MW00667268

GORDIAN®

# Square Foot Costs with RSMeans data

**Matt Doheny**, Senior Editor

# 2023

44th annual edition




**RSMeans data from Gordian**
Construction Publishers & Consultants
30 Patewood Dr., Suite 350
Greenville, SC 29615
United States of America
1.800.448.8182
rsmeans.com





Printed in the United States of America
ISSN 1540-6326
ISBN 978-1-955341-68-4





0053

$498.00 per copy (in United States)
Price is subject to change without prior notice.

# Related Data and Services

Our engineers recommend the following products and services to complement *Square Foot Costs with RSMeans data*:

## Annual Cost Data Books

*2023 Assemblies Costs with RSMeans data*
*2023 Building Construction Costs with RSMeans data*
*2023 Residential Costs with RSMeans data*
*2023 Light Commercial Costs with RSMeans data*
*2023 Square Foot Renovation Costs with RSMeans data*
*Life Cycle Cost Package*

## Reference Books

*Estimating Building Costs*
*RSMeans Estimating Handbook*
*Green Building: Project Planning & Estimating*
*How to Estimate with RSMeans data*
*Plan Reading & Material Takeoff*
*Project Scheduling & Management for Construction*
*Universal Design for Style, Comfort & Safety*

## Virtual, Instructor-led & On-site Training Offerings

Training for Conceptual Estimating on CD
Training for Our Online Estimating Solution
Plan Reading & Material Take Off

## RSMeans data

For access to the latest cost data, an intuitive search, and an easy-to-use estimate builder, take advantage of the time savings available from our online application.

To learn more visit: **RSMeans.com/online**

## Enterprise Solutions

Building owners, facility managers, building product manufacturers and attorneys across the public and private sectors engage with RSMeans data Enterprise to solve unique challenges where trusted construction cost data is critical.

To learn more visit: **RSMeans.com/Enterprise**

## Custom Built Data Sets

Building and Space Models: Quickly plan construction costs across multiple locations based on geography, project size, building system component, product options and other variables for precise budgeting and cost control.

Predictive Analytics: Accurately plan future builds with custom graphical interactive dashboards, negotiate future costs of tenant build-outs and identify and compare national account pricing.

## Consulting

Building Product Manufacturing Analytics: Validate your claims and assist with new product launches.

Third-Party Legal Resources: Used in cases of construction cost or estimate disputes, construction product failure vs. installation failure, eminent domain, class action construction product liability and more.

## API

For resellers or internal application integration, RSMeans data is offered via API. Deliver Unit, Assembly and Square Foot Model data within your interface. To learn more about how you can provide your customers with the latest in localized construction cost data visit: **RSMeans.com/API**

GORDIAN®

# Table of Contents

# Foreword

## The Value of RSMeans data from Gordian

Since 1942, RSMeans data has been the industry-standard materials, labor, and equipment cost information database for contractors, facility owners and managers, architects, engineers and anyone else that requires the latest localized construction cost information. More than 75 years later, the objective remains the same: to provide facility and construction professionals with the most current and comprehensive construction cost database possible.

With the constant influx of new construction methods and materials, in addition to ever-changing labor and material costs, last year's cost data is not reliable for today's designs, estimates or budgets. Gordian's cost engineers apply real-world construction experience to identify and quantify new building products and methodologies, adjust productivity rates and adjust costs to local market conditions across the nation. This adds up to more than 30,000 hours in cost research annually. This unparalleled construction cost expertise is why so many facility and construction professionals rely on RSMeans data year over year.

## About Gordian

Gordian is the leading provider of facility and construction cost data, software, and services for all phases of the building lifecycle. From planning to design, procurement, construction, and operations, Gordian delivers groundbreaking solutions to contractors, architects, engineers, business and financial officers, and facility owners in local, state, and federal governments, education, healthcare, and other industries. A pioneer of Job Order Contracting (JOC), Gordian's offerings also include our proprietary RSMeans data and Facility Intelligence solutions. We develop and maintain the largest collection of labor, material, and equipment data and associated costs for all areas of construction. Gordian's solutions are accessed through our innovative software platforms and supported by a team of industry experts proven to help clients maximize efficiency, optimize cost savings, and increase building quality.

## Our Commitment

At Gordian, we do more than talk about the quality of our data and the usefulness of its application. We stand behind all of our RSMeans data — from historical cost indexes to construction materials and techniques — to craft current costs and predict future trends. If you have any questions about our products or services, please call us toll-free at 800.448.8182 or visit our website at gordian.com.

# How the Cost Data Is Built: An Overview

## Unit Prices*

All cost data have been divided into 50 divisions according to the MasterFormat® system of classification and numbering.

## Assemblies*

The cost data in this section have been organized in an "Assemblies" format. These assemblies are the functional elements of a building and are arranged according to the seven elements of the UNIFORMAT II classification system. For a complete explanation of a typical "Assembly", see "RSMeans data: Assemblies—How They Work."

### *Residential Models**

Model buildings for four classes of construction – economy, average, custom, and luxury – are developed and shown with complete costs per square foot.

### *Commercial/Industrial/ Institutional Models**

This section contains complete costs for 77 typical model buildings expressed as costs per square foot.

### *Green Commercial/Industrial/ Institutional Models**

This section contains complete costs for 25 green model buildings expressed as costs per square foot.

### *References**

This section includes information on Equipment Rental Costs, Crew Listings, Historical Cost Indexes, City Cost Indexes, Location Factors, Reference Tables and Change Orders, as well as a listing of abbreviations.

- **Equipment Rental Costs:** Included are the average costs to rent and operate hundreds of pieces of construction equipment.
- **Crew Listings**: This section lists all the crews referenced in the cost data. A crew is composed of more than one trade classification and/or the addition of power equipment to any trade classification. Power equipment is included in the cost of the crew. Costs are shown both with bare labor rates and with the installing contractor's overhead and profit added. For each, the total crew cost per eight-hour day and the composite cost per labor-hour are listed.

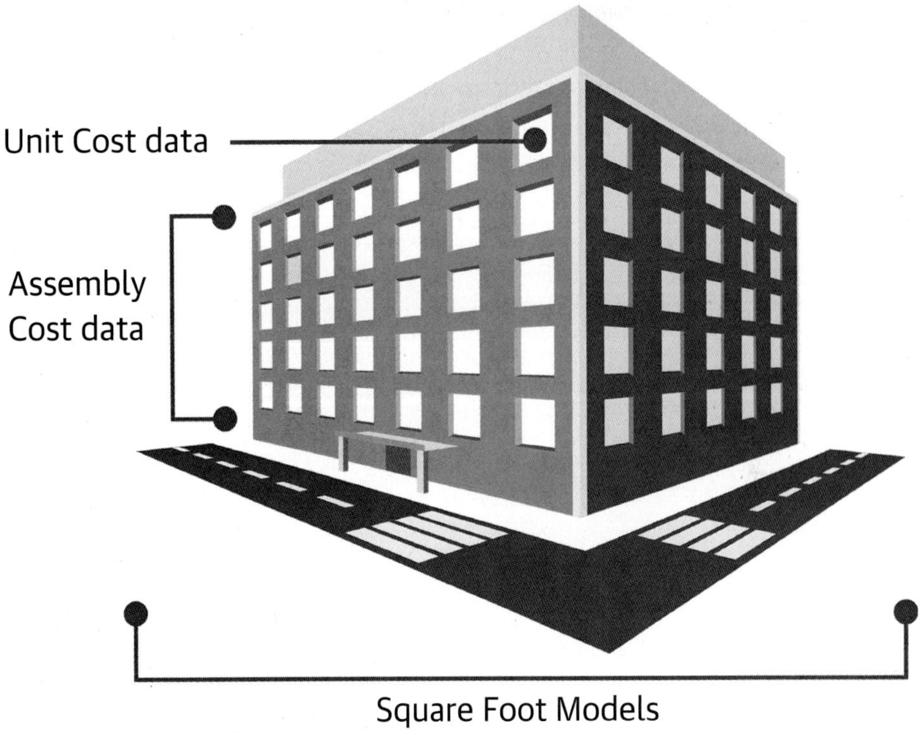


- **Historical Cost Indexes**: These indexes provide you with data to adjust construction costs over time.
- **City Cost Indexes**: All costs in this data set are U.S. national averages. Costs vary by region. You can adjust for this by CSI Division to over 730 cities in 900+ 3-digit zip codes throughout the U.S. and Canada by using this data.
- **Location Factors**: You can adjust total project costs to over 730 cities in 900+ 3-digit zip codes throughout the U.S. and Canada by using the weighted number, which applies across all divisions.
- **Reference Tables**: At the beginning of selected major classifications in the Unit Prices are reference numbers indicators. These numbers refer you to related information in the Reference Section. In this section, you'll find reference tables, explanations and estimating information that support how we develop the unit price data, technical data and estimating procedures.
- **Change Orders**: This section includes information on the factors that influence the pricing of change orders.
- **Abbreviations**: A listing of abbreviations used throughout this information, along with the terms they represent, is included.

### *Index (printed versions only)*

A comprehensive listing of all terms and subjects will help you quickly find what you need when you are not sure where it occurs in MasterFormat®.

## Conclusion

This information is designed to be as comprehensive and easy to use as possible.

---

The Construction Specifications Institute (CSI) and Construction Specifications Canada (CSC) have produced the 2018 edition of MasterFormat®, a system of titles and numbers used extensively to organize construction information.

All unit prices in the RSMeans cost data are now arranged in the 50-division MasterFormat® 2018 system.

* Not all information is available in all data sets

*Note: The material prices in RSMeans cost data are "contractor's prices." They are the prices that contractors can expect to pay at the lumberyards, suppliers'/distributors' warehouses, etc. Small orders of specialty items would be higher than the costs shown, while very large orders, such as truckload lots, would be less. The variation would depend on the size, timing, and negotiating power of the contractor. The labor costs are primarily for new construction or major renovation rather than repairs or minor alterations. With reasonable exercise of judgment, the figures can be used for any building work.*

# Residential Section

## Table of Contents

# Introduction to the Residential Square Foot Cost Section

The Residential Square Foot Cost Section contains costs per square foot for four classes of construction in seven building types. Costs are listed for various exterior wall materials which are typical of the class and building type. There are cost tables for wings and ells with modification tables to adjust the base cost of each class of building. Non-standard items can easily be added to the standard structures.

Cost estimating for a residence is a three-step process:

1. Identification
2. Listing dimensions
3. Calculations

Guidelines and a sample cost estimating procedure are shown on the following pages.

## Identification

To properly identify a residential building, the class of construction, type, and exterior wall material must be determined. The "Building Classes" information has drawings and guidelines for determining the class of construction. There are also detailed specifications and additional drawings at the beginning of each set of tables to further aid in proper building class and type identification.

Profiles for eight types of residential buildings and their configurations follow. Definitions of living area are next to each profile. Sketches and definitions of garage types follow.

## Selection of Appropriate Costs

To select the appropriate cost from the base tables, the following information is needed:

1. Class of construction
   - Economy
   - Average
   - Custom
   - Luxury
2. Type of residence
   - 1 story
   - 1-1/2 story
   - 2 story
   - 2-1/2 story
   - 3 story
   - Bi-level
   - Tri-level
3. Occupancy
   - One family
   - Two family
   - Three family
4. Building configuration
   - Detached
   - Town/Rowhouse
   - Semi-detached
5. Exterior wall construction
   - Wood frame
   - Brick veneer
   - Solid masonry
6. Living areas

Modifications are classified by class, type, and size.

## Computations

The computation process should take the following sequence:

1. Multiply the base cost by the area.
2. Add or subtract the modifications, adjustments, and alternatives.
3. Apply the location modifier.

When selecting costs, interpolate or use the cost that most nearly matches the structure under study. This applies to size, exterior wall construction, and class.

## Base Tables and Modifications

Base cost tables show the base cost per square foot without a basement, with one full bath and one full kitchen for economy and average homes, and an additional half bath for custom and luxury models. Adjustments for finished and unfinished basements are part of the base cost tables. Adjustments for multi-family residences, additional bathrooms, townhouses, alternative roofs, and air conditioning and heating systems are listed in Modifications, Adjustments, and Alternatives tables below the base cost tables.

Costs for other modifications, adjustments, and alternatives, including garages, breezeways, and site improvements, follow the base tables.

## Listing of Dimensions

To use this section, only the dimensions used to calculate the horizontal area of the building and additions, modifications, adjustments, and alternatives are needed. The dimensions, normally the length and width, can come from drawings or field measurements. For ease in calculation, consider measuring in tenths of feet, i.e., 9 ft. 6 in. = 9.5 ft. and 9 ft. 4 in. = 9.3 ft.

In all cases, make a sketch of the building. Any protrusions or other variations in shape should be noted on the sketch with dimensions.

## Calculations

The calculations portion of the estimate is a two-step activity:

1. The selection of appropriate costs from the tables
2. Computations

## Living Area

Base cost tables are prepared as costs per square foot of living area. The living area of a residence is the area which is suitable and normally designed for full time living. It does not include basement recreation rooms or finished attics, although these areas are often considered full time living areas by the owners.

Living area is calculated from the exterior dimensions without the need to adjust for exterior wall thickness. When calculating the living area of a 1-1/2 story, two story, three story, or tri-level residence, overhangs and other differences in size and shape between floors must be considered.

Only the floor area with a ceiling height of seven feet or more in a 1-1/2 story residence is considered living area. In bi-levels and tri-levels, the areas that are below grade are considered living areas, even when these areas may not be completely finished.

# How to Use the Residential Square Foot Cost Section

*The following is a detailed explanation of a sample entry in the Residential Square Foot Cost Section. Each bold number below corresponds to the item being described in the following list with the appropriate component of the sample entry in parentheses. Prices listed are costs that include overhead and profit of the installing contractor. Total model costs include an additional markup for the general contractor's overhead and profit and fees specific to the class of construction.*

## RESIDENTIAL | Average | 2 Story

- **Simple design from standard plans**
- **Single family — 1 full bath, 1 kitchen**
- **No basement**
- **Asphalt shingles on roof**
- **Hot air heat**
- **Gypsum wallboard interior finishes**
- **Materials and workmanship are average**
- **Detail specifications on p. 27**

*Note: The illustration shown may contain some optional components (for example: garages and/or fireplaces) whose costs are shown in the modifications, adjustments, & alternatives below or at the end of the square foot section.*

### Base cost per square foot of living area

| Exterior Wall | Living Area 1000 | 1200 | 1400 | 1600 | 1800 | 2000 | 2200 | 2600 | 3000 | 3400 | 3800 |
|---|---|---|---|---|---|---|---|---|---|---|---|
| Wood Siding - Wood Frame | 186.25 | 169.00 | 160.35 | 154.50 | 148.7[illegible] | 142.60 | 138.20 | 129.95 | 122.25 | 118.60 | 115.50 |
| Brick Veneer - Wood Frame | 191.80 | 174.10 | 165.15 | 159.05 | 153.05 | 146.75 | 142.15 | 133.55 | 125.55 | 121.75 | 118.50 |
| Stucco on Wood Frame | 179.40 | 162.65 | 154.40 | 148.75 | 143.35 | 137.40 | 133.30 | 125.60 | 118.10 | 114.65 | 111.75 |
| Solid Masonry | 214.90 | 195.55 | 185.20 | 178.15 | 171.00 | 164.05 | 158.60 | 148.45 | 139.35 | 134.80 | 130.90 |
| Finished Basement, Add | 28.40 | 28.30 | 27.60 | 27.20 | 26.65 | 26.30 | [illegible]5.90 | 25.10 | 24.55 | 24.20 | 23.90 |
| Unfinished Basement, Add | 10.85 | 10.40 | 10.00 | 9.75 | 9.45 | 9.25 | 9.00 | 8.60 | 8.25 | 8.05 | 7.90 |

### Modifications

*Add to the total cost*

| | |
|---|---|
| Upgrade Kitchen Cabinets | $ + 6715 |
| Solid Surface Countertops (Included) | |
| Full Bath - including plumbing, wall and floor finishes | + 9116 |
| Half Bath - including plumbing, wall and floor finishes | + 5121 |
| One Car Attached Garage | + 21,787 |
| One Car Detached Garage | + 28,036 |
| Fireplace & Chimney | + 10,762 |

### Adjustments

*For multi family - add to total cost*

| | |
|---|---|
| Additional Kitchen | $ + 11,862 |
| Additional Bath | + 9116 |
| Additional Entry & Exit | + 2368 |
| Separate Heating | + 1780 |
| Separate Electric | + 2210 |

*For Townhouse/Rowhouse - Multiply cost per square foot by*

| | |
|---|---|
| Inner Unit | .90 |
| End Unit | .95 |

### Alternatives

*Add to or deduct from the cost per square foot of living area*

| | |
|---|---|
| Cedar Shake Roof | + 3.70 |
| Clay Tile Roof | + 3.55 |
| Slate Roof | + 5.10 |
| Upgrade Walls to Skim Coat Plaster | + .72 |
| Upgrade Ceilings to Textured Finish | + .67 |
| Air Conditioning, in Heating Ductwork | + 3.22 |
| In Separate Ductwork | + 6.92 |
| Heating Systems, Hot Water | + 2.01 |
| Heat Pump | + .88 |
| Electric Heat | – 1.49 |
| Not Heated | – 1.85 |

### Additional upgrades or components


| | |
|---|---|
| Kitchen Cabinets & Countertops | Page 58 |
| Bathroom Vanities | 59 |
| Fireplaces & Chimneys | 59 |
| Windows, Skylights & Dormers | 59 |
| Appliances | 60 |
| Breezeways & Porches | 60 |
| Finished Attic | 60 |
| Garages | 61 |
| Site Improvements | 61 |
| Wings & Ells | 37 |

## 1 Class of Construction (Average)

The class of construction depends upon the design and specifications of the plan. The four classes are economy, average, custom, and luxury.

## 2 Type of Residence (2 Story)

The building type describes the number of stories or levels in the model. The seven building types are 1 story, 1-1/2 story, 2 story, 2-1/2 story, 3 story, bi-level, and tri-level.

## 3 Specification Highlights (Hot Air Heat)

These specifications include information concerning the components of the model, including the number of baths, roofing types, HVAC systems, materials, and workmanship. If the components listed are not appropriate, modifications can be made by consulting the information shown below or in the Assemblies Section.

## 4 Exterior Wall System (Wood Siding-Wood Frame)

This section includes the types of exterior wall systems and the structural frames used. The exterior wall systems shown are typical of the class of construction and the building type shown.

## 5 Living Areas (2,000 S.F.)

The living area is that area of the residence which is suitable and normally designed for full time living. It does not include basement recreation rooms or finished attics. Living area is calculated from the exterior dimensions without the need to adjust for exterior wall thickness. When calculating the living area of a 1-1/2 story, 2 story, 3 story, or tri-level residence, overhangs and other differences in size and shape between floors must be considered. Only the floor area with a ceiling height of seven feet or more in a 1-1/2 story residence is considered living area. In bi-levels and tri-levels, the areas that are below grade are considered living areas, even when these areas may not be completely finished. A range of various living areas for the residential model is shown to aid in the selection of values from the matrix.

## 6 Base Costs per Square Foot of Living Area ($142.60)

Base cost tables show the cost per square foot of living area without a basement, with one full bath and one full kitchen for economy and average homes, and an additional half bath for custom and luxury models. When selecting costs, interpolate or use the cost that most nearly matches the residence under consideration for size, exterior wall system, and class of construction. Prices listed are costs that include overhead and profit of the installing contractor, a general contractor markup, and an allowance for plans that vary by class of construction. For additional information on contractor overhead and architectural fees, see the Reference Section.

## 7 Basement Types (Finished)

The two types of basements are finished and unfinished. The specifications and components for both are shown under Building Classes in the Introduction to this section.

## 8 Additional Costs for Basements ($26.30 or $9.25)

These values indicate the additional cost per square foot of living area for either a finished or an unfinished basement.

## 9 Modifications and Adjustments (Upgrade Kitchen Cabinets $6,715)

Modifications and Adjustments are costs added to or subtracted from the total cost of the residence. The total cost of the residence is equal to the cost per square foot of living area times the living area. Typical modifications and adjustments include kitchens, baths, garages, and fireplaces.

## 10 Multiplier for Townhouse/Rowhouse (Inner Unit 0.90)

The multipliers shown adjust the base costs per square foot of living area for the common wall condition encountered in townhouses or rowhouses.

## 11 Alternatives (Skim Coat Plaster $0.72)

Alternatives are costs added to or subtracted from the base cost per square foot of living area. Typical alternatives include variations in kitchens, baths, roofing, and air conditioning and heating systems.

## 12 Additional Upgrades or Components (Wings & Ells)

Costs for additional upgrades or components, including wings or ells, breezeways, porches, finished attics, and site improvements, are shown at the end of each quality section and at the end of the Residential Square Foot Section.

# Building Classes

## Economy Class

An economy class residence is usually built from stock plans. The materials and workmanship are sufficient to satisfy building codes. Low construction cost is more important than distinctive features. The overall shape of the foundation and structure is seldom other than square or rectangular.

An unfinished basement includes a 7' high, 8" thick foundation wall composed of either concrete block or cast-in-place concrete.

Included in the finished basement cost are inexpensive paneling or drywall as the interior finish on the foundation walls, a low cost sponge backed carpeting adhered to the concrete floor, a drywall ceiling, and overhead lighting.

## Custom Class

A custom class residence is usually built from plans and specifications with enough features to give the building a distinct design. Materials and workmanship are generally above average with obvious attention given to construction details. Construction normally exceeds building code requirements.

An unfinished basement includes a 7'-6" high, 10" thick cast-in-place concrete foundation wall or a 7'-6" high, 12" thick concrete block foundation wall.

A finished basement includes painted drywall on insulated 2" × 4" wood furring as the interior finish to the concrete walls, a suspended ceiling, carpeting adhered to the concrete floor, overhead lighting, and heating.

## Average Class

An average class residence is a simple design and built from standard plans. Materials and workmanship are average but often exceed minimum building codes. There are frequently special features that give the residence some distinctive characteristics.

An unfinished basement includes a 7'-6" high, 8" thick foundation wall composed of either cast-in-place concrete or concrete block.

Included in the finished basement are plywood paneling or drywall on furring that is fastened to the foundation walls, sponge backed carpeting adhered to the concrete floor, a suspended ceiling, overhead lighting, and heating.

## Luxury Class

A luxury class residence is built from an architect's plan for a specific owner. It is unique both in design and workmanship. There are many special features, and construction usually exceeds all building codes. It is obvious that primary attention is placed on the owner's comfort and pleasure. Construction is supervised by an architect.

An unfinished basement includes an 8' high, 12" thick foundation wall that is composed of cast-in-place concrete or concrete block.

A finished basement includes painted drywall on 2" × 4" wood furring as the interior finish, a suspended ceiling, tackless carpet on wood subfloor with sleepers, overhead lighting, and heating.

# Configurations

## Detached House

This category of residence is a free-standing separate building with or without an attached garage. It has four complete walls.

## Semi-Detached House

This category of residence has two side-by-side living units. The common wall is fireproof. Semi-detached residences can be treated as a rowhouse with two end units. Semi-detached residences can be any of the building types.

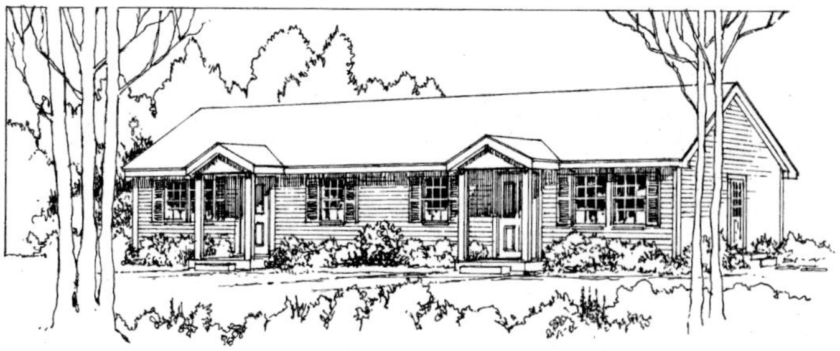

## Town/Rowhouse

This category of residence has a number of attached units made up of inner units and end units. The units are joined by common walls. The inner units have only two exterior walls. The common walls are fireproof. The end units have three walls and a common wall. Town/rowhouses can be any of the building types.

# Building Types

## One Story

This is an example of a one-story dwelling. The living area of this type of residence is confined to the ground floor. The headroom in the attic is usually too low for use as a living area.

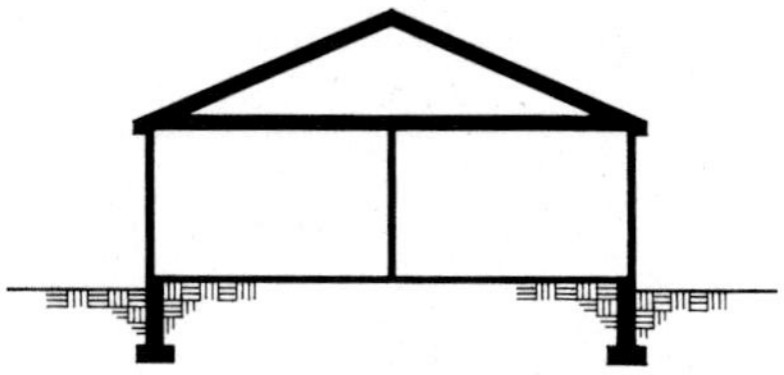

## One-and-one-half Story

The living area on the upper level of this type of residence is 50% to 90% of the ground floor. This is made possible by a combination of this design's high-peaked roof and/or dormers. Only the upper level area with a ceiling height of seven feet or more is considered living area. The living area of this residence is the sum of the ground floor area plus the area on the second level with a ceiling height of seven feet or more.

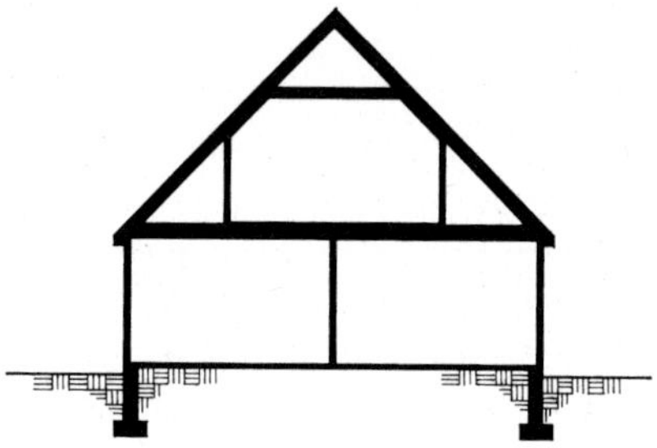

## One Story with Finished Attic

The main living area in this type of residence is the ground floor. The upper level or attic area has sufficient headroom for use as a living area. This is made possible by a high-peaked roof. The living area in the attic is less than 50% of the ground floor. The living area of this type of residence is the ground floor area only. The finished attic is considered an adjustment.

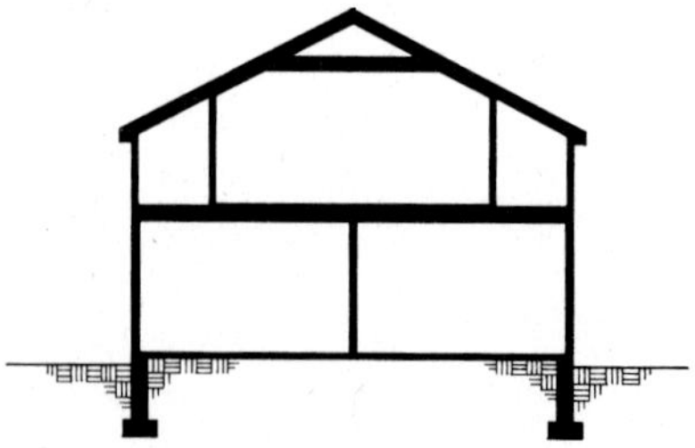

## Two Story

This type of residence has a second floor or upper level area which is equal or nearly equal to the ground floor area. The upper level of this type of residence can range from 90% to 110% of the ground floor area, depending on setbacks or overhangs. The living area is the sum of the ground floor area and the upper level floor area.

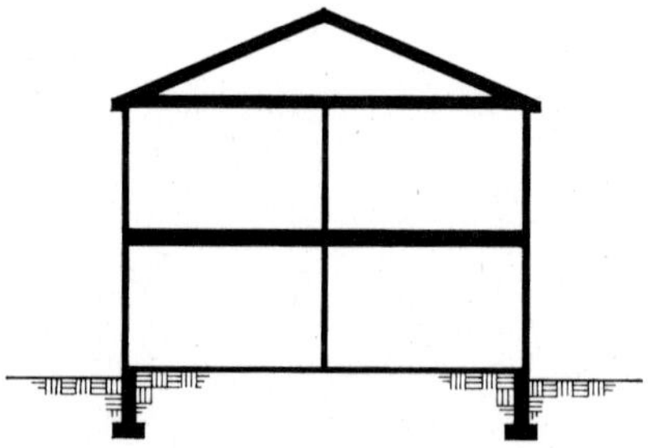

## Two-and-one-half Story

This type of residence has two levels of equal or nearly equal area and a third level which has a living area that is 50% to 90% of the ground floor. This is made possible by a high-peaked roof, extended wall heights, and/or dormers. Only the upper level area with a ceiling height of seven feet or more is considered living area. The living area of this residence is the sum of the ground floor area, the second floor area, and the area on the third level with a ceiling height of seven feet or more.

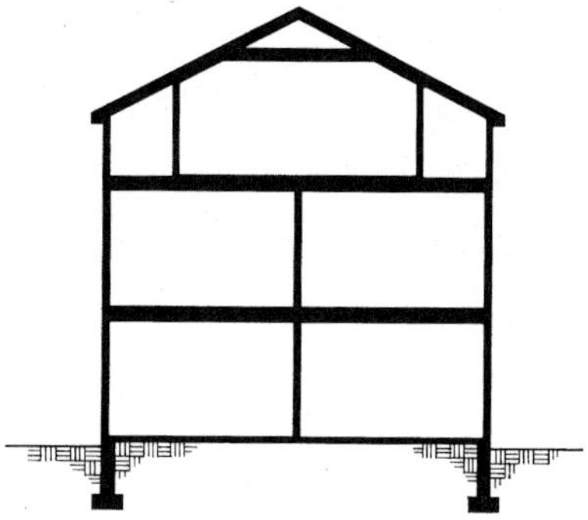

## Bi-level

This type of residence has two living areas, one above the other. One area is about four feet below grade and the second is about four feet above grade. Both areas are equal in size. The lower level in this type of residence is designed and built to serve as a living area and not as a basement. Both levels have full ceiling heights. The living area is the sum of the lower level area and the upper level area.

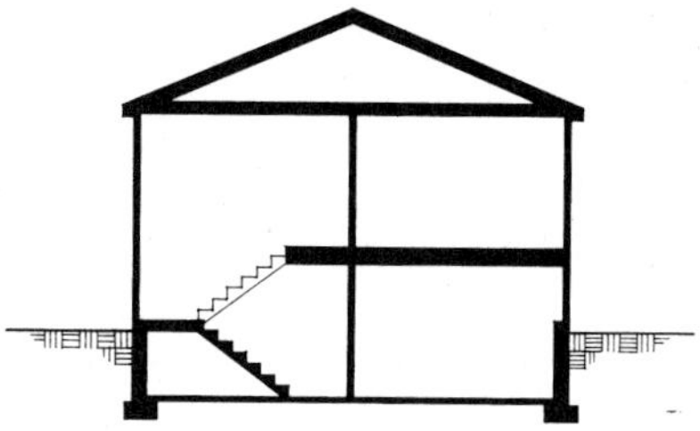

## Three Story

This type of residence has three levels which are equal or nearly equal. As in the two story residence, the second and third floor areas may vary slightly depending on setbacks or overhangs. The living area is the sum of the ground floor area and the two upper level floor areas.

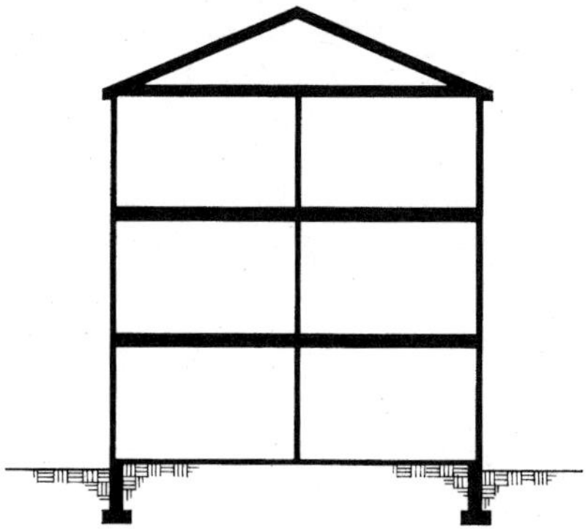

## Tri-level

This type of residence has three levels of living area: one at grade level, one about four feet below grade, and one about four feet above grade. All levels are designed to serve as living areas. All levels have full ceiling heights. The living area is a sum of the areas of each of the three levels.

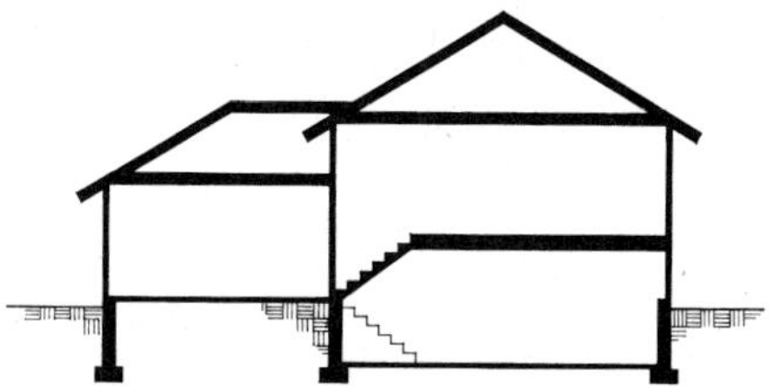

# Garage Types

## Attached Garage

Shares a common wall with the dwelling. Access is typically through a door between the dwelling and garage.

## Basement Garage

Constructed under the roof of the dwelling but below the living area.

## Built-In Garage

Constructed under the second floor living space and above the basement level of the dwelling. Reduces gross square feet of the living area.

## Detached Garage

Constructed apart from the main dwelling. Shares no common area or wall with the dwelling.

# Building Components

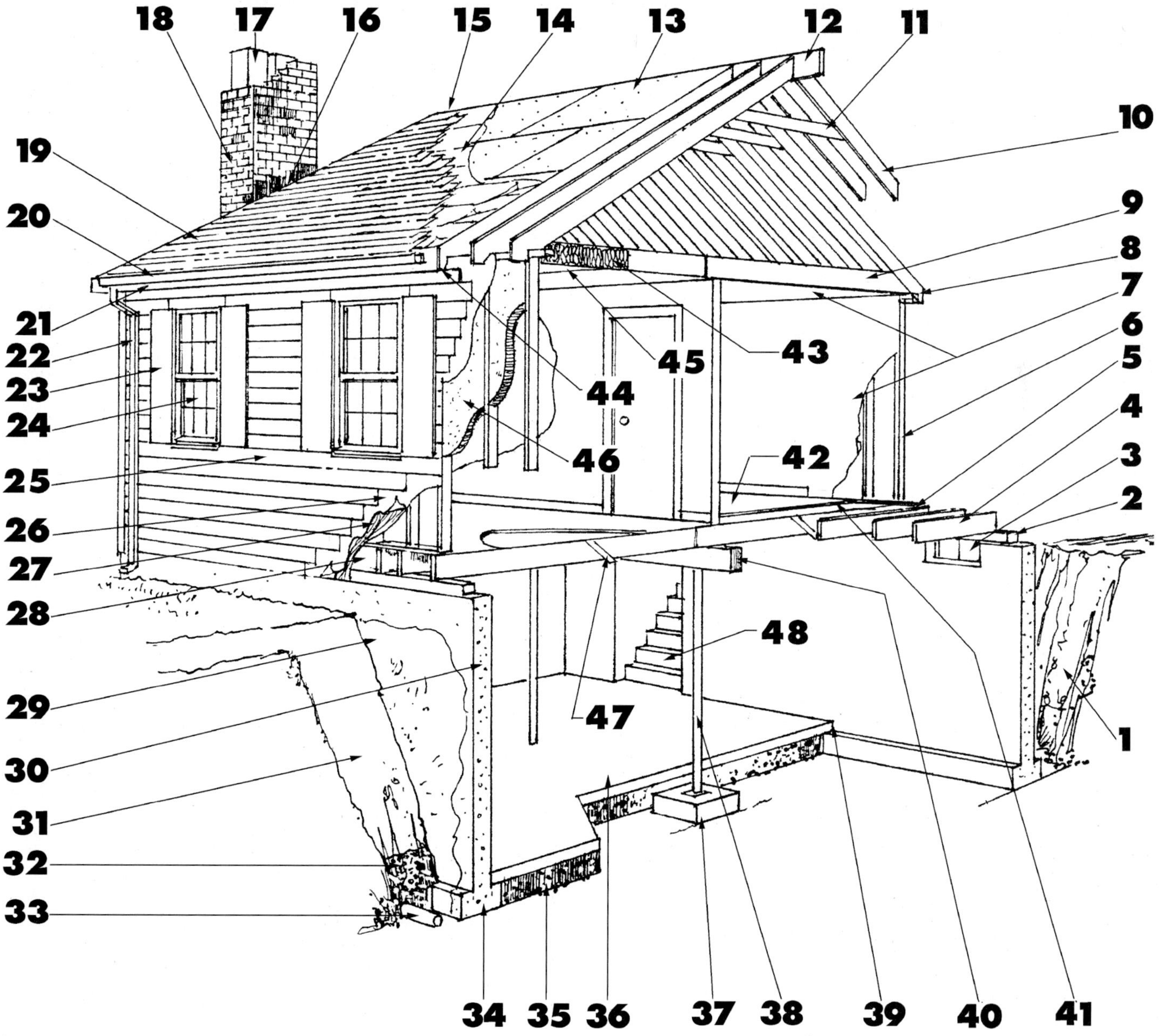


1. Excavation
2. Sill Plate
3. Basement Window
4. Floor Joist
5. Shoe Plate
6. Studs
7. Drywall
8. Plate
9. Ceiling Joists
10. Rafters
11. Collar Ties
12. Ridge Board
13. Roof Sheathing
14. Roof Felt
15. Roof Shingles
16. Flashing
17. Flue Lining
18. Chimney
19. Roof Shingles
20. Gutter
21. Fascia
22. Downspout
23. Shutter
24. Window
25. Wall Shingles
26. Weather Barrier
27. Wall Sheathing
28. Fire Stop
29. Dampproofing
30. Foundation Wall
31. Backfill
32. Drainage Stone
33. Drainage Tile
34. Wall Footing
35. Gravel
36. Concrete Slab
37. Column Footing
38. Pipe Column
39. Expansion Joint
40. Girder
41. Sub-floor
42. Finish Floor
43. Attic Insulation
44. Soffit
45. Ceiling Strapping
46. Wall Insulation
47. Cross Bridging
48. Bulkhead Stairs

# Exterior Wall Construction

## Typical Frame Construction

Typical wood frame construction consists of wood studs with insulation between them. A typical exterior surface is made up of sheathing, building paper, and exterior siding consisting of wood, vinyl, aluminum, or stucco over the wood sheathing.

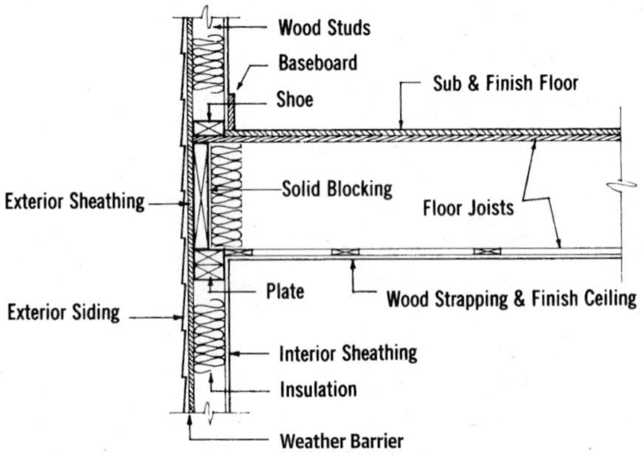


## Brick Veneer

Typical brick veneer construction consists of wood studs with insulation between them. A typical exterior surface is sheathing, building paper, and an exterior of brick tied to the sheathing with metal strips.

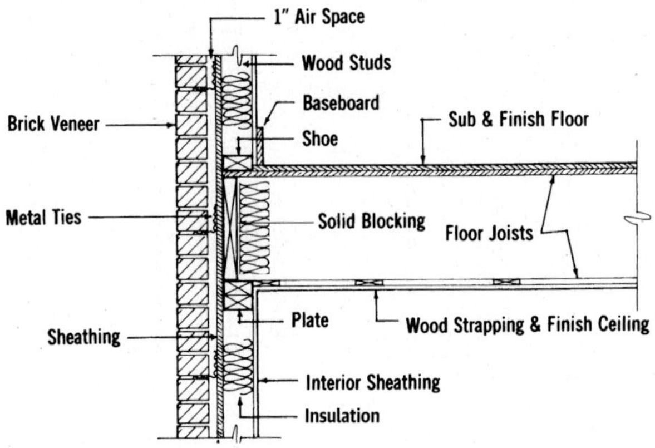


## Stone

Typical solid masonry construction consists of a stone or block wall covered on the exterior with brick, stone, or other masonry.

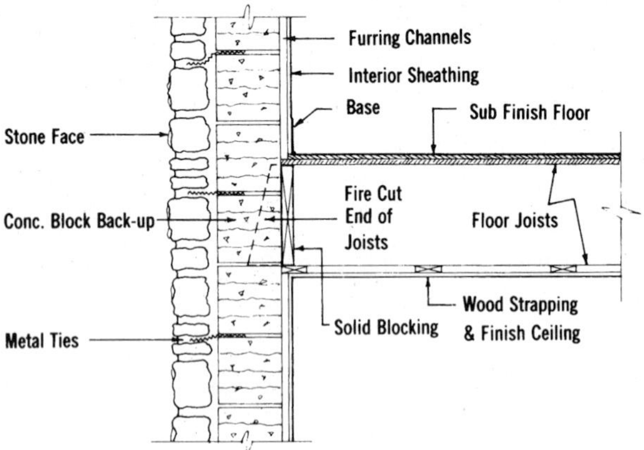

# Residential Cost Estimate Worksheet

## Worksheet Instructions

The residential cost estimate worksheet can be used as an outline for developing a residential construction or replacement cost. It is also useful for insurance appraisals. The design of the worksheet helps eliminate errors and omissions. To use the worksheet, follow the example below.

1. Fill out the owner's name, residence address, the estimator or appraiser's name, some type of project identifying number or code, and the date.
2. Determine from the plans, specifications, owner's description, photographs, or any other means possible the class of construction. The models in this data set use economy, average, custom, and luxury as classes. Fill in the appropriate box.
3. Fill in the appropriate box for the residence type, configuration, occupancy, and exterior wall. If you require clarification, the pages preceding this worksheet describe each of these.
4. Next, the living area of the residence must be established. The heated or air conditioned space of the residence, not including the basement, should be measured. It is easiest to break the structure up into separate components as shown in the example: the main house (A), a one-and-one-half story wing (B), and a one-story wing (C). The breezeway (D), garage (E), and open covered porch (F) will be treated differently. Data entry blocks for the living area are included on the worksheet for your use. Keep each level of each component separate, and fill out the blocks as shown.
5. By using the information on the worksheet, find the model, wing, or ell in the following square foot cost pages that best matches the class, type, exterior finish, and size of the residence being estimated. Use the Modifications, Adjustments, and Alternatives to determine the adjusted cost per square foot of living area for each component.
6. For each component, multiply the cost per square foot by the living area square footage. If the residence is a town/rowhouse, a multiplier should be applied based upon the configuration.
7. The second page of the residential cost estimate worksheet has space for the additional components of a house. The cost for additional bathrooms, finished attic space, breezeways, porches, fireplaces, appliance or cabinet upgrades, and garages should be added on this page. The information for each of these components is found with the model being used or in the Modifications, Adjustments, and Alternatives.
8. Add the total from page one of the estimate worksheet and the items listed on page two. The sum is the adjusted total building cost.
9. Depending on the use of the final estimated cost, one of the remaining two boxes should be filled out. Any additional items or exclusions should be added or subtracted at this time. The data contained in this data set are a national average. Construction costs are different throughout the country. To allow for this difference, a location factor based upon the first three digits of the residence's zip code must be applied. The location factor is a multiplier that increases or decreases the adjusted total building cost. Find the appropriate location factor and calculate the local cost. If depreciation is a concern, a dollar figure should be subtracted at this point.
10. No residence will match a model exactly. Many differences will be found. At this level of estimating, a variation of +/- 10% should be expected.

## Adjustments Instructions

No residence matches a model exactly in shape, material, or specifications. The common differences are:

1. Two or more exterior wall systems:
   - Partial basement
   - Partly finished basement
2. Specifications or features that are between two classes
3. Crawl space instead of a basement

### *Examples*

Below are quick examples. See pages 15-17 for complete examples of cost adjustments for these differences:

1. Residence "A" is an average one-story structure with 1,600 S.F. of living area and no basement. Three walls are wood siding on wood frame, and the fourth wall is brick veneer on wood frame. The brick veneer wall is 35% of the exterior wall area.

   **Use page 28 to calculate the Base Cost per S.F. of Living Area. Wood Siding for 1,600 S.F. = $148.05 per S.F. and Brick Veneer for 1,600 S.F. = $151.40 per S.F.**

   **0.65 ($148.05) + 0.35 ($151.40) = $149.22 per S.F. of Living Area.**

2a. Residence "B" is the same as Residence "A" but it has an unfinished basement under 50% of the building. To adjust the $149.22 per S.F. of living area for this partial basement, use page 28.

$149.22 + 0.50 ($15.85) = $137.08 per S.F. of Living Area.

2b. Residence "C" is the same as Residence "A" but it has a full basement under the entire building. 640 S.F. or 40% of the basement area is finished.

Using Page 28:

$149.22 + 0.40 ($43.30) + 0.60 ($15.85) =
$176.05 per S.F. of Living Area.

3. When specifications or features of a building are between classes, estimate the percent deviation, and use two tables to calculate the cost per S.F.

   A two-story residence with wood siding and 1,800 S.F. of living area has features 30% better than Average, but 70% less than Custom.

   From pages 30 and 42:

| | | |
|---|---|---|
| **Custom 1,800 S.F. Base Cost** | = | **$182.30 per S.F.** |
| **Average 1,800 S.F. Base Cost** | = | **$148.70 per S.F.** |
| **DIFFERENCE** | = | **$33.60 per S.F.** |
| **Cost is $148.70 + 0.30 ($33.60)** | = | **$158.78 per S.F. of Living Area.** |

4. To add the cost of a crawl space, use the cost of an unfinished basement as a maximum. For specific costs of components to be added or deducted, such as vapor barrier, underdrain, and floor, see the "Assemblies" section (pages 285 to 518).

# Model Residence Example

First Floor Plan

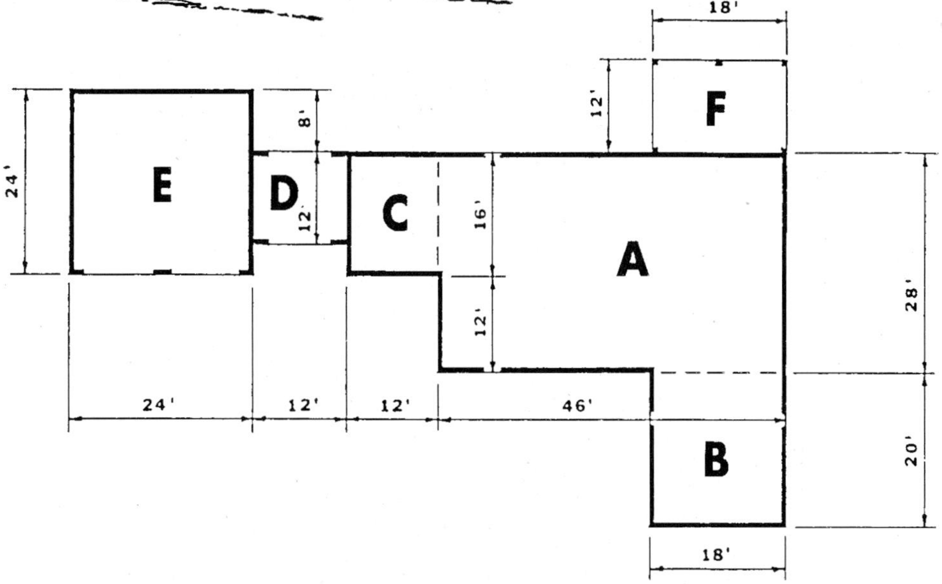


Second Floor Plan

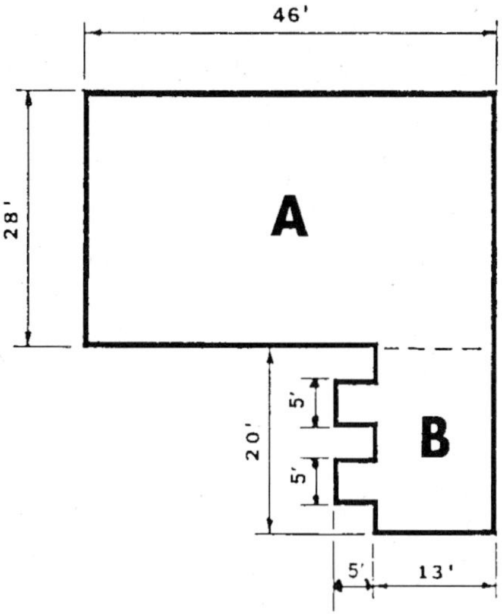


**A** = Main House
**B** = 1-1/2 Story Wing
**C** = 1 Story Wing
**D** = Breezeway
**E** = Garage
**F** = Open Covered Porch

**RESIDENTIAL**
**COST ESTIMATE**

| | | | |
|---|---|---|---|
| OWNERS NAME: | **Albert Westenberg** | APPRAISER: | **Nicole Wojtowicz** |
| RESIDENCE ADDRESS: | **300 Sygiel Road** | PROJECT: | **# 55** |
| CITY, STATE, ZIP CODE: | **Three Rivers, MA 01080** | DATE: | **Jan. 1, 2023** |

| CLASS OF CONSTRUCTION | RESIDENCE TYPE | CONFIGURATION | EXTERIOR WALL SYSTEM |
|---|---|---|---|
| ☐ ECONOMY | ☐ 1 STORY | ☑ DETACHED | ☑ WOOD SIDING - WOOD FRAME |
| ☑ AVERAGE | ☐ 11/2 STORY | ☐ TOWN/ROW HOUSE | ☐ BRICK VENEER - WOOD FRAME |
| ☐ CUSTOM | ☑ 2 STORY | ☐ SEMI-DETACHED | ☐ STUCCO ON WOOD FRAME |
| ☐ LUXURY | ☐ 2 1/2 STORY | | ☐ PAINTED CONCRETE BLOCK |
| | ☐ 3 STORY | OCCUPANCY | ☐ SOLID MASONRY (AVERAGE & CUSTOM) |
| | ☐ BI-LEVEL | ☑ ONE FAMILY | ☐ STONE VENEER - WOOD FRAME |
| | ☐ TRI-LEVEL | ☐ TWO FAMILY | ☐ SOLID BRICK (LUXURY) |
| | | ☐ THREE FAMILY | ☐ SOLID STONE (LUXURY) |
| | | ☐ OTHER | |

| * LIVING AREA (Main Building) | | * LIVING AREA (~~Wing~~ or Ell) (B) | | * LIVING AREA (Wing or ~~Ell~~) (C) | |
|---|---|---|---|---|---|
| First Level | **1288** S.F. | First Level | **360** S.F. | First Level | **192** S.F. |
| Second level | **1288** S.F. | Second level | **310** S.F. | Second level | S.F. |
| Third Level | S.F. | Third Level | S.F. | Third Level | S.F. |
| Total | **2576** S.F. | Total | **670** S.F. | Total | **192** S.F. |

* Basement Area is not part of living area.

| MAIN BUILDING | COSTS PER S.F. LIVING AREA |
|---|---|
| Cost per Square Foot of Living Area, from Page **30** | $ **129.95** |
| Basement Addition: ______ % Finished, **100** % Unfinished | + **8.60** |
| Roof Cover Adjustment: **Cedar Shake** Type, Page **30** (Add or Deduct) | ( ) **1.65** |
| Central Air Conditioning: ☐ Separate Ducts ☑ Heating Ducts, Page **30** | + **2.96** |
| Heating System Adjustment: ______ Type, Page ______ (Add or Deduct) | ( ) —— |
| Main Building: Adjusted Cost per S.F. of Living Area | $ **# 143.16** |

| MAIN BUILDING TOTAL COST | $ **143.16** /S.F. | x | **2,576** S.F. | x | —— | = | $ **368,780** |
|---|---|---|---|---|---|---|---|
| | Cost per S.F. Living Area | | Living Area | | Town/Row House Multiplier (Use 1 for Detached) | | TOTAL COST |

| ~~WING~~ OR ELL (B) **1 - 1/2** STORY | COSTS PER S.F. LIVING AREA |
|---|---|
| Cost per Square Foot of Living Area, from Page **37** | $ **132.05** |
| Basement Addition: - % Finished, **100** - % Unfinished | + **14.80** |
| Roof Cover Adjustment: - Type, Page - - (Add or Deduct) | ( ) — |
| Central Air Conditioning: ☐ Separate Ducts ☑ Heating Ducts, Page **30** | + **2.96** |
| Heating System Adjustment: ______ Type, Page ______ (Add or Deduct) | ( ) — |
| ~~Wing~~ or Ell ( **B** ): Adjusted Cost per S.F. of Living Area | $ **149.81** |

| WING OR ELL (B) TOTAL COST | $ **149.81** /S.F. | x | **670** S.F. | = | $ **100,372** |
|---|---|---|---|---|---|
| | Cost per S.F. Living Area | | Living Area | | TOTAL COST |

| WING OR ~~ELL~~ (C) **1** STORY | COSTS PER S.F. LIVING AREA |
|---|---|
| Cost per Square Foot of Living Area, from Page **# 37 (WOOD SIDING)** | $ **194.15** |
| Basement Addition: ______ % Finished, ______ % Unfinished | + — |
| Roof Cover Adjustment: - Type, Page # (Add or Deduct) | ( ) — |
| Central Air Conditioning: ☐ Separate Ducts ☐ Heating Ducts, Page ____ | + — |
| Heating System Adjustment: ______ Type, Page ______ (Add or Deduct) | ( ) — |
| Wing or Ell (C) Adjusted Cost per S.F. of Living Area | $ **# 194.15** |

| WING OR ELL (C) TOTAL COST | $ **194.15** /S.F. | x | **192** S.F. | = | $ **37,276** |
|---|---|---|---|---|---|
| | Cost per S.F. Living Area | | Living Area | | TOTAL COST |

TOTAL THIS PAGE **506,428**

Page 1 of 2

**RESIDENTIAL**
**COST ESTIMATE**

| | | | | |
|---|---|---|---|---|
| Total Page 1 | | | | $ **506,428** |
| | | QUANTITY | UNIT COST | |
| Additional Bathrooms: **2** Full, **1** Half | **2 @ 9116 1 @ 5121** | | | + **23,353** |
| Finished Attic: **N/A** Ft. x ____ Ft. | | S.F. | | |
| Breezeway: ☑ Open ☐ Enclosed **12** Ft. x **12** Ft. | | **144** S.F. | **50.78** | + **7,312** |
| Covered Porch: ☑ Open ☐ Enclosed **18** Ft. x **12** Ft. | | **216** S.F. | **52.46** | + **11,331** |
| Fireplace: ☑ Interior Chimney ☐ Exterior Chimney<br>☑ No. of Flues ( **2** ) ☑ Additional Fireplaces | **1 - 2nd Story** | | | + **18,039** |
| Appliances: | | | | + — |
| Kitchen Cabinets Adjustments: | (±) | | | — |
| ☑ Garage ☐ Carport: **2** Car(s) Description **Wood, Attached** | (±) | | | **37,225** |
| Miscellaneous: | | | | + |

ADJUSTED TOTAL BUILDING COST $ **603,688**

| REPLACEMENT COST | | |
|---|---|---|
| ADJUSTED TOTAL BUILDING COST | $ | **603,688** |
| Site Improvements | | |
| (A) Paving & Sidewalks | $ | |
| (B) Landscaping | $ | |
| (C) Fences | $ | |
| (D) Swimming Pools | $ | |
| (E) Miscellaneous | $ | |
| TOTAL | $ | **603,688** |
| Location Factor | x | **1.050** |
| Location Replacement Cost | $ | **633,872** |
| Depreciation | -$ | |
| LOCAL DEPRECIATED COST | $ | |

| INSURANCE COST | | |
|---|---|---|
| ADJUSTED TOTAL BUILDING COST | $ | |
| Insurance Exclusions | | |
| (A) Footings, sitework, Underground Piping | -$ | |
| (B) Architects Fees | -$ | |
| Total Building Cost Less Exclusion | $ | |
| Location Factor | x | |
| LOCAL INSURABLE REPLACEMENT COST | $ | |

*Estimated

**SKETCH AND ADDITIONAL CALCULATIONS**

## 1 Story

## 1-1/2 Story

## 2 Story

## Bi-Level

## Tri-Level

©Design Basics, Inc.

| | Components |
|---|---|
| **1 Site Work** | Site preparation for slab or excavation for lower level; 4′ deep trench excavation for foundation wall. |
| **2 Foundations** | Continuous reinforced concrete footing, 8″ deep x 18″ wide; dampproofed and insulated 8″ thick reinforced concrete block foundation wall, 4′ deep; 4″ concrete slab on 4″ crushed stone base and polyethylene vapor barrier, trowel finish. |
| **3 Framing** | Exterior walls—2 x 4 wood studs, 16″ O.C.; 1/2″ insulation board sheathing; wood truss roof 24″ O.C. or 2 x 6 rafters 16″ O.C. with 1/2″ plywood sheathing, 4 in 12 or 8 in 12 roof pitch. |
| **4 Exterior Walls** | Beveled wood siding and #15 felt building paper on insulated wood frame walls; sliding sash or double hung wood windows; 2 flush solid core wood exterior doors.<br>**Alternates:**<br>• Brick veneer on wood frame, has 4″ veneer of common brick.<br>• Stucco on wood frame has 1″ thick colored stucco finish.<br>• Painted concrete block has 8″ concrete block sealed and painted on exterior and furring on the interior for the drywall. |
| **5 Roofing** | 20 year asphalt shingles; #15 felt building paper; aluminum gutters, downspouts, drip edge and flashings. |
| **6 Interiors** | Walls and ceilings—1/2″ taped and finished drywall, primed and painted with 2 coats; painted baseboard and trim; rubber backed carpeting 80%, asphalt tile 20%; hollow core wood interior doors. |
| **7 Specialties** | Economy grade kitchen cabinets—6 L.F. wall and base with plastic laminate counter top and kitchen sink; 30 gallon electric water heater. |
| **8 Mechanical** | 1 lavatory, white, wall hung; 1 water closet, white; 1 bathtub, enameled steel, white; gas fired warm air heat. |
| **9 Electrical** | 100 Amp. service; romex wiring; incandescent lighting fixtures, switches, receptacles. |
| **10 Overhead and Profit** | General Contractor overhead and profit. |

## Adjustments

***Unfinished Basement:***
7′ high 8″ concrete block or cast-in-place concrete walls.

***Finished Basement:***
Includes inexpensive paneling or drywall on foundation walls. Inexpensive sponge backed carpeting on concrete floor, drywall ceiling, and lighting.

# RESIDENTIAL | Economy | 1 Story

- **Mass produced from stock plans**
- **Single family – 1 full bath, 1 kitchen**
- **No basement**
- **Asphalt shingles on roof**
- **Hot air heat**
- **Gypsum wallboard interior finishes**
- **Materials and workmanship are sufficient to meet codes**
- **Detail specifications on page 19**

*Note: The illustration shown may contain some optional components (for example: garages and/or fireplaces) whose costs are shown in the modifications, adjustments, & alternatives below or at the end of the square foot section.*

©Home Planners, Inc.

## Base cost per square foot of living area

| Exterior Wall | Living Area 600 | 800 | 1000 | 1200 | 1400 | 1600 | 1800 | 2000 | 2400 | 2800 | 3200 |
|---|---|---|---|---|---|---|---|---|---|---|---|
| Wood Siding - Wood Frame | 188.70 | 170.20 | 157.05 | 145.70 | 135.95 | 129.75 | 126.80 | 122.50 | 114.25 | 108.15 | 103.90 |
| Brick Veneer - Wood Frame | 204.95 | 184.65 | 170.15 | 157.55 | 146.70 | 139.80 | 136.55 | 131.60 | 122.60 | 115.90 | 111.00 |
| Stucco on Wood Frame | 177.85 | 160.50 | 148.25 | 137.75 | 128.70 | 122.95 | 120.30 | 116.40 | 108.65 | 103.00 | 99.10 |
| Painted Concrete Block | 176.90 | 159.65 | 147.50 | 137.10 | 128.10 | 122.35 | 119.70 | 115.80 | 108.20 | 102.55 | 98.70 |
| Finished Basement, Add | 41.10 | 39.50 | 38.20 | 37.05 | 36.05 | 35.40 | 35.10 | 34.55 | 33.80 | 33.25 | 32.75 |
| Unfinished Basement, Add | 16.70 | 15.40 | 14.45 | 13.55 | 12.80 | 12.30 | 12.05 | 11.65 | 11.05 | 10.60 | 10.20 |

## Modifications

*Add to the total cost*

| | |
|---|---|
| Upgrade Kitchen Cabinets | $ + 1366 |
| Solid Surface Countertops | + 997 |
| Full Bath - including plumbing, wall and floor finishes | + 7293 |
| Half Bath - including plumbing, wall and floor finishes | + 4097 |
| One Car Attached Garage | + 20,336 |
| One Car Detached Garage | + 25,718 |
| Fireplace & Chimney | + 9005 |

## Adjustments

*For multi family - add to total cost*

| | |
|---|---|
| Additional Kitchen | $ + 6765 |
| Additional Bath | + 7293 |
| Additional Entry & Exit | + 2368 |
| Separate Heating | + 1780 |
| Separate Electric | + 1268 |

*For Townhouse/Rowhouse - Multiply cost per square foot by*

| | |
|---|---|
| Inner Unit | .95 |
| End Unit | .97 |

## Alternatives

*Add to or deduct from the cost per square foot of living area*

| | |
|---|---|
| Composition Roll Roofing | – 1.35 |
| Cedar Shake Roof | + 7.85 |
| Upgrade Walls and Ceilings to Skim Coat Plaster | + .97 |
| Upgrade Ceilings to Textured Finish | + .67 |
| Air Conditioning, in Heating Ductwork | + 5.17 |
| In Separate Ductwork | + 8.38 |
| Heating Systems, Hot Water | + 2.14 |
| Heat Pump | + .72 |
| Electric Heat | – 3.43 |
| Not Heated | – 3.19 |

## Additional upgrades or components


| | |
|---|---|
| Kitchen Cabinets & Countertops | Page 58 |
| Bathroom Vanities | 59 |
| Fireplaces & Chimneys | 59 |
| Windows, Skylights & Dormers | 59 |
| Appliances | 60 |
| Breezeways & Porches | 60 |
| Finished Attic | 60 |
| Garages | 61 |
| Site Improvements | 61 |
| Wings & Ells | 25 |

- **Mass produced from stock plans**
- **Single family – 1 full bath, 1 kitchen**
- **No basement**
- **Asphalt shingles on roof**
- **Hot air heat**
- **Gypsum wallboard interior finishes**
- **Materials and workmanship are sufficient to meet codes**
- **Detail specifications on page 19**

*Note: The illustration shown may contain some optional components (for example: garages and/or fireplaces) whose costs are shown in the modifications, adjustments, & alternatives below or at the end of the square foot section.*

## Base cost per square foot of living area

| Exterior Wall | Living Area 600 | 800 | 1000 | 1200 | 1400 | 1600 | 1800 | 2000 | 2400 | 2800 | 3200 |
|---|---|---|---|---|---|---|---|---|---|---|---|
| Wood Siding - Wood Frame | 222.55 | 183.90 | 166.05 | 157.20 | 150.85 | 141.40 | 136.50 | 131.55 | 121.15 | 117.10 | 112.90 |
| Brick Veneer - Wood Frame | 245.80 | 200.75 | 181.65 | 171.80 | 164.75 | 154.05 | 148.45 | 142.90 | 131.20 | 126.70 | 121.70 |
| Stucco on Wood Frame | 206.90 | 172.60 | 155.60 | 147.35 | 141.45 | 132.90 | 128.45 | 123.85 | 114.40 | 110.75 | 106.95 |
| Painted Concrete Block | 205.40 | 171.55 | 154.60 | 146.40 | 140.55 | 132.10 | 127.65 | 123.15 | 113.75 | 110.15 | 106.40 |
| Finished Basement, Add | 30.30 | 26.45 | 25.70 | 25.10 | 24.65 | 23.90 | 23.55 | 23.20 | 22.35 | 22.05 | 21.60 |
| Unfinished Basement, Add | 13.95 | 11.05 | 10.40 | 10.00 | 9.65 | 9.05 | 8.75 | 8.50 | 7.85 | 7.65 | 7.30 |

## Modifications

*Add to the total cost*

| | |
|---|---|
| Upgrade Kitchen Cabinets | $ + 1366 |
| Solid Surface Countertops | + 997 |
| Full Bath - including plumbing, wall and floor finishes | + 7293 |
| Half Bath - including plumbing, wall and floor finishes | + 4097 |
| One Car Attached Garage | + 20,336 |
| One Car Detached Garage | + 25,718 |
| Fireplace & Chimney | + 9005 |

## Adjustments

*For multi family - add to total cost*

| | |
|---|---|
| Additional Kitchen | $ + 6765 |
| Additional Bath | + 7293 |
| Additional Entry & Exit | + 2368 |
| Separate Heating | + 1780 |
| Separate Electric | + 1268 |

*For Townhouse/Rowhouse - Multiply cost per square foot by*

| | |
|---|---|
| Inner Unit | .95 |
| End Unit | .97 |

## Alternatives

*Add to or deduct from the cost per square foot of living area*

| | |
|---|---|
| Composition Roll Roofing | – .95 |
| Cedar Shake Roof | + 5.70 |
| Upgrade Walls and Ceilings to Skim Coat Plaster | + .98 |
| Upgrade Ceilings to Textured Finish | + .67 |
| Air Conditioning, in Heating Ductwork | + 3.84 |
| In Separate Ductwork | + 7.36 |
| Heating Systems, Hot Water | + 2.01 |
| Heat Pump | + .80 |
| Electric Heat | – 2.73 |
| Not Heated | – 2.20 |

## Additional upgrades or components



| | |
|---|---|
| Kitchen Cabinets & Countertops | Page 58 |
| Bathroom Vanities | 59 |
| Fireplaces & Chimneys | 59 |
| Windows, Skylights & Dormers | 59 |
| Appliances | 60 |
| Breezeways & Porches | 60 |
| Finished Attic | 60 |
| Garages | 61 |
| Site Improvements | 61 |
| Wings & Ells | 25 |

- **Mass produced from stock plans**
- **Single family — 1 full bath, 1 kitchen**
- **No basement**
- **Asphalt shingles on roof**
- **Hot air heat**
- **Gypsum wallboard interior finishes**
- **Materials and workmanship are sufficient to meet codes**
- **Detail specifications on page 19**

*Note: The illustration shown may contain some optional components (for example: garages and/or fireplaces) whose costs are shown in the modifications, adjustments, & alternatives below or at the end of the square foot section.*

## Base cost per square foot of living area

| | Living Area | | | | | | | | | | |
|---|---|---|---|---|---|---|---|---|---|---|---|
| Exterior Wall | 1000 | 1200 | 1400 | 1600 | 1800 | 2000 | 2200 | 2600 | 3000 | 3400 | 3800 |
| Wood Siding - Wood Frame | 169.10 | 153.80 | 146.15 | 140.95 | 135.90 | 130.20 | 126.20 | 118.65 | 111.50 | 108.15 | 105.35 |
| Brick Veneer - Wood Frame | 185.85 | 169.30 | 160.60 | 154.75 | 148.95 | 142.80 | 138.15 | 129.45 | 121.50 | 117.60 | 114.35 |
| Stucco on Wood Frame | 157.90 | 143.40 | 136.40 | 131.60 | 127.15 | 121.80 | 118.20 | 111.40 | 104.80 | 101.75 | 99.30 |
| Painted Concrete Block | 157.10 | 142.70 | 135.75 | 131.05 | 126.55 | 121.20 | 117.65 | 110.90 | 104.35 | 101.35 | 98.85 |
| Finished Basement, Add | 21.20 | 20.60 | 20.10 | 19.75 | 19.40 | 19.15 | 18.90 | 18.30 | 17.95 | 17.65 | 17.45 |
| Unfinished Basement, Add | 8.85 | 8.40 | 7.95 | 7.70 | 7.45 | 7.25 | 7.00 | 6.60 | 6.30 | 6.10 | 5.95 |

## Modifications

*Add to the total cost*

| | |
|---|---|
| Upgrade Kitchen Cabinets | $ + 1366 |
| Solid Surface Countertops | + 997 |
| Full Bath - including plumbing, wall and floor finishes | + 7293 |
| Half Bath - including plumbing, wall and floor finishes | + 4097 |
| One Car Attached Garage | + 20,336 |
| One Car Detached Garage | + 25,718 |
| Fireplace & Chimney | + 9950 |

## Adjustments

*For multi family - add to total cost*

| | |
|---|---|
| Additional Kitchen | $ + 6765 |
| Additional Bath | + 7293 |
| Additional Entry & Exit | + 2368 |
| Separate Heating | + 1780 |
| Separate Electric | + 1268 |

*For Townhouse/Rowhouse - Multiply cost per square foot by*

| | |
|---|---|
| Inner Unit | .93 |
| End Unit | .96 |

## Alternatives

*Add to or deduct from the cost per square foot of living area*

| | |
|---|---|
| Composition Roll Roofing | – .70 |
| Cedar Shake Roof | + 3.95 |
| Upgrade Walls and Ceilings to Skim Coat Plaster | + .99 |
| Upgrade Ceilings to Textured Finish | + .67 |
| Air Conditioning, in Heating Ductwork | + 3.12 |
| In Separate Ductwork | + 6.77 |
| Heating Systems, Hot Water | + 1.96 |
| Heat Pump | + .84 |
| Electric Heat | – 2.38 |
| Not Heated | – 2.07 |

## Additional upgrades or components


| | |
|---|---|
| Kitchen Cabinets & Countertops | Page 58 |
| Bathroom Vanities | 59 |
| Fireplaces & Chimneys | 59 |
| Windows, Skylights & Dormers | 59 |
| Appliances | 60 |
| Breezeways & Porches | 60 |
| Finished Attic | 60 |
| Garages | 61 |
| Site Improvements | 61 |
| Wings & Ells | 25 |




**Important: See the Reference Section for Location Factors (to adjust for your city) and Estimating Forms.**

- Mass produced from stock plans
- Single family — 1 full bath, 1 kitchen
- No basement
- Asphalt shingles on roof
- Hot air heat
- Gypsum wallboard interior finishes
- Materials and workmanship are sufficient to meet codes
- Detail specifications on page 19

*Note: The illustration shown may contain some optional components (for example: garages and/or fireplaces) whose costs are shown in the modifications, adjustments, & alternatives below or at the end of the square foot section.*

## Base cost per square foot of living area

| Exterior Wall | Living Area 1000 | 1200 | 1400 | 1600 | 1800 | 2000 | 2200 | 2600 | 3000 | 3400 | 3800 |
|---|---|---|---|---|---|---|---|---|---|---|---|
| Wood Siding - Wood Frame | 154.90 | 140.65 | 133.85 | 129.25 | 124.80 | 119.55 | 116.10 | 109.50 | 103.05 | 100.10 | 97.70 |
| Brick Veneer - Wood Frame | 167.60 | 152.45 | 144.85 | 139.70 | 134.75 | 129.15 | 125.15 | 117.70 | 110.65 | 107.30 | 104.55 |
| Stucco on Wood Frame | 146.30 | 132.75 | 126.40 | 122.10 | 118.20 | 113.15 | 110.00 | 103.95 | 97.90 | 95.25 | 93.10 |
| Painted Concrete Block | 145.70 | 132.15 | 125.90 | 121.60 | 117.65 | 112.70 | 109.50 | 103.55 | 97.50 | 94.85 | 92.75 |
| Finished Basement, Add | 21.20 | 20.60 | 20.10 | 19.75 | 19.40 | 19.15 | 18.90 | 18.30 | 17.95 | 17.65 | 17.45 |
| Unfinished Basement, Add | 8.85 | 8.40 | 7.95 | 7.70 | 7.45 | 7.25 | 7.00 | 6.60 | 6.30 | 6.10 | 5.95 |

## Modifications

*Add to the total cost*

| | |
|---|---|
| Upgrade Kitchen Cabinets | $ + 1366 |
| Solid Surface Countertops | + 997 |
| Full Bath - including plumbing, wall and floor finishes | + 7293 |
| Half Bath - including plumbing, wall and floor finishes | + 4097 |
| One Car Attached Garage | + 20,336 |
| One Car Detached Garage | + 25,718 |
| Fireplace & Chimney | + 9005 |

## Adjustments

*For multi family - add to total cost*

| | |
|---|---|
| Additional Kitchen | $ + 6765 |
| Additional Bath | + 7293 |
| Additional Entry & Exit | + 2368 |
| Separate Heating | + 1780 |
| Separate Electric | + 1268 |

*For Townhouse/Rowhouse - Multiply cost per square foot by*

| | |
|---|---|
| Inner Unit | .94 |
| End Unit | .97 |

## Alternatives

*Add to or deduct from the cost per square foot of living area*

| | |
|---|---|
| Composition Roll Roofing | – .70 |
| Cedar Shake Roof | + 3.95 |
| Upgrade Walls and Ceilings to Skim Coat Plaster | + .94 |
| Upgrade Ceilings to Textured Finish | + .67 |
| Air Conditioning, in Heating Ductwork | + 3.12 |
| In Separate Ductwork | + 6.77 |
| Heating Systems, Hot Water | + 1.96 |
| Heat Pump | + .84 |
| Electric Heat | – 2.38 |
| Not Heated | – 2.07 |

## Additional upgrades or components


| | |
|---|---|
| Kitchen Cabinets & Countertops | Page 58 |
| Bathroom Vanities | 59 |
| Fireplaces & Chimneys | 59 |
| Windows, Skylights & Dormers | 59 |
| Appliances | 60 |
| Breezeways & Porches | 60 |
| Finished Attic | 60 |
| Garages | 61 |
| Site Improvements | 61 |
| Wings & Ells | 25 |


**Important: See the Reference Section for Location Factors (to adjust for your city) and Estimating Forms.**

- **Mass produced from stock plans**
- **Single family – 1 full bath, 1 kitchen**
- **No basement**
- **Asphalt shingles on roof**
- **Hot air heat**
- **Gypsum wallboard interior finishes**
- **Materials and workmanship are sufficient to meet codes**
- **Detail specifications on page 19**

*Note: The illustration shown may contain some optional components (for example: garages and/or fireplaces) whose costs are shown in the modifications, adjustments, & alternatives below or at the end of the square foot section.*

## Base cost per square foot of living area

| Exterior Wall | Living Area 1200 | 1500 | 1800 | 2000 | 2200 | 2400 | 2800 | 3200 | 3600 | 4000 | 4400 |
|---|---|---|---|---|---|---|---|---|---|---|---|
| Wood Siding - Wood Frame | 144.35 | 133.25 | 124.30 | 120.75 | 115.70 | 111.55 | 108.50 | 103.95 | 98.90 | 97.00 | 93.05 |
| Brick Veneer - Wood Frame | 156.25 | 144.00 | 134.00 | 130.00 | 124.50 | 119.80 | 116.40 | 111.30 | 105.70 | 103.70 | 99.25 |
| Stucco on Wood Frame | 136.45 | 126.00 | 117.80 | 114.50 | 109.80 | 105.95 | 103.15 | 99.05 | 94.30 | 92.60 | 88.85 |
| Solid Masonry | 135.80 | 125.50 | 117.30 | 114.00 | 109.30 | 105.55 | 102.70 | 98.65 | 93.95 | 92.25 | 88.60 |
| Finished Basement, Add* | 26.35 | 25.50 | 24.70 | 24.35 | 24.05 | 23.60 | 23.35 | 22.95 | 22.55 | 22.40 | 22.10 |
| Unfinished Basement, Add* | 10.25 | 9.65 | 9.05 | 8.80 | 8.50 | 8.20 | 8.00 | 7.65 | 7.40 | 7.25 | 7.05 |

*Basement under middle level only.

## Modifications

*Add to the total cost*

| | |
|---|---|
| Upgrade Kitchen Cabinets | $ + 1366 |
| Solid Surface Countertops | + 997 |
| Full Bath - including plumbing, wall and floor finishes | + 7293 |
| Half Bath - including plumbing, wall and floor finishes | + 4097 |
| One Car Attached Garage | + 20,336 |
| One Car Detached Garage | + 25,718 |
| Fireplace & Chimney | + 9950 |

## Adjustments

*For multi family - add to total cost*

| | |
|---|---|
| Additional Kitchen | $ + 6765 |
| Additional Bath | + 7293 |
| Additional Entry & Exit | + 2368 |
| Separate Heating | + 1780 |
| Separate Electric | + 1268 |

*For Townhouse/Rowhouse - Multiply cost per square foot by*

| | |
|---|---|
| Inner Unit | .93 |
| End Unit | .96 |

## Alternatives

*Add to or deduct from the cost per square foot of living area*

| | |
|---|---|
| Composition Roll Roofing | – .95 |
| Cedar Shake Roof | + 5.70 |
| Upgrade Walls and Ceilings to Skim Coat Plaster | + .85 |
| Upgrade Ceilings to Textured Finish | + .67 |
| Air Conditioning, in Heating Ductwork | + 2.67 |
| In Separate Ductwork | + 6.28 |
| Heating Systems, Hot Water | + 1.89 |
| Heat Pump | + .88 |
| Electric Heat | – 2.05 |
| Not Heated | – 2.01 |

## Additional upgrades or components


| | |
|---|---|
| Kitchen Cabinets & Countertops | Page 58 |
| Bathroom Vanities | 59 |
| Fireplaces & Chimneys | 59 |
| Windows, Skylights & Dormers | 59 |
| Appliances | 60 |
| Breezeways & Porches | 60 |
| Finished Attic | 60 |
| Garages | 61 |
| Site Improvements | 61 |
| Wings & Ells | 25 |




**Important: See the Reference Section for Location Factors (to adjust for your city) and Estimating Forms.**

## 1 Story — Base cost per square foot of living area

| Exterior Wall | Living Area 50 | 100 | 200 | 300 | 400 | 500 | 600 | 700 |
|---|---|---|---|---|---|---|---|---|
| Wood Siding - Wood Frame | 263.85 | 201.65 | 174.90 | 143.25 | 134.50 | 129.20 | 125.65 | 125.95 |
| Brick Veneer - Wood Frame | 301.10 | 228.30 | 197.05 | 158.00 | 147.75 | 141.65 | 137.50 | 137.40 |
| Stucco on Wood Frame | 238.75 | 183.75 | 159.95 | 133.30 | 125.50 | 120.85 | 117.70 | 118.30 |
| Painted Concrete Block | 237.50 | 182.85 | 159.15 | 132.80 | 125.10 | 120.45 | 117.30 | 117.90 |
| Finished Basement, Add | 63.30 | 52.70 | 48.25 | 40.90 | 39.45 | 38.55 | 37.95 | 37.55 |
| Unfinished Basement, Add | 33.70 | 25.55 | 22.15 | 16.50 | 15.40 | 14.70 | 14.25 | 13.95 |

## 1-1/2 Story — Base cost per square foot of living area

| Exterior Wall | Living Area 100 | 200 | 300 | 400 | 500 | 600 | 700 | 800 |
|---|---|---|---|---|---|---|---|---|
| Wood Siding - Wood Frame | 209.20 | 169.15 | 144.20 | 126.80 | 119.25 | 115.40 | 110.75 | 109.55 |
| Brick Veneer - Wood Frame | 242.50 | 195.75 | 166.40 | 144.10 | 135.25 | 130.45 | 125.00 | 123.70 |
| Stucco on Wood Frame | 186.85 | 151.25 | 129.30 | 115.15 | 108.55 | 105.25 | 101.20 | 100.05 |
| Painted Concrete Block | 185.70 | 150.30 | 128.55 | 114.55 | 107.95 | 104.70 | 100.65 | 99.55 |
| Finished Basement, Add | 43.05 | 38.65 | 35.70 | 32.45 | 31.60 | 31.00 | 30.45 | 30.35 |
| Unfinished Basement, Add | 21.15 | 17.80 | 15.50 | 13.00 | 12.30 | 11.90 | 11.45 | 11.40 |

## 2 Story — Base cost per square foot of living area

| Exterior Wall | Living Area 100 | 200 | 400 | 600 | 800 | 1000 | 1200 | 1400 |
|---|---|---|---|---|---|---|---|---|
| Wood Siding - Wood Frame | 216.80 | 161.40 | 137.40 | 110.40 | 102.60 | 97.90 | 94.75 | 95.30 |
| Brick Veneer - Wood Frame | 254.05 | 188.00 | 159.60 | 125.25 | 115.90 | 110.35 | 106.60 | 106.70 |
| Stucco on Wood Frame | 191.75 | 143.50 | 122.50 | 100.45 | 93.65 | 89.55 | 86.80 | 87.65 |
| Painted Concrete Block | 190.40 | 142.50 | 121.70 | 99.95 | 93.20 | 89.15 | 86.40 | 87.20 |
| Finished Basement, Add | 31.65 | 26.35 | 24.15 | 20.45 | 19.80 | 19.30 | 19.05 | 18.80 |
| Unfinished Basement, Add | 16.90 | 12.80 | 11.10 | 8.25 | 7.75 | 7.40 | 7.15 | 7.00 |

Base costs do not include bathroom or kitchen facilities. Use Modifications/Adjustments/Alternatives on pages 58-61 where appropriate.

## 1 Story

## 1-1/2 Story

## 2 Story

## 2-1/2 Story

## Bi-Level

## Tri-Level

| | Components |
|---|---|
| **1 Site Work** | Site preparation for slab or excavation for lower level; 4′ deep trench excavation for foundation wall. |
| **2 Foundations** | Continuous reinforced concrete footing, 8″ deep x 18″ wide; dampproofed and insulated 8″ thick reinforced concrete foundation wall, 4′ deep; 4″ concrete slab on 4″ crushed stone base and polyethylene vapor barrier, trowel finish. |
| **3 Framing** | Exterior walls—2 x 4 wood studs, 16″ O.C.; 1/2″ plywood sheathing; 2 x 6 rafters 16″ O.C. with 1/2″ plywood sheathing, 4 in 12 or 8 in 12 roof pitch, 2 x 6 ceiling joists; 1/2″ plywood subfloor on 1 x 2 wood sleepers 16″ O.C.; 2 x 8 floor joists with 5/8″ plywood subfloor on models with more than one level. |
| **4 Exterior Walls** | Beveled wood siding and #15 felt building paper on insulated wood frame walls; double hung windows; 3 flush solid core wood exterior doors with storms.<br>**Alternates:**<br>• Brick veneer on wood frame, has 4″ veneer of common brick.<br>• Stucco on wood frame has 1″ thick colored stucco finish.<br>• Solid masonry has a 6″ concrete block load bearing wall with insulation and a brick or stone exterior. Also solid brick or stone walls. |
| **5 Roofing** | 25 year asphalt shingles; #15 felt building paper; aluminum gutters, downspouts, drip edge and flashings. |
| **6 Interiors** | Walls and ceilings—1/2″ taped and finished drywall, primed and painted with 2 coats; painted baseboard and trim, finished hardwood floor 40%, carpet with 1/2″ underlayment 40%, vinyl tile with 1/2″ underlayment 15%, ceramic tile with 1/2″ underlayment 5%; hollow core and louvered interior doors. |
| **7 Specialties** | Average grade kitchen cabinets—14 L.F. wall and base with plastic laminate counter top and kitchen sink; 40 gallon electric water heater. |
| **8 Mechanical** | 1 lavatory, white, wall hung; 1 water closet, white; 1 bathtub, enameled steel, white; gas fired warm air heat. |
| **9 Electrical** | 100 Amp. service; romex wiring; incandescent lighting fixtures, switches, receptacles. |
| **10 Overhead and Profit** | General Contractor overhead and profit. |

## Adjustments

***Unfinished Basement:***

7′-6″ high cast-in-place concrete walls 8″ thick or 8″ concrete block.

***Finished Basement:***

Includes plywood paneling or drywall on furring on foundation walls, sponge backed carpeting on concrete floor, suspended ceiling, lighting and heating.

# RESIDENTIAL | Average | 1 Story

- **Simple design from standard plans**
- **Single family — 1 full bath, 1 kitchen**
- **No basement**
- **Asphalt shingles on roof**
- **Hot air heat**
- **Gypsum wallboard interior finishes**
- **Materials and workmanship are average**
- **Detail specifications on p. 27**

*Note: The illustration shown may contain some optional components (for example: garages and/or fireplaces) whose costs are shown in the modifications, adjustments, & alternatives below or at the end of the square foot section.*

## Base cost per square foot of living area

| Exterior Wall | Living Area 600 | 800 | 1000 | 1200 | 1400 | 1600 | 1800 | 2000 | 2400 | 2800 | 3200 |
|---|---|---|---|---|---|---|---|---|---|---|---|
| Wood Siding - Wood Frame | 216.40 | 194.30 | 178.85 | 166.00 | 155.10 | 148.05 | 144.50 | 139.65 | 130.60 | 123.95 | 119.15 |
| Brick Veneer - Wood Frame | 221.75 | 199.05 | 183.15 | 169.90 | 158.70 | 151.40 | 147.65 | 142.70 | 133.35 | 126.50 | 121.55 |
| Stucco on Wood Frame | 209.60 | 188.20 | 173.35 | 161.05 | 150.60 | 143.80 | 140.35 | 135.85 | 127.05 | 120.70 | 116.15 |
| Solid Masonry | 242.60 | 217.65 | 200.00 | 185.15 | 172.55 | 164.35 | 160.20 | 154.45 | 144.05 | 136.35 | 130.70 |
| Finished Basement, Add | 49.85 | 48.95 | 47.20 | 45.55 | 44.15 | 43.30 | 42.85 | 42.05 | 41.10 | 40.25 | 39.55 |
| Unfinished Basement, Add | 20.30 | 19.05 | 18.05 | 17.10 | 16.30 | 15.85 | 15.55 | 15.10 | 14.55 | 14.10 | 13.70 |

## Modifications

*Add to the total cost*

| | |
|---|---|
| Upgrade Kitchen Cabinets | $ + 6715 |
| Solid Surface Countertops (Included) | |
| Full Bath - including plumbing, wall and floor finishes | + 9116 |
| Half Bath - including plumbing, wall and floor finishes | + 5121 |
| One Car Attached Garage | + 21,787 |
| One Car Detached Garage | + 28,036 |
| Fireplace & Chimney | + 9740 |

## Adjustments

*For multi family - add to total cost*

| | |
|---|---|
| Additional Kitchen | $ + 11,862 |
| Additional Bath | + 9116 |
| Additional Entry & Exit | + 2368 |
| Separate Heating | + 1780 |
| Separate Electric | + 2210 |

*For Townhouse/Rowhouse - Multiply cost per square foot by*

| | |
|---|---|
| Inner Unit | .92 |
| End Unit | .96 |

## Alternatives

*Add to or deduct from the cost per square foot of living area*

| | |
|---|---|
| Cedar Shake Roof | + 7.40 |
| Clay Tile Roof | + 7.10 |
| Slate Roof | + 10.15 |
| Upgrade Walls to Skim Coat Plaster | + .61 |
| Upgrade Ceilings to Textured Finish | + .67 |
| Air Conditioning, in Heating Ductwork | + 5.34 |
| In Separate Ductwork | + 8.70 |
| Heating Systems, Hot Water | + 2.16 |
| Heat Pump | + .76 |
| Electric Heat | – 1.90 |
| Not Heated | – 1.99 |

## Additional upgrades or components



| | |
|---|---|
| Kitchen Cabinets & Countertops | Page 58 |
| Bathroom Vanities | 59 |
| Fireplaces & Chimneys | 59 |
| Windows, Skylights & Dormers | 59 |
| Appliances | 60 |
| Breezeways & Porches | 60 |
| Finished Attic | 60 |
| Garages | 61 |
| Site Improvements | 61 |
| Wings & Ells | 37 |





**Important: See the Reference Section for Location Factors (to adjust for your city) and Estimating Forms.**

- **Simple design from standard plans**
- **Single family — 1 full bath, 1 kitchen**
- **No basement**
- **Asphalt shingles on roof**
- **Hot air heat**
- **Gypsum wallboard interior finishes**
- **Materials and workmanship are average**
- **Detail specifications on p. 27**

*Note: The illustration shown may contain some optional components (for example: garages and/or fireplaces) whose costs are shown in the modifications, adjustments, & alternatives below or at the end of the square foot section.*

©By Designer

## Base cost per square foot of living area

| | Living Area | | | | | | | | | | |
|---|---|---|---|---|---|---|---|---|---|---|---|
| **Exterior Wall** | **600** | **800** | **1000** | **1200** | **1400** | **1600** | **1800** | **2000** | **2400** | **2800** | **3200** |
| Wood Siding - Wood Frame | 244.65 | 202.95 | 182.20 | 172.00 | 164.60 | 154.35 | 148.75 | 143.25 | 132.05 | 127.45 | 122.80 |
| Brick Veneer - Wood Frame | 252.35 | 208.50 | 187.35 | 176.80 | 169.20 | 158.55 | 152.75 | 147.05 | 135.35 | 130.60 | 125.70 |
| Stucco on Wood Frame | 234.80 | 195.80 | 175.60 | 165.80 | 158.70 | 148.95 | 143.65 | 138.40 | 127.75 | 123.40 | 119.05 |
| Solid Masonry | 280.90 | 229.20 | 206.50 | 194.75 | 186.30 | 174.10 | 167.50 | 161.05 | 147.75 | 142.30 | 136.55 |
| Finished Basement, Add | 39.30 | 35.05 | 34.00 | 33.20 | 32.60 | 31.50 | 30.95 | 30.50 | 29.35 | 28.90 | 28.35 |
| Unfinished Basement, Add | 16.45 | 13.50 | 12.85 | 12.40 | 12.05 | 11.45 | 11.15 | 10.80 | 10.20 | 9.95 | 9.60 |

## Modifications

*Add to the total cost*

| | |
|---|---|
| Upgrade Kitchen Cabinets | $ + 6715 |
| Solid Surface Countertops (Included) | |
| Full Bath - including plumbing, wall and floor finishes | + 9116 |
| Half Bath - including plumbing, wall and floor finishes | + 5121 |
| One Car Attached Garage | + 21,787 |
| One Car Detached Garage | + 28,036 |
| Fireplace & Chimney | + 9740 |

## Adjustments

*For multi family - add to total cost*

| | |
|---|---|
| Additional Kitchen | $ + 11,862 |
| Additional Bath | + 9116 |
| Additional Entry & Exit | + 2368 |
| Separate Heating | + 1780 |
| Separate Electric | + 2210 |

*For Townhouse/Rowhouse - Multiply cost per square foot by*

| | |
|---|---|
| Inner Unit | .92 |
| End Unit | .96 |

## Alternatives

*Add to or deduct from the cost per square foot of living area*

| | |
|---|---|
| Cedar Shake Roof | + 5.30 |
| Clay Tile Roof | + 5.10 |
| Slate Roof | + 7.35 |
| Upgrade Walls to Skim Coat Plaster | + .70 |
| Upgrade Ceilings to Textured Finish | + .67 |
| Air Conditioning, in Heating Ductwork | + 4.05 |
| In Separate Ductwork | + 7.61 |
| Heating Systems, Hot Water | + 2.05 |
| Heat Pump | + .83 |
| Electric Heat | − 1.72 |
| Not Heated | − 1.92 |

## Additional upgrades or components



**Important: See the Reference Section for Location Factors (to adjust for your city) and Estimating Forms.**

- **Simple design from standard plans**
- **Single family — 1 full bath, 1 kitchen**
- **No basement**
- **Asphalt shingles on roof**
- **Hot air heat**
- **Gypsum wallboard interior finishes**
- **Materials and workmanship are average**
- **Detail specifications on p. 27**

*Note: The illustration shown may contain some optional components (for example: garages and/or fireplaces) whose costs are shown in the modifications, adjustments, & alternatives below or at the end of the square foot section.*

## Base cost per square foot of living area

| Exterior Wall | Living Area 1000 | 1200 | 1400 | 1600 | 1800 | 2000 | 2200 | 2600 | 3000 | 3400 | 3800 |
|---|---|---|---|---|---|---|---|---|---|---|---|
| Wood Siding - Wood Frame | 186.25 | 169.00 | 160.35 | 154.50 | 148.70 | 142.60 | 138.20 | 129.95 | 122.25 | 118.60 | 115.50 |
| Brick Veneer - Wood Frame | 191.80 | 174.10 | 165.15 | 159.05 | 153.05 | 146.75 | 142.15 | 133.55 | 125.55 | 121.75 | 118.50 |
| Stucco on Wood Frame | 179.40 | 162.65 | 154.40 | 148.75 | 143.35 | 137.40 | 133.30 | 125.60 | 118.10 | 114.65 | 111.75 |
| Solid Masonry | 214.90 | 195.55 | 185.20 | 178.15 | 171.00 | 164.05 | 158.60 | 148.45 | 139.35 | 134.80 | 130.90 |
| Finished Basement, Add | 28.40 | 28.30 | 27.60 | 27.20 | 26.65 | 26.30 | 25.90 | 25.10 | 24.55 | 24.20 | 23.90 |
| Unfinished Basement, Add | 10.85 | 10.40 | 10.00 | 9.75 | 9.45 | 9.25 | 9.00 | 8.60 | 8.25 | 8.05 | 7.90 |

## Modifications

*Add to the total cost*

| | |
|---|---|
| Upgrade Kitchen Cabinets | $ + 6715 |
| Solid Surface Countertops (Included) | |
| Full Bath - including plumbing, wall and floor finishes | + 9116 |
| Half Bath - including plumbing, wall and floor finishes | + 5121 |
| One Car Attached Garage | + 21,787 |
| One Car Detached Garage | + 28,036 |
| Fireplace & Chimney | + 10,762 |

## Adjustments

*For multi family - add to total cost*

| | |
|---|---|
| Additional Kitchen | $ + 11,862 |
| Additional Bath | + 9116 |
| Additional Entry & Exit | + 2368 |
| Separate Heating | + 1780 |
| Separate Electric | + 2210 |

*For Townhouse/Rowhouse - Multiply cost per square foot by*

| | |
|---|---|
| Inner Unit | .90 |
| End Unit | .95 |

## Alternatives

*Add to or deduct from the cost per square foot of living area*

| | |
|---|---|
| Cedar Shake Roof | + 3.70 |
| Clay Tile Roof | + 3.55 |
| Slate Roof | + 5.10 |
| Upgrade Walls to Skim Coat Plaster | + .72 |
| Upgrade Ceilings to Textured Finish | + .67 |
| Air Conditioning, in Heating Ductwork | + 3.22 |
| In Separate Ductwork | + 6.92 |
| Heating Systems, Hot Water | + 2.01 |
| Heat Pump | + .88 |
| Electric Heat | – 1.49 |
| Not Heated | – 1.85 |

## Additional upgrades or components


| | |
|---|---|
| Kitchen Cabinets & Countertops | Page 58 |
| Bathroom Vanities | 59 |
| Fireplaces & Chimneys | 59 |
| Windows, Skylights & Dormers | 59 |
| Appliances | 60 |
| Breezeways & Porches | 60 |
| Finished Attic | 60 |
| Garages | 61 |
| Site Improvements | 61 |
| Wings & Ells | 37 |




**Important: See the Reference Section for Location Factors (to adjust for your city) and Estimating Forms.**

- **Simple design from standard plans**
- **Single family — 1 full bath, 1 kitchen**
- **No basement**
- **Asphalt shingles on roof**
- **Hot air heat**
- **Gypsum wallboard interior finishes**
- **Materials and workmanship are average**
- **Detail specifications on p. 27**

*Note: The illustration shown may contain some optional components (for example: garages and/or fireplaces) whose costs are shown in the modifications, adjustments, & alternatives below or at the end of the square foot section.*

## Base cost per square foot of living area

| Exterior Wall | Living Area 1200 | 1400 | 1600 | 1800 | 2000 | 2400 | 2800 | 3200 | 3600 | 4000 | 4400 |
|---|---|---|---|---|---|---|---|---|---|---|---|
| Wood Siding - Wood Frame | 185.45 | 173.75 | 158.95 | 156.05 | 150.30 | 141.40 | 134.45 | 127.10 | 123.30 | 116.80 | 114.70 |
| Brick Veneer - Wood Frame | 191.50 | 179.20 | 163.95 | 161.10 | 155.00 | 145.65 | 138.50 | 130.80 | 126.85 | 120.05 | 117.85 |
| Stucco on Wood Frame | 177.85 | 166.85 | 152.60 | 149.70 | 144.30 | 136.00 | 129.30 | 122.45 | 118.90 | 112.70 | 110.70 |
| Solid Masonry | 215.75 | 201.10 | 184.15 | 181.30 | 174.00 | 162.75 | 154.90 | 145.65 | 140.90 | 133.10 | 130.45 |
| Finished Basement, Add | 23.85 | 23.55 | 22.85 | 22.85 | 22.40 | 21.65 | 21.35 | 20.75 | 20.45 | 20.05 | 19.90 |
| Unfinished Basement, Add | 8.95 | 8.40 | 8.05 | 8.05 | 7.75 | 7.35 | 7.15 | 6.80 | 6.65 | 6.40 | 6.30 |

## Modifications

*Add to the total cost*

| | |
|---|---|
| Upgrade Kitchen Cabinets | $ + 6715 |
| Solid Surface Countertops (Included) | |
| Full Bath - including plumbing, wall and floor finishes | + 9116 |
| Half Bath - including plumbing, wall and floor finishes | + 5121 |
| One Car Attached Garage | + 21,787 |
| One Car Detached Garage | + 28,036 |
| Fireplace & Chimney | + 11,805 |

## Adjustments

*For multi family - add to total cost*

| | |
|---|---|
| Additional Kitchen | $ + 11,862 |
| Additional Bath | + 9116 |
| Additional Entry & Exit | + 2368 |
| Separate Heating | + 1780 |
| Separate Electric | + 2210 |

*For Townhouse/Rowhouse - Multiply cost per square foot by*

| | |
|---|---|
| Inner Unit | .90 |
| End Unit | .95 |

## Alternatives

*Add to or deduct from the cost per square foot of living area*

| | |
|---|---|
| Cedar Shake Roof | + 3.20 |
| Clay Tile Roof | + 3.05 |
| Slate Roof | + 4.40 |
| Upgrade Walls to Skim Coat Plaster | + .70 |
| Upgrade Ceilings to Textured Finish | + .67 |
| Air Conditioning, in Heating Ductwork | + 2.93 |
| In Separate Ductwork | + 6.71 |
| Heating Systems, Hot Water | + 1.84 |
| Heat Pump | + .90 |
| Electric Heat | – 2.65 |
| Not Heated | – 2.16 |

## Additional upgrades or components


| | |
|---|---|
| Kitchen Cabinets & Countertops | Page 58 |
| Bathroom Vanities | 59 |
| Fireplaces & Chimneys | 59 |
| Windows, Skylights & Dormers | 59 |
| Appliances | 60 |
| Breezeways & Porches | 60 |
| Finished Attic | 60 |
| Garages | 61 |
| Site Improvements | 61 |
| Wings & Ells | 37 |


**Important: See the Reference Section for Location Factors (to adjust for your city) and Estimating Forms.**

- **Simple design from standard plans**
- **Single family — 1 full bath, 1 kitchen**
- **No basement**
- **Asphalt shingles on roof**
- **Hot air heat**
- **Gypsum wallboard interior finishes**
- **Materials and workmanship are average**
- **Detail specifications on p. 27**

*Note: The illustration shown may contain some optional components (for example: garages and/or fireplaces) whose costs are shown in the modifications, adjustments, & alternatives below or at the end of the square foot section.*

## Base cost per square foot of living area

| | Living Area | | | | | | | | | | |
|---|---|---|---|---|---|---|---|---|---|---|---|
| Exterior Wall | 1500 | 1800 | 2100 | 2500 | 3000 | 3500 | 4000 | 4500 | 5000 | 5500 | 6000 |
| Wood Siding - Wood Frame | 168.45 | 153.05 | 146.00 | 140.40 | 130.40 | 125.70 | 119.35 | 112.55 | 110.35 | 107.90 | 105.20 |
| Brick Veneer - Wood Frame | 173.90 | 158.10 | 150.70 | 144.90 | 134.45 | 129.55 | 122.80 | 115.80 | 113.45 | 110.95 | 108.00 |
| Stucco on Wood Frame | 161.70 | 146.85 | 140.15 | 134.80 | 125.30 | 120.95 | 115.00 | 108.55 | 106.50 | 104.15 | 101.70 |
| Solid Masonry | 197.25 | 179.75 | 170.90 | 164.20 | 151.95 | 146.15 | 137.90 | 129.70 | 126.90 | 123.90 | 120.25 |
| Finished Basement, Add | 20.60 | 20.55 | 20.10 | 19.85 | 19.25 | 18.95 | 18.45 | 18.10 | 17.95 | 17.80 | 17.50 |
| Unfinished Basement, Add | 7.35 | 7.00 | 6.75 | 6.65 | 6.30 | 6.10 | 5.80 | 5.60 | 5.55 | 5.45 | 5.25 |

## Modifications

*Add to the total cost*

| | |
|---|---|
| Upgrade Kitchen Cabinets | $ + 6715 |
| Solid Surface Countertops (Included) | |
| Full Bath - including plumbing, wall and floor finishes | + 9116 |
| Half Bath - including plumbing, wall and floor finishes | + 5121 |
| One Car Attached Garage | + 21,787 |
| One Car Detached Garage | + 28,036 |
| Fireplace & Chimney | + 11,805 |

## Adjustments

*For multi family - add to total cost*

| | |
|---|---|
| Additional Kitchen | $ + 11,862 |
| Additional Bath | + 9116 |
| Additional Entry & Exit | + 2368 |
| Separate Heating | + 1780 |
| Separate Electric | + 2210 |

*For Townhouse/Rowhouse - Multiply cost per square foot by*

| | |
|---|---|
| Inner Unit | .88 |
| End Unit | .94 |

## Alternatives

*Add to or deduct from the cost per square foot of living area*

| | |
|---|---|
| Cedar Shake Roof | + 2.45 |
| Clay Tile Roof | + 2.35 |
| Slate Roof | + 3.40 |
| Upgrade Walls to Skim Coat Plaster | + .72 |
| Upgrade Ceilings to Textured Finish | + .67 |
| Air Conditioning, in Heating Ductwork | + 2.93 |
| In Separate Ductwork | + 6.71 |
| Heating Systems, Hot Water | + 1.84 |
| Heat Pump | + .90 |
| Electric Heat | – 2.05 |
| Not Heated | – 2.02 |

## Additional upgrades or components

| | |
|---|---|
| Kitchen Cabinets & Countertops | Page 58 |
| Bathroom Vanities | 59 |
| Fireplaces & Chimneys | 59 |
| Windows, Skylights & Dormers | 59 |
| Appliances | 60 |
| Breezeways & Porches | 60 |
| Finished Attic | 60 |
| Garages | 61 |
| Site Improvements | 61 |
| Wings & Ells | 37 |

- **Simple design from standard plans**
- **Single family — 1 full bath, 1 kitchen**
- **No basement**
- **Asphalt shingles on roof**
- **Hot air heat**
- **Gypsum wallboard interior finishes**
- **Materials and workmanship are average**
- **Detail specifications on p. 27**

*Note: The illustration shown may contain some optional components (for example: garages and/or fireplaces) whose costs are shown in the modifications, adjustments, & alternatives below or at the end of the square foot section.*

## Base cost per square foot of living area

| | Living Area | | | | | | | | | | |
|---|---|---|---|---|---|---|---|---|---|---|---|
| Exterior Wall | 1000 | 1200 | 1400 | 1600 | 1800 | 2000 | 2200 | 2600 | 3000 | 3400 | 3800 |
| Wood Siding - Wood Frame | 172.80 | 156.55 | 148.75 | 143.30 | 138.25 | 132.45 | 128.55 | 121.30 | 114.30 | 110.95 | 108.25 |
| Brick Veneer - Wood Frame | 177.05 | 160.45 | 152.40 | 146.80 | 141.55 | 135.65 | 131.55 | 124.05 | 116.75 | 113.40 | 110.55 |
| Stucco on Wood Frame | 167.55 | 151.70 | 144.20 | 138.95 | 134.20 | 128.50 | 124.85 | 117.95 | 111.10 | 108.00 | 105.45 |
| Solid Masonry | 194.20 | 176.40 | 167.30 | 161.05 | 154.95 | 148.55 | 143.80 | 135.15 | 127.05 | 123.10 | 119.75 |
| Finished Basement, Add | 28.40 | 28.30 | 27.60 | 27.20 | 26.65 | 26.30 | 25.90 | 25.10 | 24.55 | 24.20 | 23.90 |
| Unfinished Basement, Add | 10.85 | 10.40 | 10.00 | 9.75 | 9.45 | 9.25 | 9.00 | 8.60 | 8.25 | 8.05 | 7.90 |

## Modifications

***Add to the total cost***

| | |
|---|---|
| Upgrade Kitchen Cabinets | $ + 6715 |
| Solid Surface Countertops (Included) | |
| Full Bath - including plumbing, wall and floor finishes | + 9116 |
| Half Bath - including plumbing, wall and floor finishes | + 5121 |
| One Car Attached Garage | + 21,787 |
| One Car Detached Garage | + 28,036 |
| Fireplace & Chimney | + 9740 |

## Adjustments

***For multi family - add to total cost***

| | |
|---|---|
| Additional Kitchen | $ + 11,862 |
| Additional Bath | + 9116 |
| Additional Entry & Exit | + 2368 |
| Separate Heating | + 1780 |
| Separate Electric | + 2210 |

***For Townhouse/Rowhouse - Multiply cost per square foot by***

| | |
|---|---|
| Inner Unit | .91 |
| End Unit | .96 |

## Alternatives

***Add to or deduct from the cost per square foot of living area***

| | |
|---|---|
| Cedar Shake Roof | + 3.70 |
| Clay Tile Roof | + 3.55 |
| Slate Roof | + 5.10 |
| Upgrade Walls to Skim Coat Plaster | + .67 |
| Upgrade Ceilings to Textured Finish | + .67 |
| Air Conditioning, in Heating Ductwork | + 3.22 |
| In Separate Ductwork | + 6.92 |
| Heating Systems, Hot Water | + 2.01 |
| Heat Pump | + .88 |
| Electric Heat | – 1.49 |
| Not Heated | – 1.85 |

## Additional upgrades or components


| | |
|---|---|
| Kitchen Cabinets & Countertops | Page 58 |
| Bathroom Vanities | 59 |
| Fireplaces & Chimneys | 59 |
| Windows, Skylights & Dormers | 59 |
| Appliances | 60 |
| Breezeways & Porches | 60 |
| Finished Attic | 60 |
| Garages | 61 |
| Site Improvements | 61 |
| Wings & Ells | 37 |


**Important: See the Reference Section for Location Factors (to adjust for your city) and Estimating Forms.**

- **Simple design from standard plans**
- **Single family — 1 full bath, 1 kitchen**
- **No basement**
- **Asphalt shingles on roof**
- **Hot air heat**
- **Gypsum wallboard interior finishes**
- **Materials and workmanship are average**
- **Detail specifications on p. 27**

*Note: The illustration shown may contain some optional components (for example: garages and/or fireplaces) whose costs are shown in the modifications, adjustments, & alternatives below or at the end of the square foot section.*

## Base cost per square foot of living area

| | Living Area | | | | | | | | | | |
|---|---|---|---|---|---|---|---|---|---|---|---|
| Exterior Wall | 1200 | 1500 | 1800 | 2100 | 2400 | 2700 | 3000 | 3400 | 3800 | 4200 | 4600 |
| Wood Siding - Wood Frame | 161.50 | 148.80 | 138.85 | 130.35 | 124.75 | 121.85 | 118.20 | 114.90 | 109.70 | 105.35 | 103.20 |
| Brick Veneer - Wood Frame | 165.35 | 152.30 | 142.05 | 133.30 | 127.50 | 124.50 | 120.70 | 117.30 | 111.90 | 107.45 | 105.25 |
| Stucco on Wood Frame | 156.55 | 144.30 | 134.75 | 126.70 | 121.30 | 118.55 | 115.10 | 111.95 | 106.90 | 102.75 | 100.70 |
| Solid Masonry | 181.05 | 166.55 | 154.85 | 144.95 | 138.40 | 135.05 | 130.60 | 126.90 | 120.80 | 115.80 | 113.30 |
| Finished Basement, Add* | 33.50 | 33.30 | 32.20 | 31.25 | 30.65 | 30.35 | 29.85 | 29.60 | 29.05 | 28.60 | 28.40 |
| Unfinished Basement, Add* | 12.85 | 12.15 | 11.55 | 11.05 | 10.70 | 10.50 | 10.25 | 10.10 | 9.80 | 9.55 | 9.40 |

*Basement under middle level only.

## Modifications

*Add to the total cost*

| | |
|---|---|
| Upgrade Kitchen Cabinets | $ + 6715 |
| Solid Surface Countertops (Included) | |
| Full Bath - including plumbing, wall and floor finishes | + 9116 |
| Half Bath - including plumbing, wall and floor finishes | + 5121 |
| One Car Attached Garage | + 21,787 |
| One Car Detached Garage | + 28,036 |
| Fireplace & Chimney | + 10,762 |

## Adjustments

*For multi family - add to total cost*

| | |
|---|---|
| Additional Kitchen | $ + 11,862 |
| Additional Bath | + 9116 |
| Additional Entry & Exit | + 2368 |
| Separate Heating | + 1780 |
| Separate Electric | + 2210 |

*For Townhouse/Rowhouse - Multiply cost per square foot by*

| | |
|---|---|
| Inner Unit | .90 |
| End Unit | .95 |

## Alternatives

*Add to or deduct from the cost per square foot of living area*

| | |
|---|---|
| Cedar Shake Roof | + 5.30 |
| Clay Tile Roof | + 5.10 |
| Slate Roof | + 7.35 |
| Upgrade Walls to Skim Coat Plaster | + .58 |
| Upgrade Ceilings to Textured Finish | + .67 |
| Air Conditioning, in Heating Ductwork | + 2.71 |
| In Separate Ductwork | + 6.50 |
| Heating Systems, Hot Water | + 1.96 |
| Heat Pump | + .92 |
| Electric Heat | – 1.25 |
| Not Heated | – 1.79 |

## Additional upgrades or components

| | |
|---|---|
| Kitchen Cabinets & Countertops | Page 58 |
| Bathroom Vanities | 59 |
| Fireplaces & Chimneys | 59 |
| Windows, Skylights & Dormers | 59 |
| Appliances | 60 |
| Breezeways & Porches | 60 |
| Finished Attic | 60 |
| Garages | 61 |
| Site Improvements | 61 |
| Wings & Ells | 37 |



**Important: See the Reference Section for Location Factors (to adjust for your city) and Estimating Forms.**

- **Post and beam frame**
- **Log exterior walls**
- **Simple design from standard plans**
- **Single family — 1 full bath, 1 kitchen**
- **No basement**
- **Asphalt shingles on roof**
- **Hot air heat**
- **Gypsum wallborad interior finishes**
- **Materials and workmanship are average**
- **Detail specification on page 27**

*Note: The illustration shown may contain some optional components (for example: garages and/or fireplaces) whose costs are shown in the modifications, adjustments, & alternatives below or at the end of the square foot section.*

## Base cost per square foot of living area

| Exterior Wall | Living Area 600 | 800 | 1000 | 1200 | 1400 | 1600 | 1800 | 2000 | 2400 | 2800 | 3200 |
|---|---|---|---|---|---|---|---|---|---|---|---|
| 6" Log - Solid Wall | 224.90 | 202.95 | 187.60 | 174.90 | 164.15 | 157.15 | 153.60 | 148.85 | 139.80 | 133.25 | 128.50 |
| 8" Log - Solid Wall | 212.35 | 191.80 | 177.50 | 165.80 | 155.85 | 149.40 | 146.10 | 141.85 | 133.40 | 127.25 | 123.05 |
| Finished Basement, Add | 49.85 | 48.95 | 47.20 | 45.55 | 44.15 | 43.30 | 42.85 | 42.05 | 41.10 | 40.25 | 39.55 |
| Unfinished Basement, Add | 20.30 | 19.05 | 18.05 | 17.10 | 16.30 | 15.85 | 15.55 | 15.10 | 14.55 | 14.10 | 13.70 |

## Modifications

*Add to the total cost*

| | |
|---|---|
| Upgrade Kitchen Cabinets | $ + 6715 |
| Solid Surface Countertops (Included) | |
| Full Bath - including plumbing, wall and floor finishes | + 9116 |
| Half Bath - including plumbing, wall and floor finishes | + 5121 |
| One Car Attached Garage | + 21,787 |
| One Car Detached Garage | + 28,036 |
| Fireplace & Chimney | + 9740 |

## Adjustments

*For multi family - add to total cost*

| | |
|---|---|
| Additional Kitchen | $ + 11,862 |
| Additional Bath | + 9116 |
| Additional Entry & Exit | + 2368 |
| Separate Heating | + 1780 |
| Separate Electric | + 2210 |

*For Townhouse/Rowhouse - Multiply cost per square foot by*

| | |
|---|---|
| Inner Unit | .92 |
| End Unit | .96 |

## Alternatives

*Add to or deduct from the cost per square foot of living area*

| | |
|---|---|
| Cedar Shake Roof | + 7.40 |
| Air Conditioning, in Heating Ductwork | + 5.34 |
| In Separate Ductwork | + 8.69 |
| Heating Systems, Hot Water | + 2.16 |
| Heat Pump | + .76 |
| Electric Heat | − 1.98 |
| Not Heated | − 1.99 |

## Additional upgrades or components


| | |
|---|---|
| Kitchen Cabinets & Countertops | Page 58 |
| Bathroom Vanities | 59 |
| Fireplaces & Chimneys | 59 |
| Windows, Skylights & Dormers | 59 |
| Appliances | 60 |
| Breezeways & Porches | 60 |
| Finished Attic | 60 |
| Garages | 61 |
| Site Improvements | 61 |
| Wings & Ells | 37 |


**Important: See the Reference Section for Location Factors (to adjust for your city) and Estimating Forms.**

- **Post and beam frame**
- **Log exterior walls**
- **Simple design from standard plans**
- **Single family — 1 full bath, 1 kitchen**
- **No basement**
- **Asphalt shingles on roof**
- **Hot air heat**
- **Gypsum wallborad interior finishes**
- **Materials and workmanship are average**
- **Detail specification on page 27**

*Note: The illustration shown may contain some optional components (for example: garages and/or fireplaces) whose costs are shown in the modifications, adjustments, & alternatives below or at the end of the square foot section.*

## Base cost per square foot of living area

| Exterior Wall | Living Area 1000 | 1200 | 1400 | 1600 | 1800 | 2000 | 2200 | 2600 | 3000 | 3400 | 3800 |
|---|---|---|---|---|---|---|---|---|---|---|---|
| 6" Log - Solid Wall | 187.50 | 170.35 | 161.90 | 156.05 | 150.40 | 144.25 | 139.95 | 131.95 | 124.25 | 120.65 | 117.65 |
| 8" Log - Solid Wall | 174.50 | 158.40 | 150.70 | 145.35 | 140.30 | 134.55 | 130.75 | 123.60 | 116.55 | 113.35 | 110.65 |
| Finished Basement, Add | 28.40 | 28.30 | 27.60 | 27.20 | 26.65 | 26.30 | 25.90 | 25.10 | 24.55 | 24.20 | 23.90 |
| Unfinished Basement, Add | 10.85 | 10.40 | 10.00 | 9.75 | 9.45 | 9.25 | 9.00 | 8.60 | 8.25 | 8.05 | 7.90 |

## Modifications

***Add to the total cost***

| | |
|---|---|
| Upgrade Kitchen Cabinets | $ + 6715 |
| Solid Surface Countertops (Included) | |
| Full Bath - including plumbing, wall and floor finishes | + 9116 |
| Half Bath - including plumbing, wall and floor finishes | + 5121 |
| One Car Attached Garage | + 21,787 |
| One Car Detached Garage | + 28,036 |
| Fireplace & Chimney | + 9740 |

## Adjustments

***For multi family - add to total cost***

| | |
|---|---|
| Additional Kitchen | $ + 11,862 |
| Additional Bath | + 9116 |
| Additional Entry & Exit | + 2368 |
| Separate Heating | + 1780 |
| Separate Electric | + 2210 |

***For Townhouse/Rowhouse - Multiply cost per square foot by***

| | |
|---|---|
| Inner Unit | .92 |
| End Unit | .96 |

## Alternatives

***Add to or deduct from the cost per square foot of living area***

| | |
|---|---|
| Cedar Shake Roof | + 3.70 |
| Air Conditioning, in Heating Ductwork | + 3.22 |
| In Separate Ductwork | + 6.92 |
| Heating Systems, Hot Water | + 2.01 |
| Heat Pump | + .88 |
| Electric Heat | – 1.49 |
| Not Heated | – 1.85 |

## Additional upgrades or components


| | |
|---|---|
| Kitchen Cabinets & Countertops | Page 58 |
| Bathroom Vanities | 59 |
| Fireplaces & Chimneys | 59 |
| Windows, Skylights & Dormers | 59 |
| Appliances | 60 |
| Breezeways & Porches | 60 |
| Finished Attic | 60 |
| Garages | 61 |
| Site Improvements | 61 |
| Wings & Ells | 37 |




**Important: See the Reference Section for Location Factors (to adjust for your city) and Estimating Forms.**

## 1 Story — Base cost per square foot of living area

| Exterior Wall | Living Area 50 | 100 | 200 | 300 | 400 | 500 | 600 | 700 |
|---|---|---|---|---|---|---|---|---|
| Wood Siding - Wood Frame | 285.20 | 221.65 | 194.15 | 163.50 | 154.50 | 149.10 | 145.40 | 146.35 |
| Brick Veneer - Wood Frame | 278.50 | 211.50 | 182.55 | 149.45 | 140.00 | 134.25 | 130.40 | 131.15 |
| Stucco on Wood Frame | 269.85 | 210.70 | 184.95 | 157.30 | 148.90 | 143.80 | 140.40 | 141.45 |
| Solid Masonry | 358.50 | 274.05 | 237.80 | 192.65 | 180.75 | 173.50 | 171.75 | 171.40 |
| Finished Basement, Add | 80.15 | 67.50 | 61.30 | 51.00 | 48.95 | 47.70 | 46.90 | 46.30 |
| Unfinished Basement, Add | 37.85 | 29.50 | 26.00 | 20.20 | 19.00 | 18.30 | 17.85 | 17.50 |

## 1-1/2 Story — Base cost per square foot of living area

| Exterior Wall | Living Area 100 | 200 | 300 | 400 | 500 | 600 | 700 | 800 |
|---|---|---|---|---|---|---|---|---|
| Wood Siding - Wood Frame | 232.20 | 187.60 | 161.10 | 144.15 | 136.05 | 132.05 | 127.15 | 125.70 |
| Brick Veneer - Wood Frame | 276.40 | 213.05 | 179.50 | 158.15 | 148.05 | 142.55 | 136.60 | 134.50 |
| Stucco on Wood Frame | 252.00 | 193.55 | 163.20 | 145.45 | 136.35 | 131.50 | 126.20 | 124.15 |
| Solid Masonry | 330.85 | 256.60 | 215.85 | 186.50 | 174.20 | 167.25 | 159.95 | 157.70 |
| Finished Basement, Add | 54.80 | 50.15 | 46.05 | 41.50 | 40.25 | 39.45 | 38.65 | 38.55 |
| Unfinished Basement, Add | 24.35 | 20.85 | 18.55 | 16.00 | 15.30 | 14.80 | 14.35 | 14.35 |

## 2 Story — Base cost per square foot of living area

| Exterior Wall | Living Area 100 | 200 | 400 | 600 | 800 | 1000 | 1200 | 1400 |
|---|---|---|---|---|---|---|---|---|
| Wood Siding - Wood Frame | 229.45 | 173.00 | 148.40 | 122.70 | 114.65 | 109.85 | 106.60 | 107.75 |
| Brick Veneer - Wood Frame | 280.85 | 201.40 | 165.55 | 134.10 | 123.95 | 117.85 | 113.75 | 114.25 |
| Stucco on Wood Frame | 253.55 | 181.85 | 149.25 | 123.25 | 114.15 | 108.75 | 105.10 | 105.95 |
| Solid Masonry | 341.85 | 244.95 | 201.80 | 158.35 | 145.70 | 138.15 | 133.15 | 133.00 |
| Finished Basement, Add | 42.65 | 36.45 | 33.35 | 28.20 | 27.15 | 26.55 | 26.10 | 25.85 |
| Unfinished Basement, Add | 19.15 | 14.95 | 13.20 | 10.30 | 9.70 | 9.35 | 9.15 | 9.00 |

Base costs do not include bathroom or kitchen facilities. Use Modifications/Adjustments/Alternatives on pages 58-61 where appropriate.

**Important: See the Reference Section for Location Factors (to adjust for your city) and Estimating Forms.**

## 1 Story

## 1-1/2 Story

## 2 Story

## 2-1/2 Story

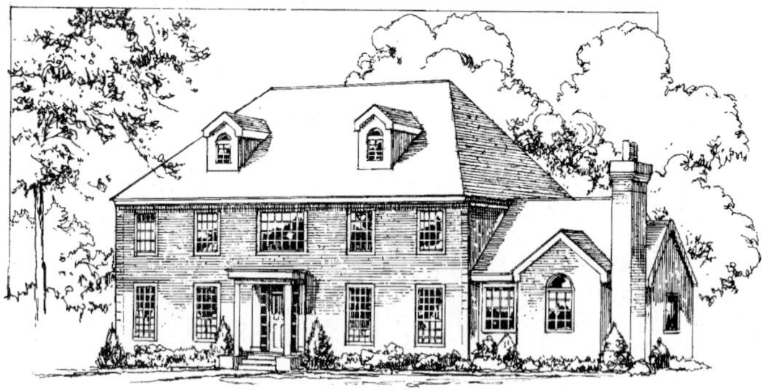

## Bi-Level

## Tri-Level

| | Components |
|---|---|
| **1 Site Work** | Site preparation for slab or excavation for lower level; 4′ deep trench excavation for foundation wall. |
| **2 Foundations** | Continuous reinforced concrete footing, 8″ deep x 18″ wide; dampproofed and insulated 8″ thick reinforced concrete foundation wall, 4′ deep; 4″ concrete slab on 4″ crushed stone base and polyethylene vapor barrier, trowel finish. |
| **3 Framing** | Exterior walls—2 x 6 wood studs, 16″ O.C.; 1/2″ plywood sheathing; 2 x 8 rafters 16″ O.C. with 1/2″ plywood sheathing, 4 in 12, 6 in 12 or 8 in 12 roof pitch, 2 x 6 or 2 x 8 ceiling joists; 1/2″ plywood subfloor on 1 x 3 wood sleepers 16″ O.C.; 2 x 10 floor joists with 5/8″ plywood subfloor on models with more than one level. |
| **4 Exterior Walls** | Horizontal beveled wood siding and #15 felt building paper on insulated wood frame walls; double hung windows; 3 flush solid core wood exterior doors with storms.<br>**Alternates:**<br>• Brick veneer on wood frame, has 4″ veneer high quality face brick or select common brick.<br>• Stone veneer on wood frame has exterior veneer of field stone or 2″ thick limestone.<br>• Solid masonry has an 8″ concrete block wall with insulation and a brick or stone facing. It may be a solid brick or stone structure. |
| **5 Roofing** | 30 year asphalt shingles; #15 felt building paper; aluminum gutters, downspouts and drip edge; copper flashings. |
| **6 Interiors** | Walls and ceilings—5/8″ drywall, skim coat plaster, primed and painted with 2 coats; hardwood baseboard and trim; sanded and finished, hardwood floor 70%, ceramic tile with 1/2″ underlayment 20%, vinyl tile with 1/2″ underlayment 10%; wood panel interior doors, primed and painted with 2 coats. |
| **7 Specialties** | Custom grade kitchen cabinets—20 L.F. wall and base with plastic laminate counter top and kitchen sink; 4 L.F. bathroom vanity; 75 gallon electric water heater; medicine cabinet. |
| **8 Mechanical** | Gas fired warm air heat/air conditioning; one full bath including bathtub, corner shower, built in lavatory and water closet; one 1/2 bath including built in lavatory and water closet. |
| **9 Electrical** | 100 Amp. service; romex wiring; incandescent lighting fixtures, switches, receptacles. |
| **10 Overhead and Profit** | General Contractor overhead and profit. |

## Adjustments

***Unfinished Basement:***
7′-6″ high cast-in-place concrete walls 10″ thick or 12″ concrete block.

***Finished Basement:***
Includes painted drywall on 2 x 4 wood furring with insulation, suspended ceiling, carpeting on concrete floor, heating and lighting.

# RESIDENTIAL | Custom | 1 Story

- **A distinct residence from designer's plans**
- **Single family — 1 full bath, 1 half bath, 1 kitchen**
- **No basement**
- **Asphalt shingles on roof**
- **Forced hot air heat/air conditioning**
- **Gypsum wallboard interior finishes**
- **Materials and workmanship are above average**
- **Detail specifications on page 39**

*Note: The illustration shown may contain some optional components (for example: garages and/or fireplaces) whose costs are shown in the modifications, adjustments, & alternatives below or at the end of the square foot section.*

## Base cost per square foot of living area

| Exterior Wall | Living Area 800 | 1000 | 1200 | 1400 | 1600 | 1800 | 2000 | 2400 | 2800 | 3200 | 3600 |
|---|---|---|---|---|---|---|---|---|---|---|---|
| Wood Siding - Wood Frame | 258.75 | 234.60 | 215.85 | 200.85 | 190.50 | 184.60 | 177.85 | 165.50 | 156.60 | 150.25 | 143.75 |
| Brick Veneer - Wood Frame | 269.10 | 244.05 | 224.35 | 208.55 | 197.65 | 191.50 | 184.40 | 171.50 | 162.05 | 155.35 | 148.50 |
| Stone Veneer - Wood Frame | 293.10 | 265.80 | 243.95 | 226.45 | 214.40 | 207.65 | 199.60 | 185.30 | 174.90 | 167.20 | 159.50 |
| Solid Masonry | 273.80 | 248.25 | 228.15 | 212.00 | 200.95 | 194.70 | 187.35 | 174.20 | 164.60 | 157.65 | 150.60 |
| Finished Basement, Add | 74.60 | 74.55 | 71.50 | 69.15 | 67.50 | 66.65 | 65.35 | 63.55 | 62.15 | 60.95 | 59.85 |
| Unfinished Basement, Add | 31.70 | 30.40 | 29.10 | 28.00 | 27.35 | 26.95 | 26.40 | 25.60 | 24.90 | 24.40 | 23.85 |

## Modifications

*Add to the total cost*

| | |
|---|---|
| Upgrade Kitchen Cabinets | $ + 2070 |
| Solid Surface Countertops (Included) | |
| Full Bath - including plumbing, wall and floor finishes | + 10,939 |
| Half Bath - including plumbing, wall and floor finishes | + 6146 |
| Two Car Attached Garage | + 39,741 |
| Two Car Detached Garage | + 45,377 |
| Fireplace & Chimney | + 9780 |

## Adjustments

*For multi family - add to total cost*

| | |
|---|---|
| Additional Kitchen | $ + 25,614 |
| Additional Full Bath & Half Bath | + 17,085 |
| Additional Entry & Exit | + 2368 |
| Separate Heating & Air Conditioning | + 7781 |
| Separate Electric | + 2210 |

*For Townhouse/Rowhouse - Multiply cost per square foot by*

| | |
|---|---|
| Inner Unit | .90 |
| End Unit | .95 |

## Alternatives

*Add to or deduct from the cost per square foot of living area*

| | |
|---|---|
| Cedar Shake Roof | + 6.35 |
| Clay Tile Roof | + 6.05 |
| Slate Roof | + 9.15 |
| Upgrade Ceilings to Textured Finish | + .67 |
| Air Conditioning, in Heating Ductwork | Base System |
| Heating Systems, Hot Water | + 2.21 |
| Heat Pump | + .76 |
| Electric Heat | − 5.55 |
| Not Heated | − 2.50 |

## Additional upgrades or components

| | |
|---|---|
| Kitchen Cabinets & Countertops | Page 58 |
| Bathroom Vanities | 59 |
| Fireplaces & Chimneys | 59 |
| Windows, Skylights & Dormers | 59 |
| Appliances | 60 |
| Breezeways & Porches | 60 |
| Finished Attic | 60 |
| Garages | 61 |
| Site Improvements | 61 |
| Wings & Ells | 47 |

- **A distinct residence from designer's plans**
- **Single family — 1 full bath, 1 half bath, 1 kitchen**
- **No basement**
- **Asphalt shingles on roof**
- **Forced hot air heat/air conditioning**
- **Gypsum wallboard interior finishes**
- **Materials and workmanship are above average**
- **Detail specifications on page 39**

*Note: The illustration shown may contain some optional components (for example: garages and/or fireplaces) whose costs are shown in the modifications, adjustments, & alternatives below or at the end of the square foot section.*

## Base cost per square foot of living area

| Exterior Wall | 1000 | 1200 | 1400 | 1600 | 1800 | 2000 | 2400 | 2800 | 3200 | 3600 | 4000 |
|---|---|---|---|---|---|---|---|---|---|---|---|
| | Living Area | | | | | | | | | | |
| Wood Siding - Wood Frame | 232.80 | 217.10 | 205.95 | 192.30 | 184.65 | 177.20 | 162.95 | 156.50 | 150.30 | 145.75 | 139.30 |
| Brick Veneer - Wood Frame | 243.90 | 227.55 | 215.95 | 201.35 | 193.20 | 185.35 | 170.15 | 163.30 | 156.60 | 151.80 | 144.95 |
| Stone Veneer - Wood Frame | 269.80 | 251.85 | 239.05 | 222.35 | 213.15 | 204.25 | 186.85 | 179.15 | 171.25 | 165.95 | 158.10 |
| Solid Masonry | 248.90 | 232.25 | 220.40 | 205.35 | 197.00 | 188.95 | 173.35 | 166.35 | 159.45 | 154.50 | 147.45 |
| Finished Basement, Add | 49.30 | 49.70 | 48.45 | 46.60 | 45.55 | 44.65 | 42.75 | 41.85 | 40.85 | 40.30 | 39.50 |
| Unfinished Basement, Add | 20.90 | 20.25 | 19.80 | 18.95 | 18.55 | 18.15 | 17.30 | 16.95 | 16.50 | 16.25 | 15.90 |

## Modifications

*Add to the total cost*

| | |
|---|---|
| Upgrade Kitchen Cabinets | $ + 2070 |
| Solid Surface Countertops (Included) | |
| Full Bath - including plumbing, wall and floor finishes | + 10,939 |
| Half Bath - including plumbing, wall and floor finishes | + 6146 |
| Two Car Attached Garage | + 39,741 |
| Two Car Detached Garage | + 45,377 |
| Fireplace & Chimney | + 9780 |

## Adjustments

*For multi family - add to total cost*

| | |
|---|---|
| Additional Kitchen | $ + 25,614 |
| Additional Full Bath & Half Bath | + 17,085 |
| Additional Entry & Exit | + 2368 |
| Separate Heating & Air Conditioning | + 7781 |
| Separate Electric | + 12,296 |

*For Townhouse/Rowhouse - Multiply cost per square foot by*

| | |
|---|---|
| Inner Unit | .90 |
| End Unit | .95 |

## Alternatives

*Add to or deduct from the cost per square foot of living area*

| | |
|---|---|
| Cedar Shake Roof | + 4.60 |
| Clay Tile Roof | + 4.35 |
| Slate Roof | + 6.60 |
| Upgrade Ceilings to Textured Finish | + .67 |
| Air Conditioning, in Heating Ductwork | Base System |
| Heating Systems, Hot Water | + 2.14 |
| Heat Pump | + .79 |
| Electric Heat | − 4.87 |
| Not Heated | − 2.30 |

## Additional upgrades or components

| | |
|---|---|
| Kitchen Cabinets & Countertops | Page 58 |
| Bathroom Vanities | 59 |
| Fireplaces & Chimneys | 59 |
| Windows, Skylights & Dormers | 59 |
| Appliances | 60 |
| Breezeways & Porches | 60 |
| Finished Attic | 60 |
| Garages | 61 |
| Site Improvements | 61 |
| Wings & Ells | 47 |

**Important: See the Reference Section for Location Factors (to adjust for your city) and Estimating Forms.**

- **A distinct residence from designer's plans**
- **Single family — 1 full bath, 1 half bath, 1 kitchen**
- **No basement**
- **Asphalt shingles on roof**
- **Forced hot air heat/air conditioning**
- **Gypsum wallboard interior finishes**
- **Materials and workmanship are above average**
- **Detail specifications on page 39**

*Note: The illustration shown may contain some optional components (for example: garages and/or fireplaces) whose costs are shown in the modifications, adjustments, & alternatives below or at the end of the square foot section.*

## Base cost per square foot of living area

| | Living Area | | | | | | | | | | |
|---|---|---|---|---|---|---|---|---|---|---|---|
| Exterior Wall | 1200 | 1400 | 1600 | 1800 | 2000 | 2400 | 2800 | 3200 | 3600 | 4000 | 4400 |
| Wood Siding - Wood Frame | 211.80 | 199.30 | 190.30 | 182.30 | 174.15 | 162.00 | 151.80 | 145.05 | 141.05 | 136.70 | 133.15 |
| Brick Veneer - Wood Frame | 222.90 | 209.65 | 200.20 | 191.60 | 183.10 | 170.05 | 159.20 | 151.90 | 147.70 | 142.95 | 139.25 |
| Stone Veneer - Wood Frame | 248.60 | 233.70 | 223.20 | 213.25 | 203.95 | 188.85 | 176.25 | 167.95 | 163.10 | 157.45 | 153.25 |
| Solid Masonry | 228.10 | 214.60 | 204.90 | 196.00 | 187.30 | 173.80 | 162.60 | 155.15 | 150.80 | 145.90 | 142.05 |
| Finished Basement, Add | 39.60 | 39.95 | 39.00 | 37.95 | 37.35 | 35.80 | 34.60 | 33.80 | 33.35 | 32.65 | 32.30 |
| Unfinished Basement, Add | 16.75 | 16.20 | 15.85 | 15.45 | 15.15 | 14.55 | 14.00 | 13.70 | 13.50 | 13.15 | 13.05 |

## Modifications

*Add to the total cost*

| | |
|---|---|
| Upgrade Kitchen Cabinets | $ + 2070 |
| Solid Surface Countertops (Included) | |
| Full Bath - including plumbing, wall and floor finishes | + 10,939 |
| Half Bath - including plumbing, wall and floor finishes | + 6146 |
| Two Car Attached Garage | + 39,741 |
| Two Car Detached Garage | + 45,377 |
| Fireplace & Chimney | + 11,040 |

## Adjustments

*For multi family - add to total cost*

| | |
|---|---|
| Additional Kitchen | $ + 25,614 |
| Additional Full Bath & Half Bath | + 17,085 |
| Additional Entry & Exit | + 2368 |
| Separate Heating & Air Conditioning | + 7781 |
| Separate Electric | + 12,296 |

*For Townhouse/Rowhouse - Multiply cost per square foot by*

| | |
|---|---|
| Inner Unit | .87 |
| End Unit | .93 |

## Alternatives

*Add to or deduct from the cost per square foot of living area*

| | |
|---|---|
| Cedar Shake Roof | + 3.20 |
| Clay Tile Roof | + 3.05 |
| Slate Roof | + 4.60 |
| Upgrade Ceilings to Textured Finish | + .67 |
| Air Conditioning, in Heating Ductwork | Base System |
| Heating Systems, Hot Water | + 2.05 |
| Heat Pump | + .88 |
| Electric Heat | – 4.87 |
| Not Heated | – 2.17 |

## Additional upgrades or components



| | |
|---|---|
| Kitchen Cabinets & Countertops | Page 58 |
| Bathroom Vanities | 59 |
| Fireplaces & Chimneys | 59 |
| Windows, Skylights & Dormers | 59 |
| Appliances | 60 |
| Breezeways & Porches | 60 |
| Finished Attic | 60 |
| Garages | 61 |
| Site Improvements | 61 |
| Wings & Ells | 47 |





**Important: See the Reference Section for Location Factors (to adjust for your city) and Estimating Forms.**

- **A distinct residence from designer's plans**
- **Single family — 1 full bath, 1 half bath, 1 kitchen**
- **No basement**
- **Asphalt shingles on roof**
- **Forced hot air heat/air conditioning**
- **Gypsum wallboard interior finishes**
- **Materials and workmanship are above average**
- **Detail specifications on page 39**

*Note: The illustration shown may contain some optional components (for example: garages and/or fireplaces) whose costs are shown in the modifications, adjustments, & alternatives below or at the end of the square foot section.*

## Base cost per square foot of living area

| Exterior Wall | Living Area 1500 | 1800 | 2100 | 2400 | 2800 | 3200 | 3600 | 4000 | 4500 | 5000 | 5500 |
|---|---|---|---|---|---|---|---|---|---|---|---|
| Wood Siding - Wood Frame | 208.45 | 188.55 | 176.55 | 169.25 | 160.15 | 151.25 | 146.30 | 138.65 | 134.55 | 131.00 | 127.20 |
| Brick Veneer - Wood Frame | 220.25 | 199.45 | 186.30 | 178.50 | 168.95 | 159.25 | 153.90 | 145.70 | 141.25 | 137.30 | 133.25 |
| Stone Veneer - Wood Frame | 247.80 | 224.75 | 208.95 | 199.95 | 189.50 | 177.85 | 171.50 | 162.10 | 156.75 | 152.05 | 147.35 |
| Solid Masonry | 225.75 | 204.50 | 190.85 | 182.75 | 173.00 | 162.95 | 157.40 | 149.00 | 144.30 | 140.30 | 136.05 |
| Finished Basement, Add | 31.40 | 31.45 | 29.95 | 29.20 | 28.55 | 27.50 | 26.95 | 26.25 | 25.75 | 25.40 | 25.00 |
| Unfinished Basement, Add | 13.35 | 12.85 | 12.20 | 11.90 | 11.65 | 11.15 | 10.95 | 10.65 | 10.40 | 10.25 | 10.05 |

## Modifications

*Add to the total cost*

| | |
|---|---|
| Upgrade Kitchen Cabinets | $ + 2070 |
| Solid Surface Countertops (Included) | |
| Full Bath - including plumbing, wall and floor finishes | + 10,939 |
| Half Bath - including plumbing, wall and floor finishes | + 6146 |
| Two Car Attached Garage | + 39,741 |
| Two Car Detached Garage | + 45,377 |
| Fireplace & Chimney | + 12,467 |

## Adjustments

*For multi family - add to total cost*

| | |
|---|---|
| Additional Kitchen | $ + 25,614 |
| Additional Full Bath & Half Bath | + 17,085 |
| Additional Entry & Exit | + 2368 |
| Separate Heating & Air Conditioning | + 7781 |
| Separate Electric | + 12,296 |

*For Townhouse/Rowhouse - Multiply cost per square foot by*

| | |
|---|---|
| Inner Unit | .87 |
| End Unit | .94 |

## Alternatives

*Add to or deduct from the cost per square foot of living area*

| | |
|---|---|
| Cedar Shake Roof | + 2.75 |
| Clay Tile Roof | + 2.60 |
| Slate Roof | + 3.95 |
| Upgrade Ceilings to Textured Finish | + .67 |
| Air Conditioning, in Heating Ductwork | Base System |
| Heating Systems, Hot Water | + 1.87 |
| Heat Pump | + .90 |
| Electric Heat | – 8.61 |
| Not Heated | – 2.17 |

## Additional upgrades or components


| | |
|---|---|
| Kitchen Cabinets & Countertops | Page 58 |
| Bathroom Vanities | 59 |
| Fireplaces & Chimneys | 59 |
| Windows, Skylights & Dormers | 59 |
| Appliances | 60 |
| Breezeways & Porches | 60 |
| Finished Attic | 60 |
| Garages | 61 |
| Site Improvements | 61 |
| Wings & Ells | 47 |


**Important: See the Reference Section for Location Factors (to adjust for your city) and Estimating Forms.**

- **A distinct residence from designer's plans**
- **Single family — 1 full bath, 1 half bath, 1 kitchen**
- **No basement**
- **Asphalt shingles on roof**
- **Forced hot air heat/air conditioning**
- **Gypsum wallboard interior finishes**
- **Materials and workmanship are above average**
- **Detail specifications on page 39**

*Note: The illustration shown may contain some optional components (for example: garages and/or fireplaces) whose costs are shown in the modifications, adjustments, & alternatives below or at the end of the square foot section.*

## Base cost per square foot of living area

| | Living Area | | | | | | | | | | |
|---|---|---|---|---|---|---|---|---|---|---|---|
| Exterior Wall | 1500 | 1800 | 2100 | 2500 | 3000 | 3500 | 4000 | 4500 | 5000 | 5500 | 6000 |
| Wood Siding - Wood Frame | 203.55 | 184.05 | 174.30 | 166.30 | 153.80 | 147.65 | 139.95 | 132.05 | 129.35 | 126.15 | 122.95 |
| Brick Veneer - Wood Frame | 215.35 | 194.95 | 184.50 | 176.00 | 162.65 | 156.00 | 147.60 | 139.10 | 136.10 | 132.65 | 129.10 |
| Stone Veneer - Wood Frame | 242.70 | 220.30 | 208.20 | 198.65 | 183.20 | 175.40 | 165.25 | 155.45 | 151.85 | 147.85 | 143.40 |
| Solid Masonry | 220.90 | 200.10 | 189.40 | 180.65 | 166.80 | 160.00 | 151.20 | 142.40 | 139.35 | 135.85 | 132.00 |
| Finished Basement, Add | 27.50 | 27.55 | 26.65 | 25.95 | 24.85 | 24.25 | 23.45 | 22.80 | 22.50 | 22.20 | 21.80 |
| Unfinished Basement, Add | 11.60 | 11.20 | 10.85 | 10.60 | 10.15 | 9.85 | 9.55 | 9.20 | 9.10 | 9.00 | 8.75 |

## Modifications

***Add to the total cost***

| | |
|---|---|
| Upgrade Kitchen Cabinets | $ + 2070 |
| Solid Surface Countertops (Included) | |
| Full Bath - including plumbing, wall and floor finishes | + 10,939 |
| Half Bath - including plumbing, wall and floor finishes | + 6146 |
| Two Car Attached Garage | + 39,741 |
| Two Car Detached Garage | + 45,377 |
| Fireplace & Chimney | + 12,467 |

## Adjustments

***For multi family - add to total cost***

| | |
|---|---|
| Additional Kitchen | $ + 25,614 |
| Additional Full Bath & Half Bath | + 17,085 |
| Additional Entry & Exit | + 2368 |
| Separate Heating & Air Conditioning | + 7781 |
| Separate Electric | + 12,296 |

***For Townhouse/Rowhouse - Multiply cost per square foot by***

| | |
|---|---|
| Inner Unit | .85 |
| End Unit | .93 |

## Alternatives

***Add to or deduct from the cost per square foot of living area***

| | |
|---|---|
| Cedar Shake Roof | + 2.10 |
| Clay Tile Roof | + 2 |
| Slate Roof | + 3.05 |
| Upgrade Ceilings to Textured Finish | + .67 |
| Air Conditioning, in Heating Ductwork | Base System |
| Heating Systems, Hot Water | + 1.87 |
| Heat Pump | + .90 |
| Electric Heat | – 8.61 |
| Not Heated | – 2.11 |

## Additional upgrades or components


| | |
|---|---|
| Kitchen Cabinets & Countertops | Page 58 |
| Bathroom Vanities | 59 |
| Fireplaces & Chimneys | 59 |
| Windows, Skylights & Dormers | 59 |
| Appliances | 60 |
| Breezeways & Porches | 60 |
| Finished Attic | 60 |
| Garages | 61 |
| Site Improvements | 61 |
| Wings & Ells | 47 |




**Important: See the Reference Section for Location Factors (to adjust for your city) and Estimating Forms.**

- A distinct residence from designer's plans
- Single family — 1 full bath, 1 half bath, 1 kitchen
- No basement
- Asphalt shingles on roof
- Forced hot air heat/air conditioning
- Gypsum wallboard interior finishes
- Materials and workmanship are above average
- Detail specifications on page 39

*Note: The illustration shown may contain some optional components (for example: garages and/or fireplaces) whose costs are shown in the modifications, adjustments, & alternatives below or at the end of the square foot section.*

## Base cost per square foot of living area

| Exterior Wall | Living Area 1200 | 1400 | 1600 | 1800 | 2000 | 2400 | 2800 | 3200 | 3600 | 4000 | 4400 |
|---|---|---|---|---|---|---|---|---|---|---|---|
| Wood Siding - Wood Frame | 200.15 | 188.45 | 180.00 | 172.60 | 164.70 | 153.45 | 144.00 | 137.80 | 134.05 | 130.10 | 126.80 |
| Brick Veneer - Wood Frame | 208.55 | 196.30 | 187.50 | 179.65 | 171.55 | 159.60 | 149.65 | 143.05 | 139.10 | 134.90 | 131.45 |
| Stone Veneer - Wood Frame | 228.20 | 214.60 | 204.95 | 196.10 | 187.40 | 173.90 | 162.65 | 155.25 | 150.85 | 145.95 | 142.15 |
| Solid Masonry | 212.50 | 200.00 | 190.95 | 182.95 | 174.75 | 162.45 | 152.25 | 145.50 | 141.45 | 137.10 | 133.55 |
| Finished Basement, Add | 39.60 | 39.95 | 39.00 | 37.95 | 37.35 | 35.80 | 34.60 | 33.80 | 33.35 | 32.65 | 32.30 |
| Unfinished Basement, Add | 16.75 | 16.20 | 15.85 | 15.45 | 15.15 | 14.55 | 14.00 | 13.70 | 13.50 | 13.15 | 13.05 |

## Modifications

*Add to the total cost*

| | |
|---|---|
| Upgrade Kitchen Cabinets | $ + 2070 |
| Solid Surface Countertops (Included) | |
| Full Bath - including plumbing, wall and floor finishes | + 10,939 |
| Half Bath - including plumbing, wall and floor finishes | + 6146 |
| Two Car Attached Garage | + 39,741 |
| Two Car Detached Garage | + 45,377 |
| Fireplace & Chimney | + 9780 |

## Adjustments

*For multi family - add to total cost*

| | |
|---|---|
| Additional Kitchen | $ + 25,614 |
| Additional Full Bath & Half Bath | + 17,085 |
| Additional Entry & Exit | + 2368 |
| Separate Heating & Air Conditioning | + 7781 |
| Separate Electric | + 12,296 |

*For Townhouse/Rowhouse - Multiply cost per square foot by*

| | |
|---|---|
| Inner Unit | .89 |
| End Unit | .95 |

## Alternatives

*Add to or deduct from the cost per square foot of living area*

| | |
|---|---|
| Cedar Shake Roof | + 3.20 |
| Clay Tile Roof | + 3.05 |
| Slate Roof | + 4.60 |
| Upgrade Ceilings to Textured Finish | + .67 |
| Air Conditioning, in Heating Ductwork | Base System |
| Heating Systems, Hot Water | + 2.05 |
| Heat Pump | + .88 |
| Electric Heat | – 4.87 |
| Not Heated | – 2.11 |

## Additional upgrades or components


| | |
|---|---|
| Kitchen Cabinets & Countertops | Page 58 |
| Bathroom Vanities | 59 |
| Fireplaces & Chimneys | 59 |
| Windows, Skylights & Dormers | 59 |
| Appliances | 60 |
| Breezeways & Porches | 60 |
| Finished Attic | 60 |
| Garages | 61 |
| Site Improvements | 61 |
| Wings & Ells | 47 |


**Important: See the Reference Section for Location Factors (to adjust for your city) and Estimating Forms.**

- A distinct residence from designer's plans
- Single family — 1 full bath, 1 half bath, 1 kitchen
- No basement
- Asphalt shingles on roof
- Forced hot air heat/air conditioning
- Gypsum wallboard interior finishes
- Materials and workmanship are above average
- Detail specifications on page 39

*Note: The illustration shown may contain some optional components (for example: garages and/or fireplaces) whose costs are shown in the modifications, adjustments, & alternatives below or at the end of the square foot section.*

## Base cost per square foot of living area

| Exterior Wall | Living Area 1200 | 1500 | 1800 | 2100 | 2400 | 2800 | 3200 | 3600 | 4000 | 4500 | 5000 |
|---|---|---|---|---|---|---|---|---|---|---|---|
| Wood Siding - Wood Frame | 207.95 | 189.30 | 175.35 | 163.85 | 156.20 | 150.50 | 143.95 | 137.05 | 133.95 | 127.40 | 123.95 |
| Brick Veneer - Wood Frame | 216.40 | 197.00 | 182.30 | 170.15 | 162.10 | 156.20 | 149.15 | 141.90 | 138.70 | 131.80 | 128.05 |
| Stone Veneer - Wood Frame | 236.05 | 214.80 | 198.35 | 184.80 | 175.80 | 169.35 | 161.40 | 153.25 | 149.70 | 141.95 | 137.60 |
| Solid Masonry | 220.30 | 200.45 | 185.50 | 173.05 | 164.85 | 158.80 | 151.55 | 144.15 | 140.90 | 133.80 | 129.95 |
| Finished Basement, Add* | 49.70 | 49.70 | 47.70 | 46.10 | 45.00 | 44.30 | 43.30 | 42.35 | 41.95 | 41.10 | 40.40 |
| Unfinished Basement, Add* | 21.10 | 20.25 | 19.35 | 18.65 | 18.20 | 17.95 | 17.45 | 17.00 | 16.85 | 16.45 | 16.15 |

*Basement under middle level only.

## Modifications

*Add to the total cost*

| | |
|---|---|
| Upgrade Kitchen Cabinets | $ + 2070 |
| Solid Surface Countertops (Included) | |
| Full Bath - including plumbing, wall and floor finishes | + 10,939 |
| Half Bath - including plumbing, wall and floor finishes | + 6146 |
| Two Car Attached Garage | + 39,741 |
| Two Car Detached Garage | + 45,377 |
| Fireplace & Chimney | + 11,040 |

## Adjustments

*For multi family - add to total cost*

| | |
|---|---|
| Additional Kitchen | $ + 25,614 |
| Additional Full Bath & Half Bath | + 17,085 |
| Additional Entry & Exit | + 2368 |
| Separate Heating & Air Conditioning | + 7781 |
| Separate Electric | + 12,296 |

*For Townhouse/Rowhouse - Multiply cost per square foot by*

| | |
|---|---|
| Inner Unit | .87 |
| End Unit | .94 |

## Alternatives

*Add to or deduct from the cost per square foot of living area*

| | |
|---|---|
| Cedar Shake Roof | + 4.60 |
| Clay Tile Roof | + 4.35 |
| Slate Roof | + 6.60 |
| Upgrade Ceilings to Textured Finish | + .67 |
| Air Conditioning, in Heating Ductwork | Base System |
| Heating Systems, Hot Water | + 1.98 |
| Heat Pump | + .91 |
| Electric Heat | – 4.37 |
| Not Heated | – 2.11 |

## Additional upgrades or components


| | |
|---|---|
| Kitchen Cabinets & Countertops | Page 58 |
| Bathroom Vanities | 59 |
| Fireplaces & Chimneys | 59 |
| Windows, Skylights & Dormers | 59 |
| Appliances | 60 |
| Breezeways & Porches | 60 |
| Finished Attic | 60 |
| Garages | 61 |
| Site Improvements | 61 |
| Wings & Ells | 47 |




**Important: See the Reference Section for Location Factors (to adjust for your city) and Estimating Forms.**

## 1 Story — Base cost per square foot of living area

| Exterior Wall | Living Area 50 | 100 | 200 | 300 | 400 | 500 | 600 | 700 |
|---|---|---|---|---|---|---|---|---|
| Wood Siding - Wood Frame | 317.55 | 248.95 | 219.15 | 186.55 | 176.85 | 171.00 | 167.05 | 168.15 |
| Brick Veneer - Wood Frame | 344.15 | 268.00 | 235.00 | 197.15 | 186.35 | 179.85 | 175.55 | 176.30 |
| Stone Veneer - Wood Frame | 406.10 | 312.25 | 271.90 | 221.70 | 208.45 | 200.50 | 195.20 | 195.20 |
| Solid Masonry | 361.45 | 280.35 | 245.35 | 204.00 | 192.60 | 185.65 | 181.00 | 181.55 |
| Finished Basement, Add | 117.65 | 101.10 | 92.00 | 76.80 | 73.75 | 71.95 | 70.75 | 69.90 |
| Unfinished Basement, Add | 59.90 | 47.20 | 41.90 | 33.65 | 31.95 | 31.00 | 30.30 | 29.85 |

## 1-1/2 Story — Base cost per square foot of living area

| Exterior Wall | Living Area 100 | 200 | 300 | 400 | 500 | 600 | 700 | 800 |
|---|---|---|---|---|---|---|---|---|
| Wood Siding - Wood Frame | 251.20 | 207.20 | 180.25 | 163.60 | 155.45 | 151.50 | 146.45 | 145.00 |
| Brick Veneer - Wood Frame | 275.00 | 226.20 | 196.10 | 176.00 | 166.85 | 162.25 | 156.65 | 155.10 |
| Stone Veneer - Wood Frame | 330.30 | 270.45 | 233.00 | 204.75 | 193.40 | 187.30 | 180.35 | 178.60 |
| Solid Masonry | 290.45 | 238.60 | 206.45 | 184.00 | 174.25 | 169.30 | 163.35 | 161.75 |
| Finished Basement, Add | 79.10 | 73.60 | 67.55 | 60.85 | 59.10 | 57.80 | 56.70 | 56.60 |
| Unfinished Basement, Add | 38.95 | 33.60 | 30.20 | 26.60 | 25.60 | 24.90 | 24.30 | 24.20 |

## 2 Story — Base cost per square foot of living area

| Exterior Wall | Living Area 100 | 200 | 400 | 600 | 800 | 1000 | 1200 | 1400 |
|---|---|---|---|---|---|---|---|---|
| Wood Siding - Wood Frame | 249.55 | 191.25 | 165.70 | 140.20 | 131.90 | 126.85 | 123.50 | 124.95 |
| Brick Veneer - Wood Frame | 276.20 | 210.25 | 181.55 | 150.75 | 141.40 | 135.70 | 131.95 | 133.15 |
| Stone Veneer - Wood Frame | 338.15 | 254.50 | 218.40 | 175.30 | 163.55 | 156.35 | 151.60 | 152.10 |
| Solid Masonry | 293.50 | 222.65 | 191.85 | 157.60 | 147.60 | 141.50 | 137.50 | 138.40 |
| Finished Basement, Add | 58.80 | 50.55 | 46.00 | 38.45 | 36.90 | 36.00 | 35.40 | 35.00 |
| Unfinished Basement, Add | 29.95 | 23.60 | 20.95 | 16.85 | 16.00 | 15.45 | 15.15 | 14.90 |

Base costs do not include bathroom or kitchen facilities. Use Modifications/Adjustments/Alternatives on pages 58-61 where appropriate.

## 1 Story

## 1-1/2 Story

## 2 Story

## 2-1/2 Story

## Bi-Level

## Tri-Level

| | Components |
|---|---|
| **1 Site Work** | Site preparation for slab or excavation for lower level; 4′ deep trench excavation for foundation wall. |
| **2 Foundations** | Continuous reinforced concrete footing, 8″ deep x 18″ wide; dampproofed and insulated 12″ thick reinforced concrete foundation wall, 4′ deep; 4″ concrete slab on 4″ crushed stone base and polyethylene vapor barrier, trowel finish. |
| **3 Framing** | Exterior walls—2 x 6 wood studs, 16″ O.C.; 1/2″ plywood sheathing; 2 x 8 rafters 16″ O.C. with 1/2″ plywood sheathing, 4 in 12, 6 in 12 or 8 in 12 roof pitch, 2 x 6 or 2 x 8 ceiling joists; 1/2″ plywood subfloor on 1 x 3 wood sleepers 16″ O.C.; 2 x 10 floor joists with 5/8″ plywood subfloor on models with more than one level. |
| **4 Exterior Walls** | Face brick veneer and #15 felt building paper on insulated wood frame walls; double hung windows; 3 flush solid core wood exterior doors with storms.<br>**Alternates:**<br>• Wood siding on wood frame, has top quality cedar or redwood siding or hand split cedar shingles or shakes.<br>• Solid brick may have solid brick exterior wall or brick on concrete block.<br>• Solid stone concrete block with selected fieldstone or limestone exterior. |
| **5 Roofing** | Red cedar shingles; #15 felt building paper; aluminum gutters, downspouts and drip edge; copper flashings. |
| **6 Interiors** | Walls and ceilings—5/8″ drywall, skim coat plaster, primed and painted with 2 coats; hardwood baseboard and trim; sanded and finished, hardwood floor 70%, ceramic tile with 1/2″ underlayment 20%, vinyl tile with 1/2″ underlayment 10%; wood panel interior doors, primed and painted with 2 coats. |
| **7 Specialties** | Luxury grade kitchen cabinets—25 L.F. wall and base with plastic laminate counter top and kitchen sink; 6 L.F. bathroom vanity; 75 gallon electric water heater; medicine cabinet. |
| **8 Mechanical** | Gas fired warm air heat/air conditioning; one full bath including bathtub, corner shower, built in lavatory and water closet; one 1/2 bath including built in lavatory and water closet. |
| **9 Electrical** | 100 Amp. service; romex wiring; incandescent lighting fixtures, switches, receptacles. |
| **10 Overhead and Profit** | General Contractor overhead and profit. |

## Adjustments

***Unfinished Basement:***

8′-0″ high cast-in-place concrete walls 12″ thick or 12″ concrete block.

***Finished Basement:***

Includes painted drywall on 2 x 4 wood furring with insulation, suspended ceiling, carpeting on subfloor with sleepers, heating and lighting.

- **Unique residence built from an architect's plan**
- **Single family – 1 full bath, 1 half bath, 1 kitchen**
- **No basement**
- **Cedar shakes on roof**
- **Forced hot air heat/air conditioning**
- **Gypsum wallboard interior finishes**
- **Many special features**
- **Extraordinary materials and workmanship**
- **Detail specifications on page 49**

*Note: The illustration shown may contain some optional components (for example: garages and/or fireplaces) whose costs are shown in the modifications, adjustments, & alternatives below or at the end of the square foot section.*

## Base cost per square foot of living area

| Exterior Wall | Living Area 1000 | 1200 | 1400 | 1600 | 1800 | 2000 | 2400 | 2800 | 3200 | 3600 | 4000 |
|---|---|---|---|---|---|---|---|---|---|---|---|
| Wood Siding - Wood Frame | 286.05 | 262.50 | 243.75 | 230.95 | 223.80 | 215.30 | 200.00 | 189.15 | 181.20 | 173.20 | 166.65 |
| Brick Veneer - Wood Frame | 296.55 | 271.90 | 252.35 | 239.00 | 231.65 | 222.60 | 206.70 | 195.30 | 186.90 | 178.50 | 171.65 |
| Solid Brick | 306.75 | 281.05 | 260.65 | 246.85 | 239.15 | 229.65 | 213.20 | 201.25 | 192.40 | 183.65 | 176.45 |
| Solid Stone | 325.65 | 298.15 | 276.25 | 261.40 | 253.15 | 242.90 | 225.25 | 212.35 | 202.75 | 193.20 | 185.50 |
| Finished Basement, Add | 73.15 | 78.90 | 75.95 | 74.00 | 72.80 | 71.20 | 69.00 | 67.20 | 65.70 | 64.35 | 63.20 |
| Unfinished Basement, Add | 33.65 | 32.00 | 30.70 | 29.85 | 29.40 | 28.70 | 27.70 | 26.95 | 26.20 | 25.60 | 25.05 |

## Modifications

***Add to the total cost***

| | |
|---|---|
| Upgrade Kitchen Cabinets | $ + 2915 |
| Solid Surface Countertops (Included) | |
| Full Bath - including plumbing, wall and floor finishes | + 13,127 |
| Half Bath - including plumbing, wall and floor finishes | + 7375 |
| Two Car Attached Garage | + 44,884 |
| Two Car Detached Garage | + 50,881 |
| Fireplace & Chimney | + 14,512 |

## Adjustments

***For multi family - add to total cost***

| | |
|---|---|
| Additional Kitchen | $ + 34,672 |
| Additional Full Bath & Half Bath | + 20,502 |
| Additional Entry & Exit | + 3010 |
| Separate Heating & Air Conditioning | + 7781 |
| Separate Electric | + 12,296 |

***For Townhouse/Rowhouse - Multiply cost per square foot by***

| | |
|---|---|
| Inner Unit | .90 |
| End Unit | .95 |

## Alternatives

***Add to or deduct from the cost per square foot of living area***

| | |
|---|---|
| Heavyweight Asphalt Shingles | – 6.35 |
| Clay Tile Roof | – .30 |
| Slate Roof | + 2.80 |
| Upgrade Ceilings to Textured Finish | + .67 |
| Air Conditioning, in Heating Ductwork | Base System |
| Heating Systems, Hot Water | + 2.39 |
| Heat Pump | + .81 |
| Electric Heat | – 4.87 |
| Not Heated | – 2.72 |

## Additional upgrades or components



| | |
|---|---|
| Kitchen Cabinets & Countertops | Page 58 |
| Bathroom Vanities | 59 |
| Fireplaces & Chimneys | 59 |
| Windows, Skylights & Dormers | 59 |
| Appliances | 60 |
| Breezeways & Porches | 60 |
| Finished Attic | 60 |
| Garages | 61 |
| Site Improvements | 61 |
| Wings & Ells | 57 |





**Important: See the Reference Section for Location Factors (to adjust for your city) and Estimating Forms.**

- **Unique residence built from an architect's plan**
- **Single family — 1 full bath, 1 half bath, 1 kitchen**
- **No basement**
- **Cedar shakes on roof**
- **Forced hot air heat/air conditioning**
- **Gypsum wallboard interior finishes**
- **Many special features**
- **Extraordinary materials and workmanship**
- **Detail specifications on page 49**

*Note: The illustration shown may contain some optional components (for example: garages and/or fireplaces) whose costs are shown in the modifications, adjustments, & alternatives below or at the end of the square foot section.*

## Base cost per square foot of living area

| Exterior Wall | Living Area 1000 | 1200 | 1400 | 1600 | 1800 | 2000 | 2400 | 2800 | 3200 | 3600 | 4000 |
|---|---|---|---|---|---|---|---|---|---|---|---|
| Wood Siding - Wood Frame | 284.75 | 264.75 | 250.55 | 234.35 | 224.50 | 215.20 | 197.60 | 189.45 | 181.90 | 176.20 | 168.35 |
| Brick Veneer - Wood Frame | 297.20 | 276.40 | 261.70 | 244.40 | 234.10 | 224.25 | 205.65 | 197.05 | 188.95 | 183.00 | 174.70 |
| Solid Brick | 308.55 | 287.05 | 271.80 | 253.60 | 242.80 | 232.55 | 212.90 | 203.95 | 195.30 | 189.15 | 180.45 |
| Solid Stone | 331.65 | 308.80 | 292.50 | 272.45 | 260.60 | 249.50 | 227.85 | 218.15 | 208.45 | 201.85 | 192.10 |
| Finished Basement, Add | 51.15 | 55.60 | 54.00 | 51.70 | 50.45 | 49.25 | 46.90 | 45.85 | 44.55 | 43.90 | 42.85 |
| Unfinished Basement, Add | 23.40 | 22.60 | 22.05 | 21.00 | 20.50 | 20.05 | 18.90 | 18.50 | 17.95 | 17.70 | 17.20 |

## Modifications

*Add to the total cost*

| | |
|---|---|
| Upgrade Kitchen Cabinets | $ + 2915 |
| Solid Surface Countertops (Included) | |
| Full Bath - including plumbing, wall and floor finishes | + 13,127 |
| Half Bath - including plumbing, wall and floor finishes | + 7375 |
| Two Car Attached Garage | + 44,884 |
| Two Car Detached Garage | + 50,881 |
| Fireplace & Chimney | + 14,512 |

## Adjustments

*For multi family - add to total cost*

| | |
|---|---|
| Additional Kitchen | $ + 34,672 |
| Additional Full Bath & Half Bath | + 20,502 |
| Additional Entry & Exit | + 3010 |
| Separate Heating & Air Conditioning | + 7781 |
| Separate Electric | + 12,296 |

*For Townhouse/Rowhouse - Multiply cost per square foot by*

| | |
|---|---|
| Inner Unit | .90 |
| End Unit | .95 |

## Alternatives

*Add to or deduct from the cost per square foot of living area*

| | |
|---|---|
| Heavyweight Asphalt Shingles | – 4.60 |
| Clay Tile Roof | – .25 |
| Slate Roof | + 2 |
| Upgrade Ceilings to Textured Finish | + .67 |
| Air Conditioning, in Heating Ductwork | Base System |
| Heating Systems, Hot Water | + 2.29 |
| Heat Pump | + .90 |
| Electric Heat | – 4.87 |
| Not Heated | – 2.50 |

## Additional upgrades or components


| | |
|---|---|
| Kitchen Cabinets & Countertops | Page 58 |
| Bathroom Vanities | 59 |
| Fireplaces & Chimneys | 59 |
| Windows, Skylights & Dormers | 59 |
| Appliances | 60 |
| Breezeways & Porches | 60 |
| Finished Attic | 60 |
| Garages | 61 |
| Site Improvements | 61 |
| Wings & Ells | 57 |


**Important: See the Reference Section for Location Factors (to adjust for your city) and Estimating Forms.**

- **Unique residence built from an architect's plan**
- **Single family — 1 full bath, 1 half bath, 1 kitchen**
- **No basement**
- **Cedar shakes on roof**
- **Forced hot air heat/air conditioning**
- **Gypsum wallboard interior finishes**
- **Many special features**
- **Extraordinary materials and workmanship**
- **Detail specifications on page 49**

*Note: The illustration shown may contain some optional components (for example: garages and/or fireplaces) whose costs are shown in the modifications, adjustments, & alternatives below or at the end of the square foot section.*

## Base cost per square foot of living area

| Exterior Wall | Living Area 1200 | 1400 | 1600 | 1800 | 2000 | 2400 | 2800 | 3200 | 3600 | 4000 | 4400 |
|---|---|---|---|---|---|---|---|---|---|---|---|
| Wood Siding - Wood Frame | 258.60 | 242.95 | 231.70 | 222.05 | 211.95 | 196.85 | 184.35 | 175.95 | 171.20 | 165.70 | 161.35 |
| Brick Veneer - Wood Frame | 271.00 | 254.50 | 242.70 | 232.45 | 222.00 | 205.85 | 192.55 | 183.65 | 178.65 | 172.70 | 168.10 |
| Solid Brick | 284.25 | 266.85 | 254.55 | 243.60 | 232.75 | 215.50 | 201.30 | 191.90 | 186.55 | 180.20 | 175.35 |
| Solid Stone | 305.65 | 286.80 | 273.70 | 261.55 | 249.95 | 231.10 | 215.50 | 205.20 | 199.35 | 192.20 | 186.95 |
| Finished Basement, Add | 41.05 | 44.60 | 43.50 | 42.15 | 41.40 | 39.50 | 38.00 | 37.00 | 36.45 | 35.65 | 35.15 |
| Unfinished Basement, Add | 18.75 | 18.05 | 17.65 | 17.10 | 16.85 | 15.95 | 15.35 | 14.90 | 14.70 | 14.30 | 14.15 |

## Modifications

***Add to the total cost***

| | |
|---|---|
| Upgrade Kitchen Cabinets | $ + 2915 |
| Solid Surface Countertops (Included) | |
| Full Bath - including plumbing, wall and floor finishes | + 13,127 |
| Half Bath - including plumbing, wall and floor finishes | + 7375 |
| Two Car Attached Garage | + 44,884 |
| Two Car Detached Garage | + 50,881 |
| Fireplace & Chimney | + 15,909 |

## Adjustments

***For multi family - add to total cost***

| | |
|---|---|
| Additional Kitchen | $ + 34,672 |
| Additional Full Bath & Half Bath | + 20,502 |
| Additional Entry & Exit | + 3010 |
| Separate Heating & Air Conditioning | + 7781 |
| Separate Electric | + 12,296 |

***For Townhouse/Rowhouse - Multiply cost per square foot by***

| | |
|---|---|
| Inner Unit | .86 |
| End Unit | .93 |

## Alternatives

***Add to or deduct from the cost per square foot of living area***

| | |
|---|---|
| Heavyweight Asphalt Shingles | – 3.20 |
| Clay Tile Roof | – .15 |
| Slate Roof | + 1.40 |
| Upgrade Ceilings to Textured Finish | + .67 |
| Air Conditioning, in Heating Ductwork | Base System |
| Heating Systems, Hot Water | + 2.21 |
| Heat Pump | + .95 |
| Electric Heat | – 4.44 |
| Not Heated | – 2.37 |

## Additional upgrades or components

| | |
|---|---|
| Kitchen Cabinets & Countertops | Page 58 |
| Bathroom Vanities | 59 |
| Fireplaces & Chimneys | 59 |
| Windows, Skylights & Dormers | 59 |
| Appliances | 60 |
| Breezeways & Porches | 60 |
| Finished Attic | 60 |
| Garages | 61 |
| Site Improvements | 61 |
| Wings & Ells | 57 |

- Unique residence built from an architect's plan
- Single family — 1 full bath, 1 half bath, 1 kitchen
- No basement
- Cedar shakes on roof
- Forced hot air heat/air conditioning
- Gypsum wallboard interior finishes
- Many special features
- Extraordinary materials and workmanship
- Detail specifications on page 49

*Note: The illustration shown may contain some optional components (for example: garages and/or fireplaces) whose costs are shown in the modifications, adjustments, & alternatives below or at the end of the square foot section.*

## Base cost per square foot of living area

| | Living Area | | | | | | | | | | |
|---|---|---|---|---|---|---|---|---|---|---|---|
| **Exterior Wall** | **1500** | **1800** | **2100** | **2500** | **3000** | **3500** | **4000** | **4500** | **5000** | **5500** | **6000** |
| Wood Siding - Wood Frame | 253.25 | 229.30 | 214.30 | 203.65 | 188.90 | 178.10 | 168.05 | 162.85 | 158.65 | 154.00 | 149.30 |
| Brick Veneer - Wood Frame | 266.50 | 241.50 | 225.20 | 214.00 | 198.20 | 186.60 | 175.90 | 170.35 | 165.75 | 160.75 | 155.80 |
| Solid Brick | 279.85 | 253.85 | 236.25 | 224.35 | 207.60 | 195.15 | 183.90 | 177.85 | 172.90 | 167.55 | 162.35 |
| Solid Stone | 303.30 | 275.45 | 255.55 | 242.60 | 224.25 | 210.30 | 197.85 | 191.10 | 185.50 | 179.60 | 173.90 |
| Finished Basement, Add | 32.70 | 35.25 | 33.40 | 32.35 | 30.95 | 29.70 | 28.80 | 28.20 | 27.65 | 27.20 | 26.75 |
| Unfinished Basement, Add | 15.00 | 14.40 | 13.60 | 13.15 | 12.55 | 12.05 | 11.60 | 11.35 | 11.15 | 10.90 | 10.75 |

## Modifications

*Add to the total cost*

| | |
|---|---|
| Upgrade Kitchen Cabinets | $ + 2915 |
| Solid Surface Countertops (Included) | |
| Full Bath - including plumbing, wall and floor finishes | + 13,127 |
| Half Bath - including plumbing, wall and floor finishes | + 7375 |
| Two Car Attached Garage | + 44,884 |
| Two Car Detached Garage | + 50,881 |
| Fireplace & Chimney | + 17,409 |

## Adjustments

*For multi family - add to total cost*

| | |
|---|---|
| Additional Kitchen | $ + 34,672 |
| Additional Full Bath & Half Bath | + 20,502 |
| Additional Entry & Exit | + 3010 |
| Separate Heating & Air Conditioning | + 7781 |
| Separate Electric | + 12,296 |

*For Townhouse/Rowhouse - Multiply cost per square foot by*

| | |
|---|---|
| Inner Unit | .86 |
| End Unit | .93 |

## Alternatives

*Add to or deduct from the cost per square foot of living area*

| | |
|---|---|
| Heavyweight Asphalt Shingles | – 2.75 |
| Clay Tile Roof | – .15 |
| Slate Roof | + 1.20 |
| Upgrade Ceilings to Textured Finish | + .67 |
| Air Conditioning, in Heating Ductwork | Base System |
| Heating Systems, Hot Water | + 2 |
| Heat Pump | + .98 |
| Electric Heat | – 8.70 |
| Not Heated | – 2.37 |

## Additional upgrades or components



**Important: See the Reference Section for Location Factors (to adjust for your city) and Estimating Forms.**

- **Unique residence built from an architect's plan**
- **Single family – 1 full bath, 1 half bath, 1 kitchen**
- **No basement**
- **Cedar shakes on roof**
- **Forced hot air heat/air conditioning**
- **Gypsum wallboard interior finishes**
- **Many special features**
- **Extraordinary materials and workmanship**
- **Detail specifications on page 49**

*Note: The illustration shown may contain some optional components (for example: garages and/or fireplaces) whose costs are shown in the modifications, adjustments, & alternatives below or at the end of the square foot section.*

## Base cost per square foot of living area

| Exterior Wall | Living Area 1500 | 1800 | 2100 | 2500 | 3000 | 3500 | 4000 | 4500 | 5000 | 5500 | 6000 |
|---|---|---|---|---|---|---|---|---|---|---|---|
| Wood Siding - Wood Frame | 248.05 | 224.45 | 212.25 | 202.10 | 187.20 | 179.40 | 169.95 | 160.50 | 157.00 | 153.20 | 149.20 |
| Brick Veneer - Wood Frame | 261.25 | 236.65 | 223.65 | 213.00 | 197.05 | 188.70 | 178.45 | 168.30 | 164.60 | 160.50 | 156.05 |
| Solid Brick | 275.75 | 250.15 | 236.30 | 225.05 | 208.00 | 199.05 | 187.85 | 177.00 | 172.95 | 168.55 | 163.65 |
| Solid Stone | 298.10 | 270.80 | 255.55 | 243.55 | 224.65 | 214.90 | 202.25 | 190.30 | 185.75 | 180.90 | 175.30 |
| Finished Basement, Add | 28.60 | 30.90 | 29.75 | 28.90 | 27.55 | 26.80 | 25.80 | 25.00 | 24.60 | 24.20 | 23.75 |
| Unfinished Basement, Add | 13.00 | 12.50 | 12.05 | 11.75 | 11.20 | 10.90 | 10.40 | 10.05 | 9.95 | 9.80 | 9.55 |

## Modifications

*Add to the total cost*

| | |
|---|---|
| Upgrade Kitchen Cabinets | $ + 2915 |
| Solid Surface Countertops (Included) | |
| Full Bath - including plumbing, wall and floor finishes | + 13,127 |
| Half Bath - including plumbing, wall and floor finishes | + 7375 |
| Two Car Attached Garage | + 44,884 |
| Two Car Detached Garage | + 50,881 |
| Fireplace & Chimney | + 17,409 |

## Adjustments

*For multi family - add to total cost*

| | |
|---|---|
| Additional Kitchen | $ + 34,672 |
| Additional Full Bath & Half Bath | + 20,502 |
| Additional Entry & Exit | + 3010 |
| Separate Heating & Air Conditioning | + 7781 |
| Separate Electric | + 12,296 |

*For Townhouse/Rowhouse - Multiply cost per square foot by*

| | |
|---|---|
| Inner Unit | .84 |
| End Unit | .92 |

## Alternatives

*Add to or deduct from the cost per square foot of living area*

| | |
|---|---|
| Heavyweight Asphalt Shingles | – 2.10 |
| Clay Tile Roof | – .10 |
| Slate Roof | + .95 |
| Upgrade Ceilings to Textured Finish | + .67 |
| Air Conditioning, in Heating Ductwork | Base System |
| Heating Systems, Hot Water | + 2 |
| Heat Pump | + .98 |
| Electric Heat | – 8.70 |
| Not Heated | – 2.30 |

## Additional upgrades or components

Kitchen Cabinets & Countertops Page 58
Bathroom Vanities 59
Fireplaces & Chimneys 59
Windows, Skylights & Dormers 59
Appliances 60
Breezeways & Porches 60
Finished Attic 60
Garages 61
Site Improvements 61
Wings & Ells 57



**Important: See the Reference Section for Location Factors (to adjust for your city) and Estimating Forms.**

- **Unique residence built from an architect's plan**
- **Single family — 1 full bath, 1 half bath, 1 kitchen**
- **No basement**
- **Cedar shakes on roof**
- **Forced hot air heat/air conditioning**
- **Gypsum wallboard interior finishes**
- **Many special features**
- **Extraordinary materials and workmanship**
- **Detail specifications on page 49**

*Note: The illustration shown may contain some optional components (for example: garages and/or fireplaces) whose costs are shown in the modifications, adjustments, & alternatives below or at the end of the square foot section.*

## Base cost per square foot of living area

| | Living Area | | | | | | | | | | |
|---|---|---|---|---|---|---|---|---|---|---|---|
| Exterior Wall | 1200 | 1400 | 1600 | 1800 | 2000 | 2400 | 2800 | 3200 | 3600 | 4000 | 4400 |
| Wood Siding - Wood Frame | 243.95 | 229.20 | 218.60 | 209.70 | 200.05 | 186.10 | 174.55 | 166.80 | 162.40 | 157.40 | 153.30 |
| Brick Veneer - Wood Frame | 253.35 | 237.95 | 227.00 | 217.65 | 207.70 | 193.00 | 180.80 | 172.65 | 168.00 | 162.75 | 158.50 |
| Solid Brick | 263.10 | 247.10 | 235.70 | 225.85 | 215.60 | 200.10 | 187.30 | 178.70 | 173.85 | 168.25 | 163.80 |
| Solid Stone | 279.65 | 262.55 | 250.45 | 239.75 | 228.95 | 212.15 | 198.25 | 189.00 | 183.80 | 177.55 | 172.80 |
| Finished Basement, Add | 41.05 | 44.60 | 43.50 | 42.15 | 41.40 | 39.50 | 38.00 | 37.00 | 36.45 | 35.65 | 35.15 |
| Unfinished Basement, Add | 18.75 | 18.05 | 17.65 | 17.10 | 16.85 | 15.95 | 15.35 | 14.90 | 14.70 | 14.30 | 14.15 |

## Modifications

***Add to the total cost***

| | |
|---|---|
| Upgrade Kitchen Cabinets | $ + 2915 |
| Solid Surface Countertops (Included) | |
| Full Bath - including plumbing, wall and floor finishes | + 13,127 |
| Half Bath - including plumbing, wall and floor finishes | + 7375 |
| Two Car Attached Garage | + 44,884 |
| Two Car Detached Garage | + 50,881 |
| Fireplace & Chimney | + 14,512 |

## Adjustments

***For multi family - add to total cost***

| | |
|---|---|
| Additional Kitchen | $ + 34,672 |
| Additional Full Bath & Half Bath | + 20,502 |
| Additional Entry & Exit | + 3010 |
| Separate Heating & Air Conditioning | + 7781 |
| Separate Electric | + 12,296 |

***For Townhouse/Rowhouse - Multiply cost per square foot by***

| | |
|---|---|
| Inner Unit | .89 |
| End Unit | .94 |

## Alternatives

***Add to or deduct from the cost per square foot of living area***

| | |
|---|---|
| Heavyweight Asphalt Shingles | – 3.20 |
| Clay Tile Roof | – .15 |
| Slate Roof | + 1.40 |
| Upgrade Ceilings to Textured Finish | + .67 |
| Air Conditioning, in Heating Ductwork | Base System |
| Heating Systems, Hot Water | + 2.21 |
| Heat Pump | + .95 |
| Electric Heat | – 4.44 |
| Not Heated | – 2.37 |

## Additional upgrades or components

- **Unique residence built from an architect's plan**
- **Single family – 1 full bath, 1 half bath, 1 kitchen**
- **No basement**
- **Cedar shakes on roof**
- **Forced hot air heat/air conditioning**
- **Gypsum wallboard interior finishes**
- **Many special features**
- **Extraordinary materials and workmanship**
- **Detail specifications on page 49**

*Note: The illustration shown may contain some optional components (for example: garages and/or fireplaces) whose costs are shown in the modifications, adjustments, & alternatives below or at the end of the square foot section.*

©Home Planners, Inc.

## Base cost per square foot of living area

| Exterior Wall | Living Area 1500 | 1800 | 2100 | 2400 | 2800 | 3200 | 3600 | 4000 | 4500 | 5000 | 5500 |
|---|---|---|---|---|---|---|---|---|---|---|---|
| Wood Siding - Wood Frame | 230.20 | 212.85 | 198.70 | 189.05 | 182.30 | 174.00 | 165.65 | 161.80 | 153.90 | 149.60 | 144.55 |
| Brick Veneer - Wood Frame | 238.75 | 220.60 | 205.75 | 195.65 | 188.65 | 179.90 | 171.10 | 167.10 | 158.80 | 154.15 | 148.90 |
| Solid Brick | 247.40 | 228.40 | 212.85 | 202.30 | 195.05 | 185.85 | 176.55 | 172.45 | 163.75 | 158.80 | 153.35 |
| Solid Stone | 262.65 | 242.10 | 225.35 | 214.05 | 206.30 | 196.30 | 186.25 | 181.85 | 172.35 | 166.95 | 161.05 |
| Finished Basement, Add* | 48.75 | 52.65 | 50.60 | 49.30 | 48.45 | 47.15 | 45.95 | 45.45 | 44.40 | 43.60 | 42.90 |
| Unfinished Basement, Add* | 22.40 | 21.35 | 20.50 | 19.90 | 19.60 | 19.00 | 18.45 | 18.25 | 17.75 | 17.35 | 17.05 |

*Basement under middle level only.

## Modifications

***Add to the total cost***

| | |
|---|---|
| Upgrade Kitchen Cabinets | $ + 2915 |
| Solid Surface Countertops (Included) | |
| Full Bath - including plumbing, wall and floor finishes | + 13,127 |
| Half Bath - including plumbing, wall and floor finishes | + 7375 |
| Two Car Attached Garage | + 44,884 |
| Two Car Detached Garage | + 50,881 |
| Fireplace & Chimney | + 15,909 |

## Adjustments

***For multi family - add to total cost***

| | |
|---|---|
| Additional Kitchen | $ + 34,672 |
| Additional Full Bath & Half Bath | + 20,502 |
| Additional Entry & Exit | + 3010 |
| Separate Heating & Air Conditioning | + 7781 |
| Separate Electric | + 12,296 |

***For Townhouse/Rowhouse - Multiply cost per square foot by***

| | |
|---|---|
| Inner Unit | .86 |
| End Unit | .93 |

## Alternatives

***Add to or deduct from the cost per square foot of living area***

| | |
|---|---|
| Heavyweight Asphalt Shingles | – 4.60 |
| Clay Tile Roof | – .25 |
| Slate Roof | + 2 |
| Upgrade Ceilings to Textured Finish | + .67 |
| Air Conditioning, in Heating Ductwork | Base System |
| Heating Systems, Hot Water | + 2.15 |
| Heat Pump | + .99 |
| Electric Heat | – 3.89 |
| Not Heated | – 2.30 |

## Additional upgrades or components


| | |
|---|---|
| Kitchen Cabinets & Countertops | Page 58 |
| Bathroom Vanities | 59 |
| Fireplaces & Chimneys | 59 |
| Windows, Skylights & Dormers | 59 |
| Appliances | 60 |
| Breezeways & Porches | 60 |
| Finished Attic | 60 |
| Garages | 61 |
| Site Improvements | 61 |
| Wings & Ells | 57 |




**Important: See the Reference Section for Location Factors (to adjust for your city) and Estimating Forms.**

## 1 Story — Base cost per square foot of living area

| Exterior Wall | Living Area 50 | 100 | 200 | 300 | 400 | 500 | 600 | 700 |
|---|---|---|---|---|---|---|---|---|
| Wood Siding - Wood Frame | 364.50 | 285.85 | 251.65 | 213.70 | 202.55 | 195.80 | 191.35 | 192.40 |
| Brick Veneer - Wood Frame | 395.20 | 307.75 | 269.90 | 225.85 | 213.45 | 206.00 | 201.10 | 201.80 |
| Solid Brick | 438.85 | 338.95 | 295.85 | 243.20 | 229.10 | 220.60 | 214.95 | 215.15 |
| Solid Stone | 487.50 | 373.70 | 324.80 | 262.50 | 246.50 | 236.80 | 230.45 | 230.05 |
| Finished Basement, Add | 128.40 | 117.20 | 105.55 | 86.15 | 82.25 | 79.95 | 78.40 | 77.25 |
| Unfinished Basement, Add | 67.45 | 53.20 | 47.25 | 37.30 | 35.30 | 34.10 | 33.30 | 32.75 |

## 1-1/2 Story — Base cost per square foot of living area

| Exterior Wall | Living Area 100 | 200 | 300 | 400 | 500 | 600 | 700 | 800 |
|---|---|---|---|---|---|---|---|---|
| Wood Siding - Wood Frame | 288.10 | 237.65 | 206.65 | 187.00 | 177.70 | 173.00 | 167.25 | 165.70 |
| Brick Veneer - Wood Frame | 315.50 | 259.55 | 224.85 | 201.30 | 190.90 | 185.45 | 179.00 | 177.30 |
| Solid Brick | 354.50 | 290.75 | 250.85 | 221.60 | 209.55 | 203.15 | 195.65 | 193.90 |
| Solid Stone | 397.90 | 325.50 | 279.80 | 244.10 | 230.40 | 222.80 | 214.30 | 212.30 |
| Finished Basement, Add | 85.05 | 84.50 | 76.75 | 68.20 | 65.85 | 64.35 | 62.90 | 62.65 |
| Unfinished Basement, Add | 43.75 | 37.80 | 33.80 | 29.40 | 28.20 | 27.45 | 26.70 | 26.60 |

## 2 Story — Base cost per square foot of living area

| Exterior Wall | Living Area 100 | 200 | 400 | 600 | 800 | 1000 | 1200 | 1400 |
|---|---|---|---|---|---|---|---|---|
| Wood Siding - Wood Frame | 282.45 | 215.20 | 185.75 | 155.75 | 146.20 | 140.40 | 136.65 | 138.10 |
| Brick Veneer - Wood Frame | 313.20 | 237.15 | 204.05 | 168.00 | 157.20 | 150.65 | 146.35 | 147.55 |
| Solid Brick | 356.90 | 268.30 | 230.00 | 185.30 | 172.80 | 165.20 | 160.20 | 160.85 |
| Solid Stone | 405.50 | 303.05 | 258.95 | 204.60 | 190.15 | 181.40 | 175.70 | 175.75 |
| Finished Basement, Add | 64.25 | 58.65 | 52.80 | 43.10 | 41.15 | 40.00 | 39.25 | 38.65 |
| Unfinished Basement, Add | 33.75 | 26.55 | 23.60 | 18.60 | 17.65 | 17.05 | 16.65 | 16.35 |

Base costs do not include bathroom or kitchen facilities. Use Modifications/Adjustments/Alternatives on pages 58-61 where appropriate.

## Kitchen cabinets - Base units, hardwood *(Cost per Unit)*

| | Economy | Average | Custom | Luxury |
|---|---|---|---|---|
| **24" deep, 35" high,** | | | | |
| One top drawer, | | | | |
| One door below | | | | |
| 12" wide | $ 510 | $ 680 | $ 904 | $ 1190 |
| 15" wide | 525 | 700 | 931 | 1225 |
| 18" wide | 394 | 525 | 698 | 919 |
| 21" wide | 405 | 540 | 718 | 945 |
| 24" wide | 439 | 585 | 778 | 1024 |
| Four drawers | | | | |
| 12" wide | 668 | 890 | 1184 | 1558 |
| 15" wide | 671 | 895 | 1190 | 1566 |
| 18" wide | 701 | 935 | 1244 | 1636 |
| 24" wide | 739 | 985 | 1310 | 1724 |
| Two top drawers, | | | | |
| Two doors below | | | | |
| 27" wide | 450 | 600 | 798 | 1050 |
| 30" wide | 476 | 635 | 845 | 1111 |
| 33" wide | 499 | 665 | 884 | 1164 |
| 36" wide | 506 | 675 | 898 | 1181 |
| 42" wide | 608 | 810 | 1077 | 1418 |
| 48" wide | 630 | 840 | 1117 | 1470 |
| **Range or sink base** | | | | |
| *(Cost per unit)* | | | | |
| Two doors below | | | | |
| 30" wide | 353 | 470 | 625 | 823 |
| 33" wide | 375 | 500 | 665 | 875 |
| 36" wide | 390 | 520 | 692 | 910 |
| 42" wide | 409 | 545 | 725 | 954 |
| 48" wide | 428 | 570 | 758 | 998 |
| **Corner Base Cabinet** | | | | |
| *(Cost per unit)* | | | | |
| 36" wide | 510 | 680 | 904 | 1190 |
| **Lazy Susan** *(Cost per unit)* | | | | |
| With revolving door | 488 | 650 | 865 | 1138 |

## Kitchen cabinets - Wall cabinets, hardwood *(Cost per Unit)*

| | Economy | Average | Custom | Luxury |
|---|---|---|---|---|
| **12" deep, 2 doors** | | | | |
| 12" high | | | | |
| 30" wide | $ 224 | $ 298 | $ 396 | $ 522 |
| 36" wide | | | | |
| 15" high | | | | |
| 30" wide | 315 | 420 | 559 | 735 |
| 33" wide | 161 | 214 | 285 | 375 |
| 36" wide | 168 | 224 | 298 | 392 |
| 24" high | | | | |
| 30" wide | 176 | 235 | 313 | 411 |
| 36" wide | 446 | 595 | 791 | 1041 |
| 42" wide | 296 | 395 | 525 | 691 |
| 30" high, 1 door | | | | |
| 12" wide | 128 | 171 | 227 | 299 |
| 15" wide | 248 | 330 | 439 | 578 |
| 18" wide | 274 | 365 | 485 | 639 |
| 24" wide | 311 | 415 | 552 | 726 |
| 30" high, 2 doors | | | | |
| 27" wide | 196 | 261 | 347 | 457 |
| 30" wide | 386 | 515 | 685 | 901 |
| 36" wide | 375 | 500 | 665 | 875 |
| 42" wide | 435 | 580 | 771 | 1015 |
| 48" wide | 716 | 955 | 1270 | 1671 |
| Corner wall, 30" high | | | | |
| 24" wide | 216 | 288 | 383 | 504 |
| 30" wide | 503 | 670 | 891 | 1173 |
| 36" wide | 454 | 605 | 805 | 1059 |
| **Broom closet** | | | | |
| 84" high, 24" deep | | | | |
| 18" wide | 788 | 1050 | 1397 | 1838 |
| **Oven Cabinet** | | | | |
| 84" high, 24" deep | | | | |
| 27" wide | 1013 | 1350 | 1796 | 2363 |

## Kitchen countertops *(Cost per L.F.)*

| | Economy | Average | Custom | Luxury |
|---|---|---|---|---|
| Solid Surface | | | | |
| 24" wide, no backsplash | $ 125 | $ 166 | $ 221 | $ 291 |
| with backsplash | 141 | 188 | 250 | 329 |
| Stock plastic laminate, 24" wide | | | | |
| with backsplash | 28 | 37 | 50 | 66 |
| Custom plastic laminate, no splash | | | | |
| 7/8" thick, alum. molding | 47 | 62 | 82 | 109 |
| 1-1/4" thick, no splash | 51 | 67 | 90 | 118 |
| Marble | | | | |
| 1/2" - 3/4" thick w/splash | 71 | 94 | 125 | 165 |
| Maple, laminated | | | | |
| 1-1/2" thick w/splash | 110 | 146 | 194 | 256 |
| Stainless steel | | | | |
| (per S.F.) | 188 | 250 | 333 | 438 |
| Cutting blocks, recessed | | | | |
| 16" x 20" x 1" (each) | 171 | 228 | 303 | 399 |

## Vanity bases *(Cost per Unit)*

| | Economy | Average | Custom | Luxury |
|---|---|---|---|---|
| 2 door, 30″ high, 21″ deep | | | | |
| 24″ wide | $ 431 | $ 575 | $ 765 | $ 1006 |
| 30″ wide | 465 | 620 | 825 | 1085 |
| 36″ wide | 409 | 545 | 725 | 954 |
| 48″ wide | 525 | 700 | 931 | 1225 |

## Solid surface vanity tops *(Cost Each)*

| | Economy | Average | Custom | Luxury |
|---|---|---|---|---|
| Center bowl | | | | |
| 22″ x 25″ | $ 400 | $ 432 | $ 467 | $ 504 |
| 22″ x 31″ | 460 | 497 | 537 | 580 |
| 22″ x 37″ | 530 | 572 | 618 | 667 |
| 22″ x 49″ | 655 | 707 | 764 | 825 |

## Fireplaces & Chimneys *(Cost per Unit)*

| | 1-1/2 Story | 2 Story | 3 Story |
|---|---|---|---|
| **Economy (prefab metal)** | | | |
| Exterior chimney & 1 fireplace | $ 9005 | $ 9950 | $ 10914 |
| Interior chimney & 1 fireplace | 8629 | 9593 | 10036 |
| **Average (masonry)** | | | |
| Exterior chimney & 1 fireplace | 9740 | 10762 | 11805 |
| Interior chimney & 1 fireplace | 9333 | 10376 | 10856 |
| For more than 1 flue, add | 663 | 1128 | 1891 |
| For more than 1 fireplace, add | 6535 | 6535 | 6535 |
| **Custom (masonry)** | | | |
| Exterior chimney & 1 fireplace | 9780 | 11040 | 12467 |
| Interior chimney & 1 fireplace | 9170 | 10381 | 11188 |
| For more than 1 flue, add | 767 | 1328 | 2223 |
| For more than 1 fireplace, add | 7025 | 7025 | 7025 |
| **Luxury (masonry)** | | | |
| Exterior chimney & 1 fireplace | 14512 | 15909 | 17409 |
| Interior chimney & 1 fireplace | 13846 | 15138 | 16023 |
| For more than 1 flue, add | 1198 | 2000 | 2792 |
| For more than 1 fireplace, add | 11439 | 11439 | 11439 |

## Windows and Skylights *(Cost Each)*

| | Economy | Average | Custom | Luxury |
|---|---|---|---|---|
| Fixed Picture Windows | | | | |
| 3′-6″ x 4′-0″ | $ 505 | $ 672 | $ 895 | $ 1178 |
| 4′-0″ x 6′-0″ | 555 | 740 | 985 | 1296 |
| 5′-0″ x 6′-0″ | 606 | 808 | 1075 | 1414 |
| 6′-0″ x 6′-0″ | 648 | 864 | 1150 | 1513 |
| Bay/Bow Windows | | | | |
| 8′-0″ x 5′-0″ | 1142 | 1522 | 2025 | 2664 |
| 10′-0″ x 5′-0″ | 1241 | 1654 | 2200 | 2895 |
| 10′-0″ x 6′-0″ | 2016 | 2687 | 3575 | 4704 |
| 12′-0″ x 6′-0″ | 2636 | 3515 | 4675 | 6151 |
| Palladian Windows | | | | |
| 3′-2″ x 6′-4″ | | 1973 | 2625 | 3454 |
| 4′-0″ x 6′-0″ | | 2612 | 3475 | 4572 |
| 5′-5″ x 6′-10″ | | 3045 | 4050 | 5329 |
| 8′-0″ x 6′-0″ | | 3665 | 4875 | 6414 |
| Skylights | | | | |
| 46″ x 21-1/2″ | 637 | 980 | 1180 | 1298 |
| 46″ x 28″ | 660 | 1015 | 1240 | 1364 |
| 57″ x 44″ | 728 | 1120 | 1235 | 1359 |

## Dormers *(Cost/S.F. of plan area )*

| | Economy | Average | Custom | Luxury |
|---|---|---|---|---|
| **Framing and Roofing Only** | | | | |
| Gable dormer, 2″ x 6″ roof frame | $ 43 | $ 47 | $ 51 | $ 84 |
| 2″ x 8″ roof frame | 44 | 48 | 52 | 87 |
| Shed dormer, 2″ x 6″ roof frame | 26 | 32 | 35 | 55 |
| 2″ x 8″ roof frame | 29 | 33 | 36 | 56 |
| 2″ x 10″ roof frame | 32 | 35 | 37 | 58 |

## Appliances *(Cost per Unit)*

| | Economy | Average | Custom | Luxury |
|---|---|---|---|---|
| **Range** | | | | |
| 30″ free standing, 1 oven | $ 850 | $ 1038 | $ 1132 | $ 1225 |
| 2 oven | 3925 | 4463 | 4732 | 5000 |
| 30″ built-in, 1 oven | 1525 | 2275 | 2650 | 3025 |
| 2 oven | 3100 | 3565 | 3798 | 4030 |
| 21″ free standing | | | | |
| 1 oven | 955 | 1099 | 1171 | 1242 |
| **Counter Top Ranges** | | | | |
| 4 burner standard | 440 | 615 | 703 | 790 |
| As above with griddle | 6050 | 6958 | 7412 | 7865 |
| **Microwave Oven** | 320 | 553 | 669 | 785 |
| **Compactor** | | | | |
| 4 to 1 compaction | 1550 | 1688 | 1757 | 1825 |
| **Deep Freeze** | | | | |
| 15 to 23 C.F. | 1050 | 1208 | 1287 | 1365 |
| 30 C.F. | 1150 | 1388 | 1507 | 1625 |
| **Dehumidifier,** portable, auto. | | | | |
| 15 pint | 345 | 397 | 423 | 449 |
| 30 pint | 520 | 598 | 637 | 676 |
| **Washing Machine,** automatic | 920 | 1123 | 1224 | 1325 |
| **Water Heater** | | | | |
| **Electric,** glass lined | | | | |
| 30 gal. | 965 | 1170 | 1273 | 1375 |
| 80 gal. | 2650 | 3275 | 3588 | 3900 |
| **Water Heater, Gas,** glass lined | | | | |
| 30 gal. | 2325 | 2800 | 3038 | 3275 |
| 50 gal. | 1275 | 1575 | 1725 | 1875 |
| **Dishwasher,** built-in | | | | |
| 2 cycles | 725 | 1075 | 1250 | 1425 |
| 4 or more cycles | 920 | 1175 | 1200 | 1225 |
| **Dryer,** automatic | 1375 | 1650 | 1788 | 1925 |
| **Garage Door Opener** | 540 | 638 | 687 | 735 |
| **Garbage Disposal** | 207 | 279 | 315 | 350 |
| **Heater, Electric,** built-in | | | | |
| 1250 watt ceiling type | 294 | 385 | 430 | 475 |
| 1250 watt wall type | 274 | 307 | 324 | 340 |
| Wall type w/blower | 345 | | | 720 |
| 1500 watt | 395 | 455 | 485 | 514 |
| 3000 watt | 440 | 506 | 539 | 572 |
| **Hood For Range,** 2 speed | | | | |
| 30″ wide | 251 | 863 | 1169 | 1475 |
| 42″ wide | 320 | 380 | 410 | 440 |
| **Humidifier,** portable | | | | |
| 7 gal. per day | 187 | 215 | 229 | 243 |
| 15 gal. per day | 305 | 351 | 374 | 397 |
| **Ice Maker,** automatic | | | | |
| 13 lb. per day | 1625 | 1869 | 1991 | 2113 |
| 51 lb. per day | 3200 | 3680 | 3920 | 4160 |
| **Refrigerator,** no frost | | | | |
| 10-12 C.F. | 975 | 1122 | 1195 | 1268 |
| 14-16 C.F. | 865 | 923 | 952 | 980 |
| 18-20 C.F. | 915 | 970 | 998 | 1025 |
| 21-29 C.F. | 1975 | 2338 | 2519 | 2700 |
| **Sump Pump,** 1/3 H.P. | 340 | 450 | 505 | 560 |

## Breezeway *(Cost per S.F.)*

| Class | Type | Area (S.F.) | | | |
|---|---|---|---|---|---|
| | | 50 | 100 | 150 | 200 |
| Economy | Open | $ 58.31 | $ 47.95 | $ 41.73 | $ 38.62 |
| | Enclosed | 240.26 | 167.29 | 136.05 | 114.51 |
| Average | Open | 71.25 | 57.97 | 50.78 | 47.18 |
| | Enclosed | 234.37 | 165.66 | 135.34 | 119.94 |
| Custom | Open | 88.31 | 72.73 | 64.15 | 59.87 |
| | Enclosed | 310.67 | 228.87 | 190.00 | 170.30 |
| Luxury | Open | 98.55 | 81.47 | 72.39 | 67.86 |
| | Enclosed | 368.16 | 267.23 | 219.98 | 196.09 |

## Porches *(Cost per S.F.)*

| Class | Type | Area (S.F.) | | | | |
|---|---|---|---|---|---|---|
| | | 25 | 50 | 100 | 200 | 300 |
| Economy | Open | $ 111.54 | $ 83.72 | $ 63.41 | $ 50.33 | $ 45.91 |
| | Enclosed | 255.31 | 198.65 | 130.11 | 100.21 | 87.41 |
| Average | Open | 117.04 | 92.24 | 67.67 | 52.46 | 47.33 |
| | Enclosed | 242.45 | 200.74 | 130.40 | 99.61 | 86.51 |
| Custom | Open | 203.36 | 151.22 | 116.55 | 89.11 | 86.80 |
| | Enclosed | 292.61 | 236.06 | 160.29 | 124.04 | 125.65 |
| Luxury | Open | 213.06 | 159.11 | 122.53 | 91.79 | 84.88 |
| | Enclosed | 369.98 | 335.23 | 220.71 | 165.44 | 140.23 |

## Finished attic *(Cost per S.F.)*

| Class | Area (S.F.) | | | | |
|---|---|---|---|---|---|
| | 400 | 500 | 600 | 800 | 1000 |
| Economy | $ 29.87 | $ 28.88 | $ 27.67 | $ 27.21 | $ 26.20 |
| Average | 45.05 | 44.07 | 42.99 | 42.44 | 41.26 |
| Custom | 55.85 | 54.60 | 53.35 | 52.54 | 51.46 |
| Luxury | 74.17 | 72.37 | 70.68 | 69.00 | 67.86 |

## Alarm system *(Cost per System)*

| | Burglar Alarm | Smoke Detector |
|---|---|---|
| Economy | $ 455 | $ 84 |
| Average | 515 | 96 |
| Custom | 916 | 265 |
| Luxury | 895 | 225 |

## Sauna, prefabricated
*(Cost per unit, including heater and controls—7′ high)*

| Size | Cost |
|---|---|
| 6′ x 4′ | $ 5950 |
| 6′ x 5′ | 6975 |
| 6′ x 6′ | 7775 |
| 6′ x 9′ | 7975 |
| 8′ x 10′ | 11,200 |
| 8′ x 12′ | 26,900 |
| 10′ x 12′ | 18,800 |

## Garages *

(Costs include exterior wall systems comparable with the quality of the residence. Included in the cost is an allowance for one personnel door, manual overhead door(s) and electrical fixture.)

| Class | Type | | | | | | | | | |
|---|---|---|---|---|---|---|---|---|---|---|
| | Detached | | | Attached | | | Built-in | | Basement | |
| Economy | One Car | Two Car | Three Car | One Car | Two Car | Three Car | One Car | Two Car | One Car | Two Car |
| Wood | $25,718 | $39,875 | $54,032 | $20,336 | $35,191 | $49,348 | $ -999 | $-1998 | $3924 | $6209 |
| Masonry | 36,942 | 53,922 | 70,901 | 27,359 | 45,037 | 62,017 | -2377 | -4755 | | |
| Average | | | | | | | | | | |
| Wood | 28,036 | 42,776 | 57,517 | 21,787 | 37,225 | 51,965 | -1284 | -2567 | 4272 | 6905 |
| Masonry | 33,095 | 49,107 | 65,119 | 24,952 | 41,662 | 57,674 | -1905 | -2617 | | |
| Custom | | | | | | | | | | |
| Wood | 29,366 | 45,377 | 61,388 | 23,087 | 39,741 | 55,752 | -3378 | -2882 | 4248 | 6856 |
| Masonry | 34,378 | 51,650 | 68,921 | 26,223 | 44,138 | 61,409 | -3993 | -4113 | | |
| Luxury | | | | | | | | | | |
| Wood | 32,479 | 50,881 | 69,283 | 25,839 | 44,884 | 63,286 | -3496 | -3119 | 5682 | 9029 |
| Masonry | 45,017 | 66,572 | 88,126 | 33,684 | 55,882 | 77,437 | -5036 | -6198 | | |

*See the Introduction to this section for definitions of garage types.

## Swimming pools *(Cost per S.F.)*

| | |
|---|---|
| **Residential** | |
| In-ground | $ 40.50 - 97.50 |
| **Deck equipment** | 1.30 |
| **Paint pool,** preparation & 3 coats (epoxy) | 6.38 |
| Rubber base paint | 4.88 |
| **Pool Cover** | 2.35 |
| **Swimming Pool Heaters** | |
| (not including wiring, external piping, base or pad) | |
| **Gas** | |
| 155 MBH | $ 3075.00 |
| 190 MBH | 3750.00 |
| 500 MBH | 12,000. |
| **Electric** | |
| 15 KW 7200 gallon pool | 3425.00 |
| 24 KW 9600 gallon pool | 4325.00 |
| 54 KW 24,000 gallon pool | 6200.00 |

## Wood and coal stoves

| | |
|---|---|
| **Wood Only** | |
| Free Standing (minimum) | $ 2811 |
| Fireplace Insert (minimum) | 2327 |
| **Coal Only** | |
| Free Standing | $ 2629 |
| Fireplace Insert | 2878 |
| **Wood and Coal** | |
| Free Standing | $ 5408 |
| Fireplace Insert | 5542 |

## Sidewalks *(Cost per S.F.)*

| | | |
|---|---|---|
| Concrete, 3000 psi with wire mesh | 4" thick | $ 5.55 |
| | 5" thick | 6.31 |
| | 6" thick | 7.12 |
| Precast concrete patio blocks (natural) | 2" thick | 5.45 |
| Precast concrete patio blocks (colors) | 2" thick | 5.45 |
| Flagstone, bluestone | 1" thick | 23.70 |
| Flagstone, bluestone | 1-1/2" thick | 33.35 |
| Slate (natural, irregular) | 3/4" thick | 20.80 |
| Slate (random rectangular) | 1/2" thick | 32.25 |
| **Seeding** | | |
| Fine grading & seeding includes lime, fertilizer & seed | per S.Y. | 3.29 |
| **Lawn Sprinkler System** | per S.F. | 1.19 |

## Fencing *(Cost per L.F.)*

| | |
|---|---|
| Chain Link, 4' high, galvanized | $ 21.00 |
| Gate, 4' high (each) | 275.00 |
| Cedar Picket, 3' high, 2 rail | 21.50 |
| Gate (each) | 350.00 |
| 3 Rail, 4' high | 27.00 |
| Gate (each) | 310.00 |
| Cedar Stockade, 3 Rail, 6' high | 25.50 |
| Gate (each) | 405.00 |
| Board & Battens, 2 sides 6' high, pine | 53.50 |
| 6' high, cedar | 48.50 |
| No. 1 Cedar, basketweave, 6' high | 37.00 |
| Gate, 6' high (each) | 375.00 |

## Carport *(Cost per S.F.)*

| | |
|---|---|
| Economy | $ 13.67 |
| Average | 19.93 |
| Custom | 28.28 |
| Luxury | 34.20 |

## Insurance Exclusions

Insurance exclusions are a matter of policy coverage and are not standard or universal. When making an appraisal for insurance purposes, it is recommended that some time be taken in studying the insurance policy to determine the specific items to be excluded. Most homeowners insurance policies have, as part of their provisions, statements that read "the policy permits the insured to exclude from value, in determining whether the amount of the insurance equals or exceeds 80% of its replacement cost, such items as building excavation, basement footings, underground piping and wiring, piers and other supports which are below the undersurface of the lowest floor or where there is no basement below the ground." Loss to any of these items, however, is covered.

## Costs for Excavation, Spread and Strip Footings and Underground Piping

This chart shows excluded items expressed as a percentage of total building cost.

| | Number of Stories | | | |
|---|---|---|---|---|
| Class | 1 | 1-1/2 | 2 | 3 |
| Luxury | 3.4% | 2.7% | 2.4% | 1.9% |
| Custom | 3.5% | 2.7% | 2.4% | 1.9% |
| Average | 5.0% | 4.3% | 3.8% | 3.3% |
| Economy | 5.0% | 4.4% | 4.1% | 3.5% |

## Architect/Designer Fees

Architect/designer fees as presented in the following chart are typical ranges for 4 classes of residences. Factors affecting these ranges include economic conditions, size and scope of project, site selection, and standardization. Where superior quality and detail is required or where closer supervision is required, fees may run higher than listed. Lower quality or simplicity may dictate lower fees.

The editors have included architect/designer fees from the "mean" column in calculating costs.

Listed below are average costs expressed as a range and mean of total building cost for 4 classes of residences.

| Class | | | Range | Mean |
|---|---|---|---|---|
| Luxury | – | Architecturally designed and supervised | 5%–15% | 10% |
| Custom | – | Architecturally modified designer plans | $2000–$3500 | $2500 |
| Average | – | Designer plans | $800–$1500 | $1100 |
| Economy | – | Stock plans | $100–$500 | $300 |

Depreciation as generally defined is "the loss of value due to any cause." Specifically, depreciation can be broken down into three categories: **Physical Depreciation, Functional Obsolescence,** and **Economic Obsolescence.**

**Physical Depreciation** is the loss of value from the wearing out of the building's components. Such causes may be decay, dry rot, cracks, or structural defects.

**Functional Obsolescence** is the loss of value from features which render the residence less useful or desirable. Such features may be higher than normal ceilings, design and/or style changes, or outdated mechanical systems.

**Economic Obsolescence** is the loss of value from external features which render the residence less useful or desirable. These features may be changes in neighborhood socio-economic grouping, zoning changes, legislation, etc.

Depreciation as it applies to the residential portion of this manual deals with the observed physical condition of the residence being appraised. It is in essence *"the cost to cure."*

The ultimate method to arrive at *"the cost to cure"* is to analyze each component of the residence.

For example:

Component, Roof Covering – Cost = $2400
Average Life = 15 years
Actual Life = 5 years
Depreciation = 5 ÷ 15 = .33 or 33%

$2400 × 33% = $792 = Amount of Depreciation

The following table, however, can be used as a guide in estimating the % depreciation using the actual age and general condition of the residence.

## Depreciation Table — Residential

| Age in Years | Good | Average | Poor |
|---|---|---|---|
| 2 | 2% | 3% | 10% |
| 5 | 4 | 6 | 20 |
| 10 | 7 | 10 | 25 |
| 15 | 10 | 15 | 30 |
| 20 | 15 | 20 | 35 |
| 25 | 18 | 25 | 40 |
| 30 | 24 | 30 | 45 |
| 35 | 28 | 35 | 50 |
| 40 | 32 | 40 | 55 |
| 45 | 36 | 45 | 60 |
| 50 | 40 | 50 | 65 |

# Commercial/Industrial/Institutional Models

## Table of Contents

# Introduction to the Commercial/ Industrial/Institutional Section

## General

The Commercial/Industrial/Institutional section contains base building costs per square foot of floor area for 77 model buildings. Each model has a table of square foot costs for combinations of exterior wall and framing systems. This table is supplemented by a list of common additives and their unit costs. In printed versions, a breakdown of all component costs used to develop the base cost for the model is included. In electronic products, the cost breakdown is available as a printable report. Modifications to the standard models can be performed manually in printed products and automatically using the "swapper" feature in electronic products.

This data may be used directly to estimate the construction cost of most types of buildings when only the floor area, exterior wall construction, and framing systems are known. To adjust the base cost for components that are different from the model, use the tables from the Assemblies Section.

## Building Identification & Model Selection

The building models in this section represent structures by use. Occupancy, however, does not necessarily identify the building, i.e., a restaurant could be a converted warehouse. In all instances, the building should be described and identified by its own physical characteristics. The model selection should also be guided by comparing specifications with the model. In the case of converted use, data from one model may be used to supplement data from another.

## Green Models

Consistent with expanding green trends in the design and construction industry, 25 green building models are currently included. Although similar to our standard models in building type and structural system, the green models align with Energy Star requirements and address many of the items necessary to obtain LEED certification. Although our models do not include site-specific information, our design assumption is that they are located in climate zone 5. DOE's eQuest software was used to perform an energy analysis of the model buildings. By reducing energy use, we were able to reduce the size of the service entrances, switchgear, power feeds, and generators. Each of the following building systems was researched and analyzed: building envelope, HVAC, plumbing fixtures, lighting, and electrical service. These systems were targeted because of their impact on energy usage and green building.

Wall and roof insulation was increased to reduce heat loss and a recycled vapor barrier was added to the foundation. White roofs were specified for models with flat roofs. Interior finishes include materials with recycled content and low VOC paint. Stainless steel toilet partitions were selected because the recycled material is easy to maintain. Plumbing fixtures were selected to conserve water. Water closets are low-flow and equipped with auto-sensor valves. Waterless urinals are specified throughout. Faucets use auto-sensor flush valves and are powered by a hydroelectric power unit inside the faucet. Energy-efficient, low-flow water coolers were specified to reduce energy consumption and water usage throughout each building model.

Lighting efficiency was achieved by specifying LED fixtures in place of standard fluorescents. Daylight on/off lighting control systems were incorporated into the models. These controls are equipped with sensors that automatically turn off the lights when sufficient daylight is available. Energy monitoring systems were also included in all green models.

## Adjustments

The base cost tables represent the base cost per square foot of floor area for buildings without a basement and without unusual special features. Basement costs and other common additives are available. Cost adjustments can also be made to the model by using the tables from the Assemblies Section.

## Dimensions

All base cost tables are developed so that measurements can be readily made during the inspection process. Areas are calculated from exterior dimensions and story heights are measured from the top surface of one floor to the top surface of the floor above. Roof areas are measured by horizontal area covered and costs related to inclines are converted with appropriate factors. The precision of measurement is a matter of the user's choice and discretion. For ease in calculation, consider measuring in tenths of a foot, i.e., 9 ft. 6 in. = 9.5 ft. and 9 ft. 4 in. = 9.3 ft.

## Floor Area

The term "Floor Area" as used in this section includes the sum of floor plate at grade level and above. This dimension is measured from the outside face of the foundation wall. Basement costs are calculated separately. The user must exercise his/her own judgment, where the lowest level floor is slightly below grade, whether to consider it at grade level or make the basement adjustment.

# How to Use the Commercial/ Industrial/Institutional Section

*The following is a detailed explanation of a sample entry in the Commercial/Industrial/Institutional Square Foot Cost Section. Each bold number below corresponds to the described item on the following page with the appropriate component or cost of the sample entry following in parentheses.*

*Prices listed are costs that include overhead and profit of the installing contractor and additional markups for general conditions and architects' fees.*

## COMMERCIAL/INDUSTRIAL/ INSTITUTIONAL | M.010 (1) | Apartment, 1-3 Story (2)

### Costs per square foot of floor area

| Exterior Wall (3) | S.F. Area | 8000 | 12000 | 15000 | 19000 | 22500 | 25000 | 29000 | 32000 | 36000 |
|---|---|---|---|---|---|---|---|---|---|---|
| | L.F. Perimeter | 213 | 280 | 330 | 350 | 400 (4) | 433 | 442 | 480 | 520 |
| Fiber Cement | Wood Frame | 242.05 | 230.45 | 225.80 | 217.25 | 215.05 | 213.60 | 208.95 | 208.10 | 206.65 |
| Stone Veneer | Wood Frame | 269.55 | 254.55 | 248.55 | 236.35 | 233.40 (5) | 231.50 | 224.70 | 223.65 | 221.55 |
| Brick Veneer | Rigid Steel | 255.40 | 241.25 | 235.50 | 224.10 | 221.35 | 219.55 | 213.25 | 212.20 | 210.30 |
| E.I.F.S. and Metal Studs | Rigid Steel | 246.85 | 234.15 | 229.00 | 219.30 | 216.80 | 215.20 | 209.85 | 208.95 | 207.25 |
| Brick Veneer | Reinforced Concrete | 282.30 | 266.25 | 259.75 | 246.45 | 243.25 | 241.20 | 233.75 | 232.60 | 230.35 |
| Stucco and Concrete Block | Reinforced Concrete | 269.00 | 254.60 | 248.75 | 237.15 | 234.40 | 232.55 | 226.15 | 225.05 | 223.15 |
| Perimeter Adj., Add or Deduct (6) | Per 100 L.F. | 23.30 | 15.50 | 12.35 | 9.85 | 8.25 (7) | 7.45 | 6.45 | 5.80 | 5.20 |
| Story Hgt. Adj., Add or Deduct | Per 1 Ft. | 3.85 | 3.40 | 3.15 | 2.70 | 2.55 | 2.50 | 2.30 | 2.20 | 2.10 |
| (8) ***For Basement**, add $57.60 per square foot of basement area* | | | | | | | | | | |

*The above costs were calculated using the basic specifications shown on the facing page. These costs should be adjusted where necessary for design alternatives and owner's requirements.*

### Common additives (9)

| Description | Unit | $ Cost |
|---|---|---|
| Appliances | | |
| Cooking range, 30" free standing | | |
| 1 oven | Ea. | 885 - 1300 |
| 2 oven | Ea. | 3975 - 5050 |
| 30" built-in | | |
| 1 oven | Ea. | 1550 - 3225 |
| 2 oven | Ea. | 3200 - 3775 |
| Counter top cook tops, 4 burner | Ea. | 480 - 860 |
| Microwave oven | Ea. | 375 - 895 |
| Combination range, refrig. & sink, 30" wide | Ea. | 2250 - 3325 |
| 72" wide | Ea. | 3650 |
| Combination range, refrigerator, sink, microwave oven & icemaker | Ea. | 8600 |
| Compactor, residential, 4-1 compaction | Ea. | 1600 - 1875 |
| Dishwasher, built-in, 2 cycles | Ea. | 965 - 1900 |
| 4 cycles | Ea. | 1150 - 1700 |
| Garbage disposer, sink type | Ea. | 300 - 445 |
| Hood for range, 2 speed, vented, 30" wide | Ea. | 425 - 1750 |
| 42" wide | Ea. | 495 - 730 |
| Refrigerator, no frost 10-12 C.F. | Ea. | 1000 - 855 |
| 18-20 C.F. | Ea. | 960 - 1100 |

| Description | Unit | $ Cost |
|---|---|---|
| Closed Circuit Surveillance, One station | | |
| Camera and monitor | Ea. | 1250 |
| For additional camera stations, add | Ea. | 475 |
| Elevators, Hydraulic passenger, 2 stops | | |
| 2000# capacity | Ea. | 87,500 |
| 2500# capacity | Ea. | 90,500 |
| 3500# capacity | Ea. | 96,000 |
| Additional stop, add | Ea. | 9875 |
| Emergency Lighting, 25 watt, battery operated | | |
| Lead battery | Ea. | 360 |
| Nickel cadmium | Ea. | 585 |
| Laundry Equipment | | |
| Dryer, gas, 16 lb. capacity | Ea. | 1725 |
| 30 lb. capacity | Ea. | 2200 |
| Washer, 4 cycle | Ea. | 1550 |
| Commercial | Ea. | 2000 |
| Smoke Detectors | | |
| Ceiling type | Ea. | 300 |
| Duct type | Ea. | 615 |

## 1 Model Number (M.010)

"M" distinguishes this section of the data and stands for model. The number designation is a sequential number. Our newest models are green and are designated with the letter "G" followed by the building type number.

## 2 Type of Building (Apartment, 1-3 Story)

There are 50 different types of commercial/industrial/institutional buildings highlighted in this section.

## 3 Exterior Wall Construction and Building Framing Options (Stone Veneer with Wood Frame)

Three or more commonly used exterior walls and, in most cases, two typical building framing systems are presented for each type of building. The model selected should be based on the actual characteristics of the building being estimated.

## 4 Total Square Foot of Floor Area and Perimeter Used to Compute Base Costs (22,500 Square Feet and 400 Linear Feet)

Square foot of floor area is the total gross area of all floors at grade and above and does not include a basement. The perimeter in linear feet used for the base cost is generally for a rectangular, economical building shape.

## 5 Cost per Square Foot of Floor Area ($233.40)

The highlighted cost is for a building of the selected exterior wall and framing system and floor area. Costs for buildings with floor areas other than those calculated may be interpolated between the costs shown.

## 6 Building Perimeter and Story Height Adjustments

Square foot costs for a building with a perimeter or floor-to-floor story height significantly different from the model used to calculate the base cost may be adjusted (added or deducted) to reflect the actual building geometry.

## 7 Cost per Square Foot of Floor Area for the Perimeter and/or Height Adjustment ($8.25 for Perimeter Difference and $2.55 for Story Height Difference)

Add (or deduct) $8.25 to the base square foot cost for each 100 feet of perimeter difference between the model and the actual building. Add (or deduct) $2.55 to the base square foot cost for each 1 foot of story height difference between the model and the actual building.

## 8 Optional Cost per Square Foot of Basement Floor Area ($57.60)

The cost of an unfinished basement for the building being estimated is $57.60 times the gross floor area of the basement.

## 9 Common Additives

Common components and/or systems used in this type of building are listed. These costs should be added to the total building cost. Additional selections may be found in the Assemblies Section.

# How to Use the Commercial/ Industrial/Institutional Section (Cont.)

*The following is a detailed explanation of the specification and costs for a model building in the Commercial/Industrial/Institutional Square Foot Cost Section. Each bold number below corresponds to the described item on the following page with the appropriate component of the sample entry following in parentheses.*

*Prices listed in the specification are costs that include overhead and profit of the installing contractor but not the general contractor's markup and architect's fees.*

**Model costs calculated for a 3 story building with 10′ story height and 22,500 square feet of floor area** **1**

**2** **Apartment, 1-3 Story**

| | | | | Unit | Unit Cost | Cost Per S.F. | % Of Sub-Total |
|---|---|---|---|---|---|---|---|
| **A. SUBSTRUCTURE** | | | | | | | |
| 1010 | Standard Foundations | Poured concrete; strip and spread footings; 4′ foundation wall | | S.F. Ground | 12.87 | 4.29 | |
| 1020 | Special Foundations | N/A | | – | – | – | |
| 1030 | Slab on Grade | 4″ reinforced concrete | | S.F. Slab | 7.22 | 2.41 | 3.9% |
| 2010 | Basement Excavation | Site preparation for slab and trench for foundation wall and footing | | S.F. Ground | .38 | .13 | |
| 2020 | Basement Walls | N/A | | – | – | – | |
| **B. SHELL** | | | | | | | |
| | **B10 Superstructure** | | | | | | |
| 1010 | Floor Construction | Wood Beam and joist on wood columns, fireproofed | | S.F. Floor | 30.50 | 20.33 | 14.1% |
| 1020 | Roof Construction | Wood roof, truss, 4/12 slope | | S.F. Roof | 13.02 | 4.34 | |
| | **B20 Exterior Enclosure** | | | | | | |
| 2010 | Exterior Walls | Ashlar stone veneer on wood stud back up, insulated | *80% of wall* | S.F. Wall | 49.01 | 20.91 | |
| 2020 | Exterior Windows | Aluminum horizontal sliding | *20% of wall* | Each | 1552 | 11.04 | 18.7% |
| 2030 | Exterior Doors | Steel door , hollow metal with frame | | Each | 4140 | .73 | |
| | **B30 Roofing** | | | | | | |
| 3010 | Roof Coverings | Asphalt roofing, strip shingles, flashing | | S.F. Roof | 2.58 | .86 | 0.5% |
| 3020 | Roof Openings | N/A | | – | – | – | |
| **C. INTERIORS** **3** | | | | | | | |
| 1010 | Partitions | Gypsum board on wood studs | *10 S.F. Floor/L.F. Partition* | S.F. Partition | 9.50 | 8.44 | |
| 1020 | Interior Doors | Interior single leaf doors, frames and hardware **4** | *130 S.F. Floor/Door* **5** | **6** Each | **7** 1351 | **8** 10.24 | |
| 1030 | Fittings | Residential wall and base wood cabinets, laminate counters | | S.F. Floor | 5.98 | 5.98 | |
| 2010 | Stair Construction | Wood Stairs with wood rails | | Flight | 4005 | 1.06 | 22.5% **9** |
| 3010 | Wall Finishes | 95% paint, 5% ceramic wall tile | | S.F. Surface | 1.60 | 2.84 | |
| 3020 | Floor Finishes | 80% Carpet tile, 10% vinyl composition tile, 10% ceramic tile | | S.F. Floor | 5.28 | 5.28 | |
| 3030 | Ceiling Finishes | Painted gypsum board ceiling on resilient channels | | S.F. Ceiling | 5.43 | 5.43 | |
| **D. SERVICES** | | | | | | | |
| | **D10 Conveying** | | | | | | |
| 1010 | Elevators & Lifts | Hydraulic passenger elevator | | Each | 137,925 | 6.13 | 3.5% |
| 1020 | Escalators & Moving Walks | N/A | | – | – | – | |
| | **D20 Plumbing** | | | | | | |
| 2010 | Plumbing Fixtures | Kitchen, bath, laundry and service fixtures, supply and drainage | *1 Fixture/285 S.F. Floor* | Each | 2710 | 9.51 | |
| 2020 | Domestic Water Distribution | Electric water heater | | S.F. Floor | 8.24 | 8.24 | 10.6% |
| 2040 | Rain Water Drainage | Roof drains | | S.F. Roof | 2.22 | .74 | |
| | **D30 HVAC** | | | | | | |
| 3010 | Energy Supply | Oil fired hot water, baseboard radiation | | S.F. Floor | 9.80 | 9.80 | |
| 3020 | Heat Generating Systems | N/A | | – | – | – | |
| 3030 | Cooling Generating Systems | Chilled water, air cooled condenser system | | S.F. Floor | 12.97 | 12.97 | 13.0% |
| 3050 | Terminal & Package Units | N/A | | – | – | – | |
| 3090 | Other HVAC Sys. & Equipment | N/A | | – | – | – | |
| | **D40 Fire Protection** | | | | | | |
| 4010 | Sprinklers | Wet pipe spinkler system, light hazard | | S.F. Floor | 5.08 | 5.08 | 2.9% |
| 4020 | Standpipes | N/A | | – | – | – | |
| | **D50 Electrical** | | | | | | |
| 5010 | Electrical Service/Distribution | 800 ampere service, panel board and feeders | | S.F. Floor | 4.01 | 4.01 | |
| 5020 | Lighting & Branch Wiring | Incandescent fixtures, receptacles, switches, A.C. and misc. power | | S.F. Floor | 9.59 | 9.59 | 9.0% |
| 5030 | Communications & Security | Addressable alarm systems, emergency lighting, internet and phone wiring | | S.F. Floor | 2.02 | 2.02 | |
| 5090 | Other Electrical Systems | N/A | | – | – | – | |
| **E. EQUIPMENT & FURNISHINGS** | | | | | | | |
| 1010 | Commercial Equipment | N/A | | – | – | – | |
| 1020 | Institutional Equipment | N/A | | – | – | – | 1.2 % |
| 1030 | Vehicular Equipment | N/A | | – | – | – | |
| 1090 | Other Equipment | Residential freestanding gas ranges, dishwashers | | S.F. Floor | 2.10 | 2.10 | |
| **F. SPECIAL CONSTRUCTION** | | | | | | | |
| 1020 | Integrated Construction | N/A | | – | – | – | 0.0 % |
| 1040 | Special Facilities | N/A | | – | – | – | |
| **G. BUILDING SITEWORK** | **N/A** | | | | | | |
| | | | | | **10** **Sub-Total** | 174.50 | **100%** |
| | CONTRACTOR FEES (General Requirements: 10%, Overhead: 5%, Profit: 10%) **11** | | | | *25%* | 43.63 | |
| | ARCHITECT FEES | | | | *7%* | 15.27 | |
| | | | | | **12** **Total Building Cost** | **233.40** | |

1. **Building Description (Model costs are calculated for a 3-story apartment building with a 10' story height and 22,500 square feet of floor area)**
   The model highlighted is described in terms of building type, number of stories, typical story height, and square footage.

2. **Type of Building (Apartment, 1-3 Story)**

3. **Division C Interiors (C1020 Interior Doors)**
   System costs are presented in divisions according to the 7-element UNIFORMAT II classifications. Each of the component systems is listed.

4. **Specification Highlights (Interior single leaf doors, frames and hardware)**
   All systems in each subdivision are described with the material and proportions used.

5. **Quantity Criteria (130 S.F. Floor/Door)**
   The criteria used in determining quantities for the calculations are shown.

6. **Unit (Each)**
   The unit of measure shown in this column is the unit of measure of the particular system shown that corresponds to the unit cost.

7. **Unit Cost ($1,351)**
   The cost per unit of measure of each system subdivision.

8. **Cost per Square Foot ($10.24)**
   The cost per square foot for each system is the unit cost of the system times the total number of units, divided by the total square feet of building area.

9. **% of Sub-Total (22.5%)**
   The percent of sub-total is the total cost per square foot of all systems in the division divided by the sub-total cost per square foot of the building.

10. **Sub-Total ($174.50)**
    The sub-total is the total of all the system costs per square foot.

11. **Project Fees (Contractors' Fee - 25%); (Architects' Fee - 7%)**
    Contractor fees to cover the general requirements, overhead, and profit of the general contractor are added as a percentage of the sub-total. An architect's fee, also as a percentage of the sub-total, is also added. These values may vary significantly with the building type or project.

12. **Total Building Cost ($233.40)**
    The total building cost per square foot of building area is the sum of the square foot costs of all the systems, the general contractor's general requirements, overhead and profit, and the architect's fee. The total building cost is the amount that appears shaded in the Cost per Square Foot of Floor Area table shown previously.

# Examples

## Example 1

This example illustrates the use of the base cost tables. The base cost is adjusted for different exterior wall systems, a different story height, and a partial basement.

**CII APPRAISAL FIELD DATA FORM**

COMMERCIAL
INDUSTRIAL
INSTITUTIONAL

*Use sheets A & D for App. Form 2*
*Use sheets A,B & C for App. Form 3*

**CII APPRAISAL**

5 DATE: **Jan. 1, 2023**

1. SUBJECT PROPERTY: **Westernberg Holdings, Inc.**
6. APPRAISER: **BA**
2. BUILDING: **# 623**
3. ADDRESS: **55 Pine wood Rd., Paterson, N.J. 07410**
4. BUILDING USE: **Apartments**
7. YEAR BUILT: **1991**

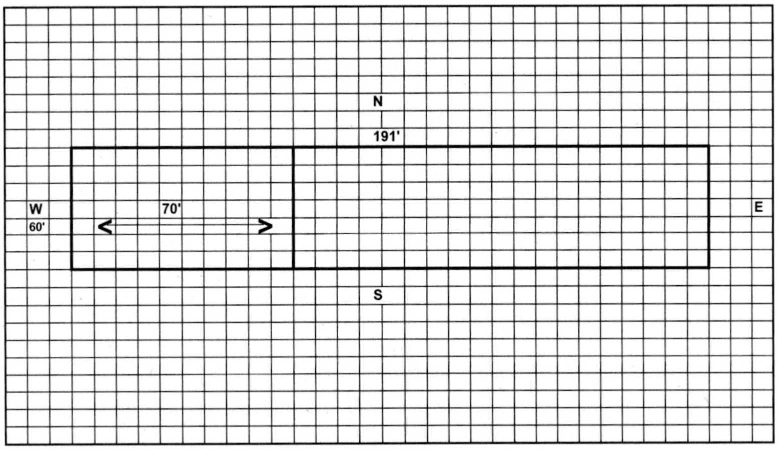


8. EXTERIOR WALL CONSTRUCTION: **North wall - Curtain wall, steel frame**
**East, West & South walls - Brick veneer, steel frame**
9. FRAME: **Steel**
10. GROUND FLOOR AREA: **60' x 191'** **11,460** S.F.
11. GROSS FLOOR AREA (EXCL. BASEMENT): **80, 220 (7 Floors)** S.F.
12. NUMBER OF STORIES: **7**
13. STORY HEIGHT: **11 ' - 4"**
14. PERIMETER: **502** L.F.
15. BASEMENT AREA: **4200 S.F.** S.F.
16. GENERAL COMMENTS:

# Example 1 (continued)

Base Cost per square area: *(from square foot table)*

Specify source: Page: **80** , Model # **M.020** , Area **80,220** S.F., Exterior wall **See Below** , Frame **Steel**

Adjustments for exterior wall variation:

**North wall is curtain wall**

$\frac{191}{502}$ = 38% **East, West, South = 62% Brick veneer**

Size Adjustment: **(.38 x 201.05) + (.62 x 203.45) = 76.39 + 126.139 = 202.53**
*(Interpolate)*

Height Adjustment: **202.538** + **2.75** = **205.29**

Adjusted Base Cost per square foot: **205.29**

| | | | | | | |
|---|---|---|---|---|---|---|
| Building Cost | $ | **205.29** *Adjusted Base Cost per square foot* | x | **80220.00** *Floor Area* | = | **16,468,203** |
| Basement Cost | $ | **57.70** *Basement Cost* | x | **4,200** *Basement Area* | = | **242,340** |

Lump Sum Additions

**70 Smoke detectors @ $284.00 each** — **19,880**

| | | |
|---|---|---|
| TOTAL BUILDING COST *(Sum of above costs)* | | **16,730,423** |
| Modifications: *(complexity, workmanship, size)* | +/- ______ % | — |
| Location Modifier: City **Paterson, NJ 07410** Date **January 2023** | x | **1.11** |
| Local cost of replacement | | **18,570,770** |
| Less depreciation: **30%** | - | **5,571,231** |
| Local cost of replacement less depreciation | $ | **12,999,539** |

Identify the source of base costs

38% = area of north wall / total wall area

**$203.45** from page 80; 80,000 S.F. Brick Veneer

**$201.05** from page 80; 80,000 S.F. Curtian Wal

**$2.75** from page 80; 80,000 S.F. Story Height Adjustmen

**$57.70** from page 80; Basement Additior

**$284.00** from page 80; Common Additives

**1.11** from page 527

**30 %** from page 232

# Example 2

This example shows how to modify a model building.

Model #M.020, 4–7 Story Apartment, page 80, matches the example quite closely. The model specifies a 6-story building with a 10' story height.

The following adjustments must be made:

- add stone ashlar wall
- adjust model to a 5-story building
- change partitions
- change floor finish

**CII APPRAISAL**

5. DATE: **Jan. 2, 2023**

1. SUBJECT PROPERTY: **Westernberg Holdings, Inc.**

6. APPRAISER: **BA**

2. BUILDING: **# 623**

3. ADDRESS: **55 Pinewood Rd., Paterson, N.J. 07410**

4. BUILDING USE: **Apartments**

7. YEAR BUILT: **1992**

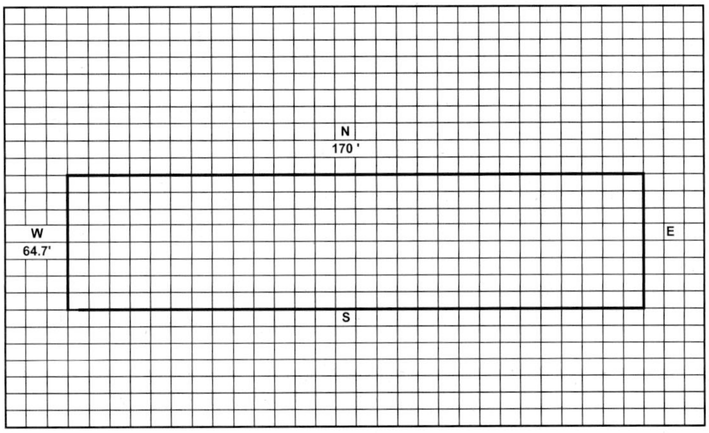


8. EXTERIOR WALL CONSTRUCTION: **North wall - 4" stone Ashlar w/8" block back up (split Face)**
**East, West & South walls - 12" Decorative concrete block**

Two exterior wall types

9. FRAME: **Steel**

10. GROUND FLOOR AREA: **11,000**

11. GROSS FLOOR AREA (EXCL. BASEMENT): **55,000** S.F.

12. NUMBER OF STORIES: **5**

13. STORY HEIGHT: **11 Ft.**

14. PERIMETER: **469.4**

15. BASEMENT AREA: None S.F.

16. GENERAL COMMENTS:

## Example 2 (continued)

Square foot area (excluding basement) from item 11: 55,000 S.F.
Perimeter from item 14: 469.4 Lin. Ft.
Item 17 - Model square foot costs (from model sub-total): $174.50

| | NO. | DESCRIPTION | | | UNIT | UNIT COST | NEW SF COST | MODEL SF COST | |
|---|---|---|---|---|---|---|---|---|---|
| **A SUBSTRUCTURE** | | | | | | | | | |
| A | 1010 | Standard Foundations | | Bay size: *Same as model* | S.F. Gnd. | 10.92 | 2.18 | 1.82 | 0.36 |
| A | 1030 | Slab on Grade | Material: | Thickness: *Same as model* | S.F. Slab | 7.22 | 1.44 | 1.20 | 0.24 |
| A | 2010 | Basement Excavation | Depth: | Area: *11,000 S.F.* | S.F. Gnd. | 0.37 | 0.07 | 0.06 | 0.01 |
| A | 2020 | Basement Walls | | | L.F. Walls | | | | |
| **B SHELL** | | | | | | | | | |
| | B10 Superstructure | | | | | | | | |
| B | 1010 | Floor Construction | Elevated floors: *Same as model* | | S.F. Floor | 29.17 | 29.17 | 24.31 | 4.86 |
| | | | | | | | | | |
| B | 1020 | Roof Construction | | | S.F. Roof | 21.30 | 4.26 | 3.55 | 0.71 |
| | B20 Exterior Closure | | | | | | | | |
| B | 2010 | Exterior Walls | Material: *North wall- 4" stone ashlar on 8" CMU* | Thickness: *36% of wall* | S.F. Walls | 36.55 | 14.75 | - | 14.75 |
| | | | Material: *East, West, & South walls- 12" split rib block* | Thickness: *64% of wall* | S.F. Walls | | | | |
| B | 2020 | Exterior Windows | Type: | *% of wall* | S.F. Wind. | | | | |
| | | | Type: | *14% of wall* Each | S.F. Wind. | 1552 | 6.80 | 10.35 | -3.55 |
| B | 2030 | Exterior Doors | Type: *Same as model* | Number: *4* | Each | 6633 | 0.48 | 0.67 | -0.19 |
| | | | Type: | Number: | Each | | | | |
| | B30 Roofing | | | | | | | | |
| B | 3010 | Roof Coverings | Material: *Same as model* | | S.F. Roof | 12.00 | 2.40 | 2.00 | 0.40 |
| | | | | | | | | | |
| B | 3020 | Roof Openings | N/A | | S.F. Opng. | | | | |
| **C INTERIORS** | | | | | | | | | |
| C | 1010 | Partitions: *High* | Material: *Gyp board on metal studs* | Density: *10 S.F. Floor/L.F. Part.* | S.F. Part. | 10.16 | 9.14 | 9.44 | -0.30 |
| | | | Material: | Density: | | | | | |
| C | 1020 | Interior Doors | Type: | Number: 140 SF | Each | 1159 | 8.28 | 8.34 | -0.06 |
| C | 1030 | Fittings | | | S.F. Floor | 6.01 | 6.01 | 6.01 | - |
| C | 2010 | Stair Construction | *14 Flights* | | Flight | 12,925 | 3.29 | 3.45 | -0.16 |
| C | 3010 | Wall Finishes | Material: *Same as model* | % of Wall *9'-0" High* | S.F. Walls | 1.37 | 2.47 | 2.43 | 0.04 |
| | | | Material: | | | | | | |
| C | 3020 | Floor Finishes | Material: *Hardwood - 60% of floor* | | S.F. Floor | 5.28 | 5.28 | 5.28 | - |
| | | | Material: *Carpet - 30% of floor* | | | | | | |
| | | | Material: *Tile -10% of floor* | | | | | | |
| C | 3030 | Ceiling Finishes | Material: *Same as model* | | S.F. Ceil. | 5.43 | 5.43 | 5.43 | - |

**From page 81, Model #M.020 Sub-total**

**$ .37 /S.F. ground area / 5 Stories**

**Area of elevated floors(16.91/S.F. x 5 x 11000 S.F.) / S.F. Building Floor Area 55,000**

**21.30 / S.F. roof / 5 stories**

**Windows are 14% of wall area,**
**15 S.F. / window (use B2020 106 6650 for windows)**

**(1552/15) x .14 x 469.4 x 11 x 5 /55,000 = 6.799**

**From Table C1010 126 7600 on page 403**

**$ 10.16/S.F. partition x 9 ft. high / 10 S.F. fllor / L.F. partition**

**North wall is 36% of wall area, e.g.** 170 x 11 / 469.4 x 11
**From Table B2010 128 2350 page 361**
**Stone ashlar @ 54.50 / S.F. wall**
**East, West and south walls are 64% of wall area**
**From Table B2010 113 1530 page 355**
**Split ribbed block @26.45 / S.F. wall**

**New wall cost**
**(.36 x $54.50 / S.F.) + (.64 x $26.45 / S.F.) = $36.55 / S.F.**

**Convert Cost per S.F. wall to cost per S.F. of floor**
**Windows are 14% of wall area**

**$14.75 S.F. floor = $36.55 / S.F. wall x .86 x 469.4 L.F. x 11 ft. high x 5 stories / 55,000 S.F. of floor**

# Example 2 (continued)

| | NO. | SYSTEM/COMPONENT | DESCRIPTION | UNIT | UNIT COST | NEW S.F. COST | MODEL S.F. COST | +/- CHANGE |
|---|---|---|---|---|---|---|---|---|
| **D SERVICES** | | | | | | | | |
| | **D10 Conveying** | | | | | | | |
| D | 1010 | Elevators & Lifts | 2 Type: *Same as model* Capacity: Stops: | Each | 288,900 | 10.51 | 9.63 | 0.88 |
| D | 1020 | Escalators & Moving Walks | Type: | Each | | | | |
| | **D20 Plumbing** | | | | | | | |
| D | 2010 | Plumbing | *Kitchen, bath, + service fixtures* *1 Fixture/285 S.F. Floor* | Each | 2,700 | 9.47 | 9.44 | 0.03 |
| D | 2020 | Domestic Water Distribution | | S.F. Floor | 8.29 | 8.29 | 8.29 | - |
| D | 2040 | Rain Water Drainage | | S.F. Roof | 2.28 | 0.46 | 0.38 | 0.08 |
| | **D30 HVAC** | | | | | | | |
| D | 3010 | Energy Supply | | S.F. Floor | 9.50 | 9.50 | 9.50 | - |
| D | 3020 | Heat Generating Systems | Type: *Same as model* | S.F. Floor | | | | |
| D | 3030 | Cooling Generating Systems | Type: *Same as model* | S.F. Floor | 10.65 | 10.65 | 10.65 | - |
| D | 3090 | Other HVAC Sys. & Equipment | | Each | | | | |
| | **D40 Fire Protection** | | | | | | | |
| D | 4010 | Sprinklers | *Same as model* | S.F. Floor | 4.22 | 4.22 | 4.22 | - |
| D | 4020 | Standpipes | *Same as model* | S.F. Floor | 1.44 | 1.44 | 1.44 | - |
| | **D50 Electrical** | | | | | | | |
| D | 5010 | Electrical Service/Distribution | *Same as model* | S.F. Floor | 4.72 | 4.72 | 4.72 | - |
| D | 5020 | Lighting & Branch Wiring | | S.F. Floor | 9.55 | 9.55 | 9.55 | - |
| D | 5030 | Communications & Security | | S.F. Floor | 2.07 | 2.07 | 2.07 | - |
| D | 5090 | Other Electrical Systems | | S.F. Floor | | | | |
| **E EQUIPMENT & FURNISHINGS** | | | | | | | | |
| E | 1010 | Commercial Equipment | | Each | | | | |
| E | 1020 | Institutional Equipment | | Each | | | | |
| E | 1030 | Vehicular Equipment | | Each | | | | |
| E | 1090 | Other Equipment | | S.F. Floor | 1.78 | 1.78 | 1.78 | - |
| **F SPECIAL CONSTRUCTION** | | | | | | | | |
| F | 1020 | Integrated Construction | N/A | S.F. | | | | |
| F | 1040 | Special Facilities | N/A | S.F. | | | | |
| **G BUILDING SITEWORK** | | | | | | | | |

| ITEM | | | | Total Change | 18.11 |
|---|---|---|---|---|---|
| 17 | Model 020 total | $ **156.01** | | | |
| 18 | Adjusted S.F. cost | $ **174.12** | item 17 +/- changes | | |
| 19 | Building area - from item 11 | **55,000** | S.F. x adjusted S.F. cost | $ | 9,576,720 |
| 20 | Basement area - from item 15 | | S.F. x S.F. cost $ | $ | |
| 21 | Base building sub-total - item 20 + item 19 | | | $ | 9,576,720 |
| 22 | Miscellaneous addition (quality, etc.) | | | $ | |
| 23 | Sub-total - item 22 + 21 | | | $ | 9,576,720 |
| 24 | General conditions -25 % of item 23 | | | $ | 2,394,180 |
| 25 | Sub-total - item 24 + item 23 | | | $ | 11,970,900 |
| 26 | Architects fees | **5.5** | % of item 25 | $ | 658,399 |
| 27 | Sub-total - item 26 + item 25 | | | $ | 12,629,299 |
| 28 | Location modifier | zip code 07410 | | x | 1.11 |
| 29 | Local replacement cost - item 28 x item 27 | | | $ | 14,018,522 |
| 30 | Depreciation | **20** | % of item 29 | $ | 4,205,557 |
| 31 | Depreciated local replacement cost - item 29 less item 30 | | | $ | 9,812,965 |
| 32 | Exclusions | | | $ | |
| 33 | Net depreciated replacement cost - item 31 less item 32 | | | $ | 9,812,965 |

**From page 527**

**Use table on page 232**

## Costs per square foot of floor area

| Exterior Wall | S.F. Area | 8000 | 12000 | 15000 | 19000 | 22500 | 25000 | 29000 | 32000 | 36000 |
|---|---|---|---|---|---|---|---|---|---|---|
| | L.F. Perimeter | 213 | 280 | 330 | 350 | 400 | 433 | 442 | 480 | 520 |
| Fiber Cement | Wood Frame | 242.05 | 230.45 | 225.80 | 217.25 | 215.05 | 213.60 | 208.95 | 208.10 | 206.65 |
| Stone Veneer | Wood Frame | 269.55 | 254.55 | 248.55 | 236.35 | **233.40** | 231.50 | 224.70 | 223.65 | 221.55 |
| Brick Veneer | Rigid Steel | 255.40 | 241.25 | 235.50 | 224.10 | 221.35 | 219.55 | 213.25 | 212.20 | 210.30 |
| E.I.F.S. and Metal Studs | Rigid Steel | 246.85 | 234.15 | 229.00 | 219.30 | 216.80 | 215.20 | 209.85 | 208.95 | 207.25 |
| Brick Veneer | Reinforced Concrete | 282.30 | 266.25 | 259.75 | 246.45 | 243.25 | 241.20 | 233.75 | 232.60 | 230.35 |
| Stucco and Concrete Block | Reinforced Concrete | 269.00 | 254.60 | 248.75 | 237.15 | 234.40 | 232.55 | 226.15 | 225.05 | 223.15 |
| Perimeter Adj., Add or Deduct | Per 100 L.F. | 23.30 | 15.50 | 12.35 | 9.85 | 8.25 | 7.45 | 6.45 | 5.80 | 5.20 |
| Story Hgt. Adj., Add or Deduct | Per 1 Ft. | 3.85 | 3.40 | 3.15 | 2.70 | 2.55 | 2.50 | 2.30 | 2.20 | 2.10 |
| ***For Basement**, add $57.60 per square foot of basement area* | | | | | | | | | | |

*The above costs were calculated using the basic specifications shown on the facing page. These costs should be adjusted where necessary for design alternatives and owner's requirements.*

## Common additives

| Description | Unit | $ Cost |
|---|---|---|
| Appliances | | |
| Cooking range, 30" free standing | | |
| 1 oven | Ea. | 885 - 1300 |
| 2 oven | Ea. | 3975 - 5050 |
| 30" built-in | | |
| 1 oven | Ea. | 1550 - 3225 |
| 2 oven | Ea. | 3200 - 3775 |
| Counter top cook tops, 4 burner | Ea. | 480 - 860 |
| Microwave oven | Ea. | 375 - 895 |
| Combination range, refrig. & sink, 30" wide | Ea. | 2250 - 3325 |
| 72" wide | Ea. | 3650 |
| Combination range, refrigerator, sink, microwave oven & icemaker | Ea. | 8600 |
| Compactor, residential, 4-1 compaction | Ea. | 1600 - 1875 |
| Dishwasher, built-in, 2 cycles | Ea. | 965 - 1900 |
| 4 cycles | Ea. | 1150 - 1700 |
| Garbage disposer, sink type | Ea. | 300 - 445 |
| Hood for range, 2 speed, vented, 30" wide | Ea. | 425 - 1750 |
| 42" wide | Ea. | 495 - 730 |
| Refrigerator, no frost 10-12 C.F. | Ea. | 1000 - 855 |
| 18-20 C.F. | Ea. | 960 - 1100 |

| Description | Unit | $ Cost |
|---|---|---|
| Closed Circuit Surveillance, One station | | |
| Camera and monitor | Ea. | 1250 |
| For additional camera stations, add | Ea. | 475 |
| Elevators, Hydraulic passenger, 2 stops | | |
| 2000# capacity | Ea. | 87,500 |
| 2500# capacity | Ea. | 90,500 |
| 3500# capacity | Ea. | 96,000 |
| Additional stop, add | Ea. | 9875 |
| Emergency Lighting, 25 watt, battery operated | | |
| Lead battery | Ea. | 360 |
| Nickel cadmium | Ea. | 585 |
| Laundry Equipment | | |
| Dryer, gas, 16 lb. capacity | Ea. | 1725 |
| 30 lb. capacity | Ea. | 2200 |
| Washer, 4 cycle | Ea. | 1550 |
| Commercial | Ea. | 2000 |
| Smoke Detectors | | |
| Ceiling type | Ea. | 300 |
| Duct type | Ea. | 615 |

## Model costs calculated for a 3 story building with 10′ story height and 22,500 square feet of floor area

# Apartment, 1-3 Story

| | | | Unit | Unit Cost | Cost Per S.F. | % Of Sub-Total |
|---|---|---|---|---|---|---|
| **A. SUBSTRUCTURE** | | | | | | |
| 1010 | Standard Foundations | Poured concrete; strip and spread footings; 4′ foundation wall | S.F. Ground | 12.87 | 4.29 | 3.9% |
| 1020 | Special Foundations | N/A | — | — | — | |
| 1030 | Slab on Grade | 4″ reinforced concrete | S.F. Slab | 7.22 | 2.41 | |
| 2010 | Basement Excavation | Site preparation for slab and trench for foundation wall and footing | S.F. Ground | .38 | .13 | |
| 2020 | Basement Walls | N/A | — | — | — | |
| **B. SHELL** | | | | | | |
| | **B10 Superstructure** | | | | | |
| 1010 | Floor Construction | Wood Beam and joist on wood columns, fireproofed | S.F. Floor | 30.50 | 20.33 | 14.1% |
| 1020 | Roof Construction | Wood roof, truss, 4/12 slope | S.F. Roof | 13.02 | 4.34 | |
| | **B20 Exterior Enclosure** | | | | | |
| 2010 | Exterior Walls | Ashlar stone veneer on wood stud back up, insulated *80% of wall* | S.F. Wall | 49.01 | 20.91 | 18.7% |
| 2020 | Exterior Windows | Aluminum horizontal sliding *20% of wall* | Each | 1552 | 11.04 | |
| 2030 | Exterior Doors | Steel door , hollow metal with frame | Each | 4140 | .73 | |
| | **B30 Roofing** | | | | | |
| 3010 | Roof Coverings | Asphalt roofing, strip shingles, flashing | S.F. Roof | 2.58 | .86 | 0.5% |
| 3020 | Roof Openings | N/A | — | — | — | |
| **C. INTERIORS** | | | | | | |
| 1010 | Partitions | Gypsum board on wood studs *10 S.F. Floor/L.F. Partition* | S.F. Partition | 9.50 | 8.44 | 22.5% |
| 1020 | Interior Doors | Interior single leaf doors, frames and hardware *130 S.F. Floor/Door* | Each | 1351 | 10.24 | |
| 1030 | Fittings | Residential wall and base wood cabinets, laminate counters | S.F. Floor | 5.98 | 5.98 | |
| 2010 | Stair Construction | Wood Stairs with wood rails | Flight | 4005 | 1.06 | |
| 3010 | Wall Finishes | 95% paint, 5% ceramic wall tile | S.F. Surface | 1.60 | 2.84 | |
| 3020 | Floor Finishes | 80% Carpet tile, 10% vinyl composition tile, 10% ceramic tile | S.F. Floor | 5.28 | 5.28 | |
| 3030 | Ceiling Finishes | Painted gypsum board ceiling on resilient channels | S.F. Ceiling | 5.43 | 5.43 | |
| **D. SERVICES** | | | | | | |
| | **D10 Conveying** | | | | | |
| 1010 | Elevators & Lifts | Hydraulic passenger elevator | Each | 137,925 | 6.13 | 3.5% |
| 1020 | Escalators & Moving Walks | N/A | — | — | — | |
| | **D20 Plumbing** | | | | | |
| 2010 | Plumbing Fixtures | Kitchen, bath, laundry and service fixtures, supply and drainage *1 Fixture/285 S.F. Floor* | Each | 2710 | 9.51 | 10.6% |
| 2020 | Domestic Water Distribution | Electric water heater | S.F. Floor | 8.24 | 8.24 | |
| 2040 | Rain Water Drainage | Roof drains | S.F. Roof | 2.22 | .74 | |
| | **D30 HVAC** | | | | | |
| 3010 | Energy Supply | Oil fired hot water, baseboard radiation | S.F. Floor | 9.80 | 9.80 | 13.0% |
| 3020 | Heat Generating Systems | N/A | — | — | — | |
| 3030 | Cooling Generating Systems | Chilled water, air cooled condenser system | S.F. Floor | 12.97 | 12.97 | |
| 3050 | Terminal & Package Units | N/A | — | — | — | |
| 3090 | Other HVAC Sys. & Equipment | N/A | — | — | — | |
| | **D40 Fire Protection** | | | | | |
| 4010 | Sprinklers | Wet pipe spinkler system, light hazard | S.F. Floor | 5.08 | 5.08 | 2.9% |
| 4020 | Standpipes | N/A | — | — | — | |
| | **D50 Electrical** | | | | | |
| 5010 | Electrical Service/Distribution | 800 ampere service, panel board and feeders | S.F. Floor | 4.01 | 4.01 | 9.0% |
| 5020 | Lighting & Branch Wiring | Incandescent fixtures, receptacles, switches, A.C. and misc. power | S.F. Floor | 9.59 | 9.59 | |
| 5030 | Communications & Security | Addressable alarm systems, emergency lighting, internet and phone wiring | S.F. Floor | 2.02 | 2.02 | |
| 5090 | Other Electrical Systems | N/A | — | — | — | |
| **E. EQUIPMENT & FURNISHINGS** | | | | | | |
| 1010 | Commercial Equipment | N/A | — | — | — | 1.2 % |
| 1020 | Institutional Equipment | N/A | — | — | — | |
| 1030 | Vehicular Equipment | N/A | — | — | — | |
| 1090 | Other Equipment | Residential freestanding gas ranges, dishwashers | S.F. Floor | 2.10 | 2.10 | |
| **F. SPECIAL CONSTRUCTION** | | | | | | |
| 1020 | Integrated Construction | N/A | — | — | — | 0.0 % |
| 1040 | Special Facilities | N/A | — | — | — | |
| **G. BUILDING SITEWORK** | **N/A** | | | | | |
| | | | | **Sub-Total** | 174.50 | **100%** |
| | CONTRACTOR FEES (General Requirements: 10%, Overhead: 5%, Profit: 10%) | | | *25%* | 43.63 | |
| | ARCHITECT FEES | | | *7%* | 15.27 | |
| | | | | **Total Building Cost** | **233.40** | |

## Costs per square foot of floor area

| Exterior Wall | S.F. Area | 40000 | 45000 | 50000 | 55000 | 60000 | 70000 | 80000 | 90000 | 100000 |
|---|---|---|---|---|---|---|---|---|---|---|
| | L.F. Perimeter | 366 | 400 | 433 | 466 | 500 | 510 | 530 | 550 | 594 |
| Curtain Wall | Rigid Steel | 219.20 | 216.55 | 214.30 | 212.50 | 211.05 | 205.00 | 201.05 | 197.95 | 196.60 |
| Brick Veneer | Rigid Steel | 222.40 | 219.70 | 217.30 | 215.45 | 214.00 | 207.55 | 203.45 | 200.15 | 198.70 |
| E.I.F.S. and Metal Studs | Rigid Steel | 214.05 | 211.50 | 209.40 | 207.70 | 206.40 | 200.90 | 197.35 | 194.50 | 193.25 |
| Precast Concrete | Reinforced Concrete | 260.25 | 256.75 | 253.65 | 251.25 | **249.35** | 239.65 | 233.45 | 228.55 | 226.65 |
| Brick Veneer | Reinforced Concrete | 244.30 | 241.25 | 238.55 | 236.50 | 234.80 | 226.90 | 221.85 | 217.85 | 216.15 |
| Stucco | Reinforced Concrete | 228.30 | 225.50 | 223.15 | 221.25 | 219.80 | 213.15 | 208.90 | 205.50 | 204.10 |
| Perimeter Adj., Add or Deduct | Per 100 L.F. | 11.50 | 10.20 | 9.20 | 8.40 | 7.75 | 6.55 | 5.75 | 5.10 | 4.60 |
| Story Hgt. Adj., Add or Deduct | Per 1 Ft. | 3.70 | 3.60 | 3.45 | 3.40 | 3.40 | 2.95 | 2.75 | 2.50 | 2.40 |
| ***For Basement**, add $ 57.70 per square foot of basement area* | | | | | | | | | | |

*The above costs were calculated using the basic specifications shown on the facing page. These costs should be adjusted where necessary for design alternatives and owner's requirements.*

## Common additives

| Description | Unit | $ Cost |
|---|---|---|
| Appliances | | |
| Cooking range, 30" free standing | | |
| 1 oven | Ea. | 885 - 1300 |
| 2 oven | Ea. | 3975 - 5050 |
| 30" built-in | | |
| 1 oven | Ea. | 1550 - 3225 |
| 2 oven | Ea. | 3200 - 3775 |
| Counter top cook tops, 4 burner | Ea. | 480 - 860 |
| Microwave oven | Ea. | 375 - 895 |
| Combination range, refrig. & sink, 30" wide | Ea. | 2250 - 3325 |
| 72" wide | Ea. | 3650 |
| Combination range, refrigerator, sink, microwave oven & icemaker | Ea. | 8600 |
| Compactor, residential, 4-1 compaction | Ea. | 1600 - 1875 |
| Dishwasher, built-in, 2 cycles | Ea. | 965 - 1900 |
| 4 cycles | Ea. | 1150 - 1700 |
| Garbage disposer, sink type | Ea. | 300 - 445 |
| Hood for range, 2 speed, vented, 30" wide | Ea. | 425 - 1750 |
| 42" wide | Ea. | 495 - 730 |
| Refrigerator, no frost 10-12 C.F. | Ea. | 1000 - 855 |
| 18-20 C.F. | Ea. | 960 - 1100 |

| Description | Unit | $ Cost |
|---|---|---|
| Closed Circuit Surveillance, One station | | |
| Camera and monitor | Ea. | 1250 |
| For additional camera stations, add | Ea. | 475 |
| Elevators, Electric passenger, 5 stops | | |
| 2000# capacity | Ea. | 213,000 |
| 3500# capacity | Ea. | 220,500 |
| 5000# capacity | Ea. | 229,000 |
| Additional stop, add | Ea. | 12,600 |
| Emergency Lighting, 25 watt, battery operated | | |
| Lead battery | Ea. | 360 |
| Nickel cadmium | Ea. | 585 |
| Laundry Equipment | | |
| Dryer, gas, 16 lb. capacity | Ea. | 1725 |
| 30 lb. capacity | Ea. | 2200 |
| Washer, 4 cycle | Ea. | 1550 |
| Commercial | Ea. | 2000 |
| Smoke Detectors | | |
| Ceiling type | Ea. | 300 |
| Duct type | Ea. | 615 |



**Important: See the Reference Section for Location Factors.**

## Model costs calculated for a 6 story building with 10'-4" story height and 60,000 square feet of floor area

# Apartment, 4-7 Story

| | | | Unit | Unit Cost | Cost Per S.F. | % Of Sub-Total |
|---|---|---|---|---|---|---|
| **A. SUBSTRUCTURE** | | | | | | |
| 1010 | Standard Foundations | Poured concrete; strip and spread footings and 4' foundation wall; 4' foundation wall | S.F. Ground | 10.92 | 1.82 | |
| 1020 | Special Foundations | N/A | — | — | — | |
| 1030 | Slab on Grade | 4" reinforced concrete with vapor barrier and granular base | S.F. Slab | 7.22 | 1.20 | 1.7% |
| 2010 | Basement Excavation | Site preparation for slab and trench for foundation wall and footing | S.F. Ground | .37 | .06 | |
| 2020 | Basement Walls | N/A | — | — | — | |
| **B. SHELL** | | | | | | |
| | **B10 Superstructure** | | | | | |
| 1010 | Floor Construction | Open web steel joists, slab form, concrete, steel columns | S.F. Floor | 29.17 | 24.31 | 14.9% |
| 1020 | Roof Construction | Open web steel joists with rib metal deck, steel columns | S.F. Roof | 21.30 | 3.55 | |
| | **B20 Exterior Enclosure** | | | | | |
| 2010 | Exterior Walls | Face brick with concrete block backup *86% of wall* | S.F. Wall | 75 | 30.10 | |
| 2020 | Exterior Windows | Aluminum horizontal sliding *14% of wall* | Each | 1552 | 10.35 | 22.1% |
| 2030 | Exterior Doors | Aluminum and glass | Each | 6633 | .67 | |
| | **B30 Roofing** | | | | | |
| 3010 | Roof Coverings | Built-up tar and gravel with flashing; perlite/EPS composite insulation | S.F. Roof | 12 | 2 | 1.1% |
| 3020 | Roof Openings | N/A | — | — | — | |
| **C. INTERIORS** | | | | | | |
| 1010 | Partitions | Gypsum board and sound deadening board on metal studs *8 S.F. Floor/L.F. Partitions* | S.F. Partition | 10.62 | 9.44 | |
| 1020 | Interior Doors | 15% solid core wood, 85% hollow core wood *80 S.F Floor/Door* | Each | 1159 | 8.34 | |
| 1030 | Fittings | Kitchen cabinets | S.F. Floor | 6.01 | 6.01 | |
| 2010 | Stair Construction | Concrete filled metal pan | Flight | 12,925 | 3.45 | 21.7% |
| 3010 | Wall Finishes | 70% paint, 25% vinyl wall covering, 5% ceramic tile | S.F. Surface | 1.37 | 2.43 | |
| 3020 | Floor Finishes | 60% carpet, 30% vinyl composition tile, 10% ceramic tile | S.F. Floor | 5.28 | 5.28 | |
| 3030 | Ceiling Finishes | Painted gypsum board on resilient channels | S.F. Ceiling | 5.43 | 5.43 | |
| **D. SERVICES** | | | | | | |
| | **D10 Conveying** | | | | | |
| 1010 | Elevators & Lifts | Two geared passenger elevators | Each | 288,900 | 9.63 | 5.2% |
| 1020 | Escalators & Moving Walks | N/A | — | — | — | |
| | **D20 Plumbing** | | | | | |
| 2010 | Plumbing Fixtures | Kitchen, bathroom and service fixtures, supply and drainage *1 Fixture/215 S.F. Floor* | Each | 2700 | 9.44 | |
| 2020 | Domestic Water Distribution | Gas fired water heater | S.F. Floor | 8.29 | 8.29 | 9.7% |
| 2040 | Rain Water Drainage | Roof drains | S.F. Roof | 2.28 | .38 | |
| | **D30 HVAC** | | | | | |
| 3010 | Energy Supply | Oil fired hot water, baseboard radiation | S.F. Floor | 9.50 | 9.50 | |
| 3020 | Heat Generating Systems | N/A | — | — | — | |
| 3030 | Cooling Generating Systems | Chilled water, air cooled condenser system | S.F. Floor | 10.65 | 10.65 | 10.8% |
| 3050 | Terminal & Package Units | N/A | — | — | — | |
| 3090 | Other HVAC Sys. & Equipment | N/A | — | — | — | |
| | **D40 Fire Protection** | | | | | |
| 4010 | Sprinklers | Wet pipe sprinkler system | S.F. Floor | 4.22 | 4.22 | 3.0% |
| 4020 | Standpipes | Standpipe with pumps | S.F. Floor | 1.44 | 1.44 | |
| | **D50 Electrical** | | | | | |
| 5010 | Electrical Service/Distribution | 1600 ampere service, panel board and feeders | S.F. Floor | 4.72 | 4.72 | |
| 5020 | Lighting & Branch Wiring | Incandescent fixtures, receptacles, switches, A.C. and misc. power | S.F. Floor | 9.55 | 9.55 | 8.8% |
| 5030 | Communications & Security | Alarm systems and fire command center | S.F. Floor | 2.07 | 2.07 | |
| 5090 | Other Electrical Systems | | | | | |
| **E. EQUIPMENT & FURNISHINGS** | | | | | | |
| 1010 | Commercial Equipment | N/A | — | — | — | |
| 1020 | Institutional Equipment | N/A | — | — | — | 1.1 % |
| 1030 | Vehicular Equipment | N/A | — | — | — | |
| 1090 | Other Equipment | N/A | — | — | — | |
| **F. SPECIAL CONSTRUCTION** | | | | | | |
| 1020 | Integrated Construction | N/A | — | — | — | 0.0 % |
| 1040 | Special Facilities | N/A | — | — | — | |
| **G. BUILDING SITEWORK** | | **N/A** | | | | |
| | | | | **Sub-Total** | 186.45 | **100%** |
| | CONTRACTOR FEES (General Requirements: 10%, Overhead: 5%, Profit: 10%) | | | *25%* | 46.59 | |
| | ARCHITECT FEES | | | *7%* | 16.31 | |
| | | | | **Total Building Cost** | **249.35** | |

## Costs per square foot of floor area

| Exterior Wall | S.F. Area | 95000 | 112000 | 129000 | 145000 | 170000 | 200000 | 275000 | 400000 | 600000 |
|---|---|---|---|---|---|---|---|---|---|---|
| | L.F. Perimeter | 345 | 386 | 406 | 442 | 480 | 510 | 530 | 660 | 800 |
| Curtain Wall | Rigid Steel | 263.25 | 259.20 | 254.25 | **252.10** | 248.20 | 244.05 | 235.30 | 230.65 | 226.05 |
| Brick Veneer | Rigid Steel | 266.30 | 262.05 | 256.95 | 254.65 | 250.55 | 246.15 | 236.90 | 232.05 | 227.15 |
| E.I.F.S. | Rigid Steel | 258.15 | 254.35 | 249.90 | 247.85 | 244.25 | 240.45 | 232.60 | 228.40 | 224.20 |
| Precast Concrete | Reinforced Concrete | 297.15 | 291.65 | 284.35 | 281.30 | 275.70 | 269.30 | 255.65 | 248.80 | 241.60 |
| Brick Veneer | Reinforced Concrete | 281.65 | 276.90 | 270.85 | 268.30 | 263.60 | 258.40 | 247.35 | 241.75 | 235.90 |
| Stucco | Reinforced Concrete | 272.60 | 268.35 | 263.05 | 260.70 | 256.60 | 252.05 | 242.60 | 237.65 | 232.65 |
| Perimeter Adj., Add or Deduct | Per 100 L.F. | 11.95 | 10.10 | 8.85 | 7.85 | 6.70 | 5.70 | 4.15 | 2.85 | 1.95 |
| Story Hgt. Adj., Add or Deduct | Per 1 Ft. | 3.60 | 3.45 | 3.20 | 3.05 | 2.85 | 2.55 | 1.90 | 1.70 | 1.30 |
| ***For Basement**, add $ 59.10 per square foot of basement area* | | | | | | | | | | |

*The above costs were calculated using the basic specifications shown on the facing page. These costs should be adjusted where necessary for design alternatives and owner's requirements.*

## Common additives

| Description | Unit | $ Cost |
|---|---|---|
| Appliances | | |
| Cooking range, 30" free standing | | |
| 1 oven | Ea. | 885 - 1300 |
| 2 oven | Ea. | 3975 - 5050 |
| 30" built-in | | |
| 1 oven | Ea. | 1550 - 3225 |
| 2 oven | Ea. | 3200 - 3775 |
| Counter top cook tops, 4 burner | Ea. | 480 - 860 |
| Microwave oven | Ea. | 375 - 895 |
| Combination range, refrig. & sink, 30" wide | Ea. | 2250 - 3325 |
| 72" wide | Ea. | 3650 |
| Combination range, refrigerator, sink, microwave oven & icemaker | Ea. | 8600 |
| Compactor, residential, 4-1 compaction | Ea. | 1600 - 1875 |
| Dishwasher, built-in, 2 cycles | Ea. | 965 - 1900 |
| 4 cycles | Ea. | 1150 - 1700 |
| Garbage disposer, sink type | Ea. | 300 - 445 |
| Hood for range, 2 speed, vented, 30" wide | Ea. | 425 - 1750 |
| 42" wide | Ea. | 495 - 730 |
| Refrigerator, no frost 10-12 C.F. | Ea. | 1000 - 855 |
| 18-20 C.F. | Ea. | 960 - 1100 |

| Description | Unit | $ Cost |
|---|---|---|
| Closed Circuit Surveillance, One station | | |
| Camera and monitor | Ea. | 1250 |
| For additional camera stations, add | Ea. | 475 |
| Elevators, Electric passenger, 10 stops | | |
| 3000# capacity | Ea. | 484,000 |
| 4000# capacity | Ea. | 487,000 |
| 5000# capacity | Ea. | 494,500 |
| Additional stop, add | Ea. | 12,600 |
| Emergency Lighting, 25 watt, battery operated | | |
| Lead battery | Ea. | 360 |
| Nickel cadmium | Ea. | 585 |
| Laundry Equipment | | |
| Dryer, gas, 16 lb. capacity | Ea. | 1725 |
| 30 lb. capacity | Ea. | 2200 |
| Washer, 4 cycle | Ea. | 1550 |
| Commercial | Ea. | 2000 |
| Smoke Detectors | | |
| Ceiling type | Ea. | 300 |
| Duct type | Ea. | 615 |



**Important: See the Reference Section for Location Factors.**

## Model costs calculated for a 15 story building with 10'-6" story height and 145,000 square feet of floor area

# Apartment, 8-24 Story

| | | | | Unit | Unit Cost | Cost Per S.F. | % Of Sub-Total |
|---|---|---|---|---|---|---|---|
| **A. SUBSTRUCTURE** | | | | | | | |
| 1010 | Standard Foundations | CIP concrete pile caps; 4' foundation wall | | S.F. Ground | 29.10 | 1.94 | |
| 1020 | Special Foundations | Steel H piles, concrete grade beams | | S.F. Ground | 315 | 20.97 | |
| 1030 | Slab on Grade | 4" thick reinforced | | S.F. Slab | 7.22 | .48 | 12.3% |
| 2010 | Basement Excavation | Site preparation for slab, piles and grade beams | | S.F. Ground | .37 | .02 | |
| 2020 | Basement Walls | N/A | | – | – | – | |
| **B. SHELL** | | | | | | | |
| | **B10 Superstructure** | | | | | | |
| 1010 | Floor Construction | Open web steel joists, slab form, concrete, fireproofed steel columns | | S.F. Floor | 17.95 | 16.75 | 9.3% |
| 1020 | Roof Construction | Metal deck, open web steel joists, beams, columns | | S.F. Roof | 13.80 | .92 | |
| | **B20 Exterior Enclosure** | | | | | | |
| 2010 | Exterior Walls | N/A | | – | – | – | |
| 2020 | Exterior Windows | Curtain wall glazing system, thermo-break frame | *100% of wall* | S.F. Wall | 57 | 20.84 | 12.1 % |
| 2030 | Exterior Doors | Aluminum and glass single and double doors | | Each | 2454 | 2.18 | |
| | **B30 Roofing** | | | | | | |
| 3010 | Roof Coverings | Single ply membrane, stone ballast, rigid insulation | | S.F. Roof | 11.70 | .78 | 0.4% |
| 3020 | Roof Openings | N/A | | – | – | – | |
| **C. INTERIORS** | | | | | | | |
| 1010 | Partitions | Gypsum board on metal studs | *10 S.F. Floor/L.F. Partition* | S.F. Partition | 14.29 | 12.70 | |
| 1020 | Interior Doors | Interior single leaf doors, frames and hardware | *140 S.F. Floor/Door* | Each | 1160 | 8.11 | |
| 1030 | Fittings | Residential wall and base wood cabinets, laminate counters | | S.F. Floor | 6 | 6 | |
| 2010 | Stair Construction | Cement filled metal pan | | Flight | 12,925 | 3.83 | 23.0% |
| 3010 | Wall Finishes | 95% paint, 5% ceramic wall tile | | S.F. Surface | 1.37 | 2.43 | |
| 3020 | Floor Finishes | 80% Carpet tile, 10% vinyl composition tile, 10% ceramic tile | | S.F. Floor | 5.28 | 5.28 | |
| 3030 | Ceiling Finishes | Painted gypsum board ceiling on resilient channels | | S.F. Ceiling | 5.43 | 5.43 | |
| **D. SERVICES** | | | | | | | |
| | **D10 Conveying** | | | | | | |
| 1010 | Elevators & Lifts | Four geared passenger elevators | | Each | 578,550 | 15.96 | 8.4% |
| 1020 | Escalators & Moving Walks | N/A | | – | – | – | |
| | **D20 Plumbing** | | | | | | |
| 2010 | Plumbing Fixtures | Kitchen, bath, laundry and service fixtures, supply and drainage | *1 Fixture/280 S.F. Floor* | Each | 2626 | 9.38 | |
| 2020 | Domestic Water Distribution | Electric water heater | | S.F. Floor | 8.27 | 8.27 | 9.5% |
| 2040 | Rain Water Drainage | Roof drains | | S.F. Roof | 5.10 | .34 | |
| | **D30 HVAC** | | | | | | |
| 3010 | Energy Supply | Oil fired hot water, baseboard radiation | | S.F. Floor | 9.50 | 9.50 | |
| 3020 | Heat Generating Systems | N/A | | – | – | – | |
| 3030 | Cooling Generating Systems | Chilled water, air cooled condenser system | | S.F. Floor | 10.65 | 10.65 | 10.6% |
| 3050 | Terminal & Package Units | N/A | | – | – | – | |
| 3090 | Other HVAC Sys. & Equipment | N/A | | – | – | – | |
| | **D40 Fire Protection** | | | | | | |
| 4010 | Sprinklers | Wet pipe spinkler system, light hazard and accessory package | | S.F. Floor | 4.30 | 4.30 | 3.8% |
| 4020 | Standpipes | Standpipes and hose systems, with pumps | | S.F. Floor | 2.85 | 2.85 | |
| | **D50 Electrical** | | | | | | |
| 5010 | Electrical Service/Distribution | 2000 Ampere service, panel boards and feeders | | S.F. Floor | 3.41 | 3.41 | |
| 5020 | Lighting & Branch Wiring | Incandescent fixtures, receptacles, switches, A.C. and misc. power | | S.F. Floor | 10.56 | 10.56 | 9.6% |
| 5030 | Communications & Security | Addressable alarm systems, emergency lighting, internet and phone wiring | | S.F. Floor | 4.27 | 4.27 | |
| 5090 | Other Electrical Systems | N/A | | – | – | – | |
| **E. EQUIPMENT & FURNISHINGS** | | | | | | | |
| 1010 | Commercial Equipment | N/A | | – | – | – | |
| 1020 | Institutional Equipment | N/A | | – | – | – | 1.1 % |
| 1030 | Vehicular Equipment | N/A | | – | – | – | |
| 1090 | Other Equipment | Residential freestanding gas ranges, dishwashers | | S.F. Floor | 2.11 | 2.11 | |
| **F. SPECIAL CONSTRUCTION** | | | | | | | |
| 1020 | Integrated Construction | N/A | | – | – | – | 0.0 % |
| 1040 | Special Facilities | N/A | | – | – | – | |
| **G. BUILDING SITEWORK** | | **N/A** | | | | | |
| | | | | | **Sub-Total** | 190.26 | **100%** |
| | CONTRACTOR FEES (General Requirements: 10%, Overhead: 5%, Profit: 10%) | | | | *25%* | 47.57 | |
| | ARCHITECT FEES | | | | *6%* | 14.27 | |
| | | | | | **Total Building Cost** | **252.10** | |

## Costs per square foot of floor area

| Exterior Wall | S.F. Area | 2000 | 3000 | 4000 | 5000 | 7500 | 10000 | 15000 | 25000 | 50000 |
|---|---|---|---|---|---|---|---|---|---|---|
| | L.F. Perimeter | 188 | 224 | 260 | 300 | 356 | 400 | 504 | 700 | 1200 |
| Brick Veneer | Wood Frame | 336.85 | 301.10 | 283.20 | 273.25 | 254.75 | **244.45** | 235.05 | 227.15 | 221.45 |
| | Rigid Steel | 399.00 | 363.45 | 345.65 | 335.70 | 317.35 | 307.10 | 297.75 | 289.95 | 284.30 |
| Brick Veneer and Concrete Block | Wood Truss | 339.60 | 302.40 | 283.85 | 273.45 | 254.05 | 243.20 | 233.35 | 225.00 | 219.00 |
| | Bearing Walls | 415.35 | 376.40 | 357.00 | 346.15 | 325.60 | 314.05 | 303.60 | 294.80 | 288.45 |
| Wood Clapboard | Wood Frame | 322.55 | 289.75 | 273.35 | 264.10 | 247.50 | 238.35 | 229.95 | 222.90 | 217.80 |
| Vinyl Clapboard | Wood Frame | 319.85 | 287.60 | 271.50 | 262.40 | 246.10 | 237.20 | 228.95 | 222.10 | 217.10 |
| Perimeter Adj., Add or Deduct | Per 100 L.F. | 43.75 | 29.15 | 21.90 | 17.45 | 11.60 | 8.80 | 5.85 | 3.55 | 1.70 |
| Story Hgt. Adj., Add or Deduct | Per 1 Ft. | 5.05 | 4.00 | 3.55 | 3.20 | 2.50 | 2.15 | 1.85 | 1.50 | 1.25 |
| ***For Basement**, add $51.95 per square foot of basement area* | | | | | | | | | | |

*The above costs were calculated using the basic specifications shown on the facing page. These costs should be adjusted where necessary for design alternatives and owner's requirements.*

## Common additives

| Description | Unit | $ Cost |
|---|---|---|
| Appliances | | |
| Cooking range, 30" free standing | | |
| 1 oven | Ea. | 885 - 1300 |
| 2 oven | Ea. | 3975 - 5050 |
| 30" built-in | | |
| 1 oven | Ea. | 1550 - 3225 |
| 2 oven | Ea. | 3200 - 3775 |
| Counter top cook tops, 4 burner | Ea. | 480 - 860 |
| Microwave oven | Ea. | 375 - 895 |
| Combination range, refrig. & sink, 30" wide | Ea. | 2250 - 3325 |
| 60" wide | Ea. | 3450 |
| 72" wide | Ea. | 3650 |
| Combination range, refrigerator, sink, microwave oven & icemaker | Ea. | 8600 |
| Compactor, residential, 4-1 compaction | Ea. | 1600 - 1875 |
| Dishwasher, built-in, 2 cycles | Ea. | 965 - 1900 |
| 4 cycles | Ea. | 1150 - 1700 |
| Garbage disposer, sink type | Ea. | 300 - 445 |
| Hood for range, 2 speed, vented, 30" wide | Ea. | 425 - 1750 |
| 42" wide | Ea. | 495 - 730 |

| Description | Unit | $ Cost |
|---|---|---|
| Appliances, cont. | | |
| Refrigerator, no frost 10-12 C.F. | Ea. | 1000 - 855 |
| 14-16 C.F. | Ea. | 905 - 1050 |
| 18-20 C.F. | Ea. | 960 - 1100 |
| Laundry Equipment | | |
| Dryer, gas, 16 lb. capacity | Ea. | 1725 |
| 30 lb. capacity | Ea. | 2200 |
| Washer, 4 cycle | Ea. | 1550 |
| Commercial | Ea. | 2000 |
| Sound System | | |
| Amplifier, 250 watts | Ea. | 2425 |
| Speaker, ceiling or wall | Ea. | 320 |
| Trumpet | Ea. | 580 |



**Important: See the Reference Section for Location Factors.**

## Model costs calculated for a 1 story building with 10′ story height and 10,000 square feet of floor area

# Assisted - Senior Living

| | | | | Unit | Unit Cost | Cost Per S.F. | % Of Sub-Total |
|---|---|---|---|---|---|---|---|
| **A. SUBSTRUCTURE** | | | | | | | |
| 1010 | Standard Foundations | Poured concrete strip footings; 4′ foundation wall | | S.F. Ground | 9.31 | 9.31 | 9.8% |
| 1020 | Special Foundations | N/A | | — | — | — | |
| 1030 | Slab on Grade | 4″ reinforced concrete with vapor barrier and granular base | | S.F. Slab | 7.22 | 7.22 | |
| 2010 | Basement Excavation | Site preparation for slab and trench for foundation wall and footing | | S.F. Ground | .66 | .66 | |
| 2020 | Basement Walls | N/A | | — | — | — | |
| **B. SHELL** | | | | | | | |
| | **B10 Superstructure** | | | | | | |
| 1010 | Floor Construction | Steel column | | S.F. Floor | .75 | .75 | 7.6% |
| 1020 | Roof Construction | Plywood on wood trusses (pitched); fiberglass batt insulation | | S.F. Roof | 12.67 | 12.67 | |
| | **B20 Exterior Enclosure** | | | | | | |
| 2010 | Exterior Walls | Brick veneer on wood studs, insulated | *80% of wall* | S.F. Wall | 32.34 | 10.35 | 9.8% |
| 2020 | Exterior Windows | Double hung wood | *20% of wall* | Each | 850 | 4.25 | |
| 2030 | Exterior Doors | Aluminum and glass; 18 ga. steel flush | | Each | 4425 | 2.65 | |
| | **B30 Roofing** | | | | | | |
| 3010 | Roof Coverings | Asphalt shingles with flashing (pitched); al. gutters & downspouts | | S.F. Roof | 3.90 | 3.90 | 2.2% |
| 3020 | Roof Openings | N/A | | — | — | — | |
| **C. INTERIORS** | | | | | | | |
| 1010 | Partitions | Gypsum board on wood studs | *6 S.F. Floor/L.F. Partition* | S.F. Partition | 7.19 | 9.59 | 26.1% |
| 1020 | Interior Doors | Single leaf wood | *80 S.F. Floor/Door* | Each | 1231 | 14.48 | |
| 1030 | Fittings | N/A | | — | — | — | |
| 2010 | Stair Construction | N/A | | — | — | — | |
| 3010 | Wall Finishes | Paint on drywall | | S.F. Surface | .96 | 2.56 | |
| 3020 | Floor Finishes | 80% carpet, 20% ceramic tile | | S.F. Floor | 8.43 | 8.43 | |
| 3030 | Ceiling Finishes | Gypsum board on wood furring, painted | | S.F. Ceiling | 10.86 | 10.86 | |
| **D. SERVICES** | | | | | | | |
| | **D10 Conveying** | | | | | | |
| 1010 | Elevators & Lifts | N/A | | — | — | — | 0.0 % |
| 1020 | Escalators & Moving Walks | N/A | | — | — | — | |
| | **D20 Plumbing** | | | | | | |
| 2010 | Plumbing Fixtures | Kitchen, toilet and service fixtures, supply and drainage | *1 Fixture/200 S.F. Floor* | Each | 4570 | 22.85 | 14.7% |
| 2020 | Domestic Water Distribution | Gas water heater | | S.F. Floor | 2.97 | 2.97 | |
| 2040 | Rain Water Drainage | N/A | | — | — | — | |
| | **D30 HVAC** | | | | | | |
| 3010 | Energy Supply | N/A | | — | — | — | 3.1 % |
| 3020 | Heat Generating Systems | N/A | | — | — | — | |
| 3030 | Cooling Generating Systems | N/A | | — | — | — | |
| 3050 | Terminal & Package Units | Gas fired hot water boiler; terminal package heat/A/C units | | S.F. Floor | 5.41 | 5.41 | |
| 3090 | Other HVAC Sys. & Equipment | N/A | | — | — | — | |
| | **D40 Fire Protection** | | | | | | |
| 4010 | Sprinklers | Wet pipe sprinkler system | | S.F. Floor | 5.07 | 5.07 | 3.7% |
| 4020 | Standpipes | Standpipes | | S.F. Floor | 1.48 | 1.48 | |
| | **D50 Electrical** | | | | | | |
| 5010 | Electrical Service/Distribution | 600 ampere service, panel board, feeders and branch wiring | | S.F. Floor | 11.56 | 11.56 | 21.6% |
| 5020 | Lighting & Branch Wiring | Fuorescent & incandescent fixtures, receptacles, switches, A.C. and misc. power | | S.F. Floor | 15.10 | 15.10 | |
| 5030 | Communications & Security | Addressable alarm, fire detection and command center, communication system | | S.F. Floor | 11.16 | 11.16 | |
| 5090 | Other Electrical Systems | Emergency generator, 7.5 kW | | S.F. Floor | .22 | .22 | |
| **E. EQUIPMENT & FURNISHINGS** | | | | | | | |
| 1010 | Commercial Equipment | Residential washers and dryers | | S.F. Floor | .67 | .67 | 1.5% |
| 1020 | Institutional Equipment | N/A | | — | — | — | |
| 1030 | Vehicular Equipment | N/A | | — | — | — | |
| 1090 | Other Equipment | Residential ranges & refrigerators | | S.F. Floor | 2 | 2 | |
| **F. SPECIAL CONSTRUCTION** | | | | | | | |
| 1020 | Integrated Construction | N/A | | — | — | — | 0.0 % |
| 1040 | Special Facilities | N/A | | — | — | — | |
| **G. BUILDING SITEWORK** | **N/A** | | | | | | |
| | | | | | **Sub-Total** | 176.17 | **100%** |
| | CONTRACTOR FEES (General Requirements: 10%, Overhead: 5%, Profit: 10%) | | | | *25%* | 44.06 | |
| | ARCHITECT FEES | | | | *11%* | 24.22 | |
| | | | | | **Total Building Cost** | **244.45** | |

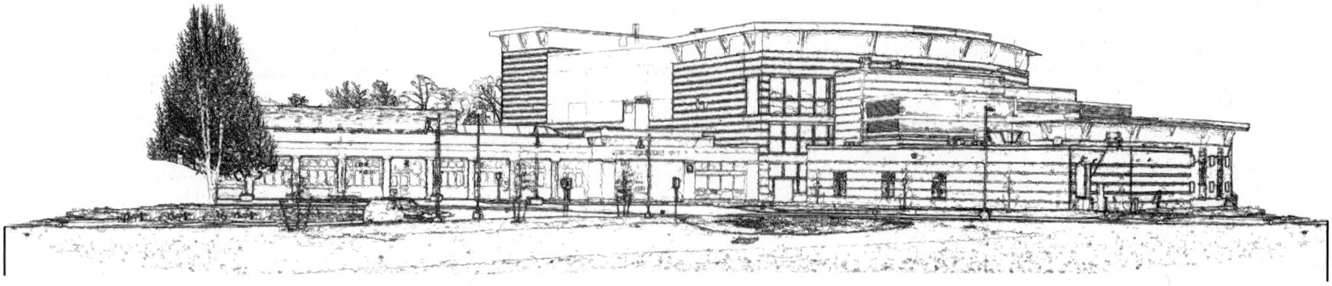

## Costs per square foot of floor area

| Exterior Wall | S.F. Area | 12000 | 15000 | 18000 | 21000 | 24000 | 27000 | 30000 | 33000 | 36000 |
|---|---|---|---|---|---|---|---|---|---|---|
| | L.F. Perimeter | 440 | 500 | 540 | 590 | 640 | 665 | 700 | 732 | 770 |
| Face Brick and Concrete Block | Rigid Steel | 266.15 | 259.00 | 251.90 | 247.85 | 244.85 | 240.55 | 237.85 | 235.45 | 233.75 |
| | Bearing Walls | 255.20 | 248.00 | 240.95 | 236.95 | 233.85 | 229.60 | 226.90 | 224.45 | 222.85 |
| Precast Concrete | Rigid Steel | 269.15 | 260.15 | 251.20 | 246.05 | **242.20** | 236.80 | 233.35 | 230.25 | 228.15 |
| Decorative Concrete Block | Bearing Walls | 237.35 | 231.85 | 226.45 | 223.30 | 220.90 | 217.70 | 215.55 | 213.70 | 212.45 |
| Concrete Block | Rigid Steel | 219.70 | 216.80 | 213.95 | 212.35 | 211.10 | 209.40 | 208.35 | 207.35 | 206.70 |
| | Bearing Walls | 228.75 | 223.95 | 219.35 | 216.70 | 214.65 | 211.90 | 210.10 | 208.50 | 207.40 |
| Perimeter Adj., Add or Deduct | Per 100 L.F. | 17.05 | 13.60 | 11.35 | 9.75 | 8.50 | 7.60 | 6.80 | 6.20 | 5.75 |
| Story Hgt. Adj., Add or Deduct | Per 1 Ft. | 2.60 | 2.40 | 2.20 | 2.05 | 1.90 | 1.75 | 1.70 | 1.55 | 1.55 |

***For Basement**, add $ 47.20 per square foot of basement area*

*The above costs were calculated using the basic specifications shown on the facing page. These costs should be adjusted where necessary for design alternatives and owner's requirements.*

## Common additives

| Description | Unit | $ Cost |
|---|---|---|
| Closed Circuit Surveillance, One station | | |
| Camera and monitor | Ea. | 1250 |
| For additional camera stations, add | Ea. | 475 |
| Emergency Lighting, 25 watt, battery operated | | |
| Lead battery | Ea. | 360 |
| Nickel cadmium | Ea. | 585 |
| Seating | | |
| Auditorium chair, all veneer | Ea. | 480 |
| Veneer back, padded seat | Ea. | 430 |
| Upholstered, spring seat | Ea. | 385 |
| Classroom, movable chair & desk | Set | 81 - 171 |
| Lecture hall, pedestal type | Ea. | 385 - 775 |
| Smoke Detectors | | |
| Ceiling type | Ea. | 300 |
| Duct type | Ea. | 615 |
| Sound System | | |
| Amplifier, 250 watts | Ea. | 2425 |
| Speaker, ceiling or wall | Ea. | 320 |
| Trumpet | Ea. | 580 |



**Important: See the Reference Section for Location Factors.**

## Model costs calculated for a 1 story building with 24′ story height and 24,000 square feet of floor area

# Auditorium

| | | | | Unit | Unit Cost | Cost Per S.F. | % Of Sub-Total |
|---|---|---|---|---|---|---|---|
| **A. SUBSTRUCTURE** | | | | | | | |
| 1010 | Standard Foundations | Poured concrete; strip and spread footings; 4′ foundation wall | | S.F. Ground | 5.32 | 5.32 | |
| 1020 | Special Foundations | N/A | | — | — | — | |
| 1030 | Slab on Grade | 6″ reinforced concrete with vapor barrier and granular base | | S.F. Slab | 9.16 | 9.16 | 8.1% |
| 2010 | Basement Excavation | Site preparation for slab and trench for foundation wall and footing | | S.F. Ground | .22 | .22 | |
| 2020 | Basement Walls | N/A | | — | — | — | |
| **B. SHELL** | | | | | | | |
| | **B10 Superstructure** | | | | | | |
| 1010 | Floor Construction | Open web steel joists, slab form, concrete | *(balcony)* | S.F. Floor | 29.84 | 3.73 | 3.1% |
| 1020 | Roof Construction | Metal deck on steel truss | | S.F. Roof | 1.86 | 1.86 | |
| | **B20 Exterior Enclosure** | | | | | | |
| 2010 | Exterior Walls | Precast concrete panel | *80% of wall (adjusted for end walls)* | S.F. Wall | 71 | 36.54 | |
| 2020 | Exterior Windows | Glass curtain wall | *20% of wall* | Each | 55 | 6.99 | 26.2% |
| 2030 | Exterior Doors | Double aluminum and glass and hollow metal | | Each | 7890 | 3.95 | |
| | **B30 Roofing** | | | | | | |
| 3010 | Roof Coverings | Built-up tar and gravel with flashing; perlite/EPS composite insulation | | S.F. Roof | 8.25 | 8.25 | 4.7% |
| 3020 | Roof Openings | Roof hatches | | S.F. Roof | .28 | .28 | |
| **C. INTERIORS** | | | | | | | |
| 1010 | Partitions | Concrete Block and toilet partitions | *40 S.F. Floor/L.F. Partition* | S.F. Partition | 10.85 | 4.34 | |
| 1020 | Interior Doors | Single leaf hollow metal | *400 S.F. Floor/Door* | Each | 1159 | 2.90 | |
| 1030 | Fittings | N/A | | — | — | — | |
| 2010 | Stair Construction | Concrete filled metal pan | | Flight | 19,225 | 2.41 | 17.2% |
| 3010 | Wall Finishes | 70% paint, 30% epoxy coating | | S.F. Surface | 6.19 | 4.95 | |
| 3020 | Floor Finishes | 70% vinyl tile, 30% carpet | | S.F. Floor | 7.07 | 7.07 | |
| 3030 | Ceiling Finishes | Fiberglass board, suspended | | S.F. Ceiling | 9.48 | 9.48 | |
| **D. SERVICES** | | | | | | | |
| | **D10 Conveying** | | | | | | |
| 1010 | Elevators & Lifts | One hydraulic passenger elevator | | Each | 118,560 | 4.94 | 2.7% |
| 1020 | Escalators & Moving Walks | N/A | | — | — | — | |
| | **D20 Plumbing** | | | | | | |
| 2010 | Plumbing Fixtures | Toilet and service fixtures, supply and drainage | *1 Fixture/800 S.F. Floor* | Each | 9288 | 11.61 | |
| 2020 | Domestic Water Distribution | Gas fired water heater | | S.F. Floor | 5.30 | 5.30 | 10.1% |
| 2040 | Rain Water Drainage | Roof drains | | S.F. Roof | 1.43 | 1.43 | |
| | **D30 HVAC** | | | | | | |
| 3010 | Energy Supply | N/A | | — | — | — | |
| 3020 | Heat Generating Systems | Included in D3050 | | — | — | — | |
| 3030 | Cooling Generating Systems | N/A | | — | — | — | 9.3 % |
| 3050 | Terminal & Package Units | Single zone rooftop unit, gas heating, electric cooling | | S.F. Floor | 16.85 | 16.85 | |
| 3090 | Other HVAC Sys. & Equipment | N/A | | — | — | — | |
| | **D40 Fire Protection** | | | | | | |
| 4010 | Sprinklers | Wet pipe sprinkler system | | S.F. Floor | 5.07 | 5.07 | 3.1% |
| 4020 | Standpipes | Standpipe | | S.F. Floor | .62 | .62 | |
| | **D50 Electrical** | | | | | | |
| 5010 | Electrical Service/Distribution | 800 ampere service, panel board and feeders | | S.F. Floor | 2.73 | 2.73 | |
| 5020 | Lighting & Branch Wiring | Fluorescent fixtures, receptacles, switches, A.C. and misc. power | | S.F. Floor | 18.16 | 18.16 | 15.4% |
| 5030 | Communications & Security | Addressable alarm systems, emergency lighting and public address system | | S.F. Floor | 5.28 | 5.28 | |
| 5090 | Other Electrical Systems | Emergency generator, 100 kW | | S.F. Floor | 1.64 | 1.64 | |
| **E. EQUIPMENT & FURNISHINGS** | | | | | | | |
| 1010 | Commercial Equipment | N/A | | — | — | — | |
| 1020 | Institutional Equipment | N/A | | — | — | — | 0.0 % |
| 1030 | Vehicular Equipment | N/A | | — | — | — | |
| 1090 | Other Equipment | N/A | | — | — | — | |
| **F. SPECIAL CONSTRUCTION** | | | | | | | |
| 1020 | Integrated Construction | N/A | | — | — | — | 0.0 % |
| 1040 | Special Facilities | N/A | | — | — | — | |
| **G. BUILDING SITEWORK** | | **N/A** | | | | | |
| | | | | | **Sub-Total** | 181.08 | **100%** |
| | CONTRACTOR FEES (General Requirements: 10%, Overhead: 5%, Profit: 10%) | | | | *25%* | 45.28 | |
| | ARCHITECT FEES | | | | *7%* | 15.84 | |
| | | | | | **Total Building Cost** | **242.20** | |

## Costs per square foot of floor area

| Exterior Wall | S.F. Area | 2000 | 2700 | 3400 | 4100 | 4800 | 5500 | 6200 | 6900 | 7600 |
|---|---|---|---|---|---|---|---|---|---|---|
| | L.F. Perimeter | 180 | 208 | 236 | 256 | 280 | 303 | 317 | 337 | 357 |
| Face Brick and Concrete Block | Rigid Steel | 342.65 | 320.35 | 307.25 | 295.75 | 288.85 | 283.40 | 277.05 | 273.35 | 270.25 |
| | Reinforced Concrete | 364.55 | 342.25 | 329.20 | **317.70** | 310.75 | 305.30 | 298.95 | 295.25 | 292.15 |
| Precast Concrete | Rigid Steel | 366.70 | 340.80 | 325.65 | 312.20 | 304.15 | 297.85 | 290.40 | 286.05 | 282.45 |
| | Reinforced Concrete | 389.35 | 363.50 | 348.30 | 334.90 | 326.80 | 320.50 | 313.05 | 308.70 | 305.10 |
| Limestone and Concrete Block | Rigid Steel | 370.35 | 344.05 | 328.65 | 315.00 | 306.80 | 300.35 | 292.80 | 288.35 | 284.70 |
| | Reinforced Concrete | 392.25 | 365.95 | 350.55 | 336.90 | 328.75 | 322.25 | 314.70 | 310.25 | 306.60 |
| Perimeter Adj., Add or Deduct | Per 100 L.F. | 73.85 | 54.75 | 43.45 | 36.05 | 30.80 | 26.85 | 23.85 | 21.35 | 19.40 |
| Story Hgt. Adj., Add or Deduct | Per 1 Ft. | 7.30 | 6.20 | 5.60 | 5.05 | 4.75 | 4.45 | 4.10 | 3.85 | 3.75 |

***For Basement**, add $54.55 per square foot of basement area*

*The above costs were calculated using the basic specifications shown on the facing page. These costs should be adjusted where necessary for design alternatives and owner's requirements.*

## Common additives

| Description | Unit | $ Cost |
|---|---|---|
| Bulletproof Teller Window, 44" x 60" | Ea. | 6150 |
| 60" x 48" | Ea. | 9775 |
| Closed Circuit Surveillance, One station | | |
| Camera and monitor | Ea. | 1250 |
| For additional camera stations, add | Ea. | 475 |
| Counters, Complete | Station | 7750 |
| Door & Frame, 3' x 6'-8", bullet resistant steel | | |
| with vision panel | Ea. | 5625 - 10,800 |
| Drive-up Window, Drawer & micr., not incl. glass | Ea. | 6325 - 9850 |
| Emergency Lighting, 25 watt, battery operated | | |
| Lead battery | Ea. | 360 |
| Nickel cadmium | Ea. | 585 |
| Night Depository | Ea. | 2650 - 5750 |
| Package Receiver, painted | Ea. | 4875 |
| stainless steel | Ea. | 2525 |
| Partitions, Bullet resistant to 8' high | L.F. | 415 - 660 |
| Pneumatic Tube Systems, 2 station | Ea. | 41,900 |
| With TV viewer | Ea. | 77,000 |

| Description | Unit | $ Cost |
|---|---|---|
| Service Windows, Pass thru, steel | | |
| 24" x 36" | Ea. | 6050 |
| 48" x 48" | Ea. | 8625 |
| 72" x 40" | Ea. | 8000 |
| Smoke Detectors | | |
| Ceiling type | Ea. | 300 |
| Duct type | Ea. | 615 |
| Twenty-four Hour Teller | | |
| Automatic deposit cash & memo | Ea. | 12,900 |
| Vault Front, Door & frame | | |
| 1 hour test, 32"x 78" | Opng. | 7450 |
| 2 hour test, 32" door | Opng. | 7450 |
| 40" door | Opng. | 7925 |
| 4 hour test, 32" door | Opng. | 7425 |
| 40" door | Opng. | 7625 |
| Time lock, two movement, add | Ea. | 2050 |



**Important: See the Reference Section for Location Factors.**

## Model costs calculated for a 1 story building with 14' story height and 4,100 square feet of floor area

## Bank

| | | | | Unit | Unit Cost | Cost Per S.F. | % Of Sub-Total |
|---|---|---|---|---|---|---|---|
| **A. SUBSTRUCTURE** | | | | | | | |
| 1010 | Standard Foundations | Poured concrete; strip and spread footings; 4' foundation wall | | S.F. Ground | 14.20 | 14.20 | |
| 1020 | Special Foundations | N/A | | — | — | — | |
| 1030 | Slab on Grade | 4" reinforced concrete with vapor barrier and granular base | | S.F. Slab | 7.22 | 7.22 | 9.3% |
| 2010 | Basement Excavation | Site preparation for slab and trench for foundation wall and footing | | S.F. Ground | .38 | .38 | |
| 2020 | Basement Walls | N/A | | — | — | — | |
| **B. SHELL** | | | | | | | |
| | **B10 Superstructure** | | | | | | |
| 1010 | Floor Construction | Cast-in-place columns | | L.F. Column | 161 | 7.83 | 12.7% |
| 1020 | Roof Construction | Cast-in-place concrete flat plate | | S.F. Roof | 22.10 | 22.10 | |
| | **B20 Exterior Enclosure** | | | | | | |
| 2010 | Exterior Walls | Face brick with concrete block backup | *80% of wall* | S.F. Wall | 40.65 | 28.43 | |
| 2020 | Exterior Windows | Horizontal aluminum sliding | *20% of wall* | Each | 1677 | 19.54 | 21.7% |
| 2030 | Exterior Doors | Double aluminum and glass and hollow metal | | Each | 6225 | 3.03 | |
| | **B30 Roofing** | | | | | | |
| 3010 | Roof Coverings | Built-up tar and gravel with flashing; perlite/EPS composite insulation | | S.F. Roof | 10.49 | 10.49 | 4.5% |
| 3020 | Roof Openings | N/A | | — | — | — | |
| **C. INTERIORS** | | | | | | | |
| 1010 | Partitions | Gypsum board on metal studs | *20 S.F. of Floor/L.F. Partition* | S.F. Partition | 13.80 | 6.90 | |
| 1020 | Interior Doors | Single leaf hollow metal | *200 S.F. Floor/Door* | Each | 1159 | 5.80 | |
| 1030 | Fittings | N/A | | — | — | — | |
| 2010 | Stair Construction | N/A | | — | — | — | 13.0% |
| 3010 | Wall Finishes | 50% vinyl wall covering, 50% paint | | S.F. Surface | 2.64 | 2.64 | |
| 3020 | Floor Finishes | 50% carpet tile, 40% vinyl composition tile, 10% quarry tile | | S.F. Floor | 6.17 | 6.17 | |
| 3030 | Ceiling Finishes | Mineral fiber tile on concealed zee bars | | S.F. Ceiling | 9 | 9 | |
| **D. SERVICES** | | | | | | | |
| | **D10 Conveying** | | | | | | |
| 1010 | Elevators & Lifts | N/A | | — | — | — | 0.0 % |
| 1020 | Escalators & Moving Walks | N/A | | — | — | — | |
| | **D20 Plumbing** | | | | | | |
| 2010 | Plumbing Fixtures | Toilet and service fixtures, supply and drainage | *1 Fixture/580 S.F. Floor* | Each | 7888 | 13.60 | |
| 2020 | Domestic Water Distribution | Gas fired water heater | | S.F. Floor | 2.22 | 2.22 | 7.7% |
| 2040 | Rain Water Drainage | Roof drains | | S.F. Roof | 2.30 | 2.30 | |
| | **D30 HVAC** | | | | | | |
| 3010 | Energy Supply | N/A | | — | — | — | |
| 3020 | Heat Generating Systems | Included in D3050 | | — | — | — | |
| 3030 | Cooling Generating Systems | N/A | | — | — | — | 5.5 % |
| 3050 | Terminal & Package Units | Single zone rooftop unit, gas heating, electric cooling | | S.F. Floor | 12.95 | 12.95 | |
| 3090 | Other HVAC Sys. & Equipment | N/A | | — | — | — | |
| | **D40 Fire Protection** | | | | | | |
| 4010 | Sprinklers | Wet pipe sprinkler system | | S.F. Floor | 6.60 | 6.60 | 5.0% |
| 4020 | Standpipes | Standpipe | | S.F. Floor | 5.06 | 5.06 | |
| | **D50 Electrical** | | | | | | |
| 5010 | Electrical Service/Distribution | 200 ampere service, panel board and feeders | | S.F. Floor | 3.42 | 3.42 | |
| 5020 | Lighting & Branch Wiring | Fluorescent fixtures, receptacles, switches, A.C. and misc. power | | S.F. Floor | 11.54 | 11.54 | 11.8% |
| 5030 | Communications & Security | Alarm systems, internet and phone wiring, emergency lighting, and security television | | S.F. Floor | 12.66 | 12.66 | |
| 5090 | Other Electrical Systems | Emergency generator, 15 kW, Uninterruptible power supply | | S.F. Floor | .20 | .20 | |
| **E. EQUIPMENT & FURNISHINGS** | | | | | | | |
| 1010 | Commercial Equipment | Automatic teller, drive up window, night depository | | S.F. Floor | 5.30 | 5.30 | |
| 1020 | Institutional Equipment | Closed circuit TV monitoring system | | S.F. Floor | 3.25 | 3.25 | 3.6% |
| 1030 | Vehicular Equipment | N/A | | — | — | — | |
| 1090 | Other Equipment | N/A | | — | — | — | |
| **F. SPECIAL CONSTRUCTION** | | | | | | | |
| 1020 | Integrated Construction | N/A | | — | — | — | 5.3 % |
| 1040 | Special Facilities | Security vault door | | S.F. Floor | 12.49 | 12.49 | |
| **G. BUILDING SITEWORK** | **N/A** | | | | | | |
| | | | | | **Sub-Total** | 235.32 | **100%** |
| | CONTRACTOR FEES (General Requirements: 10%, Overhead: 5%, Profit: 10%) | | | | *25%* | 58.85 | |
| | ARCHITECT FEES | | | | *8%* | 23.53 | |
| | | | | | **Total Building Cost** | **317.70** | |

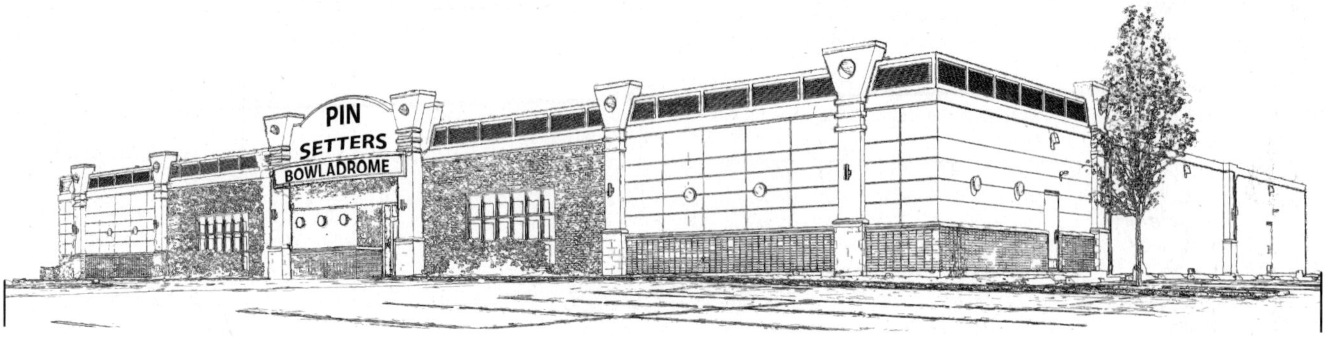


## Costs per square foot of floor area

| Exterior Wall | S.F. Area | 12000 | 14000 | 16000 | 18000 | 20000 | 22000 | 24000 | 26000 | 28000 |
|---|---|---|---|---|---|---|---|---|---|---|
| | L.F. Perimeter | 460 | 491 | 520 | 540 | 566 | 593 | 620 | 645 | 670 |
| Concrete Block | Steel Roof Deck | 221.85 | 217.65 | 214.40 | 211.45 | **209.40** | 207.65 | 206.20 | 205.00 | 203.95 |
| Decorative Concrete Block | Steel Roof Deck | 228.65 | 223.80 | 220.10 | 216.80 | 214.35 | 212.40 | 210.80 | 209.35 | 208.15 |
| Face Brick and Concrete Block | Steel Roof Deck | 237.70 | 232.15 | 227.85 | 223.90 | 221.05 | 218.80 | 216.90 | 215.25 | 213.85 |
| Jumbo Brick and Concrete Block | Steel Roof Deck | 233.80 | 228.55 | 224.50 | 220.85 | 218.20 | 216.05 | 214.30 | 212.70 | 211.40 |
| Stucco and Concrete Block | Steel Roof Deck | 226.30 | 221.65 | 218.15 | 214.95 | 212.65 | 210.70 | 209.20 | 207.90 | 206.70 |
| Precast Concrete | Steel Roof Deck | 238.35 | 232.75 | 228.40 | 224.45 | 221.55 | 219.25 | 217.35 | 215.70 | 214.25 |
| Perimeter Adj., Add or Deduct | Per 100 L.F. | 6.70 | 5.65 | 4.95 | 4.45 | 3.95 | 3.65 | 3.40 | 3.05 | 2.85 |
| Story Hgt. Adj., Add or Deduct | Per 1 Ft. | 1.40 | 1.30 | 1.20 | 1.15 | 1.05 | 1.00 | 1.00 | 0.90 | 0.85 |
| ***For Basement**, add $ 53.80 per square foot of basement area* | | | | | | | | | | |

*The above costs were calculated using the basic specifications shown on the facing page. These costs should be adjusted where necessary for design alternatives and owner's requirements.*

## Common additives

| Description | Unit | $ Cost |
|---|---|---|
| Bowling Alleys, Incl. alley, pinsetter, | | |
| scorer, counter & misc. supplies, average | Lane | 73,500 |
| For automatic scorer, add (maximum) | Lane | 12,000 |
| Emergency Lighting, 25 watt, battery operated | | |
| Lead battery | Ea. | 360 |
| Nickel cadmium | Ea. | 585 |
| Lockers, Steel, Single tier, 60" or 72" | Opng. | 285 - 520 |
| 2 tier, 60" or 72" total | Opng. | 216 - 265 |
| 5 tier, box lockers | Opng. | 465 - 153 |
| Locker bench, lam., maple top only | L.F. | 148 |
| Pedestals, steel pipe | Ea. | 87 |
| Seating | | |
| Auditorium chair, all veneer | Ea. | 480 |
| Veneer back, padded seat | Ea. | 430 |
| Upholstered, spring seat | Ea. | 385 |
| Sound System | | |
| Amplifier, 250 watts | Ea. | 2425 |
| Speaker, ceiling or wall | Ea. | 320 |
| Trumpet | Ea. | 580 |



**Important: See the Reference Section for Location Factors.**

## Model costs calculated for a 1 story building with 14′ story height and 20,000 square feet of floor area

# Bowling Alley

| | | | | Unit | Unit Cost | Cost Per S.F. | % Of Sub-Total |
|---|---|---|---|---|---|---|---|
| **A. SUBSTRUCTURE** | | | | | | | |
| 1010 | Standard Foundations | Poured concrete; strip and spread footings; 4′ foundation wall | | S.F. Ground | 4.86 | 4.86 | |
| 1020 | Special Foundations | N/A | | — | — | — | |
| 1030 | Slab on Grade | 4″ reinforced concrete with vapor barrier and granular base | | S.F. Slab | 7.22 | 7.22 | 8.1% |
| 2010 | Basement Excavation | Site preparation for slab and trench for foundation wall and footing | | S.F. Ground | .66 | .66 | |
| 2020 | Basement Walls | N/A | | — | — | — | |
| **B. SHELL** | | | | | | | |
| | **B10 Superstructure** | | | | | | |
| 1010 | Floor Construction | N/A | | — | — | — | 9.2 % |
| 1020 | Roof Construction | Metal deck on open web steel joists with columns and beams | | S.F. Roof | 14.51 | 14.51 | |
| | **B20 Exterior Enclosure** | | | | | | |
| 2010 | Exterior Walls | Concrete block | *90% of wall* | S.F. Wall | 15.90 | 5.67 | |
| 2020 | Exterior Windows | Horizontal pivoted | *10% of wall* | Each | 2405 | 3.97 | 6.8% |
| 2030 | Exterior Doors | Double aluminum and glass and hollow metal | | Each | 4620 | 1.17 | |
| | **B30 Roofing** | | | | | | |
| 3010 | Roof Coverings | Built-up tar and gravel with flashing; perlite/EPS composite insulation | | S.F. Roof | 8.02 | 8.02 | 5.3% |
| 3020 | Roof Openings | Roof hatches | | S.F. Roof | .35 | .35 | |
| **C. INTERIORS** | | | | | | | |
| 1010 | Partitions | Concrete block | *50 S.F. Floor/L.F. Partition* | S.F. Partition | 12.50 | 2.50 | |
| 1020 | Interior Doors | Hollow metal single leaf | *1000 S.F. Floor/Door* | Each | 1159 | 1.16 | |
| 1030 | Fittings | N/A | | — | — | — | |
| 2010 | Stair Construction | N/A | | — | — | — | 6.0% |
| 3010 | Wall Finishes | Paint and block filler | | S.F. Surface | 7.20 | 2.88 | |
| 3020 | Floor Finishes | Vinyl tile | *25% of floor* | S.F. Floor | 2.36 | .59 | |
| 3030 | Ceiling Finishes | Suspended fiberglass board | *25% of area* | S.F. Ceiling | 9.48 | 2.37 | |
| **D. SERVICES** | | | | | | | |
| | **D10 Conveying** | | | | | | |
| 1010 | Elevators & Lifts | N/A | | — | — | — | 0.0 % |
| 1020 | Escalators & Moving Walks | N/A | | — | — | — | |
| | **D20 Plumbing** | | | | | | |
| 2010 | Plumbing Fixtures | Toilet and service fixtures, supply and drainage | *1 Fixture/2200 S.F. Floor* | Each | 4598 | 2.09 | |
| 2020 | Domestic Water Distribution | Gas fired water heater | | S.F. Floor | .40 | .40 | 2.2% |
| 2040 | Rain Water Drainage | Roof drains | | S.F. Roof | 1.03 | 1.03 | |
| | **D30 HVAC** | | | | | | |
| 3010 | Energy Supply | N/A | | — | — | — | |
| 3020 | Heat Generating Systems | Included in D3050 | | — | — | — | |
| 3030 | Cooling Generating Systems | N/A | | — | — | — | 12.1 % |
| 3050 | Terminal & Package Units | Single zone rooftop unit, gas heating, electric cooling | | S.F. Floor | 19.10 | 19.10 | |
| 3090 | Other HVAC Sys. & Equipment | N/A | | — | — | — | |
| | **D40 Fire Protection** | | | | | | |
| 4010 | Sprinklers | Sprinklers, light hazard | | S.F. Floor | 5.07 | 5.07 | 3.9% |
| 4020 | Standpipes | Standpipe, wet, Class III | | S.F. Floor | 1.04 | 1.04 | |
| | **D50 Electrical** | | | | | | |
| 5010 | Electrical Service/Distribution | 800 ampere service, panel board and feeders | | S.F. Floor | 3.29 | 3.29 | |
| 5020 | Lighting & Branch Wiring | High efficiency fluorescent fixtures, receptacles, switches, A.C. and misc. power | | S.F. Floor | 16.59 | 16.59 | 13.6% |
| 5030 | Communications & Security | Addressable alarm systems and emergency lighting | | S.F. Floor | 1.48 | 1.48 | |
| 5090 | Other Electrical Systems | Emergency generator, 7.5 kW | | S.F. Floor | .09 | .09 | |
| **E. EQUIPMENT & FURNISHINGS** | | | | | | | |
| 1010 | Commercial Equipment | N/A | | — | — | — | |
| 1020 | Institutional Equipment | N/A | | — | — | — | 32.9 % |
| 1030 | Vehicular Equipment | N/A | | — | — | — | |
| 1090 | Other Equipment | Bowling Alley, ballrack, automatic scorers | | S.F. Floor | 52 | 51.91 | |
| **F. SPECIAL CONSTRUCTION** | | | | | | | |
| 1020 | Integrated Construction | N/A | | — | — | — | 0.0 % |
| 1040 | Special Facilities | N/A | | — | — | — | |
| **G. BUILDING SITEWORK** | **N/A** | | | | | | |
| | | | | | **Sub-Total** | 158.02 | **100%** |
| | CONTRACTOR FEES (General Requirements: 10%, Overhead: 5%, Profit: 10%) | | | | *25%* | 39.53 | |
| | ARCHITECT FEES | | | | *6%* | 11.85 | |
| | | | | | **Total Building Cost** | **209.40** | |

## Costs per square foot of floor area

| Exterior Wall | S.F. Area | 6000 | 8000 | 10000 | 12000 | 14000 | 16000 | 18000 | 20000 | 22000 |
|---|---|---|---|---|---|---|---|---|---|---|
| | L.F. Perimeter | 320 | 386 | 453 | 475 | 505 | 530 | 570 | 600 | 630 |
| Face Brick and Concrete Block | Bearing Walls | 225.25 | 217.30 | 212.70 | **205.45** | 200.90 | 197.15 | 195.15 | 193.05 | 191.30 |
| | Rigid Steel | 228.95 | 221.10 | 216.60 | 209.45 | 205.00 | 201.25 | 199.35 | 197.30 | 195.50 |
| Decorative Concrete Block | Bearing Walls | 215.40 | 208.35 | 204.35 | 198.10 | 194.25 | 191.00 | 189.35 | 187.55 | 186.00 |
| | Rigid Steel | 219.15 | 212.25 | 208.20 | 202.15 | 198.35 | 195.15 | 193.50 | 191.75 | 190.25 |
| Precast Concrete | Bearing Walls | 231.75 | 223.15 | 218.20 | 210.25 | 205.30 | 201.20 | 199.05 | 196.75 | 194.75 |
| | Rigid Steel | 235.50 | 227.00 | 222.10 | 214.30 | 209.40 | 205.30 | 203.25 | 200.95 | 199.00 |
| Perimeter Adj., Add or Deduct | Per 100 L.F. | 18.25 | 13.70 | 10.90 | 9.05 | 7.80 | 6.85 | 6.05 | 5.50 | 4.95 |
| Story Hgt. Adj., Add or Deduct | Per 1 Ft. | 2.90 | 2.65 | 2.45 | 2.15 | 1.95 | 1.80 | 1.80 | 1.70 | 1.55 |
| **Basement**—Not Applicable | | | | | | | | | | |

*The above costs were calculated using the basic specifications shown on the facing page. These costs should be adjusted where necessary for design alternatives and owner's requirements.*

## Common additives

| Description | Unit | $ Cost |
|---|---|---|
| Directory Boards, Plastic, glass covered | | |
| 30″ x 20″ | Ea. | 705 |
| 36″ x 48″ | Ea. | 1475 |
| Aluminum, 24″ x 18″ | Ea. | 705 |
| 36″ x 24″ | Ea. | 985 |
| 48″ x 32″ | Ea. | 1975 |
| 48″ x 60″ | Ea. | 2650 |
| Emergency Lighting, 25 watt, battery operated | | |
| Lead battery | Ea. | 360 |
| Nickel cadmium | Ea. | 585 |
| Benches, Hardwood | L.F. | 234 - 520 |
| Ticket Printer | Ea. | 12,100 |
| Turnstiles, One way | | |
| 4 arm, 46″ dia., manual | Ea. | 2725 |
| Electric | Ea. | 7125 |
| High security, 3 arm | | |
| 65″ dia., manual | Ea. | 10,600 |
| Electric | Ea. | 17,400 |
| Gate with horizontal bars | | |
| 65″ dia., 7′ high transit type | Ea. | 10,900 |



**Important: See the Reference Section for Location Factors.**

## Model costs calculated for a 1 story building with 14′ story height and 12,000 square feet of floor area

# Bus Terminal

| | | | Unit | Unit Cost | Cost Per S.F. | % Of Sub-Total |
|---|---|---|---|---|---|---|
| **A. SUBSTRUCTURE** | | | | | | |
| 1010 | Standard Foundations | Poured concrete; strip and spread footings; 4′ foundation wall | S.F. Ground | 7.83 | 7.83 | 12.5% |
| 1020 | Special Foundations | N/A | — | — | — | |
| 1030 | Slab on Grade | 6″ reinforced concrete with vapor barrier and granular base | S.F. Slab | 11.10 | 11.10 | |
| 2010 | Basement Excavation | Site preparation for slab and trench for foundation wall and footing | S.F. Ground | .38 | .38 | |
| 2020 | Basement Walls | N/A | — | — | — | |
| **B. SHELL** | | | | | | |
| | **B10 Superstructure** | | | | | |
| 1010 | Floor Construction | N/A | — | — | — | 6.0 % |
| 1020 | Roof Construction | Metal deck on open web steel joists with columns and beams | S.F. Roof | 9.26 | 9.26 | |
| | **B20 Exterior Enclosure** | | | | | |
| 2010 | Exterior Walls | Face brick with concrete block backup *70% of wall* | S.F. Wall | 40.65 | 15.77 | 16.6% |
| 2020 | Exterior Windows | Store front *30% of wall* | Each | 41.75 | 6.94 | |
| 2030 | Exterior Doors | Double aluminum and glass | Each | 9150 | 3.05 | |
| | **B30 Roofing** | | | | | |
| 3010 | Roof Coverings | Built-up tar and gravel with flashing; perlite/EPS composite insulation | S.F. Roof | 9.05 | 9.05 | 5.8% |
| 3020 | Roof Openings | N/A | — | — | — | |
| **C. INTERIORS** | | | | | | |
| 1010 | Partitions | Lightweight concrete block *15 S.F. Floor/L.F. Partition* | S.F. Partition | 12.48 | 8.32 | 21.7% |
| 1020 | Interior Doors | Hollow metal *150 S.F. Floor/Door* | Each | 1159 | .77 | |
| 1030 | Fittings | N/A | — | — | — | |
| 2010 | Stair Construction | N/A | — | — | — | |
| 3010 | Wall Finishes | Glazed coating | S.F. Surface | 2.14 | 2.85 | |
| 3020 | Floor Finishes | Quarry tile and vinyl composition tile | S.F. Floor | 12.22 | 12.22 | |
| 3030 | Ceiling Finishes | Mineral fiber tile on concealed zee bars | S.F. Ceiling | 9.48 | 9.48 | |
| **D. SERVICES** | | | | | | |
| | **D10 Conveying** | | | | | |
| 1010 | Elevators & Lifts | N/A | — | — | — | 0.0 % |
| 1020 | Escalators & Moving Walks | N/A | — | — | — | |
| | **D20 Plumbing** | | | | | |
| 2010 | Plumbing Fixtures | Toilet and service fixtures, supply and drainage *1 Fixture/850 S.F. Floor* | Each | 10,064 | 11.84 | 10.4% |
| 2020 | Domestic Water Distribution | Electric water heater | S.F. Floor | 2.56 | 2.56 | |
| 2040 | Rain Water Drainage | Roof drains | S.F. Roof | 1.77 | 1.77 | |
| | **D30 HVAC** | | | | | |
| 3010 | Energy Supply | N/A | — | — | — | 9.4 % |
| 3020 | Heat Generating Systems | Included in D3050 | — | — | — | |
| 3030 | Cooling Generating Systems | N/A | — | — | — | |
| 3050 | Terminal & Package Units | Single zone rooftop unit, gas heating, electric cooling | S.F. Floor | 14.50 | 14.50 | |
| 3090 | Other HVAC Sys. & Equipment | N/A | — | — | — | |
| | **D40 Fire Protection** | | | | | |
| 4010 | Sprinklers | Wet pipe sprinkler system | S.F. Floor | 6.66 | 6.66 | 5.4% |
| 4020 | Standpipes | Standpipe | S.F. Floor | 1.73 | 1.73 | |
| | **D50 Electrical** | | | | | |
| 5010 | Electrical Service/Distribution | 400 ampere service, panel board and feeders | S.F. Floor | 2.34 | 2.34 | 12.2% |
| 5020 | Lighting & Branch Wiring | Fluorescent fixtures, receptacles, switches, A.C. and misc. power | S.F. Floor | 13.65 | 13.65 | |
| 5030 | Communications & Security | Alarm systems and emergency lighting | S.F. Floor | 2.51 | 2.51 | |
| 5090 | Other Electrical Systems | Emergency generator, 7.5 kW | S.F. Floor | .45 | .45 | |
| **E. EQUIPMENT & FURNISHINGS** | | | | | | |
| 1010 | Commercial Equipment | N/A | — | — | — | 0.0 % |
| 1020 | Institutional Equipment | N/A | — | — | — | |
| 1030 | Vehicular Equipment | N/A | — | — | — | |
| 1090 | Other Equipment | N/A | — | — | — | |
| **F. SPECIAL CONSTRUCTION** | | | | | | |
| 1020 | Integrated Construction | N/A | — | — | — | 0.0 % |
| 1040 | Special Facilities | N/A | — | — | — | |
| **G. BUILDING SITEWORK** | | **N/A** | | | | |
| | | | | **Sub-Total** | 155.03 | **100%** |
| | CONTRACTOR FEES (General Requirements: 10%, Overhead: 5%, Profit: 10%) | | | *25%* | 38.79 | |
| | ARCHITECT FEES | | | *6%* | 11.63 | |
| | | | | **Total Building Cost** | **205.45** | |

## Costs per square foot of floor area

| Exterior Wall | S.F. Area | 600 | 800 | 1000 | 1200 | 1600 | 2000 | 2400 | 3000 | 4000 |
|---|---|---|---|---|---|---|---|---|---|---|
| | L.F. Perimeter | 100 | 114 | 128 | 139 | 164 | 189 | 210 | 235 | 280 |
| Face Brick and Concrete Block | Rigid Steel | 428.75 | 410.10 | 398.90 | 389.50 | 379.20 | 373.05 | 367.65 | 360.55 | 354.10 |
| | Bearing Walls | 419.35 | 400.70 | 389.50 | 380.10 | 369.80 | 363.65 | 358.25 | 351.15 | 344.75 |
| Concrete Block | Rigid Steel | 375.45 | 364.50 | 357.90 | 352.45 | 346.40 | 342.80 | 339.60 | 335.45 | 331.70 |
| | Bearing Walls | 366.05 | 355.10 | 348.55 | 343.05 | 337.00 | 333.45 | 330.25 | 326.10 | 322.35 |
| Metal Panel | Rigid Steel | 380.55 | 368.85 | 361.95 | 356.05 | 349.65 | 345.85 | 342.50 | 338.05 | 334.10 |
| Metal Sandwich Panel | Rigid Steel | 380.65 | 368.75 | 361.65 | 355.65 | 349.10 | 345.15 | 341.75 | 337.25 | 333.15 |
| Perimeter Adj., Add or Deduct | Per 100 L.F. | 128.70 | 96.50 | 77.20 | 64.35 | 48.30 | 38.55 | 32.15 | 25.75 | 19.30 |
| Story Hgt. Adj., Add or Deduct | Per 1 Ft. | 7.75 | 6.60 | 5.90 | 5.35 | 4.75 | 4.40 | 4.05 | 3.65 | 3.25 |
| **Basement**—Not Applicable | | | | | | | | | | |

*The above costs were calculated using the basic specifications shown on the facing page. These costs should be adjusted where necessary for design alternatives and owner's requirements.*

## Common additives

| Description | Unit | $ Cost |
|---|---|---|
| Air Compressors, Electric | | |
| 1-1/2 H.P., standard controls | Ea. | 2575 |
| Dual controls | Ea. | 2525 |
| 5 H.P., 115/230 volt, standard control | Ea. | 3800 |
| Dual controls | Ea. | 3800 |
| Emergency Lighting, 25 watt, battery operated | | |
| Lead battery | Ea. | 360 |
| Nickel cadmium | Ea. | 585 |
| Fence, Chain link, 6' high | | |
| 9 ga. wire, galvanized | L.F. | 33.50 |
| 6 ga. wire | L.F. | 41 |
| Gate | Ea. | 485 |
| Product Dispenser with vapor recovery for 6 nozzles | Ea. | 31,300 |
| Laundry Equipment | | |
| Dryer, gas, 16 lb. capacity | Ea. | 1725 |
| 30 lb. capacity | Ea. | 2200 |
| Washer, 4 cycle | Ea. | 1550 |
| Commercial | Ea. | 2000 |
| Lockers, Steel, single tier, 60" or 72" | Opng. | 285 - 520 |
| 2 tier, 60" or 72" total | Opng. | 216 - 265 |
| 5 tier, box lockers | Opng. | 465 - 153 |
| Locker bench, lam. maple top only | L.F. | 148 |
| Pedestals, steel pipe | Ea. | 87 |
| Paving, Bituminous | | |
| Wearing course plus base course | S.Y. | 9.85 |
| Safe, Office type, 1 hour rating | | |
| 30" x 18" x 18" | Ea. | 1900 |
| 60" x 36" x 18", double door | Ea. | 8625 |
| Sidewalks, Concrete 4" thick | S.F. | 6.40 |
| Yard Lighting, 20' aluminum pole with 400 watt high pressure sodium fixture | Ea. | 3200 |



**Important: See the Reference Section for Location Factors.**

## Model costs calculated for a 1 story building with 12′ story height and 800 square feet of floor area

# Car Wash

| | | | | Unit | Unit Cost | Cost Per S.F. | % Of Sub-Total |
|---|---|---|---|---|---|---|---|
| **A. SUBSTRUCTURE** | | | | | | | |
| 1010 | Standard Foundations | Poured concrete; strip and spread footings; 4′ foundation wall | | S.F. Ground | 18.64 | 18.64 | |
| 1020 | Special Foundations | N/A | | — | — | — | |
| 1030 | Slab on Grade | 5″ reinforced concrete with vapor barrier and granular base | | S.F. Slab | 9.63 | 9.63 | 9.6% |
| 2010 | Basement Excavation | Site preparation for slab and trench for foundation wall and footing | | S.F. Ground | 1.25 | 1.25 | |
| 2020 | Basement Walls | N/A | | — | — | — | |
| **B. SHELL** | | | | | | | |
| | **B10 Superstructure** | | | | | | |
| 1010 | Floor Construction | N/A | | — | — | — | 4.0 % |
| 1020 | Roof Construction | Metal deck, open web steel joists, beams, columns | | S.F. Roof | 12.15 | 12.15 | |
| | **B20 Exterior Enclosure** | | | | | | |
| 2010 | Exterior Walls | Face brick with concrete block backup | *70% of wall* | S.F. Wall | 40.65 | 48.66 | |
| 2020 | Exterior Windows | Horizontal pivoted steel | *5% of wall* | Each | 1128 | 10.72 | 27.2% |
| 2030 | Exterior Doors | Steel overhead hollow metal | | Each | 4820 | 24.10 | |
| | **B30 Roofing** | | | | | | |
| 3010 | Roof Coverings | Built-up tar and gravel with flashing; perlite/EPS composite insulation | | S.F. Roof | 12.11 | 12.11 | 3.9% |
| 3020 | Roof Openings | N/A | | — | — | — | |
| **C. INTERIORS** | | | | | | | |
| 1010 | Partitions | Concrete block | *20 S.F. Floor/S.F. Partition* | S.F. Partition | 12.18 | 6.09 | |
| 1020 | Interior Doors | Hollow metal | *600 S.F. Floor/Door* | Each | 1159 | 1.94 | |
| 1030 | Fittings | N/A | | — | — | — | |
| 2010 | Stair Construction | N/A | | — | — | — | 3.1% |
| 3010 | Wall Finishes | Paint | | S.F. Surface | 1.49 | 1.49 | |
| 3020 | Floor Finishes | N/A | | — | — | — | |
| 3030 | Ceiling Finishes | N/A | | — | — | — | |
| **D. SERVICES** | | | | | | | |
| | **D10 Conveying** | | | | | | |
| 1010 | Elevators & Lifts | N/A | | — | — | — | 0.0 % |
| 1020 | Escalators & Moving Walks | N/A | | — | — | — | |
| | **D20 Plumbing** | | | | | | |
| 2010 | Plumbing Fixtures | Toilet and service fixtures, supply and drainage | *1 Fixture/160 S.F. Floor* | Each | 3693 | 23.08 | |
| 2020 | Domestic Water Distribution | Gas fired water heater | | S.F. Floor | 36.07 | 36.07 | 21.0% |
| 2040 | Rain Water Drainage | Roof drains | | S.F. Roof | 5.22 | 5.22 | |
| | **D30 HVAC** | | | | | | |
| 3010 | Energy Supply | N/A | | — | — | — | |
| 3020 | Heat Generating Systems | N/A | | — | — | — | |
| 3030 | Cooling Generating Systems | N/A | | — | — | — | 3.7 % |
| 3050 | Terminal & Package Units | Single zone rooftop unit, gas heating, electric cooling | | S.F. Floor | 11.41 | 11.41 | |
| 3090 | Other HVAC Sys. & Equipment | N/A | | — | — | — | |
| | **D40 Fire Protection** | | | | | | |
| 4010 | Sprinklers | N/A | | — | — | — | 0.0 % |
| 4020 | Standpipes | N/A | | — | — | — | |
| | **D50 Electrical** | | | | | | |
| 5010 | Electrical Service/Distribution | 400 ampere service, panel board and feeders | | S.F. Floor | 30.81 | 30.81 | |
| 5020 | Lighting & Branch Wiring | Fluorescent fixtures, receptacles, switches and misc. power | | S.F. Floor | 51 | 51.29 | 27.4% |
| 5030 | Communications & Security | N/A | | — | — | — | |
| 5090 | Other Electrical Systems | Emergency generator, 7.5 kW | | S.F. Floor | 1.94 | 1.94 | |
| **E. EQUIPMENT & FURNISHINGS** | | | | | | | |
| 1010 | Commercial Equipment | N/A | | — | — | — | |
| 1020 | Institutional Equipment | N/A | | — | — | — | 0.0 % |
| 1030 | Vehicular Equipment | N/A | | — | — | — | |
| 1090 | Other Equipment | N/A | | — | — | — | |
| **F. SPECIAL CONSTRUCTION** | | | | | | | |
| 1020 | Integrated Construction | N/A | | — | — | — | 0.0 % |
| 1040 | Special Facilities | N/A | | — | — | — | |
| **G. BUILDING SITEWORK** | | **N/A** | | | | | |
| | | | | | **Sub-Total** | 306.60 | **100%** |
| | CONTRACTOR FEES (General Requirements: 10%, Overhead: 5%, Profit: 10%) | | | | *25%* | 76.67 | |
| | ARCHITECT FEES | | | | *7%* | 26.83 | |
| | | | | | **Total Building Cost** | **410.10** | |

# Church

## Costs per square foot of floor area

| Exterior Wall | S.F. Area | 2000 | 7000 | 12000 | 17000 | 22000 | 27000 | 32000 | 37000 | 42000 |
|---|---|---|---|---|---|---|---|---|---|---|
| | L.F. Perimeter | 180 | 340 | 470 | 540 | 640 | 740 | 762 | 793 | 860 |
| Decorative Concrete Block | Wood Arch | 333.55 | 252.05 | 234.45 | 221.50 | 216.60 | 213.60 | 207.60 | 203.55 | 201.85 |
| | Steel Truss | 329.35 | 247.85 | 230.20 | 217.25 | 212.40 | 209.30 | 203.40 | 199.35 | 197.65 |
| Stone and Concrete Block | Wood Arch | 413.10 | 295.00 | 269.10 | 249.60 | 242.35 | 237.80 | 228.65 | 222.50 | 220.00 |
| | Steel Truss | 408.90 | 290.80 | 264.80 | 245.40 | 238.10 | 233.55 | 224.45 | 218.30 | 215.70 |
| Face Brick and Concrete Block | Wood Arch | 374.05 | 273.95 | 252.05 | 235.80 | 229.70 | 225.90 | 218.30 | 213.20 | 211.10 |
| | Steel Truss | 369.85 | 269.70 | 247.80 | 231.55 | 225.45 | 221.65 | 214.05 | 208.95 | 206.85 |
| Perimeter Adj., Add or Deduct | Per 100 L.F. | 80.55 | 23.00 | 13.45 | 9.50 | 7.40 | 5.90 | 5.05 | 4.35 | 3.90 |
| Story Hgt. Adj., Add or Deduct | Per 1 Ft. | 4.45 | 2.40 | 1.90 | 1.60 | 1.45 | 1.35 | 1.15 | 1.10 | 1.05 |
| ***For Basement**, add $ 56.20 per square foot of basement area* | | | | | | | | | | |

*The above costs were calculated using the basic specifications shown on the facing page. These costs should be adjusted where necessary for design alternatives and owner's requirements.*

## Common additives

| Description | Unit | $ Cost |
|---|---|---|
| Altar, Wood, custom design, plain | Ea. | 3250 |
| Deluxe | Ea. | 16,700 |
| Granite or marble, average | Ea. | 15,600 |
| Deluxe | Ea. | 41,600 |
| Ark, Prefabricated, plain | Ea. | 11,500 |
| Deluxe | Ea. | 146,000 |
| Baptistry, Fiberglass, incl. plumbing | Ea. | 5825 - 14,800 |
| Bells & Carillons, 48 bells | Ea. | 1,253,000 |
| 24 bells | Ea. | 589,500 |
| Confessional, Prefabricated wood | | |
| Single, plain | Ea. | 4350 |
| Deluxe | Ea. | 9625 |
| Double, plain | Ea. | 7525 |
| Deluxe | Ea. | 21,500 |
| Emergency Lighting, 25 watt, battery operated | | |
| Lead battery | Ea. | 360 |
| Nickel cadmium | Ea. | 585 |
| Lecterns, Wood, plain | Ea. | 450 |
| Deluxe | Ea. | 6800 |

| Description | Unit | $ Cost |
|---|---|---|
| Pews/Benches, Hardwood | L.F. | 234 - 520 |
| Pulpits, Prefabricated, hardwood | Ea. | 1875 - 13,700 |
| Railing, Hardwood | L.F. | 251 |
| Steeples, translucent fiberglass | | |
| 30" square, 15' high | Ea. | 4975 |
| 25' high | Ea. | 9375 |
| Painted fiberglass, 24" square, 14' high | Ea. | 4975 |
| 28' high | Ea. | 14,100 |
| Aluminum | | |
| 20' high, 3'- 6" base | Ea. | 10,900 |
| 35' high, 8'- 0" base | Ea. | 18,100 |
| 60' high, 14'- 0" base | Ea. | 97,000 |

## Model costs calculated for a 1 story building with 24′ story height and 17,000 square feet of floor area

# Church

| | | | Unit | Unit Cost | Cost Per S.F. | % Of Sub-Total |
|---|---|---|---|---|---|---|
| **A. SUBSTRUCTURE** | | | | | | |
| 1010 | Standard Foundations | Poured concrete; strip and spread footings; 4′ foundation wall | S.F. Ground | 10.88 | 10.88 | 10.7% |
| 1020 | Special Foundations | N/A | — | — | — | |
| 1030 | Slab on Grade | 4″ reinforced concrete with vapor barrier and granular base | S.F. Slab | 7.22 | 7.22 | |
| 2010 | Basement Excavation | Site preparation for slab and trench for foundation wall and footing | S.F. Ground | .22 | .22 | |
| 2020 | Basement Walls | N/A | — | — | — | |
| **B. SHELL** | | | | | | |
| | **B10 Superstructure** | | | | | |
| 1010 | Floor Construction | N/A | — | — | — | 18.1 % |
| 1020 | Roof Construction | Wood deck on laminated wood arches | S.F. Roof | 29.08 | 31.03 | |
| | **B20 Exterior Enclosure** | | | | | |
| 2010 | Exterior Walls | Face brick with concrete block backup *80% of wall (adjusted for end walls)* | S.F. Wall | 48.27 | 29.44 | 20.6% |
| 2020 | Exterior Windows | Aluminum, top hinged, in-swinging and curtain wall panels *20% of wall* | S.F. Window | 30.37 | 4.63 | |
| 2030 | Exterior Doors | Double hollow metal swinging, single hollow metal | Each | 3430 | 1.21 | |
| | **B30 Roofing** | | | | | |
| 3010 | Roof Coverings | Asphalt shingles with flashing; polystyrene insulation | S.F. Roof | 9.18 | 9.18 | 5.4% |
| 3020 | Roof Openings | N/A | — | — | — | |
| **C. INTERIORS** | | | | | | |
| 1010 | Partitions | Plaster on metal studs *40 S.F. Floor/L.F. Partitions* | S.F. Partition | 18.98 | 11.39 | 12.6% |
| 1020 | Interior Doors | Hollow metal *400 S.F. Floor/Door* | Each | 1159 | 2.90 | |
| 1030 | Fittings | N/A | — | — | — | |
| 2010 | Stair Construction | N/A | — | — | — | |
| 3010 | Wall Finishes | Paint | S.F. Surface | 1.39 | 1.67 | |
| 3020 | Floor Finishes | Carpet | S.F. Floor | 5.73 | 5.73 | |
| 3030 | Ceiling Finishes | N/A | — | — | — | |
| **D. SERVICES** | | | | | | |
| | **D10 Conveying** | | | | | |
| 1010 | Elevators & Lifts | N/A | — | — | — | 0.0 % |
| 1020 | Escalators & Moving Walks | N/A | — | — | — | |
| | **D20 Plumbing** | | | | | |
| 2010 | Plumbing Fixtures | Kitchen, toilet and service fixtures, supply and drainage *1 Fixture/2430 S.F. Floor* | Each | 11,543 | 4.75 | 3.1% |
| 2020 | Domestic Water Distribution | Gas fired hot water heater | S.F. Floor | .54 | .54 | |
| 2040 | Rain Water Drainage | N/A | — | — | — | |
| | **D30 HVAC** | | | | | |
| 3010 | Energy Supply | Oil fired hot water, wall fin radiation | S.F. Floor | 14.25 | 14.25 | 15.4% |
| 3020 | Heat Generating Systems | N/A | — | — | — | |
| 3030 | Cooling Generating Systems | N/A | — | — | — | |
| 3050 | Terminal & Package Units | Split systems with air cooled condensing units | S.F. Floor | 12.18 | 12.18 | |
| 3090 | Other HVAC Sys. & Equipment | N/A | — | — | — | |
| | **D40 Fire Protection** | | | | | |
| 4010 | Sprinklers | Wet pipe sprinkler system | S.F. Floor | 5.07 | 5.07 | 4.2% |
| 4020 | Standpipes | Standpipe | S.F. Floor | 2.09 | 2.09 | |
| | **D50 Electrical** | | | | | |
| 5010 | Electrical Service/Distribution | 400 ampere service, panel board and feeders | S.F. Floor | 1.02 | 1.02 | 10.0% |
| 5020 | Lighting & Branch Wiring | Fluorescent fixtures, receptacles, switches, A.C. and misc. power | S.F. Floor | 12.32 | 12.32 | |
| 5030 | Communications & Security | Alarm systems, sound system and emergency lighting | S.F. Floor | 3.64 | 3.64 | |
| 5090 | Other Electrical Systems | Emergency generator, 7.5 kW | S.F. Floor | .13 | .13 | |
| **E. EQUIPMENT & FURNISHINGS** | | | | | | |
| 1010 | Commercial Equipment | N/A | — | — | — | 0.0 % |
| 1020 | Institutional Equipment | N/A | — | — | — | |
| 1030 | Vehicular Equipment | N/A | — | — | — | |
| 1090 | Other Equipment | N/A | — | — | — | |
| **F. SPECIAL CONSTRUCTION** | | | | | | |
| 1020 | Integrated Construction | N/A | — | — | — | 0.0 % |
| 1040 | Special Facilities | N/A | — | — | — | |
| **G. BUILDING SITEWORK** | | **N/A** | | | | |
| | | | | **Sub-Total** | 171.49 | **100%** |
| | CONTRACTOR FEES (General Requirements: 10%, Overhead: 5%, Profit: 10%) | | | *25%* | 42.87 | |
| | ARCHITECT FEES | | | *10%* | 21.44 | |
| | | | | **Total Building Cost** | **235.80** | |

# M.100 Club, Country

## Costs per square foot of floor area

| Exterior Wall | S.F. Area | 2000 | 4000 | 6000 | 8000 | 12000 | 15000 | 18000 | 20000 | 22000 |
|---|---|---|---|---|---|---|---|---|---|---|
| | L.F. Perimeter | 180 | 280 | 340 | 386 | 460 | 535 | 560 | 600 | 640 |
| Stone Ashlar and Concrete Block | Wood Truss | 370.05 | 329.25 | 305.60 | 291.15 | 274.40 | 269.70 | 262.40 | 260.45 | 258.85 |
| | Steel Joists | 375.25 | 333.30 | 308.95 | 294.05 | 276.80 | 271.90 | 264.35 | 262.40 | 260.75 |
| Stucco and Concrete Block | Wood Truss | 335.70 | 302.50 | 284.00 | 272.75 | 259.80 | 256.10 | 250.50 | 249.05 | 247.75 |
| | Steel Joists | 340.90 | 306.60 | 287.30 | 275.65 | 262.20 | 258.30 | 252.50 | 250.95 | 249.65 |
| Brick Veneer | Wood Frame | 350.10 | 313.75 | 293.00 | 280.45 | 265.95 | 261.80 | 255.50 | 253.80 | 252.45 |
| Wood Shingles | Wood Frame | 337.10 | 303.55 | 284.80 | 273.45 | 260.40 | 256.65 | 251.00 | 249.45 | 248.20 |
| Perimeter Adj., Add or Deduct | Per 100 L.F. | 75.15 | 37.55 | 25.00 | 18.75 | 12.55 | 10.00 | 8.35 | 7.50 | 6.85 |
| Story Hgt. Adj., Add or Deduct | Per 1 Ft. | 9.20 | 7.15 | 5.75 | 4.90 | 3.90 | 3.65 | 3.15 | 3.05 | 3.00 |

***For Basement**, add $49.25 per square foot of basement area*

*The above costs were calculated using the basic specifications shown on the facing page. These costs should be adjusted where necessary for design alternatives and owner's requirements.*

## Common additives

| Description | Unit | $ Cost |
|---|---|---|
| Bar, Front bar | L.F. | 490 |
| Back bar | L.F. | 395 |
| Booth, Upholstered, custom, straight | L.F. | 281 - 1500 |
| "L" or "U" shaped | L.F. | 291 - 490 |
| Fireplaces, Brick not incl. chimney | | |
| or foundation, 30" x 24" opening | Ea. | 3750 |
| Chimney, standard brick | | |
| Single flue 16" x 20" | V.L.F. | 161 |
| 20" x 20" | V.L.F. | 187 |
| 2 flue, 20" x 32" | V.L.F. | 305 |
| Lockers, Steel, single tier, 60" or 72" | Opng. | 285 - 520 |
| 2 tier, 60" or 72" total | Opng. | 216 - 265 |
| 5 tier, box lockers | Opng. | 465 - 153 |
| Locker bench, lam. maple top only | L.F. | 148 |
| Pedestals, steel pipe | Ea. | 87 |
| Refrigerators, Prefabricated, walk-in | | |
| 7'-6" High, 6' x 6' | S.F. | 141 |
| 10' x 10' | S.F. | 110 |
| 12' x 14' | S.F. | 96 |
| 12' x 20' | S.F. | 139 |

| Description | Unit | $ Cost |
|---|---|---|
| Sauna, Prefabricated, complete, 6' x 4' | Ea. | 7500 |
| 6' x 9' | Ea. | 10,500 |
| 8' x 8' | Ea. | 13,500 |
| 10' x 12' | Ea. | 19,700 |
| Smoke Detectors | | |
| Ceiling type | Ea. | 300 |
| Duct type | Ea. | 615 |
| Sound System | | |
| Amplifier, 250 watts | Ea. | 2425 |
| Speaker, ceiling or wall | Ea. | 320 |
| Trumpet | Ea. | 580 |
| Steam Bath, Complete, to 140 C.F. | Ea. | 3325 |
| To 300 C.F. | Ea. | 7900 |
| To 800 C.F. | Ea. | 8375 |
| To 2500 C.F. | Ea. | 9850 |
| Swimming Pool Complete, gunite | S.F. | 127 - 158 |
| Tennis Court, Complete with fence | | |
| Bituminous | Ea. | 62,500 - 112,000 |
| Clay | Ea. | 67,000 - 103,500 |

# Model costs calculated for a 1 story building with 12′ story height and 6,000 square feet of floor area

# Club, Country

| | | | | Unit | Unit Cost | Cost Per S.F. | % Of Sub-Total |
|---|---|---|---|---|---|---|---|
| **A. SUBSTRUCTURE** | | | | | | | |
| 1010 | Standard Foundations | Poured concrete; strip and spread footings; 4′ foundation wall | | S.F. Ground | 11.54 | 11.54 | |
| 1020 | Special Foundations | N/A | | — | — | — | |
| 1030 | Slab on Grade | 4″ reinforced concrete with vapor barrier and granular base | | S.F. Slab | 7.22 | 7.22 | 8.5% |
| 2010 | Basement Excavation | Site preparation for slab and trench for foundation wall and footing | | S.F. Ground | .38 | .38 | |
| 2020 | Basement Walls | N/A | | — | — | — | |
| **B. SHELL** | | | | | | | |
| | **B10 Superstructure** | | | | | | |
| 1010 | Floor Construction | 6 x 6 wood columns | | S.F. Floor | .36 | .36 | 5.9% |
| 1020 | Roof Construction | Wood truss with plywood sheathing | | S.F. Roof | 13.03 | 13.03 | |
| | **B20 Exterior Enclosure** | | | | | | |
| 2010 | Exterior Walls | Stone ashlar veneer on concrete block | *65% of wall* | S.F. Wall | 55 | 24.09 | |
| 2020 | Exterior Windows | Aluminum horizontal sliding | *35% of wall* | Each | 1552 | 24.63 | 23.9% |
| 2030 | Exterior Doors | Double aluminum and glass, hollow metal | | Each | 5333 | 5.33 | |
| | **B30 Roofing** | | | | | | |
| 3010 | Roof Coverings | Asphalt shingles | | S.F. Roof | 22.59 | 3.87 | 1.7% |
| 3020 | Roof Openings | N/A | | — | — | — | |
| **C. INTERIORS** | | | | | | | |
| 1010 | Partitions | Gypsum board on metal studs, load bearing | *14 S.F. Floor/L.F. Partition* | S.F. Partition | 10.86 | 7.76 | |
| 1020 | Interior Doors | Single leaf wood | *140 S.F. Floor/Door* | Each | 1231 | 8.79 | |
| 1030 | Fittings | N/A | | — | — | — | |
| 2010 | Stair Construction | N/A | | — | — | — | 16.5% |
| 3010 | Wall Finishes | 40% vinyl wall covering, 40% paint, 20% ceramic tile | | S.F. Surface | 3.91 | 5.58 | |
| 3020 | Floor Finishes | 50% carpet, 30% hardwood tile, 20% ceramic tile | | S.F. Floor | 9.72 | 9.72 | |
| 3030 | Ceiling Finishes | Gypsum plaster on wood furring | | S.F. Ceiling | 5.53 | 5.53 | |
| **D. SERVICES** | | | | | | | |
| | **D10 Conveying** | | | | | | |
| 1010 | Elevators & Lifts | N/A | | — | — | — | 0.0 % |
| 1020 | Escalators & Moving Walks | N/A | | — | — | — | |
| | **D20 Plumbing** | | | | | | |
| 2010 | Plumbing Fixtures | Kitchen, toilet and service fixtures, supply and drainage | *1 Fixture/125 S.F. Floor* | Each | 3034 | 24.27 | |
| 2020 | Domestic Water Distribution | Gas fired hot water | | S.F. Floor | 11.26 | 11.26 | 15.7% |
| 2040 | Rain Water Drainage | N/A | | — | — | — | |
| | **D30 HVAC** | | | | | | |
| 3010 | Energy Supply | N/A | | — | — | — | |
| 3020 | Heat Generating Systems | Included in D3050 | | — | — | — | |
| 3030 | Cooling Generating Systems | N/A | | — | — | — | 14.5 % |
| 3050 | Terminal & Package Units | Multizone rooftop unit, gas heating, electric cooling | | S.F. Floor | 32.77 | 32.77 | |
| 3090 | Other HVAC Sys. & Equipment | N/A | | — | — | — | |
| | **D40 Fire Protection** | | | | | | |
| 4010 | Sprinklers | Wet pipe sprinkler system | | S.F. Floor | 7.71 | 7.71 | 4.7% |
| 4020 | Standpipes | Standpipe | | S.F. Floor | 2.96 | 2.96 | |
| | **D50 Electrical** | | | | | | |
| 5010 | Electrical Service/Distribution | 400 ampere service, panel board and feeders | | S.F. Floor | 4.70 | 4.70 | |
| 5020 | Lighting & Branch Wiring | High efficiency fluorescent fixtures, receptacles, switches, A.C. and misc. power | | S.F. Floor | 12.78 | 12.78 | 8.6% |
| 5030 | Communications & Security | Addressable alarm systems and emergency lighting | | S.F. Floor | 1.83 | 1.83 | |
| 5090 | Other Electrical Systems | Emergency generator, 11.5 kW | | S.F. Floor | .25 | .25 | |
| **E. EQUIPMENT & FURNISHINGS** | | | | | | | |
| 1010 | Commercial Equipment | N/A | | — | — | — | |
| 1020 | Institutional Equipment | N/A | | — | — | — | 0.0 % |
| 1030 | Vehicular Equipment | N/A | | — | — | — | |
| 1090 | Other Equipment | N/A | | — | — | — | |
| **F. SPECIAL CONSTRUCTION** | | | | | | | |
| 1020 | Integrated Construction | N/A | | — | — | — | 0.0 % |
| 1040 | Special Facilities | N/A | | — | — | — | |
| **G. BUILDING SITEWORK** | **N/A** | | | | | | |

| | | | |
|---|---|---|---|
| | **Sub-Total** | 226.36 | **100%** |
| CONTRACTOR FEES (General Requirements: 10%, Overhead: 5%, Profit: 10%) | *25%* | 56.60 | |
| ARCHITECT FEES | *8%* | 22.64 | |
| | **Total Building Cost** | **305.60** | |

## Costs per square foot of floor area

| Exterior Wall | S.F. Area | 4000 | 8000 | 12000 | 17000 | 22000 | 27000 | 32000 | 37000 | 42000 |
|---|---|---|---|---|---|---|---|---|---|---|
| | L.F. Perimeter | 280 | 386 | 520 | 585 | 640 | 740 | 840 | 940 | 940 |
| Stone Ashlar and Concrete Block | Steel Joists | 286.40 | 249.85 | 240.60 | 227.40 | **219.50** | 216.80 | 214.95 | 213.55 | 209.40 |
| | Wood Joists | 278.95 | 243.70 | 234.80 | 222.10 | 214.55 | 211.95 | 210.15 | 208.80 | 204.85 |
| Face Brick and Concrete Block | Steel Joists | 276.25 | 242.80 | 234.35 | 222.40 | 215.25 | 212.85 | 211.10 | 209.90 | 206.15 |
| | Wood Joists | 269.25 | 237.00 | 228.75 | 217.30 | 210.50 | 208.15 | 206.50 | 205.25 | 201.75 |
| Decorative Concrete Block | Steel Joists | 265.90 | 235.65 | 227.95 | 217.35 | 211.00 | 208.80 | 207.25 | 206.10 | 202.85 |
| | Wood Joists | 258.45 | 229.60 | 222.10 | 212.05 | 206.05 | 203.90 | 202.40 | 201.35 | 198.30 |
| Perimeter Adj., Add or Deduct | Per 100 L.F. | 32.45 | 16.20 | 10.85 | 7.70 | 5.95 | 4.80 | 4.05 | 3.50 | 3.10 |
| Story Hgt. Adj., Add or Deduct | Per 1 Ft. | 5.80 | 4.00 | 3.60 | 2.85 | 2.40 | 2.25 | 2.15 | 2.10 | 1.90 |

***For Basement**, add $50.20 per square foot of basement area*

*The above costs were calculated using the basic specifications shown on the facing page. These costs should be adjusted where necessary for design alternatives and owner's requirements.*

## Common additives

| Description | Unit | $ Cost |
|---|---|---|
| Bar, Front bar | L.F. | 490 |
| Back bar | L.F. | 395 |
| Booth, Upholstered, custom, straight | L.F. | 281 - 1500 |
| "L" or "U" shaped | L.F. | 291 - 490 |
| Emergency Lighting, 25 watt, battery operated | | |
| Lead battery | Ea. | 360 |
| Nickel cadmium | Ea. | 585 |
| Flagpoles, Complete | | |
| Aluminum, 20′ high | Ea. | 2050 |
| 40′ High | Ea. | 5275 |
| 70′ High | Ea. | 14,300 |
| Fiberglass, 23′ High | Ea. | 3025 |
| 39′-5″ High | Ea. | 3725 |
| 59′ High | Ea. | 12,300 |
| Kitchen Equipment | | |
| Broiler | Ea. | 4425 |
| Coffee urn, twin 6 gallon | Ea. | 4075 |
| Cooler, 6 ft. long, reach-in | Ea. | 4525 |
| Dishwasher, 10-12 racks per hr. | Ea. | 42,900 |
| Food warmer, counter 1.2 kw | Ea. | 720 |

| Description | Unit | $ Cost |
|---|---|---|
| Kitchen Equipment, cont. | | |
| Freezer, 44 C.F., reach-in | Ea. | 3600 |
| Ice cube maker, 50 lb. per day | Ea. | 2525 |
| Lockers, Steel, single tier, 60″ or 72″ | Opng. | 285 - 520 |
| 2 tier, 60″ or 72″ total | Opng. | 216 - 265 |
| 5 tier, box lockers | Opng. | 465 - 153 |
| Locker bench, lam. maple top only | L.F. | 148 |
| Pedestals, steel pipe | Ea. | 87 |
| Refrigerators, Prefabricated, walk-in | | |
| 7′-6″ High, 6′ x 6′ | S.F. | 141 |
| 10′ x 10′ | S.F. | 110 |
| 12′ x 14′ | S.F. | 96 |
| 12′ x 20′ | S.F. | 139 |
| Smoke Detectors | | |
| Ceiling type | Ea. | 300 |
| Duct type | Ea. | 615 |
| Sound System | | |
| Amplifier, 250 watts | Ea. | 2425 |
| Speaker, ceiling or wall | Ea. | 320 |
| Trumpet | Ea. | 580 |

# Model costs calculated for a 1 story building with 12′ story height and 22,000 square feet of floor area

# Club, Social

| | | | | Unit | Unit Cost | Cost Per S.F. | % Of Sub-Total |
|---|---|---|---|---|---|---|---|
| **A. SUBSTRUCTURE** | | | | | | | |
| 1010 | Standard Foundations | Poured concrete; strip and spread footings; 4′ foundation wall | | S.F. Ground | 5.15 | 5.15 | |
| 1020 | Special Foundations | N/A | | – | – | – | |
| 1030 | Slab on Grade | 4″ reinforced concrete with vapor barrier and granular base | | S.F. Slab | 7.22 | 7.22 | 7.7% |
| 2010 | Basement Excavation | Site preparation for slab and trench for foundation wall and footing | | S.F. Ground | .22 | .22 | |
| 2020 | Basement Walls | N/A | | – | – | – | |
| **B. SHELL** | | | | | | | |
| **B10 Superstructure** | | | | | | | |
| 1010 | Floor Construction | Steel column | | S.F. Floor | .80 | .80 | 7.2% |
| 1020 | Roof Construction | Metal deck on open web steel joists | | S.F. Roof | 10.96 | 10.96 | |
| **B20 Exterior Enclosure** | | | | | | | |
| 2010 | Exterior Walls | Stone, ashlar veneer on concrete block | *65% of wall* | S.F. Wall | 55 | 12.37 | |
| 2020 | Exterior Windows | Window wall | *35% of wall* | Each | 65 | 7.91 | 13.2% |
| 2030 | Exterior Doors | Double aluminum and glass doors | | Each | 5333 | 1.46 | |
| **B30 Roofing** | | | | | | | |
| 3010 | Roof Coverings | Built-up tar and gravel with flashing; perlite/EPS composite insulation | | S.F. Roof | 8.39 | 8.39 | 5.1% |
| 3020 | Roof Openings | N/A | | – | – | – | |
| **C. INTERIORS** | | | | | | | |
| 1010 | Partitions | Lightweight concrete block | *14 S.F. Floor/L.F. Partition* | S.F. Partition | 14.14 | 10.10 | |
| 1020 | Interior Doors | Single leaf wood | *140 S.F. Floor/Door* | Each | 1231 | 8.79 | |
| 1030 | Fittings | N/A | | – | – | – | |
| 2010 | Stair Construction | N/A | | – | – | – | 25.0% |
| 3010 | Wall Finishes | 65% paint, 25% vinyl wall covering, 10% ceramic tile | | S.F. Surface | 2.61 | 3.73 | |
| 3020 | Floor Finishes | 60% carpet, 35% hardwood, 15% ceramic tile | | S.F. Floor | 8.97 | 8.97 | |
| 3030 | Ceiling Finishes | Mineral fiber tile on concealed zee bars | | S.F. Ceiling | 9.48 | 9.48 | |
| **D. SERVICES** | | | | | | | |
| **D10 Conveying** | | | | | | | |
| 1010 | Elevators & Lifts | N/A | | – | – | – | 0.0 % |
| 1020 | Escalators & Moving Walks | N/A | | – | – | – | |
| **D20 Plumbing** | | | | | | | |
| 2010 | Plumbing Fixtures | Kitchen, toilet and service fixtures, supply and drainage | *1 Fixture/1050 S.F. Floor* | Each | 12,390 | 11.80 | |
| 2020 | Domestic Water Distribution | Gas fired hot water heater | | S.F. Floor | .34 | .34 | 8.1% |
| 2040 | Rain Water Drainage | Roof drains | | S.F. Roof | 1.18 | 1.18 | |
| **D30 HVAC** | | | | | | | |
| 3010 | Energy Supply | N/A | | – | – | – | |
| 3020 | Heat Generating Systems | Included in D3050 | | – | – | – | |
| 3030 | Cooling Generating Systems | N/A | | – | – | – | 19.3 % |
| 3050 | Terminal & Package Units | Multizone rooftop unit, gas heating, electric cooling | | S.F. Floor | 31.60 | 31.60 | |
| 3090 | Other HVAC Sys. & Equipment | N/A | | – | – | – | |
| **D40 Fire Protection** | | | | | | | |
| 4010 | Sprinklers | Wet pipe sprinkler system | | S.F. Floor | 6.74 | 6.74 | 4.6% |
| 4020 | Standpipes | Standpipe | | S.F. Floor | .80 | .80 | |
| **D50 Electrical** | | | | | | | |
| 5010 | Electrical Service/Distribution | 400 ampere service, panel board and feeders | | S.F. Floor | 1.56 | 1.56 | |
| 5020 | Lighting & Branch Wiring | High efficiency fluorescent fixtures, receptacles, switches, A.C. and misc. power | | S.F. Floor | 12.57 | 12.57 | 9.8% |
| 5030 | Communications & Security | Addressable alarm systems and emergency lighting | | S.F. Floor | 1.84 | 1.84 | |
| 5090 | Other Electrical Systems | Emergency generator, 11.5 kW | | S.F. Floor | .14 | .14 | |
| **E. EQUIPMENT & FURNISHINGS** | | | | | | | |
| 1010 | Commercial Equipment | N/A | | – | – | – | |
| 1020 | Institutional Equipment | N/A | | – | – | – | 0.0 % |
| 1030 | Vehicular Equipment | N/A | | – | – | – | |
| 1090 | Other Equipment | N/A | | – | – | – | |
| **F. SPECIAL CONSTRUCTION** | | | | | | | |
| 1020 | Integrated Construction | N/A | | – | – | – | 0.0 % |
| 1040 | Special Facilities | N/A | | – | – | – | |
| **G. BUILDING SITEWORK** | **N/A** | | | | | | |
| | | | | | **Sub-Total** | 164.12 | **100%** |
| | CONTRACTOR FEES (General Requirements: 10%, Overhead: 5%, Profit: 10%) | | | | *25%* | 41.02 | |
| | ARCHITECT FEES | | | | *7%* | 14.36 | |
| | | | | | **Total Building Cost** | **219.50** | |

## Costs per square foot of floor area

| Exterior Wall | S.F. Area | 15000 | 20000 | 28000 | 38000 | 50000 | 65000 | 85000 | 100000 | 150000 |
|---|---|---|---|---|---|---|---|---|---|---|
| | L.F. Perimeter | 350 | 400 | 480 | 550 | 630 | 660 | 750 | 825 | 1035 |
| Fiber Cement | Wood Frame | 232.75 | 221.60 | 212.05 | 204.65 | 199.60 | 194.45 | 191.20 | 189.75 | 186.55 |
| Stone Veneer | Wood Frame | 255.55 | 241.10 | 228.65 | 218.60 | 211.65 | 204.05 | 199.45 | 197.45 | 192.85 |
| Brick Veneer | Rigid Steel | 246.95 | 233.40 | 221.65 | 212.35 | 205.85 | 198.95 | 194.70 | 192.80 | 188.60 |
| Curtain Wall | Rigid Steel | 248.70 | 234.40 | 222.05 | 212.15 | 205.35 | 197.85 | 193.35 | 191.35 | 186.85 |
| Brick Veneer | Reinforced Concrete | 267.90 | 253.10 | 240.30 | 230.05 | 222.95 | 215.10 | 210.35 | 208.30 | 203.60 |
| Stone Veneer | Reinforced Concrete | 284.15 | 267.05 | 252.30 | 240.15 | 231.70 | 222.20 | 216.55 | 214.10 | 208.45 |
| Perimeter Adj., Add or Deduct | Per 100 L.F. | 9.10 | 6.80 | 4.85 | 3.60 | 2.75 | 2.05 | 1.60 | 1.30 | 0.95 |
| Story Hgt. Adj., Add or Deduct | Per 1 Ft. | 1.20 | 1.05 | 0.80 | 0.80 | 0.65 | 0.50 | 0.45 | 0.40 | 0.30 |

***For Basement**, add $58.55 per square foot of basement area*

*The above costs were calculated using the basic specifications shown on the facing page. These costs should be adjusted where necessary for design alternatives and owner's requirements.*

## Common additives

| Description | Unit | $ Cost |
|---|---|---|
| Carrels Hardwood | Ea. | 395 - 2350 |
| Clock System | | |
| 20 Room | Ea. | 23,000 |
| 50 Room | Ea. | 55,000 |
| Elevators, Hydraulic passenger, 2 stops | | |
| 1500# capacity | Ea. | 86,500 |
| 2500# capacity | Ea. | 90,500 |
| 3500# capacity | Ea. | 96,000 |
| Additional stop, add | Ea. | 9875 |
| Emergency Lighting, 25 watt, battery operated | | |
| Lead battery | Ea. | 360 |
| Nickel cadmium | Ea. | 585 |
| Flagpoles, Complete | | |
| Aluminum, 20' high | Ea. | 2050 |
| 40' High | Ea. | 5275 |
| 70' High | Ea. | 14,300 |
| Fiberglass, 23' High | Ea. | 3025 |
| 39'-5" High | Ea. | 3725 |
| 59' High | Ea. | 12,300 |

| Description | Unit | $ Cost |
|---|---|---|
| Lockers, Steel, single tier, 60" or 72" | Opng. | 285 - 520 |
| 2 tier, 60" or 72" total | Opng. | 216 - 265 |
| 5 tier, box lockers | Opng. | 465 - 153 |
| Locker bench, lam. maple top only | L.F. | 148 |
| Pedestals, steel pipe | Ea. | 87 |
| Seating | | |
| Auditorium chair, all veneer | Ea. | 480 |
| Veneer back, padded seat | Ea. | 430 |
| Upholstered, spring seat | Ea. | 385 |
| Classroom, movable chair & desk | Set | 81 - 171 |
| Lecture hall, pedestal type | Ea. | 385 - 775 |
| Smoke Detectors | | |
| Ceiling type | Ea. | 300 |
| Duct type | Ea. | 615 |
| Sound System | | |
| Amplifier, 250 watts | Ea. | 2425 |
| Speaker, ceiling or wall | Ea. | 320 |
| Trumpet | Ea. | 580 |
| TV Antenna, Master system, 12 outlet | Outlet | 284 |
| 30 outlet | Outlet | 370 |
| 100 outlet | Outlet | 395 |



**Important: See the Reference Section for Location Factors.**

## Model costs calculated for a 2 story building with 12′ story height and 50,000 square feet of floor area

# College, Classroom, 2-3 Story

| | | | Unit | Unit Cost | Cost Per S.F. | % Of Sub-Total |
|---|---|---|---|---|---|---|
| **A. SUBSTRUCTURE** | | | | | | |
| 1010 | Standard Foundations | Poured concrete; strip and spread footings; 4′ foundation wall | S.F. Ground | 5.52 | 2.76 | 4.3% |
| 1020 | Special Foundations | N/A | — | — | — | |
| 1030 | Slab on Grade | 4″ reinforced slab on grade | S.F. Slab | 7.22 | 3.61 | |
| 2010 | Basement Excavation | Site preparation for slab and trench for foundation wall and footing | S.F. Ground | .37 | .19 | |
| 2020 | Basement Walls | N/A | — | — | — | |
| **B. SHELL** | | | | | | |
| | **B10 Superstructure** | | | | | |
| 1010 | Floor Construction | Open web steel joists, slab form, concrete, fireproofed steel columns | S.F. Floor | 19.36 | 9.68 | 10.8% |
| 1020 | Roof Construction | Metal deck on open web steel joints, columns | S.F. Roof | 13.72 | 6.86 | |
| | **B20 Exterior Enclosure** | | | | | |
| 2010 | Exterior Walls | N/A | — | — | — | 9.7 % |
| 2020 | Exterior Windows | Curtain wall glazing system, thermo-break frame *100% of wall* | S.F. Wall | 57 | 13.79 | |
| 2030 | Exterior Doors | Aluminum and glass double doors | Each | 9150 | 1.10 | |
| | **B30 Roofing** | | | | | |
| 3010 | Roof Coverings | Single ply membrane, stone ballast, rigid insulation | S.F. Roof | 10.44 | 5.22 | 3.5% |
| 3020 | Roof Openings | Roof and smoke hatches | S.F. Roof | 4547 | .18 | |
| **C. INTERIORS** | | | | | | |
| 1010 | Partitions | Gypsum board on Metal studs *20 S.F. Floor/L.F. Partition* | S.F. Partition | 8.18 | 4.09 | 19.1% |
| 1020 | Interior Doors | Single leaf hollow metal doors *420 S.F. Floor/Door* | Each | 1159 | 2.75 | |
| 1030 | Fittings | Toilet partitions, chalkboards, classroom cabinetry | S.F. Floor | 5.46 | 5.46 | |
| 2010 | Stair Construction | Cement filled metal pan | Flight | 19,225 | 1.92 | |
| 3010 | Wall Finishes | 95% paint, 5% ceramic wall tile | S.F. Surface | 1.60 | 1.60 | |
| 3020 | Floor Finishes | 25% Carpet tile, 35% vinyl composition tile, 5% ceramic tile | S.F. Floor | 4.09 | 4.09 | |
| 3030 | Ceiling Finishes | Acoustic ceiling tiles on suspended channel grid | S.F. Ceiling | 9.48 | 9.48 | |
| **D. SERVICES** | | | | | | |
| | **D10 Conveying** | | | | | |
| 1010 | Elevators & Lifts | Two hydraulic passenger elevators | Each | 107,000 | 4.28 | 2.8% |
| 1020 | Escalators & Moving Walks | N/A | — | — | — | |
| | **D20 Plumbing** | | | | | |
| 2010 | Plumbing Fixtures | Restroom and service fixtures, supply and drainage *1 Fixture/395 S.F. Floor* | Each | 3113 | 7.90 | 8.0% |
| 2020 | Domestic Water Distribution | Gas fired water heater | S.F. Floor | 3.89 | 3.89 | |
| 2040 | Rain Water Drainage | Roof drains | S.F. Roof | 1.08 | .54 | |
| | **D30 HVAC** | | | | | |
| 3010 | Energy Supply | N/A | — | — | — | 16.1 % |
| 3020 | Heat Generating Systems | Included in D3050 | — | — | — | |
| 3030 | Cooling Generating Systems | N/A | — | — | — | |
| 3050 | Terminal & Package Units | Multizone gas heating, electric cooling unit | S.F. Floor | 24.70 | 24.70 | |
| 3090 | Other HVAC Sys. & Equipment | N/A | — | — | — | |
| | **D40 Fire Protection** | | | | | |
| 4010 | Sprinklers | Wet pipe spinkler system, light hazard | S.F. Floor | 4.57 | 4.57 | 3.3% |
| 4020 | Standpipes | Standpipes | S.F. Floor | .57 | .57 | |
| | **D50 Electrical** | | | | | |
| 5010 | Electrical Service/Distribution | 2000 ampere service,panel board and feeders | S.F. Floor | 5.74 | 5.74 | 22.3% |
| 5020 | Lighting & Branch Wiring | Incandescent fixtures, receptacles, switches, A.C. and misc. power | S.F. Floor | 19.45 | 19.45 | |
| 5030 | Communications & Security | Addressable alarm systems, emergency lighting, internet and phone wiring | S.F. Floor | 9.10 | 9.10 | |
| 5090 | Other Electrical Systems | N/A | — | — | — | |
| **E. EQUIPMENT & FURNISHINGS** | | | | | | |
| 1010 | Commercial Equipment | N/A | — | — | — | 0.0 % |
| 1020 | Institutional Equipment | N/A | — | — | — | |
| 1030 | Vehicular Equipment | N/A | — | — | — | |
| 1090 | Other Equipment | N/A | — | — | — | |
| **F. SPECIAL CONSTRUCTION** | | | | | | |
| 1020 | Integrated Construction | N/A | — | — | — | 0.0 % |
| 1040 | Special Facilities | N/A | — | — | — | |
| **G. BUILDING SITEWORK** | | **N/A** | | | | |
| | | | | **Sub-Total** | 153.52 | **100%** |
| | CONTRACTOR FEES (General Requirements: 10%, Overhead: 5%, Profit: 10%) | | | *25%* | 38.40 | |
| | ARCHITECT FEES | | | *7%* | 13.43 | |
| | | | | **Total Building Cost** | **205.35** | |

## Costs per square foot of floor area

| Exterior Wall | S.F. Area | 10000 | 15000 | 25000 | 40000 | 55000 | 70000 | 80000 | 90000 | 100000 |
|---|---|---|---|---|---|---|---|---|---|---|
| | L.F. Perimeter | 260 | 320 | 400 | 476 | 575 | 628 | 684 | 721 | 772 |
| Fiber Cement | Wood Frame | 266.40 | 245.80 | 226.90 | 214.60 | 209.70 | 205.85 | 204.50 | 203.05 | 202.20 |
| Stone Veneer | Wood Frame | 303.55 | 276.00 | 249.30 | 231.20 | 224.20 | 218.30 | 216.35 | 214.20 | 212.85 |
| Brick Veneer | Rigid Steel | 280.75 | 255.05 | 230.50 | 214.00 | 207.55 | 202.25 | 200.45 | 198.50 | 197.35 |
| Curtain Wall | Rigid Steel | 292.85 | 265.55 | 239.20 | 221.40 | 214.50 | 208.70 | 206.75 | 204.65 | 203.35 |
| Brick Veneer | Reinforced Concrete | 302.25 | 274.75 | 248.10 | 230.05 | 223.05 | 217.15 | 215.20 | 213.10 | 211.80 |
| Stone Veneer | Reinforced Concrete | 334.40 | 301.10 | 267.95 | 244.80 | 235.95 | 228.30 | 225.75 | 222.95 | 221.30 |
| Perimeter Adj., Add or Deduct | Per 100 L.F. | 15.25 | 10.15 | 6.10 | 3.85 | 2.75 | 2.20 | 1.85 | 1.70 | 1.55 |
| Story Hgt. Adj., Add or Deduct | Per 1 Ft. | 2.25 | 1.85 | 1.35 | 1.00 | 0.90 | 0.80 | 0.70 | 0.70 | 0.65 |

***For Basement**, add $ 57.00 per square foot of basement area*

*The above costs were calculated using the basic specifications shown on the facing page. These costs should be adjusted where necessary for design alternatives and owner's requirements.*

## Common additives

| Description | Unit | $ Cost |
|---|---|---|
| Carrels Hardwood | Ea. | 395 - 2350 |
| Closed Circuit Surveillance, One station | | |
| Camera and monitor | Ea. | 1250 |
| For additional camera stations, add | Ea. | 475 |
| Elevators, Hydraulic passenger, 2 stops | | |
| 2000# capacity | Ea. | 87,500 |
| 2500# capacity | Ea. | 90,500 |
| 3500# capacity | Ea. | 96,000 |
| Additional stop, add | Ea. | 9875 |
| Emergency Lighting, 25 watt, battery operated | | |
| Lead battery | Ea. | 360 |
| Nickel cadmium | Ea. | 585 |
| Furniture | Student | 2800 - 5350 |
| Intercom System, 25 station capacity | | |
| Master station | Ea. | 3175 |
| Intercom outlets | Ea. | 228 |
| Handset | Ea. | 400 |

| Description | Unit | $ Cost |
|---|---|---|
| Kitchen Equipment | | |
| Broiler | Ea. | 4425 |
| Coffee urn, twin 6 gallon | Ea. | 4075 |
| Cooler, 6 ft. long | Ea. | 4525 |
| Dishwasher, 10-12 racks per hr. | Ea. | 42,900 |
| Food warmer | Ea. | 720 |
| Freezer, 44 C.F., reach-in | Ea. | 3600 |
| Ice cube maker, 50 lb. per day | Ea. | 2525 |
| Range with 1 oven | Ea. | 2050 |
| Laundry Equipment | | |
| Dryer, gas, 16 lb. capacity | Ea. | 1725 |
| 30 lb. capacity | Ea. | 2200 |
| Washer, 4 cycle | Ea. | 1550 |
| Commercial | Ea. | 2000 |
| Smoke Detectors | | |
| Ceiling type | Ea. | 300 |
| Duct type | Ea. | 615 |
| TV Antenna, Master system, 12 outlet | Outlet | 284 |
| 30 outlet | Outlet | 370 |
| 100 outlet | Outlet | 395 |



**Important: See the Reference Section for Location Factors.**

## Model costs calculated for a 3 story building with 12′ story height and 25,000 square feet of floor area

# College, Dormitory, 2-3 Story

| | | | | Unit | Unit Cost | Cost Per S.F. | % Of Sub-Total |
|---|---|---|---|---|---|---|---|
| **A. SUBSTRUCTURE** | | | | | | | |
| 1010 | Standard Foundations | Poured concrete; strip and spread footings; 4′ foundation wall | | S.F. Ground | 18.18 | 6.06 | 5.0% |
| 1020 | Special Foundations | N/A | | — | — | — | |
| 1030 | Slab on Grade | 4″ reinforced slab on grade | | S.F. Slab | 7.22 | 2.41 | |
| 2010 | Basement Excavation | Site preparation for slab and trench for foundation wall and footing | | S.F. Ground | .22 | .07 | |
| 2020 | Basement Walls | N/A | | — | — | — | |
| **B. SHELL** | | | | | | | |
| | **B10 Superstructure** | | | | | | |
| 1010 | Floor Construction | Wood-Beam and Joist on wood columns, fireproofed | | S.F. Floor | 31.20 | 20.80 | 14.8% |
| 1020 | Roof Construction | Wood roof, truss, 4/12 slope | | S.F. Roof | 13.02 | 4.34 | |
| | **B20 Exterior Enclosure** | | | | | | |
| 2010 | Exterior Walls | Vinyl siding on wood studs, insulated | *80% of wall* | S.F. Wall | 16.17 | 7.45 | 8.4% |
| 2020 | Exterior Windows | Aluminum awning windows | *20% of wall* | Each | 839 | 4.21 | |
| 2030 | Exterior Doors | Aluminum and glass double doors | | Each | 10,800 | 2.59 | |
| | **B30 Roofing** | | | | | | |
| 3010 | Roof Coverings | Asphalt roofing, strip shingles, flashing, gutters and downspouts | | S.F. Roof | 5.55 | 1.85 | 1.1% |
| 3020 | Roof Openings | N/A | | — | — | — | |
| **C. INTERIORS** | | | | | | | |
| 1010 | Partitions | Sound deadening gypsum board on wood studs | *10 S.F. Floor/L.F. Partition* | S.F. Partition | 11.39 | 12.65 | 22.1% |
| 1020 | Interior Doors | Single leaf solid core wood doors | *100 S.F. Floor/Door* | Each | 1159 | 4.83 | |
| 1030 | Fittings | Toilet partitions and bathroom accessories | | S.F. Floor | 3.83 | 3.83 | |
| 2010 | Stair Construction | Prefabricated wood stairs with rails | | Flight | 12,925 | 5.69 | |
| 3010 | Wall Finishes | 95% paint, 5% ceramic wall tile | | S.F. Surface | 1.97 | 4.37 | |
| 3020 | Floor Finishes | 80% Carpet tile, 10% vinyl composition tile, 10% ceramic tile | | S.F. Floor | 5.15 | 5.15 | |
| 3030 | Ceiling Finishes | Acoustic ceiling tiles on suspended channel grid | | S.F. Ceiling | .95 | .95 | |
| **D. SERVICES** | | | | | | | |
| | **D10 Conveying** | | | | | | |
| 1010 | Elevators & Lifts | Hydraulic passenger elevator | | Each | 145,250 | 5.81 | 3.4% |
| 1020 | Escalators & Moving Walks | N/A | | — | — | — | |
| | **D20 Plumbing** | | | | | | |
| 2010 | Plumbing Fixtures | Restroom and service fixtures, supply and drainage | *1 Fixture/300 S.F. Floor* | Each | 6002 | 19.94 | 16.2% |
| 2020 | Domestic Water Distribution | Electric water heater | | S.F. Floor | 7.59 | 7.59 | |
| 2040 | Rain Water Drainage | Roof drains | | S.F. Roof | | | |
| | **D30 HVAC** | | | | | | |
| 3010 | Energy Supply | N/A | | — | — | — | 8.7 % |
| 3020 | Heat Generating Systems | Included in D3050 | | — | — | — | |
| 3030 | Cooling Generating Systems | N/A | | — | — | — | |
| 3050 | Terminal & Package Units | Multizone gas heating, electric cooling unit | | S.F. Floor | 14.75 | 14.75 | |
| 3090 | Other HVAC Sys. & Equipment | N/A | | — | — | — | |
| | **D40 Fire Protection** | | | | | | |
| 4010 | Sprinklers | Wet pipe spinkler system, light hazard | | S.F. Floor | 4.39 | 4.39 | 3.4% |
| 4020 | Standpipes | Standpipes | | S.F. Floor | 1.44 | 1.44 | |
| | **D50 Electrical** | | | | | | |
| 5010 | Electrical Service/Distribution | 600 ampere service, panel board and feeders | | S.F. Floor | 3.24 | 3.24 | 15.7% |
| 5020 | Lighting & Branch Wiring | Fluorescent fixtures, receptacles, switches, A.C. and misc. power | | S.F. Floor | 13.80 | 13.80 | |
| 5030 | Communications & Security | Addressable alarm systems, emergency lighting, internet and phone wiring | | S.F. Floor | 9.63 | 9.63 | |
| 5090 | Other Electrical Systems | N/A | | — | — | — | |
| **E. EQUIPMENT & FURNISHINGS** | | | | | | | |
| 1010 | Commercial Equipment | N/A | | — | — | — | 1.1 % |
| 1020 | Institutional Equipment | N/A | | — | — | — | |
| 1030 | Vehicular Equipment | N/A | | — | — | — | |
| 2020 | Moveable Furnishings | Dormitory furniture | | S.F. Floor | 1.80 | 1.80 | |
| **F. SPECIAL CONSTRUCTION** | | | | | | | |
| 1020 | Integrated Construction | N/A | | — | — | — | 0.0 % |
| 1040 | Special Facilities | N/A | | — | — | — | |
| **G. BUILDING SITEWORK** | **N/A** | | | | | | |
| | | | | | **Sub-Total** | 169.64 | **100%** |
| | CONTRACTOR FEES (General Requirements: 10%, Overhead: 5%, Profit: 10%) | | | | *25%* | 42.42 | |
| | ARCHITECT FEES | | | | *7%* | 14.84 | |
| | | | | | **Total Building Cost** | **226.90** | |

## Costs per square foot of floor area

| Exterior Wall | S.F. Area | 20000 | 35000 | 45000 | 65000 | 85000 | 110000 | 135000 | 160000 | 200000 |
|---|---|---|---|---|---|---|---|---|---|---|
| | L.F. Perimeter | 260 | 340 | 400 | 440 | 500 | 540 | 560 | 590 | 640 |
| Brick Veneer | Rigid Steel | 250.50 | 227.75 | 221.85 | 208.30 | 202.55 | 196.50 | 191.80 | 188.90 | 185.85 |
| Curtain Wall | Rigid Steel | 256.45 | 232.30 | 226.00 | 211.65 | 205.50 | 199.05 | 194.05 | 190.95 | 187.70 |
| E.I.F.S. | Rigid Steel | 238.45 | 218.80 | 213.75 | 202.25 | 197.35 | 192.20 | 188.25 | 185.85 | 183.25 |
| Precast Concrete | Precast Concrete | 294.35 | 262.20 | 253.90 | 234.35 | 226.05 | 217.20 | 210.40 | 206.15 | 201.70 |
| Brick Veneer | Reinforced Concrete | 308.40 | 274.40 | 265.65 | 244.95 | 236.15 | 226.75 | 219.50 | 215.00 | 210.30 |
| Stone Veneer | Reinforced Concrete | 336.35 | 294.35 | 283.65 | 257.75 | 246.80 | 235.05 | 225.95 | 220.30 | 214.40 |
| Perimeter Adj., Add or Deduct | Per 100 L.F. | 29.00 | 16.55 | 12.85 | 8.95 | 6.80 | 5.25 | 4.30 | 3.55 | 2.95 |
| Story Hgt. Adj., Add or Deduct | Per 1 Ft. | 5.45 | 4.05 | 3.70 | 2.90 | 2.50 | 2.05 | 1.75 | 1.50 | 1.30 |

***For Basement**, add $57.00 per square foot of basement area*

*The above costs were calculated using the basic specifications shown on the facing page. These costs should be adjusted where necessary for design alternatives and owner's requirements.*

## Common additives

| Description | Unit | $ Cost |
|---|---|---|
| Carrels Hardwood | Ea. | 395 - 2350 |
| Closed Circuit Surveillance, One station | | |
| Camera and monitor | Ea. | 1250 |
| For additional camera stations, add | Ea. | 475 |
| Elevators, Electric passenger, 5 stops | | |
| 2000# capacity | Ea. | 213,000 |
| 2500# capacity | Ea. | 218,500 |
| 3500# capacity | Ea. | 220,500 |
| Additional stop, add | Ea. | 12,600 |
| Emergency Lighting, 25 watt, battery operated | | |
| Lead battery | Ea. | 360 |
| Nickel cadmium | Ea. | 585 |
| Furniture | Student | 2800 - 5350 |
| Intercom System, 25 station capacity | | |
| Master station | Ea. | 3175 |
| Intercom outlets | Ea. | 228 |
| Handset | Ea. | 400 |

| Description | Unit | $ Cost |
|---|---|---|
| Kitchen Equipment | | |
| Broiler | Ea. | 4425 |
| Coffee urn, twin, 6 gallon | Ea. | 4075 |
| Cooler, 6 ft. long | Ea. | 4525 |
| Dishwasher, 10-12 racks per hr. | Ea. | 42,900 |
| Food warmer | Ea. | 720 |
| Freezer, 44 C.F., reach-in | Ea. | 3600 |
| Ice cube maker, 50 lb. per day | Ea. | 2525 |
| Range with 1 oven | Ea. | 2050 |
| Laundry Equipment | | |
| Dryer, gas, 16 lb. capacity | Ea. | 1725 |
| 30 lb. capacity | Ea. | 2200 |
| Washer, 4 cycle | Ea. | 1550 |
| Commercial | Ea. | 2000 |
| Smoke Detectors | | |
| Ceiling type | Ea. | 300 |
| Duct type | Ea. | 615 |
| TV Antenna, Master system, 12 outlet | Outlet | 284 |
| 30 outlet | Outlet | 370 |
| 100 outlet | Outlet | 395 |



**Important: See the Reference Section for Location Factors.**

**Model costs calculated for a 6 story building with 12′ story height and 85,000 square feet of floor area**

# College, Dormitory, 4-8 Story

| | | | Unit | Unit Cost | Cost Per S.F. | % Of Sub-Total |
|---|---|---|---|---|---|---|
| **A. SUBSTRUCTURE** | | | | | | |
| 1010 | Standard Foundations | Poured concrete; strip and spread footings; 4′ foundation wall | S.F. Ground | 12.42 | 2.07 | 2.0% |
| 1020 | Special Foundations | N/A | – | – | – | |
| 1030 | Slab on Grade | 4″ reinforced slab on grade | S.F. Slab | 7.22 | 1.20 | |
| 2010 | Basement Excavation | Site preparation for slab and trench for foundation wall and footing | S.F. Ground | .37 | .06 | |
| 2020 | Basement Walls | N/A | – | – | – | |
| **B. SHELL** | | | | | | |
| | **B10 Superstructure** | | | | | |
| 1010 | Floor Construction | Cast-in-place column, I beam, precast double T beam & topping | S.F. Floor | 22.30 | 18.58 | 13.2% |
| 1020 | Roof Construction | Precast double T beams with 2″ topping | S.F. Roof | 22.44 | 3.74 | |
| | **B20 Exterior Enclosure** | | | | | |
| 2010 | Exterior Walls | Precast concrete panels, insulated *80% of wall* | S.F. Wall | 75 | 25.50 | 20.6% |
| 2020 | Exterior Windows | Aluminum sliding windows *20% of wall* | Each | 1552 | 8.76 | |
| 2030 | Exterior Doors | Aluminum and glass double doors and single doors | Each | 5994 | .56 | |
| | **B30 Roofing** | | | | | |
| 3010 | Roof Coverings | Single ply membrane, stone ballast, rigid insulation | S.F. Roof | 11.04 | 1.84 | 1.2% |
| 3020 | Roof Openings | Roof and smoke hatches | S.F. Roof | 4547 | .21 | |
| **C. INTERIORS** | | | | | | |
| 1010 | Partitions | Sound deadening gypsum board on metal studs, CMU partitions *10 S.F. Floor/L.F. Partition* | S.F. Partition | 7.79 | 8.65 | 19.2% |
| 1020 | Interior Doors | Single leaf solid core wood doors *100 S.F. Floor/Door* | Each | 1159 | 4.83 | |
| 1030 | Fittings | Toilet partitions and bathroom accessories | S.F. Floor | 1.69 | 1.69 | |
| 2010 | Stair Construction | Cement filled metal pan with rails | Flight | 19,225 | 4.53 | |
| 3010 | Wall Finishes | 95% paint, 5% ceramic wall tile | S.F. Surface | 3.01 | 6.68 | |
| 3020 | Floor Finishes | 80% Carpet tile, 10% vinyl composition tile, 10% ceramic tile | S.F. Floor | 5.15 | 5.15 | |
| 3030 | Ceiling Finishes | Acoustic ceiling tiles on suspended channel grid | S.F. Ceiling | .95 | .95 | |
| **D. SERVICES** | | | | | | |
| | **D10 Conveying** | | | | | |
| 1010 | Elevators & Lifts | Traction geared passenger elevators | Each | 304,938 | 14.35 | 8.5% |
| 1020 | Escalators & Moving Walks | N/A | – | – | – | |
| | **D20 Plumbing** | | | | | |
| 2010 | Plumbing Fixtures | Restroom and service fixtures, supply and drainage *1 Fixture/300 S.F. Floor* | Each | 2754 | 9.15 | 7.7% |
| 2020 | Domestic Water Distribution | Electric water heater | S.F. Floor | 3.47 | 3.47 | |
| 2040 | Rain Water Drainage | Roof drains | S.F. Roof | 2.28 | .38 | |
| | **D30 HVAC** | | | | | |
| 3010 | Energy Supply | Oil fired hot water, wall fin radiation | S.F. Floor | 6.16 | 6.16 | 9.9% |
| 3020 | Heat Generating Systems | N/A | – | – | – | |
| 3030 | Cooling Generating Systems | Chilled water, air cooled condenser system | S.F. Floor | 10.65 | 10.65 | |
| 3050 | Terminal & Package Units | N/A | – | – | – | |
| 3090 | Other HVAC Sys. & Equipment | N/A | – | – | – | |
| | **D40 Fire Protection** | | | | | |
| 4010 | Sprinklers | Wet pipe spinkler system, light hazard | S.F. Floor | 4.33 | 4.33 | 3.2% |
| 4020 | Standpipes | Standpipes | S.F. Floor | 1.03 | 1.03 | |
| | **D50 Electrical** | | | | | |
| 5010 | Electrical Service/Distribution | 800 ampere service, panel board and feeders | S.F. Floor | 1.26 | 1.26 | 14.0% |
| 5020 | Lighting & Branch Wiring | Fluorescent fixtures, receptacles, switches, A.C. and misc. power | S.F. Floor | 13.96 | 13.96 | |
| 5030 | Communications & Security | Addressable alarm systems, emergency lighting, internet and phone wiring | S.F. Floor | 8.49 | 8.49 | |
| 5090 | Other Electrical Systems | N/A | – | – | – | |
| **E. EQUIPMENT & FURNISHINGS** | | | | | | |
| 1010 | Commercial Equipment | N/A | – | – | – | 0.5 % |
| 1020 | Institutional Equipment | N/A | – | – | – | |
| 1030 | Vehicular Equipment | N/A | – | – | – | |
| 2020 | Moveable Furnishings | Dormitory furniture | S.F. Floor | .79 | .79 | |
| **F. SPECIAL CONSTRUCTION** | | | | | | |
| 1020 | Integrated Construction | N/A | – | – | – | 0.0 % |
| 1040 | Special Facilities | N/A | – | – | – | |
| **G. BUILDING SITEWORK** | **N/A** | | | | | |
| | | | | **Sub-Total** | 169.02 | **100%** |
| | CONTRACTOR FEES (General Requirements: 10%, Overhead: 5%, Profit: 10%) | | | *25%* | 42.24 | |
| | ARCHITECT FEES | | | *7%* | 14.79 | |
| | | | | **Total Building Cost** | **226.05** | |

## Costs per square foot of floor area

| Exterior Wall | S.F. Area | 12000 | 20000 | 28000 | 37000 | 45000 | 57000 | 68000 | 80000 | 92000 |
|---|---|---|---|---|---|---|---|---|---|---|
| | L.F. Perimeter | 470 | 600 | 698 | 793 | 900 | 1000 | 1075 | 1180 | 1275 |
| Brick Veneer | Rigid Steel | 306.90 | 267.20 | 247.90 | 235.45 | 229.55 | 221.75 | 216.50 | 213.10 | 210.25 |
| Curtain Wall | Rigid Steel | 316.70 | 273.55 | 252.35 | 238.60 | **232.10** | 223.35 | 217.45 | 213.65 | 210.45 |
| E.I.F.S. | Rigid Steel | 301.70 | 263.80 | 245.55 | 233.75 | 228.10 | 220.70 | 215.85 | 212.65 | 209.95 |
| Precast Concrete | Reinforced Concrete | 339.25 | 294.45 | 272.35 | 257.90 | 251.20 | 241.95 | 235.80 | 231.75 | 228.40 |
| Brick Veneer | Reinforced Concrete | 327.20 | 285.20 | 264.60 | 251.30 | 245.05 | 236.60 | 230.95 | 227.20 | 224.10 |
| Stone Veneer | Reinforced Concrete | 342.00 | 296.50 | 274.05 | 259.40 | 252.55 | 243.15 | 236.90 | 232.75 | 229.35 |
| Perimeter Adj., Add or Deduct | Per 100 L.F. | 15.65 | 9.35 | 6.70 | 5.10 | 4.15 | 3.25 | 2.75 | 2.30 | 2.05 |
| Story Hgt. Adj., Add or Deduct | Per 1 Ft. | 1.70 | 1.35 | 1.15 | 1.00 | 0.90 | 0.80 | 0.75 | 0.60 | 0.65 |
| ***For Basement**, add $ 36.85 per square foot of basement area* | | | | | | | | | | |

*The above costs were calculated using the basic specifications shown on the facing page. These costs should be adjusted where necessary for design alternatives and owner's requirements.*

## Common additives

| Description | Unit | $ Cost |
|---|---|---|
| Cabinets, Base, door units, metal | L.F. | 2875 |
| Drawer units | L.F. | 1075 |
| Tall storage cabinets, open | L.F. | 475 |
| With doors | L.F. | 1125 |
| Wall, metal 12-1/2" deep, open | L.F. | 284 |
| With doors | L.F. | 425 |
| Carrels Hardwood | Ea. | 395 - 2350 |
| Countertops, not incl. base cabinets, acid proof | S.F. | 148 - 143 |
| Stainless steel | S.F. | 95 |
| Fume Hood, Not incl. ductwork | L.F. | 1250 - 3050 |
| Ductwork | Hood | 7700 - 11,400 |
| Glassware Washer, Distilled water rinse | Ea. | 10,100 - 21,800 |
| Seating | | |
| Auditorium chair, all veneer | Ea. | 480 |
| Veneer back, padded seat | Ea. | 430 |
| Upholstered, spring seat | Ea. | 385 |
| Classroom, movable chair & desk | Set | 81 - 171 |
| Lecture hall, pedestal type | Ea. | 385 - 775 |

| Description | Unit | $ Cost |
|---|---|---|
| Safety Equipment, Eye wash, hand held | Ea. | 460 |
| Deluge shower | Ea. | 325 |
| Sink, One piece plastic | | |
| Flask wash, freestanding | Ea. | 915 |
| Tables, acid resist. top, drawers | L.F. | 266 |
| Titration Unit, Four 2000 ml reservoirs | Ea. | 8275 |



**Important: See the Reference Section for Location Factors.**

## Model costs calculated for a 1 story building with 12′ story height and 45,000 square feet of floor area

# College, Laboratory

| | | | | Unit | Unit Cost | Cost Per S.F. | % Of Sub-Total |
|---|---|---|---|---|---|---|---|
| **A. SUBSTRUCTURE** | | | | | | | |
| 1010 | Standard Foundations | Poured concrete; strip and spread footings; 4′ foundation wall | | S.F. Ground | 4.79 | 4.79 | 7.2% |
| 1020 | Special Foundations | N/A | | — | — | — | |
| 1030 | Slab on Grade | 4″ reinforced slab on grade | | S.F. Slab | 7.22 | 7.22 | |
| 2010 | Basement Excavation | Site preparation for slab and trench for foundation wall and footing | | S.F. Ground | .22 | .22 | |
| 2020 | Basement Walls | N/A | | — | — | — | |
| **B. SHELL** | | | | | | | |
| **B10 Superstructure** | | | | | | | |
| 1010 | Floor Construction | Structural fireproofing | | S.F. Floor | 9 | 1.17 | 8.7% |
| 1020 | Roof Construction | Metal deck on open web steel joints, columns | | S.F. Roof | 13.70 | 13.70 | |
| **B20 Exterior Enclosure** | | | | | | | |
| 2010 | Exterior Walls | N/A | | — | — | — | 10.0 % |
| 2020 | Exterior Windows | Curtain wall glazing system, thermo-break frame | *100% of wall* | S.F. Wall | 57 | 13.53 | |
| 2030 | Exterior Doors | Aluminum and glass single and double doors | | Each | 7785 | 3.46 | |
| **B30 Roofing** | | | | | | | |
| 3010 | Roof Coverings | Single ply membrane, stone ballast, rigid insulation | | S.F. Roof | 10.12 | 10.12 | 6.3% |
| 3020 | Roof Openings | Roof and smoke hatches | | S.F. Roof | .63 | .63 | |
| **C. INTERIORS** | | | | | | | |
| 1010 | Partitions | Gypsum board on metal studs | *10 S.F. Floor/L.F. Partition* | S.F. Partition | 7.25 | 7.25 | 17.1% |
| 1020 | Interior Doors | Single leaf steel doors | *820 S.F. Floor/Door* | Each | 2060 | 2.51 | |
| 1030 | Fittings | Toilet partitions and lockers | | S.F. Floor | .71 | .71 | |
| 2010 | Stair Construction | N/A | | — | — | — | |
| 3010 | Wall Finishes | 80% paint, 20% ceramic wall tile | | S.F. Surface | .96 | 1.92 | |
| 3020 | Floor Finishes | 80% Carpet tile, 10% vinyl composition tile, 10% ceramic tile | | S.F. Floor | 7.24 | 7.24 | |
| 3030 | Ceiling Finishes | Acoustic ceiling tiles on suspended channel grid | | S.F. Ceiling | 9.48 | 9.48 | |
| **D. SERVICES** | | | | | | | |
| **D10 Conveying** | | | | | | | |
| 1010 | Elevators & Lifts | N/A | | — | — | — | 0.0 % |
| 1020 | Escalators & Moving Walks | N/A | | — | — | — | |
| **D20 Plumbing** | | | | | | | |
| 2010 | Plumbing Fixtures | Toilet and service fixtures, supply and drainage | *1 Fixture/260 S.F. Floor* | Each | 1898 | 7.30 | 7.1% |
| 2020 | Domestic Water Distribution | Gas fired water heater | | S.F. Floor | 4.33 | 4.33 | |
| 2040 | Rain Water Drainage | Roof drains | | S.F. Roof | .52 | .52 | |
| **D30 HVAC** | | | | | | | |
| 3010 | Energy Supply | N/A | | — | — | — | 14.5 % |
| 3020 | Heat Generating Systems | Included in D3050 | | — | — | — | |
| 3030 | Cooling Generating Systems | N/A | | — | — | — | |
| 3050 | Terminal & Package Units | Multizone gas heating, electric cooling unit | | S.F. Floor | 24.70 | 24.70 | |
| 3090 | Other HVAC Sys. & Equipment | N/A | | — | — | — | |
| **D40 Fire Protection** | | | | | | | |
| 4010 | Sprinklers | Wet pipe spinkler system, light hazard | | S.F. Floor | 4.46 | 4.46 | 2.9% |
| 4020 | Standpipes | Standpipes | | S.F. Floor | .54 | .54 | |
| **D50 Electrical** | | | | | | | |
| 5010 | Electrical Service/Distribution | 1000 ampere service, panel board and feeders | | S.F. Floor | 2.30 | 2.30 | 13.7% |
| 5020 | Lighting & Branch Wiring | Fluorescent fixtures, receptacles, switches, A.C. and misc. power | | S.F. Floor | 16.61 | 16.61 | |
| 5030 | Communications & Security | Addressable alarm systems, emergency lighting, internet and phone wiring | | S.F. Floor | 4.32 | 4.32 | |
| 5090 | Other Electrical Systems | Emergency generator, 11.5 kW, Uninterruptible power supply | | S.F. Floor | .11 | .11 | |
| **E. EQUIPMENT & FURNISHINGS** | | | | | | | |
| 1010 | Commercial Equipment | N/A | | — | — | — | 12.5 % |
| 1020 | Institutional Equipment | Laboratory equipment | | S.F. Floor | 21.22 | 21.22 | |
| 1030 | Vehicular Equipment | N/A | | — | — | — | |
| 1090 | Other Equipment | N/A | | — | — | — | |
| **F. SPECIAL CONSTRUCTION** | | | | | | | |
| 1020 | Integrated Construction | N/A | | — | — | — | 0.0 % |
| 1040 | Special Facilities | N/A | | — | — | — | |
| **G. BUILDING SITEWORK** | **N/A** | | | | | | |
| | | | | | **Sub-Total** | 170.36 | **100%** |
| | CONTRACTOR FEES (General Requirements: 10%, Overhead: 5%, Profit: 10%) | | | | 25% | 42.57 | |
| | ARCHITECT FEES | | | | 9% | 19.17 | |
| | | | | | **Total Building Cost** | **232.10** | |

## Costs per square foot of floor area

| Exterior Wall | S.F. Area | 15000 | 20000 | 25000 | 30000 | 35000 | 40000 | 45000 | 50000 | 55000 |
|---|---|---|---|---|---|---|---|---|---|---|
| | L.F. Perimeter | 354 | 425 | 457 | 513 | 568 | 583 | 629 | 644 | 683 |
| Face Brick and Concrete Block | Rigid Steel | 240.65 | 233.30 | 225.90 | 222.55 | 220.00 | 216.35 | 214.70 | 212.30 | 211.05 |
| | Reinforced Concrete | 228.85 | 221.50 | **214.10** | 210.70 | 208.20 | 204.55 | 202.90 | 200.50 | 199.25 |
| Precast Concrete | Rigid Steel | 257.60 | 248.75 | 239.30 | 235.15 | 232.05 | 227.25 | 225.15 | 222.05 | 220.40 |
| | Reinforced Concrete | 246.20 | 237.10 | 227.50 | 223.30 | 220.15 | 215.25 | 213.15 | 209.95 | 208.35 |
| Limestone and Concrete Block | Rigid Steel | 252.20 | 243.70 | 234.85 | 230.90 | 227.95 | 223.45 | 221.55 | 218.60 | 217.10 |
| | Reinforced Concrete | 240.45 | 231.95 | 223.05 | 219.15 | 216.15 | 211.70 | 209.75 | 206.80 | 205.30 |
| Perimeter Adj., Add or Deduct | Per 100 L.F. | 12.35 | 9.15 | 7.40 | 6.05 | 5.25 | 4.60 | 4.10 | 3.70 | 3.35 |
| Story Hgt. Adj., Add or Deduct | Per 1 Ft. | 3.05 | 2.70 | 2.35 | 2.15 | 2.05 | 1.90 | 1.75 | 1.65 | 1.55 |
| ***For Basement**, add $61.10 per square foot of basement area* | | | | | | | | | | |

*The above costs were calculated using the basic specifications shown on the facing page. These costs should be adjusted where necessary for design alternatives and owner's requirements.*

## Common additives

| Description | Unit | $ Cost |
|---|---|---|
| Carrels Hardwood | Ea. | 395 - 2350 |
| Elevators, Hydraulic passenger, 2 stops | | |
| 2000# capacity | Ea. | 87,500 |
| 2500# capacity | Ea. | 90,500 |
| 3500# capacity | Ea. | 96,000 |
| Emergency Lighting, 25 watt, battery operated | | |
| Lead battery | Ea. | 360 |
| Nickel cadmium | Ea. | 585 |
| Escalators, Metal | | |
| 32" wide, 10' story height | Ea. | 183,500 |
| 20' story height | Ea. | 228,000 |
| 48" wide, 10' Story height | Ea. | 194,500 |
| 20' story height | Ea. | 239,000 |
| Glass | | |
| 32" wide, 10' story height | Ea. | 174,500 |
| 20' story height | Ea. | 216,500 |
| 48" wide, 10' story height | Ea. | 182,500 |
| 20' story height | Ea. | 226,500 |

| Description | Unit | $ Cost |
|---|---|---|
| Lockers, Steel, Single tier, 60" or 72" | Opng. | 285 - 520 |
| 2 tier, 60" or 72" total | Opng. | 216 - 265 |
| 5 tier, box lockers | Opng. | 465 - 153 |
| Locker bench, lam. maple top only | L.F. | 148 |
| Pedestals, steel pipe | Ea. | 87 |
| Sound System | | |
| Amplifier, 250 watts | Ea. | 2425 |
| Speaker, ceiling or wall | Ea. | 320 |
| Trumpet | Ea. | 580 |

## Model costs calculated for a 2 story building with 12′ story height and 25,000 square feet of floor area

# College, Student Union

| | | | Unit | Unit Cost | Cost Per S.F. | % Of Sub-Total |
|---|---|---|---|---|---|---|
| **A. SUBSTRUCTURE** | | | | | | |
| 1010 | Standard Foundations | Poured concrete; strip and spread footings; 4′ foundation wall | S.F. Ground | 10.54 | 5.27 | |
| 1020 | Special Foundations | N/A | — | — | — | |
| 1030 | Slab on Grade | 4″ reinforced concrete with vapor barrier and granular base | S.F. Slab | 7.22 | 3.61 | 5.6% |
| 2010 | Basement Excavation | Site preparation for slab and trench for foundation wall and footing | S.F. Ground | .22 | .11 | |
| 2020 | Basement Walls | N/A | — | — | — | |
| **B. SHELL** | | | | | | |
| | **B10 Superstructure** | | | | | |
| 1010 | Floor Construction | Concrete flat plate | S.F. Floor | 36.88 | 18.44 | 18.2% |
| 1020 | Roof Construction | Concrete flat plate | S.F. Roof | 21.32 | 10.66 | |
| | **B20 Exterior Enclosure** | | | | | |
| 2010 | Exterior Walls | Face brick with concrete block backup *75% of wall* | S.F. Wall | 40.63 | 13.37 | |
| 2020 | Exterior Windows | Window wall *25% of wall* | Each | 55 | 6.05 | 12.6% |
| 2030 | Exterior Doors | Double aluminum and glass | Each | 4400 | .71 | |
| | **B30 Roofing** | | | | | |
| 3010 | Roof Coverings | Built-up tar and gravel with flashing; perlite/EPS composite insulation | S.F. Roof | 8.88 | 4.44 | 2.8% |
| 3020 | Roof Openings | Roof hatches | S.F. Roof | .20 | .10 | |
| **C. INTERIORS** | | | | | | |
| 1010 | Partitions | Gypsum board on metal studs *14 S.F. Floor/L.F. Partition* | S.F. Partition | 7.92 | 5.66 | |
| 1020 | Interior Doors | Single leaf hollow metal *140 S.F. Floor/Door* | Each | 1159 | 2.32 | |
| 1030 | Fittings | N/A | — | — | — | |
| 2010 | Stair Construction | Cast in place concrete | Flight | 10,225 | 1.64 | 18.4% |
| 3010 | Wall Finishes | 50% paint, 50% vinyl wall covering | S.F. Surface | 3.79 | 5.42 | |
| 3020 | Floor Finishes | 50% carpet, 50% vinyl composition tile | S.F. Floor | 4.90 | 4.90 | |
| 3030 | Ceiling Finishes | Suspended fiberglass board | S.F. Ceiling | 9.48 | 9.48 | |
| **D. SERVICES** | | | | | | |
| | **D10 Conveying** | | | | | |
| 1010 | Elevators & Lifts | One hydraulic passenger elevator | Each | 107,000 | 4.28 | 2.7% |
| 1020 | Escalators & Moving Walks | N/A | — | — | — | |
| | **D20 Plumbing** | | | | | |
| 2010 | Plumbing Fixtures | Toilet and service fixtures, supply and drainage *1 Fixture/1040 S.F. Floor* | Each | 4659 | 4.48 | |
| 2020 | Domestic Water Distribution | Gas fired water heater | S.F. Floor | 1.17 | 1.17 | 4.1% |
| 2040 | Rain Water Drainage | Roof drains | S.F. Roof | 1.70 | .85 | |
| | **D30 HVAC** | | | | | |
| 3010 | Energy Supply | N/A | — | — | — | |
| 3020 | Heat Generating Systems | Included in D3050 | — | — | — | |
| 3030 | Cooling Generating Systems | N/A | — | — | — | 15.4 % |
| 3050 | Terminal & Package Units | Multizone unit, gas heating, electric cooling | S.F. Floor | 24.70 | 24.70 | |
| 3090 | Other HVAC Sys. & Equipment | N/A | — | — | — | |
| | **D40 Fire Protection** | | | | | |
| 4010 | Sprinklers | Wet pipe sprinkler system | S.F. Floor | 4.57 | 4.57 | 3.8% |
| 4020 | Standpipes | Standpipe, wet, Class III | S.F. Floor | 1.47 | 1.47 | |
| | **D50 Electrical** | | | | | |
| 5010 | Electrical Service/Distribution | 600 ampere service, panel board and feeders | S.F. Floor | 2.49 | 2.49 | |
| 5020 | Lighting & Branch Wiring | High efficiency fluorescent fixtures, receptacles, switches, A.C. and misc. power | S.F. Floor | 18.98 | 18.98 | 16.5% |
| 5030 | Communications & Security | Addressable alarm systems, internet wiring, communications systems and emergency lighting | S.F. Floor | 4.73 | 4.73 | |
| 5090 | Other Electrical Systems | Emergency generator, 11.5 kW | S.F. Floor | .17 | .17 | |
| **E. EQUIPMENT & FURNISHINGS** | | | | | | |
| 1010 | Commercial Equipment | N/A | — | — | — | |
| 1020 | Institutional Equipment | N/A | — | — | — | 0.0 % |
| 1030 | Vehicular Equipment | N/A | — | — | — | |
| 1090 | Other Equipment | N/A | — | — | — | |
| **F. SPECIAL CONSTRUCTION** | | | | | | |
| 1020 | Integrated Construction | N/A | — | — | — | 0.0 % |
| 1040 | Special Facilities | N/A | — | — | — | |
| **G. BUILDING SITEWORK** | | **N/A** | | | | |
| | | | | **Sub-Total** | 160.07 | **100%** |
| | CONTRACTOR FEES (General Requirements: 10%, Overhead: 5%, Profit: 10%) | | | *25%* | 40.02 | |
| | ARCHITECT FEES | | | *7%* | 14.01 | |
| | | | | **Total Building Cost** | **214.10** | |

## Costs per square foot of floor area

| Exterior Wall | S.F. Area | 4000 | 6000 | 8000 | 10000 | 12000 | 14000 | 16000 | 18000 | 20000 |
|---|---|---|---|---|---|---|---|---|---|---|
| | L.F. Perimeter | 260 | 340 | 420 | 453 | 460 | 510 | 560 | 610 | 600 |
| Face Brick and Concrete Block | Bearing Walls | 220.45 | 209.00 | 203.20 | 194.35 | 185.85 | 183.35 | 181.55 | 180.10 | 175.45 |
| | Rigid Steel | 225.00 | 213.55 | 207.80 | 198.90 | 190.40 | 187.95 | 186.10 | 184.65 | 180.05 |
| Decorative Concrete Block | Bearing Walls | 204.40 | 195.00 | 190.25 | 183.15 | 176.35 | 174.35 | 172.90 | 171.70 | 168.10 |
| | Rigid Steel | 209.00 | 199.55 | 194.85 | 187.70 | 180.90 | 178.95 | 177.45 | 176.25 | 172.65 |
| Tilt-up Concrete Panels | Bearing Walls | 198.65 | 190.00 | 185.60 | 179.10 | 173.00 | 171.15 | 169.85 | 168.75 | 165.40 |
| | Rigid Steel | 203.25 | 194.55 | 190.20 | 183.70 | 177.55 | 175.75 | 174.40 | 173.35 | 170.00 |
| Perimeter Adj., Add or Deduct | Per 100 L.F. | 29.10 | 19.35 | 14.50 | 11.60 | 9.70 | 8.30 | 7.25 | 6.40 | 5.80 |
| Story Hgt. Adj., Add or Deduct | Per 1 Ft. | 4.45 | 3.85 | 3.65 | 3.05 | 2.60 | 2.55 | 2.35 | 2.30 | 2.10 |

***For Basement**, add $53.45 per square foot of basement area*

*The above costs were calculated using the basic specifications shown on the facing page. These costs should be adjusted where necessary for design alternatives and owner's requirements.*

## Common additives

| Description | Unit | $ Cost |
|---|---|---|
| Bar, Front bar | L.F. | 490 |
| Back bar | L.F. | 395 |
| Booth, Upholstered, custom straight | L.F. | 281 - 1500 |
| "L" or "U" shaped | L.F. | 291 - 490 |
| Bowling Alleys, incl. alley, pinsetter | | |
| Scorer, counter & misc. supplies, average | Lane | 73,500 |
| For automatic scorer, add | Lane | 12,000 |
| Emergency Lighting, 25 watt, battery operated | | |
| Lead battery | Ea. | 360 |
| Nickel cadmium | Ea. | 585 |
| Kitchen Equipment | | |
| Broiler | Ea. | 4425 |
| Coffee urn, twin 6 gallon | Ea. | 4075 |
| Cooler, 6 ft. long | Ea. | 4525 |
| Dishwasher, 10-12 racks per hr. | Ea. | 42,900 |
| Food warmer | Ea. | 720 |
| Freezer, 44 C.F., reach-in | Ea. | 3600 |
| Ice cube maker, 50 lb. per day | Ea. | 2525 |
| Range with 1 oven | Ea. | 2050 |

| Description | Unit | $ Cost |
|---|---|---|
| Movie Equipment | | |
| Projector, 35mm | Ea. | 15,500 - 21,400 |
| Screen, wall or ceiling hung | S.F. | 11.95 - 17.35 |
| Partitions, Folding leaf, wood | | |
| Acoustic type | S.F. | 132 - 213 |
| Seating | | |
| Auditorium chair, all veneer | Ea. | 480 |
| Veneer back, padded seat | Ea. | 430 |
| Upholstered, spring seat | Ea. | 385 |
| Classroom, movable chair & desk | Set | 81 - 171 |
| Lecture hall, pedestal type | Ea. | 385 - 775 |
| Sound System | | |
| Amplifier, 250 watts | Ea. | 2425 |
| Speaker, ceiling or wall | Ea. | 320 |
| Trumpet | Ea. | 580 |
| Stage Curtains, Medium weight | S.F. | 13.95 - 46 |
| Curtain Track, Light duty | L.F. | 104 |
| Swimming Pools, Complete, gunite | S.F. | 127 - 158 |



**Important: See the Reference Section for Location Factors.**

## Model costs calculated for a 1 story building with 12′ story height and 10,000 square feet of floor area

# Community Center

| | | | | Unit | Unit Cost | Cost Per S.F. | % Of Sub-Total |
|---|---|---|---|---|---|---|---|
| **A. SUBSTRUCTURE** | | | | | | | |
| 1010 | Standard Foundations | Poured concrete; strip and spread footings; 4′ foundation wall | | S.F. Ground | 8.69 | 8.69 | |
| 1020 | Special Foundations | N/A | | — | — | — | |
| 1030 | Slab on Grade | 4″ reinforced concrete with vapor barrier and granular base | | S.F. Slab | 7.22 | 7.22 | 11.3% |
| 2010 | Basement Excavation | Site preparation for slab and trench for foundation wall and footing | | S.F. Ground | .38 | .38 | |
| 2020 | Basement Walls | N/A | | — | — | — | |
| **B. SHELL** | | | | | | | |
| | **B10 Superstructure** | | | | | | |
| 1010 | Floor Construction | N/A | | — | — | — | 8.1 % |
| 1020 | Roof Construction | Metal deck on open web steel joists | | S.F. Roof | 11.61 | 11.61 | |
| | **B20 Exterior Enclosure** | | | | | | |
| 2010 | Exterior Walls | Face brick with concrete block backup | *80% of wall* | S.F. Wall | 40.65 | 17.68 | |
| 2020 | Exterior Windows | Aluminum sliding | *20% of wall* | Each | 2440 | 8.29 | 19.4% |
| 2030 | Exterior Doors | Double aluminum and glass and hollow metal | | Each | 4888 | 1.96 | |
| | **B30 Roofing** | | | | | | |
| 3010 | Roof Coverings | Built-up tar and gravel with flashing; perlite/EPS composite insulation | | S.F. Roof | 9.42 | 9.42 | 6.7% |
| 3020 | Roof Openings | Roof hatches | | S.F. Roof | .21 | .21 | |
| **C. INTERIORS** | | | | | | | |
| 1010 | Partitions | Gypsum board on metal studs | *14 S.F. Floor/L.F. Partition* | S.F. Partition | 10.65 | 7.61 | |
| 1020 | Interior Doors | Single leaf hollow metal | *140 S.F. Floor/Door* | Each | 1159 | 1.16 | |
| 1030 | Fittings | Toilet partitions, directory board, mailboxes | | S.F. Floor | 2.91 | 2.91 | |
| 2010 | Stair Construction | N/A | | — | — | — | 20.1% |
| 3010 | Wall Finishes | Paint | | S.F. Surface | 2.11 | 3.02 | |
| 3020 | Floor Finishes | 50% carpet, 50% vinyl tile | | S.F. Floor | 4.78 | 4.78 | |
| 3030 | Ceiling Finishes | Mineral fiber tile on concealed zee bars | | S.F. Ceiling | 9.48 | 9.48 | |
| **D. SERVICES** | | | | | | | |
| | **D10 Conveying** | | | | | | |
| 1010 | Elevators & Lifts | N/A | | — | — | — | 0.0 % |
| 1020 | Escalators & Moving Walks | N/A | | — | — | — | |
| | **D20 Plumbing** | | | | | | |
| 2010 | Plumbing Fixtures | Kitchen, toilet and service fixtures, supply and drainage | *1 Fixture/910 S.F. Floor* | Each | 4932 | 5.42 | |
| 2020 | Domestic Water Distribution | Electric water heater | | S.F. Floor | 10.56 | 10.56 | 11.6% |
| 2040 | Rain Water Drainage | Roof drains | | S.F. Roof | .75 | .75 | |
| | **D30 HVAC** | | | | | | |
| 3010 | Energy Supply | N/A | | — | — | — | |
| 3020 | Heat Generating Systems | Included in D3050 | | — | — | — | |
| 3030 | Cooling Generating Systems | N/A | | — | — | — | 9.3 % |
| 3050 | Terminal & Package Units | Single zone rooftop unit, gas heating, electric cooling | | S.F. Floor | 13.35 | 13.35 | |
| 3090 | Other HVAC Sys. & Equipment | N/A | | — | — | — | |
| | **D40 Fire Protection** | | | | | | |
| 4010 | Sprinklers | Wet pipe sprinkler system | | S.F. Floor | 5.07 | 5.07 | 3.5% |
| 4020 | Standpipes | N/A | | — | — | — | |
| | **D50 Electrical** | | | | | | |
| 5010 | Electrical Service/Distribution | 200 ampere service, panel board and feeders | | S.F. Floor | 1.41 | 1.41 | |
| 5020 | Lighting & Branch Wiring | High efficiency fluorescent fixtures, receptacles, switches, A.C. and misc. power | | S.F. Floor | 8.78 | 8.78 | 8.2% |
| 5030 | Communications & Security | Addressable alarm systems and emergency lighting | | S.F. Floor | 1.51 | 1.51 | |
| 5090 | Other Electrical Systems | Emergency generator, 15 kW | | S.F. Floor | .17 | .17 | |
| **E. EQUIPMENT & FURNISHINGS** | | | | | | | |
| 1010 | Commercial Equipment | Freezer, chest type | | S.F. Floor | .81 | .81 | |
| 1020 | Institutional Equipment | N/A | | — | — | — | 1.7% |
| 1030 | Vehicular Equipment | N/A | | — | — | — | |
| 1090 | Other Equipment | Kitchen equipment, directory board, mailboxes, built-in coat racks | | S.F. Floor | 1.68 | 1.68 | |
| **F. SPECIAL CONSTRUCTION** | | | | | | | |
| 1020 | Integrated Construction | N/A | | — | — | — | 0.0 % |
| 1040 | Special Facilities | N/A | | — | — | — | |
| **G. BUILDING SITEWORK** | **N/A** | | | | | | |
| | | | | | **Sub-Total** | 143.93 | **100%** |
| | CONTRACTOR FEES (General Requirements: 10%, Overhead: 5%, Profit: 10%) | | | | *25%* | 36.03 | |
| | ARCHITECT FEES | | | | *8%* | 14.39 | |
| | | | | | **Total Building Cost** | **194.35** | |

## Costs per square foot of floor area

| Exterior Wall | S.F. Area | 10000 | 12500 | 15000 | 17500 | 20000 | 22500 | 25000 | 30000 | 40000 |
|---|---|---|---|---|---|---|---|---|---|---|
| | L.F. Perimeter | 400 | 450 | 500 | 550 | 600 | 625 | 650 | 700 | 800 |
| Fiber Cement | Wood Frame | 422.85 | 419.15 | 416.65 | 414.85 | 413.55 | 411.55 | 409.85 | 407.45 | 404.40 |
| Stone Veneer | Wood Frame | 450.95 | 444.20 | 439.70 | 436.35 | 434.00 | 430.25 | 427.25 | 422.80 | 417.25 |
| Curtain Wall | Rigid Steel | 449.75 | 443.50 | 439.30 | 436.25 | 434.10 | 430.65 | 427.90 | 423.70 | 418.55 |
| E.I.F.S. | Rigid Steel | 430.70 | 426.55 | 423.85 | 421.80 | 420.45 | 418.10 | 416.35 | 413.65 | 410.30 |
| Brick Veneer | Reinforced Concrete | 464.45 | 457.40 | 452.75 | 449.25 | 446.80 | 442.90 | 439.80 | 435.10 | 429.25 |
| Metal Panel | Reinforced Concrete | 462.70 | 456.15 | 451.85 | 448.65 | 446.40 | 442.80 | 439.90 | 435.55 | 430.15 |
| Perimeter Adj., Add or Deduct | Per 100 L.F. | 9.00 | 7.10 | 6.00 | 5.15 | 4.50 | 3.95 | 3.70 | 2.95 | 2.30 |
| Story Hgt. Adj., Add or Deduct | Per 1 Ft. | 1.20 | 1.10 | 1.00 | 0.95 | 0.90 | 0.85 | 0.80 | 0.70 | 0.60 |
| ***For Basement**, add $58.75 per square foot of basement area* | | | | | | | | | | |

*The above costs were calculated using the basic specifications shown on the facing page. These costs should be adjusted where necessary for design alternatives and owner's requirements.*

## Common additives

| Description | Unit | $ Cost |
|---|---|---|
| Clock System | | |
| 20 room | Ea. | 23,000 |
| 50 room | Ea. | 55,000 |
| Closed Circuit Surveillance, one station | | |
| Camera and monitor | Total | 1250 |
| For additional camera stations, add | Ea. | 475 |
| For zoom lens - remote control, add | Ea. | 2150 - 5250 |
| For automatic iris for low light, add | Ea. | 1375 |
| Directory Boards, plastic, glass covered | | |
| 30" x 20" | Ea. | 705 |
| 36" x 48" | Ea. | 1475 |
| Aluminum, 24" x 18" | Ea. | 705 |
| 36" x 24" | Ea. | 985 |
| 48" x 32" | Ea. | 1975 |
| 48" x 60" | Ea. | 2650 |
| Emergency Lighting, 25 watt, battery operated | | |
| Lead battery | Ea. | 360 |
| Nickel cadmium | Ea. | 585 |

| Description | Unit | $ Cost |
|---|---|---|
| Smoke Detectors | | |
| Ceiling type | Ea. | 300 |
| Duct type | Ea. | 615 |
| Sound System | | |
| Amplifier, 250 watts | Ea. | 2425 |
| Speakers, ceiling or wall | Ea. | 320 |
| Trumpets | Ea. | 580 |



**Important: See the Reference Section for Location Factors.**

## Model costs calculated for a 1 story building with 16'-6" story height and 22,500 square feet of floor area

# Computer Data Center

| | | | | Unit | Unit Cost | Cost Per S.F. | % Of Sub-Total |
|---|---|---|---|---|---|---|---|
| **A. SUBSTRUCTURE** | | | | | | | |
| 1010 | Standard Foundations | Poured concrete; strip and spread footings; 4' foundation wall | | S.F. Ground | 5.10 | 5.10 | 4.1% |
| 1020 | Special Foundations | N/A | | — | — | — | |
| 1030 | Slab on Grade | 4" reinforced concrete | | S.F. Slab | 7.22 | 7.22 | |
| 2010 | Basement Excavation | Site preparation for slab and trench for foundation wall and footing | | S.F. Ground | .22 | .24 | |
| 2020 | Basement Walls | N/A | | — | — | — | |
| **B. SHELL** | | | | | | | |
| | **B10 Superstructure** | | | | | | |
| 1010 | Floor Construction | Wood columns, fireproofed | | S.F. Floor | 4.44 | 4.44 | 5.8% |
| 1020 | Roof Construction | Wood roof truss 4:12 pitch | | S.F. Roof | 13.43 | 13.43 | |
| | **B20 Exterior Enclosure** | | | | | | |
| 2010 | Exterior Walls | Fiber cement siding on wood studs, insulated | *95% of wall* | S.F. Wall | 19.91 | 8.67 | 4.2% |
| 2020 | Exterior Windows | Aluminum horizontal sliding | *5% of wall* | Each | 1677 | 2.56 | |
| 2030 | Exterior Doors | Aluminum and glass single and double doors | | Each | 6200 | 1.66 | |
| | **B30 Roofing** | | | | | | |
| 3010 | Roof Coverings | Asphalt roofing, strip shingles, gutters and downspouts | | S.F. Roof | 2.78 | 2.78 | 1.0% |
| 3020 | Roof Openings | Roof hatch | | S.F. Roof | .44 | .44 | |
| **C. INTERIORS** | | | | | | | |
| 1010 | Partitions | Sound deadening gypsum board on wood studs | *15 S.F. Floor/L.F. Partition* | S.F. Partition | 11.49 | 10.61 | 11.2% |
| 1020 | Interior Doors | Solid core wood doors in metal frames | *370 S.F. Floor/Door* | Each | 1296 | 3.50 | |
| 1030 | Fittings | Plastic laminate toilet partitions | | S.F. Floor | .27 | .27 | |
| 2010 | Stair Construction | N/A | | — | — | — | |
| 3010 | Wall Finishes | 90% Paint, 10% ceramic wall tile | | S.F. Surface | 2 | 3.69 | |
| 3020 | Floor Finishes | 65% Carpet, 10% porcelain tile, 10% quarry tile | | S.F. Floor | 7.43 | 7.43 | |
| 3030 | Ceiling Finishes | Acoustic ceiling tiles on suspended channel grid | | S.F. Ceiling | 9 | 9 | |
| **D. SERVICES** | | | | | | | |
| | **D10 Conveying** | | | | | | |
| 1010 | Elevators & Lifts | N/A | | — | — | — | 0.0 % |
| 1020 | Escalators & Moving Walks | N/A | | — | — | — | |
| | **D20 Plumbing** | | | | | | |
| 2010 | Plumbing Fixtures | Restroom and service fixtures, supply and drainage | *1 Fixture/1180 S.F. Floor* | Each | 2891 | 2.45 | 1.1% |
| 2020 | Domestic Water Distribution | Gas fired water heater | | S.F. Floor | .91 | .91 | |
| 2040 | Rain Water Drainage | N/A | | — | — | — | |
| | **D30 HVAC** | | | | | | |
| 3010 | Energy Supply | Hot water reheat system | | S.F. Floor | 9.36 | 9.36 | 41.5% |
| 3020 | Heat Generating Systems | Oil fired hot water boiler and pumps | | Each | 68,625 | 13.72 | |
| 3030 | Cooling Generating Systems | Cooling tower and chiller | | S.F. Floor | 12.01 | 12.01 | |
| 3050 | Terminal & Package Units | N/A | | — | — | — | |
| 3090 | Other HVAC Sys. & Equipment | Plate heat exchanger, ductwork, AHUs and VAV terminals | | S.F. Floor | 93 | 92.65 | |
| | **D40 Fire Protection** | | | | | | |
| 4010 | Sprinklers | 85% light hazard wet pipe sprinkler system, 15% preaction system | | S.F. Floor | 6.97 | 6.97 | 2.6% |
| 4020 | Standpipes | Standpipes and hose systems | | S.F. Floor | 1.11 | 1.11 | |
| | **D50 Electrical** | | | | | | |
| 5010 | Electrical Service/Distribution | 1200 ampere service, panel boards and feeders | | S.F. Floor | 5.46 | 5.46 | 27.3% |
| 5020 | Lighting & Branch Wiring | Fluorescent fixtures, receptacles, switches, A.C. and misc. power | | S.F. Floor | 22.97 | 22.97 | |
| 5030 | Communications & Security | Telephone systems, internet wiring, and addressable alarm systems | | S.F. Floor | 39.63 | 39.63 | |
| 5090 | Other Electrical Systems | Emergency generator, UPS system with 15 minute pack | | S.F. Floor | 16.03 | 16.03 | |
| **E. EQUIPMENT & FURNISHINGS** | | | | | | | |
| 1010 | Commercial Equipment | N/A | | — | — | — | 0.0 % |
| 1020 | Institutional Equipment | N/A | | — | — | — | |
| 1030 | Vehicular Equipment | N/A | | — | — | — | |
| 1090 | Other Equipment | N/A | | — | — | — | |
| **F. SPECIAL CONSTRUCTION & DEMOLITION** | | | | | | | |
| 1020 | Integrated Construction | Pedestal access floor | | S.F. Floor | 3.37 | 3.37 | 1.1% |
| 1040 | Special Facilities | N/A | | — | — | — | |
| **G. BUILDING SITEWORK** | | **N/A** | | | | | |
| | | | | | **Sub-Total** | 307.68 | **100%** |
| | CONTRACTOR FEES (General Requirements: 10%, Overhead: 5%, Profit: 10%) | | | | *25%* | 76.95 | |
| | ARCHITECT FEES | | | | *7%* | 26.92 | |
| | | | | | **Total Building Cost** | **411.55** | |

## Costs per square foot of floor area

| Exterior Wall | S.F. Area | 16000 | 23000 | 30000 | 37000 | 44000 | 51000 | 58000 | 65000 | 72000 |
|---|---|---|---|---|---|---|---|---|---|---|
| | L.F. Perimeter | 597 | 763 | 821 | 954 | 968 | 1066 | 1090 | 1132 | 1220 |
| Limestone and Concrete Block | Reinforced Concrete | 310.05 | 298.00 | **285.70** | 281.40 | 274.00 | 271.35 | 267.25 | 264.55 | 263.35 |
| | Rigid Steel | 306.05 | 293.90 | 281.70 | 277.35 | 270.00 | 267.35 | 263.25 | 260.50 | 259.30 |
| Face Brick and Concrete Block | Reinforced Concrete | 291.80 | 281.75 | 272.35 | 268.75 | 263.25 | 261.15 | 258.10 | 256.00 | 255.05 |
| | Rigid Steel | 287.80 | 277.70 | 268.35 | 264.75 | 259.25 | 257.10 | 254.10 | 252.00 | 251.05 |
| Stone and Concrete Block | Reinforced Concrete | 299.05 | 288.15 | 277.65 | 273.75 | 267.50 | 265.20 | 261.75 | 259.40 | 258.35 |
| | Rigid Steel | 295.00 | 284.15 | 273.65 | 269.75 | 263.50 | 261.15 | 257.75 | 255.40 | 254.35 |
| Perimeter Adj., Add or Deduct | Per 100 L.F. | 10.10 | 7.00 | 5.40 | 4.35 | 3.70 | 3.20 | 2.85 | 2.45 | 2.25 |
| Story Hgt. Adj., Add or Deduct | Per 1 Ft. | 3.45 | 3.05 | 2.60 | 2.40 | 2.05 | 1.90 | 1.75 | 1.65 | 1.60 |
| ***For Basement**, add $ 50.50 per square foot of basement area* | | | | | | | | | | |

*The above costs were calculated using the basic specifications shown on the facing page. These costs should be adjusted where necessary for design alternatives and owner's requirements.*

## Common additives

| Description | Unit | $ Cost |
|---|---|---|
| Benches, Hardwood | L.F. | 234 - 520 |
| Clock System | | |
| 20 room | Ea. | 23,000 |
| 50 room | Ea. | 55,000 |
| Closed Circuit Surveillance, One station | | |
| Camera and monitor | Ea. | 1250 |
| For additional camera stations, add | Ea. | 475 |
| Directory Boards, Plastic, glass covered | | |
| 30″ x 20″ | Ea. | 705 |
| 36″ x 48″ | Ea. | 1475 |
| Aluminum, 24″ x 18″ | Ea. | 705 |
| 36″ x 24″ | Ea. | 985 |
| 48″ x 32″ | Ea. | 1975 |
| 48″ x 60″ | Ea. | 2650 |
| Emergency Lighting, 25 watt, battery operated | | |
| Lead battery | Ea. | 360 |
| Nickel cadmium | Ea. | 585 |

| Description | Unit | $ Cost |
|---|---|---|
| Flagpoles, Complete | | |
| Aluminum, 20′ high | Ea. | 2050 |
| 40′ high | Ea. | 5275 |
| 70′ high | Ea. | 14,300 |
| Fiberglass, 23′ high | Ea. | 3025 |
| 39′-5″ high | Ea. | 3725 |
| 59′ high | Ea. | 12,300 |
| Intercom System, 25 station capacity | | |
| Master station | Ea. | 3175 |
| Intercom outlets | Ea. | 228 |
| Handset | Ea. | 400 |
| Safe, Office type, 1 hour rating | | |
| 30″ x 18″ x 18″ | Ea. | 1900 |
| 60″ x 36″ x 18″, double door | Ea. | 8625 |
| Smoke Detectors | | |
| Ceiling type | Ea. | 300 |
| Duct type | Ea. | 615 |



**Important: See the Reference Section for Location Factors.**

## Model costs calculated for a 1 story building with 14' story height and 30,000 square feet of floor area

# Courthouse, 1 Story

| | | | | Unit | Unit Cost | Cost Per S.F. | % Of Sub-Total |
|---|---|---|---|---|---|---|---|
| **A. SUBSTRUCTURE** | | | | | | | |
| 1010 | Standard Foundations | Poured concrete; strip and spread footings; 4' foundation wall | | S.F. Ground | 5.81 | 5.81 | 6.2% |
| 1020 | Special Foundations | N/A | | – | – | – | |
| 1030 | Slab on Grade | 4" reinforced concrete with vapor barrier and granular base | | S.F. Slab | 7.22 | 7.22 | |
| 2010 | Basement Excavation | Site preparation for slab and trench for foundation wall and footing | | S.F. Ground | .22 | .22 | |
| 2020 | Basement Walls | N/A | | – | – | – | |
| **B. SHELL** | | | | | | | |
| | **B10 Superstructure** | | | | | | |
| 1010 | Floor Construction | Cast-in-place columns | | L.F. Column | 95 | 2.13 | 15.6% |
| 1020 | Roof Construction | Cast-in-place concrete waffle slab | | S.F. Roof | 31.25 | 31.25 | |
| | **B20 Exterior Enclosure** | | | | | | |
| 2010 | Exterior Walls | Limestone panels with concrete block backup | *75% of wall* | S.F. Wall | 76 | 21.70 | 12.3% |
| 2020 | Exterior Windows | Aluminum with insulated glass | *25% of wall* | Each | 839 | 3.50 | |
| 2030 | Exterior Doors | Double wood | | Each | 4600 | 1.08 | |
| | **B30 Roofing** | | | | | | |
| 3010 | Roof Coverings | Built-up tar and gravel with flashing; perlite/EPS composite insulation | | S.F. Roof | 7.97 | 7.97 | 3.8% |
| 3020 | Roof Openings | Roof hatches | | S.F. Roof | .21 | .21 | |
| **C. INTERIORS** | | | | | | | |
| 1010 | Partitions | Plaster on metal studs | *10 S.F. Floor/L.F. Partition* | S.F. Partition | 18.13 | 21.76 | 34.1% |
| 1020 | Interior Doors | Single leaf wood | *100 S.F. Floor/Door* | Each | 1231 | 12.31 | |
| 1030 | Fittings | Toilet partitions | | S.F. Floor | .89 | .89 | |
| 2010 | Stair Construction | N/A | | – | – | – | |
| 3010 | Wall Finishes | 70% paint, 20% wood paneling, 10% vinyl wall covering | | S.F. Surface | 2.88 | 6.91 | |
| 3020 | Floor Finishes | 60% hardwood, 20% carpet, 20% terrazzo | | S.F. Floor | 18.05 | 18.05 | |
| 3030 | Ceiling Finishes | Gypsum plaster on metal lath, suspended | | S.F. Ceiling | 12.97 | 12.97 | |
| **D. SERVICES** | | | | | | | |
| | **D10 Conveying** | | | | | | |
| 1010 | Elevators & Lifts | N/A | | – | – | – | 0.0 % |
| 1020 | Escalators & Moving Walks | N/A | | – | – | – | |
| | **D20 Plumbing** | | | | | | |
| 2010 | Plumbing Fixtures | Toilet and service fixtures, supply and drainage | *1 Fixture/1110 S.F. Floor* | Each | 6627 | 5.97 | 5.4% |
| 2020 | Domestic Water Distribution | Electric hot water heater | | S.F. Floor | 3.79 | 3.79 | |
| 2040 | Rain Water Drainage | Roof drains | | S.F. Roof | 1.68 | 1.68 | |
| | **D30 HVAC** | | | | | | |
| 3010 | Energy Supply | N/A | | – | – | – | 11.6 % |
| 3020 | Heat Generating Systems | Included in D3050 | | – | – | – | |
| 3030 | Cooling Generating Systems | N/A | | – | – | – | |
| 3050 | Terminal & Package Units | Multizone unit, gas heating, electric cooling | | S.F. Floor | 24.70 | 24.70 | |
| 3090 | Other HVAC Sys. & Equipment | N/A | | – | – | – | |
| | **D40 Fire Protection** | | | | | | |
| 4010 | Sprinklers | Wet pipe sprinkler system | | S.F. Floor | 4.46 | 4.46 | 2.5% |
| 4020 | Standpipes | Standpipe, wet, Class III | | S.F. Floor | .80 | .80 | |
| | **D50 Electrical** | | | | | | |
| 5010 | Electrical Service/Distribution | 400 ampere service, panel board and feeders | | S.F. Floor | 1.32 | 1.32 | 8.5% |
| 5020 | Lighting & Branch Wiring | High efficiency fluorescent fixtures, receptacles, switches, A.C. and misc. power | | S.F. Floor | 14.69 | 14.69 | |
| 5030 | Communications & Security | Addressable alarm systems, internet wiring, and emergency lighting | | S.F. Floor | 2.09 | 2.09 | |
| 5090 | Other Electrical Systems | Emergency generator, 11.5 kW | | S.F. Floor | .14 | .14 | |
| **E. EQUIPMENT & FURNISHINGS** | | | | | | | |
| 1010 | Commercial Equipment | N/A | | – | – | – | 0.0 % |
| 1020 | Institutional Equipment | N/A | | – | – | – | |
| 1030 | Vehicular Equipment | N/A | | – | – | – | |
| 1090 | Other Equipment | N/A | | – | – | – | |
| **F. SPECIAL CONSTRUCTION** | | | | | | | |
| 1020 | Integrated Construction | N/A | | – | – | – | 0.0 % |
| 1040 | Special Facilities | N/A | | – | – | – | |
| **G. BUILDING SITEWORK** | | **N/A** | | | | | |
| | | | | | **Sub-Total** | 213.62 | **100%** |
| | CONTRACTOR FEES (General Requirements: 10%, Overhead: 5%, Profit: 10%) | | | | *25%* | 53.39 | |
| | ARCHITECT FEES | | | | *7%* | 18.69 | |
| | | | | | **Total Building Cost** | **285.70** | |

## Costs per square foot of floor area

| Exterior Wall | S.F. Area | 30000 | 40000 | 45000 | 50000 | 60000 | 70000 | 80000 | 90000 | 100000 |
|---|---|---|---|---|---|---|---|---|---|---|
| | L.F. Perimeter | 400 | 466 | 500 | 533 | 600 | 666 | 733 | 800 | 867 |
| Limestone and Concrete Block | Reinforced Concrete | 326.65 | 312.00 | 307.35 | 303.40 | 297.65 | 293.40 | 290.35 | 287.90 | 285.95 |
| | Rigid Steel | 327.45 | 312.80 | 308.10 | 304.10 | 298.40 | 294.15 | 291.10 | 288.65 | 286.75 |
| Face Brick and Concrete Block | Reinforced Concrete | 310.00 | 297.50 | 293.50 | 290.10 | 285.20 | 281.55 | 278.90 | 276.85 | 275.15 |
| | Rigid Steel | 310.80 | 298.25 | 294.25 | 290.80 | **285.90** | 282.30 | 279.70 | 277.55 | 275.95 |
| Stone and Concrete Block | Reinforced Concrete | 316.65 | 303.25 | 299.00 | 295.35 | 290.10 | 286.25 | 283.45 | 281.25 | 279.45 |
| | Rigid Steel | 317.35 | 304.00 | 299.75 | 296.10 | 290.90 | 287.05 | 284.25 | 281.95 | 280.25 |
| Perimeter Adj., Add or Deduct | Per 100 L.F. | 14.80 | 11.05 | 9.80 | 8.85 | 7.35 | 6.30 | 5.55 | 4.95 | 4.50 |
| Story Hgt. Adj., Add or Deduct | Per 1 Ft. | 4.60 | 4.00 | 3.80 | 3.60 | 3.40 | 3.25 | 3.15 | 3.05 | 3.00 |
| ***For Basement**, add $51.55 per square foot of basement area* | | | | | | | | | | |

*The above costs were calculated using the basic specifications shown on the facing page. These costs should be adjusted where necessary for design alternatives and owner's requirements.*

## Common additives

| Description | Unit | $ Cost |
|---|---|---|
| Benches, Hardwood | L.F. | 234 - 520 |
| Clock System | | |
| 20 room | Ea. | 23,000 |
| 50 room | Ea. | 55,000 |
| Closed Circuit Surveillance, One station | | |
| Camera and monitor | Ea. | 1250 |
| For additional camera stations, add | Ea. | 475 |
| Directory Boards, Plastic, glass covered | | |
| 30" x 20" | Ea. | 705 |
| 36" x 48" | Ea. | 1475 |
| Aluminum, 24" x 18" | Ea. | 705 |
| 36" x 24" | Ea. | 985 |
| 48" x 32" | Ea. | 1975 |
| 48" x 60" | Ea. | 2650 |
| Elevators, Hydraulic passenger, 2 stops | | |
| 1500# capacity | Ea. | 86,500 |
| 2500# capacity | Ea. | 90,500 |
| 3500# capacity | Ea. | 96,000 |
| Additional stop, add | Ea. | 9875 |

| Description | Unit | $ Cost |
|---|---|---|
| Emergency Lighting, 25 watt, battery operated | | |
| Lead battery | Ea. | 360 |
| Nickel cadmium | Ea. | 585 |
| Flagpoles, Complete | | |
| Aluminum, 20' high | Ea. | 2050 |
| 40' high | Ea. | 5275 |
| 70' high | Ea. | 14,300 |
| Fiberglass, 23' high | Ea. | 3025 |
| 39'-5" high | Ea. | 3725 |
| 59' high | Ea. | 12,300 |
| Intercom System, 25 station capacity | | |
| Master station | Ea. | 3175 |
| Intercom outlets | Ea. | 228 |
| Handset | Ea. | 400 |
| Safe, Office type, 1 hour rating | | |
| 30" x 18" x 18" | Ea. | 1900 |
| 60" x 36" x 18", double door | Ea. | 8625 |
| Smoke Detectors | | |
| Ceiling type | Ea. | 300 |
| Duct type | Ea. | 615 |



**Important: See the Reference Section for Location Factors.**

# Model costs calculated for a 3 story building with 12′ story height and 60,000 square feet of floor area

# Courthouse, 2-3 Story

| | | | | Unit | Unit Cost | Cost Per S.F. | % Of Sub-Total |
|---|---|---|---|---|---|---|---|
| **A. SUBSTRUCTURE** | | | | | | | |
| 1010 | Standard Foundations | Poured concrete; strip and spread footings; 4′ foundation wall | | S.F. Ground | 6.66 | 2.22 | 2.2% |
| 1020 | Special Foundations | N/A | | — | — | — | |
| 1030 | Slab on Grade | 4″ reinforced concrete with vapor barrier and granular base | | S.F. Slab | 7.22 | 2.41 | |
| 2010 | Basement Excavation | Site preparation for slab and trench for foundation wall and footing | | S.F. Ground | .22 | .07 | |
| 2020 | Basement Walls | N/A | | — | — | — | |
| **B. SHELL** | | | | | | | |
| **B10 Superstructure** | | | | | | | |
| 1010 | Floor Construction | Concrete slab with metal deck and beams | | S.F. Floor | 46.65 | 31.10 | 18.6% |
| 1020 | Roof Construction | Concrete slab with metal deck and beams | | S.F. Roof | 27.21 | 9.07 | |
| **B20 Exterior Enclosure** | | | | | | | |
| 2010 | Exterior Walls | Face brick with concrete block backup | *75% of wall* | S.F. Wall | 44.37 | 11.98 | 10.0% |
| 2020 | Exterior Windows | Horizontal pivoted steel | *25% of wall* | Each | 906 | 9.06 | |
| 2030 | Exterior Doors | Double aluminum and glass and hollow metal | | Each | 5875 | .60 | |
| **B30 Roofing** | | | | | | | |
| 3010 | Roof Coverings | Built-up tar and gravel with flashing; perlite/EPS composite insulation | | S.F. Roof | 8.49 | 2.83 | 1.3% |
| 3020 | Roof Openings | N/A | | — | — | — | |
| **C. INTERIORS** | | | | | | | |
| 1010 | Partitions | Plaster on metal studs | *10 S.F. Floor/L.F. Partition* | S.F. Partition | 18.33 | 18.33 | 32.3% |
| 1020 | Interior Doors | Single leaf wood | *100 S.F. Floor/Door* | Each | 1231 | 12.31 | |
| 1030 | Fittings | Toilet partitions | | S.F. Floor | .44 | .44 | |
| 2010 | Stair Construction | Concrete filled metal pan | | Flight | 22,275 | 1.86 | |
| 3010 | Wall Finishes | 70% paint, 20% wood paneling, 10% vinyl wall covering | | S.F. Surface | 2.89 | 5.77 | |
| 3020 | Floor Finishes | 60% hardwood, 20% terrazzo, 20% carpet | | S.F. Floor | 18.05 | 18.05 | |
| 3030 | Ceiling Finishes | Gypsum plaster on metal lath, suspended | | S.F. Ceiling | 12.97 | 12.97 | |
| **D. SERVICES** | | | | | | | |
| **D10 Conveying** | | | | | | | |
| 1010 | Elevators & Lifts | Five hydraulic passenger elevators | | Each | 169,920 | 14.16 | 6.6% |
| 1020 | Escalators & Moving Walks | N/A | | — | — | — | |
| **D20 Plumbing** | | | | | | | |
| 2010 | Plumbing Fixtures | Toilet and service fixtures, supply and drainage | *1 Fixture/665 S.F. Floor* | Each | 4715 | 7.09 | 6.6% |
| 2020 | Domestic Water Distribution | Electric water heater | | S.F. Floor | 6.21 | 6.21 | |
| 2040 | Rain Water Drainage | Roof drains | | S.F. Roof | 3.03 | 1.01 | |
| **D30 HVAC** | | | | | | | |
| 3010 | Energy Supply | N/A | | — | — | — | 11.4 % |
| 3020 | Heat Generating Systems | Included in D3050 | | — | — | — | |
| 3030 | Cooling Generating Systems | N/A | | — | — | — | |
| 3050 | Terminal & Package Units | Multizone unit, gas heating, electric cooling | | S.F. Floor | 24.70 | 24.70 | |
| 3090 | Other HVAC Sys. & Equipment | N/A | | — | — | — | |
| **D40 Fire Protection** | | | | | | | |
| 4010 | Sprinklers | Wet pipe sprinkler system | | S.F. Floor | 4.49 | 4.49 | 2.4% |
| 4020 | Standpipes | Standpipe, wet, Class III | | S.F. Floor | .74 | .74 | |
| **D50 Electrical** | | | | | | | |
| 5010 | Electrical Service/Distribution | 800 ampere service, panel board and feeders | | S.F. Floor | 1.39 | 1.39 | 8.5% |
| 5020 | Lighting & Branch Wiring | High efficiency fluorescent fixtures, receptacles, switches, A.C. and misc. power | | S.F. Floor | 14.84 | 14.84 | |
| 5030 | Communications & Security | Addressable alarm systems, internet wiring, and emergency lighting | | S.F. Floor | 1.90 | 1.90 | |
| 5090 | Other Electrical Systems | Emergency generator, 15 kW | | S.F. Floor | .20 | .20 | |
| **E. EQUIPMENT & FURNISHINGS** | | | | | | | |
| 1010 | Commercial Equipment | N/A | | — | — | — | 0.0 % |
| 1020 | Institutional Equipment | N/A | | — | — | — | |
| 1030 | Vehicular Equipment | N/A | | — | — | — | |
| 1090 | Other Equipment | N/A | | — | — | — | |
| **F. SPECIAL CONSTRUCTION** | | | | | | | |
| 1020 | Integrated Construction | N/A | | — | — | — | 0.0 % |
| 1040 | Special Facilities | N/A | | — | — | — | |
| **G. BUILDING SITEWORK** | **N/A** | | | | | | |
| | | | | | **Sub-Total** | 215.80 | **100%** |
| | CONTRACTOR FEES (General Requirements: 10%, Overhead: 5%, Profit: 10%) | | | | *25%* | 53.91 | |
| | ARCHITECT FEES | | | | *6%* | 16.19 | |
| | | | | | **Total Building Cost** | **285.90** | |

## Costs per square foot of floor area

| Exterior Wall | S.F. Area | 2000 | 5000 | 7000 | 10000 | 12000 | 15000 | 18000 | 21000 | 25000 |
|---|---|---|---|---|---|---|---|---|---|---|
| | L.F. Perimeter | 200 | 310 | 360 | 440 | 480 | 520 | 560 | 600 | 660 |
| Tilt-up Concrete Panels | Steel Joists | 293.10 | 254.25 | 244.40 | 237.45 | 233.85 | 229.35 | 226.40 | 224.30 | 222.40 |
| Decorative Concrete Block | Bearing Walls | 299.45 | 257.10 | 246.25 | 238.55 | 234.65 | 229.65 | 226.35 | 224.00 | 221.95 |
| Face Brick and Concrete Block | Steel Joists | 343.10 | 284.70 | 269.70 | 259.05 | 253.55 | 246.55 | 241.95 | 238.60 | 235.70 |
| Stucco and Concrete Block | Wood Truss | 290.65 | 255.60 | 246.45 | 240.00 | 236.65 | 232.35 | 229.50 | 227.50 | 225.75 |
| Brick Veneer | Wood Frame | 308.60 | 267.65 | 256.90 | **249.30** | 245.30 | 240.20 | 236.80 | 234.40 | 232.20 |
| Wood Clapboard | Wood Frame | 288.95 | 255.45 | 246.80 | 240.65 | 237.50 | 233.40 | 230.65 | 228.80 | 227.05 |
| Perimeter Adj., Add or Deduct | Per 100 L.F. | 36.30 | 14.50 | 10.40 | 7.20 | 6.10 | 4.85 | 4.05 | 3.45 | 2.90 |
| Story Hgt. Adj., Add or Deduct | Per 1 Ft. | 3.55 | 2.15 | 1.85 | 1.55 | 1.40 | 1.25 | 1.10 | 1.00 | 0.95 |
| ***For Basement**, add $50.15 per square foot of basement area* | | | | | | | | | | |

*The above costs were calculated using the basic specifications shown on the facing page. These costs should be adjusted where necessary for design alternatives and owner's requirements.*

## Common additives

| Description | Unit | $ Cost |
|---|---|---|
| Emergency Lighting, 25 watt, battery operated | | |
| Lead battery | Ea. | 360 |
| Nickel cadmium | Ea. | 585 |
| Flagpoles, Complete | | |
| Aluminum, 20′ high | Ea. | 2050 |
| 40′ high | Ea. | 5275 |
| 70′ high | Ea. | 14,300 |
| Fiberglass, 23′ high | Ea. | 3025 |
| 39′-5″ high | Ea. | 3725 |
| 59′ high | Ea. | 12,300 |
| Gym Floor, Incl. sleepers and finish, maple | S.F. | 23 |
| Intercom System, 25 Station capacity | | |
| Master station | Ea. | 3175 |
| Intercom outlets | Ea. | 228 |
| Handset | Ea. | 400 |

| Description | Unit | $ Cost |
|---|---|---|
| Lockers, Steel, single tier, 60″ to 72″ | Opng. | 285 - 520 |
| 2 tier, 60″ to 72″ total | Opng. | 216 - 265 |
| 5 tier, box lockers | Opng. | 465 - 153 |
| Locker bench, lam. maple top only | L.F. | 148 |
| Pedestals, steel pipe | Ea. | 87 |
| Smoke Detectors | | |
| Ceiling type | Ea. | 300 |
| Duct type | Ea. | 615 |
| Sound System | | |
| Amplifier, 250 watts | Ea. | 2425 |
| Speaker, ceiling or wall | Ea. | 320 |
| Trumpet | Ea. | 580 |

# Model costs calculated for a 1 story building with 12′ story height and 10,000 square feet of floor area

# Day Care Center

| | | | | Unit | Unit Cost | Cost Per S.F. | % Of Sub-Total |
|---|---|---|---|---|---|---|---|
| **A. SUBSTRUCTURE** | | | | | | | |
| 1010 | Standard Foundations | Poured concrete; strip and spread footings; 4′ foundation wall | | S.F. Ground | 7.82 | 7.82 | 8.0% |
| 1020 | Special Foundations | N/A | | — | — | — | |
| 1030 | Slab on Grade | 4″ concrete with vapor barrier and granular base | | S.F. Slab | 6.49 | 6.49 | |
| 2010 | Basement Excavation | Site preparation for slab and trench for foundation wall and footing | | S.F. Ground | .38 | .38 | |
| 2020 | Basement Walls | N/A | | — | — | — | |
| **B. SHELL** | | | | | | | |
| | **B10 Superstructure** | | | | | | |
| 1010 | Floor Construction | Wood beams on columns | | S.F. Floor | .42 | .42 | 7.6% |
| 1020 | Roof Construction | Wood trusses | | S.F. Roof | 13.43 | 13.43 | |
| | **B20 Exterior Enclosure** | | | | | | |
| 2010 | Exterior Walls | Brick veneer on wood studs | *85% of wall* | S.F. Wall | 33.44 | 15.01 | 15.7% |
| 2020 | Exterior Windows | Window wall | *15% of wall* | Each | 65 | 5.13 | |
| 2030 | Exterior Doors | Aluminum and glass; steel | | Each | 4505 | 8.56 | |
| | **B30 Roofing** | | | | | | |
| 3010 | Roof Coverings | Asphalt shingles, 9″ fiberglass batt insulation, gutters and downspouts | | S.F. Roof | 6.84 | 6.84 | 3.7% |
| 3020 | Roof Openings | N/A | | — | — | — | |
| **C. INTERIORS** | | | | | | | |
| 1010 | Partitions | Gypsum board on wood studs | *8 S.F. Floor/S.F. Partition* | S.F. Partition | 11.12 | 7.41 | 14.6% |
| 1020 | Interior Doors | Single leaf hollow metal | *700 S.F. Floor/Door* | Each | 1159 | 3.09 | |
| 1030 | Fittings | Toilet partitions | | S.F. Floor | .80 | .80 | |
| 2010 | Stair Construction | N/A | | — | — | — | |
| 3010 | Wall Finishes | Paint | | S.F. Surface | 1.86 | 2.48 | |
| 3020 | Floor Finishes | 5% quarry tile, 95% vinyl composition tile | | S.F. Floor | 3.51 | 3.51 | |
| 3030 | Ceiling Finishes | Fiberglass tile on tee grid | | S.F. Ceiling | 9.48 | 9.48 | |
| **D. SERVICES** | | | | | | | |
| | **D10 Conveying** | | | | | | |
| 1010 | Elevators & Lifts | N/A | | — | — | — | 0.0 % |
| 1020 | Escalators & Moving Walks | N/A | | — | — | — | |
| | **D20 Plumbing** | | | | | | |
| 2010 | Plumbing Fixtures | Toilet and service fixtures, supply and drainage | *1 Fixture/455 S.F. Floor* | Each | 4799 | 26.96 | 16.6% |
| 2020 | Domestic Water Distribution | Electric water heater | | S.F. Floor | 3.38 | 3.38 | |
| 2040 | Rain Water Drainage | N/A | | — | — | — | |
| | **D30 HVAC** | | | | | | |
| 3010 | Energy Supply | Oil fired hot water, wall fin radiation | | S.F. Floor | 15.68 | 15.68 | 17.5% |
| 3020 | Heat Generating Systems | N/A | | — | — | — | |
| 3030 | Cooling Generating Systems | N/A | | — | — | — | |
| 3050 | Terminal & Package Units | Split systems with air cooled condensing units | | S.F. Floor | 16.40 | 16.40 | |
| 3090 | Other HVAC Sys. & Equipment | N/A | | — | — | — | |
| | **D40 Fire Protection** | | | | | | |
| 4010 | Sprinklers | Sprinkler, light hazard | | S.F. Floor | 5.07 | 5.07 | 3.6% |
| 4020 | Standpipes | Standpipe | | S.F. Floor | 1.48 | 1.48 | |
| | **D50 Electrical** | | | | | | |
| 5010 | Electrical Service/Distribution | 200 ampere service, panel board and feeders | | S.F. Floor | 1.41 | 1.41 | 8.3% |
| 5020 | Lighting & Branch Wiring | High efficiency fluorescent fixtures, receptacles, switches, A.C. and misc. power | | S.F. Floor | 12.14 | 12.14 | |
| 5030 | Communications & Security | Addressable alarm systems and emergency lighting | | S.F. Floor | 1.53 | 1.53 | |
| 5090 | Other Electrical Systems | Emergency generator, 15 kW | | S.F. Floor | .09 | .09 | |
| **E. EQUIPMENT & FURNISHINGS** | | | | | | | |
| 1010 | Commercial Equipment | N/A | | — | — | — | 4.4 % |
| 1020 | Institutional Equipment | Cabinets and countertop | | S.F. Floor | 7.97 | 7.97 | |
| 1030 | Vehicular Equipment | N/A | | — | — | — | |
| 1090 | Other Equipment | N/A | | — | — | — | |
| **F. SPECIAL CONSTRUCTION** | | | | | | | |
| 1020 | Integrated Construction | N/A | | — | — | — | 0.0 % |
| 1040 | Special Facilities | N/A | | — | — | — | |
| **G. BUILDING SITEWORK** | **N/A** | | | | | | |
| | | | | | **Sub-Total** | 182.96 | **100%** |
| | CONTRACTOR FEES (General Requirements: 10%, Overhead: 5%, Profit: 10%) | | | | *25%* | 45.76 | |
| | ARCHITECT FEES | | | | *9%* | 20.58 | |
| | | | | | **Total Building Cost** | **249.30** | |

# Factory, 1 Story

## Costs per square foot of floor area

| Exterior Wall | S.F. Area | 12000 | 18000 | 24000 | 30000 | 36000 | 42000 | 48000 | 54000 | 60000 |
|---|---|---|---|---|---|---|---|---|---|---|
| | L.F. Perimeter | 460 | 580 | 713 | 730 | 826 | 880 | 965 | 1006 | 1045 |
| Concrete Block | Rigid Steel | 196.05 | 184.95 | 180.10 | 172.65 | 170.30 | 167.40 | 166.00 | 163.95 | 162.30 |
| | Bearing Walls | 193.05 | 181.95 | 177.15 | 169.60 | 167.30 | 164.35 | 163.00 | 160.95 | 159.25 |
| Precast Concrete | Rigid Steel | 209.25 | 196.05 | 190.35 | 181.05 | 178.25 | 174.60 | 172.90 | 170.40 | 168.30 |
| Metal Panel | Rigid Steel | 198.40 | 186.95 | 181.95 | 174.15 | 171.75 | 168.65 | 167.25 | 165.10 | 163.40 |
| Face Brick and Common Brick | Rigid Steel | 222.25 | 206.95 | 200.35 | 189.20 | 186.00 | 181.65 | 179.70 | 176.70 | 174.20 |
| Tilt-up Concrete Panels | Rigid Steel | 199.40 | 187.80 | 182.70 | 174.75 | 172.35 | 169.20 | 167.75 | 165.60 | 163.85 |
| Perimeter Adj., Add or Deduct | Per 100 L.F. | 9.60 | 6.45 | 4.80 | 3.85 | 3.20 | 2.75 | 2.45 | 2.15 | 1.90 |
| Story Hgt. Adj., Add or Deduct | Per 1 Ft. | 1.50 | 1.35 | 1.20 | 1.00 | 0.95 | 0.80 | 0.80 | 0.80 | 0.75 |
| ***For Basement**, add $51.10 per square foot of basement area* | | | | | | | | | | |

*The above costs were calculated using the basic specifications shown on the facing page. These costs should be adjusted where necessary for design alternatives and owner's requirements.*

## Common additives

| Description | Unit | $ Cost |
|---|---|---|
| Clock System | | |
| 20 room | Ea. | 23,000 |
| 50 room | Ea. | 55,000 |
| Dock Bumpers, Rubber blocks | | |
| 4-1/2" thick, 10" high, 14" long | Ea. | 90.50 |
| 24" long | Ea. | 131 |
| 36" long | Ea. | 525 |
| 12" high, 14" long | Ea. | 106 |
| 24" long | Ea. | 106 |
| 36" long | Ea. | 237 |
| 6" thick, 10" high, 14" long | Ea. | 115 |
| 24" long | Ea. | 169 |
| 36" long | Ea. | 245 |
| 20" high, 11" long | Ea. | 184 |
| Dock Boards, Heavy | | |
| 60" x 60" Aluminum, 5,000# cap. | Ea. | 1525 |
| 9000# cap. | Ea. | 2000 |
| 15,000# cap. | Ea. | 2125 |

| Description | Unit | $ Cost |
|---|---|---|
| Dock Levelers, Hinged 10 ton cap. | | |
| 6' x 8' | Ea. | 8025 |
| 7' x 8' | Ea. | 9675 |
| Partitions, Woven wire, 10 ga., 1-1/2" mesh | | |
| 4' wide x 7' high | Ea. | 320 |
| 8' high | Ea. | 273 |
| 10' High | Ea. | 300 |
| Platform Lifter, Portable, 6'x 6' | | |
| 3000# cap. | Ea. | 9975 |
| 4000# cap. | Ea. | 7000 |
| Fixed, 6' x 8', 5000# cap. | Ea. | 14,900 |



**Important: See the Reference Section for Location Factors.**

## Model costs calculated for a 1 story building with 20′ story height and 30,000 square feet of floor area

# Factory, 1 Story

| | | | | Unit | Unit Cost | Cost Per S.F. | % Of Sub-Total |
|---|---|---|---|---|---|---|---|
| **A. SUBSTRUCTURE** | | | | | | | |
| 1010 | Standard Foundations | Poured concrete; strip and spread footings; 4′ foundation wall | | S.F. Ground | 5.34 | 5.34 | |
| 1020 | Special Foundations | N/A | | — | — | — | |
| 1030 | Slab on Grade | 4″ reinforced concrete with vapor barrier and granular base | | S.F. Slab | 9.63 | 9.63 | 11.8% |
| 2010 | Basement Excavation | Site preparation for slab and trench for foundation wall and footing | | S.F. Ground | .22 | .22 | |
| 2020 | Basement Walls | N/A | | — | — | — | |
| **B. SHELL** | | | | | | | |
| **B10 Superstructure** | | | | | | | |
| 1010 | Floor Construction | N/A | | — | — | — | 10.9 % |
| 1020 | Roof Construction | Metal deck, open web steel joists, beams and columns | | S.F. Roof | 14.09 | 14.09 | |
| **B20 Exterior Enclosure** | | | | | | | |
| 2010 | Exterior Walls | Concrete block | *75% of wall* | S.F. Wall | 10.44 | 3.81 | |
| 2020 | Exterior Windows | Industrial horizontal pivoted steel | *25% of wall* | Each | 2490 | 9.47 | 11.9% |
| 2030 | Exterior Doors | Double aluminum and glass, hollow metal, steel overhead | | Each | 4130 | 2.06 | |
| **B30 Roofing** | | | | | | | |
| 3010 | Roof Coverings | Built-up tar and gravel with flashing; perlite/EPS composite insulation | | S.F. Roof | 8.09 | 8.09 | 6.9% |
| 3020 | Roof Openings | Roof hatches | | S.F. Roof | .80 | .80 | |
| **C. INTERIORS** | | | | | | | |
| 1010 | Partitions | Concrete block | *60 S.F. Floor/L.F. Partition* | S.F. Partition | 10.55 | 2.11 | |
| 1020 | Interior Doors | Single leaf hollow metal and fire doors | *600 S.F. Floor/Door* | Each | 1159 | 1.94 | |
| 1030 | Fittings | Toilet partitions | | S.F. Floor | 1.76 | 1.76 | |
| 2010 | Stair Construction | N/A | | — | — | — | 7.1% |
| 3010 | Wall Finishes | Paint | | S.F. Surface | 5.58 | 2.23 | |
| 3020 | Floor Finishes | Vinyl composition tile | *10%of floor* | S.F. Floor | 2.60 | .26 | |
| 3030 | Ceiling Finishes | Fiberglass board on exposed grid system | *10% of area* | S.F. Ceiling | 9 | .91 | |
| **D. SERVICES** | | | | | | | |
| **D10 Conveying** | | | | | | | |
| 1010 | Elevators & Lifts | N/A | | — | — | — | 0.0 % |
| 1020 | Escalators & Moving Walks | N/A | | — | — | — | |
| **D20 Plumbing** | | | | | | | |
| 2010 | Plumbing Fixtures | Toilet and service fixtures, supply and drainage | *1 Fixture/1000 S.F. Floor* | Each | 7460 | 7.46 | |
| 2020 | Domestic Water Distribution | Gas fired water heater | | S.F. Floor | .57 | .57 | 7.3% |
| 2040 | Rain Water Drainage | Roof drains | | S.F. Roof | 1.43 | 1.43 | |
| **D30 HVAC** | | | | | | | |
| 3010 | Energy Supply | Oil fired hot water, unit heaters | | S.F. Floor | 14.25 | 14.25 | |
| 3020 | Heat Generating Systems | N/A | | — | — | — | |
| 3030 | Cooling Generating Systems | Chilled water, air cooled condenser system | | S.F. Floor | 13.51 | 13.51 | 21.5% |
| 3050 | Terminal & Package Units | N/A | | — | — | — | |
| 3090 | Other HVAC Sys. & Equipment | N/A | | — | — | — | |
| **D40 Fire Protection** | | | | | | | |
| 4010 | Sprinklers | Sprinklers, ordinary hazard | | S.F. Floor | 6.26 | 6.26 | 5.6% |
| 4020 | Standpipes | Standpipe, wet, Class III | | S.F. Floor | 1.02 | 1.02 | |
| **D50 Electrical** | | | | | | | |
| 5010 | Electrical Service/Distribution | 600 ampere service, panel board and feeders | | S.F. Floor | 1.44 | 1.44 | |
| 5020 | Lighting & Branch Wiring | High intensity discharge fixtures, receptacles, switches, A.C. and misc. power | | S.F. Floor | 17.98 | 17.98 | 16.5% |
| 5030 | Communications & Security | Addressable alarm systems and emergency lighting | | S.F. Floor | 1.83 | 1.83 | |
| 5090 | Other Electrical Systems | N/A | | — | — | — | |
| **E. EQUIPMENT & FURNISHINGS** | | | | | | | |
| 1010 | Commercial Equipment | N/A | | — | — | — | |
| 1020 | Institutional Equipment | N/A | | — | — | — | 0.5 % |
| 1030 | Vehicular Equipment | Dock shelters | | S.F. Floor | .61 | .61 | |
| 1090 | Other Equipment | N/A | | — | — | — | |
| **F. SPECIAL CONSTRUCTION** | | | | | | | |
| 1020 | Integrated Construction | N/A | | — | — | — | 0.0 % |
| 1040 | Special Facilities | N/A | | — | — | — | |
| **G. BUILDING SITEWORK** | | **N/A** | | | | | |
| | | | | | **Sub-Total** | 129.08 | **100%** |
| | CONTRACTOR FEES (General Requirements: 10%, Overhead: 5%, Profit: 10%) | | | | *25%* | 32.28 | |
| | ARCHITECT FEES | | | | *7%* | 11.29 | |
| | | | | | **Total Building Cost** | **172.65** | |

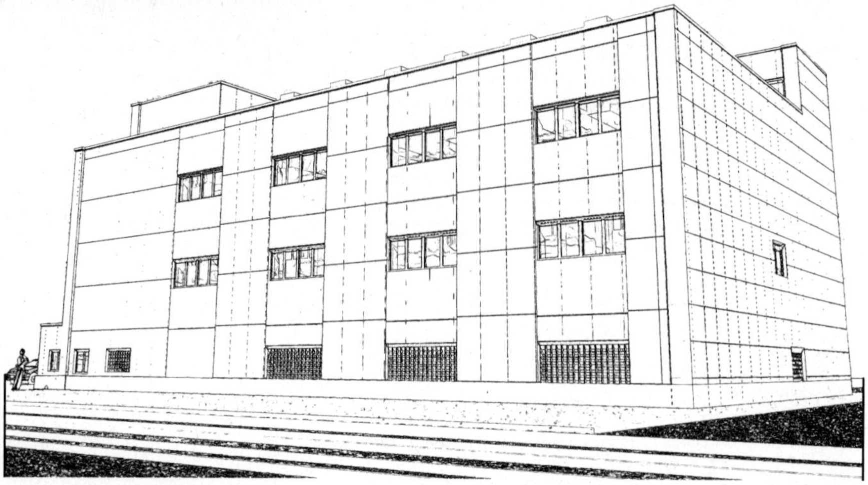

## Costs per square foot of floor area

| Exterior Wall | S.F. Area | 20000 | 30000 | 40000 | 50000 | 60000 | 70000 | 80000 | 90000 | 100000 |
|---|---|---|---|---|---|---|---|---|---|---|
| | L.F. Perimeter | 625 | 750 | 850 | 950 | 1015 | 1095 | 1150 | 1275 | 1300 |
| Face Brick and Common Brick | Rigid Steel | 263.10 | 239.10 | 225.00 | 216.55 | 209.05 | 204.45 | 199.90 | 198.90 | 194.90 |
| | Reinforced Concrete | 251.15 | 227.05 | 213.05 | 204.55 | 197.10 | 192.50 | 187.95 | 186.90 | 182.90 |
| Face Brick and Concrete Block | Rigid Steel | 259.10 | 235.90 | 222.25 | 214.10 | 206.90 | 202.45 | 198.10 | 197.10 | 193.25 |
| | Reinforced Concrete | 247.15 | 223.90 | 210.30 | 202.15 | 194.95 | 190.50 | 186.10 | 185.15 | 181.30 |
| Stucco and Concrete Block | Rigid Steel | 235.75 | 217.15 | 206.40 | 199.95 | 194.25 | 190.75 | 187.35 | 186.50 | 183.50 |
| | Reinforced Concrete | 223.80 | 205.20 | 194.45 | 187.95 | 182.30 | 178.80 | 175.40 | 174.55 | 171.55 |
| Perimeter Adj., Add or Deduct | Per 100 L.F. | 16.00 | 10.65 | 8.05 | 6.45 | 5.40 | 4.55 | 4.05 | 3.60 | 3.20 |
| Story Hgt. Adj., Add or Deduct | Per 1 Ft. | 7.60 | 6.05 | 5.15 | 4.60 | 4.15 | 3.80 | 3.50 | 3.45 | 3.15 |

***For Basement**, add $ 55.70 per square foot of basement area*

*The above costs were calculated using the basic specifications shown on the facing page. These costs should be adjusted where necessary for design alternatives and owner's requirements.*

## Common additives

| Description | Unit | $ Cost |
|---|---|---|
| Clock System | | |
| 20 room | Ea. | 23,000 |
| 50 room | Ea. | 55,000 |
| Dock Bumpers, Rubber blocks | | |
| 4-1/2" thick, 10" high, 14" long | Ea. | 90.50 |
| 24" long | Ea. | 131 |
| 36" long | Ea. | 525 |
| 12" high, 14" long | Ea. | 106 |
| 24" long | Ea. | 106 |
| 36" long | Ea. | 237 |
| 6" thick, 10" high, 14" long | Ea. | 115 |
| 24" long | Ea. | 169 |
| 36" long | Ea. | 245 |
| 20" high, 11" long | Ea. | 184 |
| Dock Boards, Heavy | | |
| 60" x 60" Aluminum, 5,000# cap. | Ea. | 1525 |
| 9000# cap. | Ea. | 2000 |
| 15,000# cap. | Ea. | 2125 |

| Description | Unit | $ Cost |
|---|---|---|
| Dock Levelers, Hinged 10 ton cap. | | |
| 6'x 8' | Ea. | 8025 |
| 7'x 8' | Ea. | 9675 |
| Elevator, Hydraulic freight, 2 stops | | |
| 3500# capacity | Ea. | 176,400 |
| 4000# capacity | Ea. | 182,900 |
| Additional stop, add | Ea. | 11,600 |
| Partitions, Woven wire, 10 ga., 1-1/2" mesh | | |
| 4' Wide x 7" high | Ea. | 320 |
| 8' High | Ea. | 273 |
| 10' High | Ea. | 300 |
| Platform Lifter, Portable, 6'x 6' | | |
| 3000# cap. | Ea. | 9975 |
| 4000# cap. | Ea. | 7000 |
| Fixed, 6'x 8', 5000# cap. | Ea. | 14,900 |



**Important: See the Reference Section for Location Factors.**

## Model costs calculated for a 3 story building with 12′ story height and 90,000 square feet of floor area

# Factory, 3 Story

| | | | | Unit | Unit Cost | Cost Per S.F. | % Of Sub-Total |
|---|---|---|---|---|---|---|---|
| **A. SUBSTRUCTURE** | | | | | | | |
| 1010 | Standard Foundations | Poured concrete; strip and spread footings; 4′ foundation wall | | S.F. Ground | 7.77 | 2.59 | |
| 1020 | Special Foundations | N/A | | — | — | — | |
| 1030 | Slab on Grade | 4″ reinforced concrete with vapor barrier and granular base | | S.F. Slab | 14.35 | 4.78 | 5.3% |
| 2010 | Basement Excavation | Site preparation for slab and trench for foundation wall and footing | | S.F. Ground | .22 | .07 | |
| 2020 | Basement Walls | N/A | | — | — | — | |
| **B. SHELL** | | | | | | | |
| | **B10 Superstructure** | | | | | | |
| 1010 | Floor Construction | Concrete flat slab | | S.F. Floor | 30.20 | 20.13 | 19.5% |
| 1020 | Roof Construction | Concrete flat slab | | S.F. Roof | 22.11 | 7.37 | |
| | **B20 Exterior Enclosure** | | | | | | |
| 2010 | Exterior Walls | Face brick with common brick backup | *70% of wall* | S.F. Wall | 44.45 | 15.87 | |
| 2020 | Exterior Windows | Industrial, horizontal pivoted steel | *30% of wall* | Each | 1605 | 15.35 | 22.7% |
| 2030 | Exterior Doors | Double aluminum & glass, hollow metal, overhead doors | | Each | 4047 | .77 | |
| | **B30 Roofing** | | | | | | |
| 3010 | Roof Coverings | Built-up tar and gravel with flashing; perlite/EPS composite insulation | | S.F. Roof | 8.73 | 2.91 | 2.3% |
| 3020 | Roof Openings | Roof hatches | | S.F. Roof | .81 | .27 | |
| **C. INTERIORS** | | | | | | | |
| 1010 | Partitions | Gypsum board on metal studs | *50 S.F. Floor/L.F. Partition* | S.F. Partition | 5.65 | 1.13 | |
| 1020 | Interior Doors | Single leaf fire doors | *500 S.F. Floor/Door* | Each | 2060 | 4.12 | |
| 1030 | Fittings | Toilet partitions | | S.F. Floor | .89 | .89 | |
| 2010 | Stair Construction | Concrete | | Flight | 10,225 | .46 | 9.2% |
| 3010 | Wall Finishes | Paint | | S.F. Surface | .98 | .39 | |
| 3020 | Floor Finishes | 90% metallic hardener, 10% vinyl composition tile | | S.F. Floor | 5.04 | 5.04 | |
| 3030 | Ceiling Finishes | Fiberglass board on exposed grid systems | *10% of area* | S.F. Ceiling | 9.48 | .95 | |
| **D. SERVICES** | | | | | | | |
| | **D10 Conveying** | | | | | | |
| 1010 | Elevators & Lifts | Two hydraulic freight elevators | | Each | 252,000 | 5.60 | 4.0% |
| 1020 | Escalators & Moving Walks | N/A | | — | — | — | |
| | **D20 Plumbing** | | | | | | |
| 2010 | Plumbing Fixtures | Toilet and service fixtures, supply and drainage | *1 Fixture/1345 S.F. Floor* | Each | 11,903 | 8.85 | |
| 2020 | Domestic Water Distribution | Gas fired water heater | | S.F. Floor | .35 | .35 | 7.0% |
| 2040 | Rain Water Drainage | Roof drains | | S.F. Roof | 1.89 | .63 | |
| | **D30 HVAC** | | | | | | |
| 3010 | Energy Supply | Oil fired hot water, unit heaters | | S.F. Floor | 6.93 | 6.93 | |
| 3020 | Heat Generating Systems | N/A | | — | — | — | |
| 3030 | Cooling Generating Systems | Chilled water, air cooled condenser system | | S.F. Floor | 13.51 | 13.51 | 14.5% |
| 3050 | Terminal & Package Units | N/A | | — | — | — | |
| 3090 | Other HVAC Sys. & Equipment | N/A | | — | — | — | |
| | **D40 Fire Protection** | | | | | | |
| 4010 | Sprinklers | Wet pipe sprinkler system | | S.F. Floor | 5.46 | 5.46 | 4.6% |
| 4020 | Standpipes | Standpipe, wet, Class III | | S.F. Floor | .98 | .98 | |
| | **D50 Electrical** | | | | | | |
| 5010 | Electrical Service/Distribution | 800 ampere service, panel board and feeders | | S.F. Floor | .91 | .91 | |
| 5020 | Lighting & Branch Wiring | High intensity discharge fixtures, switches, A.C. and misc. power | | S.F. Floor | 12.85 | 12.85 | 11.0% |
| 5030 | Communications & Security | Addressable alarm systems and emergency lighting | | S.F. Floor | 1.50 | 1.50 | |
| 5090 | Other Electrical Systems | Emergency generator, 30 kW | | S.F. Floor | .22 | .22 | |
| **E. EQUIPMENT & FURNISHINGS** | | | | | | | |
| 1010 | Commercial Equipment | N/A | | — | — | — | |
| 1020 | Institutional Equipment | N/A | | — | — | — | 0.1 % |
| 1030 | Vehicular Equipment | Dock Shelters | | S.F. Floor | .20 | .20 | |
| 1090 | Other Equipment | N/A | | — | — | — | |
| **F. SPECIAL CONSTRUCTION** | | | | | | | |
| 1020 | Integrated Construction | N/A | | — | — | — | 0.0 % |
| 1040 | Special Facilities | N/A | | — | — | — | |
| **G. BUILDING SITEWORK** | **N/A** | | | | | | |
| | | | | | **Sub-Total** | 141.08 | **100%** |
| | CONTRACTOR FEES (General Requirements: 10%, Overhead: 5%, Profit: 10%) | | | | *25%* | 35.24 | |
| | ARCHITECT FEES | | | | *6%* | 10.58 | |
| | | | | | **Total Building Cost** | **186.90** | |

For customer support on your Square Foot Costs with RSMeans data, call 800.448.8182.

# M.220 Fire Station, 1 Story

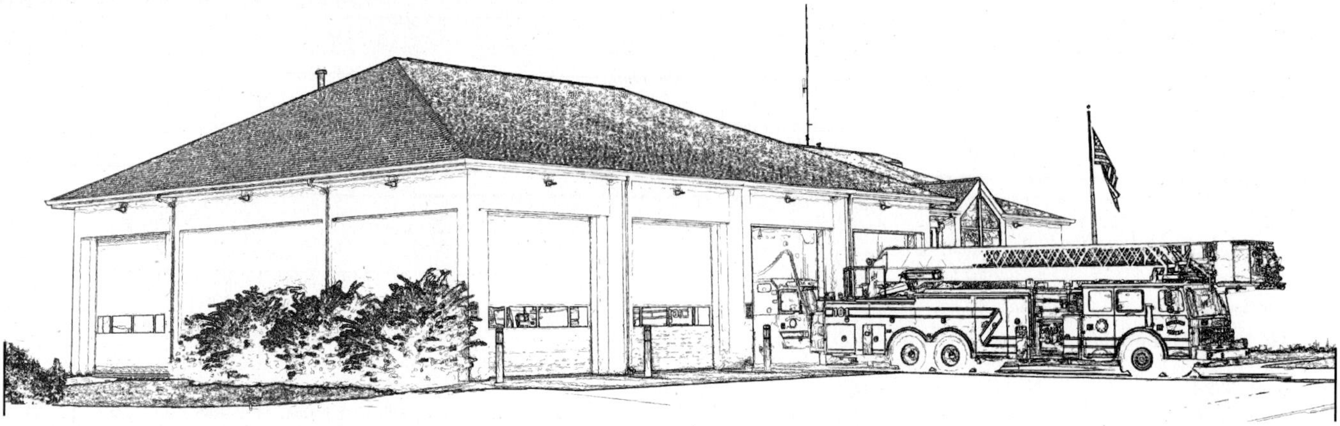

## Costs per square foot of floor area

| Exterior Wall | S.F. Area | 4000 | 4500 | 5000 | 5500 | 6000 | 6500 | 7000 | 7500 | 8000 |
|---|---|---|---|---|---|---|---|---|---|---|
| | L.F. Perimeter | 260 | 280 | 300 | 310 | 320 | 336 | 353 | 370 | 386 |
| Face Brick and Concrete Block | Steel Joists | 246.45 | 241.75 | 238.00 | 232.75 | **228.45** | 225.85 | 223.75 | 222.05 | 220.25 |
| | Bearing Walls | 241.40 | 236.70 | 233.00 | 227.75 | 223.45 | 220.85 | 218.75 | 217.00 | 215.25 |
| Decorative Concrete Block | Steel Joists | 228.90 | 224.95 | 221.80 | 217.55 | 214.05 | 211.85 | 210.15 | 208.70 | 207.25 |
| | Bearing Walls | 223.90 | 219.95 | 216.80 | 212.55 | 208.95 | 206.85 | 205.15 | 203.70 | 202.20 |
| Limestone and Concrete Block | Steel Joists | 265.20 | 259.70 | 255.30 | 249.00 | 243.80 | 240.75 | 238.35 | 236.25 | 234.20 |
| | Bearing Walls | 260.20 | 254.70 | 250.30 | 244.00 | 238.80 | 235.70 | 233.30 | 231.25 | 229.15 |
| Perimeter Adj., Add or Deduct | Per 100 L.F. | 28.95 | 25.70 | 23.15 | 21.10 | 19.30 | 17.80 | 16.55 | 15.40 | 14.50 |
| Story Hgt. Adj., Add or Deduct | Per 1 Ft. | 3.95 | 3.75 | 3.60 | 3.40 | 3.20 | 3.10 | 3.05 | 2.95 | 2.95 |
| ***For Basement**, add $62.45 per square foot of basement area* | | | | | | | | | | |

*The above costs were calculated using the basic specifications shown on the facing page. These costs should be adjusted where necessary for design alternatives and owner's requirements.*

## Common additives

| Description | Unit | $ Cost |
|---|---|---|
| Appliances | | |
| Cooking range, 30" free standing | | |
| 1 oven | Ea. | 885 - 1300 |
| 2 oven | Ea. | 3975 - 5050 |
| 30" built-in | | |
| 1 oven | Ea. | 1550 - 3225 |
| 2 oven | Ea. | 3200 - 3775 |
| Counter top cook tops, 4 burner | Ea. | 480 - 860 |
| Microwave oven | Ea. | 375 - 895 |
| Combination range, refrig. & sink, 30" wide | Ea. | 2250 - 3325 |
| 60" wide | Ea. | 3450 |
| 72" wide | Ea. | 3650 |
| Combination range refrigerator, sink microwave oven & icemaker | Ea. | 8600 |
| Compactor, residential, 4-1 compaction | Ea. | 1600 - 1875 |
| Dishwasher, built-in, 2 cycles | Ea. | 965 - 1900 |
| 4 cycles | Ea. | 1150 - 1700 |
| Garbage disposer, sink type | Ea. | 300 - 445 |
| Hood for range, 2 speed, vented, 30" wide | Ea. | 425 - 1750 |
| 42" wide | Ea. | 495 - 730 |

| Description | Unit | $ Cost |
|---|---|---|
| Appliances, cont. | | |
| Refrigerator, no frost 10-12 C.F. | Ea. | 1000 - 855 |
| 14-16 C.F. | Ea. | 905 - 1050 |
| 18-20 C.F. | Ea. | 960 - 1100 |
| Lockers, Steel, single tier, 60" or 72" | Opng. | 285 - 520 |
| 2 tier, 60" or 72" total | Opng. | 216 - 265 |
| 5 tier, box lockers | Opng. | 465 - 153 |
| Locker bench, lam. maple top only | L.F. | 148 |
| Pedestals, steel pipe | Ea. | 87 |
| Sound System | | |
| Amplifier, 250 watts | Ea. | 2425 |
| Speaker, ceiling or wall | Ea. | 320 |
| Trumpet | Ea. | 580 |



**Important: See the Reference Section for Location Factors.**

## Model costs calculated for a 1 story building with 14′ story height and 6,000 square feet of floor area

# Fire Station, 1 Story

| | | | | Unit | Unit Cost | Cost Per S.F. | % Of Sub-Total |
|---|---|---|---|---|---|---|---|
| **A. SUBSTRUCTURE** | | | | | | | |
| 1010 | Standard Foundations | Poured concrete; strip and spread footings; 4′ foundation wall | | S.F. Ground | 9.61 | 9.61 | |
| 1020 | Special Foundations | N/A | | — | — | — | |
| 1030 | Slab on Grade | 6″ reinforced concrete with vapor barrier and granular base | | S.F. Slab | 9.63 | 9.63 | 11.8% |
| 2010 | Basement Excavation | Site preparation for slab and trench for foundation wall and footing | | S.F. Ground | .66 | .66 | |
| 2020 | Basement Walls | N/A | | — | — | — | |
| **B. SHELL** | | | | | | | |
| **B10 Superstructure** | | | | | | | |
| 1010 | Floor Construction | N/A | | — | — | — | 8.9 % |
| 1020 | Roof Construction | Metal deck, open web steel joists, beams on columns | | S.F. Roof | 15.13 | 15.13 | |
| **B20 Exterior Enclosure** | | | | | | | |
| 2010 | Exterior Walls | Face brick with concrete block backup | *75% of wall* | S.F. Wall | 40.64 | 22.76 | |
| 2020 | Exterior Windows | Aluminum insulated glass | *10% of wall* | Each | 2490 | 5.81 | 21.3% |
| 2030 | Exterior Doors | Single aluminum and glass, overhead, hollow metal | *15% of wall* | S.F. Door | 67 | 7.53 | |
| **B30 Roofing** | | | | | | | |
| 3010 | Roof Coverings | Built-up tar and gravel with flashing; perlite/EPS composite insulation | | S.F. Roof | 9.91 | 9.91 | 6.1% |
| 3020 | Roof Openings | Skylights, roof hatches | | S.F. Roof | .36 | .36 | |
| **C. INTERIORS** | | | | | | | |
| 1010 | Partitions | Concrete block | *17 S.F. Floor/L.F. Partition* | S.F. Partition | 10.86 | 6.39 | |
| 1020 | Interior Doors | Single leaf hollow metal | *500 S.F. Floor/Door* | Each | 1159 | 2.32 | |
| 1030 | Fittings | Toilet partitions | | S.F. Floor | .89 | .89 | |
| 2010 | Stair Construction | N/A | | — | — | — | 12.2% |
| 3010 | Wall Finishes | Paint | | S.F. Surface | 3.58 | 4.21 | |
| 3020 | Floor Finishes | 50% vinyl tile, 50% paint | | S.F. Floor | 2.35 | 2.35 | |
| 3030 | Ceiling Finishes | Fiberglass board on exposed grid, suspended | *50% of area* | S.F. Ceiling | 9 | 4.51 | |
| **D. SERVICES** | | | | | | | |
| **D10 Conveying** | | | | | | | |
| 1010 | Elevators & Lifts | N/A | | — | — | — | 0.0 % |
| 1020 | Escalators & Moving Walks | N/A | | — | — | — | |
| **D20 Plumbing** | | | | | | | |
| 2010 | Plumbing Fixtures | Kitchen, toilet and service fixtures, supply and drainage | *1 Fixture/375 S.F. Floor* | Each | 5824 | 15.53 | |
| 2020 | Domestic Water Distribution | Gast fired water heater | | S.F. Floor | 2.87 | 2.87 | 11.9% |
| 2040 | Rain Water Drainage | Roof drains | | S.F. Roof | 1.80 | 1.80 | |
| **D30 HVAC** | | | | | | | |
| 3010 | Energy Supply | N/A | | — | — | — | |
| 3020 | Heat Generating Systems | Included in D3050 | | — | — | — | |
| 3030 | Cooling Generating Systems | N/A | | — | — | — | 15.5 % |
| 3050 | Terminal & Package Units | Rooftop multizone unit system | | S.F. Floor | 26.18 | 26.18 | |
| 3090 | Other HVAC Sys. & Equipment | N/A | | — | — | — | |
| **D40 Fire Protection** | | | | | | | |
| 4010 | Sprinklers | Wet pipe sprinkler system | | S.F. Floor | 6.60 | 6.60 | 5.4% |
| 4020 | Standpipes | Standpipe, wet, Class III | | S.F. Floor | 2.47 | 2.47 | |
| **D50 Electrical** | | | | | | | |
| 5010 | Electrical Service/Distribution | 200 ampere service, panel board and feeders | | S.F. Floor | 2 | 2 | |
| 5020 | Lighting & Branch Wiring | High efficiency fluorescent fixtures, receptacles, switches, A.C. and misc. power | | S.F. Floor | 7.85 | 7.85 | 6.9% |
| 5030 | Communications & Security | Addressable alarm systems | | S.F. Floor | 1.83 | 1.83 | |
| 5090 | Other Electrical Systems | N/A | | — | — | — | |
| **E. EQUIPMENT & FURNISHINGS** | | | | | | | |
| 1010 | Commercial Equipment | N/A | | — | — | — | |
| 1020 | Institutional Equipment | N/A | | — | — | — | 0.0 % |
| 1030 | Vehicular Equipment | N/A | | — | — | — | |
| 1090 | Other Equipment | N/A | | — | — | — | |
| **F. SPECIAL CONSTRUCTION** | | | | | | | |
| 1020 | Integrated Construction | N/A | | — | — | — | 0.0 % |
| 1040 | Special Facilities | N/A | | — | — | — | |
| **G. BUILDING SITEWORK** | **N/A** | | | | | | |
| | | | | | **Sub-Total** | 169.20 | **100%** |
| | CONTRACTOR FEES (General Requirements: 10%, Overhead: 5%, Profit: 10%) | | | | *25%* | 42.33 | |
| | ARCHITECT FEES | | | | *8%* | 16.92 | |
| | | | | | **Total Building Cost** | **228.45** | |

## Costs per square foot of floor area

| Exterior Wall | S.F. Area | 6000 | 7000 | 8000 | 9000 | 10000 | 11000 | 12000 | 13000 | 14000 |
|---|---|---|---|---|---|---|---|---|---|---|
| | L.F. Perimeter | 220 | 240 | 260 | 280 | 286 | 303 | 320 | 336 | 353 |
| Face Brick and Concrete Block | Steel Joists | 257.60 | 249.60 | 243.75 | 239.05 | 232.85 | 229.50 | 226.75 | 224.35 | 222.40 |
| | Precast Concrete | 267.30 | 259.30 | 253.40 | 248.75 | 242.50 | 239.20 | 236.45 | 234.05 | 232.10 |
| Decorative Concrete Block | Steel Joists | 239.80 | 232.75 | 227.60 | 223.50 | **218.30** | 215.35 | 213.00 | 210.85 | 209.15 |
| | Precast Concrete | 252.55 | 245.50 | 240.35 | 236.25 | 231.05 | 228.10 | 225.70 | 223.60 | 221.90 |
| Limestone and Concrete Block | Steel Joists | 275.75 | 266.35 | 259.45 | 254.00 | 246.25 | 242.35 | 239.10 | 236.15 | 233.90 |
| | Precast Concrete | 288.45 | 279.10 | 272.20 | 266.70 | 259.00 | 255.10 | 251.85 | 248.90 | 246.60 |
| Perimeter Adj., Add or Deduct | Per 100 L.F. | 30.90 | 26.50 | 23.15 | 20.65 | 18.50 | 16.80 | 15.45 | 14.25 | 13.20 |
| Story Hgt. Adj., Add or Deduct | Per 1 Ft. | 4.00 | 3.80 | 3.55 | 3.45 | 3.10 | 3.00 | 2.95 | 2.80 | 2.70 |

***For Basement**, add $60.65 per square foot of basement area*

*The above costs were calculated using the basic specifications shown on the facing page. These costs should be adjusted where necessary for design alternatives and owner's requirements.*

## Common additives

| Description | Unit | $ Cost |
|---|---|---|
| Appliances | | |
| Cooking range, 30" free standing | | |
| 1 oven | Ea. | 885 - 1300 |
| 2 oven | Ea. | 3975 - 5050 |
| 30" built-in | | |
| 1 oven | Ea. | 1550 - 3225 |
| 2 oven | Ea. | 3200 - 3775 |
| Counter top cook tops, 4 burner | Ea. | 480 - 860 |
| Microwave oven | Ea. | 375 - 895 |
| Combination range, refrig. & sink, 30" wide | Ea. | 2250 - 3325 |
| 60" wide | Ea. | 3450 |
| 72" wide | Ea. | 3650 |
| Combination range, refrigerator, sink, microwave oven & icemaker | Ea. | 8600 |
| Compactor, residential, 4-1 compaction | Ea. | 1600 - 1875 |
| Dishwasher, built-in, 2 cycles | Ea. | 965 - 1900 |
| 4 cycles | Ea. | 1150 - 1700 |
| Garbage diposer, sink type | Ea. | 300 - 445 |
| Hood for range, 2 speed, vented, 30" wide | Ea. | 425 - 1750 |
| 42" wide | Ea. | 495 - 730 |

| Description | Unit | $ Cost |
|---|---|---|
| Appliances, cont. | | |
| Refrigerator, no frost 10-12 C.F. | Ea. | 1000 - 855 |
| 14-16 C.F. | Ea. | 905 - 1050 |
| 18-20 C.F. | Ea. | 960 - 1100 |
| Elevators, Hydraulic passenger, 2 stops | | |
| 1500# capacity | Ea. | 86,500 |
| 2500# capacity | Ea. | 90,500 |
| 3500# capacity | Ea. | 96,000 |
| Lockers, Steel, single tier, 60" or 72" | Opng. | 285 - 520 |
| 2 tier, 60" or 72" total | Opng. | 216 - 265 |
| 5 tier, box lockers | Opng. | 465 - 153 |
| Locker bench, lam. maple top only | L.F. | 148 |
| Pedestals, steel pipe | Ea. | 87 |
| Sound System | | |
| Amplifier, 250 watts | Ea. | 2425 |
| Speaker, ceiling or wall | Ea. | 320 |
| Trumpet | Ea. | 580 |



**Important: See the Reference Section for Location Factors.**

## Model costs calculated for a 2 story building with 14′ story height and 10,000 square feet of floor area

# Fire Station, 2 Story

| | | | | Unit | Unit Cost | Cost Per S.F. | % Of Sub-Total |
|---|---|---|---|---|---|---|---|
| **A. SUBSTRUCTURE** | | | | | | | |
| 1010 | Standard Foundations | Poured concrete; strip and spread footings; 4′ foundation wall | | S.F. Ground | 10.34 | 5.17 | 6.4% |
| 1020 | Special Foundations | N/A | | — | — | — | |
| 1030 | Slab on Grade | 6″ reinforced concrete with vapor barrier and granular base | | S.F. Slab | 9.63 | 4.82 | |
| 2010 | Basement Excavation | Site preparation for slab and trench for foundation wall and footing | | S.F. Ground | .66 | .33 | |
| 2020 | Basement Walls | N/A | | — | — | — | |
| **B. SHELL** | | | | | | | |
| | **B10 Superstructure** | | | | | | |
| 1010 | Floor Construction | Open web steel joists, slab form, concrete | | S.F. Floor | 22.54 | 11.27 | 9.5% |
| 1020 | Roof Construction | Metal deck on open web steel joists | | S.F. Roof | 8.16 | 4.08 | |
| | **B20 Exterior Enclosure** | | | | | | |
| 2010 | Exterior Walls | Decorative concrete block | *75% of wall* | S.F. Wall | 26.46 | 15.89 | 15.3% |
| 2020 | Exterior Windows | Aluminum insulated glass | *10% of wall* | Each | 839 | 2.92 | |
| 2030 | Exterior Doors | Single aluminum and glass, steel overhead, hollow metal | *15% of wall* | S.F. Door | 49.95 | 6 | |
| | **B30 Roofing** | | | | | | |
| 3010 | Roof Coverings | Built-up tar and gravel with flashing; perlite/EPS composite insulation | | S.F. Roof | 10.18 | 5.09 | 3.1% |
| 3020 | Roof Openings | N/A | | — | — | — | |
| **C. INTERIORS** | | | | | | | |
| 1010 | Partitions | Concrete block | *10 S.F. Floor/L.F. Partition* | S.F. Partition | 10.86 | 6.39 | 17.2% |
| 1020 | Interior Doors | Single leaf hollow metal | *500 S.F. Floor/Door* | Each | 2060 | 4.12 | |
| 1030 | Fittings | Toilet partitions | | S.F. Floor | .80 | .80 | |
| 2010 | Stair Construction | Concrete filled metal pan | | Flight | 22,275 | 4.46 | |
| 3010 | Wall Finishes | Paint | | S.F. Surface | 4.22 | 4.96 | |
| 3020 | Floor Finishes | 50% vinyl tile, 50% paint | | S.F. Floor | 2.35 | 2.35 | |
| 3030 | Ceiling Finishes | Fiberglass board on exposed grid, suspended | *50% of area* | S.F. Ceiling | 9.48 | 4.75 | |
| **D. SERVICES** | | | | | | | |
| | **D10 Conveying** | | | | | | |
| 1010 | Elevators & Lifts | One hydraulic passenger elevator | | Each | 107,000 | 10.70 | 6.6% |
| 1020 | Escalators & Moving Walks | N/A | | — | — | — | |
| | **D20 Plumbing** | | | | | | |
| 2010 | Plumbing Fixtures | Kitchen toilet and service fixtures, supply and drainage | *1 Fixture/400 S.F. Floor* | Each | 5968 | 14.92 | 11.9% |
| 2020 | Domestic Water Distribution | Gas fired water heater | | S.F. Floor | 3.15 | 3.15 | |
| 2040 | Rain Water Drainage | Roof drains | | S.F. Roof | 2.32 | 1.16 | |
| | **D30 HVAC** | | | | | | |
| 3010 | Energy Supply | N/A | | — | — | — | 16.2 % |
| 3020 | Heat Generating Systems | Included in D3050 | | — | — | — | |
| 3030 | Cooling Generating Systems | N/A | | — | — | — | |
| 3050 | Terminal & Package Units | Rooftop multizone unit system | | S.F. Floor | 26.18 | 26.18 | |
| 3090 | Other HVAC Sys. & Equipment | N/A | | — | — | — | |
| | **D40 Fire Protection** | | | | | | |
| 4010 | Sprinklers | Wet pipe sprinkler system | | S.F. Floor | 5.47 | 5.47 | 5.0% |
| 4020 | Standpipes | Standpipe, wet, Class III | | S.F. Floor | 2.56 | 2.56 | |
| | **D50 Electrical** | | | | | | |
| 5010 | Electrical Service/Distribution | 400 ampere service, panel board and feeders | | S.F. Floor | 2.14 | 2.14 | 8.7% |
| 5020 | Lighting & Branch Wiring | High efficiency fluorescent fixtures, receptacles, switches, A.C. and misc. power | | S.F. Floor | 10.23 | 10.23 | |
| 5030 | Communications & Security | Addressable alarm systems and emergency lighting | | S.F. Floor | 1.53 | 1.53 | |
| 5090 | Other Electrical Systems | Emergency generator, 15 kW | | S.F. Floor | .24 | .24 | |
| **E. EQUIPMENT & FURNISHINGS** | | | | | | | |
| 1010 | Commercial Equipment | N/A | | — | — | — | 0.0 % |
| 1020 | Institutional Equipment | N/A | | — | — | — | |
| 1030 | Vehicular Equipment | N/A | | — | — | — | |
| 1090 | Other Equipment | N/A | | — | — | — | |
| **F. SPECIAL CONSTRUCTION** | | | | | | | |
| 1020 | Integrated Construction | N/A | | — | — | — | 0.0 % |
| 1040 | Special Facilities | N/A | | — | — | — | |
| **G. BUILDING SITEWORK** | **N/A** | | | | | | |
| | | | | | **Sub-Total** | 161.68 | **100%** |
| | CONTRACTOR FEES (General Requirements: 10%, Overhead: 5%, Profit: 10%) | | | | *25%* | 40.45 | |
| | ARCHITECT FEES | | | | *8%* | 16.17 | |
| | | | | | **Total Building Cost** | **218.30** | |

## Costs per square foot of floor area

| Exterior Wall | S.F. Area | 4000 | 5000 | 6000 | 8000 | 10000 | 12000 | 14000 | 16000 | 18000 |
|---|---|---|---|---|---|---|---|---|---|---|
| | L.F. Perimeter | 180 | 205 | 230 | 260 | 300 | 340 | 353 | 386 | 420 |
| Wood Clapboard | Wood Frame | 277.95 | 266.60 | 259.05 | 247.30 | **241.20** | 237.15 | 232.45 | 230.10 | 228.30 |
| Aluminum Clapboard | Wood Frame | 274.05 | 263.05 | 255.75 | 244.50 | 238.65 | 234.70 | 230.30 | 228.05 | 226.30 |
| Wood Board and Batten | Wood Frame | 276.85 | 265.60 | 258.10 | 246.55 | 240.50 | 236.50 | 231.85 | 229.55 | 227.80 |
| Face Brick and Concrete Block | Bearing Walls | 290.50 | 277.10 | 268.15 | 253.50 | 246.10 | 241.15 | 234.90 | 232.00 | 229.80 |
| Stucco and Concrete Block | Bearing Walls | 267.10 | 255.80 | 248.30 | 236.60 | 230.50 | 226.45 | 221.80 | 219.45 | 217.70 |
| Decorative Concrete Block | Wood Joists | 283.00 | 271.20 | 263.35 | 251.00 | 244.60 | 240.30 | 235.25 | 232.80 | 230.95 |
| Perimeter Adj., Add or Deduct | Per 100 L.F. | 22.50 | 17.95 | 14.95 | 11.20 | 9.00 | 7.45 | 6.35 | 5.65 | 4.95 |
| Story Hgt. Adj., Add or Deduct | Per 1 Ft. | 2.95 | 2.70 | 2.45 | 2.10 | 2.00 | 1.90 | 1.60 | 1.60 | 1.55 |
| ***For Basement**, add $ 38.60 per square foot of basement area* | | | | | | | | | | |

*The above costs were calculated using the basic specifications shown on the facing page. These costs should be adjusted where necessary for design alternatives and owner's requirements.*

## Common additives

| Description | Unit | $ Cost |
|---|---|---|
| Appliances | | |
| Cooking range, 30" free standing | | |
| 1 oven | Ea. | 885 - 1300 |
| 2 oven | Ea. | 3975 - 5050 |
| 30" built-in | | |
| 1 oven | Ea. | 1550 - 3225 |
| 2 oven | Ea. | 3200 - 3775 |
| Counter top cook tops, 4 burner | Ea. | 480 - 860 |
| Microwave oven | Ea. | 375 - 895 |
| Combination range, refrig. & sink, 30" wide | Ea. | 2250 - 3325 |
| 60" wide | Ea. | 3450 |
| 72" wide | Ea. | 3650 |
| Combination range, refrigerator, sink, microwave oven & icemaker | Ea. | 8600 |
| Compactor, residential, 4-1 compaction | Ea. | 1600 - 1875 |
| Dishwasher, built-in, 2 cycles | Ea. | 965 - 1900 |
| 4 cycles | Ea. | 1150 - 1700 |
| Garbage disposer, sink type | Ea. | 300 - 445 |
| Hood for range, 2 speed, vented, 30" wide | Ea. | 425 - 1750 |
| 42" wide | Ea. | 495 - 730 |

| Description | Unit | $ Cost |
|---|---|---|
| Appliances, cont. | | |
| Refrigerator, no frost 10-12 C.F. | Ea. | 1000 - 855 |
| 14-16 C.F. | Ea. | 905 - 1050 |
| 18-20 C.F. | Ea. | 960 - 1100 |
| Elevators, Hydraulic passenger, 2 stops | | |
| 1500# capacity | Ea. | 86,500 |
| 2500# capacity | Ea. | 90,500 |
| 3500# capacity | Ea. | 96,000 |
| Laundry Equipment | | |
| Dryer, gas, 16 lb. capacity | Ea. | 1725 |
| 30 lb. capacity | Ea. | 2200 |
| Washer, 4 cycle | Ea. | 1550 |
| Commercial | Ea. | 2000 |
| Sound System | | |
| Amplifier, 250 watts | Ea. | 2425 |
| Speaker, ceiling or wall | Ea. | 320 |
| Trumpet | Ea. | 580 |



**Important: See the Reference Section for Location Factors.**

## Model costs calculated for a 2 story building with 10′ story height and 10,000 square feet of floor area

# Fraternity/Sorority House

| | | | | Unit | Unit Cost | Cost Per S.F. | % Of Sub-Total |
|---|---|---|---|---|---|---|---|
| **A. SUBSTRUCTURE** | | | | | | | |
| 1010 | Standard Foundations | Poured concrete; strip and spread footings; 4′ foundation wall | | S.F. Ground | 9.94 | 4.97 | 5.0% |
| 1020 | Special Foundations | N/A | | — | — | — | |
| 1030 | Slab on Grade | 4″ reinforced concrete with vapor barrier and granular base | | S.F. Slab | 7.22 | 3.61 | |
| 2010 | Basement Excavation | Site preparation for slab and trench for foundation wall and footing | | S.F. Ground | .66 | .33 | |
| 2020 | Basement Walls | N/A | | — | — | — | |
| **B. SHELL** | | | | | | | |
| | **B10 Superstructure** | | | | | | |
| 1010 | Floor Construction | Plywood on wood joists | | S.F. Floor | 35.86 | 17.93 | 12.2% |
| 1020 | Roof Construction | Plywood on wood rafters (pitched) | | S.F. Roof | 6.57 | 3.68 | |
| | **B20 Exterior Enclosure** | | | | | | |
| 2010 | Exterior Walls | Cedar bevel siding on wood studs, insulated | *80% of wall* | S.F. Wall | 18.65 | 8.95 | 8.9% |
| 2020 | Exterior Windows | Double hung wood | *20% of wall* | Each | 850 | 4.08 | |
| 2030 | Exterior Doors | Solid core wood | | Each | 4004 | 2.81 | |
| | **B30 Roofing** | | | | | | |
| 3010 | Roof Coverings | Asphalt shingles with flashing (pitched); rigid fiberglass insulation | | S.F. Roof | 7.12 | 3.56 | 2.0% |
| 3020 | Roof Openings | N/A | | — | — | — | |
| **C. INTERIORS** | | | | | | | |
| 1010 | Partitions | Gypsum board on wood studs | *25 S.F. Floor/L.F. Partition* | S.F. Partition | 10.66 | 3.41 | 14.9% |
| 1020 | Interior Doors | Single leaf wood | *200 S.F. Floor/Door* | Each | 1231 | 6.16 | |
| 1030 | Fittings | N/A | | — | — | — | |
| 2010 | Stair Construction | Wood | | Flight | 4005 | 1.20 | |
| 3010 | Wall Finishes | Paint | | S.F. Surface | .95 | .61 | |
| 3020 | Floor Finishes | 10% hardwood, 70% carpet, 20% ceramic tile | | S.F. Floor | 9.40 | 9.40 | |
| 3030 | Ceiling Finishes | Gypsum board on wood furring | | S.F. Ceiling | 5.53 | 5.53 | |
| **D. SERVICES** | | | | | | | |
| | **D10 Conveying** | | | | | | |
| 1010 | Elevators & Lifts | One hydraulic passenger elevator | | Each | 107,000 | 10.70 | 6.0% |
| 1020 | Escalators & Moving Walks | N/A | | — | — | — | |
| | **D20 Plumbing** | | | | | | |
| 2010 | Plumbing Fixtures | Kitchen toilet and service fixtures, supply and drainage | *1 Fixture/150 S.F. Floor* | Each | 3192 | 21.28 | 13.8% |
| 2020 | Domestic Water Distribution | Gas fired water heater | | S.F. Floor | 3.17 | 3.17 | |
| 2040 | Rain Water Drainage | N/A | | — | — | — | |
| | **D30 HVAC** | | | | | | |
| 3010 | Energy Supply | Oil fired hot water, baseboard radiation | | S.F. Floor | 10.23 | 10.23 | 10.9% |
| 3020 | Heat Generating Systems | N/A | | — | — | — | |
| 3030 | Cooling Generating Systems | N/A | | — | — | — | |
| 3050 | Terminal & Package Units | Split system with air cooled condensing unit | | S.F. Floor | 9.09 | 9.09 | |
| 3090 | Other HVAC Sys. & Equipment | N/A | | — | — | — | |
| | **D40 Fire Protection** | | | | | | |
| 4010 | Sprinklers | Wet pipe sprinkler system | | S.F. Floor | 5.47 | 5.47 | 4.1% |
| 4020 | Standpipes | Standpipe | | S.F. Floor | 1.83 | 1.83 | |
| | **D50 Electrical** | | | | | | |
| 5010 | Electrical Service/Distribution | 600 ampere service, panel board and feeders | | S.F. Floor | 5.58 | 5.58 | 22.1% |
| 5020 | Lighting & Branch Wiring | High efficiency fluorescent fixtures, receptacles, switches, A.C. and misc. power | | S.F. Floor | 14.19 | 14.19 | |
| 5030 | Communications & Security | Addressable alarm, communication system, internet and phone wiring, and generator set | | S.F. Floor | 19.05 | 19.05 | |
| 5090 | Other Electrical Systems | Emergency generator, 7.5 kW | | S.F. Floor | .22 | .22 | |
| **E. EQUIPMENT & FURNISHINGS** | | | | | | | |
| 1010 | Commercial Equipment | N/A | | — | — | — | 0.0 % |
| 1020 | Institutional Equipment | N/A | | — | — | — | |
| 1030 | Vehicular Equipment | N/A | | — | — | — | |
| 1090 | Other Equipment | N/A | | — | — | — | |
| **F. SPECIAL CONSTRUCTION** | | | | | | | |
| 1020 | Integrated Construction | N/A | | — | — | — | 0.0 % |
| 1040 | Special Facilities | N/A | | — | — | — | |
| **G. BUILDING SITEWORK** | | **N/A** | | | | | |
| | | | | | **Sub-Total** | 177.04 | **100%** |
| | CONTRACTOR FEES (General Requirements: 10%, Overhead: 5%, Profit: 10%) | | | | *25%* | 44.24 | |
| | ARCHITECT FEES | | | | *9%* | 19.92 | |
| | | | | | **Total Building Cost** | **241.20** | |

## Costs per square foot of floor area

| Exterior Wall | S.F. Area | 4000 | 6000 | 8000 | 10000 | 12000 | 14000 | 16000 | 18000 | 20000 |
|---|---|---|---|---|---|---|---|---|---|---|
| | L.F. Perimeter | 260 | 320 | 384 | 424 | 460 | 484 | 510 | 540 | 576 |
| Wood Board and Batten | Wood Frame | 286.70 | 252.65 | 236.00 | **224.35** | 216.35 | 210.05 | 205.40 | 201.95 | 199.40 |
| Brick Veneer | Wood Frame | 296.45 | 260.65 | 243.20 | 230.70 | 222.10 | 215.25 | 210.20 | 206.45 | 203.70 |
| Aluminum Clapboard | Wood Frame | 277.25 | 244.95 | 229.05 | 218.25 | 210.80 | 205.05 | 200.80 | 197.60 | 195.20 |
| Face Brick and Concrete Block | Wood Truss | 303.40 | 266.15 | 248.00 | 234.80 | 225.70 | 218.35 | 212.95 | 209.00 | 206.10 |
| Limestone and Concrete Block | Wood Truss | 323.40 | 282.55 | 262.75 | 247.85 | 237.50 | 228.95 | 222.75 | 218.20 | 214.90 |
| Stucco and Concrete Block | Wood Truss | 280.60 | 247.45 | 231.15 | 219.90 | 212.25 | 206.20 | 201.75 | 198.45 | 195.95 |
| Perimeter Adj., Add or Deduct | Per 100 L.F. | 17.20 | 11.50 | 8.60 | 6.85 | 5.75 | 4.85 | 4.25 | 3.80 | 3.40 |
| Story Hgt. Adj., Add or Deduct | Per 1 Ft. | 2.50 | 2.05 | 1.85 | 1.65 | 1.50 | 1.30 | 1.30 | 1.20 | 1.15 |
| ***For Basement**, add $51.45 per square foot of basement area* | | | | | | | | | | |

*The above costs were calculated using the basic specifications shown on the facing page. These costs should be adjusted where necessary for design alternatives and owner's requirements.*

## Common additives

| Description | Unit | $ Cost |
|---|---|---|
| Autopsy Table, Standard | Ea. | 10,300 |
| Deluxe | Ea. | 4925 |
| Directory Boards, Plastic, glass covered | | |
| 30" x 20" | Ea. | 705 |
| 36" x 48" | Ea. | 1475 |
| Aluminum, 24" x 18" | Ea. | 705 |
| 36" x 24" | Ea. | 985 |
| 48" x 32" | Ea. | 1975 |
| 48" x 60" | Ea. | 2650 |
| Emergency Lighting, 25 watt, battery operated | | |
| Lead battery | Ea. | 360 |
| Nickel cadmium | Ea. | 585 |
| Mortuary Refrigerator, End operated | | |
| Two capacity | Ea. | 6750 |
| Six capacity | Ea. | 14,900 |

| Description | Unit | $ Cost |
|---|---|---|
| Planters, Precast concrete | | |
| 48" diam., 24" high | Ea. | 745 |
| 7" diam., 36" high | Ea. | 2175 |
| Fiberglass, 36" diam., 24" high | Ea. | 565 |
| 60" diam., 24" high | Ea. | 1225 |
| Smoke Detectors | | |
| Ceiling type | Ea. | 300 |
| Duct type | Ea. | 615 |



**Important: See the Reference Section for Location Factors.**

## Model costs calculated for a 1 story building with 12′ story height and 10,000 square feet of floor area

# Funeral Home

| | | | | Unit | Unit Cost | Cost Per S.F. | % Of Sub-Total |
|---|---|---|---|---|---|---|---|
| **A. SUBSTRUCTURE** | | | | | | | |
| 1010 | Standard Foundations | Poured concrete; strip and spread footings; 4′ foundation wall | | S.F. Ground | 7.74 | 7.74 | |
| 1020 | Special Foundations | N/A | | – | – | – | |
| 1030 | Slab on Grade | 4″ reinforced concrete with vapor barrier and granular base | | S.F. Slab | 7.22 | 7.22 | 9.3% |
| 2010 | Basement Excavation | Site preparation for slab and trench for foundation wall and footing | | S.F. Ground | .38 | .38 | |
| 2020 | Basement Walls | N/A | | – | – | – | |
| **B. SHELL** | | | | | | | |
| | **B10 Superstructure** | | | | | | |
| 1010 | Floor Construction | Wood beams on columns | | S.F. Floor | 1.35 | 1.35 | 6.5% |
| 1020 | Roof Construction | Plywood on wood truss | | S.F. Roof | 9.32 | 9.32 | |
| | **B20 Exterior Enclosure** | | | | | | |
| 2010 | Exterior Walls | 1″ x 4″ vertical T & G redwood siding on wood studs | *90% of wall* | S.F. Wall | 23.26 | 10.65 | |
| 2020 | Exterior Windows | Double hung wood | *10% of wall* | Each | 670 | 2.84 | 9.9% |
| 2030 | Exterior Doors | Wood swinging double doors, single leaf hollow metal | | Each | 4795 | 2.88 | |
| | **B30 Roofing** | | | | | | |
| 3010 | Roof Coverings | Single ply membrane, fully adhered; polyisocyanurate sheets | | S.F. Roof | 8.34 | 8.34 | 5.1% |
| 3020 | Roof Openings | N/A | | – | – | – | |
| **C. INTERIORS** | | | | | | | |
| 1010 | Partitions | Gypsum board on wood studs with sound deadening board | *15 S.F. Floor/L.F. Partition* | S.F. Partition | 12.96 | 6.91 | |
| 1020 | Interior Doors | Single leaf wood | *150 S.F. Floor/Door* | Each | 1231 | 8.21 | |
| 1030 | Fittings | N/A | | – | – | – | |
| 2010 | Stair Construction | N/A | | – | – | – | 24.2% |
| 3010 | Wall Finishes | 50% wallpaper, 25% wood paneling, 25% paint | | S.F. Surface | 3.96 | 4.22 | |
| 3020 | Floor Finishes | 70% carpet, 30% ceramic tile | | S.F. Floor | 11.02 | 11.02 | |
| 3030 | Ceiling Finishes | Fiberglass board on exposed grid, suspended | | S.F. Ceiling | 9.48 | 9.48 | |
| **D. SERVICES** | | | | | | | |
| | **D10 Conveying** | | | | | | |
| 1010 | Elevators & Lifts | N/A | | – | – | – | 0.0 % |
| 1020 | Escalators & Moving Walks | N/A | | – | – | – | |
| | **D20 Plumbing** | | | | | | |
| 2010 | Plumbing Fixtures | Toilet and service fixtures, supply and drainage | *1 Fixture/770 S.F. Floor* | Each | 4435 | 5.76 | |
| 2020 | Domestic Water Distribution | Electric water heater | | S.F. Floor | 20.51 | 20.51 | 16.0% |
| 2040 | Rain Water Drainage | Roof drain | | S.F. Roof | | | |
| | **D30 HVAC** | | | | | | |
| 3010 | Energy Supply | N/A | | – | – | – | |
| 3020 | Heat Generating Systems | Included in D3030 | | – | – | – | |
| 3030 | Cooling Generating Systems | Multizone rooftop unit, gas heating, electric cooling | | S.F. Floor | 27.10 | 27.10 | 16.5 % |
| 3050 | Terminal & Package Units | N/A | | – | – | – | |
| 3090 | Other HVAC Sys. & Equipment | N/A | | – | – | – | |
| | **D40 Fire Protection** | | | | | | |
| 4010 | Sprinklers | Wet pipe sprinkler system | | S.F. Floor | 5.07 | 5.07 | 4.0% |
| 4020 | Standpipes | Standpipe, wet, Class III | | S.F. Floor | 1.48 | 1.48 | |
| | **D50 Electrical** | | | | | | |
| 5010 | Electrical Service/Distribution | 400 ampere service, panel board and feeders | | S.F. Floor | 2.41 | 2.41 | |
| 5020 | Lighting & Branch Wiring | High efficiency fluorescent fixtures, receptacles, switches, A.C. and misc. power | | S.F. Floor | 10.15 | 10.15 | 8.6% |
| 5030 | Communications & Security | Addressable alarm systems and emergency lighting | | S.F. Floor | 1.53 | 1.53 | |
| 5090 | Other Electrical Systems | Emergency generator, 15 kW | | S.F. Floor | .09 | .09 | |
| **E. EQUIPMENT & FURNISHINGS** | | | | | | | |
| 1010 | Commercial Equipment | N/A | | – | – | – | |
| 1020 | Institutional Equipment | N/A | | – | – | – | 0.0 % |
| 1030 | Vehicular Equipment | N/A | | – | – | – | |
| 1090 | Other Equipment | N/A | | – | – | – | |
| **F. SPECIAL CONSTRUCTION** | | | | | | | |
| 1020 | Integrated Construction | N/A | | – | – | – | 0.0 % |
| 1040 | Special Facilities | N/A | | – | – | – | |
| **G. BUILDING SITEWORK** | **N/A** | | | | | | |
| | | | | | **Sub-Total** | 164.66 | **100%** |
| | CONTRACTOR FEES (General Requirements: 10%, Overhead: 5%, Profit: 10%) | | | | 25% | 41.17 | |
| | ARCHITECT FEES | | | | 9% | 18.52 | |
| | | | | | **Total Building Cost** | **224.35** | |

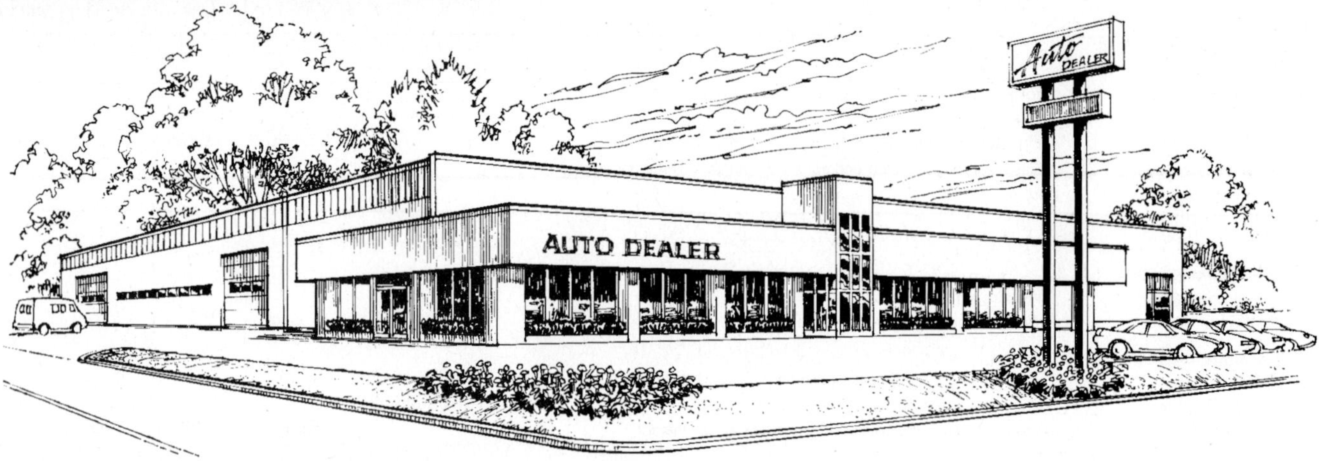


## Costs per square foot of floor area

| Exterior Wall | S.F. Area | 12000 | 14000 | 16000 | 19000 | 21000 | 23000 | 26000 | 28000 | 30000 |
|---|---|---|---|---|---|---|---|---|---|---|
| | L.F. Perimeter | 440 | 474 | 510 | 556 | 583 | 607 | 648 | 670 | 695 |
| E.I.F.S. and Concrete Block | Rigid Steel | 174.65 | 170.80 | 168.10 | 164.70 | 162.80 | 161.00 | 159.15 | 157.85 | 156.90 |
| Tilt-up Concrete Panels | Rigid Steel | 172.30 | 168.60 | 166.10 | 162.75 | 160.95 | 159.30 | 157.50 | 156.35 | 155.35 |
| Face Brick and Concrete Block | Bearing Walls | 174.50 | 169.90 | 166.75 | 162.60 | 160.30 | 158.20 | 155.95 | 154.40 | 153.25 |
| | Rigid Steel | 184.15 | 179.55 | 176.35 | 172.30 | 169.90 | 167.85 | 165.60 | 164.05 | 162.90 |
| Stucco and Concrete Block | Bearing Walls | 163.05 | 159.35 | 156.80 | 153.50 | 151.65 | 149.95 | 148.15 | 146.95 | 146.05 |
| | Rigid Steel | 172.65 | 168.95 | 166.40 | 163.10 | 161.25 | 159.60 | 157.80 | 156.55 | 155.65 |
| Perimeter Adj., Add or Deduct | Per 100 L.F. | 9.00 | 7.75 | 6.80 | 5.65 | 5.05 | 4.70 | 4.10 | 3.85 | 3.65 |
| Story Hgt. Adj., Add or Deduct | Per 1 Ft. | 1.90 | 1.75 | 1.65 | 1.55 | 1.45 | 1.40 | 1.25 | 1.25 | 1.25 |
| ***For Basement**, add $58.50 per square foot of basement area* | | | | | | | | | | |

*The above costs were calculated using the basic specifications shown on the facing page. These costs should be adjusted where necessary for design alternatives and owner's requirements.*

## Common additives

| Description | Unit | $ Cost |
|---|---|---|
| Emergency Lighting, 25 watt, battery operated | | |
| Lead battery | Ea. | 360 |
| Nickel cadmium | Ea. | 585 |
| Smoke Detectors | | |
| Ceiling type | Ea. | 300 |
| Duct type | Ea. | 615 |
| Sound System | | |
| Amplifier, 250 watts | Ea. | 2425 |
| Speaker, ceiling or wall | Ea. | 320 |
| Trumpet | Ea. | 580 |



**Important: See the Reference Section for Location Factors.**

## Model costs calculated for a 1 story building with 14′ story height and 21,000 square feet of floor area

# Garage, Auto Sales

| | | | Unit | Unit Cost | Cost Per S.F. | % Of Sub-Total |
|---|---|---|---|---|---|---|
| **A. SUBSTRUCTURE** | | | | | | |
| 1010 | Standard Foundations | Poured concrete; strip and spread footings; 4′ foundation wall | S.F. Ground | 5.09 | 5.09 | |
| 1020 | Special Foundations | N/A | — | — | — | |
| 1030 | Slab on Grade | 4″ reinforced concrete with vapor barrier and granular base | S.F. Slab | 11.10 | 11.10 | 13.6% |
| 2010 | Basement Excavation | Site preparation for slab and trench for foundation wall and footing | S.F. Ground | .38 | .38 | |
| 2020 | Basement Walls | N/A | — | — | — | |
| **B. SHELL** | | | | | | |
| | **B10 Superstructure** | | | | | |
| 1010 | Floor Construction | N/A | — | — | — | 13.8 % |
| 1020 | Roof Construction | Metal deck, open web steel joists, beams, columns | S.F. Roof | 16.76 | 16.76 | |
| | **B20 Exterior Enclosure** | | | | | |
| 2010 | Exterior Walls | E.I.F.S. *70% of wall* | S.F. Wall | 22.35 | 6.08 | |
| 2020 | Exterior Windows | Window wall *30% of wall* | Each | 72 | 8.39 | 14.8% |
| 2030 | Exterior Doors | Double aluminum and glass, hollow metal, steel overhead | Each | 4129 | 3.55 | |
| | **B30 Roofing** | | | | | |
| 3010 | Roof Coverings | Built-up tar and gravel with flashing; perlite/EPS composite insulation | S.F. Roof | 9.26 | 9.26 | 7.6% |
| 3020 | Roof Openings | N/A | — | — | — | |
| **C. INTERIORS** | | | | | | |
| 1010 | Partitions | Gypsum board on metal studs *28 S.F. Floor/L.F. Partition* | S.F. Partition | 6.93 | 2.97 | |
| 1020 | Interior Doors | Hollow metal *280 S.F. Floor/Door* | Each | 1159 | 4.14 | |
| 1030 | Fittings | N/A | — | — | — | |
| 2010 | Stair Construction | N/A | — | — | — | 12.6% |
| 3010 | Wall Finishes | Paint | S.F. Surface | 1.26 | 1.08 | |
| 3020 | Floor Finishes | 50% vinyl tile, 50% paint | S.F. Floor | 2.35 | 2.35 | |
| 3030 | Ceiling Finishes | Fiberglass board on exposed grid, suspended *50% of area* | S.F. Ceiling | 9.48 | 4.75 | |
| **D. SERVICES** | | | | | | |
| | **D10 Conveying** | | | | | |
| 1010 | Elevators & Lifts | N/A | — | — | — | 0.0 % |
| 1020 | Escalators & Moving Walks | N/A | — | — | — | |
| | **D20 Plumbing** | | | | | |
| 2010 | Plumbing Fixtures | Toilet and service fixtures, supply and drainage *1 Fixture/1500 S.F. Floor* | Each | 4650 | 3.10 | |
| 2020 | Domestic Water Distribution | Gas fired water heater | S.F. Floor | 1.88 | 1.88 | 7.6% |
| 2040 | Rain Water Drainage | Roof drains | S.F. Roof | 4.31 | 4.31 | |
| | **D30 HVAC** | | | | | |
| 3010 | Energy Supply | N/A | — | — | — | |
| 3020 | Heat Generating Systems | N/A | — | — | — | |
| 3030 | Cooling Generating Systems | N/A | — | — | — | 10.3 % |
| 3050 | Terminal & Package Units | Single zone rooftop unit, gas heating, electric cooling | S.F. Floor | 11.72 | 11.72 | |
| 3090 | Other HVAC Sys. & Equipment | Underfloor garage exhaust system | S.F. Floor | .79 | .79 | |
| | **D40 Fire Protection** | | | | | |
| 4010 | Sprinklers | Wet pipe sprinkler system | S.F. Floor | 6.66 | 6.66 | 6.1% |
| 4020 | Standpipes | Standpipe | S.F. Floor | .77 | .77 | |
| | **D50 Electrical** | | | | | |
| 5010 | Electrical Service/Distribution | 200 ampere service, panel board and feeders | S.F. Floor | .61 | .61 | |
| 5020 | Lighting & Branch Wiring | T-8 fluorescent fixtures, receptacles, switches, A.C. and misc. power | S.F. Floor | 10.11 | 10.11 | 12.3% |
| 5030 | Communications & Security | Addressable alarm systems, partial internet wiring and emergency lighting | S.F. Floor | 4.14 | 4.14 | |
| 5090 | Other Electrical Systems | Emergency generator, 7.5 kW | S.F. Floor | .08 | .08 | |
| **E. EQUIPMENT & FURNISHINGS** | | | | | | |
| 1010 | Commercial Equipment | N/A | — | — | — | |
| 1020 | Institutional Equipment | N/A | — | — | — | 1.3 % |
| 1030 | Vehicular Equipment | Hoists, compressor, fuel pump | S.F. Floor | 1.61 | 1.61 | |
| 1090 | Other Equipment | N/A | — | — | — | |
| **F. SPECIAL CONSTRUCTION** | | | | | | |
| 1020 | Integrated Construction | N/A | — | — | — | 0.0 % |
| 1040 | Special Facilities | N/A | — | — | — | |
| **G. BUILDING SITEWORK** | **N/A** | | | | | |
| | | | | **Sub-Total** | 121.68 | **100%** |
| | CONTRACTOR FEES (General Requirements: 10%, Overhead: 5%, Profit: 10%) | | | *25%* | 30.47 | |
| | ARCHITECT FEES | | | *7%* | 10.65 | |
| | | | | **Total Building Cost** | **162.80** | |

## Costs per square foot of floor area

| Exterior Wall | S.F. Area | 85000 | 115000 | 145000 | 175000 | 205000 | 235000 | 265000 | 295000 | 325000 |
|---|---|---|---|---|---|---|---|---|---|---|
| | L.F. Perimeter | 529 | 638 | 723 | 823 | 875 | 910 | 975 | 1027 | 1075 |
| Face Brick and Concrete Block | Rigid Steel | 105.55 | 103.45 | 101.90 | 101.00 | 100.05 | 99.10 | 98.60 | 98.15 | 97.70 |
| | Precast Concrete | 97.50 | 95.40 | 93.85 | 93.00 | 92.00 | 91.05 | 90.60 | 90.05 | 89.65 |
| Precast Concrete | Rigid Steel | 118.25 | 114.75 | 112.10 | 110.65 | 108.75 | 107.00 | 106.15 | 105.25 | 104.45 |
| | Precast Concrete | 110.20 | 106.70 | 104.05 | 102.60 | 100.70 | 99.00 | 98.05 | 97.20 | 96.40 |
| Cast in Place Concrete | Rigid Steel | 103.10 | 101.25 | 99.95 | 99.20 | 98.40 | 97.55 | 97.15 | 96.75 | 96.40 |
| | Reinforced Concrete | 95.45 | 93.60 | 92.30 | 91.60 | 90.75 | 89.95 | 89.50 | 89.10 | 88.80 |
| Perimeter Adj., Add or Deduct | Per 100 L.F. | 2.20 | 1.65 | 1.30 | 1.15 | 0.95 | 0.80 | 0.70 | 0.60 | 0.60 |
| Story Hgt. Adj., Add or Deduct | Per 1 Ft. | 1.00 | 0.90 | 0.80 | 0.80 | 0.65 | 0.65 | 0.60 | 0.50 | 0.55 |
| **Basement**—Not Applicable | | | | | | | | | | |

*The above costs were calculated using the basic specifications shown on the facing page. These costs should be adjusted where necessary for design alternatives and owner's requirements.*

## Common additives

| Description | Unit | $ Cost |
|---|---|---|
| Elevators, Electric passenger, 5 stops | | |
| 2000# capacity | Ea. | 213,000 |
| 3500# capacity | Ea. | 220,500 |
| 5000# capacity | Ea. | 229,000 |
| Barrier gate w/programmable controller | Ea. | 3800 |
| Booth for attendant, average | Ea. | 11,900 |
| Fee computer | Ea. | 4250 |
| Ticket spitter with time/date stamp | Ea. | 12,100 |
| Mag strip encoding | Ea. | 18,900 |
| Collection station, pay on foot | Ea. | 114,500 |
| Parking control software | Ea. | 2850 - 7775 |
| Painting, Parking stalls | Stall | 11.45 |
| Parking Barriers | | |
| Timber with saddles, 4″ x 4″ | L.F. | 11.20 |
| Precast concrete, 6″ x 10″ x 6′ | Ea. | 76.50 |
| Traffic Signs, directional, 12″ x 18″, high density | Ea. | 85.50 |



**Important: See the Reference Section for Location Factors.**

# Model costs calculated for a 5 story building with 10' story height and 145,000 square feet of floor area

# Garage, Parking

| | | | Unit | Unit Cost | Cost Per S.F. | % Of Sub-Total |
|---|---|---|---|---|---|---|
| **A. SUBSTRUCTURE** | | | | | | |
| 1010 | Standard Foundations | Poured concrete; strip and spread footings; 4' foundation wall | S.F. Ground | 5.95 | 1.19 | |
| 1020 | Special Foundations | N/A | — | — | — | |
| 1030 | Slab on Grade | 6" reinforced concrete with vapor barrier and granular base | S.F. Slab | 9.42 | 1.88 | 4.4% |
| 2010 | Basement Excavation | Site preparation for slab and trench for foundation wall and footing | S.F. Ground | .22 | .04 | |
| 2020 | Basement Walls | N/A | — | — | — | |
| **B. SHELL** | | | | | | |
| | **B10 Superstructure** | | | | | |
| 1010 | Floor Construction | Double tee precast concrete slab, precast concrete columns | S.F. Floor | 41.96 | 33.57 | 47.4% |
| 1020 | Roof Construction | N/A | — | — | — | |
| | **B20 Exterior Enclosure** | | | | | |
| 2010 | Exterior Walls | Face brick with concrete block backup *40% of story height* | S.F. Wall | 61 | 6.08 | |
| 2020 | Exterior Windows | N/A | — | — | — | 8.6% |
| 2030 | Exterior Doors | N/A | — | — | — | |
| | **B30 Roofing** | | | | | |
| 3010 | Roof Coverings | N/A | — | — | — | 0.0 % |
| 3020 | Roof Openings | N/A | — | — | — | |
| **C. INTERIORS** | | | | | | |
| 1010 | Partitions | Concrete block | S.F. Partition | 40.30 | 1.55 | |
| 1020 | Interior Doors | Hollow metal | Each | 23,180 | .16 | |
| 1030 | Fittings | N/A | — | — | — | |
| 2010 | Stair Construction | Concrete | Flight | 12,925 | 1.42 | 14.5% |
| 3010 | Wall Finishes | Paint | S.F. Surface | 2.21 | .17 | |
| 3020 | Floor Finishes | Parking deck surface coating | S.F. Floor | 6.95 | 6.95 | |
| 3030 | Ceiling Finishes | N/A | — | — | — | |
| **D. SERVICES** | | | | | | |
| | **D10 Conveying** | | | | | |
| 1010 | Elevators & Lifts | Two hydraulic passenger elevators | Each | 205,900 | 2.84 | 4.0% |
| 1020 | Escalators & Moving Walks | N/A | — | — | — | |
| | **D20 Plumbing** | | | | | |
| 2010 | Plumbing Fixtures | Toilet and service fixtures, supply and drainage *1 Fixture/18,125 S.F. Floor* | Each | 725 | .04 | |
| 2020 | Domestic Water Distribution | Electric water heater | S.F. Floor | .12 | .12 | 3.8% |
| 2040 | Rain Water Drainage | Roof drains | S.F. Roof | 12.50 | 2.50 | |
| | **D30 HVAC** | | | | | |
| 3010 | Energy Supply | N/A | — | — | — | |
| 3020 | Heat Generating Systems | N/A | — | — | — | |
| 3030 | Cooling Generating Systems | N/A | — | — | — | 0.0 % |
| 3050 | Terminal & Package Units | N/A | — | — | — | |
| 3090 | Other HVAC Sys. & Equipment | N/A | — | — | — | |
| | **D40 Fire Protection** | | | | | |
| 4010 | Sprinklers | Dry pipe sprinkler system | S.F. Floor | 5.93 | 5.93 | 8.6% |
| 4020 | Standpipes | Standpipes and hose systems | S.F. Floor | .15 | .15 | |
| | **D50 Electrical** | | | | | |
| 5010 | Electrical Service/Distribution | 400 ampere service, panel board and feeders | S.F. Floor | .34 | .34 | |
| 5020 | Lighting & Branch Wiring | T-8 fluorescent fixtures, receptacles, switches and misc. power | S.F. Floor | 4.34 | 4.34 | 6.9% |
| 5030 | Communications & Security | Addressable alarm systems and emergency lighting | S.F. Floor | .13 | .13 | |
| 5090 | Other Electrical Systems | Emergency generator, 7.5 kW | S.F. Floor | .06 | .06 | |
| **E. EQUIPMENT & FURNISHINGS** | | | | | | |
| 1010 | Commercial Equipment | N/A | — | — | — | |
| 1020 | Institutional Equipment | N/A | — | — | — | 1.9 % |
| 1030 | Vehicular Equipment | Ticket dispensers, booths, automatic gates | S.F. Floor | 1.37 | 1.37 | |
| 1090 | Other Equipment | N/A | — | — | — | |
| **F. SPECIAL CONSTRUCTION** | | | | | | |
| 1020 | Integrated Construction | N/A | — | — | — | 0.0 % |
| 1040 | Special Facilities | N/A | — | — | — | |
| **G. BUILDING SITEWORK** | **N/A** | | | | | |
| | | | | **Sub-Total** | 70.83 | **100%** |
| | CONTRACTOR FEES (General Requirements: 10%, Overhead: 5%, Profit: 10%) | | | *25%* | 17.71 | |
| | ARCHITECT FEES | | | *6%* | 5.31 | |
| | | | | **Total Building Cost** | **93.85** | |

## Costs per square foot of floor area

| Exterior Wall | S.F. Area | 20000 | 30000 | 40000 | 50000 | 75000 | 100000 | 125000 | 150000 | 175000 |
|---|---|---|---|---|---|---|---|---|---|---|
| | L.F. Perimeter | 400 | 500 | 600 | 650 | 775 | 900 | 1000 | 1100 | 1185 |
| Cast in Place Concrete | Reinforced Concrete | 137.65 | 128.85 | 124.45 | 120.20 | 114.60 | 111.75 | 109.75 | 108.40 | 107.30 |
| Perimeter Adj., Add or Deduct | Per 100 L.F. | 7.90 | 5.25 | 3.90 | 3.20 | 2.10 | 1.55 | 1.30 | 1.05 | 0.90 |
| Story Hgt. Adj., Add or Deduct | Per 1 Ft. | 3.00 | 2.50 | 2.25 | 1.95 | 1.50 | 1.35 | 1.20 | 1.10 | 1.00 |
| **Basement**—Not Applicable | | | | | | | | | | |

*The above costs were calculated using the basic specifications shown on the facing page. These costs should be adjusted where necessary for design alternatives and owner's requirements.*

## Common additives

| Description | Unit | $ Cost |
|---|---|---|
| Elevators, Hydraulic passenger, 2 stops | | |
| 1500# capacity | Ea. | 86,500 |
| 2500# capacity | Ea. | 90,500 |
| 3500# capacity | Ea. | 96,000 |
| Barrier gate w/programmable controller | Ea. | 3800 |
| Booth for attendant, average | Ea. | 11,900 |
| Fee computer | Ea. | 4250 |
| Ticket spitter with time/date stamp | Ea. | 12,100 |
| Mag strip encoding | Ea. | 18,900 |
| Collection station, pay on foot | Ea. | 114,500 |
| Parking control software | Ea. | 2850 - 7775 |
| Painting, Parking stalls | Stall | 11.45 |
| Parking Barriers | | |
| Timber with saddles, 4″ x 4″ | L.F. | 11.20 |
| Precast concrete, 6″ x 10″ x 6′ | Ea. | 76.50 |
| Traffic Signs, directional, 12″ x 18″ | Ea. | 85.50 |

# Model costs calculated for a 2 story building with 10′ story height and 100,000 square feet of floor area

# Garage, Underground Parking

| | | | Unit | Unit Cost | Cost Per S.F. | % Of Sub-Total |
|---|---|---|---|---|---|---|
| **A. SUBSTRUCTURE** | | | | | | |
| 1010 | Standard Foundations | Poured concrete; strip and spread footings and waterproofing | S.F. Ground | 10.18 | 5.09 | 20.0% |
| 1020 | Special Foundations | N/A | – | – | – | |
| 1030 | Slab on Grade | 5″ reinforced concrete with vapor barrier and granular base | S.F. Slab | 9.63 | 4.82 | |
| 2010 | Basement Excavation | Excavation 24′ deep | S.F. Ground | 13.35 | 6.68 | |
| 2020 | Basement Walls | N/A | – | – | – | |
| **B. SHELL** | | | | | | |
| | **B10 Superstructure** | | | | | |
| 1010 | Floor Construction | Cast-in-place concrete beam and slab, concrete columns | S.F. Floor | 41.98 | 20.99 | 46.6% |
| 1020 | Roof Construction | Cast-in-place concrete beam and slab, concrete columns | S.F. Roof | 35.16 | 17.58 | |
| | **B20 Exterior Enclosure** | | | | | |
| 2010 | Exterior Walls | Cast-in place concrete | S.F. Wall | 30.89 | 5.56 | 7.0% |
| 2020 | Exterior Windows | N/A | – | – | – | |
| 2030 | Exterior Doors | Steel overhead, hollow metal | Each | 6888 | .27 | |
| | **B30 Roofing** | | | | | |
| 3010 | Roof Coverings | Neoprene membrane traffic deck | S.F. Roof | 7.92 | 3.96 | 4.8% |
| 3020 | Roof Openings | N/A | – | – | – | |
| **C. INTERIORS** | | | | | | |
| 1010 | Partitions | Concrete block | S.F. Partition | 53 | 1.01 | 2.0% |
| 1020 | Interior Doors | Hollow metal | Each | 9272 | .09 | |
| 1030 | Fittings | N/A | – | – | – | |
| 2010 | Stair Construction | Concrete | Flight | 8475 | .43 | |
| 3010 | Wall Finishes | Paint | S.F. Surface | 3.12 | .12 | |
| 3020 | Floor Finishes | N/A | – | – | – | |
| 3030 | Ceiling Finishes | N/A | – | – | – | |
| **D. SERVICES** | | | | | | |
| | **D10 Conveying** | | | | | |
| 1010 | Elevators & Lifts | Two hydraulic passenger elevators | Each | 107,000 | 2.14 | 2.6% |
| 1020 | Escalators & Moving Walks | N/A | – | – | – | |
| | **D20 Plumbing** | | | | | |
| 2010 | Plumbing Fixtures | Drainage in parking areas, toilets, & service fixtures *1 Fixture/5000 S.F. Floor* | Each | .08 | .08 | 2.6% |
| 2020 | Domestic Water Distribution | Electric water heater | S.F. Floor | .17 | .17 | |
| 2040 | Rain Water Drainage | Roof drains | S.F. Roof | 3.80 | 1.90 | |
| | **D30 HVAC** | | | | | |
| 3010 | Energy Supply | N/A | – | – | – | 0.3 % |
| 3020 | Heat Generating Systems | N/A | – | – | – | |
| 3030 | Cooling Generating Systems | N/A | – | – | – | |
| 3050 | Terminal & Package Units | Exhaust fans | S.F. Floor | .21 | .21 | |
| 3090 | Other HVAC Sys. & Equipment | N/A | – | – | – | |
| | **D40 Fire Protection** | | | | | |
| 4010 | Sprinklers | Dry pipe sprinkler system | S.F. Floor | 5.94 | 5.94 | 7.5% |
| 4020 | Standpipes | Dry standpipe system, class III | S.F. Floor | .25 | .25 | |
| | **D50 Electrical** | | | | | |
| 5010 | Electrical Service/Distribution | 200 ampere service, panel board and feeders | S.F. Floor | .18 | .18 | 6.2% |
| 5020 | Lighting & Branch Wiring | T-8 fluorescent fixtures, receptacles, switches and misc. power | S.F. Floor | 4.68 | 4.68 | |
| 5030 | Communications & Security | Addressable alarm systems and emergency lighting | S.F. Floor | .17 | .17 | |
| 5090 | Other Electrical Systems | Emergency generator, 11.5 kW | S.F. Floor | .07 | .07 | |
| **E. EQUIPMENT & FURNISHINGS** | | | | | | |
| 1010 | Commercial Equipment | N/A | – | – | – | 0.5 % |
| 1020 | Institutional Equipment | N/A | – | – | – | |
| 1030 | Vehicular Equipment | Ticket dispensers, booths, automatic gates | S.F. Floor | .38 | .38 | |
| 1090 | Other Equipment | N/A | – | – | – | |
| **F. SPECIAL CONSTRUCTION** | | | | | | |
| 1020 | Integrated Construction | N/A | – | – | – | 0.0 % |
| 1040 | Special Facilities | N/A | – | – | – | |
| **G. BUILDING SITEWORK** | **N/A** | | | | | |
| | | | | **Sub-Total** | 82.77 | **100%** |
| | CONTRACTOR FEES (General Requirements: 10%, Overhead: 5%, Profit: 10%) | | | *25%* | 20.70 | |
| | ARCHITECT FEES | | | *8%* | 8.28 | |
| | | | | **Total Building Cost** | **111.75** | |

## Costs per square foot of floor area

| Exterior Wall | S.F. Area | 2000 | 4000 | 6000 | 8000 | 10000 | 12000 | 14000 | 16000 | 18000 |
|---|---|---|---|---|---|---|---|---|---|---|
| | L.F. Perimeter | 180 | 260 | 340 | 420 | 450 | 500 | 550 | 575 | 600 |
| Concrete Block | Wood Joists | 216.10 | 190.30 | 181.75 | 177.45 | 171.30 | 168.40 | 166.30 | 163.65 | 161.60 |
| | Steel Joists | 229.80 | 199.20 | 189.00 | 183.90 | **176.95** | 173.60 | 171.20 | 168.25 | 165.90 |
| Cast in Place Concrete | Wood Joists | 234.70 | 204.00 | 193.80 | 188.70 | 180.95 | 177.35 | 174.75 | 171.45 | 168.75 |
| | Steel Joists | 249.90 | 213.75 | 201.65 | 195.65 | 187.00 | 182.90 | 180.00 | 176.30 | 173.35 |
| Stucco | Wood Frame | 217.45 | 191.80 | 183.20 | 178.90 | 172.55 | 169.65 | 167.50 | 164.75 | 162.60 |
| Metal Panel | Rigid Steel | 245.75 | 210.45 | 198.65 | 192.75 | 184.55 | 180.65 | 177.85 | 174.30 | 171.60 |
| Perimeter Adj., Add or Deduct | Per 100 L.F. | 35.60 | 17.80 | 11.85 | 8.90 | 7.05 | 5.95 | 5.05 | 4.45 | 3.95 |
| Story Hgt. Adj., Add or Deduct | Per 1 Ft. | 3.00 | 2.20 | 1.90 | 1.75 | 1.50 | 1.45 | 1.30 | 1.15 | 1.10 |
| ***For Basement**, add $55.00 per square foot of basement area* | | | | | | | | | | |

*The above costs were calculated using the basic specifications shown on the facing page. These costs should be adjusted where necessary for design alternatives and owner's requirements.*

## Common additives

| Description | Unit | $ Cost |
|---|---|---|
| Air Compressors | | |
| Electric 1-1/2 H.P., standard controls | Ea. | 2575 |
| Dual controls | Ea. | 2525 |
| 5 H.P. 115/230 Volt, standard controls | Ea. | 3800 |
| Dual controls | Ea. | 3800 |
| Product Dispenser | | |
| with vapor recovery for 6 nozzles | Ea. | 31,300 |
| Lifts, Single post | | |
| 8000# cap., swivel arm | Ea. | 12,400 |
| Two post, adjustable frames, 12,000# cap. | Ea. | 8450 |
| 24,000# cap. | Ea. | 51,500 |
| 30,000# cap. | Ea. | 49,000 |
| Four post, roll on ramp, 25,000# cap. | Ea. | 16,600 |
| Lockers, Steel, single tier, 60" or 72" | Opng. | 285 - 520 |
| 2 tier, 60" or 72" total | Opng. | 216 - 265 |
| 5 tier, box lockers | Opng. | 465 - 153 |
| Locker bench, lam. maple top only | L.F. | 148 |
| Pedestals, steel pipe | Ea. | 87 |
| Lube Equipment | | |
| 3 reel type, with pumps, no piping | Ea. | 16,900 |
| Spray Painting Booth, 26' long, complete | Ea. | 32,200 |



**Important: See the Reference Section for Location Factors.**

## Model costs calculated for a 1 story building with 14' story height and 10,000 square feet of floor area

# Garage, Repair

| | | | | Unit | Unit Cost | Cost Per S.F. | % Of Sub-Total |
|---|---|---|---|---|---|---|---|
| **A. SUBSTRUCTURE** | | | | | | | |
| 1010 | Standard Foundations | Poured concrete; strip and spread footings; 4' foundation wall | | S.F. Ground | 7.68 | 7.68 | |
| 1020 | Special Foundations | N/A | | — | — | — | |
| 1030 | Slab on Grade | 6" reinforced concrete with vapor barrier and granular base | | S.F. Slab | 11.10 | 11.10 | 14.6% |
| 2010 | Basement Excavation | Site preparation for slab and trench for foundation wall and footing | | S.F. Ground | .38 | .38 | |
| 2020 | Basement Walls | N/A | | — | — | — | |
| **B. SHELL** | | | | | | | |
| | **B10 Superstructure** | | | | | | |
| 1010 | Floor Construction | N/A | | — | — | — | 6.9 % |
| 1020 | Roof Construction | Metal deck on open web steel joists | | S.F. Roof | 9.05 | 9.05 | |
| | **B20 Exterior Enclosure** | | | | | | |
| 2010 | Exterior Walls | Concrete block | *80% of wall* | S.F. Wall | 15.91 | 8.02 | |
| 2020 | Exterior Windows | Hopper type commercial steel | *5% of wall* | Each | 1552 | 3.26 | 11.4% |
| 2030 | Exterior Doors | Steel overhead and hollow metal | *15% of wall* | S.F. Door | 38.41 | 3.63 | |
| | **B30 Roofing** | | | | | | |
| 3010 | Roof Coverings | Built-up tar and gravel; perlite/EPS composite insulation | | S.F. Roof | 8.86 | 8.86 | 6.8% |
| 3020 | Roof Openings | Skylight | | S.F. Roof | .02 | .02 | |
| **C. INTERIORS** | | | | | | | |
| 1010 | Partitions | Concrete block | *50 S.F. Floor/L.F. Partition* | S.F. Partition | 27 | 5.40 | |
| 1020 | Interior Doors | Single leaf hollow metal | *3000 S.F. Floor/Door* | Each | 1159 | .39 | |
| 1030 | Fittings | Toilet partitions | | S.F. Floor | .27 | .27 | |
| 2010 | Stair Construction | N/A | | — | — | — | 9.0% |
| 3010 | Wall Finishes | Paint | | S.F. Surface | 8.60 | 3.44 | |
| 3020 | Floor Finishes | 90% metallic floor hardener, 10% vinyl composition tile | | S.F. Floor | 1.67 | 1.67 | |
| 3030 | Ceiling Finishes | Gypsum board on wood joists in office and washrooms | *10% of area* | S.F. Ceiling | 6.80 | .68 | |
| **D. SERVICES** | | | | | | | |
| | **D10 Conveying** | | | | | | |
| 1010 | Elevators & Lifts | N/A | | — | — | — | 0.0 % |
| 1020 | Escalators & Moving Walks | N/A | | — | — | — | |
| | **D20 Plumbing** | | | | | | |
| 2010 | Plumbing Fixtures | Toilet and service fixtures, supply and drainage | *1 Fixture/500 S.F. Floor* | Each | 2400 | 4.80 | |
| 2020 | Domestic Water Distribution | Gas fired water heater | | S.F. Floor | .91 | .91 | 7.5% |
| 2040 | Rain Water Drainage | Roof drains | | S.F. Roof | 4.12 | 4.12 | |
| | **D30 HVAC** | | | | | | |
| 3010 | Energy Supply | N/A | | — | — | — | |
| 3020 | Heat Generating Systems | N/A | | — | — | — | |
| 3030 | Cooling Generating Systems | N/A | | — | — | — | 10.0 % |
| 3050 | Terminal & Package Units | Single zone AC unit | | S.F. Floor | 12 | 12 | |
| 3090 | Other HVAC Sys. & Equipment | Garage exhaust system | | S.F. Floor | 1.14 | 1.14 | |
| | **D40 Fire Protection** | | | | | | |
| 4010 | Sprinklers | Sprinklers, ordinary hazard | | S.F. Floor | 6.66 | 6.66 | 6.3% |
| 4020 | Standpipes | Standpipe | | S.F. Floor | 1.62 | 1.62 | |
| | **D50 Electrical** | | | | | | |
| 5010 | Electrical Service/Distribution | 200 ampere service, panel board and feeders | | S.F. Floor | .63 | .63 | |
| 5020 | Lighting & Branch Wiring | T-8 fluorescent fixtures, receptacles, switches, A.C. and misc. power | | S.F. Floor | 12.32 | 12.32 | 13.3% |
| 5030 | Communications & Security | Addressable alarm systems, partial internet wiring and emergency lighting | | S.F. Floor | 4.35 | 4.35 | |
| 5090 | Other Electrical Systems | Emergency generator, 15 kW | | S.F. Floor | .09 | .09 | |
| **E. EQUIPMENT & FURNISHINGS** | | | | | | | |
| 1010 | Commercial Equipment | N/A | | — | — | — | |
| 1020 | Institutional Equipment | N/A | | — | — | — | 14.2 % |
| 1030 | Vehicular Equipment | Hoists | | S.F. Floor | 18.57 | 18.57 | |
| 1090 | Other Equipment | N/A | | — | — | — | |
| **F. SPECIAL CONSTRUCTION** | | | | | | | |
| 1020 | Integrated Construction | N/A | | — | — | — | 0.0 % |
| 1040 | Special Facilities | N/A | | — | — | — | |
| **G. BUILDING SITEWORK** | **N/A** | | | | | | |
| | | | | | **Sub-Total** | 131.06 | **100%** |
| | CONTRACTOR FEES (General Requirements: 10%, Overhead: 5%, Profit: 10%) | | | | *25%* | 32.78 | |
| | ARCHITECT FEES | | | | *8%* | 13.11 | |
| | | | | | **Total Building Cost** | **176.95** | |

## Costs per square foot of floor area

| Exterior Wall | S.F. Area | 600 | 800 | 1000 | 1200 | 1400 | 1600 | 1800 | 2000 | 2200 |
|---|---|---|---|---|---|---|---|---|---|---|
| | L.F. Perimeter | 100 | 120 | 126 | 140 | 153 | 160 | 170 | 180 | 190 |
| Face Brick and Concrete Block | Wood Truss | 383.05 | 359.30 | 331.65 | 319.55 | 310.25 | 299.75 | 293.15 | 287.85 | 283.55 |
| | Steel Joists | 409.25 | 383.95 | 354.60 | 341.80 | 331.90 | 320.75 | 313.80 | 308.20 | 303.60 |
| Metal Sandwich Panel | Rigid Steel | 359.55 | 337.00 | 311.65 | 300.40 | 291.75 | 282.10 | 276.05 | 271.15 | 267.15 |
| Face Brick and Glazed Block | Steel Joists | 428.40 | 401.25 | 369.15 | 355.25 | 344.55 | 332.30 | 324.70 | 318.60 | 313.55 |
| Aluminum Clapboard | Wood Frame | 332.00 | 312.10 | 290.50 | 280.70 | 273.25 | 265.05 | 259.85 | 255.70 | 252.20 |
| Wood Clapboard | Wood Frame | 333.45 | 313.40 | 291.60 | 281.75 | 274.15 | 265.90 | 260.65 | 256.50 | 253.00 |
| Perimeter Adj., Add or Deduct | Per 100 L.F. | 159.00 | 119.25 | 95.40 | 79.55 | 68.20 | 59.65 | 53.05 | 47.70 | 43.35 |
| Story Hgt. Adj., Add or Deduct | Per 1 Ft. | 10.20 | 9.15 | 7.75 | 7.20 | 6.75 | 6.10 | 5.80 | 5.55 | 5.25 |
| **Basement**—Not Applicable | | | | | | | | | | |

*The above costs were calculated using the basic specifications shown on the facing page. These costs should be adjusted where necessary for design alternatives and owner's requirements.*

## Common additives

| Description | Unit | $ Cost |
|---|---|---|
| Air Compressors | | |
| Electric 1-1/2 H.P., standard controls | Ea. | 2575 |
| Dual controls | Ea. | 2525 |
| 5 H.P. 115/230 volt, standard controls | Ea. | 3800 |
| Dual controls | Ea. | 3800 |
| Product Dispenser | | |
| with vapor recovery for 6 nozzles | Ea. | 31,300 |
| Lifts, Single post | | |
| 8000# cap. swivel arm | Ea. | 12,400 |
| Two post, adjustable frames, 12,000# cap. | Ea. | 8450 |
| 24,000# cap. | Ea. | 51,500 |
| 30,000# cap. | Ea. | 49,000 |
| Four post, roll on ramp, 25,000# cap. | Ea. | 16,600 |
| Lockers, Steel, single tier, 60" or 72" | Opng. | 285 - 520 |
| 2 tier, 60" or 72" total | Opng. | 216 - 265 |
| 5 tier, box lockers | Ea. | 465 - 153 |
| Locker bench, lam. maple top only | L.F. | 148 |
| Pedestals, steel pipe | Ea. | 87 |
| Lube Equipment | | |
| 3 reel type, with pumps, no piping | Ea. | 16,900 |



**Important: See the Reference Section for Location Factors.**

## Model costs calculated for a 1 story building with 12′ story height and 1,400 square feet of floor area

# Garage, Service Station

| | | | | Unit | Unit Cost | Cost Per S.F. | % Of Sub-Total |
|---|---|---|---|---|---|---|---|
| **A. SUBSTRUCTURE** | | | | | | | |
| 1010 | Standard Foundations | Poured concrete; strip and spread footings; 4′ foundation wall | | S.F. Ground | 16.60 | 16.60 | 12.6% |
| 1020 | Special Foundations | N/A | | – | – | – | |
| 1030 | Slab on Grade | 6″ reinforced concrete with vapor barrier and granular base | | S.F. Slab | 11.10 | 11.10 | |
| 2010 | Basement Excavation | Site preparation for slab and trench for foundation wall and footing | | S.F. Ground | 1.25 | 1.25 | |
| 2020 | Basement Walls | N/A | | – | – | – | |
| **B. SHELL** | | | | | | | |
| | **B10 Superstructure** | | | | | | |
| 1010 | Floor Construction | N/A | | – | – | – | 6.0 % |
| 1020 | Roof Construction | Plywood on wood trusses | | S.F. Roof | 13.74 | 13.74 | |
| | **B20 Exterior Enclosure** | | | | | | |
| 2010 | Exterior Walls | Face brick with concrete block backup | *60% of wall* | S.F. Wall | 40.64 | 31.98 | 29.1% |
| 2020 | Exterior Windows | Store front and metal top hinged outswinging | *20% of wall* | Each | 55 | 14.46 | |
| 2030 | Exterior Doors | Steel overhead, aluminum & glass and hollow metal | *20% of wall* | Each | 78 | 20.41 | |
| | **B30 Roofing** | | | | | | |
| 3010 | Roof Coverings | Asphalt shingles with flashing; perlite/EPS composite insulation | | S.F. Roof | 7.05 | 7.05 | 3.1% |
| 3020 | Roof Openings | N/A | | – | – | – | |
| **C. INTERIORS** | | | | | | | |
| 1010 | Partitions | Concrete block | *25 S.F. Floor/L.F. Partition* | S.F. Partition | 9.03 | 2.89 | 6.7% |
| 1020 | Interior Doors | Single leaf hollow metal | *700 S.F. Floor/Door* | Each | 1159 | 1.65 | |
| 1030 | Fittings | Toilet partitions | | S.F. Floor | 3.79 | 3.79 | |
| 2010 | Stair Construction | N/A | | – | – | – | |
| 3010 | Wall Finishes | Paint | | S.F. Surface | 6.78 | 4.34 | |
| 3020 | Floor Finishes | Vinyl composition tile | *35% of floor area* | S.F. Floor | 2.57 | .90 | |
| 3030 | Ceiling Finishes | Painted gypsum board on furring in sales area & washrooms | *35% of floor area* | S.F. Ceiling | 5.53 | 1.94 | |
| **D. SERVICES** | | | | | | | |
| | **D10 Conveying** | | | | | | |
| 1010 | Elevators & Lifts | N/A | | – | – | – | 0.0 % |
| 1020 | Escalators & Moving Walks | N/A | | – | – | – | |
| | **D20 Plumbing** | | | | | | |
| 2010 | Plumbing Fixtures | Toilet and service fixtures, supply and drainage | *1 Fixture/235 S.F. Floor* | Each | 3057 | 13.01 | 8.5% |
| 2020 | Domestic Water Distribution | Gas fired water heater | | S.F. Floor | 6.50 | 6.50 | |
| 2040 | Rain Water Drainage | N/A | | – | – | – | |
| | **D30 HVAC** | | | | | | |
| 3010 | Energy Supply | N/A | | – | – | – | 13.3 % |
| 3020 | Heat Generating Systems | N/A | | – | – | – | |
| 3030 | Cooling Generating Systems | N/A | | – | – | – | |
| 3050 | Terminal & Package Units | Single zone AC unit | | S.F. Floor | 23.75 | 23.75 | |
| 3090 | Other HVAC Sys. & Equipment | Underfloor exhaust system | | S.F. Floor | 6.87 | 6.87 | |
| | **D40 Fire Protection** | | | | | | |
| 4010 | Sprinklers | Wet pipe sprinkler system | | S.F. Floor | 17.29 | 17.29 | 10.4% |
| 4020 | Standpipes | Standpipe | | S.F. Floor | 6.50 | 6.50 | |
| | **D50 Electrical** | | | | | | |
| 5010 | Electrical Service/Distribution | 200 ampere service, panel board and feeders | | S.F. Floor | 6.19 | 6.19 | 10.4% |
| 5020 | Lighting & Branch Wiring | High efficiency fluorescent fixtures, receptacles, switches, A.C. and misc. power | | S.F. Floor | 9.03 | 9.03 | |
| 5030 | Communications & Security | Addressable alarm systems and emergency lighting | | S.F. Floor | 8 | 8 | |
| 5090 | Other Electrical Systems | Emergency generator | | S.F. Floor | .59 | .59 | |
| **E. EQUIPMENT & FURNISHINGS** | | | | | | | |
| 1010 | Commercial Equipment | N/A | | – | – | – | 0.0 % |
| 1020 | Institutional Equipment | N/A | | – | – | – | |
| 1030 | Vehicular Equipment | N/A | | – | – | – | |
| 1090 | Other Equipment | N/A | | – | – | – | |
| **F. SPECIAL CONSTRUCTION** | | | | | | | |
| 1020 | Integrated Construction | N/A | | – | – | – | 0.0 % |
| 1040 | Special Facilities | N/A | | – | – | – | |
| **G. BUILDING SITEWORK** | **N/A** | | | | | | |
| | | | | | **Sub-Total** | 229.83 | **100%** |
| | CONTRACTOR FEES (General Requirements: 10%, Overhead: 5%, Profit: 10%) | | | | 25% | 57.44 | |
| | ARCHITECT FEES | | | | 8% | 22.98 | |
| | | | | | **Total Building Cost** | **310.25** | |

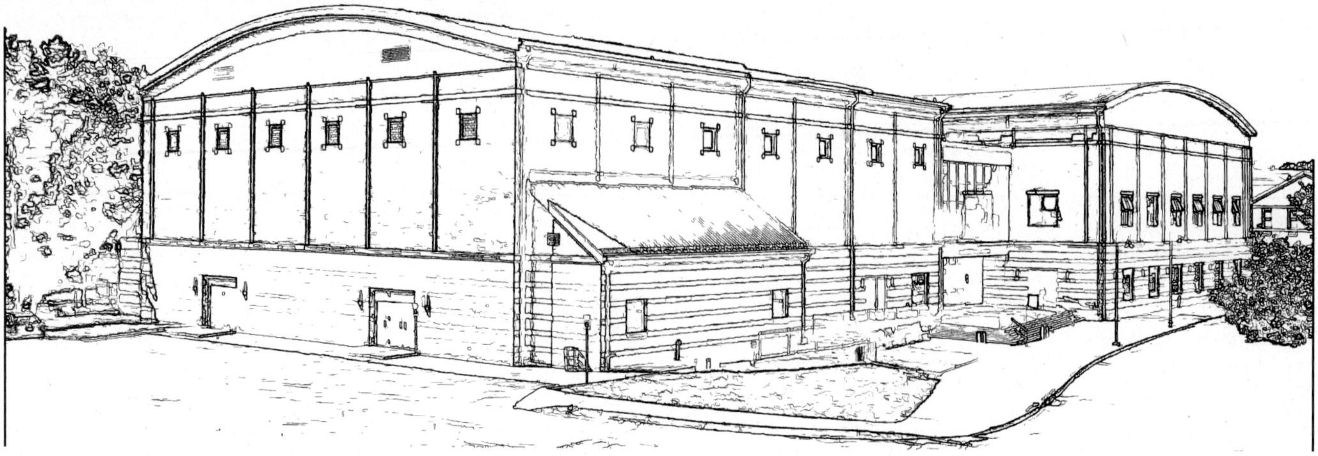

## Costs per square foot of floor area

| Exterior Wall | S.F. Area | 12000 | 16000 | 20000 | 25000 | 30000 | 35000 | 40000 | 45000 | 50000 |
|---|---|---|---|---|---|---|---|---|---|---|
| | L.F. Perimeter | 440 | 520 | 600 | 700 | 708 | 780 | 841 | 910 | 979 |
| Concrete Block | Wood Arch | 235.65 | 229.85 | 226.40 | 223.60 | 218.60 | 216.90 | 215.35 | 214.30 | 213.45 |
| | Rigid Steel | 239.85 | 233.95 | 230.45 | 227.65 | 222.55 | 220.85 | 219.25 | 218.20 | 217.35 |
| Face Brick and Concrete Block | Wood Arch | 264.60 | 255.50 | 250.10 | 245.75 | 237.25 | 234.50 | 231.95 | 230.30 | 228.95 |
| | Rigid Steel | 268.20 | 259.10 | 253.65 | 249.25 | 240.80 | 238.05 | 235.50 | 233.80 | 232.45 |
| Metal Sandwich Panel | Wood Arch | 246.55 | 239.45 | 235.30 | 231.90 | 225.55 | 223.50 | 221.60 | 220.30 | 219.30 |
| | Rigid Steel | 254.25 | 246.70 | 242.30 | 238.65 | 231.85 | 229.60 | 227.55 | 226.15 | 225.00 |
| Perimeter Adj., Add or Deduct | Per 100 L.F. | 8.60 | 6.45 | 5.15 | 4.15 | 3.40 | 2.95 | 2.55 | 2.25 | 2.10 |
| Story Hgt. Adj., Add or Deduct | Per 1 Ft. | 1.20 | 1.10 | 1.00 | 0.90 | 0.75 | 0.75 | 0.65 | 0.65 | 0.70 |
| **Basement**—Not Applicable | | | | | | | | | | |

*The above costs were calculated using the basic specifications shown on the facing page. These costs should be adjusted where necessary for design alternatives and owner's requirements.*

## Common additives

| Description | Unit | $ Cost |
|---|---|---|
| Bleachers, Telescoping, manual | | |
| To 15 tier | Seat | 162 - 299 |
| 16-20 tier | Seat | 261 - 550 |
| 21-30 tier | Seat | 390 - 605 |
| For power operation, add | Seat | 1000 - 1875 |
| Gym Divider Curtain, Mesh top | | |
| Manual roll-up | S.F. | 15.90 |
| Gym Mats | | |
| 2″ naugahyde covered | S.F. | 7.75 |
| 2″ nylon | S.F. | 7.85 |
| 1-1/2″ wall pads | S.F. | 13.20 |
| 1″ wrestling mats | S.F. | 5.90 |
| Scoreboard | | |
| Basketball, one side | Ea. | 1650 - 15,800 |
| Basketball Backstop | | |
| Wall mtd., 6′ extended, fixed | Ea. | 3550 - 4650 |
| Swing up, wall mtd. | Ea. | 3025 - 3775 |

| Description | Unit | $ Cost |
|---|---|---|
| Lockers, Steel, single tier, 60″ or 72″ | Opng. | 285 - 520 |
| 2 tier, 60″ or 72″ total | Opng. | 216 - 265 |
| 5 tier, box lockers | Opng. | 465 - 153 |
| Locker bench, lam. maple top only | L.F. | 148 |
| Pedestals, steel pipe | Ea. | 87 |
| Sound System | | |
| Amplifier, 250 watts | Ea. | 2425 |
| Speaker, ceiling or wall | Ea. | 320 |
| Trumpet | Ea. | 580 |
| Emergency Lighting, 25 watt, battery operated | | |
| Lead battery | Ea. | 360 |
| Nickel cadmium | Ea. | 585 |



**Important: See the Reference Section for Location Factors.**

## Model costs calculated for a 1 story building with 25′ story height and 20,000 square feet of floor area

# Gymnasium

| | | | | Unit | Unit Cost | Cost Per S.F. | % Of Sub-Total |
|---|---|---|---|---|---|---|---|
| **A. SUBSTRUCTURE** | | | | | | | |
| 1010 | Standard Foundations | Poured concrete; strip and spread footings; 4′ foundation wall | | S.F. Ground | 5.09 | 5.09 | 7.4% |
| 1020 | Special Foundations | N/A | | — | — | — | |
| 1030 | Slab on Grade | 4″ reinforced concrete with vapor barrier and granular base | | S.F. Slab | 7.22 | 7.22 | |
| 2010 | Basement Excavation | Site preparation for slab and trench for foundation wall and footing | | S.F. Ground | .22 | .22 | |
| 2020 | Basement Walls | N/A | | — | — | — | |
| **B. SHELL** | | | | | | | |
| | **B10 Superstructure** | | | | | | |
| 1010 | Floor Construction | Steel column | | S.F. Floor | 2.88 | 2.88 | 18.9% |
| 1020 | Roof Construction | Wood deck on laminated wood arches | | S.F. Roof | 29.16 | 29.16 | |
| | **B20 Exterior Enclosure** | | | | | | |
| 2010 | Exterior Walls | Reinforced concrete block (end walls included) | *90% of wall* | S.F. Wall | 14.39 | 9.71 | 9.9% |
| 2020 | Exterior Windows | Metal horizontal pivoted | *10% of wall* | Each | 844 | 6.33 | |
| 2030 | Exterior Doors | Aluminum and glass, hollow metal, steel overhead | | Each | 2113 | .64 | |
| | **B30 Roofing** | | | | | | |
| 3010 | Roof Coverings | EPDM, 60 mils, fully adhered; polyisocyanurate insulation | | S.F. Roof | 7.39 | 7.39 | 4.4% |
| 3020 | Roof Openings | N/A | | — | — | — | |
| **C. INTERIORS** | | | | | | | |
| 1010 | Partitions | Concrete block | *50 S.F. Floor/L.F. Partition* | S.F. Partition | 10.85 | 2.17 | 19.6% |
| 1020 | Interior Doors | Single leaf hollow metal | *500 S.F. Floor/Door* | Each | 1159 | 2.32 | |
| 1030 | Fittings | Toilet partitions | | S.F. Floor | .53 | .53 | |
| 2010 | Stair Construction | N/A | | — | — | — | |
| 3010 | Wall Finishes | 50% paint, 50% ceramic tile | | S.F. Surface | 11.98 | 4.79 | |
| 3020 | Floor Finishes | 90% hardwood, 10% ceramic tile | | S.F. Floor | 21.99 | 21.99 | |
| 3030 | Ceiling Finishes | Mineral fiber tile on concealed zee bars | *15% of area* | S.F. Ceiling | 9 | 1.35 | |
| **D. SERVICES** | | | | | | | |
| | **D10 Conveying** | | | | | | |
| 1010 | Elevators & Lifts | N/A | | — | — | — | 0.0 % |
| 1020 | Escalators & Moving Walks | N/A | | — | — | — | |
| | **D20 Plumbing** | | | | | | |
| 2010 | Plumbing Fixtures | Toilet and service fixtures, supply and drainage | *1 Fixture/515 S.F. Floor* | Each | 6561 | 12.74 | 11.5% |
| 2020 | Domestic Water Distribution | Electric water heater | | S.F. Floor | 6.76 | 6.76 | |
| 2040 | Rain Water Drainage | N/A | | — | — | — | |
| | **D30 HVAC** | | | | | | |
| 3010 | Energy Supply | N/A | | — | — | — | 8.6 % |
| 3020 | Heat Generating Systems | Included in D3050 | | — | — | — | |
| 3030 | Cooling Generating Systems | N/A | | — | — | — | |
| 3050 | Terminal & Package Units | Single zone rooftop unit, gas heating, electric cooling | | S.F. Floor | 14.50 | 14.50 | |
| 3090 | Other HVAC Sys. & Equipment | N/A | | — | — | — | |
| | **D40 Fire Protection** | | | | | | |
| 4010 | Sprinklers | Wet pipe sprinkler system | | S.F. Floor | 5.07 | 5.07 | 4.0% |
| 4020 | Standpipes | Standpipe | | S.F. Floor | 1.69 | 1.69 | |
| | **D50 Electrical** | | | | | | |
| 5010 | Electrical Service/Distribution | 400 ampere service, panel board and feeders | | S.F. Floor | 1.41 | 1.41 | 11.1% |
| 5020 | Lighting & Branch Wiring | High efficiency fluorescent fixtures, receptacles, switches, A.C. and misc. power | | S.F. Floor | 13.53 | 13.53 | |
| 5030 | Communications & Security | Addressable alarm systems, sound system and emergency lighting | | S.F. Floor | 3.70 | 3.70 | |
| 5090 | Other Electrical Systems | Emergency generator, 7.5 kW | | S.F. Floor | .22 | .22 | |
| **E. EQUIPMENT & FURNISHINGS** | | | | | | | |
| 1010 | Commercial Equipment | N/A | | — | — | — | 4.6 % |
| 1020 | Institutional Equipment | N/A | | — | — | — | |
| 1030 | Vehicular Equipment | N/A | | — | — | — | |
| 1090 | Other Equipment | Bleachers, sauna, weight room | | S.F. Floor | 7.85 | 7.85 | |
| **F. SPECIAL CONSTRUCTION** | | | | | | | |
| 1020 | Integrated Construction | N/A | | — | — | — | 0.0 % |
| 1040 | Special Facilities | N/A | | — | — | — | |
| **G. BUILDING SITEWORK** | **N/A** | | | | | | |
| | | | | | **Sub-Total** | 169.26 | **100%** |
| | CONTRACTOR FEES (General Requirements: 10%, Overhead: 5%, Profit: 10%) | | | | *25%* | 42.33 | |
| | ARCHITECT FEES | | | | *7%* | 14.81 | |
| | | | | | **Total Building Cost** | **226.40** | |

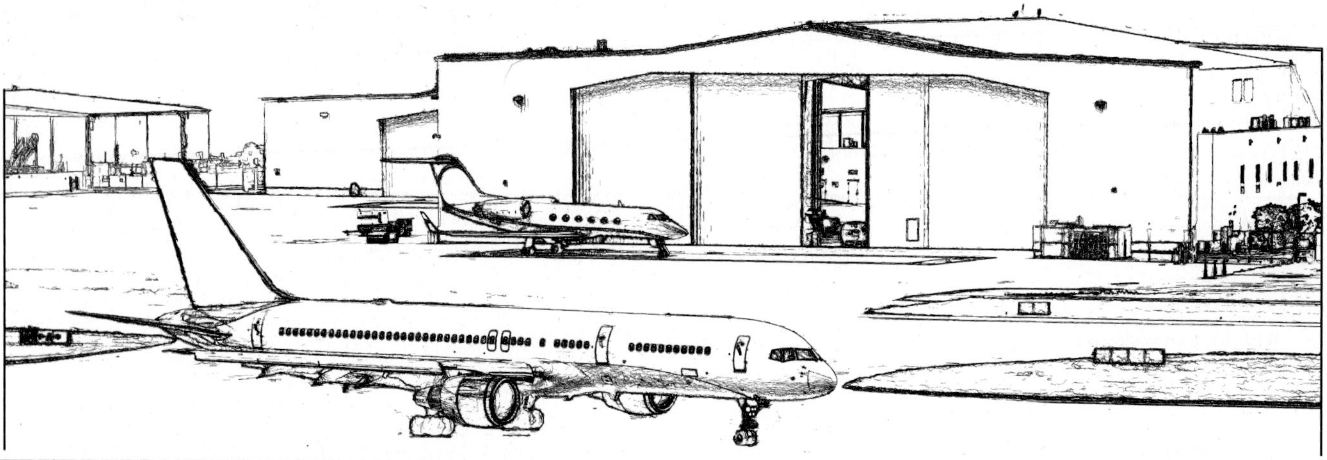

## Costs per square foot of floor area

| Exterior Wall | S.F. Area | 5000 | 10000 | 15000 | 20000 | 30000 | 40000 | 50000 | 75000 | 100000 |
|---|---|---|---|---|---|---|---|---|---|---|
| | L.F. Perimeter | 300 | 410 | 500 | 580 | 710 | 830 | 930 | 1150 | 1300 |
| Concrete Block | Rigid Steel | 247.50 | 201.85 | 184.85 | 175.80 | 165.50 | 160.05 | 156.20 | 150.70 | 147.00 |
| | Bearing Walls | 260.35 | 213.90 | 196.60 | 187.40 | 176.90 | 171.30 | 167.40 | 161.75 | 157.95 |
| Precast Concrete | Rigid Steel | 330.65 | 258.60 | 231.00 | 215.95 | 198.25 | 188.75 | 182.00 | 171.90 | 165.05 |
| | Bearing Walls | 335.20 | 262.75 | 235.00 | 219.85 | 202.05 | 192.50 | 185.65 | 175.50 | 168.55 |
| Metal Panel | Rigid Steel | 243.25 | 198.90 | 182.50 | **173.75** | 163.80 | 158.60 | 154.90 | 149.60 | 146.05 |
| Metal Sandwich Panel | Rigid Steel | 250.30 | 203.70 | 186.40 | 177.15 | 166.55 | 161.00 | 157.10 | 151.40 | 147.60 |
| Perimeter Adj., Add or Deduct | Per 100 L.F. | 25.05 | 12.45 | 8.35 | 6.25 | 4.20 | 3.10 | 2.55 | 1.65 | 1.25 |
| Story Hgt. Adj., Add or Deduct | Per 1 Ft. | 2.40 | 1.60 | 1.35 | 1.20 | 0.90 | 0.85 | 0.75 | 0.60 | 0.50 |
| **Basement**—Not Applicable | | | | | | | | | | |

*The above costs were calculated using the basic specifications shown on the facing page. These costs should be adjusted where necessary for design alternatives and owner's requirements.*

## Common additives

| Description | Unit | $ Cost |
|---|---|---|
| Closed Circuit Surveillance, One station | | |
| Camera and monitor | Ea. | 1250 |
| For additional camera stations, add | Ea. | 475 |
| Emergency Lighting, 25 watt, battery operated | | |
| Lead battery | Ea. | 360 |
| Nickel cadmium | Ea. | 585 |
| Lockers, Steel, single tier, 60" or 72" | Opng. | 285 - 520 |
| 2 tier, 60" or 72" total | Opng. | 216 - 265 |
| 5 tier, box lockers | Opng. | 465 - 153 |
| Locker bench, lam. maple top only | L.F. | 148 |
| Pedestals, steel pipe | Ea. | 87 |
| Safe, Office type, 1 hour rating | | |
| 30" x 18" x 18" | Ea. | 1900 |
| 60" x 36" x 18", double door | Ea. | 8625 |
| Sound System | | |
| Amplifier, 250 watts | Ea. | 2425 |
| Speaker, ceiling or wall | Ea. | 320 |
| Trumpet | Ea. | 580 |



**Important: See the Reference Section for Location Factors.**

## Model costs calculated for a 1 story building with 24′ story height and 20,000 square feet of floor area

# Hangar, Aircraft

| | | | | Unit | Unit Cost | Cost Per S.F. | % Of Sub-Total |
|---|---|---|---|---|---|---|---|
| **A. SUBSTRUCTURE** | | | | | | | |
| 1010 | Standard Foundations | Poured concrete; strip and spread footings; 4′ foundation wall | | S.F. Ground | 5.23 | 5.23 | |
| 1020 | Special Foundations | N/A | | – | – | – | |
| 1030 | Slab on Grade | 6″ reinforced concrete with vapor barrier and granular base | | S.F. Slab | 11.10 | 11.10 | 12.7% |
| 2010 | Basement Excavation | Site preparation for slab and trench for foundation wall and footing | | S.F. Ground | .22 | .22 | |
| 2020 | Basement Walls | N/A | | – | – | – | |
| **B. SHELL** | | | | | | | |
| | **B10 Superstructure** | | | | | | |
| 1010 | Floor Construction | N/A | | – | – | – | 11.9 % |
| 1020 | Roof Construction | Metal deck, open web steel joists, beams, columns | | S.F. Roof | 15.43 | 15.43 | |
| | **B20 Exterior Enclosure** | | | | | | |
| 2010 | Exterior Walls | Galvanized steel siding | | S.F. Wall | 14.63 | 5.09 | |
| 2020 | Exterior Windows | Industrial horizontal pivoted steel | *20% of wall* | Each | 2405 | 13.95 | 23.2% |
| 2030 | Exterior Doors | Steel overhead and sliding | *30% of wall* | Each | 53 | 11.14 | |
| | **B30 Roofing** | | | | | | |
| 3010 | Roof Coverings | Elastomeric membrane; fiberboard insulation | | S.F. Roof | 6.75 | 6.75 | 5.3% |
| 3020 | Roof Openings | Roof hatches | | S.F. Roof | .17 | .17 | |
| **C. INTERIORS** | | | | | | | |
| 1010 | Partitions | Concrete block | *200 S.F. Floor/L.F. Partition* | S.F. Partition | 12.20 | .61 | |
| 1020 | Interior Doors | Single leaf hollow metal | *5000 S.F. Floor/Door* | Each | 1159 | .23 | |
| 1030 | Fittings | Toilet partitions | | S.F. Floor | .38 | .38 | |
| 2010 | Stair Construction | N/A | | – | – | – | 1.1% |
| 3010 | Wall Finishes | Paint | | S.F. Surface | 1.50 | .15 | |
| 3020 | Floor Finishes | N/A | | – | – | – | |
| 3030 | Ceiling Finishes | N/A | | – | – | – | |
| **D. SERVICES** | | | | | | | |
| | **D10 Conveying** | | | | | | |
| 1010 | Elevators & Lifts | N/A | | – | – | – | 0.0 % |
| 1020 | Escalators & Moving Walks | N/A | | – | – | – | |
| | **D20 Plumbing** | | | | | | |
| 2010 | Plumbing Fixtures | Toilet and service fixtures, supply and drainage | *1 Fixture/1000 S.F. Floor* | Each | 3900 | 3.90 | |
| 2020 | Domestic Water Distribution | Gas fired water heater | | S.F. Floor | 3.38 | 3.38 | 7.0% |
| 2040 | Rain Water Drainage | Roof drains | | S.F. Roof | 1.84 | 1.84 | |
| | **D30 HVAC** | | | | | | |
| 3010 | Energy Supply | N/A | | – | – | – | |
| 3020 | Heat Generating Systems | Unit heaters | | S.F. Floor | 11.55 | 11.55 | |
| 3030 | Cooling Generating Systems | N/A | | – | – | – | 9.2 % |
| 3050 | Terminal & Package Units | Exhaust fan | | S.F. Floor | .35 | .35 | |
| 3090 | Other HVAC Sys. & Equipment | N/A | | – | – | – | |
| | **D40 Fire Protection** | | | | | | |
| 4010 | Sprinklers | Sprinklers, extra hazard, deluge system | | S.F. Floor | 13.22 | 13.22 | 16.3% |
| 4020 | Standpipes | Standpipe and fire pump | | S.F. Floor | 7.97 | 7.97 | |
| | **D50 Electrical** | | | | | | |
| 5010 | Electrical Service/Distribution | 200 ampere service, panel board and feeders | | S.F. Floor | 1.27 | 1.27 | |
| 5020 | Lighting & Branch Wiring | High intensity discharge fixtures, receptacles, switches and misc. power | | S.F. Floor | 14.36 | 14.36 | 13.3% |
| 5030 | Communications & Security | Addressable alarm systems and emergency lighting | | S.F. Floor | 1.48 | 1.48 | |
| 5090 | Other Electrical Systems | Emergency generator, 7.5 kW | | S.F. Floor | .15 | .15 | |
| **E. EQUIPMENT & FURNISHINGS** | | | | | | | |
| 1010 | Commercial Equipment | N/A | | – | – | – | |
| 1020 | Institutional Equipment | N/A | | – | – | – | 0.0 % |
| 1030 | Vehicular Equipment | N/A | | – | – | – | |
| 1090 | Other Equipment | N/A | | – | – | – | |
| **F. SPECIAL CONSTRUCTION** | | | | | | | |
| 1020 | Integrated Construction | N/A | | – | – | – | 0.0 % |
| 1040 | Special Facilities | N/A | | – | – | – | |
| **G. BUILDING SITEWORK** | **N/A** | | | | | | |
| | | | | | **Sub-Total** | 129.92 | **100%** |
| | CONTRACTOR FEES (General Requirements: 10%, Overhead: 5%, Profit: 10%) | | | | *25%* | 32.46 | |
| | ARCHITECT FEES | | | | *7%* | 11.37 | |
| | | | | | **Total Building Cost** | **173.75** | |

## Costs per square foot of floor area

| Exterior Wall | S.F. Area | 25000 | 40000 | 55000 | 70000 | 85000 | 100000 | 115000 | 130000 | 145000 |
|---|---|---|---|---|---|---|---|---|---|---|
| | L.F. Perimeter | 388 | 520 | 566 | 666 | 766 | 866 | 878 | 962 | 1045 |
| Face Brick and Concrete Block | Rigid Steel | 432.95 | 421.25 | 411.90 | 408.55 | 406.40 | 404.85 | 401.75 | 400.75 | 400.00 |
| Face Brick and Concrete Block | Reinforced Concrete | 441.85 | 430.15 | 420.80 | 417.40 | 415.30 | 413.70 | 410.65 | 409.65 | 408.90 |
| Stone Veneer | Steel Frame | 435.25 | 421.25 | 409.30 | 405.20 | 402.60 | 400.65 | 396.60 | 395.45 | 394.50 |
| Curtain Wall | Steel Frame | 433.40 | 419.25 | 407.25 | 403.15 | 400.55 | 398.60 | 394.45 | 393.30 | 392.30 |
| E.I.F.S. | Reinforced Concrete | 434.05 | 421.10 | 410.40 | 406.70 | 404.30 | 402.60 | 398.95 | 397.85 | 397.00 |
| Metal Panel | Reinforced Concrete | 442.75 | 428.45 | 416.35 | 412.15 | 409.45 | 407.60 | 403.40 | 402.25 | 401.20 |
| Perimeter Adj., Add or Deduct | Per 100 L.F. | 10.30 | 6.45 | 4.70 | 3.60 | 3.00 | 2.55 | 2.25 | 2.05 | 1.80 |
| Story Hgt. Adj., Add or Deduct | Per 1 Ft. | 2.65 | 2.20 | 1.75 | 1.65 | 1.55 | 1.45 | 1.30 | 1.30 | 1.25 |
| ***For Basement**, add $57.45 per square foot of basement area* | | | | | | | | | | |

*The above costs were calculated using the basic specifications shown on the facing page. These costs should be adjusted where necessary for design alternatives and owner's requirements.*

## Common additives

| Description | Unit | $ Cost |
|---|---|---|
| Cabinet, Base, door units, metal | L.F. | 2875 |
| Drawer units | L.F. | 1075 |
| Tall storage cabinets, 7' high, open | L.F. | 475 |
| With doors | L.F. | 1125 |
| Wall, metal 12-1/2" deep, open | L.F. | 284 |
| With doors | L.F. | 425 |
| Closed Circuit TV (Patient monitoring) | | |
| One station camera & monitor | Ea. | 1250 |
| For additional camera, add | Ea. | 475 |
| For automatic iris for low light, add | Ea. | 1375 |
| Hubbard Tank, with accessories | | |
| Stainless steel, 125 GPM 45 psi | Ea. | 31,800 |
| For electric hoist, add | Ea. | 3100 |
| Mortuary Refrigerator, End operated | | |
| 2 capacity | Ea. | 6750 |
| 6 capacity | Ea. | 14,900 |

| Description | Unit | $ Cost |
|---|---|---|
| Nurses Call Station | | |
| Single bedside call station | Ea. | 715 |
| Ceiling speaker station | Ea. | 266 |
| Emergency call station | Ea. | 223 |
| Pillow speaker | Ea. | 330 |
| Double bedside call station | Ea. | 475 |
| Duty station | Ea. | 655 |
| Standard call button | Ea. | 325 |
| Master control station for 20 stations | Ea. | 5800 |
| Sound System | | |
| Amplifier, 250 watts | Ea. | 2425 |
| Speaker, ceiling or wall | Ea. | 320 |
| Trumpet | Ea. | 580 |
| Station, Dietary with ice | Ea. | 700 |
| Sterilizers | | |
| Single door, steam | Ea. | 67,000 |
| Double door, steam | Ea. | 67,000 |
| Portable, countertop, steam | Ea. | 4500 - 2425 |
| Gas | Ea. | 4000 |
| Automatic washer/sterilizer | Ea. | 3950 |

## Model costs calculated for a 3 story building with 12′ story height and 55,000 square feet of floor area

# Hospital, 2-3 Story

| | | | Unit | Unit Cost | Cost Per S.F. | % Of Sub-Total |
|---|---|---|---|---|---|---|
| **A. SUBSTRUCTURE** | | | | | | |
| 1010 | Standard Foundations | Poured concrete; strip and spread footings; 4′ foundation wall | S.F. Ground | 11.01 | 3.67 | 2.0% |
| 1020 | Special Foundations | N/A | – | – | – | |
| 1030 | Slab on Grade | 4″ reinforced slab on grade | S.F. Slab | 7.22 | 2.41 | |
| 2010 | Basement Excavation | Site preparation for slab and trench for foundation wall and footing | S.F. Ground | .22 | .07 | |
| 2020 | Basement Walls | N/A | – | – | – | |
| **B. SHELL** | | | | | | |
| | **B10 Superstructure** | | | | | |
| 1010 | Floor Construction | Cast in place concrete beams, slab and columns | S.F. Floor | 33.11 | 22.07 | 10.0% |
| 1020 | Roof Construction | Case in place concrete beams, slab and columns | S.F. Roof | 26.58 | 8.86 | |
| | **B20 Exterior Enclosure** | | | | | |
| 2010 | Exterior Walls | Face brick veneer with CMU back-up | S.F. Wall | 43.19 | 12.80 | 5.0% |
| 2020 | Exterior Windows | Aluminum awning, insulated *20% of wall* | Each | 839 | 2.03 | |
| 2030 | Exterior Doors | Aluminum and glass double doors, hollow metal egress doors | Each | 5810 | .63 | |
| | **B30 Roofing** | | | | | |
| 3010 | Roof Coverings | Asphalt roofing, strip shingles, flashing, gutters and downspouts | S.F. Roof | 8.55 | 2.85 | 0.9% |
| 3020 | Roof Openings | Roof hatches | S.F. Roof | .12 | .04 | |
| **C. INTERIORS** | | | | | | |
| 1010 | Partitions | Concrete block partition, gypsum board on wood studs *10 S.F. Floor/L.F. Partition* | S.F. Partition | 11.93 | 13.26 | 17.4% |
| 1020 | Interior Doors | Hollow metal fire doors *90 S.F. Floor/Door* | Each | 1339 | 9.91 | |
| 1030 | Fittings | Hospital curtains | S.F. Floor | 1.47 | 1.47 | |
| 2010 | Stair Construction | Cast in place concrete stairs, with landings and rails | Flight | 10,225 | 1.49 | |
| 3010 | Wall Finishes | 65% paint, 35% ceramic tile | S.F. Surface | 3.80 | 8.45 | |
| 3020 | Floor Finishes | 60% vinyl tile, 20% ceramic , 15% terrazzo, 5% epoxy | S.F. Floor | 9.58 | 9.58 | |
| 3030 | Ceiling Finishes | Acoustic ceiling tiles on suspended channel grid | S.F. Ceiling | 9.48 | 9.48 | |
| **D. SERVICES** | | | | | | |
| | **D10 Conveying** | | | | | |
| 1010 | Elevators & Lifts | Two hydraulic passenger elevators | Each | 165,825 | 6.03 | 2.0% |
| 1020 | Escalators & Moving Walks | N/A | – | – | – | |
| | **D20 Plumbing** | | | | | |
| 2010 | Plumbing Fixtures | Medical, patient & specialty, supply and drainage *1 Fixture/225 S.F. Floor* | Each | 2348 | 10.48 | 9.4% |
| 2020 | Domestic Water Distribution | Electric water heater | S.F. Floor | 18.67 | 18.67 | |
| 2040 | Rain Water Drainage | Roof drains | S.F. Roof | | | |
| | **D30 HVAC** | | | | | |
| 3010 | Energy Supply | Conditioned air with hot water reheat system | S.F. Floor | 7.23 | 7.23 | 24.1% |
| 3020 | Heat Generating Systems | Boiler | Each | 153,250 | 4.52 | |
| 3030 | Cooling Generating Systems | Conditioned air, chillers, cooling towers | S.F. Floor | 8.10 | 8.10 | |
| 3050 | Terminal & Package Units | N/A | – | – | – | |
| 3090 | Other HVAC Sys. & Equipment | Conditioned air, ductwork, surgey air curtain | S.F. Floor | 55 | 54.53 | |
| | **D40 Fire Protection** | | | | | |
| 4010 | Sprinklers | Wet pipe spinkler system | S.F. Floor | 4.50 | 4.50 | 1.9% |
| 4020 | Standpipes | Standpipe | S.F. Floor | 1.29 | 1.29 | |
| | **D50 Electrical** | | | | | |
| 5010 | Electrical Service/Distribution | 1200 ampere service, panel board and feeders | S.F. Floor | 3.90 | 3.90 | 13.0% |
| 5020 | Lighting & Branch Wiring | Fluorescent fixtures, receptacles, switches, A.C. and misc. power | S.F. Floor | 24.07 | 24.07 | |
| 5030 | Communications & Security | Addressable alarm systems, emergency lighting, internet and phone wiring | S.F. Floor | 7.93 | 7.93 | |
| 5090 | Other Electrical Systems | Emergency generator, 200 Kw with fuel tank, UPS system | S.F. Floor | 4.25 | 4.25 | |
| **E. EQUIPMENT & FURNISHINGS** | | | | | | |
| 1010 | Commercial Equipment | N/A | – | – | – | 14.3 % |
| 1020 | Institutional Equipment | Laboratory and commercial kitchen equipment | S.F. Floor | 39.99 | 39.99 | |
| 1030 | Vehicular Equipment | N/A | – | – | – | |
| 2020 | Moveable Furnishings | Patient wall systems | S.F. Floor | 4.29 | 4.29 | |
| **F. SPECIAL CONSTRUCTION** | | | | | | |
| 1020 | Integrated Construction | N/A | – | – | – | 0.0 % |
| 1040 | Special Facilities | N/A | – | – | – | |
| **G. BUILDING SITEWORK** | **N/A** | | | | | |

| | | | |
|---|---|---|---|
| | **Sub-Total** | 308.85 | **100%** |
| CONTRACTOR FEES (General Requirements: 10%, Overhead: 5%, Profit: 10%) | 25% | 77.20 | |
| ARCHITECT FEES | 9% | 34.75 | |
| | **Total Building Cost** | **420.80** | |

# Hospital, 4-8 Story

## Costs per square foot of floor area

| Exterior Wall | S.F. Area | 100000 | 125000 | 150000 | 175000 | 200000 | 225000 | 250000 | 275000 | 300000 |
|---|---|---|---|---|---|---|---|---|---|---|
| | L.F. Perimeter | 594 | 705 | 816 | 783 | 866 | 950 | 1033 | 1116 | 1200 |
| Fiber Cement | Rigid Steel | 342.70 | 338.90 | 336.30 | 330.15 | 328.60 | 327.40 | 326.40 | 325.60 | 324.95 |
| Curtain Wall | Rigid Steel | 354.55 | 350.40 | 347.55 | 340.00 | 338.30 | 336.95 | 335.90 | 334.95 | 334.25 |
| Metal Panel | Rigid Steel | 347.15 | 343.40 | 340.75 | 334.45 | 332.90 | 331.75 | 330.70 | 329.90 | 329.25 |
| Brick Veneer | Reinforced Concrete | 367.25 | 362.70 | 359.60 | 351.00 | 349.10 | 347.65 | 346.40 | 345.40 | 344.55 |
| Stone Veneer | Reinforced Concrete | 379.90 | 374.70 | 371.20 | 360.50 | 358.30 | 356.60 | 355.15 | 354.05 | 353.15 |
| E.I.F.S. | Reinforced Concrete | 357.95 | 353.90 | 351.15 | 344.00 | 342.35 | 341.05 | 339.95 | 339.05 | 338.35 |
| Perimeter Adj., Add or Deduct | Per 100 L.F. | 5.40 | 4.35 | 3.70 | 3.05 | 2.70 | 2.40 | 2.15 | 2.00 | 1.80 |
| Story Hgt. Adj., Add or Deduct | Per 1 Ft. | 2.05 | 2.00 | 1.95 | 1.55 | 1.50 | 1.45 | 1.50 | 1.40 | 1.40 |
| ***For Basement**, add $59.25 per square foot of basement area* | | | | | | | | | | |

*The above costs were calculated using the basic specifications shown on the facing page. These costs should be adjusted where necessary for design alternatives and owner's requirements.*

## Common additives

| Description | Unit | $ Cost |
|---|---|---|
| Cabinets, Base, door units, metal | L.F. | 2875 |
| Drawer units | L.F. | 1075 |
| Tall storage cabinets, 7' high, open | L.F. | 475 |
| With doors | L.F. | 1125 |
| Wall, metal 12-1/2" deep, open | L.F. | 284 |
| With doors | L.F. | 425 |
| Closed Circuit TV (Patient monitoring) | | |
| One station camera & monitor | Ea. | 1250 |
| For additional camera add | Ea. | 475 |
| For automatic iris for low light add | Ea. | 1375 |
| Hubbard Tank, with accessories | | |
| Stainless steel, 125 GPM 45 psi | Ea. | 31,800 |
| For electric hoist, add | Ea. | 3100 |
| Mortuary Refrigerator, End operated | | |
| 2 capacity | Ea. | 6750 |
| 6 capacity | Ea. | 14,900 |

| Description | Unit | $ Cost |
|---|---|---|
| Nurses Call Station | | |
| Single bedside call station | Ea. | 715 |
| Ceiling speaker station | Ea. | 266 |
| Emergency call station | Ea. | 223 |
| Pillow speaker | Ea. | 330 |
| Double bedside call station | Ea. | 475 |
| Duty station | Ea. | 655 |
| Standard call button | Ea. | 325 |
| Master control station for 20 stations | Ea. | 5800 |
| Sound System | | |
| Amplifier, 250 watts | Ea. | 2425 |
| Speaker, ceiling or wall | Ea. | 320 |
| Trumpet | Ea. | 580 |
| Station, Dietary with ice | Ea. | 700 |
| Sterilizers | | |
| Single door, steam | Ea. | 67,000 |
| Double door, steam | Ea. | 67,000 |
| Portable, counter top, steam | Ea. | 4500 - 2425 |
| Gas | Ea. | 4000 |
| Automatic washer/sterilizer | Ea. | 3950 |



**Important: See the Reference Section for Location Factors.**

## Model costs calculated for a 6 story building with 12′ story height and 200,000 square feet of floor area

# Hospital, 4-8 Story

| | | | | Unit | Unit Cost | Cost Per S.F. | % Of Sub-Total |
|---|---|---|---|---|---|---|---|
| **A. SUBSTRUCTURE** | | | | | | | |
| 1010 | Standard Foundations | Poured concrete; strip and spread footings; 4′ foundation wall | | S.F. Ground | 6.18 | 1.03 | 1.7% |
| 1020 | Special Foundations | N/A | | — | — | — | |
| 1030 | Slab on Grade | 4″ reinforced slab on grade | | S.F. Slab | 18.90 | 3.15 | |
| 2010 | Basement Excavation | Site preparation for slab and trench for foundation wall and footing | | S.F. Ground | .22 | .04 | |
| 2020 | Basement Walls | N/A | | — | — | — | |
| **B. SHELL** | | | | | | | |
| | **B10 Superstructure** | | | | | | |
| 1010 | Floor Construction | Open web steel joists, slab form, concrete, fireproofed steel columns | | S.F. Floor | 17.90 | 14.92 | 7.1% |
| 1020 | Roof Construction | Metal deck on open web steel joints, columns | | S.F. Roof | 13.68 | 2.28 | |
| | **B20 Exterior Enclosure** | | | | | | |
| 2010 | Exterior Walls | Fiber cement siding on metal studs, insulated | *70% of wall* | S.F. Wall | 25.66 | 5.60 | 5.7% |
| 2020 | Exterior Windows | Aluminum sliding windows | *30% of wall* | Each | 1677 | 6.98 | |
| 2030 | Exterior Doors | Aluminum and glass double doors, hollow metal egress doors | | Each | 9049 | 1.26 | |
| | **B30 Roofing** | | | | | | |
| 3010 | Roof Coverings | Single ply membrane, stone ballast | | S.F. Roof | 10.26 | 1.71 | 0.7% |
| 3020 | Roof Openings | Roof hatches | | S.F. Roof | .36 | .06 | |
| **C. INTERIORS** | | | | | | | |
| 1010 | Partitions | Concrete block partitions, gypsum board on metal studs | *10 S.F. Floor/L.F. Partition* | S.F. Partition | 8.42 | 9.35 | 20.5% |
| 1020 | Interior Doors | Single leaf hollow metal doors, fire doors | *90 S.F. Floor/Door* | Each | 1339 | 9.91 | |
| 1030 | Fittings | Hospital curtains | | S.F. Floor | 1.61 | 1.61 | |
| 2010 | Stair Construction | Concrete filled metal pan | | Flight | 12,925 | 1.68 | |
| 3010 | Wall Finishes | 65% Paint, 35 % ceramic wall tile | | S.F. Surface | 3.78 | 8.40 | |
| 3020 | Floor Finishes | 60% vinyl tile, 20% ceramic , 20% terrazzo | | S.F. Floor | 9.05 | 9.05 | |
| 3030 | Ceiling Finishes | Acoustic ceiling tiles on suspended channel grid | | S.F. Ceiling | 9.48 | 9.48 | |
| **D. SERVICES** | | | | | | | |
| | **D10 Conveying** | | | | | | |
| 1010 | Elevators & Lifts | Six traction geared hospital elevators | | Each | 279,333 | 8.38 | 3.5% |
| 1020 | Escalators & Moving Walks | N/A | | — | — | — | |
| | **D20 Plumbing** | | | | | | |
| 2010 | Plumbing Fixtures | Medical, patient & specialty, supply and drainage | *1 Fixture/415 S.F. Floor* | Each | 4035 | 9.70 | 9.0% |
| 2020 | Domestic Water Distribution | Electric water heater | | S.F. Floor | 11.24 | 11.24 | |
| 2040 | Rain Water Drainage | Roof drains | | S.F. Roof | 4.92 | .82 | |
| | **D30 HVAC** | | | | | | |
| 3010 | Energy Supply | Conditioned air with hot water reheat system | | S.F. Floor | 6.01 | 6.01 | 25.3% |
| 3020 | Heat Generating Systems | Steam boiler for services | | Each | 44,850 | .56 | |
| 3030 | Cooling Generating Systems | Chillers | | S.F. Floor | 3.79 | 3.79 | |
| 3050 | Terminal & Package Units | N/A | | — | — | — | |
| 3090 | Other HVAC Sys. & Equipment | Hot water boilers, ductwork, VAV terminals, ventilation system | | S.F. Floor | 51 | 50.67 | |
| | **D40 Fire Protection** | | | | | | |
| 4010 | Sprinklers | Wet pipe spinkler system | | S.F. Floor | 4.28 | 4.28 | 2.1% |
| 4020 | Standpipes | Standpipe | | S.F. Floor | .86 | .86 | |
| | **D50 Electrical** | | | | | | |
| 5010 | Electrical Service/Distribution | 2000 ampere service, panel board and feeders | | S.F. Floor | 3.73 | 3.73 | 14.9% |
| 5020 | Lighting & Branch Wiring | Fluorescent fixtures, receptacles, switches, A.C. and misc. power | | S.F. Floor | 28.22 | 28.22 | |
| 5030 | Communications & Security | Addressable alarms, emergency lighting, internet and phone wiring | | S.F. Floor | 3.05 | 3.05 | |
| 5090 | Other Electrical Systems | Emergency generator, 400 Kw with fuel tank, UPS system | | S.F. Floor | 1.04 | 1.04 | |
| **E. EQUIPMENT & FURNISHINGS** | | | | | | | |
| 1010 | Commercial Equipment | N/A | | — | — | — | 9.2 % |
| 1020 | Institutional Equipment | Laboratory and kitchen equipment | | S.F. Floor | 18 | 18 | |
| 1030 | Vehicular Equipment | N/A | | — | — | — | |
| 2020 | Moveable Furnishings | Patient wall systems | | S.F. Floor | 4.30 | 4.30 | |
| **F. SPECIAL CONSTRUCTION** | | | | | | | |
| 1020 | Integrated Construction | N/A | | — | — | — | 0.0 % |
| 1040 | Special Facilities | N/A | | — | — | — | |
| **G. BUILDING SITEWORK** | | **N/A** | | | | | |
| | | | | | **Sub-Total** | 241.16 | **100%** |
| | CONTRACTOR FEES (General Requirements: 10%, Overhead: 5%, Profit: 10%) | | | | 25% | 60.31 | |
| | ARCHITECT FEES | | | | 9% | 27.13 | |
| | | | | | **Total Building Cost** | **328.60** | |

## Costs per square foot of floor area

| Exterior Wall | S.F. Area | 35000 | 55000 | 75000 | 95000 | 115000 | 135000 | 155000 | 175000 | 195000 |
|---|---|---|---|---|---|---|---|---|---|---|
| | L.F. Perimeter | 314 | 401 | 497 | 555 | 639 | 722 | 754 | 783 | 850 |
| Brick Veneer | Reinforced Concrete | 274.55 | 256.35 | 248.70 | 241.50 | 238.35 | **236.10** | 232.10 | 228.95 | 227.75 |
| Stone Veneer | Rigid Steel | 259.50 | 244.30 | 237.80 | 232.05 | 229.35 | 227.50 | 224.40 | 221.90 | 220.90 |
| E.I.F.S. | Reinforced Concrete | 241.55 | 229.90 | 224.85 | 220.75 | 218.70 | 217.25 | 215.20 | 213.55 | 212.80 |
| Curtain Wall | Rigid Steel | 259.40 | 244.25 | 237.75 | 231.90 | 229.30 | 227.45 | 224.30 | 221.85 | 220.85 |
| Precast Concrete | Reinforced Concrete | 262.15 | 245.75 | 238.80 | 232.40 | 229.55 | 227.55 | 224.05 | 221.30 | 220.25 |
| Fiber Cement | Rigid Steel | 234.40 | 223.20 | 218.30 | 214.40 | 212.40 | 211.05 | 209.05 | 207.50 | 206.80 |
| Perimeter Adj., Add or Deduct | Per 100 L.F. | 19.85 | 12.70 | 9.30 | 7.30 | 6.00 | 5.15 | 4.55 | 3.90 | 3.55 |
| Story Hgt. Adj., Add or Deduct | Per 1 Ft. | 3.45 | 2.85 | 2.50 | 2.20 | 2.15 | 2.05 | 1.90 | 1.70 | 1.65 |
| ***For Basement**, add $56.40 per square foot of basement area* | | | | | | | | | | |

*The above costs were calculated using the basic specifications shown on the facing page. These costs should be adjusted where necessary for design alternatives and owner's requirements.*

## Common additives

| Description | Unit | $ Cost |
|---|---|---|
| Bar, Front bar | L.F. | 490 |
| Back bar | L.F. | 395 |
| Booth, Upholstered, custom, straight | L.F. | 281 - 1500 |
| "L" or "U" shaped | L.F. | 291 - 490 |
| Closed Circuit Surveillance, One station | | |
| Camera and monitor | Ea. | 1250 |
| For additional camera stations, add | Ea. | 475 |
| Directory Boards, Plastic, glass covered | | |
| 30" x 20" | Ea. | 705 |
| 36" x 48" | Ea. | 1475 |
| Aluminum, 24" x 18" | Ea. | 705 |
| 48" x 32" | Ea. | 1975 |
| 48" x 60" | Ea. | 2650 |
| Elevators, Electric passenger, 5 stops | | |
| 3500# capacity | Ea. | 220,500 |
| 5000# capacity | Ea. | 229,000 |
| Additional stop, add | Ea. | 12,600 |
| Emergency Lighting, 25 watt, battery operated | | |
| Lead battery | Ea. | 360 |
| Nickel cadmium | Ea. | 585 |

| Description | Unit | $ Cost |
|---|---|---|
| Laundry Equipment | | |
| Folders, blankets & sheets, king size | Ea. | 90,500 |
| Ironers, 110" single roll | Ea. | 48,300 |
| Combination washer extractor 50# | Ea. | 19,500 |
| 125# | Ea. | 46,200 |
| Sauna, Prefabricated, complete | | |
| 6' x 4' | Ea. | 7500 |
| 6' x 6' | Ea. | 18,400 |
| 6' x 9' | Ea. | 10,500 |
| 8' x 8' | Ea. | 13,500 |
| 10' x 12' | Ea. | 19,700 |
| Smoke Detectors | | |
| Ceiling type | Ea. | 300 |
| Duct type | Ea. | 615 |
| Sound System | | |
| Amplifier, 250 watts | Ea. | 2425 |
| Speaker, ceiling or wall | Ea. | 320 |
| Trumpet | Ea. | 580 |
| TV Antenna, Master system, 12 outlet | Outlet | 284 |
| 30 outlet | Outlet | 370 |
| 100 outlet | Outlet | 395 |



**Important: See the Reference Section for Location Factors.**

## Model costs calculated for a 6 story building with 10' story height and 135,000 square feet of floor area

# Hotel, 4-7 Story

| | | | Unit | Unit Cost | Cost Per S.F. | % Of Sub-Total |
|---|---|---|---|---|---|---|
| **A. SUBSTRUCTURE** | | | | | | |
| 1010 | Standard Foundations | Poured concrete; strip and spread footings; 4' foundation wall | S.F. Ground | 7.44 | 1.24 | 1.4% |
| 1020 | Special Foundations | N/A | – | – | – | |
| 1030 | Slab on Grade | 4" reinforced slab on grade | S.F. Slab | 7.22 | 1.20 | |
| 2010 | Basement Excavation | Site preparation for slab and trench for foundation wall and footing | S.F. Ground | .22 | .04 | |
| 2020 | Basement Walls | N/A | – | – | – | |
| **B. SHELL** | | | | | | |
| | **B10 Superstructure** | | | | | |
| 1010 | Floor Construction | Cast in place concrete columns, beams, and slab, fireproofed | S.F. Floor | 35.17 | 29.31 | 16.4% |
| 1020 | Roof Construction | Included in B1010 | – | – | – | |
| | **B20 Exterior Enclosure** | | | | | |
| 2010 | Exterior Walls | Face brick with concrete block backup. Insulated *80% of wall* | S.F. Wall | 48.38 | 12.42 | 8.6% |
| 2020 | Exterior Windows | Aluminum awning windows *20% of wall* | Each | 839 | 2.34 | |
| 2030 | Exterior Doors | Aluminum and glass double doors, hollow metal egress doors | Each | 6760 | .50 | |
| | **B30 Roofing** | | | | | |
| 3010 | Roof Coverings | Single ply membrane, stone ballast, rigid insulation | S.F. Roof | 10.86 | 1.81 | 1.0% |
| 3020 | Roof Openings | Roof hatches | S.F. Roof | .36 | .06 | |
| **C. INTERIORS** | | | | | | |
| 1010 | Partitions | Fire rated gypsum board on metal studs, CMU partitions *10 S.F. Floor/L.F. Partition* | S.F. Partition | 8.18 | 7.27 | 21.9% |
| 1020 | Interior Doors | Single leaf hollow metal *90 S.F. Floor/Door* | Each | 1159 | 12.87 | |
| 1030 | Fittings | N/A | – | – | – | |
| 2010 | Stair Construction | Concrete filled metal pan | Flight | 16,075 | 3.10 | |
| 3010 | Wall Finishes | 80% paint, 20% ceramic tile | S.F. Surface | 2.72 | 4.83 | |
| 3020 | Floor Finishes | 80% carpet , 10% vinyl composition tile, 10% ceramic tile | S.F. Floor | 5.73 | 5.73 | |
| 3030 | Ceiling Finishes | Painted gypsum board ceiling on metal furring | S.F. Ceiling | 5.27 | 5.27 | |
| **D. SERVICES** | | | | | | |
| | **D10 Conveying** | | | | | |
| 1010 | Elevators & Lifts | Four geared passenger elevators | Each | 288,900 | 8.56 | 4.8% |
| 1020 | Escalators & Moving Walks | N/A | – | – | – | |
| | **D20 Plumbing** | | | | | |
| 2010 | Plumbing Fixtures | Kitchen, bath, laundry and service fixtures, supply and drainage *1 Fixture/150 S.F. Floor* | Each | 4233 | 27.31 | 15.9% |
| 2020 | Domestic Water Distribution | Gas fired water heater | S.F. Floor | .58 | .58 | |
| 2040 | Rain Water Drainage | Roof drains | S.F. Roof | 2.58 | .43 | |
| | **D30 HVAC** | | | | | |
| 3010 | Energy Supply | Gas fired hot water, wall fin radiation | S.F. Floor | 6.78 | 6.78 | 15.4% |
| 3020 | Heat Generating Systems | N/A | – | – | – | |
| 3030 | Cooling Generating Systems | Chilled water, fan coil units | S.F. Floor | 20.75 | 20.75 | |
| 3050 | Terminal & Package Units | N/A | – | – | – | |
| 3090 | Other HVAC Sys. & Equipment | N/A | – | – | – | |
| | **D40 Fire Protection** | | | | | |
| 4010 | Sprinklers | Wet pipe spinkler system, light hazard and accessory package | S.F. Floor | 4.30 | 4.30 | 2.8% |
| 4020 | Standpipes | Standpipes and hose systems, with pumps | S.F. Floor | .62 | .62 | |
| | **D50 Electrical** | | | | | |
| 5010 | Electrical Service/Distribution | 2000 Ampere service, panel boards and feeders | S.F. Floor | 2.37 | 2.37 | 11.7% |
| 5020 | Lighting & Branch Wiring | Fluorescent fixtures, receptacles, switches, A.C. and misc. power | S.F. Floor | 12.34 | 12.34 | |
| 5030 | Communications & Security | Addressable alarm systems, emergency lighting, internet and phone wiring | S.F. Floor | 5.63 | 5.63 | |
| 5090 | Other Electrical Systems | Emergency generator muffler and transfer switch, 250 kW | S.F. Floor | .54 | .54 | |
| **E. EQUIPMENT & FURNISHINGS** | | | | | | |
| 1010 | Commercial Equipment | N/A | – | – | – | 0.0 % |
| 1020 | Institutional Equipment | N/A | – | – | – | |
| 1030 | Vehicular Equipment | N/A | – | – | – | |
| 1090 | Other Equipment | N/A | – | – | – | |
| **F. SPECIAL CONSTRUCTION** | | | | | | |
| 1020 | Integrated Construction | N/A | – | – | – | 0.0 % |
| 1040 | Special Facilities | N/A | – | – | – | |
| **G. BUILDING SITEWORK** | **N/A** | | | | | |
| | | | **Sub-Total** | | 178.20 | **100%** |
| | CONTRACTOR FEES (General Requirements: 10%, Overhead: 5%, Profit: 10%) | | | *25%* | 44.53 | |
| | ARCHITECT FEES | | | *6%* | 13.37 | |
| | | | **Total Building Cost** | | **236.10** | |

## Costs per square foot of floor area

| Exterior Wall | S.F. Area | 140000 | 243000 | 346000 | 450000 | 552000 | 655000 | 760000 | 860000 | 965000 |
|---|---|---|---|---|---|---|---|---|---|---|
| | L.F. Perimeter | 403 | 587 | 672 | 800 | 936 | 1073 | 1213 | 1195 | 1312 |
| Brick Veneer | Reinforced Concrete | 280.05 | 267.60 | 257.00 | 253.00 | 250.90 | 249.55 | 248.45 | 244.20 | 243.45 |
| Stone Veneer | Rigid Steel | 260.80 | 251.70 | 244.50 | 241.70 | 240.25 | 239.25 | 238.45 | 235.80 | 235.20 |
| E.I.F.S. | Reinforced Concrete | 246.50 | 239.85 | 235.00 | 233.10 | 232.05 | 231.35 | 230.80 | 229.15 | 228.75 |
| Curtain Wall | Rigid Steel | 259.85 | 250.95 | 243.85 | 241.15 | 239.70 | 238.70 | 238.00 | 235.35 | 234.80 |
| Precast Concrete | Reinforced Concrete | 277.40 | 266.50 | 257.35 | **253.95** | 252.15 | 250.95 | 250.00 | 246.50 | 245.80 |
| Fiber Cement | Rigid Steel | 240.60 | 234.15 | 229.60 | 227.75 | 226.70 | 226.10 | 225.50 | 224.00 | 223.55 |
| Perimeter Adj., Add or Deduct | Per 100 L.F. | 14.10 | 8.15 | 5.70 | 4.40 | 3.55 | 3.00 | 2.60 | 2.35 | 2.10 |
| Story Hgt. Adj., Add or Deduct | Per 1 Ft. | 2.75 | 2.30 | 1.85 | 1.70 | 1.65 | 1.55 | 1.50 | 1.35 | 1.30 |
| ***For Basement**, add $58.55 per square foot of basement area* | | | | | | | | | | |

*The above costs were calculated using the basic specifications shown on the facing page. These costs should be adjusted where necessary for design alternatives and owner's requirements.*

## Common additives

| Description | Unit | $ Cost |
|---|---|---|
| Bar, Front bar | L.F. | 490 |
| Back bar | L.F. | 395 |
| Booth, Upholstered, custom, straight | L.F. | 281 - 1500 |
| "L" or "U" shaped | L.F. | 291 - 490 |
| Closed Circuit Surveillance, One station | | |
| Camera and monitor | Ea. | 1250 |
| For additional camera stations, add | Ea. | 475 |
| Directory Boards, Plastic, glass covered | | |
| 30" x 20" | Ea. | 705 |
| 36" x 48" | Ea. | 1475 |
| Aluminum, 24" x 18" | Ea. | 705 |
| 48" x 32" | Ea. | 1975 |
| 48" x 60" | Ea. | 2650 |
| Elevators, Electric passenger, 10 stops | | |
| 3500# capacity | Ea. | 484,000 |
| 5000# capacity | Ea. | 494,500 |
| Additional stop, add | Ea. | 12,600 |
| Emergency Lighting, 25 watt, battery operated | | |
| Lead battery | Ea. | 360 |
| Nickel cadmium | Ea. | 585 |

| Description | Unit | $ Cost |
|---|---|---|
| Laundry Equipment | | |
| Folders, blankets & sheets, king size | Ea. | 90,500 |
| Ironers, 110" single roll | Ea. | 48,300 |
| Combination washer & extractor 50# | Ea. | 19,500 |
| 125# | Ea. | 46,200 |
| Sauna, Prefabricated, complete | | |
| 6' x 4' | Ea. | 7500 |
| 6' x 6' | Ea. | 18,400 |
| 6' x 9' | Ea. | 10,500 |
| 8' x 8' | Ea. | 13,500 |
| 10' x 12' | Ea. | 19,700 |
| Smoke Detectors | | |
| Ceiling type | Ea. | 300 |
| Duct type | Ea. | 615 |
| Sound System | | |
| Amplifier, 250 watts | Ea. | 2425 |
| Speaker, ceiling or wall | Ea. | 320 |
| Trumpet | Ea. | 580 |
| TV Antenna, Master system, 12 outlet | Outlet | 284 |
| 30 outlet | Outlet | 370 |
| 100 outlet | Outlet | 395 |



**Important: See the Reference Section for Location Factors.**

## Model costs calculated for a 15 story building with 10′ story height and 450,000 square feet of floor area

# Hotel, 8-24 Story

| | | | | Unit | Unit Cost | Cost Per S.F. | % Of Sub-Total |
|---|---|---|---|---|---|---|---|
| **A. SUBSTRUCTURE** | | | | | | | |
| 1010 | Standard Foundations | CIP concrete pile caps; 4′ foundation wall | | S.F. Ground | 20.10 | 1.34 | 8.7% |
| 1020 | Special Foundations | Steel H piles, concrete grade beams | | S.F. Ground | 222 | 14.77 | |
| 1030 | Slab on Grade | 4″ reinforced slab on grade | | S.F. Slab | 7.22 | .48 | |
| 2010 | Basement Excavation | Site preparation for slab, piles and grade beams | | S.F. Ground | .22 | .01 | |
| 2020 | Basement Walls | N/A | | — | — | — | |
| **B. SHELL** | | | | | | | |
| | **B10 Superstructure** | | | | | | |
| 1010 | Floor Construction | Cast in place concrete columns, beams, and slab | | S.F. Floor | 26.20 | 24.45 | 13.5% |
| 1020 | Roof Construction | Precast double T with 2″ topping | | S.F. Roof | 21.30 | 1.42 | |
| | **B20 Exterior Enclosure** | | | | | | |
| 2010 | Exterior Walls | Precast concrete panels, insulated | *80% of wall* | S.F. Wall | 75 | 16.06 | 9.6% |
| 2020 | Exterior Windows | Aluminum awning type | *20% of wall* | Each | 839 | 1.94 | |
| 2030 | Exterior Doors | Aluminum & glass doors and entrances | | Each | 5923 | .42 | |
| | **B30 Roofing** | | | | | | |
| 3010 | Roof Coverings | Single ply membrane, stone ballast, rigid insulation | | S.F. Roof | 10.50 | .70 | 0.4% |
| 3020 | Roof Openings | Roof hatches | | S.F. Roof | .30 | .02 | |
| **C. INTERIORS** | | | | | | | |
| 1010 | Partitions | Gypsum board on metal studs, sound attenuation insulation | *10 S.F. Floor/L.F. Partition* | S.F. Partition | 8.08 | 7.18 | 19.8% |
| 1020 | Interior Doors | Single leaf hollow metal | *90 S.F. Floor/Door* | Each | 1159 | 12.87 | |
| 1030 | Fittings | N/A | | — | — | — | |
| 2010 | Stair Construction | Concrete filled metal pan with rails | | Flight | 16,075 | 2.21 | |
| 3010 | Wall Finishes | 80% Paint, 20% ceramic tile | | S.F. Surface | 2.69 | 4.78 | |
| 3020 | Floor Finishes | 80% carpet , 10% vinyl composition tile, 10% ceramic tile | | S.F. Floor | 5.73 | 5.73 | |
| 3030 | Ceiling Finishes | Gypsum board on resilient channel | | S.F. Ceiling | 5.27 | 5.27 | |
| **D. SERVICES** | | | | | | | |
| | **D10 Conveying** | | | | | | |
| 1010 | Elevators & Lifts | Five traction geared passenger elevators | | Each | 598,500 | 7.98 | 4.2% |
| 1020 | Escalators & Moving Walks | N/A | | — | — | — | |
| | **D20 Plumbing** | | | | | | |
| 2010 | Plumbing Fixtures | Kitchen, bath, laundry and service fixtures, supply and drainage | *1 Fixture/165 S.F. Floor* | Each | 4442 | 26.92 | 14.3% |
| 2020 | Domestic Water Distribution | Electric water heaters, gas fired water heaters | | S.F. Floor | .17 | .17 | |
| 2040 | Rain Water Drainage | Roof drains | | S.F. Roof | 3.75 | .25 | |
| | **D30 HVAC** | | | | | | |
| 3010 | Energy Supply | Gas fired hot water, wall fin radiation | | S.F. Floor | 3.71 | 3.71 | 12.8% |
| 3020 | Heat Generating Systems | N/A | | — | — | — | |
| 3030 | Cooling Generating Systems | Chilled water, fan coil units | | S.F. Floor | 20.75 | 20.75 | |
| 3050 | Terminal & Package Units | N/A | | — | — | — | |
| 3090 | Other HVAC Sys. & Equipment | N/A | | — | — | — | |
| | **D40 Fire Protection** | | | | | | |
| 4010 | Sprinklers | Wet pipe spinkler system, light hazard and accessory package | | S.F. Floor | 6.24 | 6.24 | 6.6% |
| 4020 | Standpipes | Standpipes and hose systems, with pumps | | S.F. Floor | 6.34 | 6.34 | |
| | **D50 Electrical** | | | | | | |
| 5010 | Electrical Service/Distribution | 2000 Ampere service, panel boards and feeders | | S.F. Floor | 1.55 | 1.55 | 10.3% |
| 5020 | Lighting & Branch Wiring | Fluorescent fixtures, receptacles, switches, A.C. and misc. power | | S.F. Floor | 12.15 | 12.15 | |
| 5030 | Communications & Security | Addressable alarm systems, emergency lighting, internet and phone wiring | | S.F. Floor | 5.63 | 5.63 | |
| 5090 | Other Electrical Systems | Emergency generator muffler and transfer switch, 250 kW | | S.F. Floor | .32 | .32 | |
| **E. EQUIPMENT & FURNISHINGS** | | | | | | | |
| 1010 | Commercial Equipment | N/A | | — | — | — | 0.0 % |
| 1020 | Institutional Equipment | N/A | | — | — | — | |
| 1030 | Vehicular Equipment | N/A | | — | — | — | |
| 1090 | Other Equipment | N/A | | — | — | — | |
| **F. SPECIAL CONSTRUCTION** | | | | | | | |
| 1020 | Integrated Construction | N/A | | — | — | — | 0.0 % |
| 1040 | Special Facilities | N/A | | — | — | — | |
| **G. BUILDING SITEWORK** | | **N/A** | | | | | |
| | | | | | **Sub-Total** | 191.66 | **100%** |
| | CONTRACTOR FEES (General Requirements: 10%, Overhead: 5%, Profit: 10%) | | | | *25%* | 47.92 | |
| | ARCHITECT FEES | | | | *6%* | 14.37 | |
| | | | | | **Total Building Cost** | **253.95** | |

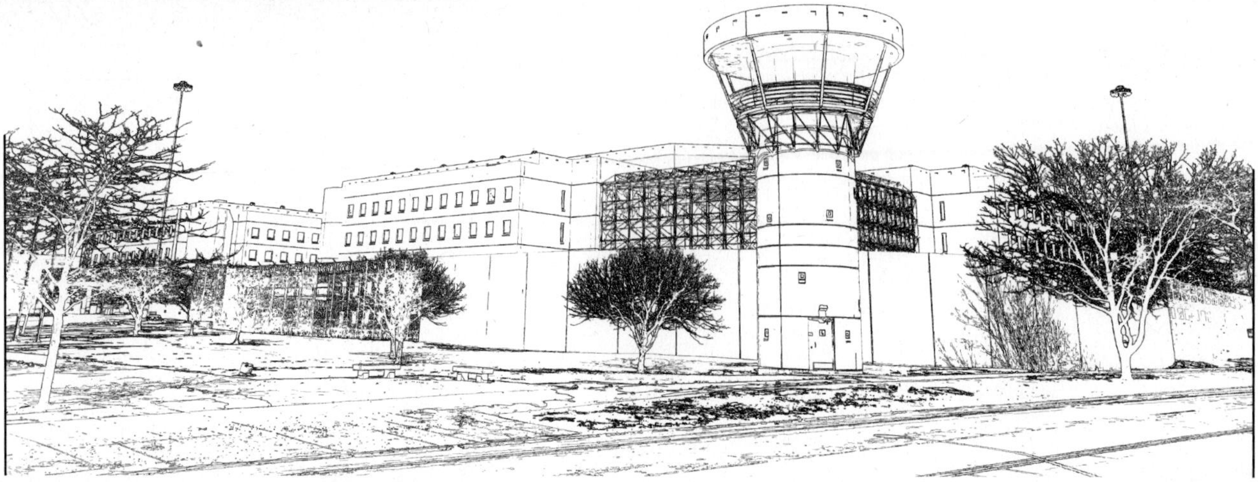

## Costs per square foot of floor area

| Exterior Wall | S.F. Area | 5500 | 12000 | 20000 | 30000 | 40000 | 60000 | 80000 | 100000 | 145000 |
|---|---|---|---|---|---|---|---|---|---|---|
| | L.F. Perimeter | 310 | 330 | 400 | 490 | 530 | 590 | 680 | 760 | 920 |
| Face Brick and Concrete Block | Rigid Steel | 671.40 | 486.75 | 433.10 | 406.60 | **388.55** | 369.05 | 360.85 | 355.40 | 348.30 |
| | Reinforced Concrete | 661.85 | 477.20 | 423.55 | 397.05 | 378.95 | 359.50 | 351.30 | 345.90 | 338.75 |
| Stucco and Concrete Block | Rigid Steel | 653.20 | 477.85 | 426.60 | 401.35 | 384.25 | 365.85 | 358.10 | 353.00 | 346.20 |
| | Reinforced Concrete | 643.60 | 468.35 | 417.05 | 391.85 | 374.70 | 356.35 | 348.55 | 343.45 | 336.70 |
| Cast in Place Concrete | Rigid Steel | 648.45 | 475.55 | 424.95 | 400.00 | 383.15 | 365.00 | 357.40 | 352.35 | 345.70 |
| | Reinforced Concrete | 638.90 | 466.05 | 415.40 | 390.45 | 373.60 | 355.50 | 347.85 | 342.80 | 336.15 |
| Perimeter Adj., Add or Deduct | Per 100 L.F. | 70.80 | 32.50 | 19.45 | 13.00 | 9.65 | 6.45 | 4.90 | 3.95 | 2.65 |
| Story Hgt. Adj., Add or Deduct | Per 1 Ft. | 16.85 | 8.25 | 6.00 | 4.90 | 3.95 | 3.00 | 2.55 | 2.30 | 1.90 |

***For Basement**, add $81.00 per square foot of basement area*

*The above costs were calculated using the basic specifications shown on the facing page. These costs should be adjusted where necessary for design alternatives and owner's requirements.*

## Common additives

| Description | Unit | $ Cost |
|---|---|---|
| Clock System | | |
| 20 room | Ea. | 23,000 |
| 50 room | Ea. | 55,000 |
| Closed Circuit Surveillance, One station | | |
| Camera and monitor | Ea. | 1250 |
| For additional camera stations, add | Ea. | 475 |
| Elevators, Hydraulic passenger, 2 stops | | |
| 1500# capacity | Ea. | 86,500 |
| 2500# capacity | Ea. | 90,500 |
| 3500# capacity | Ea. | 96,000 |
| Additional stop, add | Ea. | 9875 |
| Emergency Generators, Complete system, gas | | |
| 15 KW | Ea. | 16,500 |
| 70 KW | Ea. | 41,100 |
| 85 KW | Ea. | 46,300 |
| 115 KW | Ea. | 52,000 |
| 170 KW | Ea. | 106,000 |
| Diesel, 50 KW | Ea. | 25,700 |
| 100 KW | Ea. | 46,500 |
| 150 KW | Ea. | 35,200 |
| 350 KW | Ea. | 98,000 |

| Description | Unit | $ Cost |
|---|---|---|
| Emergency Lighting, 25 watt, battery operated | | |
| Nickel cadmium | Ea. | 585 |
| Flagpoles, Complete | | |
| Aluminum, 20′ high | Ea. | 2050 |
| 40′ High | Ea. | 5275 |
| 70′ High | Ea. | 14,300 |
| Fiberglass, 23′ High | Ea. | 3025 |
| 39′-5″ High | Ea. | 3725 |
| 59′ High | Ea. | 12,300 |
| Laundry Equipment | | |
| Folders, blankets, & sheets | Ea. | 90,500 |
| Ironers, 110″ single roll | Ea. | 48,300 |
| Combination washer & extractor, 50# | Ea. | 19,500 |
| 125# | Ea. | 46,200 |
| Safe, Office type, 1 hour rating | | |
| 30″ x 18″ x 18″ | Ea. | 1900 |
| 60″ x 36″ x 18″, double door | Ea. | 8625 |
| Sound System | | |
| Amplifier, 250 watts | Ea. | 2425 |
| Speaker, ceiling or wall | Ea. | 320 |
| Trumpet | Ea. | 580 |



**Important: See the Reference Section for Location Factors.**

# Model costs calculated for a 3 story building with 12′ story height and 40,000 square feet of floor area

# Jail

| | | | | Unit | Unit Cost | Cost Per S.F. | % Of Sub-Total |
|---|---|---|---|---|---|---|---|
| **A. SUBSTRUCTURE** | | | | | | | |
| 1010 | Standard Foundations | Poured concrete; strip and spread footings; 4′ foundation wall | | S.F. Ground | 8.13 | 2.71 | |
| 1020 | Special Foundations | N/A | | – | – | – | |
| 1030 | Slab on Grade | 4″ reinforced concrete with vapor barrier and granular base | | S.F. Slab | 7.22 | 2.41 | 1.8% |
| 2010 | Basement Excavation | Site preparation for slab and trench for foundation wall and footing | | S.F. Ground | .38 | .13 | |
| 2020 | Basement Walls | N/A | | – | – | – | |
| **B. SHELL** | | | | | | | |
| | **B10 Superstructure** | | | | | | |
| 1010 | Floor Construction | Concrete slab with metal deck and beams | | S.F. Floor | 38.76 | 25.84 | 12.4% |
| 1020 | Roof Construction | Concrete slab with metal deck and beams | | S.F. Roof | 30.51 | 10.17 | |
| | **B20 Exterior Enclosure** | | | | | | |
| 2010 | Exterior Walls | Face brick with reinforced concrete block backup | *85% of wall* | S.F. Wall | 40.65 | 16.48 | |
| 2020 | Exterior Windows | Bullet resisting and metal horizontal pivoted | *15% of wall* | Each | 246 | 17.62 | 11.9% |
| 2030 | Exterior Doors | Metal | | Each | 9020 | .45 | |
| | **B30 Roofing** | | | | | | |
| 3010 | Roof Coverings | Built-up tar and gravel with flashing; perlite/EPS composite insulation | | S.F. Roof | 8.64 | 2.88 | 1.0% |
| 3020 | Roof Openings | Roof hatches | | S.F. Roof | .15 | .05 | |
| **C. INTERIORS** | | | | | | | |
| 1010 | Partitions | Concrete block | *45 S.F. of Floor/L.F. Partition* | S.F. Partition | 12.49 | 3.33 | |
| 1020 | Interior Doors | Hollow metal fire doors | *930 S.F. Floor/Door* | Each | 1159 | 1.24 | |
| 1030 | Fittings | N/A | | – | – | – | |
| 2010 | Stair Construction | Concrete filled metal pan | | Flight | 19,225 | 2.41 | 6.7% |
| 3010 | Wall Finishes | Paint | | S.F. Surface | 5.01 | 2.67 | |
| 3020 | Floor Finishes | 70% vinyl composition tile, 20% carpet, 10% ceramic tile | | S.F. Floor | 3.48 | 3.48 | |
| 3030 | Ceiling Finishes | Mineral tile on zee runners | *30% of area* | S.F. Ceiling | 14.27 | 6.40 | |
| **D. SERVICES** | | | | | | | |
| | **D10 Conveying** | | | | | | |
| 1010 | Elevators & Lifts | One hydraulic passenger elevator | | Each | 212,400 | 5.31 | 1.8% |
| 1020 | Escalators & Moving Walks | N/A | | – | – | – | |
| | **D20 Plumbing** | | | | | | |
| 2010 | Plumbing Fixtures | Toilet and service fixtures, supply and drainage | *1 Fixture/78 S.F. Floor* | Each | 5630 | 72.18 | |
| 2020 | Domestic Water Distribution | Electric water heater | | S.F. Floor | 9.48 | 9.48 | 28.7% |
| 2040 | Rain Water Drainage | Roof drains | | S.F. Roof | 4.83 | 1.61 | |
| | **D30 HVAC** | | | | | | |
| 3010 | Energy Supply | N/A | | – | – | – | |
| 3020 | Heat Generating Systems | Included in D3050 | | – | – | – | |
| 3030 | Cooling Generating Systems | N/A | | – | – | – | 6.3 % |
| 3050 | Terminal & Package Units | Rooftop multizone unit systems | | S.F. Floor | 18.44 | 18.44 | |
| 3090 | Other HVAC Sys. & Equipment | N/A | | – | – | – | |
| | **D40 Fire Protection** | | | | | | |
| 4010 | Sprinklers | Sprinkler system, light hazard | | S.F. Floor | 4.39 | 4.39 | 1.9% |
| 4020 | Standpipes | Standpipes and hose systems | | S.F. Floor | 1.08 | 1.08 | |
| | **D50 Electrical** | | | | | | |
| 5010 | Electrical Service/Distribution | 600 ampere service, panel board and feeders | | S.F. Floor | 1.41 | 1.41 | |
| 5020 | Lighting & Branch Wiring | Fluorescent fixtures, receptacles, switches, A.C. and misc. power | | S.F. Floor | 13.62 | 13.62 | 7.7% |
| 5030 | Communications & Security | Addressable alarm systems, intercom, and emergency lighting | | S.F. Floor | 6.34 | 6.34 | |
| 5090 | Other Electrical Systems | Emergency generator, 80 kW | | S.F. Floor | .90 | .90 | |
| **E. EQUIPMENT & FURNISHINGS** | | | | | | | |
| 1010 | Commercial Equipment | N/A | | – | – | – | |
| 1020 | Institutional Equipment | Prefabricated cells, visitor cubicles | | S.F. Floor | 57 | 57.45 | 19.8 % |
| 1030 | Vehicular Equipment | N/A | | – | – | – | |
| 1090 | Other Equipment | N/A | | – | – | – | |
| **F. SPECIAL CONSTRUCTION** | | | | | | | |
| 1020 | Integrated Construction | N/A | | – | – | – | 0.0 % |
| 1040 | Special Facilities | N/A | | – | – | – | |
| **G. BUILDING SITEWORK** | **N/A** | | | | | | |
| | | | | | **Sub-Total** | 290.48 | **100%** |
| | CONTRACTOR FEES (General Requirements: 10%, Overhead: 5%, Profit: 10%) | | | | *25%* | 72.65 | |
| | ARCHITECT FEES | | | | *7%* | 25.42 | |
| | | | | | **Total Building Cost** | **388.55** | |

## Costs per square foot of floor area

| Exterior Wall | S.F. Area | 1000 | 2000 | 3000 | 4000 | 5000 | 10000 | 15000 | 20000 | 25000 |
|---|---|---|---|---|---|---|---|---|---|---|
| | L.F. Perimeter | 126 | 179 | 219 | 253 | 283 | 400 | 490 | 568 | 632 |
| Decorative Concrete Block | Rigid Steel | 366.05 | 311.75 | **291.35** | 280.35 | 273.25 | 257.50 | 251.25 | 247.80 | 245.50 |
| | Bearing Walls | 396.40 | 332.05 | 307.10 | 293.40 | 284.55 | 264.15 | 255.95 | 251.35 | 248.20 |
| Face Brick and Concrete Block | Rigid Steel | 432.20 | 358.45 | 329.25 | 313.10 | 302.45 | 277.80 | 267.70 | 262.00 | 258.05 |
| | Bearing Walls | 431.10 | 356.70 | 327.20 | 310.80 | 300.10 | 275.20 | 264.95 | 259.20 | 255.10 |
| Metal Sandwich Panel | Rigid Steel | 392.00 | 330.10 | 306.30 | 293.25 | 284.80 | 265.55 | 257.80 | 253.55 | 250.55 |
| Precast Concrete | Bearing Walls | 390.80 | 328.05 | 303.85 | 290.60 | 282.00 | 262.35 | 254.50 | 250.10 | 247.05 |
| Perimeter Adj., Add or Deduct | Per 100 L.F. | 53.30 | 26.70 | 17.70 | 13.35 | 10.70 | 5.35 | 3.55 | 2.70 | 2.10 |
| Story Hgt. Adj., Add or Deduct | Per 1 Ft. | 2.40 | 1.70 | 1.35 | 1.15 | 1.10 | 0.75 | 0.60 | 0.55 | 0.45 |
| ***For Basement**, add $53.60 per square foot of basement area* | | | | | | | | | | |

*The above costs were calculated using the basic specifications shown on the facing page. These costs should be adjusted where necessary for design alternatives and owner's requirements.*

## Common additives

| Description | Unit | $ Cost |
|---|---|---|
| Closed Circuit Surveillance, One station | | |
| Camera and monitor | Ea. | 1250 |
| For additional camera stations, add | Ea. | 475 |
| Emergency Lighting, 25 watt, battery operated | | |
| Lead battery | Ea. | 360 |
| Nickel cadmium | Ea. | 585 |
| Laundry Equipment | | |
| Dryers, coin operated 30 lb. | Ea. | 2200 |
| Double stacked | Ea. | 2750 |
| 50 lb. | Ea. | 6325 |
| Dry cleaner 20 lb. | Ea. | 53,000 |
| 30 lb. | Ea. | 81,500 |
| Washers, coin operated | Ea. | 2000 |
| Washer/extractor 20 lb. | Ea. | 7400 |
| 30 lb. | Ea. | 15,500 |
| 50 lb. | Ea. | 19,500 |
| 75 lb. | Ea. | 21,600 |
| Smoke Detectors | | |
| Ceiling type | Ea. | 300 |
| Duct type | Ea. | 615 |



**Important: See the Reference Section for Location Factors.**

# Model costs calculated for a 1 story building with 12′ story height and 3,000 square feet of floor area

# Laundromat

| | | | | Unit | Unit Cost | Cost Per S.F. | % Of Sub-Total |
|---|---|---|---|---|---|---|---|
| **A. SUBSTRUCTURE** | | | | | | | |
| 1010 | Standard Foundations | Poured concrete; strip and spread footings; 4′ foundation wall | | S.F. Ground | 11.95 | 11.95 | 9.4% |
| 1020 | Special Foundations | N/A | | — | — | — | |
| 1030 | Slab on Grade | 5″ reinforced concrete with vapor barrier and granular base | | S.F. Slab | 7.95 | 7.95 | |
| 2010 | Basement Excavation | Site preparation for slab and trench for foundation wall and footing | | S.F. Ground | .66 | .66 | |
| 2020 | Basement Walls | N/A | | — | — | — | |
| **B. SHELL** | | | | | | | |
| | **B10 Superstructure** | | | | | | |
| 1010 | Floor Construction | Steel column fireproofing | | S.F. Floor | 1.27 | 1.27 | 6.9% |
| 1020 | Roof Construction | Metal deck, open web steel joists, beams, columns | | S.F. Roof | 13.70 | 13.70 | |
| | **B20 Exterior Enclosure** | | | | | | |
| 2010 | Exterior Walls | Decorative concrete block | *90% of wall* | S.F. Wall | | | 5.5% |
| 2020 | Exterior Windows | Store front | *10% of wall* | Each | 87 | 7.64 | |
| 2030 | Exterior Doors | Double aluminum and glass | | Each | 6653 | 4.44 | |
| | **B30 Roofing** | | | | | | |
| 3010 | Roof Coverings | Built-up tar and gravel with flashing; perlite/EPS composite insulation | | S.F. Roof | 12.22 | 12.22 | 5.6% |
| 3020 | Roof Openings | N/A | | — | — | — | |
| **C. INTERIORS** | | | | | | | |
| 1010 | Partitions | Gypsum board on metal studs | *60 S.F. Floor/L.F. Partition* | S.F. Partition | 34.50 | 5.75 | 7.7% |
| 1020 | Interior Doors | Single leaf wood | *750 S.F. Floor/Door* | Each | 1231 | 1.64 | |
| 1030 | Fittings | N/A | | — | — | — | |
| 2010 | Stair Construction | N/A | | — | — | — | |
| 3010 | Wall Finishes | Paint | | S.F. Surface | .96 | .32 | |
| 3020 | Floor Finishes | Vinyl composition tile | | S.F. Floor | 2.19 | 2.19 | |
| 3030 | Ceiling Finishes | Fiberglass board on exposed grid system | | S.F. Ceiling | 6.80 | 6.80 | |
| **D. SERVICES** | | | | | | | |
| | **D10 Conveying** | | | | | | |
| 1010 | Elevators & Lifts | N/A | | — | — | — | 0.0 % |
| 1020 | Escalators & Moving Walks | N/A | | — | — | — | |
| | **D20 Plumbing** | | | | | | |
| 2010 | Plumbing Fixtures | Toilet and service fixtures, supply and drainage | *1 Fixture/600 S.F. Floor* | Each | 9654 | 16.09 | 39.8% |
| 2020 | Domestic Water Distribution | Gas fired hot water heater | | S.F. Floor | 68 | 67.53 | |
| 2040 | Rain Water Drainage | Roof drains | | S.F. Roof | 3.04 | 3.04 | |
| | **D30 HVAC** | | | | | | |
| 3010 | Energy Supply | N/A | | — | — | — | 5.0 % |
| 3020 | Heat Generating Systems | Included in D3050 | | — | — | — | |
| 3030 | Cooling Generating Systems | N/A | | — | — | — | |
| 3050 | Terminal & Package Units | Rooftop single zone unit systems | | S.F. Floor | 10.80 | 10.80 | |
| 3090 | Other HVAC Sys. & Equipment | N/A | | — | — | — | |
| | **D40 Fire Protection** | | | | | | |
| 4010 | Sprinklers | Sprinkler, ordinary hazard | | S.F. Floor | 7.37 | 7.37 | 3.4% |
| 4020 | Standpipes | N/A | | — | — | — | |
| | **D50 Electrical** | | | | | | |
| 5010 | Electrical Service/Distribution | 200 ampere service, panel board and feeders | | S.F. Floor | 5.13 | 5.13 | 16.7% |
| 5020 | Lighting & Branch Wiring | High efficiency fluorescent fixtures, receptacles, switches, A.C. and misc. power | | S.F. Floor | 28.17 | 28.17 | |
| 5030 | Communications & Security | Addressable alarm systems and emergency lighting | | S.F. Floor | 2.65 | 2.65 | |
| 5090 | Other Electrical Systems | Emergency generator, 7.5 kW | | S.F. Floor | .52 | .52 | |
| **E. EQUIPMENT & FURNISHINGS** | | | | | | | |
| 1010 | Commercial Equipment | N/A | | — | — | — | 0.0 % |
| 1020 | Institutional Equipment | N/A | | — | — | — | |
| 1030 | Vehicular Equipment | N/A | | — | — | — | |
| 1090 | Other Equipment | N/A | | — | — | — | |
| **F. SPECIAL CONSTRUCTION** | | | | | | | |
| 1020 | Integrated Construction | N/A | | — | — | — | 0.0 % |
| 1040 | Special Facilities | N/A | | — | — | — | |
| **G. BUILDING SITEWORK** | | **N/A** | | | | | |
| | | | | | **Sub-Total** | 217.83 | **100%** |
| | CONTRACTOR FEES (General Requirements: 10%, Overhead: 5%, Profit: 10%) | | | | *25%* | 54.46 | |
| | ARCHITECT FEES | | | | *7%* | 19.06 | |
| | | | | | **Total Building Cost** | **291.35** | |

## Costs per square foot of floor area

| Exterior Wall | S.F. Area | 7000 | 10000 | 13000 | 16000 | 19000 | 22000 | 25000 | 28000 | 31000 |
|---|---|---|---|---|---|---|---|---|---|---|
| | L.F. Perimeter | 240 | 300 | 336 | 386 | 411 | 435 | 472 | 510 | 524 |
| Face Brick and Concrete Block | Reinforced Concrete | 263.40 | 250.90 | 239.90 | 235.05 | 228.75 | **224.05** | 221.70 | 219.90 | 216.70 |
| | Rigid Steel | 257.80 | 245.25 | 234.25 | 229.40 | 223.10 | 218.45 | 216.05 | 214.25 | 211.05 |
| Limestone and Concrete Block | Reinforced Concrete | 294.20 | 275.80 | 260.35 | 253.30 | 244.60 | 238.15 | 234.80 | 232.20 | 227.80 |
| | Rigid Steel | 282.20 | 266.60 | 252.65 | 246.60 | 238.50 | 232.50 | 229.50 | 227.20 | 223.10 |
| Precast Concrete | Reinforced Concrete | 308.50 | 288.35 | 271.10 | 263.40 | 253.65 | 246.35 | 242.70 | 239.80 | 234.85 |
| | Rigid Steel | 302.85 | 282.70 | 265.45 | 257.75 | 248.00 | 240.75 | 237.05 | 234.20 | 229.25 |
| Perimeter Adj., Add or Deduct | Per 100 L.F. | 32.00 | 22.35 | 17.25 | 14.00 | 11.80 | 10.20 | 9.00 | 8.00 | 7.25 |
| Story Hgt. Adj., Add or Deduct | Per 1 Ft. | 4.85 | 4.25 | 3.60 | 3.35 | 3.00 | 2.80 | 2.65 | 2.55 | 2.40 |

***For Basement**, add $76.70 per square foot of basement area*

*The above costs were calculated using the basic specifications shown on the facing page. These costs should be adjusted where necessary for design alternatives and owner's requirements.*

## Common additives

| Description | Unit | $ Cost |
|---|---|---|
| Carrels Hardwood | Ea. | 395 - 2350 |
| Closed Circuit Surveillance, One station | | |
| Camera and monitor | Ea. | 1250 |
| For additional camera stations, add | Ea. | 475 |
| Elevators, Hydraulic passenger, 2 stops | | |
| 1500# capacity | Ea. | 86,500 |
| 2500# capacity | Ea. | 90,500 |
| 3500# capacity | Ea. | 96,000 |
| Emergency Lighting, 25 watt, battery operated | | |
| Lead battery | Ea. | 360 |
| Nickel cadmium | Ea. | 585 |
| Flagpoles, Complete | | |
| Aluminum, 20′ high | Ea. | 2050 |
| 40′ high | Ea. | 5275 |
| 70′ high | Ea. | 14,300 |
| Fiberglass, 23′ high | Ea. | 3025 |
| 39′-5″ high | Ea. | 3725 |
| 59′ high | Ea. | 12,300 |

| Description | Unit | $ Cost |
|---|---|---|
| Library Furnishings | | |
| Bookshelf, 90″ high, 10″ shelf double face | L.F. | 300 |
| single face | L.F. | 191 |
| Charging desk, built-in with counter | | |
| Plastic laminated top | L.F. | 710 |
| Reading table, laminated | | |
| top 60″ x 36″ | Ea. | 500 |



**Important: See the Reference Section for Location Factors.**

# Model costs calculated for a 2 story building with 14' story height and 22,000 square feet of floor area

# Library

| | | | | Unit | Unit Cost | Cost Per S.F. | % Of Sub-Total |
|---|---|---|---|---|---|---|---|
| **A. SUBSTRUCTURE** | | | | | | | |
| 1010 | Standard Foundations | Poured concrete; strip and spread footings; 4' foundation wall | | S.F. Ground | 9.82 | 4.91 | |
| 1020 | Special Foundations | N/A | | — | — | — | |
| 1030 | Slab on Grade | 4" reinforced concrete with vapor barrier and granular base | | S.F. Slab | 7.22 | 3.61 | 5.2% |
| 2010 | Basement Excavation | Site preparation for slab and trench for foundation wall and footing | | S.F. Ground | .38 | .19 | |
| 2020 | Basement Walls | N/A | | — | — | — | |
| **B. SHELL** | | | | | | | |
| | **B10 Superstructure** | | | | | | |
| 1010 | Floor Construction | Concrete waffle slab | | S.F. Floor | 38.58 | 19.29 | 20.8% |
| 1020 | Roof Construction | Concrete waffle slab | | S.F. Roof | 30.60 | 15.30 | |
| | **B20 Exterior Enclosure** | | | | | | |
| 2010 | Exterior Walls | Face brick with concrete block backup | *90% of wall* | S.F. Wall | 42.09 | 20.97 | |
| 2020 | Exterior Windows | Window wall | *10% of wall* | Each | 88 | 4.86 | 16.1% |
| 2030 | Exterior Doors | Double aluminum and glass, single leaf hollow metal | | Each | 9150 | .83 | |
| | **B30 Roofing** | | | | | | |
| 3010 | Roof Coverings | Single ply membrane, EPDM, fully adhered; perlite/EPS composite insulation | | S.F. Roof | 7.10 | 3.55 | 2.2% |
| 3020 | Roof Openings | Roof hatches | | S.F. Roof | .18 | .09 | |
| **C. INTERIORS** | | | | | | | |
| 1010 | Partitions | Gypsum board on metal studs | *30 S.F. Floor/L.F. Partition* | S.F. Partition | 15.18 | 6.07 | |
| 1020 | Interior Doors | Single leaf wood | *300 S.F. Floor/Door* | Each | 1159 | 3.86 | |
| 1030 | Fittings | N/A | | — | — | — | |
| 2010 | Stair Construction | Concrete filled metal pan | | Flight | 11,950 | 1.09 | 15.3% |
| 3010 | Wall Finishes | Paint | | S.F. Surface | .96 | .77 | |
| 3020 | Floor Finishes | 50% carpet, 50% vinyl tile | | S.F. Floor | 4.11 | 4.11 | |
| 3030 | Ceiling Finishes | Mineral fiber on concealed zee bars | | S.F. Ceiling | 9.48 | 9.48 | |
| **D. SERVICES** | | | | | | | |
| | **D10 Conveying** | | | | | | |
| 1010 | Elevators & Lifts | One hydraulic passenger elevator | | Each | 111,100 | 5.05 | 3.0% |
| 1020 | Escalators & Moving Walks | N/A | | — | — | — | |
| | **D20 Plumbing** | | | | | | |
| 2010 | Plumbing Fixtures | Toilet and service fixtures, supply and drainage | *1 Fixture/1835 S.F. Floor* | Each | 11,634 | 6.34 | |
| 2020 | Domestic Water Distribution | Gas fired water heater | | S.F. Floor | 1.31 | 1.31 | 5.2% |
| 2040 | Rain Water Drainage | Roof drains | | S.F. Roof | 1.80 | .90 | |
| | **D30 HVAC** | | | | | | |
| 3010 | Energy Supply | N/A | | — | — | — | |
| 3020 | Heat Generating Systems | Included in D3050 | | — | — | — | |
| 3030 | Cooling Generating Systems | N/A | | — | — | — | 15.8 % |
| 3050 | Terminal & Package Units | Multizone unit, gas heating, electric cooling | | S.F. Floor | 26.30 | 26.30 | |
| 3090 | Other HVAC Sys. & Equipment | N/A | | — | — | — | |
| | **D40 Fire Protection** | | | | | | |
| 4010 | Sprinklers | Wet pipe sprinkler system | | S.F. Floor | 4.57 | 4.57 | 3.7% |
| 4020 | Standpipes | Standpipe | | S.F. Floor | 1.62 | 1.62 | |
| | **D50 Electrical** | | | | | | |
| 5010 | Electrical Service/Distribution | 400 ampere service, panel board and feeders | | S.F. Floor | 1.49 | 1.49 | |
| 5020 | Lighting & Branch Wiring | High efficiency fluorescent fixtures, receptacles, switches, A.C. and misc. power | | S.F. Floor | 16.73 | 16.73 | 12.6% |
| 5030 | Communications & Security | Addressable alarm systems, internet wiring, and emergency lighting | | S.F. Floor | 2.58 | 2.58 | |
| 5090 | Other Electrical Systems | Emergency generator, 7.5 kW, Uninterruptible power supply | | S.F. Floor | .10 | .10 | |
| **E. EQUIPMENT & FURNISHINGS** | | | | | | | |
| 1010 | Commercial Equipment | N/A | | — | — | — | |
| 1020 | Institutional Equipment | N/A | | — | — | — | 0.0 % |
| 1030 | Vehicular Equipment | N/A | | — | — | — | |
| 1090 | Other Equipment | N/A | | — | — | — | |
| **F. SPECIAL CONSTRUCTION** | | | | | | | |
| 1020 | Integrated Construction | N/A | | — | — | — | 0.0 % |
| 1040 | Special Facilities | N/A | | — | — | — | |
| **G. BUILDING SITEWORK** | **N/A** | | | | | | |
| | | | | | **Sub-Total** | 165.97 | **100%** |
| | CONTRACTOR FEES (General Requirements: 10%, Overhead: 5%, Profit: 10%) | | | | *25%* | 41.48 | |
| | ARCHITECT FEES | | | | *8%* | 16.60 | |
| | | | | | **Total Building Cost** | **224.05** | |

## Costs per square foot of floor area

| Exterior Wall | S.F. Area | 4000 | 5500 | 7000 | 8500 | 10000 | 11500 | 13000 | 14500 | 16000 |
|---|---|---|---|---|---|---|---|---|---|---|
| | L.F. Perimeter | 280 | 320 | 380 | 440 | 453 | 503 | 510 | 522 | 560 |
| Vinyl Clapboard | Wood Frame | 253.20 | 241.70 | 237.65 | 235.00 | 229.10 | 227.60 | 223.45 | 220.60 | 219.60 |
| Stone Veneer | Wood Frame | 256.65 | 241.60 | **236.35** | 232.95 | 225.10 | 223.10 | 217.65 | 213.75 | 212.45 |
| Fiber Cement | Rigid Steel | 262.30 | 249.65 | 245.20 | 242.35 | 235.85 | 234.20 | 229.65 | 226.50 | 225.40 |
| E.I.F.S. | Rigid Steel | 263.35 | 250.55 | 246.05 | 243.10 | 236.55 | 234.85 | 230.25 | 227.00 | 225.85 |
| Precast Concrete | Reinforced Concrete | 312.50 | 293.15 | 286.50 | 282.20 | 272.00 | 269.45 | 262.35 | 257.30 | 255.65 |
| Brick Veneer | Reinforced Concrete | 319.65 | 298.55 | 291.25 | 286.55 | 275.40 | 272.60 | 264.80 | 259.30 | 257.50 |
| Perimeter Adj., Add or Deduct | Per 100 L.F. | 21.35 | 15.60 | 12.20 | 10.05 | 8.55 | 7.40 | 6.65 | 5.85 | 5.30 |
| Story Hgt. Adj., Add or Deduct | Per 1 Ft. | 2.65 | 2.20 | 2.00 | 1.95 | 1.70 | 1.60 | 1.50 | 1.30 | 1.35 |
| ***For Basement**, add $49.95 per square foot of basement area* | | | | | | | | | | |

*The above costs were calculated using the basic specifications shown on the facing page. These costs should be adjusted where necessary for design alternatives and owner's requirements.*

## Common additives

| Description | Unit | $ Cost |
|---|---|---|
| Cabinets, Hospital, base | | |
| Laminated plastic | L.F. | 575 |
| Stainless steel | L.F. | 940 |
| Counter top, laminated plastic | L.F. | 99.50 |
| Stainless steel | L.F. | 245 |
| For drop-in sink, add | Ea. | 1600 |
| Nurses station, door type | | |
| Laminated plastic | L.F. | 645 |
| Enameled steel | L.F. | 620 |
| Stainless steel | L.F. | 1100 |
| Wall cabinets, laminated plastic | L.F. | 420 |
| Enameled steel | L.F. | 495 |
| Stainless steel | L.F. | 890 |

| Description | Unit | $ Cost |
|---|---|---|
| Directory Boards, Plastic, glass covered | | |
| 30" x 20" | Ea. | 705 |
| 36" x 48" | Ea. | 1475 |
| Aluminum, 24" x 18" | Ea. | 705 |
| 36" x 24" | Ea. | 985 |
| 48" x 32" | Ea. | 1975 |
| 48" x 60" | Ea. | 2650 |
| Heat Therapy Unit | | |
| Humidified, 26" x 78" x 28" | Ea. | 395 |
| Smoke Detectors | | |
| Ceiling type | Ea. | 300 |
| Duct type | Ea. | 615 |
| Tables, Examining, vinyl top | | |
| with base cabinets | Ea. | 1850 - 6025 |
| Utensil Washer, Sanitizer | Ea. | 8650 |
| X-Ray, Mobile | Ea. | 16,200 - 48,400 |



**Important: See the Reference Section for Location Factors.**

## Model costs calculated for a 1 story building with 10′ story height and 7,000 square feet of floor area

# Medical Office, 1 Story

| | | | | Unit | Unit Cost | Cost Per S.F. | % Of Sub-Total |
|---|---|---|---|---|---|---|---|
| **A. SUBSTRUCTURE** | | | | | | | |
| 1010 | Standard Foundations | Poured concrete; strip and spread footings; 4′ foundation wall | | S.F. Ground | 10.27 | 10.27 | |
| 1020 | Special Foundations | N/A | | — | — | — | |
| 1030 | Slab on Grade | 4″ reinforced slab on grade | | S.F. Slab | 7.22 | 7.22 | 10.3% |
| 2010 | Basement Excavation | Site preparation for slab and trench for foundation wall and footing | | S.F. Ground | .38 | .38 | |
| 2020 | Basement Walls | N/A | | — | — | — | |
| **B. SHELL** | | | | | | | |
| | **B10 Superstructure** | | | | | | |
| 1010 | Floor Construction | Wood columns, fireproofed | | S.F. Floor | 4.92 | 4.92 | 10.6% |
| 1020 | Roof Construction | Wood roof trusses, 4:12 slope | | S.F. Roof | 13.43 | 13.43 | |
| | **B20 Exterior Enclosure** | | | | | | |
| 2010 | Exterior Walls | Ashlar stone veneer on wood stud back up | *70% of wall* | S.F. Wall | 53 | 20.10 | |
| 2020 | Exterior Windows | Double hung, insulated wood windows | *30% of wall* | Each | 850 | 8.14 | 18.0% |
| 2030 | Exterior Doors | Single leaf solid core wood doors | | Each | 3430 | 2.94 | |
| | **B30 Roofing** | | | | | | |
| 3010 | Roof Coverings | Asphalt shingles with flashing, gutters and downspouts | | S.F. Roof | 3.66 | 3.66 | 2.1% |
| 3020 | Roof Openings | N/A | | — | — | — | |
| **C. INTERIORS** | | | | | | | |
| 1010 | Partitions | Fire rated gypsum board on wood studs | *6 S.F. Floor/L.F. Partition* | S.F. Partition | 9.92 | 13.22 | |
| 1020 | Interior Doors | Single leaf solid core wood doors | *240 S.F. Floor/Door* | Each | 1159 | 4.83 | |
| 1030 | Fittings | N/A | | — | — | — | |
| 2010 | Stair Construction | N/A | | — | — | — | 20.0% |
| 3010 | Wall Finishes | Paint on drywall | | S.F. Surface | 1.10 | 2.92 | |
| 3020 | Floor Finishes | 50% carpet , 50% vinyl composition tile | | S.F. Floor | 4.11 | 4.11 | |
| 3030 | Ceiling Finishes | Acoustic ceiling tiles on suspended support system | | S.F. Ceiling | 9.67 | 9.67 | |
| **D. SERVICES** | | | | | | | |
| | **D10 Conveying** | | | | | | |
| 1010 | Elevators & Lifts | N/A | | — | — | — | 0.0 % |
| 1020 | Escalators & Moving Walks | N/A | | — | — | — | |
| | **D20 Plumbing** | | | | | | |
| 2010 | Plumbing Fixtures | Restroom, exam room and service fixtures, supply and drainage | *1 Fixture/350 S.F. Floor* | Each | 2821 | 8.06 | |
| 2020 | Domestic Water Distribution | Gas fired water heater | | S.F. Floor | 2.65 | 2.65 | 6.2% |
| 2040 | Rain Water Drainage | Roof drains | | S.F. Roof | | | |
| | **D30 HVAC** | | | | | | |
| 3010 | Energy Supply | N/A | | — | — | — | |
| 3020 | Heat Generating Systems | Included in D3050 | | — | — | — | |
| 3030 | Cooling Generating Systems | N/A | | — | — | — | 9.9 % |
| 3050 | Terminal & Package Units | Multizone unit, gas heating , electric cooling | | S.F. Floor | 17.10 | 17.10 | |
| 3090 | Other HVAC Sys. & Equipment | N/A | | — | — | — | |
| | **D40 Fire Protection** | | | | | | |
| 4010 | Sprinklers | Wet pipe spinkler system | | S.F. Floor | 6.60 | 6.60 | 5.0% |
| 4020 | Standpipes | Standpipes and hose systems, with pumps | | S.F. Floor | 2.11 | 2.11 | |
| | **D50 Electrical** | | | | | | |
| 5010 | Electrical Service/Distribution | 200 Ampere service, panel boards and feeders | | S.F. Floor | 2.06 | 2.06 | |
| 5020 | Lighting & Branch Wiring | Fluorescent fixtures, receptacles, switches, A.C. and misc. power | | S.F. Floor | 10.95 | 10.95 | 13.2% |
| 5030 | Communications & Security | Alarm systems, emergency lighting, internet and phone wiring | | S.F. Floor | 9.97 | 9.97 | |
| 5090 | Other Electrical Systems | N/A | | — | — | — | |
| **E. EQUIPMENT & FURNISHINGS** | | | | | | | |
| 1010 | Commercial Equipment | N/A | | — | — | — | |
| 1020 | Institutional Equipment | Exam room equipment, cabinets and countertops | | S.F. Floor | 8.15 | 8.15 | 4.7 % |
| 1030 | Vehicular Equipment | N/A | | — | — | — | |
| 1090 | Other Equipment | N/A | | — | — | — | |
| **F. SPECIAL CONSTRUCTION** | | | | | | | |
| 1020 | Integrated Construction | N/A | | — | — | — | 0.0 % |
| 1040 | Special Facilities | N/A | | — | — | — | |
| **G. BUILDING SITEWORK** | **N/A** | | | | | | |
| | | | | | **Sub-Total** | 173.46 | **100%** |
| | CONTRACTOR FEES (General Requirements: 10%, Overhead: 5%, Profit: 10%) | | | | 25% | 43.38 | |
| | ARCHITECT FEES | | | | 9% | 19.51 | |
| | | | | | **Total Building Cost** | **236.35** | |

**For customer support on your Square Foot Costs with RSMeans data, call 800.448.8182.**

## Costs per square foot of floor area

| Exterior Wall | S.F. Area | 4000 | 5500 | 7000 | 8500 | 10000 | 11500 | 13000 | 14500 | 16000 |
|---|---|---|---|---|---|---|---|---|---|---|
| | L.F. Perimeter | 180 | 210 | 240 | 270 | 286 | 311 | 336 | 361 | 386 |
| Vinyl Clapboard | Wood Frame | 306.75 | 291.45 | 282.75 | 277.10 | 270.80 | 267.40 | 264.80 | 262.80 | 261.15 |
| Stone Veneer | Wood Frame | 333.35 | 313.90 | 302.80 | 295.55 | 287.35 | 283.00 | 279.70 | 277.10 | 275.00 |
| Fiber Cement | Rigid Steel | 309.95 | 293.25 | **283.75** | 277.60 | 270.65 | 267.00 | 264.15 | 261.95 | 260.10 |
| E.I.F.S. | Rigid Steel | 313.05 | 296.40 | 286.90 | 280.75 | 273.80 | 270.15 | 267.30 | 265.10 | 263.30 |
| Precast Concrete | Reinforced Concrete | 366.35 | 342.60 | 329.10 | 320.35 | 310.05 | 304.80 | 300.70 | 297.55 | 294.90 |
| Brick Veneer | Reinforced Concrete | 325.00 | 305.10 | 293.80 | 286.45 | 278.00 | 273.55 | 270.20 | 267.55 | 265.40 |
| Perimeter Adj., Add or Deduct | Per 100 L.F. | 42.20 | 30.75 | 24.10 | 19.80 | 16.80 | 14.75 | 13.05 | 11.65 | 10.55 |
| Story Hgt. Adj., Add or Deduct | Per 1 Ft. | 5.35 | 4.55 | 4.05 | 3.75 | 3.40 | 3.20 | 3.10 | 2.95 | 2.85 |

***For Basement**, add $55.45 per square foot of basement area*

*The above costs were calculated using the basic specifications shown on the facing page. These costs should be adjusted where necessary for design alternatives and owner's requirements.*

## Common additives

| Description | Unit | $ Cost |
|---|---|---|
| Cabinets, Hospital, base | | |
| Laminated plastic | L.F. | 575 |
| Stainless steel | L.F. | 940 |
| Counter top, laminated plastic | L.F. | 99.50 |
| Stainless steel | L.F. | 245 |
| For drop-in sink, add | Ea. | 1600 |
| Nurses station, door type | | |
| Laminated plastic | L.F. | 645 |
| Enameled steel | L.F. | 620 |
| Stainless steel | L.F. | 1100 |
| Wall cabinets, laminated plastic | L.F. | 420 |
| Enameled steel | L.F. | 495 |
| Stainless steel | L.F. | 890 |
| Elevators, Hydraulic passenger, 2 stops | | |
| 1500# capacity | Ea. | 86,500 |
| 2500# capacity | Ea. | 90,500 |
| 3500# capacity | Ea. | 96,000 |

| Description | Unit | $ Cost |
|---|---|---|
| Directory Boards, Plastic, glass covered | | |
| 30″ x 20″ | Ea. | 705 |
| 36″ x 48″ | Ea. | 1475 |
| Aluminum, 24″ x 18″ | Ea. | 705 |
| 36″ x 24″ | Ea. | 985 |
| 48″ x 32″ | Ea. | 1975 |
| 48″ x 60″ | Ea. | 2650 |
| Emergency Lighting, 25 watt, battery operated | | |
| Lead battery | Ea. | 360 |
| Nickel cadmium | Ea. | 585 |
| Heat Therapy Unit | | |
| Humidified, 26″ x 78″ x 28″ | Ea. | 395 |
| Smoke Detectors | | |
| Ceiling type | Ea. | 300 |
| Duct type | Ea. | 615 |
| Tables, Examining, vinyl top | | |
| with base cabinets | Ea. | 1850 - 6025 |
| Utensil Washer, Sanitizer | Ea. | 8650 |
| X-Ray, Mobile | Ea. | 16,200 - 48,400 |



**Important: See the Reference Section for Location Factors.**

## Model costs calculated for a 2 story building with 10′ story height and 7,000 square feet of floor area

# Medical Office, 2 Story

| | | | | Unit | Unit Cost | Cost Per S.F. | % Of Sub-Total |
|---|---|---|---|---|---|---|---|
| **A. SUBSTRUCTURE** | | | | | | | |
| 1010 | Standard Foundations | Poured concrete; strip and spread footings; 4′ foundation wall | | S.F. Ground | 14.84 | 7.42 | |
| 1020 | Special Foundations | N/A | | — | — | — | |
| 1030 | Slab on Grade | 4″ reinforced slab on grade | | S.F. Slab | 7.22 | 3.61 | 5.5% |
| 2010 | Basement Excavation | Site preparation for slab and trench for foundation wall and footing | | S.F. Ground | .66 | .33 | |
| 2020 | Basement Walls | N/A | | — | — | — | |
| **B. SHELL** | | | | | | | |
| | **B10 Superstructure** | | | | | | |
| 1010 | Floor Construction | Open web bar joist, slab form, fireproofed columns | | S.F. Floor | 22.02 | 11.01 | 8.6% |
| 1020 | Roof Construction | Metal deck, open web steel joists, beams, columns | | S.F. Roof | 13.72 | 6.86 | |
| | **B20 Exterior Enclosure** | | | | | | |
| 2010 | Exterior Walls | Fiber cement siding on metal studs | *70% of wall* | S.F. Wall | 22.44 | 10.77 | |
| 2020 | Exterior Windows | Aluminum sliding windows | *30% of wall* | Each | 1552 | 21.29 | 17.9% |
| 2030 | Exterior Doors | Aluminum & glass entrance doors | | Each | 9150 | 5.23 | |
| | **B30 Roofing** | | | | | | |
| 3010 | Roof Coverings | Single ply membrane, stone ballast, rigid insulation | | S.F. Roof | 13.08 | 6.54 | 4.1% |
| 3020 | Roof Openings | Roof and smoke hatches | | S.F. Roof | 3.90 | 1.95 | |
| **C. INTERIORS** | | | | | | | |
| 1010 | Partitions | Fire rated gypsum board on metal studs | *6 S.F. Floor/L.F. Partition* | S.F. Partition | 7.47 | 9.96 | |
| 1020 | Interior Doors | Single leaf solid core wood doors | *240 S.F. Floor/Door* | Each | 1159 | 5.46 | |
| 1030 | Fittings | N/A | | — | — | — | |
| 2010 | Stair Construction | Concrete filled metal pan, with rails | | Flight | 16,075 | 11.48 | 21.0% |
| 3010 | Wall Finishes | Paint on drywall | | S.F. Surface | 1.13 | 3.02 | |
| 3020 | Floor Finishes | 50% carpet , 50% vinyl composition tile | | S.F. Floor | 4.11 | 4.11 | |
| 3030 | Ceiling Finishes | Acoustic ceiling tiles on suspended support system | | S.F. Ceiling | 9.67 | 9.67 | |
| **D. SERVICES** | | | | | | | |
| | **D10 Conveying** | | | | | | |
| 1010 | Elevators & Lifts | One hydraulic elevator | | Each | 141,960 | 20.28 | 9.7% |
| 1020 | Escalators & Moving Walks | N/A | | — | — | — | |
| | **D20 Plumbing** | | | | | | |
| 2010 | Plumbing Fixtures | Restroom, exam room and service fixtures, supply and drainage | *1 Fixture/350 S.F. Floor* | Each | 3133 | 8.95 | |
| 2020 | Domestic Water Distribution | Gas fired water heater | | S.F. Floor | 2.65 | 2.65 | 6.3% |
| 2040 | Rain Water Drainage | Roof drains | | S.F. Roof | 3.08 | 1.54 | |
| | **D30 HVAC** | | | | | | |
| 3010 | Energy Supply | N/A | | — | — | — | |
| 3020 | Heat Generating Systems | Included in D3050 | | — | — | — | |
| 3030 | Cooling Generating Systems | N/A | | — | — | — | 8.2 % |
| 3050 | Terminal & Package Units | Multizone unit, gas heating , electric cooling | | S.F. Floor | 17.10 | 17.10 | |
| 3090 | Other HVAC Sys. & Equipment | N/A | | — | — | — | |
| | **D40 Fire Protection** | | | | | | |
| 4010 | Sprinklers | Wet pipe spinkler system | | S.F. Floor | 5.47 | 5.47 | 4.2% |
| 4020 | Standpipes | Standpipes and hose systems, with pumps | | S.F. Floor | 3.26 | 3.26 | |
| | **D50 Electrical** | | | | | | |
| 5010 | Electrical Service/Distribution | 400 Ampere service, panel boards and feeders | | S.F. Floor | 3.15 | 3.15 | |
| 5020 | Lighting & Branch Wiring | Fluorescent fixtures, receptacles, switches, A.C. and misc. power | | S.F. Floor | 10.95 | 10.95 | 11.6% |
| 5030 | Communications & Security | Alarm systems, emergency lighting, internet and phone wiring | | S.F. Floor | 9.97 | 9.97 | |
| 5090 | Other Electrical Systems | N/A | | — | — | — | |
| **E. EQUIPMENT & FURNISHINGS** | | | | | | | |
| 1010 | Commercial Equipment | N/A | | — | — | — | |
| 1020 | Institutional Equipment | Exam room equipment, cabinets and countertops | | S.F. Floor | 6.24 | 6.24 | 3.0 % |
| 1030 | Vehicular Equipment | N/A | | — | — | — | |
| 1090 | Other Equipment | N/A | | — | — | — | |
| **F. SPECIAL CONSTRUCTION** | | | | | | | |
| 1020 | Integrated Construction | N/A | | — | — | — | 0.0 % |
| 1040 | Special Facilities | N/A | | — | — | — | |
| **G. BUILDING SITEWORK** | **N/A** | | | | | | |
| | | | | | **Sub-Total** | 208.27 | **100%** |
| | CONTRACTOR FEES (General Requirements: 10%, Overhead: 5%, Profit: 10%) | | | | *25%* | 52.05 | |
| | ARCHITECT FEES | | | | *9%* | 23.43 | |
| | | | | | **Total Building Cost** | **283.75** | |

## Costs per square foot of floor area

| Exterior Wall | S.F. Area | 2000 | 3000 | 4000 | 6000 | 8000 | 10000 | 12000 | 14000 | 16000 |
|---|---|---|---|---|---|---|---|---|---|---|
| | L.F. Perimeter | 240 | 260 | 280 | 380 | 480 | 560 | 580 | 660 | 740 |
| Brick Veneer | Wood Frame | 274.45 | 243.85 | 228.60 | 220.60 | **216.60** | 212.75 | 206.55 | 205.25 | 204.20 |
| Aluminum Clapboard | Wood Frame | 251.30 | 227.10 | 215.05 | 208.40 | 205.00 | 201.95 | 197.25 | 196.15 | 195.30 |
| Wood Clapboard | Wood Frame | 250.15 | 226.35 | 214.40 | 207.80 | 204.45 | 201.45 | 196.75 | 195.70 | 194.85 |
| Wood Shingles | Wood Frame | 258.55 | 232.35 | 219.30 | 212.25 | 208.65 | 205.35 | 200.15 | 199.00 | 198.10 |
| Concrete Block | Wood Truss | 247.85 | 224.65 | 213.10 | 206.60 | 203.30 | 200.35 | 195.85 | 194.75 | 194.00 |
| Face Brick and Concrete Block | Wood Truss | 282.75 | 249.90 | 233.45 | 225.05 | 220.75 | 216.65 | 209.90 | 208.50 | 207.45 |
| Perimeter Adj., Add or Deduct | Per 100 L.F. | 36.50 | 24.35 | 18.25 | 12.20 | 9.15 | 7.35 | 6.10 | 5.20 | 4.65 |
| Story Hgt. Adj., Add or Deduct | Per 1 Ft. | 6.55 | 4.80 | 3.85 | 3.50 | 3.30 | 3.15 | 2.65 | 2.60 | 2.60 |
| ***For Basement**, add $ 38.15 per square foot of basement area* | | | | | | | | | | |

*The above costs were calculated using the basic specifications shown on the facing page. These costs should be adjusted where necessary for design alternatives and owner's requirements.*

## Common additives

| Description | Unit | $ Cost |
|---|---|---|
| Closed Circuit Surveillance, One station | | |
| Camera and monitor | Ea. | 1250 |
| For additional camera stations, add | Ea. | 475 |
| Emergency Lighting, 25 watt, battery operated | | |
| Lead battery | Ea. | 360 |
| Nickel cadmium | Ea. | 585 |
| Laundry Equipment | | |
| Dryer, gas, 16 lb. capacity | Ea. | 1725 |
| 30 lb. capacity | Ea. | 2200 |
| Washer, 4 cycle | Ea. | 1550 |
| Commercial | Ea. | 2000 |
| Sauna, Prefabricated, complete | | |
| 6′ x 4′ | Ea. | 7500 |
| 6′ x 6′ | Ea. | 18,400 |
| 6′ x 9′ | Ea. | 10,500 |
| 8′ x 8′ | Ea. | 13,500 |
| 8′ x 10′ | Ea. | 13,000 |
| 10′ x 12′ | Ea. | 19,700 |
| Smoke Detectors | | |
| Ceiling type | Ea. | 300 |
| Duct type | Ea. | 615 |

| Description | Unit | $ Cost |
|---|---|---|
| Swimming Pools, Complete, gunite | S.F. | 127 - 158 |
| TV Antenna, Master system, 12 outlet | Outlet | 284 |
| 30 outlet | Outlet | 370 |
| 100 outlet | Outlet | 395 |



**Important: See the Reference Section for Location Factors.**

## Model costs calculated for a 1 story building with 9′ story height and 8,000 square feet of floor area

# Motel, 1 Story

| | | | | Unit | Unit Cost | Cost Per S.F. | % Of Sub-Total |
|---|---|---|---|---|---|---|---|
| **A. SUBSTRUCTURE** | | | | | | | |
| 1010 | Standard Foundations | Poured concrete; strip and spread footings; 4′ foundation wall | | S.F. Ground | 9.51 | 9.51 | 10.6% |
| 1020 | Special Foundations | N/A | | — | — | — | |
| 1030 | Slab on Grade | 4″ reinforced concrete with vapor barrier and granular base | | S.F. Slab | 7.22 | 7.22 | |
| 2010 | Basement Excavation | Site preparation for slab and trench for foundation wall and footing | | S.F. Ground | .38 | .38 | |
| 2020 | Basement Walls | N/A | | — | — | — | |
| **B. SHELL** | | | | | | | |
| **B10 Superstructure** | | | | | | | |
| 1010 | Floor Construction | N/A | | — | — | — | 8.0 % |
| 1020 | Roof Construction | Plywood on wood trusses | | S.F. Roof | 13.03 | 13.03 | |
| **B20 Exterior Enclosure** | | | | | | | |
| 2010 | Exterior Walls | Face brick on wood studs with sheathing, insulation and paper | *80% of wall* | S.F. Wall | 33.45 | 14.45 | 17.9% |
| 2020 | Exterior Windows | Wood double hung | *20% of wall* | Each | 670 | 5.16 | |
| 2030 | Exterior Doors | Wood solid core | | Each | 3430 | 9.44 | |
| **B30 Roofing** | | | | | | | |
| 3010 | Roof Coverings | Asphalt shingles with flashing (pitched); rigid fiberglass insulation | | S.F. Roof | 6.19 | 6.19 | 3.8% |
| 3020 | Roof Openings | N/A | | — | — | — | |
| **C. INTERIORS** | | | | | | | |
| 1010 | Partitions | Gypsum bd. and sound deadening bd. on wood studs | *9 S.F. Floor/L.F. Partition* | S.F. Partition | 14.02 | 12.46 | 19.3% |
| 1020 | Interior Doors | Single leaf hollow core wood | *300 S.F. Floor/Door* | Each | 825 | 2.75 | |
| 1030 | Fittings | N/A | | — | — | — | |
| 2010 | Stair Construction | N/A | | — | — | — | |
| 3010 | Wall Finishes | 90% paint, 10% ceramic tile | | S.F. Surface | 1.76 | 3.13 | |
| 3020 | Floor Finishes | 85% carpet, 15% ceramic tile | | S.F. Floor | 7.35 | 7.35 | |
| 3030 | Ceiling Finishes | Painted gypsum board on furring | | S.F. Ceiling | 5.53 | 5.53 | |
| **D. SERVICES** | | | | | | | |
| **D10 Conveying** | | | | | | | |
| 1010 | Elevators & Lifts | N/A | | — | — | — | 0.0 % |
| 1020 | Escalators & Moving Walks | N/A | | — | — | — | |
| **D20 Plumbing** | | | | | | | |
| 2010 | Plumbing Fixtures | Toilet and service fixtures, supply and drainage | *1 Fixture/90 S.F. Floor* | Each | 2731 | 30.34 | 19.8% |
| 2020 | Domestic Water Distribution | Gas fired water heater | | S.F. Floor | 1.72 | 1.72 | |
| 2040 | Rain Water Drainage | N/A | | — | — | — | |
| **D30 HVAC** | | | | | | | |
| 3010 | Energy Supply | N/A | | — | — | — | 6.1 % |
| 3020 | Heat Generating Systems | Included in D3050 | | — | — | — | |
| 3030 | Cooling Generating Systems | N/A | | — | — | — | |
| 3050 | Terminal & Package Units | Through the wall electric heating and cooling units | | S.F. Floor | 9.82 | 9.82 | |
| 3090 | Other HVAC Sys. & Equipment | N/A | | — | — | — | |
| **D40 Fire Protection** | | | | | | | |
| 4010 | Sprinklers | Wet pipe sprinkler system | | S.F. Floor | 6.60 | 6.60 | 5.2% |
| 4020 | Standpipes | Standpipe, wet, Class III | | S.F. Floor | 1.85 | 1.85 | |
| **D50 Electrical** | | | | | | | |
| 5010 | Electrical Service/Distribution | 200 ampere service, panel board and feeders | | S.F. Floor | 1.76 | 1.76 | 8.7% |
| 5020 | Lighting & Branch Wiring | Fluorescent fixtures, receptacles, switches and misc. power | | S.F. Floor | 9.43 | 9.43 | |
| 5030 | Communications & Security | Addressable alarm systems | | S.F. Floor | 2.92 | 2.92 | |
| 5090 | Other Electrical Systems | N/A | | — | — | — | |
| **E. EQUIPMENT & FURNISHINGS** | | | | | | | |
| 1010 | Commercial Equipment | Laundry equipment | | S.F. Floor | .90 | .90 | 0.6% |
| 1020 | Institutional Equipment | N/A | | — | — | — | |
| 1030 | Vehicular Equipment | N/A | | — | — | — | |
| 1090 | Other Equipment | N/A | | — | — | — | |
| **F. SPECIAL CONSTRUCTION** | | | | | | | |
| 1020 | Integrated Construction | N/A | | — | — | — | 0.0 % |
| 1040 | Special Facilities | N/A | | — | — | — | |
| **G. BUILDING SITEWORK** | | **N/A** | | | | | |
| | | | | | **Sub-Total** | 161.94 | **100%** |
| | CONTRACTOR FEES (General Requirements: 10%, Overhead: 5%, Profit: 10%) | | | | *25%* | 40.49 | |
| | ARCHITECT FEES | | | | *7%* | 14.17 | |
| | | | | | **Total Building Cost** | **216.60** | |

## Costs per square foot of floor area

| Exterior Wall | S.F. Area | 25000 | 37000 | 49000 | 61000 | 73000 | 81000 | 88000 | 96000 | 104000 |
|---|---|---|---|---|---|---|---|---|---|---|
| | L.F. Perimeter | 433 | 593 | 606 | 720 | 835 | 911 | 978 | 1054 | 1074 |
| Decorative Concrete Block | Wood Joists | 231.40 | 227.05 | 219.50 | 217.85 | 216.75 | 216.20 | 215.85 | 215.45 | 214.20 |
| | Precast Concrete | 250.75 | 245.20 | 236.75 | 234.70 | 233.35 | 232.70 | 232.20 | 231.70 | 230.35 |
| Stucco and Concrete Block | Wood Joists | 237.70 | 231.95 | 222.85 | 220.70 | 219.30 | 218.65 | 218.10 | 217.60 | 216.15 |
| | Precast Concrete | 256.20 | 249.75 | 240.10 | 237.75 | 236.20 | 235.40 | 234.85 | 234.30 | 232.70 |
| Wood Clapboard | Wood Frame | 230.25 | 225.95 | 218.60 | 217.05 | 216.00 | 215.50 | 215.05 | 214.70 | 213.50 |
| Brick Veneer | Wood Frame | 238.10 | 232.30 | 223.10 | 220.95 | 219.60 | 218.90 | 218.35 | 217.85 | 216.35 |
| Perimeter Adj., Add or Deduct | Per 100 L.F. | 7.05 | 4.80 | 3.60 | 2.85 | 2.45 | 2.20 | 2.00 | 1.80 | 1.65 |
| Story Hgt. Adj., Add or Deduct | Per 1 Ft. | 2.90 | 2.65 | 2.05 | 2.00 | 1.90 | 1.90 | 1.80 | 1.80 | 1.75 |

***For Basement**, add $ 50.05 per square foot of basement area*

*The above costs were calculated using the basic specifications shown on the facing page. These costs should be adjusted where necessary for design alternatives and owner's requirements.*

## Common additives

| Description | Unit | $ Cost |
|---|---|---|
| Closed Circuit Surveillance, One station | | |
| Camera and monitor | Ea. | 1250 |
| For additional camera station, add | Ea. | 475 |
| Elevators, Hydraulic passenger, 2 stops | | |
| 1500# capacity | Ea. | 86,500 |
| 2500# capacity | Ea. | 90,500 |
| 3500# capacity | Ea. | 96,000 |
| Additional stop, add | Ea. | 9875 |
| Emergency Lighting, 25 watt, battery operated | | |
| Lead battery | Ea. | 360 |
| Nickel cadmium | Ea. | 585 |
| Laundry Equipment | | |
| Dryer, gas, 16 lb. capacity | Ea. | 1725 |
| 30 lb. capacity | Ea. | 2200 |
| Washer, 4 cycle | Ea. | 1550 |
| Commercial | Ea. | 2000 |

| Description | Unit | $ Cost |
|---|---|---|
| Sauna, Prefabricated, complete | | |
| 6′ x 4′ | Ea. | 7500 |
| 6′ x 6′ | Ea. | 18,400 |
| 6′ x 9′ | Ea. | 10,500 |
| 8′ x 8′ | Ea. | 13,500 |
| 8′ x 10′ | Ea. | 13,000 |
| 10′ x 12′ | Ea. | 19,700 |
| Smoke Detectors | | |
| Ceiling type | Ea. | 300 |
| Duct type | Ea. | 615 |
| Swimming Pools, Complete, gunite | S.F. | 127 - 158 |
| TV Antenna, Master system, 12 outlet | Outlet | 284 |
| 30 outlet | Outlet | 370 |
| 100 outlet | Outlet | 395 |



**Important: See the Reference Section for Location Factors.**

## Model costs calculated for a 3 story building with 9′ story height and 49,000 square feet of floor area

# Motel, 2-3 Story

| | | | | Unit | Unit Cost | Cost Per S.F. | % Of Sub-Total |
|---|---|---|---|---|---|---|---|
| **A. SUBSTRUCTURE** | | | | | | | |
| 1010 | Standard Foundations | Poured concrete; strip and spread footings; 4′ foundation wall | | S.F. Ground | 7.74 | 2.58 | 2.9% |
| 1020 | Special Foundations | N/A | | — | — | — | |
| 1030 | Slab on Grade | 4″ reinforced concrete with vapor barrier and granular base | | S.F. Slab | 7.22 | 2.41 | |
| 2010 | Basement Excavation | Site preparation for slab and trench for foundation wall and footing | | S.F. Ground | .38 | .13 | |
| 2020 | Basement Walls | N/A | | — | — | — | |
| **B. SHELL** | | | | | | | |
| | **B10 Superstructure** | | | | | | |
| 1010 | Floor Construction | Precast concrete plank | | S.F. Floor | 15.54 | 10.36 | 8.3% |
| 1020 | Roof Construction | Precast concrete plank | | S.F. Roof | 13.29 | 4.43 | |
| | **B20 Exterior Enclosure** | | | | | | |
| 2010 | Exterior Walls | Decorative concrete block | *85% of wall* | S.F. Wall | 23.78 | 6.75 | 13.7% |
| 2020 | Exterior Windows | Aluminum sliding | *15% of wall* | Each | 1677 | 5.60 | |
| 2030 | Exterior Doors | Aluminum and glass doors and entrance with transom | | Each | 3672 | 12.14 | |
| | **B30 Roofing** | | | | | | |
| 3010 | Roof Coverings | Built-up tar and gravel with flashing; perlite/EPS composite insulation | | S.F. Roof | 8.46 | 2.82 | 1.6% |
| 3020 | Roof Openings | Roof hatches | | S.F. Roof | .24 | .08 | |
| **C. INTERIORS** | | | | | | | |
| 1010 | Partitions | Concrete block | *7 S.F. Floor/L.F. Partition* | S.F. Partition | 23.99 | 27.42 | 33.6% |
| 1020 | Interior Doors | Wood hollow core | *70 S.F. Floor/Door* | Each | 825 | 11.78 | |
| 1030 | Fittings | N/A | | — | — | — | |
| 2010 | Stair Construction | Concrete filled metal pan | | Flight | 16,075 | 3.94 | |
| 3010 | Wall Finishes | 90% paint, 10% ceramic tile | | S.F. Surface | 1.77 | 4.04 | |
| 3020 | Floor Finishes | 85% carpet, 5% vinyl composition tile, 10% ceramic tile | | S.F. Floor | 7.35 | 7.35 | |
| 3030 | Ceiling Finishes | Textured finish | | S.F. Ceiling | 5.53 | 5.53 | |
| **D. SERVICES** | | | | | | | |
| | **D10 Conveying** | | | | | | |
| 1010 | Elevators & Lifts | Two hydraulic passenger elevators | | Each | 137,935 | 5.63 | 3.2% |
| 1020 | Escalators & Moving Walks | N/A | | — | — | — | |
| | **D20 Plumbing** | | | | | | |
| 2010 | Plumbing Fixtures | Toilet and service fixtures, supply and drainage | *1 Fixture/180 S.F. Floor* | Each | 6203 | 34.46 | 20.3% |
| 2020 | Domestic Water Distribution | Gas fired water heater | | S.F. Floor | 1.26 | 1.26 | |
| 2040 | Rain Water Drainage | Roof drains | | S.F. Roof | 1.83 | .61 | |
| | **D30 HVAC** | | | | | | |
| 3010 | Energy Supply | N/A | | — | — | — | 5.0 % |
| 3020 | Heat Generating Systems | Included in D3050 | | — | — | — | |
| 3030 | Cooling Generating Systems | N/A | | — | — | — | |
| 3050 | Terminal & Package Units | Through the wall electric heating and cooling units | | S.F. Floor | 8.86 | 8.86 | |
| 3090 | Other HVAC Sys. & Equipment | N/A | | — | — | — | |
| | **D40 Fire Protection** | | | | | | |
| 4010 | Sprinklers | Sprinklers, wet, light hazard | | S.F. Floor | 4.39 | 4.39 | 2.7% |
| 4020 | Standpipes | Standpipe, wet, Class III | | S.F. Floor | .43 | .43 | |
| | **D50 Electrical** | | | | | | |
| 5010 | Electrical Service/Distribution | 800 ampere service, panel board and feeders | | S.F. Floor | 2.35 | 2.35 | 8.6% |
| 5020 | Lighting & Branch Wiring | Fluorescent fixtures, receptacles, switches and misc. power | | S.F. Floor | 10.59 | 10.59 | |
| 5030 | Communications & Security | Addressable alarm systems and emergency lighting | | S.F. Floor | 2.30 | 2.30 | |
| 5090 | Other Electrical Systems | Emergency generator, 7.5 kW | | S.F. Floor | .13 | .13 | |
| **E. EQUIPMENT & FURNISHINGS** | | | | | | | |
| 1010 | Commercial Equipment | Commercial laundry equipment | | S.F. Floor | .29 | .29 | 0.2% |
| 1020 | Institutional Equipment | N/A | | — | — | — | |
| 1030 | Vehicular Equipment | N/A | | — | — | — | |
| 1090 | Other Equipment | N/A | | — | — | — | |
| **F. SPECIAL CONSTRUCTION** | | | | | | | |
| 1020 | Integrated Construction | N/A | | — | — | — | 0.0 % |
| 1040 | Special Facilities | N/A | | — | — | — | |
| **G. BUILDING SITEWORK** | **N/A** | | | | | | |
| | | | | | **Sub-Total** | 178.66 | **100%** |
| | CONTRACTOR FEES (General Requirements: 10%, Overhead: 5%, Profit: 10%) | | | | 25% | 44.69 | |
| | ARCHITECT FEES | | | | 6% | 13.40 | |
| | | | | | **Total Building Cost** | **236.75** | |

# Movie Theater

## Costs per square foot of floor area

| Exterior Wall | S.F. Area | 9000 | 10000 | 12000 | 13000 | 14000 | 15000 | 16000 | 18000 | 20000 |
|---|---|---|---|---|---|---|---|---|---|---|
| | L.F. Perimeter | 385 | 410 | 440 | 460 | 480 | 500 | 510 | 547 | 583 |
| Decorative Concrete Block | Steel Joists | 243.15 | 237.60 | 227.05 | 223.50 | 220.45 | 217.80 | 214.75 | 210.75 | 207.50 |
| Concrete Block | Steel Joists | 233.50 | 228.35 | 218.75 | 215.50 | 212.75 | 210.25 | 207.55 | 203.90 | 200.90 |
| Face Brick and Concrete Block | Steel Joists | 256.15 | 250.05 | 238.20 | 234.25 | 230.90 | 227.95 | 224.45 | 219.95 | 216.35 |
| Precast Concrete | Steel Joists | 287.35 | 279.95 | 264.90 | 260.00 | 255.85 | 252.15 | 247.55 | 242.05 | 237.45 |
| Tilt-up Concrete Panels | Steel Joists | 241.25 | 235.80 | 225.45 | 221.95 | 218.95 | 216.30 | 213.35 | 209.40 | 206.20 |
| Metal Sandwich Panel | Steel Joists | 237.25 | 232.00 | 222.00 | 218.60 | 215.75 | 213.20 | 210.35 | 206.55 | 203.50 |
| Perimeter Adj., Add or Deduct | Per 100 L.F. | 14.75 | 13.20 | 11.00 | 10.10 | 9.45 | 8.80 | 8.25 | 7.35 | 6.55 |
| Story Hgt. Adj., Add or Deduct | Per 1 Ft. | 2.20 | 2.10 | 1.90 | 1.80 | 1.85 | 1.70 | 1.65 | 1.55 | 1.45 |
| **Basement**—Not Applicable | | | | | | | | | | |

*The above costs were calculated using the basic specifications shown on the facing page. These costs should be adjusted where necessary for design alternatives and owner's requirements.*

## Common additives

| Description | Unit | $ Cost |
|---|---|---|
| Emergency Lighting, 25 watt, battery operated | | |
| Lead battery | Ea. | 360 |
| Nickel cadmium | Ea. | 585 |
| Seating | | |
| Auditorium chair, all veneer | Ea. | 480 |
| Veneer back, padded seat | Ea. | 430 |
| Upholstered, spring seat | Ea. | 385 |
| Classroom, movable chair & desk | Set | 81 - 171 |
| Lecture hall, pedestal type | Ea. | 385 - 775 |
| Smoke Detectors | | |
| Ceiling type | Ea. | 300 |
| Duct type | Ea. | 615 |
| Sound System | | |
| Amplifier, 250 watts | Ea. | 2425 |
| Speaker, ceiling or wall | Ea. | 320 |
| Trumpet | Ea. | 580 |



**Important: See the Reference Section for Location Factors.**

## Model costs calculated for a 1 story building with 20′ story height and 12,000 square feet of floor area

# Movie Theater

| | | | | Unit | Unit Cost | Cost Per S.F. | % Of Sub-Total |
|---|---|---|---|---|---|---|---|
| **A. SUBSTRUCTURE** | | | | | | | |
| 1010 | Standard Foundations | Poured concrete; strip and spread footings; 4′ foundation wall | | S.F. Ground | 6.15 | 6.15 | 8.1% |
| 1020 | Special Foundations | N/A | | — | — | — | |
| 1030 | Slab on Grade | 4″ reinforced concrete with vapor barrier and granular base | | S.F. Slab | 7.22 | 7.22 | |
| 2010 | Basement Excavation | Site preparation for slab and trench for foundation wall and footing | | S.F. Ground | .38 | .38 | |
| 2020 | Basement Walls | N/A | | — | — | — | |
| **B. SHELL** | | | | | | | |
| | **B10 Superstructure** | | | | | | |
| 1010 | Floor Construction | Open web steel joists, slab form, concrete | *mezzanine 2250 S.F.* | S.F. Floor | 14.65 | 2.74 | 9.7% |
| 1020 | Roof Construction | Metal deck on open web steel joists | | S.F. Roof | 13.70 | 13.70 | |
| | **B20 Exterior Enclosure** | | | | | | |
| 2010 | Exterior Walls | Decorative concrete block | *80% of wall* | S.F. Wall | 21.15 | 15.51 | 16.7% |
| 2020 | Exterior Windows | Window wall | *20% of wall* | Each | 72 | 10.55 | |
| 2030 | Exterior Doors | Sliding mallfront aluminum and glass and hollow metal | | Each | 4483 | 2.24 | |
| | **B30 Roofing** | | | | | | |
| 3010 | Roof Coverings | Built-up tar and gravel with flashing; perlite/EPS composite insulation | | S.F. Roof | 8.44 | 8.44 | 5.0% |
| 3020 | Roof Openings | N/A | | — | — | — | |
| **C. INTERIORS** | | | | | | | |
| 1010 | Partitions | Concrete block | *40 S.F. Floor/L.F. Partition* | S.F. Partition | 10.85 | 4.34 | 17.8% |
| 1020 | Interior Doors | Single leaf hollow metal | *705 S.F. Floor/Door* | Each | 1159 | 1.65 | |
| 1030 | Fittings | Toilet partitions | | S.F. Floor | 1.02 | 1.02 | |
| 2010 | Stair Construction | Concrete filled metal pan | | Flight | 19,225 | 3.21 | |
| 3010 | Wall Finishes | Paint | | S.F. Surface | 4.90 | 3.92 | |
| 3020 | Floor Finishes | Carpet 50%, ceramic tile 5% | *50% of area* | S.F. Floor | 14.16 | 7.08 | |
| 3030 | Ceiling Finishes | Mineral fiber tile on concealed zee runners suspended | | S.F. Ceiling | 9 | 9 | |
| **D. SERVICES** | | | | | | | |
| | **D10 Conveying** | | | | | | |
| 1010 | Elevators & Lifts | N/A | | — | — | — | 0.0 % |
| 1020 | Escalators & Moving Walks | N/A | | — | — | — | |
| | **D20 Plumbing** | | | | | | |
| 2010 | Plumbing Fixtures | Toilet and service fixtures, supply and drainage | *1 Fixture/500 S.F. Floor* | Each | 7355 | 14.71 | 10.1% |
| 2020 | Domestic Water Distribution | Gas fired water heater | | S.F. Floor | .76 | .76 | |
| 2040 | Rain Water Drainage | Roof drains | | S.F. Roof | 1.70 | 1.70 | |
| | **D30 HVAC** | | | | | | |
| 3010 | Energy Supply | N/A | | — | — | — | 7.9 % |
| 3020 | Heat Generating Systems | Included in D3050 | | — | — | — | |
| 3030 | Cooling Generating Systems | N/A | | — | — | — | |
| 3050 | Terminal & Package Units | Single zone rooftop unit, gas heating, electric cooling | | S.F. Floor | 13.35 | 13.35 | |
| 3090 | Other HVAC Sys. & Equipment | N/A | | — | — | — | |
| | **D40 Fire Protection** | | | | | | |
| 4010 | Sprinklers | Wet pipe sprinkler system | | S.F. Floor | 6.17 | 6.17 | 4.5% |
| 4020 | Standpipes | Standpipe | | S.F. Floor | 1.53 | 1.53 | |
| | **D50 Electrical** | | | | | | |
| 5010 | Electrical Service/Distribution | 400 ampere service, panel board and feeders | | S.F. Floor | 2.35 | 2.35 | 8.7% |
| 5020 | Lighting & Branch Wiring | High efficiency fluorescent fixtures, receptacles, switches, A.C. and misc. power | | S.F. Floor | 9.39 | 9.39 | |
| 5030 | Communications & Security | Addressable alarm systems, sound system and emergency lighting | | S.F. Floor | 2.86 | 2.86 | |
| 5090 | Other Electrical Systems | Emergency generator, 7.5 kW | | S.F. Floor | .18 | .18 | |
| **E. EQUIPMENT & FURNISHINGS** | | | | | | | |
| 1010 | Commercial Equipment | N/A | | — | — | — | 11.5 % |
| 1020 | Institutional Equipment | Projection equipment, screen | | S.F. Floor | 8.22 | 8.22 | |
| 1030 | Vehicular Equipment | N/A | | — | — | — | |
| 2010 | Fixed Furnishings | Movie theater seating | | S.F. Floor | 11.38 | 11.38 | |
| **F. SPECIAL CONSTRUCTION** | | | | | | | |
| 1020 | Integrated Construction | N/A | | — | — | — | 0.0 % |
| 1040 | Special Facilities | N/A | | — | — | — | |
| **G. BUILDING SITEWORK** | **N/A** | | | | | | |
| | | | | | **Sub-Total** | 169.75 | **100%** |
| | CONTRACTOR FEES (General Requirements: 10%, Overhead: 5%, Profit: 10%) | | | | *25%* | 42.45 | |
| | ARCHITECT FEES | | | | *7%* | 14.85 | |
| | | | | | **Total Building Cost** | **227.05** | |

## Costs per square foot of floor area

| Exterior Wall | S.F. Area | 10000 | 15000 | 20000 | 25000 | 30000 | 35000 | 40000 | 45000 | 50000 |
|---|---|---|---|---|---|---|---|---|---|---|
| | L.F. Perimeter | 286 | 370 | 453 | 457 | 513 | 568 | 624 | 680 | 735 |
| Precast Concrete | Bearing Walls | 330.05 | 314.75 | 306.95 | 292.90 | 288.65 | 285.55 | 283.30 | 281.60 | 280.15 |
| | Rigid Steel | 336.50 | 321.30 | 313.50 | 299.60 | 295.35 | 292.25 | 290.00 | 288.30 | 286.85 |
| Face Brick and Concrete Block | Bearing Walls | 299.65 | 288.50 | 282.90 | 273.50 | 270.55 | 268.35 | 266.75 | 265.50 | 264.50 |
| | Rigid Steel | 307.50 | 296.45 | 290.90 | 281.60 | 278.60 | 276.45 | 274.85 | 273.65 | 272.65 |
| Stucco and Concrete Block | Bearing Walls | 293.30 | 283.10 | 277.90 | 269.50 | 266.75 | 264.75 | 263.30 | 262.20 | 261.25 |
| | Steel Joists | 301.20 | 291.05 | 285.85 | 277.55 | 274.85 | 272.85 | 271.45 | 270.35 | 269.40 |
| Perimeter Adj., Add or Deduct | Per 100 L.F. | 29.65 | 19.75 | 14.85 | 11.85 | 9.90 | 8.50 | 7.45 | 6.55 | 5.90 |
| Story Hgt. Adj., Add or Deduct | Per 1 Ft. | 7.60 | 6.55 | 6.05 | 4.90 | 4.60 | 4.35 | 4.20 | 4.00 | 3.85 |
| ***For Basement**, add $51.95 per square foot of basement area* | | | | | | | | | | |

*The above costs were calculated using the basic specifications shown on the facing page. These costs should be adjusted where necessary for design alternatives and owner's requirements.*

## Common additives

| Description | Unit | $ Cost |
|---|---|---|
| Beds, Manual | Ea. | 620 - 3450 |
| Elevators, Hydraulic passenger, 2 stops | | |
| 1500# capacity | Ea. | 86,500 |
| 2500# capacity | Ea. | 90,500 |
| 3500# capacity | Ea. | 96,000 |
| Emergency Lighting, 25 watt, battery operated | | |
| Lead battery | Ea. | 360 |
| Nickel cadmium | Ea. | 585 |
| Intercom System, 25 station capacity | | |
| Master station | Ea. | 3175 |
| Intercom outlets | Ea. | 228 |
| Handset | Ea. | 400 |
| Kitchen Equipment | | |
| Broiler | Ea. | 4425 |
| Coffee urn, twin 6 gallon | Ea. | 4075 |
| Cooler, 6 ft. long | Ea. | 4525 |
| Dishwasher, 10-12 racks per hr. | Ea. | 42,900 |
| Food warmer | Ea. | 720 |
| Freezer, 44 C.F., reach-in | Ea. | 3600 |

| Description | Unit | $ Cost |
|---|---|---|
| Kitchen Equipment, cont. | | |
| Ice cube maker, 50 lb. per day | Ea. | 2525 |
| Range with 1 oven | Ea. | 2050 |
| Laundry Equipment | | |
| Dryer, gas, 16 lb. capacity | Ea. | 1725 |
| 30 lb. capacity | Ea. | 2200 |
| Washer, 4 cycle | Ea. | 1550 |
| Commercial | Ea. | 2000 |
| Nurses Call System | | |
| Single bedside call station | Ea. | 715 |
| Pillow speaker | Ea. | 330 |
| Refrigerator, Prefabricated, walk-in | | |
| 7'-6" high, 6' x 6' | S.F. | 141 |
| 10' x 10' | S.F. | 110 |
| 12' x 14' | S.F. | 96 |
| 12' x 20' | S.F. | 139 |
| TV Antenna, Master system, 12 outlet | Outlet | 284 |
| 30 outlet | Outlet | 370 |
| 100 outlet | Outlet | 395 |
| Whirlpool Bath, Mobile, 18" x 24" x 60" | Ea. | 5900 |
| X-Ray, Mobile | Ea. | 16,200 - 48,400 |



**Important: See the Reference Section for Location Factors.**

## Model costs calculated for a 2 story building with 10′ story height and 25,000 square feet of floor area

# Nursing Home

| | | | | Unit | Unit Cost | Cost Per S.F. | % Of Sub-Total |
|---|---|---|---|---|---|---|---|
| **A. SUBSTRUCTURE** | | | | | | | |
| 1010 | Standard Foundations | Poured concrete; strip and spread footings; 4′ foundation wall | | S.F. Ground | 6.08 | 3.04 | 3.2% |
| 1020 | Special Foundations | N/A | | – | – | – | |
| 1030 | Slab on Grade | 4″ reinforced concrete with vapor barrier and granular base | | S.F. Slab | 7.22 | 3.61 | |
| 2010 | Basement Excavation | Site preparation for slab and trench for foundation wall and footing | | S.F. Ground | .38 | .19 | |
| 2020 | Basement Walls | N/A | | – | – | – | |
| **B. SHELL** | | | | | | | |
| **B10 Superstructure** | | | | | | | |
| 1010 | Floor Construction | Pre-cast double tees with concrete topping | | S.F. Floor | 17.82 | 8.91 | 7.8% |
| 1020 | Roof Construction | Pre-cast double tees | | S.F. Roof | 15.22 | 7.61 | |
| **B20 Exterior Enclosure** | | | | | | | |
| 2010 | Exterior Walls | Precast concrete panels | | S.F. Wall | 87 | 27.09 | 16.2% |
| 2020 | Exterior Windows | Wood double hung | *15% of wall* | Each | 1677 | 6.13 | |
| 2030 | Exterior Doors | Double aluminum & glass doors, single leaf hollow metal | | Each | 4574 | .92 | |
| **B30 Roofing** | | | | | | | |
| 3010 | Roof Coverings | Built-up tar and gravel with flashing; perlite/EPS composite insulation | | S.F. Roof | 8.46 | 4.23 | 2.0% |
| 3020 | Roof Openings | Roof hatches | | S.F. Roof | .16 | .08 | |
| **C. INTERIORS** | | | | | | | |
| 1010 | Partitions | Gypsum board on metal studs | *8 S.F. Floor/L.F. Partition* | S.F. Partition | 11.73 | 11.73 | 20.9% |
| 1020 | Interior Doors | Single leaf wood | *80 S.F. Floor/Door* | Each | 1231 | 15.39 | |
| 1030 | Fittings | N/A | | – | – | – | |
| 2010 | Stair Construction | Concrete stair | | Flight | 16,075 | 2.58 | |
| 3010 | Wall Finishes | 50% vinyl wall coverings, 45% paint, 5% ceramic tile | | S.F. Surface | 3.03 | 6.06 | |
| 3020 | Floor Finishes | 95% vinyl tile, 5% ceramic tile | | S.F. Floor | 2.95 | 2.95 | |
| 3030 | Ceiling Finishes | Painted gypsum board | | S.F. Ceiling | 5.43 | 5.43 | |
| **D. SERVICES** | | | | | | | |
| **D10 Conveying** | | | | | | | |
| 1010 | Elevators & Lifts | One hydraulic hospital elevator | | Each | 142,000 | 5.68 | 2.7% |
| 1020 | Escalators & Moving Walks | N/A | | – | – | – | |
| **D20 Plumbing** | | | | | | | |
| 2010 | Plumbing Fixtures | Kitchen, toilet and service fixtures, supply and drainage | *1 Fixture/230 S.F. Floor* | Each | 12,195 | 53.02 | 26.1% |
| 2020 | Domestic Water Distribution | Oil fired water heater | | S.F. Floor | 1.27 | 1.27 | |
| 2040 | Rain Water Drainage | Roof drains | | S.F. Roof | 1.72 | .86 | |
| **D30 HVAC** | | | | | | | |
| 3010 | Energy Supply | Oil fired hot water, wall fin radiation | | S.F. Floor | 10.29 | 10.29 | 9.4% |
| 3020 | Heat Generating Systems | N/A | | – | – | – | |
| 3030 | Cooling Generating Systems | N/A | | – | – | – | |
| 3050 | Terminal & Package Units | Split systems with air cooled condensing units | | S.F. Floor | 9.55 | 9.55 | |
| 3090 | Other HVAC Sys. & Equipment | N/A | | – | – | – | |
| **D40 Fire Protection** | | | | | | | |
| 4010 | Sprinklers | Sprinkler, light hazard | | S.F. Floor | 4.57 | 4.57 | 2.5% |
| 4020 | Standpipes | Standpipe | | S.F. Floor | .78 | .78 | |
| **D50 Electrical** | | | | | | | |
| 5010 | Electrical Service/Distribution | 800 ampere service, panel board and feeders | | S.F. Floor | 2.31 | 2.31 | 9.1% |
| 5020 | Lighting & Branch Wiring | High efficiency fluorescent fixtures, receptacles, switches, A.C. and misc. power | | S.F. Floor | 14.61 | 14.61 | |
| 5030 | Communications & Security | Addressable alarm systems and emergency lighting | | S.F. Floor | 1.73 | 1.73 | |
| 5090 | Other Electrical Systems | Emergency generator, 15 kW | | S.F. Floor | .50 | .50 | |
| **E. EQUIPMENT & FURNISHINGS** | | | | | | | |
| 1010 | Commercial Equipment | N/A | | – | – | – | 0.0 % |
| 1020 | Institutional Equipment | N/A | | – | – | – | |
| 1030 | Vehicular Equipment | N/A | | – | – | – | |
| 1090 | Other Equipment | N/A | | – | – | – | |
| **F. SPECIAL CONSTRUCTION** | | | | | | | |
| 1020 | Integrated Construction | N/A | | – | – | – | 0.0 % |
| 1040 | Special Facilities | N/A | | – | – | – | |
| **G. BUILDING SITEWORK** | | **N/A** | | | | | |
| | | | | | **Sub-Total** | 211.12 | **100%** |
| | CONTRACTOR FEES (General Requirements: 10%, Overhead: 5%, Profit: 10%) | | | | *25%* | 52.75 | |
| | ARCHITECT FEES | | | | *11%* | 29.03 | |
| | | | | | **Total Building Cost** | **292.90** | |

**For customer support on your Square Foot Costs with RSMeans data, call 800.448.8182.**

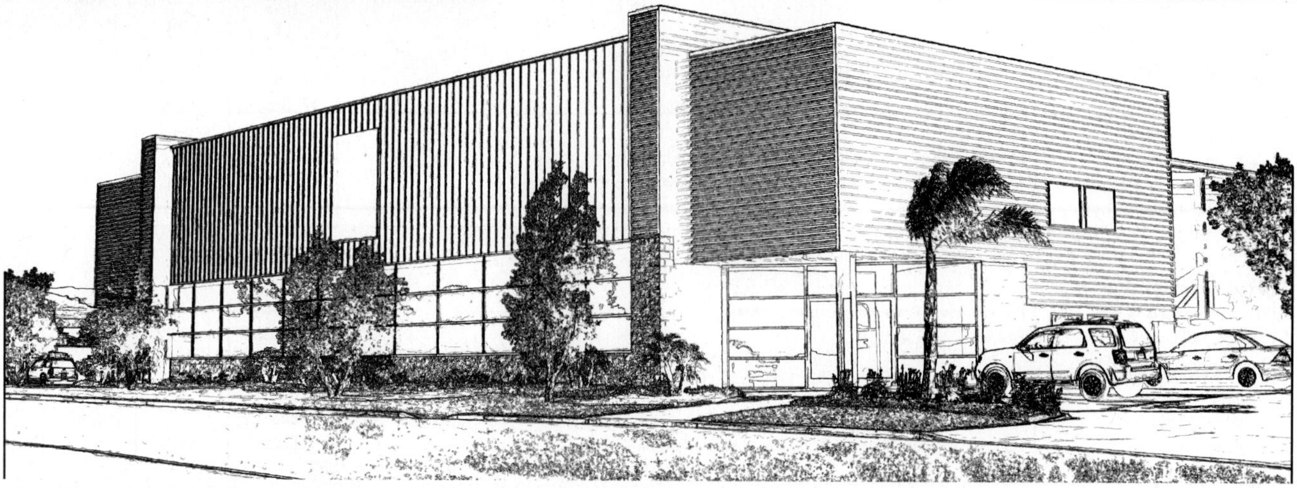

## Costs per square foot of floor area

| Exterior Wall | S.F. Area | 2000 | 3000 | 5000 | 7000 | 9000 | 12000 | 15000 | 20000 | 25000 |
|---|---|---|---|---|---|---|---|---|---|---|
| | L.F. Perimeter | 220 | 260 | 320 | 360 | 420 | 480 | 520 | 640 | 700 |
| Vinyl Clapboard | Wood Frame | 267.55 | 240.80 | 216.85 | 204.70 | 199.40 | 193.10 | 188.45 | 185.60 | 182.25 |
| Stone Veneer | Wood Frame | 313.00 | 276.75 | 243.55 | 226.25 | 218.95 | 209.95 | 203.15 | 199.20 | 194.25 |
| Fiber Cement | Rigid Steel | 295.15 | 264.05 | 235.85 | 221.35 | 215.15 | 207.65 | 201.90 | 198.60 | 194.50 |
| E.I.F.S. | Rigid Steel | 294.90 | 263.90 | 235.75 | 221.20 | 215.05 | 207.50 | 201.90 | 198.55 | 194.50 |
| Precast Concrete | Reinforced Concrete | 380.35 | 333.30 | 289.65 | **266.55** | 257.10 | 245.10 | 235.75 | 230.60 | 223.75 |
| Brick Veneer | Reinforced Concrete | 380.30 | 332.40 | 287.95 | 264.45 | 254.85 | 242.60 | 233.15 | 227.95 | 221.00 |
| Perimeter Adj., Add or Deduct | Per 100 L.F. | 33.00 | 22.10 | 13.20 | 9.40 | 7.35 | 5.55 | 4.45 | 3.30 | 2.65 |
| Story Hgt. Adj., Add or Deduct | Per 1 Ft. | 3.15 | 2.50 | 1.85 | 1.45 | 1.35 | 1.15 | 1.00 | 0.90 | 0.80 |

***For Basement**, add $52.65 per square foot of basement area*

*The above costs were calculated using the basic specifications shown on the facing page. These costs should be adjusted where necessary for design alternatives and owner's requirements.*

## Common additives

| Description | Unit | $ Cost |
|---|---|---|
| Closed circuit surveillance, one station | | |
| Camera and monitor | Ea. | 1250 |
| For additional camera stations, add | Ea. | 475 |
| Directory boards, plastic, glass covered | | |
| 30" x 20" | Ea. | 705 |
| 36" x 48" | Ea. | 1475 |
| Aluminum, 24" x 18" | Ea. | 705 |
| 36" x 24" | Ea. | 985 |
| 48" x 32" | Ea. | 1975 |
| 48" x 60" | Ea. | 2650 |
| Electronic, wall mounted | S.F. | 1175 |
| Free standing | S.F. | 1625 |
| Pedestal access floor system w/plastic laminate cover | | |
| Computer room, less than 6000 SF | S.F. | 8.80 |
| Greater than 6000 SF | S.F. | 8.65 |
| Office, greater than 6000 S.F. | S.F. | 11.95 |

| Description | Unit | $ Cost |
|---|---|---|
| Security access systems | | |
| Metal detectors, wand type | Ea. | 138 |
| Walk-through portal type, single-zone | Ea. | 1800 |
| Multi-zone | Ea. | 3125 |
| X-ray equipment | | |
| Desk top, for mail, small packages | Ea. | 3975 |
| Conveyer type, including monitor, minimum | Ea. | 21,900 |
| Maximum | Ea. | 38,700 |
| Explosive detection equipment | | |
| Hand held, battery operated | Ea. | 28,100 |
| Walk-through portal type | Ea. | 193,000 |
| Uninterruptible power supply, 15 kVA/12.75 kW | kW | 1.35 |

## Model costs calculated for a 1 story building with 12′ story height and 7,000 square feet of floor area

# Office, 1 Story

| | | | | Unit | Unit Cost | Cost Per S.F. | % Of Sub-Total |
|---|---|---|---|---|---|---|---|
| **A. SUBSTRUCTURE** | | | | | | | |
| 1010 | Standard Foundations | Poured concrete; strip and spread footings; 4′ foundation wall | | S.F. Ground | 10.45 | 10.45 | 9.1% |
| 1020 | Special Foundations | N/A | | – | – | – | |
| 1030 | Slab on Grade | 4″ reinforced concrete | | S.F. Slab | 7.22 | 7.22 | |
| 2010 | Basement Excavation | Site preparation for slab and trench for foundation wall and footing | | S.F. Ground | .38 | .38 | |
| 2020 | Basement Walls | N/A | | – | – | – | |
| **B. SHELL** | | | | | | | |
| **B10 Superstructure** | | | | | | | |
| 1010 | Floor Construction | Cast in place concrete columns | | S.F. Floor | 3.47 | 3.47 | 12.4% |
| 1020 | Roof Construction | Concrete beam and slab | | S.F. Roof | 21.30 | 21.30 | |
| **B20 Exterior Enclosure** | | | | | | | |
| 2010 | Exterior Walls | Precast concrete panels, insulated | *80% of wall* | S.F. Wall | 75 | 37.15 | 23.4% |
| 2020 | Exterior Windows | Aluminum awning windows | *20% of wall* | Each | 839 | 4.50 | |
| 2030 | Exterior Doors | Aluminum and glass single and double doors, hollow metal doors | | Each | 5775 | 4.94 | |
| **B30 Roofing** | | | | | | | |
| 3010 | Roof Coverings | Single ply membrane, stone ballast, rigid insulation | | S.F. Roof | 12.59 | 12.59 | 7.0% |
| 3020 | Roof Openings | Smoke hatches | | S.F. Roof | 1.30 | 1.30 | |
| **C. INTERIORS** | | | | | | | |
| 1010 | Partitions | Gypsum board on metal studs | *20 S.F. Floor/L.F. Partition* | S.F. Partition | 8.04 | 4.02 | 12.1% |
| 1020 | Interior Doors | 70% Single leaf solid wood doors, 30% hollow metal single leaf | *320 S.F. Floor/Door* | Each | 1159 | 3.64 | |
| 1030 | Fittings | Plastic laminate toilet partitions | | S.F. Floor | .46 | .46 | |
| 2010 | Stair Construction | N/A | | – | – | – | |
| 3010 | Wall Finishes | 90% Paint, 10% ceramic wall tile | | S.F. Surface | 1.43 | 1.43 | |
| 3020 | Floor Finishes | 65% Carpet, 10% porcelain tile, 10% quarry tile | | S.F. Floor | 5.12 | 5.12 | |
| 3030 | Ceiling Finishes | Acoustic ceiling tiles on suspended channel grid | | S.F. Ceiling | 9.48 | 9.48 | |
| **D. SERVICES** | | | | | | | |
| **D10 Conveying** | | | | | | | |
| 1010 | Elevators & Lifts | N/A | | – | – | – | 0.0 % |
| 1020 | Escalators & Moving Walks | N/A | | – | – | – | |
| **D20 Plumbing** | | | | | | | |
| 2010 | Plumbing Fixtures | Restroom and service fixtures, supply and drainage | *1 Fixture/700 S.F. Floor* | Each | 3157 | 4.51 | 3.7% |
| 2020 | Domestic Water Distribution | Gas fired water heater | | S.F. Floor | 1.72 | 1.72 | |
| 2040 | Rain Water Drainage | Roof drains | | S.F. Roof | 1.22 | 1.22 | |
| **D30 HVAC** | | | | | | | |
| 3010 | Energy Supply | N/A | | – | – | – | 11.9 % |
| 3020 | Heat Generating Systems | Included in D3050 | | – | – | – | |
| 3030 | Cooling Generating Systems | N/A | | – | – | – | |
| 3050 | Terminal & Package Units | Multizone gas heating, electric cooling unit | | S.F. Floor | 23.80 | 23.80 | |
| 3090 | Other HVAC Sys. & Equipment | N/A | | – | – | – | |
| **D40 Fire Protection** | | | | | | | |
| 4010 | Sprinklers | Wet pipe light hazard sprinkler system | | S.F. Floor | 5.07 | 5.07 | 3.8% |
| 4020 | Standpipes | Standpipes | | S.F. Floor | 2.54 | 2.54 | |
| **D50 Electrical** | | | | | | | |
| 5010 | Electrical Service/Distribution | 400 ampere service, panel boards and feeders | | S.F. Floor | 6.32 | 6.32 | 16.5% |
| 5020 | Lighting & Branch Wiring | Fluorescent fixtures, receptacles, switches, A.C. and misc. power | | S.F. Floor | 18.15 | 18.15 | |
| 5030 | Communications & Security | Telephone systems, internet wiring, and addressable alarm systems | | S.F. Floor | 8.51 | 8.51 | |
| 5090 | Other Electrical Systems | Emergency generator, 7.5 kW | | S.F. Floor | | | |
| **E. EQUIPMENT & FURNISHINGS** | | | | | | | |
| 1010 | Commercial Equipment | N/A | | – | – | – | 0.0 % |
| 1020 | Institutional Equipment | N/A | | – | – | – | |
| 1030 | Vehicular Equipment | N/A | | – | – | – | |
| 1090 | Other Equipment | N/A | | – | – | – | |
| **F. SPECIAL CONSTRUCTION** | | | | | | | |
| 1020 | Integrated Construction | N/A | | – | – | – | 0.0 % |
| 1040 | Special Facilities | N/A | | – | – | – | |
| **G. BUILDING SITEWORK** | | **N/A** | | | | | |
| | | | | | **Sub-Total** | 199.29 | **100%** |
| | CONTRACTOR FEES (General Requirements: 10%, Overhead: 5%, Profit: 10%) | | | | *25%* | 49.82 | |
| | ARCHITECT FEES | | | | *7%* | 17.44 | |
| | | | | | **Total Building Cost** | **266.55** | |

## Costs per square foot of floor area

| Exterior Wall | S.F. Area | 5000 | 8000 | 12000 | 16000 | 20000 | 35000 | 50000 | 65000 | 80000 |
|---|---|---|---|---|---|---|---|---|---|---|
| | L.F. Perimeter | 220 | 260 | 310 | 330 | 360 | 440 | 550 | 600 | 675 |
| Vinyl Clapboard | Wood Frame | 264.90 | 236.80 | 220.85 | 210.10 | 204.30 | 193.15 | 189.55 | 186.30 | 184.70 |
| Stone Veneer | Wood Frame | 319.00 | 276.85 | 252.65 | 235.55 | 226.55 | 208.75 | 203.25 | 197.75 | 195.20 |
| Fiber Cement | Rigid Steel | 274.70 | 242.25 | 223.65 | 211.00 | **204.20** | 191.00 | 186.75 | 182.75 | 180.90 |
| E.I.F.S. | Rigid Steel | 277.90 | 245.55 | 227.00 | 214.35 | 207.60 | 194.35 | 190.15 | 186.20 | 184.35 |
| Precast Concrete | Reinforced Concrete | 370.50 | 315.50 | 283.90 | 260.95 | 249.00 | 225.15 | 217.85 | 210.40 | 206.95 |
| Brick Veneer | Reinforced Concrete | 353.20 | 302.15 | 272.80 | 251.65 | 240.65 | 218.60 | 211.85 | 205.00 | 201.85 |
| Perimeter Adj., Add or Deduct | Per 100 L.F. | 29.65 | 18.60 | 12.40 | 9.25 | 7.45 | 4.25 | 2.95 | 2.35 | 1.80 |
| Story Hgt. Adj., Add or Deduct | Per 1 Ft. | 3.75 | 2.80 | 2.20 | 1.75 | 1.55 | 1.10 | 0.95 | 0.80 | 0.70 |

***For Basement**, add $58.90 per square foot of basement area*

*The above costs were calculated using the basic specifications shown on the facing page. These costs should be adjusted where necessary for design alternatives and owner's requirements.*

## Common additives

| Description | Unit | $ Cost |
|---|---|---|
| Closed circuit surveillance, one station | | |
| Camera and monitor | Ea. | 1250 |
| For additional camera stations, add | Ea. | 475 |
| Directory boards, plastic, glass covered | | |
| 30" x 20" | Ea. | 705 |
| 36" x 48" | Ea. | 1475 |
| Aluminum, 24" x 18" | Ea. | 705 |
| 36" x 24" | Ea. | 985 |
| 48" x 32" | Ea. | 1975 |
| 48" x 60" | Ea. | 2650 |
| Electronic, wall mounted | S.F. | 1175 |
| Free standing | S.F. | 1625 |
| Escalators, 10' rise, 32" wide, glass balustrade | Ea. | 174,500 |
| Metal balustrade | Ea. | 183,500 |
| 48" wide, glass balustrade | Ea. | 182,500 |
| Metal balustrade | Ea. | 194,500 |
| Pedestal access floor system w/plastic laminate cover | | |
| Computer room, less than 6000 SF | S.F. | 8.80 |
| Greater than 6000 SF | S.F. | 8.65 |
| Office, greater than 6000 S.F. | S.F. | 11.95 |

| Description | Unit | $ Cost |
|---|---|---|
| Security access systems | | |
| Metal detectors, wand type | Ea. | 138 |
| Walk-through portal type, single-zone | Ea. | 1800 |
| Multi-zone | Ea. | 3125 |
| X-ray equipment | | |
| Desk top, for mail, small packages | Ea. | 3975 |
| Conveyer type, including monitor, minimum | Ea. | 21,900 |
| Maximum | Ea. | 38,700 |
| Explosive detection equipment | | |
| Hand held, battery operated | Ea. | 28,100 |
| Walk-through portal type | Ea. | 193,000 |
| Uninterruptible power supply, 15 kVA/12.75 kW | kW | 1.35 |



**Important: See the Reference Section for Location Factors.**

**Model costs calculated for a 3 story building with 12' story height and 20,000 square feet of floor area**

# Office, 2-4 Story

| | | | | Unit | Unit Cost | Cost Per S.F. | % Of Sub-Total |
|---|---|---|---|---|---|---|---|
| **A. SUBSTRUCTURE** | | | | | | | |
| 1010 | Standard Foundations | Poured concrete; strip and spread footings; 4' foundation wall | | S.F. Ground | 12.81 | 4.27 | 4.5% |
| 1020 | Special Foundations | N/A | | – | – | – | |
| 1030 | Slab on Grade | 4" reinforced concrete with vapor barrier and granular base | | S.F. Slab | 7.22 | 2.41 | |
| 2010 | Basement Excavation | Site preparation for slab and trench for foundation wall and footing | | S.F. Ground | .38 | .13 | |
| 2020 | Basement Walls | N/A | | – | – | – | |
| **B. SHELL** | | | | | | | |
| | **B10 Superstructure** | | | | | | |
| 1010 | Floor Construction | Open web steel joists, slab form, concrete, columns | | S.F. Floor | 20.66 | 13.77 | 12.0% |
| 1020 | Roof Construction | Metal deck, open web steel joists, columns | | S.F. Roof | 13.71 | 4.57 | |
| | **B20 Exterior Enclosure** | | | | | | |
| 2010 | Exterior Walls | Face brick with concrete block backup | *80% of wall* | S.F. Wall | 22.45 | 11.64 | 11.9% |
| 2020 | Exterior Windows | Aluminum outward projecting | *20% of wall* | Each | 839 | 4.73 | |
| 2030 | Exterior Doors | Aluminum and glass, hollow metal | | Each | 5775 | 1.73 | |
| | **B30 Roofing** | | | | | | |
| 3010 | Roof Coverings | Built-up tar and gravel with flashing; perlite/EPS composite | | S.F. Roof | 12.15 | 4.05 | 3.3% |
| 3020 | Roof Openings | N/A | | – | – | – | |
| **C. INTERIORS** | | | | | | | |
| 1010 | Partitions | Gypsum board on metal studs | *20 S.F. Floor/L.F. Partition* | S.F. Partition | 8.58 | 3.43 | 18.2% |
| 1020 | Interior Doors | Single leaf hollow metal | *200 S.F. Floor/Door* | Each | 1159 | 3.72 | |
| 1030 | Fittings | Toilet partitions | | S.F. Floor | .27 | .27 | |
| 2010 | Stair Construction | Concrete filled metal pan | | Flight | 12,925 | 4.53 | |
| 3010 | Wall Finishes | 60% vinyl wall covering, 40% paint | | S.F. Surface | 1.59 | 1.27 | |
| 3020 | Floor Finishes | 60% carpet, 30% vinyl composition tile, 10% ceramic tile | | S.F. Floor | 5.12 | 5.12 | |
| 3030 | Ceiling Finishes | Mineral fiber tile on concealed zee bars | | S.F. Ceiling | 9.48 | 9.48 | |
| **D. SERVICES** | | | | | | | |
| | **D10 Conveying** | | | | | | |
| 1010 | Elevators & Lifts | Two hydraulic passenger elevators | | Each | 147,200 | 14.72 | 9.6% |
| 1020 | Escalators & Moving Walks | N/A | | – | – | – | |
| | **D20 Plumbing** | | | | | | |
| 2010 | Plumbing Fixtures | Toilet and service fixtures, supply and drainage | *1 Fixture/1320 S.F. Floor* | Each | 3359 | 3.19 | 3.0% |
| 2020 | Domestic Water Distribution | Gas fired water heater | | S.F. Floor | .60 | .60 | |
| 2040 | Rain Water Drainage | Roof drains | | S.F. Roof | 2.31 | .77 | |
| | **D30 HVAC** | | | | | | |
| 3010 | Energy Supply | N/A | | – | – | – | 13.1 % |
| 3020 | Heat Generating Systems | Included in D3030 | | – | – | – | |
| 3030 | Cooling Generating Systems | Multizone unit gas heating, electric cooling | | S.F. Floor | | | |
| 3050 | Terminal & Package Units | N/A | | – | – | – | |
| 3090 | Other HVAC Sys. & Equipment | N/A | | – | – | – | |
| | **D40 Fire Protection** | | | | | | |
| 4010 | Sprinklers | N/A | | – | – | – | 4.6 % |
| 4020 | Standpipes | Standpipes and hose systems | | S.F. Floor | 1.68 | 1.68 | |
| | **D50 Electrical** | | | | | | |
| 5010 | Electrical Service/Distribution | 1000 ampere service, panel board and feeders | | S.F. Floor | 5.16 | 5.16 | 19.8% |
| 5020 | Lighting & Branch Wiring | Fluorescent fixtures, receptacles, switches, A.C. and misc. power | | S.F. Floor | 17.57 | 17.57 | |
| 5030 | Communications & Security | Alarm systems and emergency lighting | | S.F. Floor | 7.55 | 7.55 | |
| 5090 | Other Electrical Systems | Emergency generator, 7.5 kW | | S.F. Floor | | | |
| **E. EQUIPMENT & FURNISHINGS** | | | | | | | |
| 1010 | Commercial Equipment | N/A | | – | – | – | 0.0 % |
| 1020 | Institutional Equipment | N/A | | – | – | – | |
| 1030 | Vehicular Equipment | N/A | | – | – | – | |
| 1090 | Other Equipment | N/A | | – | – | – | |
| **F. SPECIAL CONSTRUCTION** | | | | | | | |
| 1020 | Integrated Construction | N/A | | – | – | – | 0.0 % |
| 1040 | Special Facilities | N/A | | – | – | – | |
| **G. BUILDING SITEWORK** | | **N/A** | | | | | |
| | | | | | **Sub-Total** | 152.68 | **100%** |
| | CONTRACTOR FEES (General Requirements: 10%, Overhead: 5%, Profit: 10%) | | | | *25%* | 38.16 | |
| | ARCHITECT FEES | | | | *7%* | 13.36 | |
| | | | | | **Total Building Cost** | **204.20** | |

## Costs per square foot of floor area

| Exterior Wall | S.F. Area | 20000 | 40000 | 60000 | 80000 | 100000 | 150000 | 200000 | 250000 | 300000 |
|---|---|---|---|---|---|---|---|---|---|---|
| | L.F. Perimeter | 260 | 360 | 400 | 420 | 460 | 520 | 650 | 720 | 800 |
| Stone Veneer | Rigid Steel | 295.75 | 249.40 | 224.05 | 208.80 | 201.70 | 189.60 | 186.95 | 183.00 | 180.70 |
| E.I.F.S. | Rigid Steel | 243.85 | 213.45 | 197.45 | 187.85 | 183.35 | 175.80 | 174.00 | 171.45 | 170.10 |
| Curtain Wall | Rigid Steel | 271.90 | 234.05 | 213.65 | 201.45 | 195.80 | 186.05 | 183.85 | 180.70 | 178.85 |
| Brick Veneer | Reinforced Concrete | 401.05 | 323.10 | 279.35 | 252.90 | 240.65 | 219.60 | 215.20 | 208.35 | 204.35 |
| Metal Panel | Reinforced Concrete | 294.75 | 251.50 | 228.00 | 213.90 | 207.30 | 196.10 | 193.65 | 189.95 | 187.85 |
| E.I.F.S. | Reinforced Concrete | 374.75 | 304.90 | 265.85 | 242.25 | 231.30 | 212.60 | 208.60 | 202.50 | 199.00 |
| Perimeter Adj., Add or Deduct | Per 100 L.F. | 49.75 | 24.90 | 16.55 | 12.45 | 9.95 | 6.55 | 5.00 | 4.00 | 3.30 |
| Story Hgt. Adj., Add or Deduct | Per 1 Ft. | 10.15 | 7.00 | 5.20 | 4.15 | 3.65 | 2.65 | 2.55 | 2.25 | 2.10 |

***For Basement**, add $63.50 per square foot of basement area*

*The above costs were calculated using the basic specifications shown on the facing page. These costs should be adjusted where necessary for design alternatives and owner's requirements.*

## Common additives

| Description | Unit | $ Cost |
|---|---|---|
| Closed circuit surveillance, one station | | |
| Camera and monitor | Ea. | 1250 |
| For additional camera stations, add | Ea. | 475 |
| Directory boards, plastic, glass covered | | |
| 30″ x 20″ | Ea. | 705 |
| 36″ x 48″ | Ea. | 1475 |
| Aluminum, 24″ x 18″ | Ea. | 705 |
| 36″ x 24″ | Ea. | 985 |
| 48″ x 32″ | Ea. | 1975 |
| 48″ x 60″ | Ea. | 2650 |
| Electronic, wall mounted | S.F. | 1175 |
| Free standing | S.F. | 1625 |
| Escalators, 10′ rise, 32″ wide, glass balustrade | Ea. | 174,500 |
| Metal balustrade | Ea. | 183,500 |
| 48″ wide, glass balustrade | Ea. | 182,500 |
| Metal balustrade | Ea. | 194,500 |
| Pedestal access floor system w/plastic laminate cover | | |
| Computer room, less than 6000 SF | S.F. | 8.80 |
| Greater than 6000 SF | S.F. | 8.65 |
| Office, greater than 6000 S.F. | S.F. | 11.95 |

| Description | Unit | $ Cost |
|---|---|---|
| Security access systems | | |
| Metal detectors, wand type | Ea. | 138 |
| Walk-through portal type, single-zone | Ea. | 1800 |
| Multi-zone | Ea. | 3125 |
| X-ray equipment | | |
| Desk top, for mail, small packages | Ea. | 3975 |
| Conveyer type, including monitor, minimum | Ea. | 21,900 |
| Maximum | Ea. | 38,700 |
| Explosive detection equipment | | |
| Hand held, battery operated | Ea. | 28,100 |
| Walk-through portal type | Ea. | 193,000 |
| Uninterruptible power supply, 15 kVA/12.75 kW | kW | 1.35 |



**Important: See the Reference Section for Location Factors.**

## Model costs calculated for a 8 story building with 12′ story height and 80,000 square feet of floor area

# Office, 5-10 Story

| | | | | Unit | Unit Cost | Cost Per S.F. | % Of Sub-Total |
|---|---|---|---|---|---|---|---|
| **A. SUBSTRUCTURE** | | | | | | | |
| 1010 | Standard Foundations | Poured concrete; strip and spread footings; 4′ foundation wall | | S.F. Ground | 9.60 | 1.20 | |
| 1020 | Special Foundations | N/A | | — | — | — | |
| 1030 | Slab on Grade | 4″ reinforced slab on grade | | S.F. Slab | 7.22 | .91 | 1.4% |
| 2010 | Basement Excavation | Site preparation for slab and trench for foundation wall and footing | | S.F. Ground | .38 | .05 | |
| 2020 | Basement Walls | N/A | | — | — | — | |
| **B. SHELL** | | | | | | | |
| | **B10 Superstructure** | | | | | | |
| 1010 | Floor Construction | Open web steel joists, slab form, concrete, fireproofed steel columns | | S.F. Floor | 17.50 | 15.31 | 10.8% |
| 1020 | Roof Construction | Metal deck, open web steel joists, beams, columns | | S.F. Roof | 13.68 | 1.71 | |
| | **B20 Exterior Enclosure** | | | | | | |
| 2010 | Exterior Walls | Limestone stone veneer on metal studs | *80% of wall* | S.F. Wall | 62 | 24.80 | |
| 2020 | Exterior Windows | Aluminum sliding windows | *20% of wall* | Each | 1677 | 11.27 | 23.2% |
| 2030 | Exterior Doors | Aluminum and glass double doors, hollow metal egress doors | | Each | 6350 | .48 | |
| | **B30 Roofing** | | | | | | |
| 3010 | Roof Coverings | Single ply membrane, stone ballast, rigid insulation | | S.F. Roof | 11.36 | 1.42 | 1.1% |
| 3020 | Roof Openings | Roof and smoke hatches | | S.F. Roof | 4547 | .34 | |
| **C. INTERIORS** | | | | | | | |
| 1010 | Partitions | Gypsum board on metal studs | *30 S.F. Floor/L.F. Partition* | S.F. Partition | 11.79 | 3.93 | |
| 1020 | Interior Doors | Single leaf solid core wood doors, hollow metal egress doors | *350 S.F. Floor/Door* | Each | 1159 | 3.29 | |
| 1030 | Fittings | Plastic laminate toilet partitions | | S.F. Floor | .22 | .22 | |
| 2010 | Stair Construction | Concrete filled metal pan, with rails | | Flight | 12,925 | 4.20 | 17.3% |
| 3010 | Wall Finishes | Paint on drywall | | S.F. Surface | 1.55 | 1.03 | |
| 3020 | Floor Finishes | 60% Carpet tile, 30% vinyl composition tile, 10% ceramic tile | | S.F. Floor | 5.12 | 5.12 | |
| 3030 | Ceiling Finishes | Acoustic ceiling tiles on suspended support system | | S.F. Ceiling | 9.48 | 9.48 | |
| **D. SERVICES** | | | | | | | |
| | **D10 Conveying** | | | | | | |
| 1010 | Elevators & Lifts | Traction geared passenger elevators | | Each | 370,600 | 18.53 | 11.8% |
| 1020 | Escalators & Moving Walks | N/A | | — | — | — | |
| | **D20 Plumbing** | | | | | | |
| 2010 | Plumbing Fixtures | Restroom and service fixtures, supply and drainage | *1 Fixture/1600 S.F. Floor* | Each | 3760 | 2.35 | |
| 2020 | Domestic Water Distribution | Gas fired water heater | | S.F. Floor | .74 | .74 | 2.2% |
| 2040 | Rain Water Drainage | Roof drains | | S.F. Roof | 2.80 | .35 | |
| | **D30 HVAC** | | | | | | |
| 3010 | Energy Supply | N/A | | — | — | — | |
| 3020 | Heat Generating Systems | Included in D3050 | | — | — | — | |
| 3030 | Cooling Generating Systems | N/A | | — | — | — | 12.7 % |
| 3050 | Terminal & Package Units | Multizone unit, gas heating , electric cooling | | S.F. Floor | 20 | 20 | |
| 3090 | Other HVAC Sys. & Equipment | N/A | | — | — | — | |
| | **D40 Fire Protection** | | | | | | |
| 4010 | Sprinklers | Wet pipe spinkler system | | S.F. Floor | 4.33 | 4.33 | 3.9% |
| 4020 | Standpipes | Standpipes and hose systems, with pumps | | S.F. Floor | 1.83 | 1.83 | |
| | **D50 Electrical** | | | | | | |
| 5010 | Electrical Service/Distribution | 800 Ampere service, panel boards and feeders | | S.F. Floor | 1.59 | 1.59 | |
| 5020 | Lighting & Branch Wiring | Fluorescent fixtures, receptacles, switches, A.C. and misc. power | | S.F. Floor | 17.45 | 17.45 | 15.7% |
| 5030 | Communications & Security | Alarm systems, emergency lighting, internet and phone wiring | | S.F. Floor | 5.65 | 5.65 | |
| 5090 | Other Electrical Systems | Uninterruptible power supply with battery pack, 12.75kW | | S.F. Floor | | | |
| **E. EQUIPMENT & FURNISHINGS** | | | | | | | |
| 1010 | Commercial Equipment | N/A | | — | — | — | |
| 1020 | Institutional Equipment | N/A | | — | — | — | 0.0 % |
| 1030 | Vehicular Equipment | N/A | | — | — | — | |
| 1090 | Other Equipment | N/A | | — | — | — | |
| **F. SPECIAL CONSTRUCTION** | | | | | | | |
| 1020 | Integrated Construction | N/A | | — | — | — | 0.0 % |
| 1040 | Special Facilities | N/A | | — | — | — | |
| **G. BUILDING SITEWORK** | | **N/A** | | | | | |
| | | | | | **Sub-Total** | 157.58 | **100%** |
| | CONTRACTOR FEES (General Requirements: 10%, Overhead: 5%, Profit: 10%) | | | | *25%* | 39.40 | |
| | ARCHITECT FEES | | | | *6%* | 11.82 | |
| | | | | | **Total Building Cost** | **208.80** | |

## Costs per square foot of floor area

| Exterior Wall | S.F. Area | 120000 | 145000 | 170000 | 200000 | 230000 | 260000 | 400000 | 600000 | 800000 |
|---|---|---|---|---|---|---|---|---|---|---|
| | L.F. Perimeter | 420 | 450 | 470 | 490 | 510 | 530 | 650 | 800 | 900 |
| Stone Veneer | Rigid Steel | 229.65 | 220.95 | 213.85 | 207.40 | 202.65 | 198.95 | 190.10 | 184.15 | 180.10 |
| E.I.F.S. | Rigid Steel | 201.75 | 196.15 | 191.80 | 187.80 | 184.95 | 182.70 | 177.15 | 173.50 | 171.15 |
| Curtain Wall | Rigid Steel | 235.35 | 226.45 | 219.20 | 212.60 | 207.65 | 203.90 | 194.85 | 188.70 | 184.65 |
| Brick Veneer | Reinforced Concrete | 252.85 | 241.75 | 232.70 | 224.25 | 218.15 | 213.45 | 202.10 | 194.35 | 189.10 |
| Metal Panel | Reinforced Concrete | 228.35 | 220.80 | 214.85 | 209.20 | 205.15 | 202.05 | 194.45 | 189.30 | 185.95 |
| E.I.F.S. | Reinforced Concrete | 238.65 | 229.15 | 221.50 | 214.35 | 209.20 | 205.15 | 195.50 | 189.00 | 184.60 |
| Perimeter Adj., Add or Deduct | Per 100 L.F. | 12.80 | 10.65 | 9.10 | 7.70 | 6.65 | 5.95 | 3.90 | 2.55 | 1.95 |
| Story Hgt. Adj., Add or Deduct | Per 1 Ft. | 4.20 | 3.70 | 3.35 | 2.95 | 2.65 | 2.50 | 1.95 | 1.65 | 1.35 |
| ***For Basement**, add $63.50 per square foot of basement area* | | | | | | | | | | |

*The above costs were calculated using the basic specifications shown on the facing page. These costs should be adjusted where necessary for design alternatives and owner's requirements.*

## Common additives

| Description | Unit | $ Cost |
|---|---|---|
| Closed circuit surveillance, one station | | |
| Camera and monitor | Ea. | 1250 |
| For additional camera stations, add | Ea. | 475 |
| Directory boards, plastic, glass covered | | |
| 30" x 20" | Ea. | 705 |
| 36" x 48" | Ea. | 1475 |
| Aluminum, 24" x 18" | Ea. | 705 |
| 36" x 24" | Ea. | 985 |
| 48" x 32" | Ea. | 1975 |
| 48" x 60" | Ea. | 2650 |
| Electronic, wall mounted | S.F. | 1175 |
| Free standing | S.F. | 1625 |
| Escalators, 10' rise, 32" wide, glass balustrade | Ea. | 174,500 |
| Metal balustrade | Ea. | 183,500 |
| 48" wide, glass balustrade | Ea. | 182,500 |
| Metal balustrade | Ea. | 194,500 |
| Pedestal access floor system w/plastic laminate cover | | |
| Computer room, less than 6000 SF | S.F. | 8.80 |
| Greater than 6000 SF | S.F. | 8.65 |
| Office, greater than 6000 S.F. | S.F. | 11.95 |

| Description | Unit | $ Cost |
|---|---|---|
| Security access systems | | |
| Metal detectors, wand type | Ea. | 138 |
| Walk-through portal type, single-zone | Ea. | 1800 |
| Multi-zone | Ea. | 3125 |
| X-ray equipment | | |
| Desk top, for mail, small packages | Ea. | 3975 |
| Conveyer type, including monitor, minimum | Ea. | 21,900 |
| Maximum | Ea. | 38,700 |
| Explosive detection equipment | | |
| Hand held, battery operated | Ea. | 28,100 |
| Walk-through portal type | Ea. | 193,000 |
| Uninterruptible power supply, 15 kVA/12.75 kW | kW | 1.35 |

## Model costs calculated for a 16 story building with 12′ story height and 260,000 square feet of floor area

# Office, 11-20 Story

| | | | | Unit | Unit Cost | Cost Per S.F. | % Of Sub-Total |
|---|---|---|---|---|---|---|---|
| **A. SUBSTRUCTURE** | | | | | | | |
| 1010 | Standard Foundations | CIP concrete pile caps; 4′ foundation wall | | S.F. Ground | 23.04 | 1.44 | |
| 1020 | Special Foundations | Steel H-piles, concrete grade beams | | S.F. Ground | 194 | 12.10 | |
| 1030 | Slab on Grade | 4″ reinforced concrete with vapor barrier and granular base | | S.F. Slab | 7.22 | .45 | 9.3% |
| 2010 | Basement Excavation | Site preparation for slab and trench for foundation wall and footing | | S.F. Ground | .38 | .02 | |
| 2020 | Basement Walls | N/A | | – | – | – | |
| **B. SHELL** | | | | | | | |
| | **B10 Superstructure** | | | | | | |
| 1010 | Floor Construction | Open web steel joists, slab form, concrete, fireproofed steel columns | | S.F. Floor | 16.89 | 15.83 | 11.1% |
| 1020 | Roof Construction | Metal deck, open web steel joists, beams, columns | | S.F. Roof | 13.76 | .86 | |
| | **B20 Exterior Enclosure** | | | | | | |
| 2010 | Exterior Walls | Limestone stone veneer on metal studs | *80% of wall* | S.F. Wall | 49.18 | 19.25 | |
| 2020 | Exterior Windows | Curtain wall glazing system, thermo-break frame | *20% of wall* | Each | 57 | 2.02 | 14.9% |
| 2030 | Exterior Doors | Double aluminum & glass doors | | Each | 10,682 | 1.15 | |
| | **B30 Roofing** | | | | | | |
| 3010 | Roof Coverings | Single ply membrane, stone ballast, rigid insulation | | S.F. Roof | 10.72 | .67 | 0.5% |
| 3020 | Roof Openings | Roof and smoke hatches. | | S.F. Roof | 4547 | .11 | |
| **C. INTERIORS** | | | | | | | |
| 1010 | Partitions | Concrete block partitions, gypsum board on metal studs | *30 S.F. Floor/L.F. Partition* | S.F. Partition | 11.31 | 3.77 | |
| 1020 | Interior Doors | Single leaf solid core wood doors, hollow metal egress doors | *350 S.F. Floor/Door* | Each | 1159 | 3.26 | |
| 1030 | Fittings | Plastic laminate toilet partitions | | S.F. Floor | .22 | .22 | |
| 2010 | Stair Construction | Concrete filled metal pan, with rails | | Flight | 16,075 | 4.08 | 17.9% |
| 3010 | Wall Finishes | Paint on drywall | | S.F. Surface | 1.41 | .94 | |
| 3020 | Floor Finishes | 60% Carpet tile, 30% vinyl composition tile, 10% ceramic tile | | S.F. Floor | 5.12 | 5.12 | |
| 3030 | Ceiling Finishes | Acoustic ceiling tiles on suspended support system | | S.F. Ceiling | 9.48 | 9.48 | |
| **D. SERVICES** | | | | | | | |
| | **D10 Conveying** | | | | | | |
| 1010 | Elevators & Lifts | Traction geared passenger elevators | | Each | 578,500 | 8.90 | 5.9% |
| 1020 | Escalators & Moving Walks | N/A | | – | – | – | |
| | **D20 Plumbing** | | | | | | |
| 2010 | Plumbing Fixtures | Restroom and service fixtures, supply and drainage | *1 Fixture/1600 S.F. Floor* | Each | 3190 | 2 | |
| 2020 | Domestic Water Distribution | Gas fired water heater | | S.F. Floor | .33 | .33 | 1.6% |
| 2040 | Rain Water Drainage | Roof drains | | S.F. Roof | 1.60 | .10 | |
| | **D30 HVAC** | | | | | | |
| 3010 | Energy Supply | N/A | | – | – | – | |
| 3020 | Heat Generating Systems | Boiler, heat exchanger and fans | | Each | 638,725 | 3.30 | |
| 3030 | Cooling Generating Systems | Chiled water, fan coil units | | S.F. Floor | 24.64 | 24.64 | 18.6 % |
| 3050 | Terminal & Package Units | N/A | | – | – | – | |
| 3090 | Other HVAC Sys. & Equipment | N/A | | – | – | – | |
| | **D40 Fire Protection** | | | | | | |
| 4010 | Sprinklers | Sprinkler system and accessory package | | S.F. Floor | 4.21 | 4.21 | 3.4% |
| 4020 | Standpipes | Standpipes, pumps and hose systems | | S.F. Floor | .90 | .90 | |
| | **D50 Electrical** | | | | | | |
| 5010 | Electrical Service/Distribution | 1200 Ampere service, panel boards and feeders | | S.F. Floor | .92 | .92 | |
| 5020 | Lighting & Branch Wiring | Fluorescent fixtures, receptacles, switches, A.C. and misc. power | | S.F. Floor | 17.31 | 17.31 | 16.6% |
| 5030 | Communications & Security | Alarm systems, emergency lighting, internet and phone wiring | | S.F. Floor | 6.76 | 6.76 | |
| 5090 | Other Electrical Systems | Uninterruptible power supply with battery pack, 12.75kW | | S.F. Floor | | | |
| **E. EQUIPMENT & FURNISHINGS** | | | | | | | |
| 1010 | Commercial Equipment | N/A | | – | – | – | |
| 1020 | Institutional Equipment | N/A | | – | – | – | 0.0 % |
| 1030 | Vehicular Equipment | N/A | | – | – | – | |
| 1090 | Other Equipment | N/A | | – | – | – | |
| **F. SPECIAL CONSTRUCTION** | | | | | | | |
| 1020 | Integrated Construction | N/A | | – | – | – | 0.0 % |
| 1040 | Special Facilities | N/A | | – | – | – | |
| **G. BUILDING SITEWORK** | **N/A** | | | | | | |
| | | | | | **Sub-Total** | 150.14 | **100%** |
| | CONTRACTOR FEES (General Requirements: 10%, Overhead: 5%, Profit: 10%) | | | | 25% | 37.55 | |
| | ARCHITECT FEES | | | | 6% | 11.26 | |
| | | | | | **Total Building Cost** | **198.95** | |

## Costs per square foot of floor area

| Exterior Wall | S.F. Area | 5000 | 7500 | 10000 | 12500 | 15000 | 17500 | 20000 | 22500 | 25000 |
|---|---|---|---|---|---|---|---|---|---|---|
| | L.F. Perimeter | 284 | 350 | 410 | 450 | 490 | 530 | 570 | 600 | 632 |
| Brick Veneer | Wood Truss | 601.85 | 583.25 | 573.20 | 564.95 | 559.40 | 555.50 | 552.55 | 549.70 | 547.45 |
| Brick Veneer | Rigid Steel | 603.90 | 585.60 | 575.70 | 567.55 | 562.15 | 558.35 | 555.45 | 552.65 | 550.45 |
| Decorative Concrete Block | Rigid Steel | 604.25 | 585.90 | 575.95 | 567.80 | 562.40 | 558.50 | 555.65 | 552.80 | 550.60 |
| Decorative Concrete Block | Bearing Walls | 592.90 | 576.55 | 567.75 | 560.65 | 555.90 | 552.50 | 549.95 | 547.50 | 545.55 |
| Tilt-up Concrete Panels | Rigid Steel | 597.20 | 580.10 | 570.85 | **563.35** | 558.35 | 554.75 | 552.10 | 549.55 | 547.50 |
| E.I.F.S. and Concrete Block | Rigid Steel | 592.70 | 576.40 | 567.60 | 560.50 | 555.80 | 552.35 | 549.85 | 547.45 | 545.50 |
| Perimeter Adj., Add or Deduct | Per 100 L.F. | 27.35 | 18.25 | 13.70 | 10.90 | 9.15 | 7.85 | 6.85 | 6.00 | 5.50 |
| Story Hgt. Adj., Add or Deduct | Per 1 Ft. | 4.15 | 3.35 | 2.95 | 2.55 | 2.40 | 2.20 | 2.10 | 1.90 | 1.85 |
| ***For Basement**, add $49.95 per square foot of basement area* | | | | | | | | | | |

*The above costs were calculated using the basic specifications shown on the facing page. These costs should be adjusted where necessary for design alternatives and owner's requirements.*

## Common additives

| Description | Unit | $ Cost |
|---|---|---|
| Cabinets, base, door units, metal | L.F. | 2875 |
| Drawer units | L.F. | 1075 |
| Tall storage cabinets, open, 7′ high | L.F. | 475 |
| With glazed doors | L.F. | 1125 |
| Wall cabinets, metal, 12-1/2″ deep, open | L.F. | 284 |
| With doors | L.F. | 425 |
| Counter top, laminated plastic, no backsplash | L.F. | 99.50 |
| Stainless steel counter top | L.F. | 245 |
| For drop-in stainless 43″ x 21″ sink, add | Ea. | 1600 |
| Nurse Call Station | | |
| Single bedside call station | Ea. | 715 |
| Ceiling speaker station | Ea. | 266 |
| Emergency call station | Ea. | 223 |
| Pillow speaker | Ea. | 330 |
| Standard call button | Ea. | 325 |
| Master control station for 20 stations | Total | 5800 |

| Description | Unit | $ Cost |
|---|---|---|
| Directory Boards, Plastic, glass covered | | |
| Plastic, glass covered, 30″ x 20″ | Ea. | 705 |
| 36″ x 48″ | Ea. | 1475 |
| Building directory, alum., black felt panels, 1 door, 24″ x 18″ | Ea. | 705 |
| 36″ x 24″ | Ea. | 985 |
| 48″ x 32″ | Ea. | 1975 |
| 48″ x 60″ | Ea. | 2650 |
| Tables, Examining, vinyl top | | |
| with base cabinets | Ea. | 1850 |
| Utensil washer-sanitizer | Ea. | 8650 |
| X-ray, mobile, minimum | Ea. | 16,200 |



**Important: See the Reference Section for Location Factors.**

## Model costs calculated for a 1 story building with 15'-4" story height and 12,500 square feet of floor area

# Outpatient Surgery Center

| | | | | Unit | Unit Cost | Cost Per S.F. | % Of Sub-Total |
|---|---|---|---|---|---|---|---|
| **A. SUBSTRUCTURE** | | | | | | | |
| 1010 | Standard Foundations | Poured concrete; strip and spread footings; 4' foundation wall | | S.F. Ground | 6.53 | 6.53 | 3.9% |
| 1020 | Special Foundations | N/A | | — | — | — | |
| 1030 | Slab on Grade | 4" reinforced concrete with vapor barrier and granular base | | S.F. Slab | 9.01 | 9.01 | |
| 2010 | Basement Excavation | Site preparation for slab and trench for foundation wall and footing | | S.F. Ground | .38 | .38 | |
| 2020 | Basement Walls | N/A | | — | — | — | |
| **B. SHELL** | | | | | | | |
| | **B10 Superstructure** | | | | | | |
| 1010 | Floor Construction | N/A | | — | — | — | 2.5 % |
| 1020 | Roof Construction | Steel Joists and girders on columns | | S.F. Roof | 10.35 | 10.35 | |
| | **B20 Exterior Enclosure** | | | | | | |
| 2010 | Exterior Walls | Brick veneer | *85% of wall* | S.F. Wall | 25.73 | 12.07 | 6.9% |
| 2020 | Exterior Windows | Aluminum frame, fixed | *15% of wall* | Each | 1390 | 7.67 | |
| 2030 | Exterior Doors | Aluminum and glass entry; steel flush doors | | Each | 10,855 | 8.69 | |
| | **B30 Roofing** | | | | | | |
| 3010 | Roof Coverings | Single-ply membrane, loose laid and ballasted; polyisocyanurate insulation | | S.F. Roof | 11.02 | 11.02 | 2.7% |
| 3020 | Roof Openings | Roof hatches | | S.F. Roof | .16 | .16 | |
| **C. INTERIORS** | | | | | | | |
| 1010 | Partitions | Gypsum board on metal studs | *7 S.F. Floor/L.F. Partition* | S.F. Partition | 10.49 | 14.98 | 12.3% |
| 1020 | Interior Doors | Single and double leaf fire doors | *200 S.F. Floor/Door* | Each | 1883 | 9.42 | |
| 1030 | Fittings | Stainless steel toilet partitions, steel lockers | | S.F. Floor | 2.08 | 2.08 | |
| 2010 | Stair Construction | N/A | | — | — | — | |
| 3010 | Wall Finishes | 80% Paint, 10% vinyl wall covering, 10% ceramic tile | | S.F. Surface | 2.60 | 7.43 | |
| 3020 | Floor Finishes | 10% Carpet, 80% vinyl sheet, 10% ceramic tile | | S.F. Floor | 11.05 | 11.05 | |
| 3030 | Ceiling Finishes | Mineral fiber tile and plastic coated tile on suspension system | | S.F. Ceiling | 5.79 | 5.79 | |
| **D. SERVICES** | | | | | | | |
| | **D10 Conveying** | | | | | | |
| 1010 | Elevators & Lifts | N/A | | — | — | — | 0.0 % |
| 1020 | Escalators & Moving Walks | N/A | | — | — | — | |
| | **D20 Plumbing** | | | | | | |
| 2010 | Plumbing Fixtures | Medical, patient & specialty fixtures, supply and drainage | *1 fixture/350 S.F. Floor* | Each | 4788 | 13.68 | 4.9% |
| 2020 | Domestic Water Distribution | Electric water heater | | S.F. Floor | 2.70 | 2.70 | |
| 2040 | Rain Water Drainage | Roof drains | | S.F. Roof | 3.99 | 3.99 | |
| | **D30 HVAC** | | | | | | |
| 3010 | Energy Supply | Hot water reheat for surgery | | S.F. Floor | 16.80 | 16.80 | 41.2% |
| 3020 | Heat Generating Systems | Boiler | | Each | 77,500 | 8.74 | |
| 3030 | Cooling Generating Systems | N/A | | — | — | — | |
| 3050 | Terminal & Package Units | N/A | | — | — | — | |
| 3090 | Other HVAC Sys. & Equipment | Rooftop AC, CAV, roof vents, heat exchanger, surgical air curtains | | S.F. Floor | 145 | 144.91 | |
| | **D40 Fire Protection** | | | | | | |
| 4010 | Sprinklers | Wet pipe sprinkler system | | S.F. Floor | 5.07 | 5.07 | 1.9% |
| 4020 | Standpipes | Standpipe | | S.F. Floor | 2.67 | 2.67 | |
| | **D50 Electrical** | | | | | | |
| 5010 | Electrical Service/Distribution | 1200 ampere service, panel board and feeders | | S.F. Floor | 9.83 | 9.83 | 13.3% |
| 5020 | Lighting & Branch Wiring | T-8 fluorescent light fixtures, receptacles, switches, A.C. and misc. power | | S.F. Floor | 24.14 | 24.14 | |
| 5030 | Communications & Security | Addressable alarm system, internet wiring, communications system, emergency lighting | | S.F. Floor | 13.29 | 13.29 | |
| 5090 | Other Electrical Systems | Emergency generator, 300 kW with fuel tank | | S.F. Floor | 7.91 | 7.91 | |
| **E. EQUIPMENT & FURNISHINGS** | | | | | | | |
| 1010 | Commercial Equipment | N/A | | — | — | — | 10.4 % |
| 1020 | Institutional Equipment | Medical gas system, cabinetry, scrub sink, sterilizer | | S.F. Floor | 42.08 | 42.08 | |
| 1030 | Vehicular Equipment | N/A | | — | — | — | |
| 1090 | Other Equipment | Ice maker, washing machine | | S.F. Floor | 1.03 | 1.03 | |
| **F. SPECIAL CONSTRUCTION & DEMOLITION** | | | | | | | |
| 1020 | Integrated Construction | N/A | | — | — | — | 0.0 % |
| 1040 | Special Facilities | N/A | | — | — | — | |
| **G. BUILDING SITEWORK** | **N/A** | | | | | | |
| | | | | | **Sub-Total** | 413.47 | **100%** |
| | CONTRACTOR FEES (General Requirements: 10%, Overhead: 5%, Profit: 5%) | | | | 20% | 103.36 | |
| | ARCHITECT FEES | | | | 9% | 46.52 | |
| | | | | | **Total Building Cost** | **563.35** | |

# Police Station

## Costs per square foot of floor area

| Exterior Wall | S.F. Area | 7000 | 9000 | 11000 | 13000 | 15000 | 17000 | 19000 | 21000 | 23000 |
|---|---|---|---|---|---|---|---|---|---|---|
| | L.F. Perimeter | 240 | 280 | 303 | 325 | 354 | 372 | 397 | 422 | 447 |
| Limestone and Concrete Block | Bearing Walls | 348.05 | 327.30 | 309.50 | 296.95 | 289.15 | 281.25 | 276.05 | 271.90 | 268.45 |
| | Reinforced Concrete | 369.00 | 348.40 | 330.65 | 318.20 | 310.35 | 302.55 | 297.40 | 293.25 | 289.80 |
| Face Brick and Concrete Block | Bearing Walls | 316.80 | 298.95 | 284.40 | 274.20 | 267.65 | 261.30 | 257.00 | 253.60 | 250.80 |
| | Reinforced Concrete | 337.75 | 320.05 | 305.55 | 295.35 | 288.85 | 282.55 | 278.30 | 274.90 | 272.10 |
| Decorative Concrete Block | Bearing Walls | 304.00 | 287.40 | 274.15 | 264.90 | 258.85 | 253.15 | 249.20 | 246.15 | 243.55 |
| | Reinforced Concrete | 325.05 | 308.45 | 295.35 | 286.05 | 280.10 | 274.45 | 270.55 | 267.45 | 264.85 |
| Perimeter Adj., Add or Deduct | Per 100 L.F. | 43.10 | 33.55 | 27.40 | 23.20 | 20.10 | 17.70 | 15.85 | 14.40 | 13.15 |
| Story Hgt. Adj., Add or Deduct | Per 1 Ft. | 7.65 | 6.95 | 6.15 | 5.60 | 5.25 | 4.85 | 4.65 | 4.55 | 4.35 |
| ***For Basement**, add $49.95 per square foot of basement area* | | | | | | | | | | |

*The above costs were calculated using the basic specifications shown on the facing page. These costs should be adjusted where necessary for design alternatives and owner's requirements.*

## Common additives

| Description | Unit | $ Cost |
|---|---|---|
| Cells Prefabricated, 5'-6' wide, | | |
| 7'-8' high, 7'-8' deep | Ea. | 12,600 |
| Elevators, Hydraulic passenger, 2 stops | | |
| 1500# capacity | Ea. | 86,500 |
| 2500# capacity | Ea. | 90,500 |
| 3500# capacity | Ea. | 96,000 |
| Emergency Lighting, 25 watt, battery operated | | |
| Lead battery | Ea. | 360 |
| Nickel cadmium | Ea. | 585 |
| Flagpoles, Complete | | |
| Aluminum, 20' high | Ea. | 2050 |
| 40' high | Ea. | 5275 |
| 70' high | Ea. | 14,300 |
| Fiberglass, 23' high | Ea. | 3025 |
| 39'-5" high | Ea. | 3725 |
| 59' high | Ea. | 12,300 |

| Description | Unit | $ Cost |
|---|---|---|
| Lockers, Steel, Single tier, 60" to 72" | Opng. | 285 - 520 |
| 2 tier, 60" or 72" total | Opng. | 216 - 265 |
| 5 tier, box lockers | Opng. | 465 - 153 |
| Locker bench, lam. maple top only | L.F. | 148 |
| Pedestals, steel pipe | Ea. | 87 |
| Safe, Office type, 1 hour rating | | |
| 30" x 18" x 18" | Ea. | 1900 |
| 60" x 36" x 18", double door | Ea. | 8625 |
| Shooting Range, Incl. bullet traps, target provisions, and contols, not incl. structural shell | Ea. | 65,500 |
| Smoke Detectors | | |
| Ceiling type | Ea. | 300 |
| Duct type | Ea. | 615 |
| Sound System | | |
| Amplifier, 250 watts | Ea. | 2425 |
| Speaker, ceiling or wall | Ea. | 320 |
| Trumpet | Ea. | 580 |



**Important: See the Reference Section for Location Factors.**

# Model costs calculated for a 2 story building with 12′ story height and 11,000 square feet of floor area

# Police Station

| | | | | Unit | Unit Cost | Cost Per S.F. | % Of Sub-Total |
|---|---|---|---|---|---|---|---|
| **A. SUBSTRUCTURE** | | | | | | | |
| 1010 | Standard Foundations | Poured concrete; strip and spread footings; 4′ foundation wall | | S.F. Ground | 10.12 | 5.06 | 3.9% |
| 1020 | Special Foundations | N/A | | — | — | — | |
| 1030 | Slab on Grade | 4″ reinforced concrete with vapor barrier and granular base | | S.F. Slab | 7.22 | 3.61 | |
| 2010 | Basement Excavation | Site preparation for slab and trench for foundation wall and footing | | S.F. Ground | .38 | .19 | |
| 2020 | Basement Walls | N/A | | — | — | — | |
| **B. SHELL** | | | | | | | |
| | **B10 Superstructure** | | | | | | |
| 1010 | Floor Construction | Open web steel joists, slab form, concrete | | S.F. Floor | 17.76 | 8.88 | 5.4% |
| 1020 | Roof Construction | Metal deck on open web steel joists | | S.F. Roof | 6.96 | 3.48 | |
| | **B20 Exterior Enclosure** | | | | | | |
| 2010 | Exterior Walls | Limestone with concrete block backup | *80% of wall* | S.F. Wall | 76 | 39.93 | 24.4% |
| 2020 | Exterior Windows | Metal horizontal sliding | *20% of wall* | Each | 1390 | 12.26 | |
| 2030 | Exterior Doors | Hollow metal | | Each | 4409 | 3.21 | |
| | **B30 Roofing** | | | | | | |
| 3010 | Roof Coverings | Built-up tar and gravel with flashing; perlite/EPS composite insulation | | S.F. Roof | 10.04 | 5.02 | 2.2% |
| 3020 | Roof Openings | N/A | | — | — | — | |
| **C. INTERIORS** | | | | | | | |
| 1010 | Partitions | Concrete block | *20 S.F. Floor/L.F. Partition* | S.F. Partition | 17.16 | 8.58 | 17.2% |
| 1020 | Interior Doors | Single leaf kalamein fire door | *200 S.F. Floor/Door* | Each | 1159 | 5.80 | |
| 1030 | Fittings | Toilet partitions | | S.F. Floor | 1.49 | 1.49 | |
| 2010 | Stair Construction | Concrete filled metal pan | | Flight | 19,225 | 5.25 | |
| 3010 | Wall Finishes | 90% paint, 10% ceramic tile | | S.F. Surface | 4.48 | 4.48 | |
| 3020 | Floor Finishes | 70% vinyl composition tile, 20% carpet tile, 10% ceramic tile | | S.F. Floor | 3.89 | 3.89 | |
| 3030 | Ceiling Finishes | Mineral fiber tile on concealed zee bars | | S.F. Ceiling | 9.48 | 9.48 | |
| **D. SERVICES** | | | | | | | |
| | **D10 Conveying** | | | | | | |
| 1010 | Elevators & Lifts | One hydraulic passenger elevator | | Each | 107,030 | 9.73 | 4.3% |
| 1020 | Escalators & Moving Walks | N/A | | — | — | — | |
| | **D20 Plumbing** | | | | | | |
| 2010 | Plumbing Fixtures | Toilet and service fixtures, supply and drainage | *1 Fixture/580 S.F. Floor* | Each | 6873 | 11.85 | 8.5% |
| 2020 | Domestic Water Distribution | Oil fired water heater | | S.F. Floor | 4.52 | 4.52 | |
| 2040 | Rain Water Drainage | Roof drains | | S.F. Roof | 5.90 | 2.95 | |
| | **D30 HVAC** | | | | | | |
| 3010 | Energy Supply | N/A | | — | — | — | 10.5 % |
| 3020 | Heat Generating Systems | N/A | | — | — | — | |
| 3030 | Cooling Generating Systems | N/A | | — | — | — | |
| 3050 | Terminal & Package Units | Multizone HVAC air cooled system | | S.F. Floor | 23.80 | 23.80 | |
| 3090 | Other HVAC Sys. & Equipment | N/A | | — | — | — | |
| | **D40 Fire Protection** | | | | | | |
| 4010 | Sprinklers | Wet pipe sprinkler system | | S.F. Floor | 5.47 | 5.47 | 3.2% |
| 4020 | Standpipes | Standpipe | | S.F. Floor | 1.79 | 1.79 | |
| | **D50 Electrical** | | | | | | |
| 5010 | Electrical Service/Distribution | 400 ampere service, panel board and feeders | | S.F. Floor | 2.55 | 2.55 | 13.3% |
| 5020 | Lighting & Branch Wiring | T-8 fluorescent fixtures, receptacles, switches, A.C. and misc. power | | S.F. Floor | 17.96 | 17.96 | |
| 5030 | Communications & Security | Addressable alarm systems, internet wiring, intercom and emergency lighting | | S.F. Floor | 9.39 | 9.39 | |
| 5090 | Other Electrical Systems | Emergency generator, 15 kW | | S.F. Floor | .22 | .22 | |
| **E. EQUIPMENT & FURNISHINGS** | | | | | | | |
| 1010 | Commercial Equipment | N/A | | — | — | — | 7.1 % |
| 1020 | Institutional Equipment | Lockers, detention rooms, cells, gasoline dispensers | | S.F. Floor | 13.29 | 13.29 | |
| 1030 | Vehicular Equipment | Gasoline dispenser system | | S.F. Floor | 2.85 | 2.85 | |
| 1090 | Other Equipment | N/A | | — | — | — | |
| **F. SPECIAL CONSTRUCTION** | | | | | | | |
| 1020 | Integrated Construction | N/A | | — | — | — | 0.0 % |
| 1040 | Special Facilities | N/A | | — | — | — | |
| **G. BUILDING SITEWORK** | **N/A** | | | | | | |
| | | | | | **Sub-Total** | 227.16 | **100%** |
| | CONTRACTOR FEES (General Requirements: 10%, Overhead: 5%, Profit: 10%) | | | | *25%* | 56.78 | |
| | ARCHITECT FEES | | | | *9%* | 25.56 | |
| | | | | | **Total Building Cost** | **309.50** | |

## Costs per square foot of floor area

| Exterior Wall | S.F. Area | 600 | 750 | 925 | 1150 | 1450 | 1800 | 2100 | 2600 | 3200 |
|---|---|---|---|---|---|---|---|---|---|---|
| | L.F. Perimeter | 100 | 112 | 128 | 150 | 164 | 182 | 200 | 216 | 240 |
| Metal Panel and Wood Studs | Wood Truss | 110.50 | 103.60 | 99.10 | 95.75 | 89.30 | **84.75** | 82.55 | 78.10 | 75.10 |
| Aluminum Clapboard | Wood Truss | 99.80 | 93.65 | 89.60 | 86.55 | 80.85 | 76.80 | 74.85 | 70.95 | 68.30 |
| Wood Clapboard | Wood Truss | 109.70 | 102.85 | 98.40 | 95.15 | 88.70 | 84.20 | 82.00 | 77.55 | 74.65 |
| Plywood Siding | Wood Truss | 100.20 | 94.00 | 89.90 | 86.90 | 81.05 | 77.00 | 75.00 | 71.00 | 68.35 |
| Perimeter Adj., Add or Deduct | Per 100 L.F. | 57.60 | 46.00 | 37.35 | 30.05 | 23.80 | 19.20 | 16.40 | 13.25 | 10.80 |
| Story Hgt. Adj., Add or Deduct | Per 1 Ft. | 4.15 | 3.65 | 3.40 | 3.25 | 2.75 | 2.50 | 2.30 | 2.00 | 1.85 |
| **Basement**—Not Applicable | | | | | | | | | | |

*The above costs were calculated using the basic specifications shown on the facing page. These costs should be adjusted where necessary for design alternatives and owner's requirements.*

## Common additives

| Description | Unit | $ Cost |
|---|---|---|
| Slab on Grade | | |
| 4" thick, non-industrial, non-reinforced | S.F. | 6.49 |
| Reinforced | S.F. | 7.22 |
| Light industrial, non-reinforced | S.F. | 8.15 |
| Reinforced | S.F. | 9.01 |
| Industrial, non-reinforced | S.F. | 13.49 |
| Reinforced | S.F. | 14.35 |
| 6" thick, non-industrial, non-reinforced | S.F. | 7.72 |
| Reinforced | S.F. | 9.16 |
| Light industrial, non-reinforced | S.F. | 9.42 |
| Reinforced | S.F. | 11.10 |
| Heavy industrial, non-reinforced | S.F. | 17.50 |
| Reinforced | S.F. | 18.90 |
| Insulation | | |
| Fiberboard, low density, 1" thick, R2.78 | S.F. | 2.14 |
| Foil on reinforced scrim, single bubble air space, R8.8 | C.S.F. | 83 |
| Vinyl faced fiberglass, 1-1/2" thick, R5 | S.F. | 1.07 |
| Vinyl/scrim/foil (VSF), 1-1/2" thick, R5 | S.F. | 1.28 |

| Description | Unit | $ Cost |
|---|---|---|
| Roof ventilation, ridge vent, aluminum | L.F. | 8.50 |
| Mushroom vent, aluminum | Ea. | 140 |
| Gutter, aluminum, 5" K type, enameled | L.F. | 10.45 |
| Steel, half round or box, 5", enameled | L.F. | 11.60 |
| Wood, clear treated cedar, fir or hemlock, 4" x 5" | L.F. | 30.50 |
| Downspout, aluminum, 3" x 4", enameled | L.F. | 9.25 |
| Steel, round, 4" diameter | L.F. | 12.10 |

## Model costs calculated for a 1 story building with 14′ story height and 1,800 square feet of floor area

# Post Frame Barn

| | | | Unit | Unit Cost | Cost Per S.F. | % Of Sub-Total |
|---|---|---|---|---|---|---|
| **A. SUBSTRUCTURE** | | | | | | |
| 1010 | Standard Foundations | Included in B2010 Exterior Walls | – | – | – | 0.0% |
| 1020 | Special Foundations | N/A | – | – | – | |
| 1030 | Slab on Grade | N/A | – | – | – | |
| 2010 | Basement Excavation | N/A | – | – | – | |
| 2020 | Basement Walls | N/A | – | – | – | |
| **B. SHELL** | | | | | | |
| | **B10 Superstructure** | | | | | |
| 1010 | Floor Construction | N/A | – | – | – | 20.8 % |
| 1020 | Roof Construction | Wood truss, 4/12 pitch | S.F. Roof | 13.03 | 13.03 | |
| | **B20 Exterior Enclosure** | | | | | |
| 2010 | Exterior Walls | 2 x 6 Wood framing, 6 x 6 wood posts in concrete; steel siding panels | S.F. Wall | 15.40 | 20.71 | 52.3% |
| 2020 | Exterior Windows | Steel windows, fixed | Each | 656 | 5.15 | |
| 2030 | Exterior Doors | Steel overhead, hollow metal doors | Each | 3138 | 6.97 | |
| | **B30 Roofing** | | | | | |
| 3010 | Roof Coverings | Metal panel roof | S.F. Roof | 4.80 | 4.80 | 7.6% |
| 3020 | Roof Openings | N/A | – | – | – | |
| **C. INTERIORS** | | | | | | |
| 1010 | Partitions | N/A | – | – | – | 0.0 % |
| 1020 | Interior Doors | N/A | – | – | – | |
| 1030 | Fittings | N/A | – | – | – | |
| 2010 | Stair Construction | N/A | – | – | – | |
| 3010 | Wall Finishes | N/A | – | – | – | |
| 3020 | Floor Finishes | N/A | – | – | – | |
| 3030 | Ceiling Finishes | N/A | – | – | – | |
| **D. SERVICES** | | | | | | |
| | **D10 Conveying** | | | | | |
| 1010 | Elevators & Lifts | N/A | – | – | – | 0.0 % |
| 1020 | Escalators & Moving Walks | N/A | – | – | – | |
| | **D20 Plumbing** | | | | | |
| 2010 | Plumbing Fixtures | N/A | – | – | – | 0.0 % |
| 2020 | Domestic Water Distribution | N/A | – | – | – | |
| 2040 | Rain Water Drainage | N/A | – | – | – | |
| | **D30 HVAC** | | | | | |
| 3010 | Energy Supply | N/A | – | – | – | 0.0 % |
| 3020 | Heat Generating Systems | N/A | – | – | – | |
| 3030 | Cooling Generating Systems | N/A | – | – | – | |
| 3050 | Terminal & Package Units | N/A | – | – | – | |
| 3090 | Other HVAC Sys. & Equipment | N/A | – | – | – | |
| | **D40 Fire Protection** | | | | | |
| 4010 | Sprinklers | N/A | – | – | – | 0.0 % |
| 4020 | Standpipes | N/A | – | – | – | |
| | **D50 Electrical** | | | | | |
| 5010 | Electrical Service/Distribution | 60 Ampere service, panel board & feeders | S.F. Floor | 2.53 | 2.53 | 19.3% |
| 5020 | Lighting & Branch Wiring | High bay fixtures, receptacles & switches | S.F. Floor | 9.59 | 9.59 | |
| 5030 | Communications & Security | N/A | – | – | – | |
| 5090 | Other Electrical Systems | N/A | – | – | – | |
| **E. EQUIPMENT & FURNISHINGS** | | | | | | |
| 1010 | Commercial Equipment | N/A | – | – | – | 0.0 % |
| 1020 | Institutional Equipment | N/A | – | – | – | |
| 1030 | Vehicular Equipment | N/A | – | – | – | |
| 1090 | Other Equipment | N/A | – | – | – | |
| **F. SPECIAL CONSTRUCTION & DEMOLITION** | | | | | | |
| 1020 | Integrated Construction | N/A | – | – | – | 0.0 % |
| 1040 | Special Facilities | N/A | – | – | – | |
| **G. BUILDING SITEWORK** | | **N/A** | | | | |
| | | | | **Sub-Total** | 62.78 | **100%** |
| | CONTRACTOR FEES (General Requirements: 10%, Overhead: 5%, Profit: 5%) | | | *20%* | 15.69 | |
| | ARCHITECT FEES | | | *8%* | 6.28 | |
| | | | | **Total Building Cost** | **84.75** | |

# Post Office

## Costs per square foot of floor area

| Exterior Wall | S.F. Area | 5000 | 7000 | 9000 | 11000 | 13000 | 15000 | 17000 | 19000 | 21000 |
|---|---|---|---|---|---|---|---|---|---|---|
| | L.F. Perimeter | 300 | 380 | 420 | 468 | 486 | 513 | 540 | 580 | 620 |
| Face Brick and Concrete Block | Rigid Steel | 221.55 | 209.15 | 197.25 | 190.50 | **183.25** | 178.60 | 175.00 | 173.00 | 171.35 |
| | Bearing Walls | 222.10 | 209.55 | 197.60 | 190.75 | 183.35 | 178.70 | 175.05 | 173.00 | 171.35 |
| Limestone and Concrete Block | Rigid Steel | 253.40 | 238.00 | 222.15 | 213.15 | 203.15 | 196.80 | 191.90 | 189.20 | 187.05 |
| | Bearing Walls | 254.00 | 238.45 | 222.40 | 213.45 | 203.25 | 196.90 | 191.95 | 189.25 | 187.05 |
| Decorative Concrete Block | Rigid Steel | 208.55 | 197.35 | 187.15 | 181.30 | 175.15 | 171.20 | 168.15 | 166.35 | 164.95 |
| | Bearing Walls | 209.10 | 197.80 | 187.50 | 181.55 | 175.30 | 171.25 | 168.15 | 166.40 | 164.95 |
| Perimeter Adj., Add or Deduct | Per 100 L.F. | 22.50 | 16.05 | 12.55 | 10.25 | 8.65 | 7.55 | 6.65 | 5.90 | 5.40 |
| Story Hgt. Adj., Add or Deduct | Per 1 Ft. | 3.45 | 3.15 | 2.75 | 2.55 | 2.20 | 2.00 | 1.90 | 1.80 | 1.75 |

***For Basement**, add $ 48.65 per square foot of basement area*

*The above costs were calculated using the basic specifications shown on the facing page. These costs should be adjusted where necessary for design alternatives and owner's requirements.*

## Common additives

| Description | Unit | $ Cost |
|---|---|---|
| Closed Circuit Surveillance, One station | | |
| Camera and monitor | Ea. | 1250 |
| For additional camera stations, add | Ea. | 475 |
| Emergency Lighting, 25 watt, battery operated | | |
| Lead battery | Ea. | 360 |
| Nickel cadmium | Ea. | 585 |
| Flagpoles, Complete | | |
| Aluminum, 20′ high | Ea. | 2050 |
| 40′ high | Ea. | 5275 |
| 70′ high | Ea. | 14,300 |
| Fiberglass, 23′ high | Ea. | 3025 |
| 39′-5″ high | Ea. | 3725 |
| 59′ high | Ea. | 12,300 |

| Description | Unit | $ Cost |
|---|---|---|
| Mail Boxes, Horizontal, key lock, 15″ x 6″ x 5″ | Ea. | 47.50 |
| Double 15″ x 12″ x 5″ | Ea. | 150 |
| Quadruple 15″ x 12″ x 10″ | Ea. | 175 |
| Vertical, 6″ x 5″ x 15″, aluminum | Ea. | 155 |
| Bronze | Ea. | 128 |
| Steel, enameled | Ea. | 70.50 |
| Scales, Dial type, 5 ton cap. | | |
| 8′ x 6′ platform | Ea. | 14,400 |
| 9′ x 7′ platform | Ea. | 14,000 |
| Smoke Detectors | | |
| Ceiling type | Ea. | 300 |
| Duct type | Ea. | 615 |



**Important: See the Reference Section for Location Factors.**

## Model costs calculated for a 1 story building with 14′ story height and 13,000 square feet of floor area

# Post Office

| | | | | Unit | Unit Cost | Cost Per S.F. | % Of Sub-Total |
|---|---|---|---|---|---|---|---|
| **A. SUBSTRUCTURE** | | | | | | | |
| 1010 | Standard Foundations | Poured concrete; strip and spread footings; 4′ foundation wall | | S.F. Ground | 6.42 | 6.42 | 10.4% |
| 1020 | Special Foundations | N/A | | — | — | — | |
| 1030 | Slab on Grade | 4″ reinforced concrete with vapor barrier and granular base | | S.F. Slab | 7.22 | 7.22 | |
| 2010 | Basement Excavation | Site preparation for slab and trench for foundation wall and footing | | S.F. Ground | .38 | .38 | |
| 2020 | Basement Walls | N/A | | — | — | — | |
| **B. SHELL** | | | | | | | |
| | **B10 Superstructure** | | | | | | |
| 1010 | Floor Construction | Steel column fireproofing | | L.F. Column | 47.15 | .36 | 10.3% |
| 1020 | Roof Construction | Metal deck, open web steel joists, columns | | S.F. Roof | 13.55 | 13.55 | |
| | **B20 Exterior Enclosure** | | | | | | |
| 2010 | Exterior Walls | Face brick with concrete block backup | *80% of wall* | S.F. Wall | 40.65 | 17.02 | 17.1% |
| 2020 | Exterior Windows | Double strength window glass | *20% of wall* | Each | 839 | 3.82 | |
| 2030 | Exterior Doors | Double aluminum & glass, single aluminum, hollow metal, steel overhead | | Each | 4663 | 2.16 | |
| | **B30 Roofing** | | | | | | |
| 3010 | Roof Coverings | Built-up tar and gravel with flashing; perlite/EPS composite insulation | | S.F. Roof | 8.91 | 8.91 | 6.6% |
| 3020 | Roof Openings | N/A | | — | — | — | |
| **C. INTERIORS** | | | | | | | |
| 1010 | Partitions | Concrete block | *15 S.F. Floor/L.F. Partition* | S.F. Partition | 10.86 | 8.69 | 20.2% |
| 1020 | Interior Doors | Single leaf hollow metal | *150 S.F. Floor/Door* | Each | 1159 | 7.73 | |
| 1030 | Fittings | Toilet partitions, cabinets, shelving, lockers | | S.F. Floor | 1.72 | 1.72 | |
| 2010 | Stair Construction | N/A | | — | — | — | |
| 3010 | Wall Finishes | Paint | | S.F. Surface | 2.73 | 4.37 | |
| 3020 | Floor Finishes | 50% vinyl tile, 50% paint | | S.F. Floor | 2.35 | 2.35 | |
| 3030 | Ceiling Finishes | Mineral fiber tile on concealed zee bars | *25% of area* | S.F. Ceiling | 9 | 2.25 | |
| **D. SERVICES** | | | | | | | |
| | **D10 Conveying** | | | | | | |
| 1010 | Elevators & Lifts | N/A | | — | — | — | 0.0 % |
| 1020 | Escalators & Moving Walks | N/A | | — | — | — | |
| | **D20 Plumbing** | | | | | | |
| 2010 | Plumbing Fixtures | Toilet and service fixtures, supply and drainage | *1 Fixture/1180 S.F. Floor* | Each | 3599 | 3.05 | 4.2% |
| 2020 | Domestic Water Distribution | Gas fired water heater | | S.F. Floor | .70 | .70 | |
| 2040 | Rain Water Drainage | Roof drains | | S.F. Roof | 1.84 | 1.84 | |
| | **D30 HVAC** | | | | | | |
| 3010 | Energy Supply | N/A | | — | — | — | 8.5 % |
| 3020 | Heat Generating Systems | Included in D3050 | | — | — | — | |
| 3030 | Cooling Generating Systems | N/A | | — | — | — | |
| 3050 | Terminal & Package Units | Single zone, gas heating, electric cooling | | S.F. Floor | 11.40 | 11.40 | |
| 3090 | Other HVAC Sys. & Equipment | N/A | | — | — | — | |
| | **D40 Fire Protection** | | | | | | |
| 4010 | Sprinklers | Wet pipe sprinkler system | | S.F. Floor | 6.66 | 6.66 | 6.1% |
| 4020 | Standpipes | Standpipe | | S.F. Floor | 1.59 | 1.59 | |
| | **D50 Electrical** | | | | | | |
| 5010 | Electrical Service/Distribution | 600 ampere service, panel board and feeders | | S.F. Floor | 3.31 | 3.31 | 16.6% |
| 5020 | Lighting & Branch Wiring | T-8 fluorescent fixtures, receptacles, switches, A.C. and misc. power | | S.F. Floor | 13.17 | 13.17 | |
| 5030 | Communications & Security | Addressable alarm systems, internet wiring and emergency lighting | | S.F. Floor | 5.70 | 5.70 | |
| 5090 | Other Electrical Systems | Emergency generator, 15 kW | | S.F. Floor | .13 | .13 | |
| **E. EQUIPMENT & FURNISHINGS** | | | | | | | |
| 1010 | Commercial Equipment | N/A | | — | — | — | 0.0 % |
| 1020 | Institutional Equipment | N/A | | — | — | — | |
| 1030 | Vehicular Equipment | N/A | | — | — | — | |
| 1090 | Other Equipment | N/A | | — | — | — | |
| **F. SPECIAL CONSTRUCTION** | | | | | | | |
| 1020 | Integrated Construction | N/A | | — | — | — | 0.0 % |
| 1040 | Special Facilities | N/A | | — | — | — | |
| **G. BUILDING SITEWORK** | **N/A** | | | | | | |
| | | | | | **Sub-Total** | 134.50 | **100%** |
| | CONTRACTOR FEES (General Requirements: 10%, Overhead: 5%, Profit: 10%) | | | | *25%* | 33.62 | |
| | ARCHITECT FEES | | | | *9%* | 15.13 | |
| | | | | | **Total Building Cost** | **183.25** | |

## Costs per square foot of floor area

| Exterior Wall | S.F. Area | 5000 | 10000 | 15000 | 21000 | 25000 | 30000 | 40000 | 50000 | 60000 |
|---|---|---|---|---|---|---|---|---|---|---|
| | L.F. Perimeter | 287 | 400 | 500 | 600 | 660 | 700 | 834 | 900 | 1000 |
| Face Brick and Concrete Block | Rigid Steel | 315.55 | 270.30 | 253.40 | 241.85 | 236.70 | **229.80** | 223.90 | 217.65 | 214.65 |
| | Bearing Walls | 313.90 | 268.05 | 250.95 | 239.20 | 233.95 | 226.95 | 220.95 | 214.60 | 211.50 |
| Concrete Block | Rigid Steel | 269.25 | 238.05 | 226.55 | 218.80 | 215.40 | 211.00 | 207.15 | 203.15 | 201.20 |
| Brick Veneer | Rigid Steel | 298.30 | 258.25 | 243.45 | 233.30 | 228.80 | 222.80 | 217.65 | 212.25 | 209.60 |
| Metal Panel | Rigid Steel | 256.85 | 229.45 | 219.40 | 212.65 | 209.70 | 206.00 | 202.65 | 199.30 | 197.60 |
| Metal Sandwich Panel | Rigid Steel | 317.55 | 271.70 | 254.60 | 242.85 | 237.65 | 230.65 | 224.70 | 218.30 | 215.25 |
| Perimeter Adj., Add or Deduct | Per 100 L.F. | 40.70 | 20.40 | 13.60 | 9.70 | 8.20 | 6.80 | 5.15 | 4.10 | 3.35 |
| Story Hgt. Adj., Add or Deduct | Per 1 Ft. | 8.30 | 5.80 | 4.90 | 4.20 | 3.85 | 3.40 | 3.05 | 2.60 | 2.40 |

***For Basement**, add $46.85 per square foot of basement area*

*The above costs were calculated using the basic specifications shown on the facing page. These costs should be adjusted where necessary for design alternatives and owner's requirements.*

## Common additives

| Description | Unit | $ Cost |
|---|---|---|
| Bar, Front Bar | L.F. | 490 |
| Back Bar | L.F. | 395 |
| Booth, Upholstered, custom straight | L.F. | 281 - 1500 |
| "L" or "U" shaped | L.F. | 291 - 490 |
| Bleachers, Telescoping, manual | | |
| To 15 tier | Seat | 162 - 299 |
| 21-30 tier | Seat | 390 - 605 |
| Courts | | |
| Ceiling | Court | 12,100 |
| Floor | Court | 20,500 |
| Walls | Court | 34,800 |
| Emergency Lighting, 25 watt, battery operated | | |
| Lead battery | Ea. | 360 |
| Nickel cadmium | Ea. | 585 |
| Kitchen Equipment | | |
| Broiler | Ea. | 4425 |
| Cooler, 6 ft. long, reach-in | Ea. | 4525 |
| Dishwasher, 10-12 racks per hr. | Ea. | 42,900 |
| Food warmer, counter 1.2 KW | Ea. | 720 |
| Freezer, reach-in, 44 C.F. | Ea. | 3600 |
| Ice cube maker, 50 lb. per day | Ea. | 2525 |

| Description | Unit | $ Cost |
|---|---|---|
| Lockers, Steel, single tier, 60" or 72" | Opng. | 285 - 520 |
| 2 tier, 60" or 72" total | Opng. | 216 - 265 |
| 5 tier, box lockers | Opng. | 465 - 153 |
| Locker bench, lam. maple top only | L.F. | 148 |
| Pedestals, steel pipe | Ea. | 87 |
| Sauna, Prefabricated, complete | | |
| 6' x 4' | Ea. | 7500 |
| 6' x 9' | Ea. | 10,500 |
| 8' x 8' | Ea. | 13,500 |
| 8' x 10' | Ea. | 13,000 |
| 10' x 12' | Ea. | 19,700 |
| Sound System | | |
| Amplifier, 250 watts | Ea. | 2425 |
| Speaker, ceiling or wall | Ea. | 320 |
| Trumpet | Ea. | 580 |
| Steam Bath, Complete, to 140 C.F. | Ea. | 3325 |
| To 300 C.F. | Ea. | 7900 |
| To 800 C.F. | Ea. | 8375 |
| To 2500 C.F. | Ea. | 9850 |



**Important: See the Reference Section for Location Factors.**

## Model costs calculated for a 2 story building with 12′ story height and 30,000 square feet of floor area

# Racquetball Court

| | | | | Unit | Unit Cost | Cost Per S.F. | % Of Sub-Total |
|---|---|---|---|---|---|---|---|
| **A. SUBSTRUCTURE** | | | | | | | |
| 1010 | Standard Foundations | Poured concrete; strip and spread footings; 4′ foundation wall | | S.F. Ground | 8.28 | 4.14 | 5.4% |
| 1020 | Special Foundations | N/A | | — | — | — | |
| 1030 | Slab on Grade | 5″ reinforced concrete with vapor barrier and granular base | | S.F. Slab | 9.63 | 4.82 | |
| 2010 | Basement Excavation | Site preparation for slab and trench for foundation wall and footing | | S.F. Ground | .38 | .19 | |
| 2020 | Basement Walls | N/A | | — | — | — | |
| **B. SHELL** | | | | | | | |
| | **B10 Superstructure** | | | | | | |
| 1010 | Floor Construction | Open web steel joists, slab form, concrete, columns | *50% of area* | S.F. Floor | 25.58 | 12.79 | 10.6% |
| 1020 | Roof Construction | Metal deck on open web steel joists, columns | | S.F. Roof | 10.38 | 5.19 | |
| | **B20 Exterior Enclosure** | | | | | | |
| 2010 | Exterior Walls | Face brick with concrete block backup | *95% of wall* | S.F. Wall | 42.11 | 22.40 | 16.3% |
| 2020 | Exterior Windows | Storefront | *5% of wall* | S.F. Window | 164 | 4.60 | |
| 2030 | Exterior Doors | Aluminum and glass and hollow metal | | Each | 5100 | .68 | |
| | **B30 Roofing** | | | | | | |
| 3010 | Roof Coverings | Built-up tar and gravel with flashing; perlite/EPS composite insulation | | S.F. Roof | 8.98 | 4.49 | 2.7% |
| 3020 | Roof Openings | Roof hatches | | S.F. Roof | .26 | .13 | |
| **C. INTERIORS** | | | | | | | |
| 1010 | Partitions | Concrete block, gypsum board on metal studs | *25 S.F. Floor/L.F. Partition* | S.F. Partition | 17.65 | 7.06 | 12.4% |
| 1020 | Interior Doors | Single leaf hollow metal | *810 S.F. Floor/Door* | Each | 1159 | 1.43 | |
| 1030 | Fittings | Toilet partitions | | S.F. Floor | .70 | .70 | |
| 2010 | Stair Construction | Concrete filled metal pan | | Flight | 19,225 | 1.92 | |
| 3010 | Wall Finishes | Paint | | S.F. Surface | 1.64 | 1.31 | |
| 3020 | Floor Finishes | 80% carpet tile, 20% ceramic tile | *50% of floor area* | S.F. Floor | 6.44 | 3.22 | |
| 3030 | Ceiling Finishes | Mineral fiber tile on concealed zee bars | *60% of area* | S.F. Ceiling | 9 | 5.40 | |
| **D. SERVICES** | | | | | | | |
| | **D10 Conveying** | | | | | | |
| 1010 | Elevators & Lifts | N/A | | — | — | — | 0.0 % |
| 1020 | Escalators & Moving Walks | N/A | | — | — | — | |
| | **D20 Plumbing** | | | | | | |
| 2010 | Plumbing Fixtures | Kitchen, bathroom and service fixtures, supply and drainage | *1 Fixture/1000 S.F. Floor* | Each | 5550 | 5.55 | 6.2% |
| 2020 | Domestic Water Distribution | Gas fired water heater | | S.F. Floor | 4.50 | 4.50 | |
| 2040 | Rain Water Drainage | Roof drains | | S.F. Roof | 1.12 | .56 | |
| | **D30 HVAC** | | | | | | |
| 3010 | Energy Supply | N/A | | — | — | — | 21.0 % |
| 3020 | Heat Generating Systems | Included in D3050 | | — | — | — | |
| 3030 | Cooling Generating Systems | N/A | | — | — | — | |
| 3050 | Terminal & Package Units | Multizone unit, gas heating, electric cooling | | S.F. Floor | 35.70 | 35.70 | |
| 3090 | Other HVAC Sys. & Equipment | N/A | | — | — | — | |
| | **D40 Fire Protection** | | | | | | |
| 4010 | Sprinklers | Sprinklers, light hazard | | S.F. Floor | 4.82 | 4.82 | 3.2% |
| 4020 | Standpipes | Standpipe | | S.F. Floor | .65 | .65 | |
| | **D50 Electrical** | | | | | | |
| 5010 | Electrical Service/Distribution | 400 ampere service, panel board and feeders | | S.F. Floor | 1.16 | 1.16 | 8.1% |
| 5020 | Lighting & Branch Wiring | Fluorescent and high intensity discharge fixtures, receptacles, switches, A.C. and misc. power | | S.F. Floor | 11.31 | 11.31 | |
| 5030 | Communications & Security | Addressable alarm systems and emergency lighting | | S.F. Floor | 1.35 | 1.35 | |
| 5090 | Other Electrical Systems | Emergency generator, 15 kW | | S.F. Floor | .05 | .05 | |
| **E. EQUIPMENT & FURNISHINGS** | | | | | | | |
| 1010 | Commercial Equipment | N/A | | — | — | — | 14.2 % |
| 1020 | Institutional Equipment | N/A | | — | — | — | |
| 1030 | Vehicular Equipment | N/A | | — | — | — | |
| 1090 | Other Equipment | Courts, sauna baths | | S.F. Floor | 24.13 | 24.13 | |
| **F. SPECIAL CONSTRUCTION** | | | | | | | |
| 1020 | Integrated Construction | N/A | | — | — | — | 0.0 % |
| 1040 | Special Facilities | N/A | | — | — | — | |
| **G. BUILDING SITEWORK** | **N/A** | | | | | | |
| | | | | | **Sub-Total** | 170.25 | **100%** |
| | CONTRACTOR FEES (General Requirements: 10%, Overhead: 5%, Profit: 10%) | | | | *25%* | 42.53 | |
| | ARCHITECT FEES | | | | *8%* | 17.02 | |
| | | | | | **Total Building Cost** | **229.80** | |

## Costs per square foot of floor area

| Exterior Wall | S.F. Area | 5000 | 6000 | 7000 | 8000 | 9000 | 10000 | 11000 | 12000 | 13000 |
|---|---|---|---|---|---|---|---|---|---|---|
| | L.F. Perimeter | 286 | 320 | 353 | 386 | 397 | 425 | 454 | 460 | 486 |
| Face Brick and Concrete Block | Steel Joists | 258.70 | 252.70 | 248.25 | 244.85 | 239.30 | **236.90** | 235.05 | 231.15 | 229.75 |
| | Wood Joists | 253.70 | 247.55 | 243.05 | 239.65 | 234.00 | 231.60 | 229.75 | 225.80 | 224.35 |
| Stucco and Concrete Block | Steel Joists | 253.55 | 247.90 | 243.65 | 240.45 | 235.30 | 233.00 | 231.30 | 227.70 | 226.35 |
| | Wood Joists | 248.55 | 242.75 | 238.55 | 235.30 | 230.00 | 227.75 | 226.00 | 222.35 | 221.00 |
| Limestone and Concrete Block | Steel Joists | 281.55 | 273.95 | 268.35 | 264.10 | 256.90 | 253.80 | 251.50 | 246.45 | 244.70 |
| | Wood Joists | 276.50 | 268.90 | 263.20 | 258.90 | 251.60 | 248.50 | 246.20 | 241.10 | 239.30 |
| Perimeter Adj., Add or Deduct | Per 100 L.F. | 24.35 | 20.30 | 17.30 | 15.20 | 13.50 | 12.15 | 11.05 | 10.10 | 9.35 |
| Story Hgt. Adj., Add or Deduct | Per 1 Ft. | 4.40 | 4.10 | 3.85 | 3.65 | 3.35 | 3.25 | 3.10 | 2.95 | 2.90 |
| ***For Basement**, add $ 49.25 per square foot of basement area* | | | | | | | | | | |

*The above costs were calculated using the basic specifications shown on the facing page. These costs should be adjusted where necessary for design alternatives and owner's requirements.*

## Common additives

| Description | Unit | $ Cost |
|---|---|---|
| Carrels Hardwood | Ea. | 395 - 2350 |
| Emergency Lighting, 25 watt, battery operated | | |
| Lead battery | Ea. | 360 |
| Nickel cadmium | Ea. | 585 |
| Flagpoles, Complete | | |
| Aluminum, 20′ high | Ea. | 2050 |
| 40′ high | Ea. | 5275 |
| 70′ high | Ea. | 14,300 |
| Fiberglass, 23′ high | Ea. | 3025 |
| 39′-5″ high | Ea. | 3725 |
| 59′ high | Ea. | 12,300 |
| Gym Floor, Incl. sleepers and finish, maple | S.F. | 23 |
| Intercom System, 25 Station capacity | | |
| Master station | Ea. | 3175 |
| Intercom outlets | Ea. | 228 |
| Handset | Ea. | 400 |

| Description | Unit | $ Cost |
|---|---|---|
| Lockers, Steel, single tier, 60″ to 72″ | Opng. | 285 - 520 |
| 2 tier, 60″ to 72″ total | Opng. | 216 - 265 |
| 5 tier, box lockers | Opng. | 465 - 153 |
| Locker bench, lam. maple top only | L.F. | 148 |
| Pedestals, steel pipe | Ea. | 87 |
| Seating | | |
| Auditorium chair, all veneer | Ea. | 480 |
| Veneer back, padded seat | Ea. | 430 |
| Upholstered, spring seat | Ea. | 385 |
| Classroom, movable chair & desk | Set | 81 - 171 |
| Lecture hall, pedestal type | Ea. | 385 - 775 |
| Smoke Detectors | | |
| Ceiling type | Ea. | 300 |
| Duct type | Ea. | 615 |
| Sound System | | |
| Amplifier, 250 watts | Ea. | 2425 |
| Speaker, ceiling or wall | Ea. | 320 |
| Trumpet | Ea. | 580 |
| Swimming Pools, Complete, gunite | S.F. | 127 - 158 |



**Important: See the Reference Section for Location Factors.**

# Model costs calculated for a 1 story building with 12′ story height and 10,000 square feet of floor area

# Religious Education

| | | | | Unit | Unit Cost | Cost Per S.F. | % Of Sub-Total |
|---|---|---|---|---|---|---|---|
| **A. SUBSTRUCTURE** | | | | | | | |
| 1010 | Standard Foundations | Poured concrete; strip and spread footings; 4′ foundation wall | | S.F. Ground | 7.78 | 7.78 | 8.8% |
| 1020 | Special Foundations | N/A | | — | — | — | |
| 1030 | Slab on Grade | 4″ reinforced concrete with vapor barrier and granular base | | S.F. Slab | 7.22 | 7.22 | |
| 2010 | Basement Excavation | Site preparation for slab and trench for foundation wall and footing | | S.F. Ground | .38 | .38 | |
| 2020 | Basement Walls | N/A | | — | — | — | |
| **B. SHELL** | | | | | | | |
| | **B10 Superstructure** | | | | | | |
| 1010 | Floor Construction | N/A | | — | — | — | 7.2 % |
| 1020 | Roof Construction | Metal deck, open web steel joists, beams, interior columns | | S.F. Roof | 12.52 | 12.52 | |
| | **B20 Exterior Enclosure** | | | | | | |
| 2010 | Exterior Walls | Face brick with concrete block backup | *85% of wall* | S.F. Wall | 33.49 | 14.52 | 18.2% |
| 2020 | Exterior Windows | Window wall | *15% of wall* | Each | 1617 | 12.86 | |
| 2030 | Exterior Doors | Double aluminum and glass | | Each | 10,663 | 4.28 | |
| | **B30 Roofing** | | | | | | |
| 3010 | Roof Coverings | Built-up tar and gravel with flashing; perlite/EPS composite insulation | | S.F. Roof | 8.73 | 8.73 | 5.0% |
| 3020 | Roof Openings | N/A | | — | — | — | |
| **C. INTERIORS** | | | | | | | |
| 1010 | Partitions | Concrete block | *8 S.F. Floor/S.F. Partition* | S.F. Partition | 10.86 | 13.57 | 21.7% |
| 1020 | Interior Doors | Single leaf hollow metal | *700 S.F. Floor/Door* | Each | 1159 | 1.65 | |
| 1030 | Fittings | Toilet partitions | | S.F. Floor | 2.12 | 2.12 | |
| 2010 | Stair Construction | N/A | | — | — | — | |
| 3010 | Wall Finishes | Paint | | S.F. Surface | 2.64 | 6.61 | |
| 3020 | Floor Finishes | 50% vinyl tile, 50% carpet | | S.F. Floor | 4.78 | 4.78 | |
| 3030 | Ceiling Finishes | Mineral fiber tile on concealed zee bars | | S.F. Ceiling | 9 | 9 | |
| **D. SERVICES** | | | | | | | |
| | **D10 Conveying** | | | | | | |
| 1010 | Elevators & Lifts | N/A | | — | — | — | 0.0 % |
| 1020 | Escalators & Moving Walks | N/A | | — | — | — | |
| | **D20 Plumbing** | | | | | | |
| 2010 | Plumbing Fixtures | Toilet and service fixtures, supply and drainage | *1 Fixture/455 S.F. Floor* | Each | 5847 | 12.85 | 9.2% |
| 2020 | Domestic Water Distribution | Gas fired water heater | | S.F. Floor | 1.52 | 1.52 | |
| 2040 | Rain Water Drainage | Roof drains | | S.F. Roof | 1.59 | 1.59 | |
| | **D30 HVAC** | | | | | | |
| 3010 | Energy Supply | N/A | | — | — | — | 16.0 % |
| 3020 | Heat Generating Systems | N/A | | — | — | — | |
| 3030 | Cooling Generating Systems | N/A | | — | — | — | |
| 3050 | Terminal & Package Units | Multizone HVAC air cooled system | | S.F. Floor | 27.90 | 27.90 | |
| 3090 | Other HVAC Sys. & Equipment | N/A | | — | — | — | |
| | **D40 Fire Protection** | | | | | | |
| 4010 | Sprinklers | Sprinkler, light hazard | | S.F. Floor | 5.07 | 5.07 | 3.4% |
| 4020 | Standpipes | Standpipe | | S.F. Floor | .91 | .91 | |
| | **D50 Electrical** | | | | | | |
| 5010 | Electrical Service/Distribution | 200 ampere service, panel board and feeders | | S.F. Floor | 1.41 | 1.41 | 10.3% |
| 5020 | Lighting & Branch Wiring | T-8 fluorescent fixtures, receptacles, switches, A.C. and misc. power | | S.F. Floor | 12.14 | 12.14 | |
| 5030 | Communications & Security | Addressable alarm systems, partial internet wiring and emergency lighting | | S.F. Floor | 4.35 | 4.35 | |
| 5090 | Other Electrical Systems | Emergency generator, 15 kW | | S.F. Floor | .09 | .09 | |
| **E. EQUIPMENT & FURNISHINGS** | | | | | | | |
| 1010 | Commercial Equipment | N/A | | — | — | — | 0.0 % |
| 1020 | Institutional Equipment | N/A | | — | — | — | |
| 1030 | Vehicular Equipment | N/A | | — | — | — | |
| 1090 | Other Equipment | N/A | | — | — | — | |
| **F. SPECIAL CONSTRUCTION** | | | | | | | |
| 1020 | Integrated Construction | N/A | | — | — | — | 0.0 % |
| 1040 | Special Facilities | N/A | | — | — | — | |
| **G. BUILDING SITEWORK** | | **N/A** | | | | | |
| | | | | | **Sub-Total** | 173.85 | **100%** |
| | CONTRACTOR FEES (General Requirements: 10%, Overhead: 5%, Profit: 10%) | | | | 25% | 43.49 | |
| | ARCHITECT FEES | | | | 9% | 19.56 | |
| | | | | | **Total Building Cost** | **236.90** | |

## Costs per square foot of floor area

| Exterior Wall | S.F. Area | 2000 | 2800 | 3500 | 4200 | 5000 | 5800 | 6500 | 7200 | 8000 |
|---|---|---|---|---|---|---|---|---|---|---|
| | L.F. Perimeter | 180 | 212 | 240 | 268 | 300 | 314 | 336 | 344 | 368 |
| Wood Clapboard | Wood Frame | 295.95 | 280.10 | 272.10 | 266.85 | 262.60 | 257.30 | 254.85 | 251.45 | 249.65 |
| Brick Veneer | Wood Frame | 309.35 | 292.00 | 283.25 | 277.50 | 272.80 | 266.95 | 264.20 | 260.40 | 258.40 |
| Stone Veneer | Rigid Steel | 343.70 | 321.85 | 310.85 | 303.60 | 297.80 | 290.00 | 286.50 | 281.50 | 278.95 |
| Fiber Cement | Rigid Steel | 304.25 | 288.60 | 280.80 | 275.65 | 271.50 | 266.30 | 263.80 | 260.55 | 258.75 |
| E.I.F.S. | Reinforced Concrete | 334.15 | 316.45 | 307.65 | 301.80 | 297.10 | 291.05 | 288.25 | 284.40 | 282.35 |
| Stucco | Reinforced Concrete | 338.50 | 320.10 | 310.95 | 304.90 | 299.95 | 293.65 | 290.75 | 286.70 | 284.55 |
| Perimeter Adj., Add or Deduct | Per 100 L.F. | 35.80 | 25.55 | 20.50 | 17.05 | 14.35 | 12.40 | 11.00 | 9.95 | 8.95 |
| Story Hgt. Adj., Add or Deduct | Per 1 Ft. | 3.60 | 3.00 | 2.85 | 2.60 | 2.45 | 2.20 | 2.05 | 1.90 | 1.90 |

***For Basement**, add $57.00 per square foot of basement area*

*The above costs were calculated using the basic specifications shown on the facing page. These costs should be adjusted where necessary for design alternatives and owner's requirements.*

## Common additives

| Description | Unit | $ Cost |
|---|---|---|
| Bar, Front Bar | L.F. | 490 |
| Back bar | L.F. | 395 |
| Booth, Upholstered, custom straight | L.F. | 281 - 1500 |
| "L" or "U" shaped | L.F. | 291 - 490 |
| Cupola, Stock unit, redwood | | |
| 30" square, 37" high, aluminum roof | Ea. | 900 |
| Copper roof | Ea. | 545 |
| Fiberglass, 5'-0" base, 63" high | Ea. | 5100 - 5575 |
| 6'-0" base, 63" high | Ea. | 5875 - 8800 |
| Decorative Wood Beams, Non load bearing | | |
| Rough sawn, 4" x 6" | L.F. | 10.35 |
| 4" x 8" | L.F. | 11.60 |
| 4" x 10" | L.F. | 14.55 |
| 4" x 12" | L.F. | 16.05 |
| 8" x 8" | L.F. | 16.60 |
| Emergency Lighting, 25 watt, battery operated | | |
| Lead battery | Ea. | 360 |
| Nickel cadmium | Ea. | 585 |

| Description | Unit | $ Cost |
|---|---|---|
| Fireplace, Brick, not incl. chimney or foundation | | |
| 30" x 29" opening | Ea. | 3750 |
| Chimney, standard brick | | |
| Single flue, 16" x 20" | V.L.F. | 161 |
| 20" x 20" | V.L.F. | 187 |
| 2 Flue, 20" x 24" | V.L.F. | 247 |
| 20" x 32" | V.L.F. | 305 |
| Kitchen Equipment | | |
| Broiler | Ea. | 4425 |
| Coffee urn, twin 6 gallon | Ea. | 4075 |
| Cooler, 6 ft. long | Ea. | 4525 |
| Dishwasher, 10-12 racks per hr. | Ea. | 42,900 |
| Food warmer, counter, 1.2 KW | Ea. | 720 |
| Freezer, 44 C.F., reach-in | Ea. | 3600 |
| Ice cube maker, 50 lb. per day | Ea. | 2525 |
| Range with 1 oven | Ea. | 2050 |
| Refrigerators, Prefabricated, walk-in | | |
| 7'-6" high, 6' x 6' | S.F. | 141 |
| 10' x 10' | S.F. | 110 |
| 12' x 14' | S.F. | 96 |
| 12' x 20' | S.F. | 139 |



**Important: See the Reference Section for Location Factors.**

## Model costs calculated for a 1 story building with 12′ story height and 5,000 square feet of floor area

# Restaurant

| | | | | Unit | Unit Cost | Cost Per S.F. | % Of Sub-Total |
|---|---|---|---|---|---|---|---|
| **A. SUBSTRUCTURE** | | | | | | | |
| 1010 | Standard Foundations | Poured concrete; strip and spread footings; 4′ foundation wall | | S.F. Ground | 12.76 | 12.76 | 10.5% |
| 1020 | Special Foundations | N/A | | — | — | — | |
| 1030 | Slab on Grade | 4″ reinforced concrete | | S.F. Slab | 7.22 | 7.22 | |
| 2010 | Basement Excavation | Site preparation for slab and trench for foundation wall and footing | | S.F. Ground | .66 | .66 | |
| 2020 | Basement Walls | N/A | | — | — | — | |
| **B. SHELL** | | | | | | | |
| | **B10 Superstructure** | | | | | | |
| 1010 | Floor Construction | Wood columns | | S.F. Floor | .39 | .98 | 7.1% |
| 1020 | Roof Construction | Wood roof truss, 4:12 slope | | S.F. Roof | 11.63 | 13.03 | |
| | **B20 Exterior Enclosure** | | | | | | |
| 2010 | Exterior Walls | Wood siding on wood studs, insulated | *70% of wall* | S.F. Wall | 33.45 | 16.86 | 16.3% |
| 2020 | Exterior Windows | Curtain glazing wall system | *30% of wall* | Each | 59 | 5.92 | |
| 2030 | Exterior Doors | Aluminum & glass double doors, hollow metal doors | | Each | 9295 | 9.32 | |
| | **B30 Roofing** | | | | | | |
| 3010 | Roof Coverings | Asphalt strip shingles, gutters and downspouts | | S.F. Roof | 19.84 | 2.98 | 1.5% |
| 3020 | Roof Openings | N/A | | — | — | — | |
| **C. INTERIORS** | | | | | | | |
| 1010 | Partitions | Fire rated gypsum board on wood studs | *25 S.F. Floor/L.F. Partition* | S.F. Partition | 9.05 | 3.62 | 12.3% |
| 1020 | Interior Doors | Single leaf hollow core wood doors | *1000 S.F. Floor/Door* | Each | 825 | .83 | |
| 1030 | Fittings | Plastic laminate toilet partitions | | S.F. Floor | 1.07 | 1.07 | |
| 2010 | Stair Construction | N/A | | — | — | — | |
| 3010 | Wall Finishes | 80% Paint, 20% ceramic tile | | S.F. Surface | 3.18 | 2.54 | |
| 3020 | Floor Finishes | 70% Carpet tile, 30% quarry tile | | S.F. Floor | 10.54 | 10.54 | |
| 3030 | Ceiling Finishes | Gypsum board ceiling on wood furring | | S.F. Ceiling | 5.48 | 5.48 | |
| **D. SERVICES** | | | | | | | |
| | **D10 Conveying** | | | | | | |
| 1010 | Elevators & Lifts | N/A | | — | — | — | 0.0 % |
| 1020 | Escalators & Moving Walks | N/A | | — | — | — | |
| | **D20 Plumbing** | | | | | | |
| 2010 | Plumbing Fixtures | Restroom, kitchen and service fixtures, supply and drainage | *1 Fixture/350 S.F. Floor* | Each | 4494 | 12.66 | 8.8% |
| 2020 | Domestic Water Distribution | Gas fired water heater | | S.F. Floor | 4.63 | 4.63 | |
| 2040 | Rain Water Drainage | Roof drains | | S.F. Roof | | | |
| | **D30 HVAC** | | | | | | |
| 3010 | Energy Supply | N/A | | — | — | — | 22.8 % |
| 3020 | Heat Generating Systems | Included in D3050 | | — | — | — | |
| 3030 | Cooling Generating Systems | N/A | | — | — | — | |
| 3050 | Terminal & Package Units | Multizone unit gas heating, electric cooling, kitchen exhaust system | | S.F. Floor | 44.74 | 44.74 | |
| 3090 | Other HVAC Sys. & Equipment | N/A | | — | — | — | |
| | **D40 Fire Protection** | | | | | | |
| 4010 | Sprinklers | Wet pipe sprinkler system | | S.F. Floor | 13.28 | 13.28 | 8.6% |
| 4020 | Standpipes | Standpipe | | S.F. Floor | 3.55 | 3.55 | |
| | **D50 Electrical** | | | | | | |
| 5010 | Electrical Service/Distribution | 400 Ampere service, panelboards and feeders | | S.F. Floor | 5.90 | 5.90 | 12.1% |
| 5020 | Lighting & Branch Wiring | Fluorescent fixtures, receptacles, switches, a.c. and misc. power | | S.F. Floor | 14.06 | 14.06 | |
| 5030 | Communications & Security | Addressable alarm system | | S.F. Floor | 3.72 | 3.72 | |
| 5090 | Other Electrical Systems | N/A | | — | — | — | |
| **E. EQUIPMENT & FURNISHINGS** | | | | | | | |
| 1010 | Commercial Equipment | N/A | | — | — | — | 0.0 % |
| 1020 | Institutional Equipment | N/A | | — | — | — | |
| 1030 | Vehicular Equipment | N/A | | — | — | — | |
| 1090 | Other Equipment | N/A | | — | — | — | |
| **F. SPECIAL CONSTRUCTION** | | | | | | | |
| 1020 | Integrated Construction | N/A | | — | — | — | 0.0 % |
| 1040 | Special Facilities | N/A | | — | — | — | |
| **G. BUILDING SITEWORK** | | **N/A** | | | | | |
| | | | | | **Sub-Total** | 196.35 | **100%** |
| | CONTRACTOR FEES (General Requirements: 10%, Overhead: 5%, Profit: 10%) | | | | *25%* | 49.07 | |
| | ARCHITECT FEES | | | | *7%* | 17.18 | |
| | | | | | **Total Building Cost** | **262.60** | |

# Restaurant, Fast Food

## Costs per square foot of floor area

| Exterior Wall | S.F. Area | 2000 | 2800 | 3500 | 4000 | 5000 | 5800 | 6500 | 7200 | 8000 |
|---|---|---|---|---|---|---|---|---|---|---|
| | L.F. Perimeter | 180 | 212 | 240 | 260 | 300 | 314 | 336 | 344 | 368 |
| Wood Clapboard | Wood Frame | 305.30 | 294.05 | 288.40 | **285.60** | 281.60 | 277.00 | 275.10 | 272.00 | 270.65 |
| Brick Veneer | Wood Frame | 309.40 | 297.50 | 291.55 | 288.55 | 284.45 | 279.55 | 277.50 | 274.20 | 272.80 |
| Stone Veneer | Rigid Steel | 339.20 | 323.50 | 315.65 | 311.70 | 306.30 | 299.85 | 297.10 | 292.85 | 290.90 |
| Fiber Cement | Rigid Steel | 305.95 | 295.55 | 290.35 | 287.70 | 284.10 | 279.85 | 278.10 | 275.20 | 273.95 |
| E.I.F.S. | Reinforced Concrete | 333.75 | 321.45 | 315.30 | 312.20 | 307.95 | 302.90 | 300.80 | 297.45 | 295.90 |
| Stucco | Reinforced Concrete | 337.40 | 324.55 | 318.15 | 314.90 | 310.40 | 305.10 | 302.95 | 299.40 | 297.75 |
| Perimeter Adj., Add or Deduct | Per 100 L.F. | 39.30 | 28.05 | 22.50 | 19.70 | 15.80 | 13.55 | 12.05 | 10.95 | 9.80 |
| Story Hgt. Adj., Add or Deduct | Per 1 Ft. | 4.45 | 3.70 | 3.35 | 3.20 | 3.00 | 2.70 | 2.55 | 2.40 | 2.20 |
| **Basement**—Not Applicable | | | | | | | | | | |

*The above costs were calculated using the basic specifications shown on the facing page. These costs should be adjusted where necessary for design alternatives and owner's requirements.*

## Common additives

| Description | Unit | $ Cost |
|---|---|---|
| Bar, Front Bar | L.F. | 490 |
| Back bar | L.F. | 395 |
| Booth, Upholstered, custom straight | L.F. | 281 - 1500 |
| "L" or "U" shaped | L.F. | 291 - 490 |
| Drive-up Window | Ea. | 6325 - 9850 |
| Emergency Lighting, 25 watt, battery operated | | |
| Lead battery | Ea. | 360 |
| Nickel cadmium | Ea. | 585 |
| Kitchen Equipment | | |
| Broiler | Ea. | 4425 |
| Coffee urn, twin 6 gallon | Ea. | 4075 |
| Cooler, 6 ft. long | Ea. | 4525 |
| Dishwasher, 10-12 racks per hr. | Ea. | 42,900 |
| Food warmer, counter, 1.2 KW | Ea. | 720 |
| Freezer, 44 C.F., reach-in | Ea. | 3600 |
| Ice cube maker, 50 lb. per day | Ea. | 2525 |
| Range with 1 oven | Ea. | 2050 |

| Description | Unit | $ Cost |
|---|---|---|
| Refrigerators, Prefabricated, walk-in | | |
| 7'-6" High, 6' x 6' | S.F. | 141 |
| 10' x 10' | S.F. | 110 |
| 12' x 14' | S.F. | 96 |
| 12' x 20' | S.F. | 139 |
| Serving | | |
| Counter top (Stainless steel) | L.F. | 245 |
| Base cabinets | L.F. | 575 - 940 |
| Sound System | | |
| Amplifier, 250 watts | Ea. | 2425 |
| Speaker, ceiling or wall | Ea. | 320 |
| Trumpet | Ea. | 580 |
| Storage | | |
| Shelving | S.F. | 19.85 |
| Washing | | |
| Stainless steel counter | L.F. | 245 |



**Important: See the Reference Section for Location Factors.**

**Model costs calculated for a 1 story building with 10′ story height and 4,000 square feet of floor area**

# Restaurant, Fast Food

| | | | | Unit | Unit Cost | Cost Per S.F. | % Of Sub-Total |
|---|---|---|---|---|---|---|---|
| **A. SUBSTRUCTURE** | | | | | | | |
| 1010 | Standard Foundations | Poured concrete; strip and spread footings; 4′ foundation wall | | S.F. Ground | 12.01 | 12.01 | |
| 1020 | Special Foundations | N/A | | — | — | — | |
| 1030 | Slab on Grade | 4″ reinforced concrete | | S.F. Slab | 7.22 | 7.22 | 9.4% |
| 2010 | Basement Excavation | Site preparation for slab and trench for foundation wall and footing | | S.F. Ground | .66 | .66 | |
| 2020 | Basement Walls | N/A | | — | — | — | |
| **B. SHELL** | | | | | | | |
| | **B10 Superstructure** | | | | | | |
| 1010 | Floor Construction | Wood columns | | S.F. Floor | .98 | .98 | 4.2% |
| 1020 | Roof Construction | Flat wood rafter roof | | S.F. Roof | 7.89 | 7.89 | |
| | **B20 Exterior Enclosure** | | | | | | |
| 2010 | Exterior Walls | Wood siding on wood studs, insulated | *70% of wall* | S.F. Wall | 28.75 | 13.08 | |
| 2020 | Exterior Windows | Curtain glazing wall system | *30% of wall* | Each | 86 | 9.48 | 16.9% |
| 2030 | Exterior Doors | Aluminum & glass double doors, hollow metal doors | | Each | 6638 | 13.29 | |
| | **B30 Roofing** | | | | | | |
| 3010 | Roof Coverings | Single ply membrane, stone ballast, rigid insulation | | S.F. Roof | 12.16 | 12.16 | 6.3% |
| 3020 | Roof Openings | Roof and smoke hatches | | S.F. Roof | 1.14 | 1.14 | |
| **C. INTERIORS** | | | | | | | |
| 1010 | Partitions | Water resistant gypsum board on wood studs | *25 S.F. Floor/L.F. Partition* | S.F. Partition | 9.28 | 3.71 | |
| 1020 | Interior Doors | Single leaf hollow core wood doors | *1000 S.F. Floor/Door* | Each | 825 | .83 | |
| 1030 | Fittings | Stainless steel toilet partitions | | S.F. Floor | 2.65 | 2.65 | |
| 2010 | Stair Construction | N/A | | — | — | — | 19.2% |
| 3010 | Wall Finishes | 90% Paint, 10% ceramic tile | | S.F. Surface | 2.31 | 1.85 | |
| 3020 | Floor Finishes | Quarry tile | | S.F. Floor | 22.06 | 22.06 | |
| 3030 | Ceiling Finishes | Acoustic ceiling tiles on suspended support grid | | S.F. Ceiling | 9.48 | 9.48 | |
| **D. SERVICES** | | | | | | | |
| | **D10 Conveying** | | | | | | |
| 1010 | Elevators & Lifts | N/A | | — | — | — | 0.0 % |
| 1020 | Escalators & Moving Walks | N/A | | — | — | — | |
| | **D20 Plumbing** | | | | | | |
| 2010 | Plumbing Fixtures | Restroom, kitchen and service fixtures, supply and drainage | *1 Fixture/330 S.F. Floor* | Each | 4056 | 12.18 | |
| 2020 | Domestic Water Distribution | Gas fired water heater | | S.F. Floor | 4.64 | 4.64 | 9.2% |
| 2040 | Rain Water Drainage | Roof drains | | S.F. Roof | 2.54 | 2.54 | |
| | **D30 HVAC** | | | | | | |
| 3010 | Energy Supply | N/A | | — | — | — | |
| 3020 | Heat Generating Systems | Included in D3050 | | — | — | — | |
| 3030 | Cooling Generating Systems | N/A | | — | — | — | 10.7 % |
| 3050 | Terminal & Package Units | Single zone unit gas heating, electric cooling | | S.F. Floor | 22.56 | 22.56 | |
| 3090 | Other HVAC Sys. & Equipment | N/A | | — | — | — | |
| | **D40 Fire Protection** | | | | | | |
| 4010 | Sprinklers | Wet pipe sprinkler system, ordinary hazard | | S.F. Floor | 13.28 | 13.28 | 8.0% |
| 4020 | Standpipes | Standpipe | | S.F. Floor | 3.71 | 3.71 | |
| | **D50 Electrical** | | | | | | |
| 5010 | Electrical Service/Distribution | 400 Ampere service, panelboards and feeders | | S.F. Floor | 5.99 | 5.99 | |
| 5020 | Lighting & Branch Wiring | Fluorescent fixtures, receptacles, switches, a.c. and misc. power | | S.F. Floor | 15.15 | 15.15 | 12.2% |
| 5030 | Communications & Security | Addressable alarm, emergency lighting | | S.F. Floor | 4.65 | 4.65 | |
| 5090 | Other Electrical Systems | N/A | | — | — | — | |
| **E. EQUIPMENT & FURNISHINGS** | | | | | | | |
| 1010 | Commercial Equipment | N/A | | — | — | — | |
| 1020 | Institutional Equipment | N/A | | — | — | — | 3.9 % |
| 1030 | Vehicular Equipment | N/A | | — | — | — | |
| 1090 | Other Equipment | Prefabricated walk in refrigerators | | S.F. Floor | 8.33 | 8.33 | |
| **F. SPECIAL CONSTRUCTION** | | | | | | | |
| 1020 | Integrated Construction | N/A | | — | — | — | 0.0 % |
| 1040 | Special Facilities | N/A | | — | — | — | |
| **G. BUILDING SITEWORK** | **N/A** | | | | | | |
| | | | | | **Sub-Total** | 211.52 | **100%** |
| | CONTRACTOR FEES (General Requirements: 10%, Overhead: 5%, Profit: 10%) | | | | *25%* | 52.93 | |
| | ARCHITECT FEES | | | | *8%* | 21.15 | |
| | | | | | **Total Building Cost** | **285.60** | |

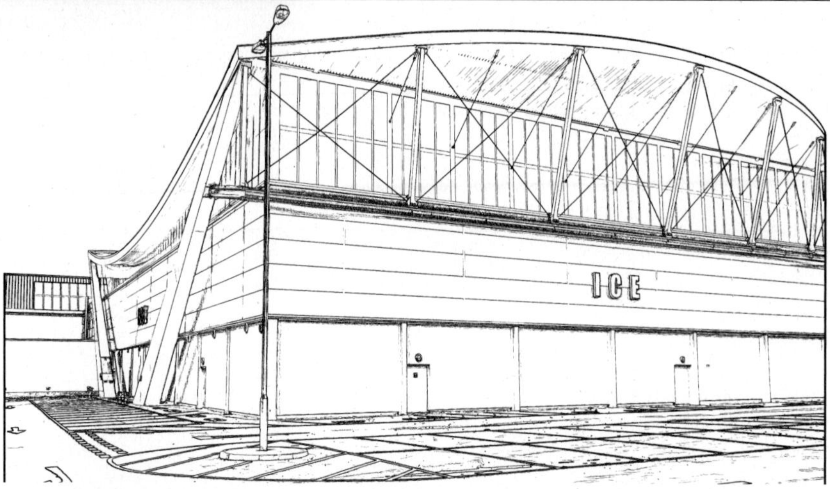


## Costs per square foot of floor area

| Exterior Wall | S.F. Area | 10000 | 15000 | 20000 | 25000 | 30000 | 35000 | 40000 | 45000 | 50000 |
|---|---|---|---|---|---|---|---|---|---|---|
| | L.F. Perimeter | 450 | 500 | 600 | 700 | 740 | 822 | 890 | 920 | 966 |
| Face Brick and Concrete Block | Steel Joists | 250.30 | 227.35 | 220.30 | 216.05 | 209.70 | 207.20 | 204.80 | 201.40 | 199.25 |
| | Wood Truss | 270.75 | 249.30 | 243.05 | 239.30 | 233.20 | 231.00 | 228.70 | 225.45 | 223.40 |
| Concrete Block | Rigid Steel | 237.80 | 223.55 | 219.05 | 216.25 | **212.35** | 210.80 | 209.30 | 207.20 | 205.95 |
| | Wood Truss | 237.15 | 224.40 | 220.70 | 218.35 | 214.75 | 213.45 | 212.10 | 210.15 | 209.00 |
| Metal Panel | Rigid Steel | 240.45 | 225.55 | 220.80 | 217.90 | 213.85 | 212.20 | 210.60 | 208.45 | 207.10 |
| Metal Sandwich Panel | Rigid Steel | 246.55 | 230.00 | 224.80 | 221.65 | 217.15 | 215.30 | 213.60 | 211.20 | 209.70 |
| Perimeter Adj., Add or Deduct | Per 100 L.F. | 17.75 | 11.80 | 8.90 | 7.10 | 5.90 | 5.10 | 4.50 | 4.00 | 3.55 |
| Story Hgt. Adj., Add or Deduct | Per 1 Ft. | 2.80 | 2.10 | 1.90 | 1.75 | 1.50 | 1.50 | 1.40 | 1.30 | 1.20 |
| **Basement**—Not Applicable | | | | | | | | | | |

*The above costs were calculated using the basic specifications shown on the facing page. These costs should be adjusted where necessary for design alternatives and owner's requirements.*

## Common additives

| Description | Unit | $ Cost |
|---|---|---|
| Bar, Front Bar | L.F. | 490 |
| Back bar | L.F. | 395 |
| Booth, Upholstered, custom straight | L.F. | 281 - 1500 |
| "L" or "U" shaped | L.F. | 291 - 490 |
| Bleachers, Telescoping, manual | | |
| To 15 tier | Seat | 162 - 299 |
| 16-20 tier | Seat | 261 - 550 |
| 21-30 tier | Seat | 390 - 605 |
| For power operation, add | Seat | 1000 - 1875 |
| Emergency Lighting, 25 watt, battery operated | | |
| Lead battery | Ea. | 360 |
| Nickel cadmium | Ea. | 585 |
| Lockers, Steel, single tier, 60" or 72" | Opng. | 285 - 520 |
| 2 tier, 60" or 72" total | Opng. | 216 - 265 |
| 5 tier, box lockers | Opng. | 465 - 153 |
| Locker bench, lam. maple top only | L.F. | 148 |
| Pedestals, steel pipe | Ea. | 87 |

| Description | Unit | $ Cost |
|---|---|---|
| Rink | | |
| Dasher boards & top guard | Ea. | 199,000 |
| Mats, rubber | S.F. | 29.50 |
| Score Board | Ea. | 21,300 - 35,700 |



**Important: See the Reference Section for Location Factors.**

## Model costs calculated for a 1 story building with 24′ story height and 30,000 square feet of floor area

# Rink, Hockey/Indoor Soccer

| | | | | Unit | Unit Cost | Cost Per S.F. | % Of Sub-Total |
|---|---|---|---|---|---|---|---|
| **A. SUBSTRUCTURE** | | | | | | | |
| 1010 | Standard Foundations | Poured concrete; strip and spread footings; 4′ foundation wall | | S.F. Ground | 4.63 | 4.63 | |
| 1020 | Special Foundations | N/A | | — | — | — | |
| 1030 | Slab on Grade | 6″ reinforced concrete with vapor barrier and granular base | | S.F. Slab | 9.16 | 9.16 | 8.8% |
| 2010 | Basement Excavation | Site preparation for slab and trench for foundation wall and footing | | S.F. Ground | .22 | .22 | |
| 2020 | Basement Walls | N/A | | — | — | — | |
| **B. SHELL** | | | | | | | |
| | **B10 Superstructure** | | | | | | |
| 1010 | Floor Construction | Wide flange beams and columns | | S.F. Floor | 53 | 36.85 | 23.2% |
| 1020 | Roof Construction | (incl. in B1010) | | | | | |
| | **B20 Exterior Enclosure** | | | | | | |
| 2010 | Exterior Walls | Concrete block | *95% of wall* | S.F. Wall | 16.16 | 9.09 | |
| 2020 | Exterior Windows | Store front | *5% of wall* | Each | 83 | 2.45 | 8.2% |
| 2030 | Exterior Doors | Aluminum and glass, hollow metal, overhead | | Each | 5288 | 1.42 | |
| | **B30 Roofing** | | | | | | |
| 3010 | Roof Coverings | Elastomeric neoprene membrane with flashing; perlite/EPS composite insulation | | S.F. Roof | 6.73 | 6.73 | 4.6% |
| 3020 | Roof Openings | Roof hatches | | S.F. Roof | .55 | .55 | |
| **C. INTERIORS** | | | | | | | |
| 1010 | Partitions | Concrete block | *140 S.F. Floor/L.F. Partition* | S.F. Partition | 10.85 | .93 | |
| 1020 | Interior Doors | Hollow metal | *2500 S.F. Floor/Door* | Each | 1159 | .46 | |
| 1030 | Fittings | N/A | | — | — | — | |
| 2010 | Stair Construction | N/A | | — | — | — | 6.0% |
| 3010 | Wall Finishes | Paint | | S.F. Surface | 14.58 | 2.50 | |
| 3020 | Floor Finishes | 80% rubber mat, 20% paint | *50% of floor area* | S.F. Floor | 9.32 | 4.66 | |
| 3030 | Ceiling Finishes | Mineral fiber tile on concealed zee bar | *10% of area* | S.F. Ceiling | 9 | .91 | |
| **D. SERVICES** | | | | | | | |
| | **D10 Conveying** | | | | | | |
| 1010 | Elevators & Lifts | N/A | | — | — | — | 0.0 % |
| 1020 | Escalators & Moving Walks | N/A | | — | — | — | |
| | **D20 Plumbing** | | | | | | |
| 2010 | Plumbing Fixtures | Toilet and service fixtures, supply and drainage | *1 Fixture/1070 S.F. Floor* | Each | 9106 | 8.51 | |
| 2020 | Domestic Water Distribution | Oil fired water heater | | S.F. Floor | 4.50 | 4.50 | 9.0% |
| 2040 | Rain Water Drainage | Roof drains | | S.F. Roof | 1.23 | 1.23 | |
| | **D30 HVAC** | | | | | | |
| 3010 | Energy Supply | Oil fired hot water, unit heaters | *10% of area* | S.F. Floor | 1.30 | 1.30 | |
| 3020 | Heat Generating Systems | N/A | | — | — | — | |
| 3030 | Cooling Generating Systems | N/A | | — | — | — | 11.7% |
| 3050 | Terminal & Package Units | Single zone, electric cooling | *90% of area* | S.F. Floor | 17.20 | 17.20 | |
| 3090 | Other HVAC Sys. & Equipment | N/A | | — | — | — | |
| | **D40 Fire Protection** | | | | | | |
| 4010 | Sprinklers | N/A | | — | — | — | 0.7 % |
| 4020 | Standpipes | Standpipe | | S.F. Floor | 1.11 | 1.11 | |
| | **D50 Electrical** | | | | | | |
| 5010 | Electrical Service/Distribution | 600 ampere service, panel board and feeders | | S.F. Floor | 2.08 | 2.08 | |
| 5020 | Lighting & Branch Wiring | High intensity discharge and fluorescent fixtures, receptacles, switches, A.C. and misc. power | | S.F. Floor | 10.72 | 10.72 | 9.9% |
| 5030 | Communications & Security | Addressable alarm systems, emergency lighting and public address | | S.F. Floor | 2.63 | 2.63 | |
| 5090 | Other Electrical Systems | Emergency generator | | S.F. Floor | .22 | .22 | |
| **E. EQUIPMENT & FURNISHINGS** | | | | | | | |
| 1010 | Commercial Equipment | N/A | | — | — | — | |
| 1020 | Institutional Equipment | N/A | | — | — | — | 0.0 % |
| 1030 | Vehicular Equipment | N/A | | — | — | — | |
| 1090 | Other Equipment | N/A | | — | — | — | |
| **F. SPECIAL CONSTRUCTION** | | | | | | | |
| 1020 | Integrated Construction | N/A | | — | — | — | 18.1 % |
| 1040 | Special Facilities | Dasher boards and rink (including ice making system) | | S.F. Floor | 28.71 | 28.71 | |
| **G. BUILDING SITEWORK** | | **N/A** | | | | | |
| | | | | | **Sub-Total** | 158.77 | **100%** |
| | CONTRACTOR FEES (General Requirements: 10%, Overhead: 5%, Profit: 10%) | | | | *25%* | 39.69 | |
| | ARCHITECT FEES | | | | *7%* | 13.89 | |
| | | | | | **Total Building Cost** | **212.35** | |

## Costs per square foot of floor area

| Exterior Wall | S.F. Area | 25000 | 30000 | 35000 | 40000 | 45000 | 50000 | 55000 | 60000 | 65000 |
|---|---|---|---|---|---|---|---|---|---|---|
| | L.F. Perimeter | 900 | 1050 | 1200 | 1350 | 1510 | 1650 | 1800 | 1970 | 2100 |
| Fiber Cement | Rigid Steel | 207.80 | 206.15 | 204.90 | 204.05 | 203.60 | 202.80 | 202.30 | 202.35 | 201.60 |
| Metal Panel | Rigid Steel | 207.60 | 206.00 | 204.65 | 203.80 | **203.40** | 202.55 | 202.10 | 202.10 | 201.40 |
| E.I.F.S. | Rigid Steel | 210.05 | 208.40 | 207.10 | 206.30 | 205.85 | 205.05 | 204.55 | 204.60 | 203.85 |
| Tilt-up Concrete Panels | Reinforced Concrete | 260.45 | 257.65 | 255.65 | 254.15 | 253.55 | 252.05 | 251.35 | 251.45 | 250.20 |
| Brick Veneer | Reinforced Concrete | 238.05 | 235.95 | 234.50 | 233.40 | 232.90 | 231.85 | 231.25 | 231.30 | 230.45 |
| Stone Veneer | Reinforced Concrete | 286.80 | 283.30 | 280.70 | 278.90 | 278.10 | 276.30 | 275.30 | 275.45 | 273.85 |
| Perimeter Adj., Add or Deduct | Per 100 L.F. | 4.20 | 3.50 | 3.05 | 2.60 | 2.30 | 2.10 | 1.90 | 1.70 | 1.65 |
| Story Hgt. Adj., Add or Deduct | Per 1 Ft. | 1.55 | 1.50 | 1.50 | 1.45 | 1.45 | 1.40 | 1.45 | 1.40 | 1.40 |
| ***For Basement**, add $ 42.25 per square foot of basement area* | | | | | | | | | | |

*The above costs were calculated using the basic specifications shown on the facing page. These costs should be adjusted where necessary for design alternatives and owner's requirements.*

## Common additives

| Description | Unit | $ Cost |
|---|---|---|
| Bleachers, Telescoping, manual | | |
| To 15 tier | Seat | 162 - 299 |
| 16-20 tier | Seat | 261 - 550 |
| 21-30 tier | Seat | 390 - 605 |
| For power operation, add | Seat | 1000 - 1875 |
| Carrels Hardwood | Ea. | 395 - 2350 |
| Clock System | | |
| 20 room | Ea. | 23,000 |
| 50 room | Ea. | 55,000 |
| Emergency Lighting, 25 watt, battery operated | | |
| Lead battery | Ea. | 360 |
| Nickel cadmium | Ea. | 585 |
| Flagpoles, Complete | | |
| Aluminum, 20′ high | Ea. | 2050 |
| 40′ high | Ea. | 5275 |
| Fiberglass, 23′ high | Ea. | 3025 |
| 39′-5″ high | Ea. | 3725 |
| Kitchen Equipment | | |
| Broiler | Ea. | 4425 |
| Cooler, 6 ft. long, reach-in | Ea. | 4525 |

| Description | Unit | $ Cost |
|---|---|---|
| Kitchen Equipment, cont. | | |
| Dishwasher, 10-12 racks per hr. | Ea. | 42,900 |
| Food warmer, counter, 1.2 KW | Ea. | 720 |
| Freezer, 44 C.F., reach-in | Ea. | 3600 |
| Ice cube maker, 50 lb. per day | Ea. | 2525 |
| Range with 1 oven | Ea. | 2050 |
| Lockers, Steel, single tier, 60″ to 72″ | Opng. | 285 - 520 |
| 2 tier, 60″ to 72″ total | Opng. | 216 - 265 |
| 5 tier, box lockers | Opng. | 465 - 153 |
| Locker bench, lam. maple top only | L.F. | 148 |
| Pedestals, steel pipe | Ea. | 87 |
| Seating | | |
| Auditorium chair, all veneer | Ea. | 480 |
| Veneer back, padded seat | Ea. | 430 |
| Upholstered, spring seat | Ea. | 385 |
| Classroom, movable chair & desk | Set | 81 - 171 |
| Lecture hall, pedestal type | Ea. | 385 - 775 |
| Sound System | | |
| Amplifier, 250 watts | Ea. | 2425 |
| Speaker, ceiling or wall | Ea. | 320 |
| Trumpet | Ea. | 580 |



**Important: See the Reference Section for Location Factors.**

## Model costs calculated for a 1 story building with 15′ story height and 45,000 square feet of floor area

# School, Elementary

| | | | | Unit | Unit Cost | Cost Per S.F. | % Of Sub-Total |
|---|---|---|---|---|---|---|---|
| **A. SUBSTRUCTURE** | | | | | | | |
| 1010 | Standard Foundations | Poured concrete; strip and spread footings; 4′ foundation wall | | S.F. Ground | 6.74 | 6.74 | 9.4% |
| 1020 | Special Foundations | N/A | | — | — | — | |
| 1030 | Slab on Grade | 4″ reinforced concrete | | S.F. Slab | 7.22 | 7.22 | |
| 2010 | Basement Excavation | Site preparation for slab and trench for foundation wall and footing | | S.F. Ground | .22 | .39 | |
| 2020 | Basement Walls | N/A | | — | — | — | |
| **B. SHELL** | | | | | | | |
| | **B10 Superstructure** | | | | | | |
| 1010 | Floor Construction | Fireproofing for structural columns | | S.F. Floor | 1.43 | 1.43 | 9.9% |
| 1020 | Roof Construction | Metal deck, open web steel joists, beams, columns | | S.F. Roof | 13.70 | 13.70 | |
| | **B20 Exterior Enclosure** | | | | | | |
| 2010 | Exterior Walls | Textured metal panel on metal stud, insulated | *70% of wall* | S.F. Wall | 23.81 | 8.39 | 11.1% |
| 2020 | Exterior Windows | Curtain wall system, thermo-break frame, aluminum awning windows | *30% of wall* | Each | 911 | 7.30 | |
| 2030 | Exterior Doors | Aluminum & glass double doors, hollow metal doors | | Each | 6350 | 1.14 | |
| | **B30 Roofing** | | | | | | |
| 3010 | Roof Coverings | Single ply membrane, stone ballast, rigid insulation | | S.F. Roof | 11.76 | 11.76 | 8.0% |
| 3020 | Roof Openings | Roof and smoke hatches | | S.F. Roof | 4547 | .41 | |
| **C. INTERIORS** | | | | | | | |
| 1010 | Partitions | Gypsum board on metal studs, sound attentuation insulation | *20 S.F. Floor/L.F. Partition* | S.F. Partition | 7.34 | 3.67 | 17.2% |
| 1020 | Interior Doors | Hollow metal doors | *700 S.F. Floor/Door* | Each | 1159 | 1.65 | |
| 1030 | Fittings | Chalkboards, lockers, toilet partitions | | S.F. Floor | 1.30 | 1.30 | |
| 2010 | Stair Construction | N/A | | — | — | — | |
| 3010 | Wall Finishes | 90% Paint, 10% ceramic tile | | S.F. Surface | 2.11 | 2.11 | |
| 3020 | Floor Finishes | 10% Carpet, 10% terrazzo, 60% VCT, 20% wood | | S.F. Floor | 8.42 | 8.42 | |
| 3030 | Ceiling Finishes | Acoustic ceiling tiles on suspended channel grid | | S.F. Ceiling | 9 | 9 | |
| **D. SERVICES** | | | | | | | |
| | **D10 Conveying** | | | | | | |
| 1010 | Elevators & Lifts | N/A | | — | — | — | 0.0 % |
| 1020 | Escalators & Moving Walks | N/A | | — | — | — | |
| | **D20 Plumbing** | | | | | | |
| 2010 | Plumbing Fixtures | Restroom, kitchen, and service fixtures, supply and drainage | *1 Fixture/325 S.F. Floor* | Each | 2951 | 9.08 | 7.3% |
| 2020 | Domestic Water Distribution | Gas fired water heater | | S.F. Floor | .64 | .64 | |
| 2040 | Rain Water Drainage | Roof drains | | S.F. Roof | 1.31 | 1.31 | |
| | **D30 HVAC** | | | | | | |
| 3010 | Energy Supply | Forced hot water heating system, fin tube radiation | | S.F. Floor | 14.25 | 14.25 | 19.0% |
| 3020 | Heat Generating Systems | N/A | | — | — | — | |
| 3030 | Cooling Generating Systems | N/A | | — | — | — | |
| 3050 | Terminal & Package Units | Split system with air cooled condensing unit | | S.F. Floor | 14.70 | 14.70 | |
| 3090 | Other HVAC Sys. & Equipment | N/A | | — | — | — | |
| | **D40 Fire Protection** | | | | | | |
| 4010 | Sprinklers | Wet pipe spinkler system | | S.F. Floor | 4.46 | 4.46 | 3.4% |
| 4020 | Standpipes | Standpipe | | S.F. Floor | .72 | .72 | |
| | **D50 Electrical** | | | | | | |
| 5010 | Electrical Service/Distribution | 800 Ampere service, panelboards and feeders | | S.F. Floor | 1.56 | 1.56 | 14.6% |
| 5020 | Lighting & Branch Wiring | Fluorescent fixtures, receptacles, switches, a.c. and misc. power | | S.F. Floor | 15.84 | 15.84 | |
| 5030 | Communications & Security | Addressable alarm system, emergency lighting, internet & phone wiring | | S.F. Floor | 4.68 | 4.68 | |
| 5090 | Other Electrical Systems | Emergency generator, 15kW | | S.F. Floor | .09 | .09 | |
| **E. EQUIPMENT & FURNISHINGS** | | | | | | | |
| 1010 | Commercial Equipment | N/A | | — | — | — | 0.1 % |
| 1020 | Institutional Equipment | Laboratory equipment | | S.F. Floor | .11 | .11 | |
| 1030 | Vehicular Equipment | N/A | | — | — | — | |
| 1090 | Other Equipment | N/A | | — | — | — | |
| **F. SPECIAL CONSTRUCTION** | | | | | | | |
| 1020 | Integrated Construction | N/A | | — | — | — | 0.0 % |
| 1040 | Special Facilities | N/A | | — | — | — | |
| **G. BUILDING SITEWORK** | **N/A** | | | | | | |
| | | | | | **Sub-Total** | 152.07 | **100%** |
| | CONTRACTOR FEES (General Requirements: 10%, Overhead: 5%, Profit: 10%) | | | | *25%* | 38.02 | |
| | ARCHITECT FEES | | | | *7%* | 13.31 | |
| | | | | | **Total Building Cost** | **203.40** | |

## Costs per square foot of floor area

| Exterior Wall | S.F. Area | 50000 | 70000 | 90000 | 110000 | 130000 | 150000 | 170000 | 190000 | 210000 |
|---|---|---|---|---|---|---|---|---|---|---|
| | L.F. Perimeter | 850 | 1140 | 1420 | 1700 | 1980 | 2280 | 2560 | 2840 | 3120 |
| Fiber Cement | Rigid Steel | 251.80 | 246.65 | 243.45 | 241.45 | 240.05 | 239.40 | 238.50 | 237.95 | 237.45 |
| Metal Panel | Rigid Steel | 257.10 | 251.90 | 248.65 | 246.65 | 245.30 | 244.60 | 243.70 | 243.10 | 242.65 |
| E.I.F.S. | Rigid Steel | 258.15 | 253.05 | 249.90 | 247.90 | 246.55 | 245.85 | 245.05 | 244.40 | 244.00 |
| Tilt-up Concrete Panels | Reinforced Concrete | 301.90 | 295.05 | 290.75 | 288.00 | 286.05 | 285.35 | 284.20 | 283.30 | 282.60 |
| Brick Veneer | Reinforced Concrete | 282.65 | 276.85 | 273.20 | 270.95 | 269.35 | 268.70 | 267.70 | 267.00 | 266.45 |
| Stone Veneer | Reinforced Concrete | 324.90 | 317.10 | 312.05 | 308.95 | 306.65 | 305.90 | 304.50 | 303.50 | 302.70 |
| Perimeter Adj., Add or Deduct | Per 100 L.F. | 5.25 | 3.75 | 2.90 | 2.40 | 2.00 | 1.75 | 1.60 | 1.35 | 1.20 |
| Story Hgt. Adj., Add or Deduct | Per 1 Ft. | 2.05 | 1.95 | 1.90 | 1.85 | 1.80 | 1.80 | 1.80 | 1.75 | 1.75 |

***For Basement**, add $55.15 per square foot of basement area*

*The above costs were calculated using the basic specifications shown on the facing page. These costs should be adjusted where necessary for design alternatives and owner's requirements.*

## Common additives

| Description | Unit | $ Cost |
|---|---|---|
| Bleachers, Telescoping, manual | | |
| To 15 tier | Seat | 162 - 299 |
| 16-20 tier | Seat | 261 - 550 |
| 21-30 tier | Seat | 390 - 605 |
| For power operation, add | Seat | 1000 - 1875 |
| Carrels Hardwood | Ea. | 395 - 2350 |
| Clock System | | |
| 20 room | Ea. | 23,000 |
| 50 room | Ea. | 55,000 |
| Elevators, Hydraulic passenger, 2 stops | | |
| 1500# capacity | Ea. | 86,500 |
| 2500# capacity | Ea. | 90,500 |
| Emergency Lighting, 25 watt, battery operated | | |
| Lead battery | Ea. | 360 |
| Nickel cadmium | Ea. | 585 |
| Flagpoles, Complete | | |
| Aluminum, 20' high | Ea. | 2050 |
| 40' high | Ea. | 5275 |
| Fiberglass, 23' high | Ea. | 3025 |
| 39'-5" high | Ea. | 3725 |

| Description | Unit | $ Cost |
|---|---|---|
| Kitchen Equipment | | |
| Broiler | Ea. | 4425 |
| Cooler, 6 ft. long, reach-in | Ea. | 4525 |
| Dishwasher, 10-12 racks per hr. | Ea. | 42,900 |
| Food warmer, counter, 1.2 KW | Ea. | 720 |
| Freezer, 44 C.F., reach-in | Ea. | 3600 |
| Lockers, Steel, single tier, 60" or 72" | Opng. | 285 - 520 |
| 2 tier, 60" or 72" total | Opng. | 216 - 265 |
| 5 tier, box lockers | Opng. | 465 - 153 |
| Locker bench, lam. maple top only | L.F. | 148 |
| Pedestals, steel pipe | Ea. | 87 |
| Seating | | |
| Auditorium chair, all veneer | Ea. | 480 |
| Veneer back, padded seat | Ea. | 430 |
| Upholstered, spring seat | Ea. | 385 |
| Classroom, movable chair & desk | Set | 81 - 171 |
| Lecture hall, pedestal type | Ea. | 385 - 775 |
| Sound System | | |
| Amplifier, 250 watts | Ea. | 2425 |
| Speaker, ceiling or wall | Ea. | 320 |
| Trumpet | Ea. | 580 |



**Important: See the Reference Section for Location Factors.**

## Model costs calculated for a 2 story building with 15′ story height and 130,000 square feet of floor area

# School, High, 2-3 Story

| | | | Unit | Unit Cost | Cost Per S.F. | % Of Sub-Total |
|---|---|---|---|---|---|---|
| **A. SUBSTRUCTURE** | | | | | | |
| 1010 | Standard Foundations | Poured concrete; strip and spread footings; 4′ foundation wall | S.F. Ground | 7.42 | 3.71 | 4.1% |
| 1020 | Special Foundations | N/A | — | — | — | |
| 1030 | Slab on Grade | 4″ reinforced concrete | S.F. Slab | 7.22 | 3.61 | |
| 2010 | Basement Excavation | Site preparation for slab and trench for foundation wall and footing | S.F. Ground | .22 | .17 | |
| 2020 | Basement Walls | N/A | — | — | — | |
| **B. SHELL** | | | | | | |
| | **B10 Superstructure** | | | | | |
| 1010 | Floor Construction | Open web steel joists, slab form, concrete, fireproofed steel columns | S.F. Floor | 19.54 | 9.77 | 9.1% |
| 1020 | Roof Construction | Metal deck, open web steel joists, beams, columns | S.F. Roof | 13.72 | 6.86 | |
| | **B20 Exterior Enclosure** | | | | | |
| 2010 | Exterior Walls | Textured metal panel on metal stud, insulated *75% of wall* | S.F. Wall | 23.78 | 8.15 | 11.4% |
| 2020 | Exterior Windows | Curtain wall system, thermo-break frame *25% of wall* | Each | 104 | 11.89 | |
| 2030 | Exterior Doors | Aluminum & glass double doors, hollow metal doors, overhead doors | Each | 4048 | .92 | |
| | **B30 Roofing** | | | | | |
| 3010 | Roof Coverings | Single ply membrane, stone ballast, rigid insulation | S.F. Roof | 11.24 | 5.62 | 3.3% |
| 3020 | Roof Openings | Roof and smoke hatches | S.F. Roof | .72 | .36 | |
| **C. INTERIORS** | | | | | | |
| 1010 | Partitions | Gypsum board on metal studs, sound attentuation insulation *25 S.F. Floor/L.F. Partition* | S.F. Partition | 8.60 | 4.13 | 20.7% |
| 1020 | Interior Doors | Hollow metal doors *700 S.F. Floor/Door* | Each | 1159 | 1.65 | |
| 1030 | Fittings | Chalkboards, lockers, toilet partitions | S.F. Floor | 11.30 | 11.30 | |
| 2010 | Stair Construction | Cement filled metal pan, picket rail | Flight | 12,925 | 1 | |
| 3010 | Wall Finishes | 90% Paint, 10% ceramic tile | S.F. Surface | 2.11 | 2.03 | |
| 3020 | Floor Finishes | 10% Carpet, 10% terrazzo, 60% VCT, 20% wood | S.F. Floor | 8.42 | 8.42 | |
| 3030 | Ceiling Finishes | Acoustic ceiling tiles on suspended channel grid | S.F. Ceiling | 9.48 | 9.48 | |
| **D. SERVICES** | | | | | | |
| | **D10 Conveying** | | | | | |
| 1010 | Elevators & Lifts | Hydraulic passenger elevator | Each | 107,900 | .83 | 0.5% |
| 1020 | Escalators & Moving Walks | N/A | — | — | — | |
| | **D20 Plumbing** | | | | | |
| 2010 | Plumbing Fixtures | Restroom, kitchen, and service fixtures, supply and drainage *1 Fixture/340 S.F. Floor* | Each | 2788 | 8.20 | 5.6% |
| 2020 | Domestic Water Distribution | Gas fired water heater | S.F. Floor | 1.53 | 1.53 | |
| 2040 | Rain Water Drainage | Roof drains | S.F. Roof | 1.20 | .60 | |
| | **D30 HVAC** | | | | | |
| 3010 | Energy Supply | Forced hot water heating system, fin tube radiation | S.F. Floor | 7.09 | 7.09 | 18.3% |
| 3020 | Heat Generating Systems | N/A | — | — | — | |
| 3030 | Cooling Generating Systems | Packaged chiller | S.F. Floor | 26.51 | 26.51 | |
| 3050 | Terminal & Package Units | N/A | — | — | — | |
| 3090 | Other HVAC Sys. & Equipment | N/A | — | — | — | |
| | **D40 Fire Protection** | | | | | |
| 4010 | Sprinklers | Wet pipe spinkler system | S.F. Floor | 3.88 | 3.88 | 2.4% |
| 4020 | Standpipes | Standpipe | S.F. Floor | .58 | .58 | |
| | **D50 Electrical** | | | | | |
| 5010 | Electrical Service/Distribution | 2000 Ampere service, panelboards and feeders | S.F. Floor | 1.58 | 1.58 | 12.0% |
| 5020 | Lighting & Branch Wiring | Fluorescent fixtures, receptacles, switches, a.c. and misc. power | S.F. Floor | 14.63 | 14.63 | |
| 5030 | Communications & Security | Addressable alarm system, emergency lighting, internet & phone wiring | S.F. Floor | 5.33 | 5.33 | |
| 5090 | Other Electrical Systems | Emergency generator, 250kW | S.F. Floor | .55 | .55 | |
| **E. EQUIPMENT & FURNISHINGS** | | | | | | |
| 1010 | Commercial Equipment | N/A | — | — | — | 12.5 % |
| 1020 | Institutional Equipment | Laboratory equipment | S.F. Floor | 18.90 | 18.90 | |
| 1030 | Vehicular Equipment | N/A | — | — | — | |
| 1090 | Other Equipment | Gym equipment, bleachers, scoreboards | S.F. Floor | 4.08 | 4.08 | |
| **F. SPECIAL CONSTRUCTION** | | | | | | |
| 1020 | Integrated Construction | N/A | — | — | — | 0.0 % |
| 1040 | Special Facilities | N/A | — | — | — | |
| **G. BUILDING SITEWORK** | **N/A** | | | | | |
| | | | | **Sub-Total** | 183.36 | **100%** |
| | CONTRACTOR FEES (General Requirements: 10%, Overhead: 5%, Profit: 10%) | | | *25%* | 45.90 | |
| | ARCHITECT FEES | | | *7%* | 16.04 | |
| | | | | **Total Building Cost** | **245.30** | |

# School, Jr High, 2-3 Story

## Costs per square foot of floor area

| Exterior Wall | S.F. Area | 50000 | 65000 | 80000 | 95000 | 110000 | 125000 | 140000 | 155000 | 170000 |
|---|---|---|---|---|---|---|---|---|---|---|
| | L.F. Perimeter | 850 | 1060 | 1280 | 1490 | 1700 | 1920 | 2140 | 2340 | 2560 |
| Fiber Cement | Rigid Steel | 212.00 | 209.60 | 208.40 | 207.35 | 206.55 | 206.15 | 205.80 | 205.30 | 205.10 |
| Metal Panel | Rigid Steel | 212.75 | 210.30 | 209.10 | 208.05 | 207.30 | 206.85 | 206.50 | 205.95 | 205.75 |
| E.I.F.S. | Rigid Steel | 215.05 | 212.75 | 211.45 | 210.45 | 209.70 | 209.25 | 208.90 | 208.40 | 208.15 |
| Tilt-up Concrete Panels | Reinforced Concrete | 248.95 | 245.65 | 244.00 | 242.45 | 241.40 | 240.85 | 240.40 | 239.60 | 239.35 |
| Brick Veneer | Reinforced Concrete | 244.30 | 241.30 | 239.85 | 238.50 | 237.60 | 237.10 | 236.70 | 236.00 | 235.80 |
| Stone Veneer | Reinforced Concrete | 269.55 | 265.30 | 263.30 | 261.40 | 260.05 | 259.35 | 258.85 | 257.80 | 257.55 |
| Perimeter Adj., Add or Deduct | Per 100 L.F. | 4.45 | 3.45 | 2.80 | 2.30 | 2.05 | 1.75 | 1.60 | 1.50 | 1.35 |
| Story Hgt. Adj., Add or Deduct | Per 1 Ft. | 1.75 | 1.70 | 1.70 | 1.65 | 1.70 | 1.65 | 1.65 | 1.55 | 1.55 |
| ***For Basement**, add $ 57.45 per square foot of basement area* | | | | | | | | | | |

*The above costs were calculated using the basic specifications shown on the facing page. These costs should be adjusted where necessary for design alternatives and owner's requirements.*

## Common additives

| Description | Unit | $ Cost |
|---|---|---|
| Bleachers, Telescoping, manual | | |
| To 15 tier | Seat | 162 - 299 |
| 16-20 tier | Seat | 261 - 550 |
| 21-30 tier | Seat | 390 - 605 |
| For power operation, add | Seat | 1000 - 1875 |
| Carrels Hardwood | Ea. | 395 - 2350 |
| Clock System | | |
| 20 room | Ea. | 23,000 |
| 50 room | Ea. | 55,000 |
| Elevators, Hydraulic passenger, 2 stops | | |
| 1500# capacity | Ea. | 86,500 |
| 2500# capacity | Ea. | 90,500 |
| Emergency Lighting, 25 watt, battery operated | | |
| Lead battery | Ea. | 360 |
| Nickel cadmium | Ea. | 585 |
| Flagpoles, Complete | | |
| Aluminum, 20′ high | Ea. | 2050 |
| 40′ high | Ea. | 5275 |
| Fiberglass, 23′ high | Ea. | 3025 |
| 39′-5″ high | Ea. | 3725 |

| Description | Unit | $ Cost |
|---|---|---|
| Kitchen Equipment | | |
| Broiler | Ea. | 4425 |
| Cooler, 6 ft. long, reach-in | Ea. | 4525 |
| Dishwasher, 10-12 racks per hr. | Ea. | 42,900 |
| Food warmer, counter, 1.2 KW | Ea. | 720 |
| Freezer, 44 C.F., reach-in | Ea. | 3600 |
| Lockers, Steel, single tier, 60″ to 72″ | Opng. | 285 - 520 |
| 2 tier, 60″ to 72″ total | Opng. | 216 - 265 |
| 5 tier, box lockers | Opng. | 465 - 153 |
| Locker bench, lam. maple top only | L.F. | 148 |
| Pedestals, steel pipe | Ea. | 87 |
| Seating | | |
| Auditorium chair, all veneer | Ea. | 480 |
| Veneer back, padded seat | Ea. | 430 |
| Upholstered, spring seat | Ea. | 385 |
| Classroom, movable chair & desk | Set | 81 - 171 |
| Lecture hall, pedestal type | Ea. | 385 - 775 |
| Sound System | | |
| Amplifier, 250 watts | Ea. | 2425 |
| Speaker, ceiling or wall | Ea. | 320 |
| Trumpet | Ea. | 580 |



**Important: See the Reference Section for Location Factors.**

**Model costs calculated for a 2 story building with 15′ story height and 110,000 square feet of floor area**

# School, Jr High, 2-3 Story

| | | | Unit | Unit Cost | Cost Per S.F. | % Of Sub-Total |
|---|---|---|---|---|---|---|
| **A. SUBSTRUCTURE** | | | | | | |
| 1010 | Standard Foundations | Poured concrete; strip and spread footings; 4′ foundation wall | S.F. Ground | 6.70 | 3.35 | 4.6% |
| 1020 | Special Foundations | N/A | — | — | — | |
| 1030 | Slab on Grade | 4″ reinforced concrete | S.F. Slab | 7.22 | 3.61 | |
| 2010 | Basement Excavation | Site preparation for slab and trench for foundation wall and footing | S.F. Ground | .22 | .19 | |
| 2020 | Basement Walls | N/A | — | — | — | |
| **B. SHELL** | | | | | | |
| | **B10 Superstructure** | | | | | |
| 1010 | Floor Construction | Open web steel joists, slab form, concrete, fireproofed steel columns | S.F. Floor | 19.76 | 9.88 | 10.8% |
| 1020 | Roof Construction | Metal deck, open web steel joists, beams, columns | S.F. Roof | 13.72 | 6.86 | |
| | **B20 Exterior Enclosure** | | | | | |
| 2010 | Exterior Walls | Fiber cement siding on wood studs, insulated *75% of wall* | S.F. Wall | 22.46 | 7.81 | 12.1% |
| 2020 | Exterior Windows | Curtain wall system, thermo-break frame *25% of wall* | Each | 84 | 9.76 | |
| 2030 | Exterior Doors | Aluminum & glass double doors, hollow metal doors, overhead doors | Each | 4218 | 1.10 | |
| | **B30 Roofing** | | | | | |
| 3010 | Roof Coverings | Single ply membrane, stone ballast, rigid insulation | S.F. Roof | 11.64 | 5.82 | 4.0% |
| 3020 | Roof Openings | Roof and smoke hatches | S.F. Roof | .66 | .33 | |
| **C. INTERIORS** | | | | | | |
| 1010 | Partitions | Gypsum board on metal studs, sound attentuation insulation *20 S.F. Floor/L.F. Partition* | S.F. Partition | 8.25 | 4.95 | 23.0% |
| 1020 | Interior Doors | Hollow metal doors *750 S.F. Floor/Door* | Each | 1159 | 1.55 | |
| 1030 | Fittings | Chalkboards, lockers, toilet partitions | S.F. Floor | 9.06 | 9.06 | |
| 2010 | Stair Construction | Cement filled metal pan, picket rail | Flight | 12,925 | .94 | |
| 3010 | Wall Finishes | 90% Paint, 10% ceramic tile | S.F. Surface | 2.05 | 2.46 | |
| 3020 | Floor Finishes | 10% Carpet, 10% terrazzo, 70% VCT, 10% wood | S.F. Floor | 7.13 | 7.13 | |
| 3030 | Ceiling Finishes | Acoustic ceiling tiles on suspended channel grid | S.F. Ceiling | 9.48 | 9.48 | |
| **D. SERVICES** | | | | | | |
| | **D10 Conveying** | | | | | |
| 1010 | Elevators & Lifts | Hydraulic passenger elevator | Each | 106,700 | .97 | 0.6% |
| 1020 | Escalators & Moving Walks | N/A | — | — | — | |
| | **D20 Plumbing** | | | | | |
| 2010 | Plumbing Fixtures | Restroom, kitchen, and service fixtures, supply and drainage *1 Fixture/350 S.F. Floor* | Each | 2919 | 8.34 | 6.2% |
| 2020 | Domestic Water Distribution | Gas fired water heater | S.F. Floor | .65 | .65 | |
| 2040 | Rain Water Drainage | Roof drains | S.F. Roof | 1.08 | .54 | |
| | **D30 HVAC** | | | | | |
| 3010 | Energy Supply | N/A | — | — | — | 16.0 % |
| 3020 | Heat Generating Systems | Included in D3050 | — | — | — | |
| 3030 | Cooling Generating Systems | N/A | — | — | — | |
| 3050 | Terminal & Package Units | Single zone unit gas heating, electric cooling | S.F. Floor | 24.70 | 24.70 | |
| 3090 | Other HVAC Sys. & Equipment | N/A | — | — | — | |
| | **D40 Fire Protection** | | | | | |
| 4010 | Sprinklers | Wet pipe spinkler system | S.F. Floor | 3.88 | 3.88 | 3.0% |
| 4020 | Standpipes | Standpipe | S.F. Floor | .68 | .68 | |
| | **D50 Electrical** | | | | | |
| 5010 | Electrical Service/Distribution | 1600 Ampere service, panelboards and feeders | S.F. Floor | 1.48 | 1.48 | 14.5% |
| 5020 | Lighting & Branch Wiring | Fluorescent fixtures, receptacles, switches, a.c. and misc. power | S.F. Floor | 14.64 | 14.64 | |
| 5030 | Communications & Security | Addressable alarm system, emergency lighting, internet & phone wiring | S.F. Floor | 5.87 | 5.87 | |
| 5090 | Other Electrical Systems | Emergency generator, 100kW | S.F. Floor | .43 | .43 | |
| **E. EQUIPMENT & FURNISHINGS** | | | | | | |
| 1010 | Commercial Equipment | N/A | — | — | — | 5.2 % |
| 1020 | Institutional Equipment | Laboratory equipment | S.F. Floor | 3.15 | 3.15 | |
| 1030 | Vehicular Equipment | N/A | — | — | — | |
| 1090 | Other Equipment | Gym equipment, bleachers, scoreboards | S.F. Floor | 4.84 | 4.84 | |
| **F. SPECIAL CONSTRUCTION** | | | | | | |
| 1020 | Integrated Construction | N/A | — | — | — | 0.0 % |
| 1040 | Special Facilities | N/A | — | — | — | |
| **G. BUILDING SITEWORK** | | **N/A** | | | | |
| | | | | **Sub-Total** | 154.45 | **100%** |
| | CONTRACTOR FEES (General Requirements: 10%, Overhead: 5%, Profit: 10%) | | | 25% | 38.59 | |
| | ARCHITECT FEES | | | 7% | 13.51 | |
| | | | | **Total Building Cost** | **206.55** | |

## Costs per square foot of floor area

| Exterior Wall | S.F. Area | 20000 | 30000 | 40000 | 50000 | 60000 | 70000 | 80000 | 90000 | 100000 |
|---|---|---|---|---|---|---|---|---|---|---|
| | L.F. Perimeter | 440 | 590 | 740 | 900 | 1050 | 1200 | 1360 | 1510 | 1660 |
| Face Brick and Concrete Block | Rigid Steel | 247.85 | 240.20 | 236.45 | 234.55 | 233.00 | 231.90 | 231.30 | 230.60 | 230.05 |
| | Bearing Walls | 242.75 | 235.10 | **231.25** | 229.45 | 227.85 | 226.70 | 226.10 | 225.40 | 224.90 |
| Decorative Concrete Block | Rigid Steel | 232.60 | 226.60 | 223.60 | 222.10 | 220.90 | 219.95 | 219.50 | 218.95 | 218.50 |
| | Bearing Walls | 227.45 | 221.45 | 218.45 | 216.95 | 215.70 | 214.85 | 214.35 | 213.85 | 213.40 |
| Metal Panel and Metal Studs | Rigid Steel | 224.95 | 219.75 | 217.15 | 215.90 | 214.80 | 214.00 | 213.60 | 213.15 | 212.75 |
| Metal Sandwich Panel | Rigid Steel | 225.25 | 220.00 | 217.40 | 216.10 | 215.05 | 214.25 | 213.85 | 213.35 | 212.95 |
| Perimeter Adj., Add or Deduct | Per 100 L.F. | 12.30 | 8.20 | 6.15 | 5.00 | 4.05 | 3.40 | 3.10 | 2.75 | 2.45 |
| Story Hgt. Adj., Add or Deduct | Per 1 Ft. | 2.95 | 2.70 | 2.50 | 2.50 | 2.35 | 2.30 | 2.30 | 2.25 | 2.20 |

***For Basement**, add $55.70 per square foot of basement area*

*The above costs were calculated using the basic specifications shown on the facing page. These costs should be adjusted where necessary for design alternatives and owner's requirements.*

## Common additives

| Description | Unit | $ Cost |
|---|---|---|
| Carrels Hardwood | Ea. | 395 - 2350 |
| Clock System | | |
| 20 room | Ea. | 23,000 |
| 50 room | Ea. | 55,000 |
| Directory Boards, Plastic, glass covered | | |
| 30" x 20" | Ea. | 705 |
| 36" x 48" | Ea. | 1475 |
| Aluminum, 24" x 18" | Ea. | 705 |
| 36" x 24" | Ea. | 985 |
| 48" x 32" | Ea. | 1975 |
| 48" x 60" | Ea. | 2650 |
| Elevators, Hydraulic passenger, 2 stops | | |
| 1500# capacity | Ea. | 86,500 |
| 2500# capacity | Ea. | 90,500 |
| 3500# capacity | Ea. | 96,000 |
| Emergency Lighting, 25 watt, battery operated | | |
| Lead battery | Ea. | 360 |
| Nickel cadmium | Ea. | 585 |

| Description | Unit | $ Cost |
|---|---|---|
| Flagpoles, Complete | | |
| Aluminum, 20' high | Ea. | 2050 |
| 40' high | Ea. | 5275 |
| Fiberglass, 23' high | Ea. | 3025 |
| 39'-5" high | Ea. | 3725 |
| Seating | | |
| Auditorium chair, all veneer | Ea. | 480 |
| Veneer back, padded seat | Ea. | 430 |
| Upholstered, spring seat | Ea. | 385 |
| Classroom, movable chair & desk | Set | 81 - 171 |
| Lecture hall, pedestal type | Ea. | 385 - 775 |
| Shops & Workroom: | | |
| Benches, metal | Ea. | 785 |
| Parts bins 6'-3" high, 3' wide, 12" deep, 72 bins | Ea. | 1475 |
| Shelving, metal 1' x 3' | S.F. | 25 |
| Wide span 6' wide x 24" deep | S.F. | 19.85 |
| Sound System | | |
| Amplifier, 250 watts | Ea. | 2425 |
| Speaker, ceiling or wall | Ea. | 320 |
| Trumpet | Ea. | 580 |



**Important: See the Reference Section for Location Factors.**

## Model costs calculated for a 2 story building with 16′ story height and 40,000 square feet of floor area

# School, Vocational

| | | | Unit | Unit Cost | Cost Per S.F. | % Of Sub-Total |
|---|---|---|---|---|---|---|
| **A. SUBSTRUCTURE** | | | | | | |
| 1010 | Standard Foundations | Poured concrete; strip and spread footings; 4′ foundation wall | S.F. Ground | 8.20 | 4.10 | 7.6% |
| 1020 | Special Foundations | N/A | — | — | — | |
| 1030 | Slab on Grade | 5″ reinforced concrete with vapor barrier and granular base | S.F. Slab | 17.70 | 8.85 | |
| 2010 | Basement Excavation | Site preparation for slab and trench for foundation wall and footing | S.F. Ground | .22 | .11 | |
| 2020 | Basement Walls | N/A | — | — | — | |
| **B. SHELL** | | | | | | |
| | **B10 Superstructure** | | | | | |
| 1010 | Floor Construction | Open web steel joists, slab form, concrete, beams, columns | S.F. Floor | 29.52 | 14.76 | 11.4% |
| 1020 | Roof Construction | Metal deck, open web steel joists, beams, columns | S.F. Roof | 9.82 | 4.91 | |
| | **B20 Exterior Enclosure** | | | | | |
| 2010 | Exterior Walls | Face brick with concrete block backup *85% of wall* | S.F. Wall | 40.66 | 20.46 | 16.7% |
| 2020 | Exterior Windows | Tubular aluminum framing with insulated glass *15% of wall* | Each | 84 | 7.47 | |
| 2030 | Exterior Doors | Metal and glass doors | Each | 4509 | .89 | |
| | **B30 Roofing** | | | | | |
| 3010 | Roof Coverings | Single-ply membrane with polyisocyanurate insulation | S.F. Roof | 10.32 | 5.16 | 3.2% |
| 3020 | Roof Openings | Roof hatches | S.F. Roof | .70 | .35 | |
| **C. INTERIORS** | | | | | | |
| 1010 | Partitions | Concrete block *20 S.F. Floor/L.F. Partition* | S.F. Partition | 10.87 | 6.52 | 17.2% |
| 1020 | Interior Doors | Single leaf kalamein fire doors *600 S.F. Floor/Door* | Each | 1159 | 1.94 | |
| 1030 | Fittings | Toilet partitions, chalkboards | S.F. Floor | .85 | .85 | |
| 2010 | Stair Construction | Concrete filled metal pan | Flight | 16,075 | 2.41 | |
| 3010 | Wall Finishes | 50% paint, 40% glazed coating, 10% ceramic tile | S.F. Surface | 5.31 | 6.37 | |
| 3020 | Floor Finishes | 70% vinyl composition tile, 20% carpet, 10% terrazzo | S.F. Floor | 6.27 | 6.27 | |
| 3030 | Ceiling Finishes | Mineral fiber tile on concealed zee bars *60% of area* | S.F. Ceiling | 9 | 5.40 | |
| **D. SERVICES** | | | | | | |
| | **D10 Conveying** | | | | | |
| 1010 | Elevators & Lifts | One hydraulic passenger elevator | Each | 107,200 | 2.68 | 1.5% |
| 1020 | Escalators & Moving Walks | N/A | — | — | — | |
| | **D20 Plumbing** | | | | | |
| 2010 | Plumbing Fixtures | Toilet and service fixtures, supply and drainage *1 Fixture/700 S.F. Floor* | Each | 4788 | 6.84 | 5.2% |
| 2020 | Domestic Water Distribution | Gas fired water heater | S.F. Floor | .98 | .98 | |
| 2040 | Rain Water Drainage | Roof drains | S.F. Roof | 2.34 | 1.17 | |
| | **D30 HVAC** | | | | | |
| 3010 | Energy Supply | Oil fired hot water, wall fin radiation | S.F. Floor | 13.73 | 13.73 | 20.9% |
| 3020 | Heat Generating Systems | N/A | | — | — | |
| 3030 | Cooling Generating Systems | Chilled water, cooling tower systems | S.F. Floor | 22.35 | 22.35 | |
| 3050 | Terminal & Package Units | N/A | — | — | — | |
| 3090 | Other HVAC Sys. & Equipment | N/A | — | — | — | |
| | **D40 Fire Protection** | | | | | |
| 4010 | Sprinklers | Sprinklers, light hazard | S.F. Floor | 4.57 | 4.57 | 3.7% |
| 4020 | Standpipes | Standpipe, wet, Class III | S.F. Floor | 1.85 | 1.85 | |
| | **D50 Electrical** | | | | | |
| 5010 | Electrical Service/Distribution | 800 ampere service, panel board and feeders | S.F. Floor | 1.75 | 1.75 | 12.6% |
| 5020 | Lighting & Branch Wiring | High efficiency fluorescent fixtures, receptacles, switches, A.C. and misc. power | S.F. Floor | 15.87 | 15.87 | |
| 5030 | Communications & Security | Addressable alarm systems, internet wiring, communications systems and emergency lighting | S.F. Floor | 4.09 | 4.09 | |
| 5090 | Other Electrical Systems | Emergency generator, 11.5 kW | S.F. Floor | .12 | .12 | |
| **E. EQUIPMENT & FURNISHINGS** | | | | | | |
| 1010 | Commercial Equipment | N/A | — | — | — | 0.1 % |
| 1020 | Institutional Equipment | Stainless steel countertops | S.F. Floor | .10 | .10 | |
| 1030 | Vehicular Equipment | N/A | — | — | — | |
| 1090 | Other Equipment | N/A | — | — | — | |
| **F. SPECIAL CONSTRUCTION** | | | | | | |
| 1020 | Integrated Construction | N/A | — | — | — | 0.0 % |
| 1040 | Special Facilities | N/A | — | — | — | |
| **G. BUILDING SITEWORK** | **N/A** | | | | | |
| | | | | **Sub-Total** | 172.92 | **100%** |
| | CONTRACTOR FEES (General Requirements: 10%, Overhead: 5%, Profit: 10%) | | | *25%* | 43.20 | |
| | ARCHITECT FEES | | | *7%* | 15.13 | |
| | | | | **Total Building Cost** | **231.25** | |

## Costs per square foot of floor area

| Exterior Wall | S.F. Area | 1000 | 2000 | 3000 | 4000 | 6000 | 8000 | 10000 | 12000 | 15000 |
|---|---|---|---|---|---|---|---|---|---|---|
| | L.F. Perimeter | 126 | 179 | 219 | 253 | 310 | 358 | 400 | 438 | 490 |
| Wood Clapboard | Wood Frame | 216.10 | 183.00 | 169.55 | 162.00 | 153.35 | 148.40 | 145.10 | 142.75 | 140.05 |
| Face Brick | Wood Frame | 238.15 | 196.10 | 178.55 | 168.60 | 157.10 | 150.50 | 146.00 | 142.75 | 139.20 |
| Stucco and Concrete Block | Rigid Steel | 237.80 | 200.45 | 185.05 | 176.35 | 166.35 | 160.65 | 156.80 | 154.00 | 150.90 |
| | Bearing Walls | 231.10 | 193.75 | 178.40 | 169.70 | 159.70 | 153.95 | 150.10 | 147.30 | 144.25 |
| Metal Sandwich Panel | Rigid Steel | 250.95 | 209.80 | 192.70 | 183.00 | 171.80 | 165.35 | 161.00 | 157.85 | 154.40 |
| Precast Concrete | Rigid Steel | 350.95 | 280.80 | 250.65 | 233.15 | 212.80 | 200.80 | 192.70 | 186.80 | 180.25 |
| Perimeter Adj., Add or Deduct | Per 100 L.F. | 56.50 | 28.25 | 18.85 | 14.10 | 9.45 | 7.05 | 5.65 | 4.65 | 3.85 |
| Story Hgt. Adj., Add or Deduct | Per 1 Ft. | 4.15 | 2.95 | 2.40 | 2.10 | 1.70 | 1.50 | 1.30 | 1.15 | 1.15 |
| ***For Basement**, add $42.05 per square foot of basement area* | | | | | | | | | | |

*The above costs were calculated using the basic specifications shown on the facing page. These costs should be adjusted where necessary for design alternatives and owner's requirements.*

## Common additives

| Description | Unit | $ Cost |
|---|---|---|
| Check Out Counter | | |
| Single belt | Ea. | 4225 |
| Double belt | Ea. | 5775 |
| Emergency Lighting, 25 watt, battery operated | | |
| Lead battery | Ea. | 360 |
| Nickel cadmium | Ea. | 585 |
| Refrigerators, Prefabricated, walk-in | | |
| 7'-6" high, 6' x 6' | S.F. | 141 |
| 10' x 10' | S.F. | 110 |
| 12' x 14' | S.F. | 96 |
| 12' x 20' | S.F. | 139 |
| Refrigerated Food Cases | | |
| Dairy, multi deck, 12' long | Ea. | 20,600 |
| Delicatessen case, single deck, 12' long | Ea. | 15,900 |
| Multi deck, 18 S.F. shelf display | Ea. | 9700 |
| Freezer, self-contained chest type, 30 C.F. | Ea. | 3000 |
| Glass door upright, 78 C.F. | Ea. | 10,700 |

| Description | Unit | $ Cost |
|---|---|---|
| Refrigerated Food Cases, cont. | | |
| Frozen food, chest type, 12' long | Ea. | 8025 |
| Glass door reach-in, 5 door | Ea. | 12,200 |
| Island case 12' long, single deck | Ea. | 10,100 |
| Multi deck | Ea. | 12,200 |
| Meat cases, 12' long, single deck | Ea. | 8675 |
| Multi deck | Ea. | 11,700 |
| Produce, 12' long single deck | Ea. | 7725 |
| Multi deck | Ea. | 9875 |
| Safe, Office type, 1 hour rating | | |
| 30" x 18" x 18" | Ea. | 1900 |
| 60" x 36" x 18", double door | Ea. | 8625 |
| Smoke Detectors | | |
| Ceiling type | Ea. | 300 |
| Duct type | Ea. | 615 |
| Sound System | | |
| Amplifier, 250 watts | Ea. | 2425 |
| Speaker, ceiling or wall | Ea. | 320 |
| Trumpet | Ea. | 580 |



**Important: See the Reference Section for Location Factors.**

**Model costs calculated for a 1 story building with 12′ story height and 4,000 square feet of floor area**

# Store, Convenience

| | | | | Unit | Unit Cost | Cost Per S.F. | % Of Sub-Total |
|---|---|---|---|---|---|---|---|
| **A. SUBSTRUCTURE** | | | | | | | |
| 1010 | Standard Foundations | Poured concrete; strip and spread footings; 4′ foundation wall | | S.F. Ground | 8.74 | 8.74 | |
| 1020 | Special Foundations | N/A | | — | — | — | |
| 1030 | Slab on Grade | 4″ reinforced concrete with vapor barrier and granular base | | S.F. Slab | 7.22 | 7.22 | 13.7% |
| 2010 | Basement Excavation | Site preparation for slab and trench for foundation wall and footing | | S.F. Ground | .66 | .66 | |
| 2020 | Basement Walls | N/A | | — | — | — | |
| **B. SHELL** | | | | | | | |
| | **B10 Superstructure** | | | | | | |
| 1010 | Floor Construction | N/A | | — | — | — | 11.1 % |
| 1020 | Roof Construction | Wood truss with plywood sheathing | | S.F. Roof | 13.03 | 13.03 | |
| | **B20 Exterior Enclosure** | | | | | | |
| 2010 | Exterior Walls | Wood siding on wood studs, insulated | *80% of wall* | S.F. Wall | 13.75 | 8.35 | |
| 2020 | Exterior Windows | Storefront | *20% of wall* | Each | 57 | 8.64 | 17.5% |
| 2030 | Exterior Doors | Double aluminum and glass, solid core wood | | Each | 5528 | 4.15 | |
| | **B30 Roofing** | | | | | | |
| 3010 | Roof Coverings | Asphalt shingles; rigid fiberglass insulation | | S.F. Roof | 4.62 | 4.62 | 3.8% |
| 3020 | Roof Openings | N/A | | — | — | — | |
| **C. INTERIORS** | | | | | | | |
| 1010 | Partitions | Gypsum board on wood studs | *60 S.F. Floor/L.F. Partition* | S.F. Partition | 16.56 | 2.76 | |
| 1020 | Interior Doors | Single leaf wood, hollow metal | *1300 S.F. Floor/Door* | Each | 2011 | 1.55 | |
| 1030 | Fittings | N/A | | — | — | — | |
| 2010 | Stair Construction | N/A | | — | — | — | 11.7% |
| 3010 | Wall Finishes | Paint | | S.F. Surface | 1.38 | .46 | |
| 3020 | Floor Finishes | Vinyl composition tile | | S.F. Floor | 2.58 | 2.58 | |
| 3030 | Ceiling Finishes | Mineral fiber tile on wood furring | | S.F. Ceiling | 6.80 | 6.80 | |
| **D. SERVICES** | | | | | | | |
| | **D10 Conveying** | | | | | | |
| 1010 | Elevators & Lifts | N/A | | — | — | — | 0.0 % |
| 1020 | Escalators & Moving Walks | N/A | | — | — | — | |
| | **D20 Plumbing** | | | | | | |
| 2010 | Plumbing Fixtures | Toilet and service fixtures, supply and drainage | *1 Fixture/1000 S.F. Floor* | Each | 6630 | 6.63 | |
| 2020 | Domestic Water Distribution | Gas fired water heater | | S.F. Floor | 2.27 | 2.27 | 7.3% |
| 2040 | Rain Water Drainage | N/A | | — | — | — | |
| | **D30 HVAC** | | | | | | |
| 3010 | Energy Supply | N/A | | — | — | — | |
| 3020 | Heat Generating Systems | Included in D3050 | | — | — | — | |
| 3030 | Cooling Generating Systems | N/A | | — | — | — | 7.4 % |
| 3050 | Terminal & Package Units | Single zone rooftop unit, gas heating, electric cooling | | S.F. Floor | 8.97 | 8.97 | |
| 3090 | Other HVAC Sys. & Equipment | N/A | | — | — | — | |
| | **D40 Fire Protection** | | | | | | |
| 4010 | Sprinklers | Sprinkler, ordinary hazard | | S.F. Floor | 6.60 | 6.60 | 8.5% |
| 4020 | Standpipes | Standpipe | | S.F. floor | 3.71 | 3.71 | |
| | **D50 Electrical** | | | | | | |
| 5010 | Electrical Service/Distribution | 200 ampere service, panel board and feeders | | S.F. Floor | 3.85 | 3.85 | |
| 5020 | Lighting & Branch Wiring | High efficiency fluorescent fixtures, receptacles, switches, A.C. and misc. power | | S.F. Floor | 16.12 | 16.12 | 18.9% |
| 5030 | Communications & Security | Addressable alarm systems and emergency lighting | | S.F. Floor | 2.56 | 2.56 | |
| 5090 | Other Electrical Systems | Emergency generator, 7.5 kW | | S.F. Floor | .39 | .39 | |
| **E. EQUIPMENT & FURNISHINGS** | | | | | | | |
| 1010 | Commercial Equipment | N/A | | — | — | — | |
| 1020 | Institutional Equipment | N/A | | — | — | — | 0.0 % |
| 1030 | Vehicular Equipment | N/A | | — | — | — | |
| 1090 | Other Equipment | N/A | | — | — | — | |
| **F. SPECIAL CONSTRUCTION** | | | | | | | |
| 1020 | Integrated Construction | N/A | | — | — | — | 0.0 % |
| 1040 | Special Facilities | N/A | | — | — | — | |
| **G. BUILDING SITEWORK** | **N/A** | | | | | | |
| | | | | | **Sub-Total** | 121.11 | **100%** |
| | CONTRACTOR FEES (General Requirements: 10%, Overhead: 5%, Profit: 10%) | | | | *25%* | 30.29 | |
| | ARCHITECT FEES | | | | *7%* | 10.60 | |
| | | | | | **Total Building Cost** | **162** | |

## Costs per square foot of floor area

| Exterior Wall | S.F. Area | 50000 | 65000 | 80000 | 95000 | 110000 | 125000 | 140000 | 155000 | 170000 |
|---|---|---|---|---|---|---|---|---|---|---|
| | L.F. Perimeter | 920 | 1065 | 1167 | 1303 | 1333 | 1433 | 1533 | 1633 | 1733 |
| Face Brick and Concrete Block | Reinforced Concrete | 168.35 | 165.00 | 162.30 | 160.75 | **158.60** | 157.60 | 156.75 | 156.10 | 155.55 |
| | Rigid Steel | 141.35 | 138.00 | 135.25 | 133.80 | 131.55 | 130.55 | 129.75 | 129.10 | 128.55 |
| Decorative Concrete Block | Reinforced Concrete | 162.75 | 160.00 | 157.85 | 156.60 | 154.90 | 154.10 | 153.45 | 152.90 | 152.45 |
| | Steel Joists | 135.70 | 133.05 | 130.80 | 129.60 | 127.85 | 127.05 | 126.40 | 125.85 | 125.40 |
| Precast Concrete | Reinforced Concrete | 168.10 | 164.75 | 162.05 | 160.60 | 158.35 | 157.35 | 156.60 | 155.95 | 155.45 |
| | Steel Joists | 141.05 | 137.75 | 135.05 | 133.55 | 131.40 | 130.40 | 129.60 | 128.95 | 128.40 |
| Perimeter Adj., Add or Deduct | Per 100 L.F. | 2.55 | 1.90 | 1.50 | 1.40 | 1.05 | 0.90 | 0.90 | 0.85 | 0.75 |
| Story Hgt. Adj., Add or Deduct | Per 1 Ft. | 1.30 | 1.15 | 1.00 | 1.00 | 0.80 | 0.75 | 0.75 | 0.75 | 0.75 |

***For Basement**, add $41.35 per square foot of basement area*

*The above costs were calculated using the basic specifications shown on the facing page. These costs should be adjusted where necessary for design alternatives and owner's requirements.*

## Common additives

| Description | Unit | $ Cost |
|---|---|---|
| Closed Circuit Surveillance, One station | | |
| Camera and monitor | Ea. | 1250 |
| For additional camera stations, add | Ea. | 475 |
| Directory Boards, Plastic, glass covered | | |
| 30" x 20" | Ea. | 705 |
| 36" x 48" | Ea. | 1475 |
| Aluminum, 24" x 18" | Ea. | 705 |
| 36" x 24" | Ea. | 985 |
| 48" x 32" | Ea. | 1975 |
| 48" x 60" | Ea. | 2650 |
| Emergency Lighting, 25 watt, battery operated | | |
| Lead battery | Ea. | 360 |
| Nickel cadmium | Ea. | 585 |
| Safe, Office type, 1 hour rating | | |
| 30" x 18" x 18" | Ea. | 1900 |
| 60" x 36" x 18", double door | Ea. | 8625 |
| Sound System | | |
| Amplifier, 250 watts | Ea. | 2425 |
| Speaker, ceiling or wall | Ea. | 320 |
| Trumpet | Ea. | 580 |



**Important: See the Reference Section for Location Factors.**

**Model costs calculated for a 1 story building with 14′ story height and 110,000 square feet of floor area**

# Store, Department, 1 Story

| | | | | Unit | Unit Cost | Cost Per S.F. | % Of Sub-Total |
|---|---|---|---|---|---|---|---|
| **A. SUBSTRUCTURE** | | | | | | | |
| 1010 | Standard Foundations | Poured concrete; strip and spread footings; 4′ foundation wall | | S.F. Ground | 2.64 | 2.64 | 8.5% |
| 1020 | Special Foundations | N/A | | — | — | — | |
| 1030 | Slab on Grade | 4″ reinforced concrete with vapor barrier and granular base | | S.F. Slab | 7.22 | 7.22 | |
| 2010 | Basement Excavation | Site preparation for slab and trench for foundation wall and footing | | S.F. Ground | .37 | .37 | |
| 2020 | Basement Walls | N/A | | — | — | — | |
| **B. SHELL** | | | | | | | |
| | **B10 Superstructure** | | | | | | |
| 1010 | Floor Construction | Cast-in-place concrete columns | | L.F. Column | 95 | 1.21 | 30.2% |
| 1020 | Roof Construction | Precast concrete beam and plank, concrete columns | | S.F. Roof | 34.91 | 34.91 | |
| | **B20 Exterior Enclosure** | | | | | | |
| 2010 | Exterior Walls | Face brick with concrete block backup | *90% of wall* | S.F. Wall | 42.11 | 6.43 | 7.0% |
| 2020 | Exterior Windows | Storefront | *10% of wall* | Each | 85 | 1.44 | |
| 2030 | Exterior Doors | Sliding electric operated entrance, hollow metal | | Each | 10,275 | .56 | |
| | **B30 Roofing** | | | | | | |
| 3010 | Roof Coverings | Built-up tar and gravel with flashing; perlite/EPS composite insulation | | S.F. Roof | 7.19 | 7.19 | 6.1% |
| 3020 | Roof Openings | Roof hatches | | S.F. Roof | .13 | .13 | |
| **C. INTERIORS** | | | | | | | |
| 1010 | Partitions | Gypsum board on metal studs | *60 S.F. Floor/L.F. Partition* | S.F. Partition | 13.44 | 2.24 | 18.5% |
| 1020 | Interior Doors | Single leaf hollow metal | *600 S.F. Floor/Door* | Each | 1159 | 1.94 | |
| 1030 | Fittings | N/A | | — | — | — | |
| 2010 | Stair Construction | N/A | | — | — | — | |
| 3010 | Wall Finishes | Paint | | S.F. Surface | .96 | .32 | |
| 3020 | Floor Finishes | 50% ceramic tile, 50% carpet tile | | S.F. Floor | 10.02 | 10.02 | |
| 3030 | Ceiling Finishes | Mineral fiber board on exposed grid system, suspended | | S.F. Ceiling | 7.68 | 7.68 | |
| **D. SERVICES** | | | | | | | |
| | **D10 Conveying** | | | | | | |
| 1010 | Elevators & Lifts | N/A | | — | — | — | 0.0 % |
| 1020 | Escalators & Moving Walks | N/A | | — | — | — | |
| | **D20 Plumbing** | | | | | | |
| 2010 | Plumbing Fixtures | Toilet and service fixtures, supply and drainage | *1 Fixture/4075 S.F. Floor* | Each | 10,595 | 2.60 | 3.3% |
| 2020 | Domestic Water Distribution | Gas fired water heater | | S.F. Floor | .36 | .36 | |
| 2040 | Rain Water Drainage | Roof drains | | S.F. Roof | .98 | .98 | |
| | **D30 HVAC** | | | | | | |
| 3010 | Energy Supply | N/A | | — | — | — | 8.8 % |
| 3020 | Heat Generating Systems | Included in D3050 | | — | — | — | |
| 3030 | Cooling Generating Systems | N/A | | — | — | — | |
| 3050 | Terminal & Package Units | Single zone unit gas heating, electric cooling | | S.F. Floor | 10.50 | 10.50 | |
| 3090 | Other HVAC Sys. & Equipment | N/A | | — | — | — | |
| | **D40 Fire Protection** | | | | | | |
| 4010 | Sprinklers | Sprinklers, light hazard | | S.F. Floor | 4.46 | 4.46 | 4.1% |
| 4020 | Standpipes | Standpipe | | S.F. Floor | .46 | .46 | |
| | **D50 Electrical** | | | | | | |
| 5010 | Electrical Service/Distribution | 1200 ampere service, panel board and feeders | | S.F. Floor | 1.11 | 1.11 | 13.4% |
| 5020 | Lighting & Branch Wiring | High efficiency fluorescent fixtures, receptacles, switches, A.C. and misc. power | | S.F. Floor | 13.34 | 13.34 | |
| 5030 | Communications & Security | Addressable alarm systems, internet wiring and emergency lighting | | S.F. Floor | 1.53 | 1.53 | |
| 5090 | Other Electrical Systems | Emergency generator, 7.5 kW | | S.F. Floor | .04 | .04 | |
| **E. EQUIPMENT & FURNISHINGS** | | | | | | | |
| 1010 | Commercial Equipment | N/A | | — | — | — | 0.0 % |
| 1020 | Institutional Equipment | N/A | | — | — | — | |
| 1030 | Vehicular Equipment | N/A | | — | — | — | |
| 1090 | Other Equipment | N/A | | — | — | — | |
| **F. SPECIAL CONSTRUCTION** | | | | | | | |
| 1020 | Integrated Construction | N/A | | — | — | — | 0.0 % |
| 1040 | Special Facilities | N/A | | — | — | — | |
| **G. BUILDING SITEWORK** | | **N/A** | | | | | |
| | | | | | **Sub-Total** | 119.68 | **100%** |
| | CONTRACTOR FEES (General Requirements: 10%, Overhead: 5%, Profit: 10%) | | | | *25%* | 29.94 | |
| | ARCHITECT FEES | | | | *6%* | 8.98 | |
| | | | | | **Total Building Cost** | **158.60** | |

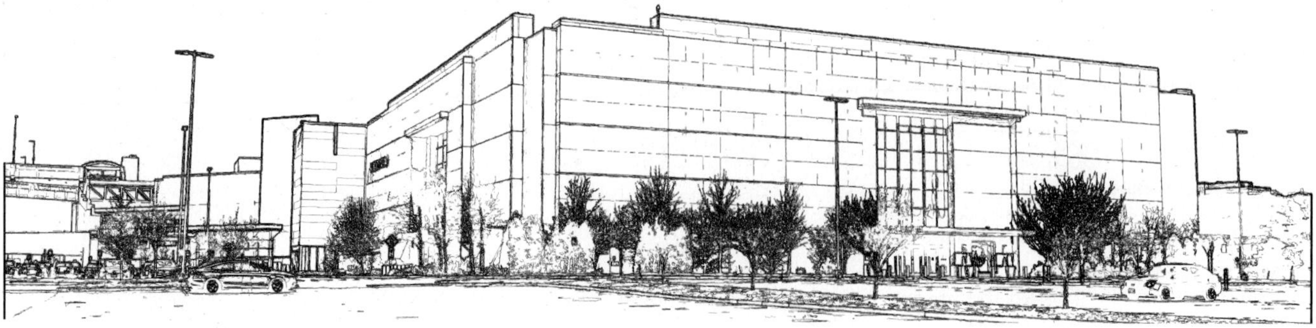

## Costs per square foot of floor area

| Exterior Wall | S.F. Area | 50000 | 65000 | 80000 | 95000 | 110000 | 125000 | 140000 | 155000 | 170000 |
|---|---|---|---|---|---|---|---|---|---|---|
| | L.F. Perimeter | 533 | 593 | 670 | 715 | 778 | 840 | 871 | 923 | 976 |
| Face Brick and Concrete Block | Rigid Steel | 200.00 | 192.20 | 188.05 | 184.00 | 181.65 | 179.85 | 177.75 | 176.40 | 175.30 |
| | Reinforced Concrete | 200.65 | 192.90 | 188.75 | 184.70 | 182.35 | 180.55 | 178.45 | 177.10 | 176.05 |
| Face Brick and Metal Studs | Rigid Steel | 194.05 | 187.10 | 183.35 | 179.80 | 177.75 | 176.10 | 174.25 | 173.10 | 172.15 |
| | Reinforced Concrete | 197.35 | 190.40 | 186.70 | 183.10 | 181.00 | 179.40 | 177.60 | 176.40 | 175.40 |
| Precast Concrete | Rigid Steel | 216.50 | 206.65 | 201.55 | 196.45 | 193.50 | 191.25 | 188.50 | 186.75 | 185.40 |
| | Reinforced Concrete | 216.60 | 206.80 | 201.65 | 196.55 | 193.60 | 191.35 | 188.60 | 186.90 | 185.55 |
| Perimeter Adj., Add or Deduct | Per 100 L.F. | 6.95 | 5.30 | 4.30 | 3.65 | 3.20 | 2.80 | 2.45 | 2.25 | 2.10 |
| Story Hgt. Adj., Add or Deduct | Per 1 Ft. | 2.10 | 1.80 | 1.65 | 1.50 | 1.40 | 1.35 | 1.20 | 1.20 | 1.20 |

***For Basement**, add $70.10 per square foot of basement area*

*The above costs were calculated using the basic specifications shown on the facing page. These costs should be adjusted where necessary for design alternatives and owner's requirements.*

## Common additives

| Description | Unit | $ Cost |
|---|---|---|
| Closed Circuit Surveillance, One station | | |
| Camera and monitor | Ea. | 1250 |
| For additional camera stations, add | Ea. | 475 |
| Directory Boards, Plastic, glass covered | | |
| 30″ x 20″ | Ea. | 705 |
| 36″ x 48″ | Ea. | 1475 |
| Aluminum, 24″ x 18″ | Ea. | 705 |
| 36″ x 24″ | Ea. | 985 |
| 48″ x 32″ | Ea. | 1975 |
| 48″ x 60″ | Ea. | 2650 |
| Elevators, Hydraulic passenger, 2 stops | | |
| 1500# capacity | Ea. | 86,500 |
| 2500# capacity | Ea. | 90,500 |
| 3500# capacity | Ea. | 96,000 |
| Additional stop, add | Ea. | 9875 |
| Emergency Lighting, 25 watt, battery operated | | |
| Lead battery | Ea. | 360 |
| Nickel cadmium | Ea. | 585 |

| Description | Unit | $ Cost |
|---|---|---|
| Escalators, Metal | | |
| 32″ wide, 10′ story height | Ea. | 183,500 |
| 20′ story height | Ea. | 228,000 |
| 48″ wide, 10′ story height | Ea. | 194,500 |
| 20′ story height | Ea. | 239,000 |
| Glass | | |
| 32″ wide, 10′ story height | Ea. | 174,500 |
| 20′ story height | Ea. | 216,500 |
| 48″ wide, 10′ story height | Ea. | 182,500 |
| 20′ story height | Ea. | 226,500 |
| Safe, Office type, 1 hour rating | | |
| 30″ x 18″ x 18″ | Ea. | 1900 |
| 60″ x 36″ x 18″, double door | Ea. | 8625 |
| Sound System | | |
| Amplifier, 250 watts | Ea. | 2425 |
| Speaker, ceiling or wall | Ea. | 320 |
| Trumpet | Ea. | 580 |



**Important: See the Reference Section for Location Factors.**

**Model costs calculated for a 3 story building with 16′ story height and 95,000 square feet of floor area**

# Store, Department, 3 Story

| | | | | Unit | Unit Cost | Cost Per S.F. | % Of Sub-Total |
|---|---|---|---|---|---|---|---|
| **A. SUBSTRUCTURE** | | | | | | | |
| 1010 | Standard Foundations | Poured concrete; strip and spread footings; 4′ foundation wall | | S.F. Ground | 7.89 | 2.63 | |
| 1020 | Special Foundations | N/A | | – | – | – | |
| 1030 | Slab on Grade | 4″ reinforced concrete with vapor barrier and granular base | | S.F. Slab | 7.22 | 2.41 | 3.7% |
| 2010 | Basement Excavation | Site preparation for slab and trench for foundation wall and footing | | S.F. Ground | .22 | .07 | |
| 2020 | Basement Walls | N/A | | – | – | – | |
| **B. SHELL** | | | | | | | |
| | **B10 Superstructure** | | | | | | |
| 1010 | Floor Construction | Concrete slab with metal deck and beams, steel columns | | S.F. Floor | 39.86 | 26.57 | 22.7% |
| 1020 | Roof Construction | Metal deck, open web steel joists, beams, columns | | S.F. Roof | 15 | 5 | |
| | **B20 Exterior Enclosure** | | | | | | |
| 2010 | Exterior Walls | Face brick with concrete block backup | *90% of wall* | S.F. Wall | 42.11 | 13.69 | |
| 2020 | Exterior Windows | Storefront | *10% of wall* | Each | 84 | 3.02 | 13.6% |
| 2030 | Exterior Doors | Revolving and sliding panel, mall-front | | Each | 15,189 | 2.24 | |
| | **B30 Roofing** | | | | | | |
| 3010 | Roof Coverings | Built-up tar and gravel with flashing; perlite/EPS composite insulation | | S.F. Roof | 7.98 | 2.66 | 2.0% |
| 3020 | Roof Openings | Roof hatches | | S.F. Roof | .48 | .16 | |
| **C. INTERIORS** | | | | | | | |
| 1010 | Partitions | Gypsum board on metal studs | *60 S.F. Floor/L.F. Partition* | S.F. Partition | 7.92 | 1.32 | |
| 1020 | Interior Doors | Single leaf hollow metal | *600 S.F. Floor/Door* | Each | 1159 | 1.94 | |
| 1030 | Fittings | N/A | | – | – | – | |
| 2010 | Stair Construction | Concrete filled metal pan | | Flight | 22,275 | 2.35 | 20.6% |
| 3010 | Wall Finishes | 70% paint, 20% vinyl wall covering, 10% ceramic tile | | S.F. Surface | 6.15 | 2.05 | |
| 3020 | Floor Finishes | 50% carpet tile, 40% marble tile, 10% terrazzo | | S.F. Floor | 11.90 | 11.90 | |
| 3030 | Ceiling Finishes | Mineral fiber tile on concealed zee bars | | S.F. Ceiling | 9 | 9 | |
| **D. SERVICES** | | | | | | | |
| | **D10 Conveying** | | | | | | |
| 1010 | Elevators & Lifts | One hydraulic passenger, one hydraulic freight | | Each | 381,900 | 4.02 | 8.7% |
| 1020 | Escalators & Moving Walks | Four escalators | | Each | 192,138 | 8.09 | |
| | **D20 Plumbing** | | | | | | |
| 2010 | Plumbing Fixtures | Toilet and service fixtures, supply and drainage | *1 Fixture/2570 S.F. Floor* | Each | 7196 | 2.80 | |
| 2020 | Domestic Water Distribution | Gas fired water heater | | S.F. Floor | .41 | .41 | 2.9% |
| 2040 | Rain Water Drainage | Roof drains | | S.F. Roof | 2.34 | .78 | |
| | **D30 HVAC** | | | | | | |
| 3010 | Energy Supply | N/A | | – | – | – | |
| 3020 | Heat Generating Systems | Included in D3050 | | – | – | – | |
| 3030 | Cooling Generating Systems | N/A | | – | – | – | 7.6 % |
| 3050 | Terminal & Package Units | Multizone rooftop unit, gas heating, electric cooling | | S.F. Floor | 10.50 | 10.50 | |
| 3090 | Other HVAC Sys. & Equipment | N/A | | – | – | – | |
| | **D40 Fire Protection** | | | | | | |
| 4010 | Sprinklers | Sprinklers, light hazard | | S.F. Floor | 3.71 | 3.71 | 4.7% |
| 4020 | Standpipes | Standpipe | | S.F. Floor | 2.85 | 2.85 | |
| | **D50 Electrical** | | | | | | |
| 5010 | Electrical Service/Distribution | 1200 ampere service, panel board and feeders | | S.F. Floor | 1.82 | 1.82 | |
| 5020 | Lighting & Branch Wiring | High efficiency fluorescent fixtures, receptacles, switches, A.C. and misc. power | | S.F. Floor | 13.55 | 13.55 | 13.5% |
| 5030 | Communications & Security | Addressable alarm systems, internet wiring and emergency lighting | | S.F. Floor | 3.07 | 3.07 | |
| 5090 | Other Electrical Systems | Emergency generator, 50 kW | | S.F. Floor | .28 | .28 | |
| **E. EQUIPMENT & FURNISHINGS** | | | | | | | |
| 1010 | Commercial Equipment | N/A | | – | – | – | |
| 1020 | Institutional Equipment | N/A | | – | – | – | 0.0 % |
| 1030 | Vehicular Equipment | N/A | | – | – | – | |
| 1090 | Other Equipment | N/A | | – | – | – | |
| **F. SPECIAL CONSTRUCTION** | | | | | | | |
| 1020 | Integrated Construction | N/A | | – | – | – | 0.0 % |
| 1040 | Special Facilities | N/A | | – | – | – | |
| **G. BUILDING SITEWORK** | **N/A** | | | | | | |
| | | | | | **Sub-Total** | 138.89 | **100%** |
| | CONTRACTOR FEES (General Requirements: 10%, Overhead: 5%, Profit: 10%) | | | | 25% | 34.69 | |
| | ARCHITECT FEES | | | | 6% | 10.42 | |
| | | | | | **Total Building Cost** | **184** | |

## Costs per square foot of floor area

| Exterior Wall | S.F. Area | 4000 | 6000 | 8000 | 10000 | 12000 | 15000 | 18000 | 20000 | 22000 |
|---|---|---|---|---|---|---|---|---|---|---|
| | L.F. Perimeter | 260 | 340 | 360 | 410 | 440 | 490 | 540 | 565 | 594 |
| Vinyl Clapboard | Wood Frame | 177.55 | 165.30 | 153.85 | 149.10 | 144.85 | 140.60 | 138.00 | 136.30 | 135.00 |
| Fiber Cement | Wood Frame | 179.75 | 167.65 | 156.20 | 151.50 | 147.20 | 143.05 | 140.40 | 138.80 | 137.45 |
| E.I.F.S. and Metal Studs | Steel Joists | 192.60 | 179.45 | 166.55 | 161.35 | 156.50 | 151.85 | 148.85 | 147.00 | 145.55 |
| Stone Veneer | Rigid Steel | 243.05 | 224.65 | 204.40 | 196.65 | 189.10 | 181.95 | 177.25 | 174.30 | 172.05 |
| Brick Veneer | Reinforced Concrete | 237.25 | 219.65 | 200.60 | 193.30 | 186.15 | 179.40 | 175.05 | 172.15 | 170.00 |
| Stucco | Reinforced Concrete | 256.40 | 235.95 | 212.85 | 204.10 | 195.50 | 187.35 | 182.00 | 178.60 | 176.00 |
| Perimeter Adj., Add or Deduct | Per 100 L.F. | 18.00 | 12.00 | 9.00 | 7.20 | 5.90 | 4.85 | 3.90 | 3.55 | 3.25 |
| Story Hgt. Adj., Add or Deduct | Per 1 Ft. | 1.95 | 1.75 | 1.35 | 1.35 | 1.05 | 1.05 | 0.85 | 0.85 | 0.85 |
| ***For Basement**, add $ 58.20 per square foot of basement area* | | | | | | | | | | |

*The above costs were calculated using the basic specifications shown on the facing page. These costs should be adjusted where necessary for design alternatives and owner's requirements.*

## Common additives

| Description | Unit | $ Cost |
|---|---|---|
| Emergency Lighting, 25 watt, battery operated | | |
| Lead battery | Ea. | 360 |
| Nickel cadmium | Ea. | 585 |
| Safe, Office type, 1 hour rating | | |
| 30" x 18" x 18" | Ea. | 1900 |
| 60" x 36" x 18", double door | Ea. | 8625 |
| Smoke Detectors | | |
| Ceiling type | Ea. | 300 |
| Duct type | Ea. | 615 |
| Sound System | | |
| Amplifier, 250 watts | Ea. | 2425 |
| Speaker, ceiling or wall | Ea. | 320 |
| Trumpet | Ea. | 580 |



**Important: See the Reference Section for Location Factors.**

## Model costs calculated for a 1 story building with 14′ story height and 8,000 square feet of floor area

# Store, Retail

| | | | | Unit | Unit Cost | Cost Per S.F. | % Of Sub-Total |
|---|---|---|---|---|---|---|---|
| **A. SUBSTRUCTURE** | | | | | | | |
| 1010 | Standard Foundations | Poured concrete; strip and spread footings; 4′ foundation wall | | S.F. Ground | 7.85 | 7.85 | |
| 1020 | Special Foundations | N/A | | — | — | — | |
| 1030 | Slab on Grade | 4″ reinforced concrete | | S.F. Slab | 7.22 | 7.22 | 13.6% |
| 2010 | Basement Excavation | Site preparation for slab and trench for foundation wall and footing | | S.F. Ground | .38 | .38 | |
| 2020 | Basement Walls | N/A | | — | — | — | |
| **B. SHELL** | | | | | | | |
| | **B10 Superstructure** | | | | | | |
| 1010 | Floor Construction | Wood columns, | | S.F. Floor | .98 | .98 | 12.6% |
| 1020 | Roof Construction | Wood roof truss 4:12 pitch | | S.F. Roof | 13.43 | 13.43 | |
| | **B20 Exterior Enclosure** | | | | | | |
| 2010 | Exterior Walls | Vinyl siding on wood studs, insulated | *85% of wall* | S.F. Wall | 14.85 | 7.95 | |
| 2020 | Exterior Windows | Storefront glazing | *15% of wall* | Each | 84 | 4.75 | 13.0% |
| 2030 | Exterior Doors | Aluminum and glass single doors, hollow metal doors | | Each | 4188 | 2.09 | |
| | **B30 Roofing** | | | | | | |
| 3010 | Roof Coverings | Asphalt roofing, strip shingles, gutters and downspouts | | S.F. Roof | 4.87 | 4.87 | 4.5% |
| 3020 | Roof Openings | Roof hatches | | S.F. Roof | .26 | .26 | |
| **C. INTERIORS** | | | | | | | |
| 1010 | Partitions | Sound deadening gypsum board on wood studs | *60 S.F. Floor/L.F. Partition* | S.F. Partition | 12.60 | 2.10 | |
| 1020 | Interior Doors | Hollow metal doors | *1150 S.F. Floor/Door* | Each | 1159 | 1.01 | |
| 1030 | Fittings | Toilet partitions | | S.F. Floor | .33 | .33 | |
| 2010 | Stair Construction | N/A | | — | — | — | 14.2% |
| 3010 | Wall Finishes | 90% Paint, 10% ceramic tile | | S.F. Surface | 3.33 | 1.11 | |
| 3020 | Floor Finishes | Vinyl composition tile | | S.F. Floor | 2.58 | 2.58 | |
| 3030 | Ceiling Finishes | Acoustic ceiling tiles on suspended channel grid | | S.F. Ceiling | 9 | 9 | |
| **D. SERVICES** | | | | | | | |
| | **D10 Conveying** | | | | | | |
| 1010 | Elevators & Lifts | N/A | | — | — | — | 0.0 % |
| 1020 | Escalators & Moving Walks | N/A | | — | — | — | |
| | **D20 Plumbing** | | | | | | |
| 2010 | Plumbing Fixtures | Restroom and service fixtures, supply and drainage | *1 Fixture/1350 S.F. Floor* | Each | 4852 | 3.64 | |
| 2020 | Domestic Water Distribution | Gas fired water heater | | S.F. Floor | 2.90 | 2.90 | 7.3% |
| 2040 | Rain Water Drainage | Roof Drains | | S.F. Roof | 1.80 | 1.80 | |
| | **D30 HVAC** | | | | | | |
| 3010 | Energy Supply | N/A | | — | — | — | |
| 3020 | Heat Generating Systems | Included in D3050 | | — | — | — | |
| 3030 | Cooling Generating Systems | N/A | | — | — | — | 9.2 % |
| 3050 | Terminal & Package Units | Single zone unit gas heating, electric cooling | | S.F. Floor | 10.50 | 10.50 | |
| 3090 | Other HVAC Sys. & Equipment | N/A | | — | — | — | |
| | **D40 Fire Protection** | | | | | | |
| 4010 | Sprinklers | Wet pipe spinkler system | | S.F. Floor | 6.66 | 6.66 | 7.5% |
| 4020 | Standpipes | Standpipe | | S.F. Floor | 1.85 | 1.85 | |
| | **D50 Electrical** | | | | | | |
| 5010 | Electrical Service/Distribution | 400 Ampere service, panelboards and feeders | | S.F. Floor | 3.52 | 3.52 | |
| 5020 | Lighting & Branch Wiring | Flourescent fixtures, receptacles, a.c. and misc. power | | S.F. Floor | 15.55 | 15.55 | 18.2% |
| 5030 | Communications & Security | Addressable alarm system, emergency lighting | | S.F. Floor | 1.63 | 1.63 | |
| 5090 | Other Electrical Systems | N/A | | — | — | — | |
| **E. EQUIPMENT & FURNISHINGS** | | | | | | | |
| 1010 | Commercial Equipment | N/A | | — | — | — | |
| 1020 | Institutional Equipment | N/A | | — | — | — | 0.0 % |
| 1030 | Vehicular Equipment | N/A | | — | — | — | |
| 1090 | Other Equipment | N/A | | — | — | — | |
| **F. SPECIAL CONSTRUCTION** | | | | | | | |
| 1020 | Integrated Construction | N/A | | — | — | — | 0.0 % |
| 1040 | Special Facilities | N/A | | — | — | — | |
| **G. BUILDING SITEWORK** | **N/A** | | | | | | |
| | | | | | **Sub-Total** | 113.96 | **100%** |
| | CONTRACTOR FEES (General Requirements: 10%, Overhead: 5%, Profit: 10%) | | | | *25%* | 28.49 | |
| | ARCHITECT FEES | | | | *8%* | 11.40 | |
| | | | | | **Total Building Cost** | **153.85** | |

## Costs per square foot of floor area

| Exterior Wall | S.F. Area | 12000 | 16000 | 20000 | 26000 | 32000 | 38000 | 44000 | 52000 | 60000 |
|---|---|---|---|---|---|---|---|---|---|---|
| | L.F. Perimeter | 450 | 510 | 570 | 650 | 716 | 780 | 840 | 920 | 1020 |
| Stucco | Reinforced Concrete | 239.65 | 219.65 | 207.65 | 195.50 | 186.80 | 180.65 | 175.90 | 171.30 | 168.85 |
| Curtain Wall | Rigid Steel | 196.05 | 181.55 | 172.90 | 164.15 | 158.05 | 153.75 | **150.40** | 147.20 | 145.40 |
| E.I.F.S. | Rigid Steel | 173.25 | 162.55 | 156.15 | 149.75 | 145.40 | 142.30 | 139.90 | 137.65 | 136.30 |
| Metal Panel | Rigid Steel | 172.10 | 161.20 | 154.70 | 148.20 | 143.70 | 140.60 | 138.20 | 135.90 | 134.50 |
| Tilt-up Concrete Panels | Reinforced Concrete | 193.70 | 181.10 | 173.50 | 165.95 | 160.70 | 157.00 | 154.15 | 151.40 | 149.90 |
| Brick Veneer | Reinforced Concrete | 251.60 | 229.75 | 216.75 | 203.45 | 193.90 | 187.20 | 182.00 | 176.95 | 174.25 |
| Perimeter Adj., Add or Deduct | Per 100 L.F. | 22.40 | 16.80 | 13.40 | 10.35 | 8.35 | 7.05 | 6.10 | 5.25 | 4.55 |
| Story Hgt. Adj., Add or Deduct | Per 1 Ft. | 2.00 | 1.65 | 1.55 | 1.35 | 1.15 | 1.10 | 1.05 | 1.00 | 0.90 |

***For Basement**, add $ 42.30 per square foot of basement area*

*The above costs were calculated using the basic specifications shown on the facing page. These costs should be adjusted where necessary for design alternatives and owner's requirements.*

## Common additives

| Description | Unit | $ Cost |
|---|---|---|
| Check Out Counter | | |
| Single belt | Ea. | 4225 |
| Double belt | Ea. | 5775 |
| Scanner, registers, guns & memory 2 lanes | Ea. | 20,600 |
| 10 lanes | Ea. | 195,500 |
| Power take away | Ea. | 6375 |
| Emergency Lighting, 25 watt, battery operated | | |
| Lead battery | Ea. | 360 |
| Nickel cadmium | Ea. | 585 |
| Refrigerators, Prefabricated, walk-in | | |
| 7'-6" High, 6' x 6' | S.F. | 141 |
| 10' x 10' | S.F. | 110 |
| 12' x 14' | S.F. | 96 |
| 12' x 20' | S.F. | 139 |
| Refrigerated Food Cases | | |
| Dairy, multi deck, 12' long | Ea. | 20,600 |
| Delicatessen case, single deck, 12' long | Ea. | 15,900 |
| Multi deck, 18 S.F. shelf display | Ea. | 9700 |
| Freezer, self-contained chest type, 30 C.F. | Ea. | 3000 |
| Glass door upright, 78 C.F. | Ea. | 10,700 |

| Description | Unit | $ Cost |
|---|---|---|
| Refrigerated Food Cases, cont. | | |
| Frozen food, chest type, 12' long | Ea. | 8025 |
| Glass door reach in, 5 door | Ea. | 12,200 |
| Island case 12' long, single deck | Ea. | 10,100 |
| Multi deck | Ea. | 12,200 |
| Meat case 12' long, single deck | Ea. | 8675 |
| Multi deck | Ea. | 11,700 |
| Produce, 12' long single deck | Ea. | 7725 |
| Multi deck | Ea. | 9875 |
| Safe, Office type, 1 hour rating | | |
| 30" x 18" x 18" | Ea. | 1900 |
| 60" x 36" x 18", double door | Ea. | 8625 |
| Smoke Detectors | | |
| Ceiling type | Ea. | 300 |
| Duct type | Ea. | 615 |
| Sound System | | |
| Amplifier, 250 watts | Ea. | 2425 |
| Speaker, ceiling or wall | Ea. | 320 |
| Trumpet | Ea. | 580 |

## Model costs calculated for a 1 story building with 18′ story height and 44,000 square feet of floor area

# Supermarket

| | | | Unit | Unit Cost | Cost Per S.F. | % Of Sub-Total |
|---|---|---|---|---|---|---|
| **A. SUBSTRUCTURE** | | | | | | |
| 1010 | Standard Foundations | Poured concrete; strip and spread footings; 4′ foundation wall | S.F. Ground | 3.53 | 3.53 | 9.8% |
| 1020 | Special Foundations | N/A | — | — | — | |
| 1030 | Slab on Grade | 4″ reinforced slab on grade | S.F. Slab | 7.22 | 7.22 | |
| 2010 | Basement Excavation | Site preparation for slab and trench for foundation wall and footing | S.F. Ground | .22 | .22 | |
| 2020 | Basement Walls | N/A | — | — | — | |
| **B. SHELL** | | | | | | |
| | **B10 Superstructure** | | | | | |
| 1010 | Floor Construction | N/A | — | — | — | 12.2 % |
| 1020 | Roof Construction | Metal deck on open web steel joints, columns | S.F. Roof | 13.70 | 13.70 | |
| | **B20 Exterior Enclosure** | | | | | |
| 2010 | Exterior Walls | N/A | — | — | — | 18.7 % |
| 2020 | Exterior Windows | Curtain wall glazing system, thermo-break frame *100% of wall* | Each | 57 | 19.38 | |
| 2030 | Exterior Doors | Glass sliding entrance doors, overhead doors, hollow metal doors | Each | 6811 | 1.70 | |
| | **B30 Roofing** | | | | | |
| 3010 | Roof Coverings | Single ply membrane, rigid insulation, gravel stop | S.F. Roof | 9.82 | 9.82 | 9.0% |
| 3020 | Roof Openings | Roof and smoke hatches | S.F. Roof | .28 | .28 | |
| **C. INTERIORS** | | | | | | |
| 1010 | Partitions | Concrete partitions, gypsum board on metal stud *50 S.F. Floor/L.F. Partition* | S.F. Partition | 10.92 | 2.62 | 14.7% |
| 1020 | Interior Doors | Hollow metal doors *2000 S.F. Floor/Door* | Each | 1159 | .58 | |
| 1030 | Fittings | Stainless steel toilet partitions | S.F. Floor | .18 | .18 | |
| 2010 | Stair Construction | N/A | — | — | — | |
| 3010 | Wall Finishes | Paint | S.F. Surface | 2.25 | 1.08 | |
| 3020 | Floor Finishes | Vinyl composition tile | S.F. Floor | 2.58 | 2.58 | |
| 3030 | Ceiling Finishes | Acoustic ceiling tiles on suspended channel grid | S.F. Ceiling | 9.48 | 9.48 | |
| **D. SERVICES** | | | | | | |
| | **D10 Conveying** | | | | | |
| 1010 | Elevators & Lifts | N/A | — | — | — | 0.0 % |
| 1020 | Escalators & Moving Walks | N/A | — | — | — | |
| | **D20 Plumbing** | | | | | |
| 2010 | Plumbing Fixtures | Restroom, food prep and service fixtures, supply and drainage *1 Fixture/1750 S.F. Floor* | Each | 3098 | 1.76 | 2.8% |
| 2020 | Domestic Water Distribution | Gas fired water heater | S.F. Floor | .23 | .23 | |
| 2040 | Rain Water Drainage | Roof drains | S.F. Roof | 1.19 | 1.19 | |
| | **D30 HVAC** | | | | | |
| 3010 | Energy Supply | N/A | — | — | — | 5.4 % |
| 3020 | Heat Generating Systems | Included in D3050 | — | — | — | |
| 3030 | Cooling Generating Systems | N/A | — | — | — | |
| 3050 | Terminal & Package Units | Single zone unit gas heating, electric cooling | S.F. Floor | 6.02 | 6.02 | |
| 3090 | Other HVAC Sys. & Equipment | N/A | — | — | — | |
| | **D40 Fire Protection** | | | | | |
| 4010 | Sprinklers | Wet pipe sprinkler system | S.F. Floor | 5.07 | 5.07 | 5.4% |
| 4020 | Standpipes | Standpipe | S.F. Floor | .98 | .98 | |
| | **D50 Electrical** | | | | | |
| 5010 | Electrical Service/Distribution | 1600 ampere service, panel board and feeders | S.F. Floor | 3.72 | 3.72 | 22.1% |
| 5020 | Lighting & Branch Wiring | Fluorescent fixtures, receptacles, switches, A.C. and misc. power | S.F. Floor | 18.30 | 18.30 | |
| 5030 | Communications & Security | Addressable alarm system, emergency lighting, internet & phone wiring | S.F. Floor | 2.76 | 2.76 | |
| 5090 | Other Electrical Systems | Emergency generator, 15kW | S.F. Floor | .04 | .04 | |
| **E. EQUIPMENT & FURNISHINGS** | | | | | | |
| 1010 | Commercial Equipment | N/A | — | — | — | 0.0 % |
| 1020 | Institutional Equipment | N/A | — | — | — | |
| 1030 | Vehicular Equipment | N/A | — | — | — | |
| 1090 | Other Equipment | N/A | — | — | — | |
| **F. SPECIAL CONSTRUCTION** | | | | | | |
| 1020 | Integrated Construction | N/A | — | — | — | 0.0 % |
| 1040 | Special Facilities | N/A | — | — | — | |
| **G. BUILDING SITEWORK** | **N/A** | | | | | |
| | | | | **Sub-Total** | 112.44 | **100%** |
| | CONTRACTOR FEES (General Requirements: 10%, Overhead: 5%, Profit: 10%) | | | 25% | 28.12 | |
| | ARCHITECT FEES | | | 7% | 9.84 | |
| | | | | **Total Building Cost** | **150.40** | |

## Costs per square foot of floor area

| Exterior Wall | S.F. Area | 10000 | 16000 | 20000 | 22000 | 24000 | 26000 | 28000 | 30000 | 32000 |
|---|---|---|---|---|---|---|---|---|---|---|
| | L.F. Perimeter | 420 | 510 | 600 | 640 | 660 | 684 | 706 | 740 | 737 |
| Face Brick and Concrete Block | Wood Truss | 387.75 | 362.75 | **357.80** | 355.50 | 351.75 | 348.80 | 346.15 | 344.80 | 341.05 |
| | Precast Concrete | 403.10 | 372.45 | 366.45 | 363.55 | 358.90 | 355.35 | 352.15 | 350.45 | 345.75 |
| Metal Sandwich Panel | Wood Truss | 372.65 | 351.30 | 347.00 | 345.05 | 341.80 | 339.35 | 337.10 | 336.00 | 332.80 |
| Precast Concrete | Precast Concrete | 419.70 | 385.85 | 379.30 | 376.15 | 370.95 | 367.05 | 363.50 | 361.65 | 356.50 |
| Concrete Block | Wood Frame | 359.20 | 341.05 | 337.40 | 335.70 | 333.00 | 330.90 | 329.00 | 328.05 | 325.40 |
| | Precast Concrete | 378.15 | 354.30 | 349.60 | 347.35 | 343.80 | 341.05 | 338.60 | 337.30 | 333.70 |
| Perimeter Adj., Add or Deduct | Per 100 L.F. | 22.40 | 14.00 | 11.25 | 10.20 | 9.30 | 8.65 | 8.05 | 7.55 | 7.00 |
| Story Hgt. Adj., Add or Deduct | Per 1 Ft. | 3.05 | 2.30 | 2.20 | 2.10 | 1.95 | 1.90 | 1.90 | 1.85 | 1.70 |

***For Basement**, add $62.75 per square foot of basement area*

*The above costs were calculated using the basic specifications shown on the facing page. These costs should be adjusted where necessary for design alternatives and owner's requirements.*

## Common additives

| Description | Unit | $ Cost |
|---|---|---|
| Bleachers, Telescoping, manual | | |
| To 15 tier | Seat | 162 - 299 |
| 16-20 tier | Seat | 261 - 550 |
| 21-30 tier | Seat | 390 - 605 |
| For power operation, add | Seat | 1000 - 1875 |
| Emergency Lighting, 25 watt, battery operated | | |
| Lead battery | Ea. | 360 |
| Nickel cadmium | Ea. | 585 |
| Lockers, Steel, single tier, 60" or 72" | Opng. | 285 - 520 |
| 2 tier, 60" or 72" total | Opng. | 216 - 265 |
| 5 tier, box lockers | Opng. | 465 - 153 |
| Locker bench, lam. maple top only | L.F. | 148 |
| Pedestal, steel pipe | Ea. | 87 |
| Pool Equipment | | |
| Diving stand, 3 meter | Ea. | 25,800 |
| 1 meter | Ea. | 19,200 |
| Diving board, 16' aluminum | Ea. | 6000 |
| Fiberglass | Ea. | 7000 |
| Lifeguard chair, fixed | Ea. | 5775 |
| Portable | Ea. | 4125 |
| Lights, underwater, 12 volt, 300 watt | Ea. | 1125 |

| Description | Unit | $ Cost |
|---|---|---|
| Sauna, Prefabricated, complete | | |
| 6' x 4' | Ea. | 7500 |
| 6' x 6' | Ea. | 18,400 |
| 6' x 9' | Ea. | 10,500 |
| 8' x 8' | Ea. | 13,500 |
| 8' x 10' | Ea. | 13,000 |
| 10' x 12' | Ea. | 19,700 |
| Sound System | | |
| Amplifier, 250 watts | Ea. | 2425 |
| Speaker, ceiling or wall | Ea. | 320 |
| Trumpet | Ea. | 580 |
| Steam Bath, Complete, to 140 C.F. | Ea. | 3325 |
| To 300 C.F. | Ea. | 7900 |
| To 800 C.F. | Ea. | 8375 |
| To 2500 C.F. | Ea. | 9850 |



**Important: See the Reference Section for Location Factors.**

# Swimming Pool, Enclosed

**Model costs calculated for a 1 story building with 24′ story height and 20,000 square feet of floor area**

| | | | | Unit | Unit Cost | Cost Per S.F. | % Of Sub-Total |
|---|---|---|---|---|---|---|---|
| **A. SUBSTRUCTURE** | | | | | | | |
| 1010 | Standard Foundations | Poured concrete; strip and spread footings; 4′ foundation wall | | S.F. Ground | 9.09 | 9.09 | 7.5% |
| 1020 | Special Foundations | N/A | | – | – | – | |
| 1030 | Slab on Grade | 4″ reinforced concrete with vapor barrier and granular base | | S.F. Slab | 7.22 | 7.22 | |
| 2010 | Basement Excavation | Site preparation for slab and trench for foundation wall and footing | | S.F. Ground | .38 | .76 | |
| 2020 | Basement Walls | N/A | | – | – | – | |
| **B. SHELL** | | | | | | | |
| **B10 Superstructure** | | | | | | | |
| 1010 | Floor Construction | N/A | | – | – | – | 11.1 % |
| 1020 | Roof Construction | Wood deck on laminated wood truss | | S.F. Roof | 29.42 | 29.42 | |
| **B20 Exterior Enclosure** | | | | | | | |
| 2010 | Exterior Walls | Face brick with concrete block backup | *80% of wall* | S.F. Wall | 42.10 | 24.25 | 14.1% |
| 2020 | Exterior Windows | Outward projecting steel | *20% of wall* | Each | 84 | 12.03 | |
| 2030 | Exterior Doors | Double aluminum and glass, hollow metal | | Each | 4670 | 1.18 | |
| **B30 Roofing** | | | | | | | |
| 3010 | Roof Coverings | Asphalt shingles with flashing; perlite/EPS composite insulation | | S.F. Roof | 5.53 | 5.53 | 2.1% |
| 3020 | Roof Openings | N/A | | – | – | – | |
| **C. INTERIORS** | | | | | | | |
| 1010 | Partitions | Concrete block | *100 S.F. Floor/L.F. Partition* | S.F. Partition | 10.90 | 1.09 | 12.4% |
| 1020 | Interior Doors | Single leaf hollow metal | *1000 S.F. Floor/Door* | Each | 1159 | 1.16 | |
| 1030 | Fittings | Toilet partitions | | S.F. Floor | .21 | .21 | |
| 2010 | Stair Construction | N/A | | – | – | – | |
| 3010 | Wall Finishes | Acrylic glazed coating | | S.F. Surface | 13.20 | 2.64 | |
| 3020 | Floor Finishes | 70% terrazzo, 30% ceramic tile | | S.F. Floor | 26.18 | 26.18 | |
| 3030 | Ceiling Finishes | Mineral fiber tile on concealed zee bars | *20% of area* | S.F. Ceiling | 7.68 | 1.54 | |
| **D. SERVICES** | | | | | | | |
| **D10 Conveying** | | | | | | | |
| 1010 | Elevators & Lifts | N/A | | – | – | – | 0.0 % |
| 1020 | Escalators & Moving Walks | N/A | | – | – | – | |
| **D20 Plumbing** | | | | | | | |
| 2010 | Plumbing Fixtures | Toilet and service fixtures, supply and drainage | *1 Fixture/210 S.F. Floor* | Each | 1751 | 8.34 | 4.6% |
| 2020 | Domestic Water Distribution | Gas fired water heater | | S.F. Floor | 3.93 | 3.93 | |
| 2040 | Rain Water Drainage | N/A | | – | – | – | |
| **D30 HVAC** | | | | | | | |
| 3010 | Energy Supply | Terminal unit heaters | *10% of area* | S.F. Floor | 1.30 | 1.30 | 14.2% |
| 3020 | Heat Generating Systems | N/A | | – | – | – | |
| 3030 | Cooling Generating Systems | N/A | | – | – | – | |
| 3050 | Terminal & Package Units | Single zone unit gas heating, electric cooling | | S.F. Floor | 36.30 | 36.30 | |
| 3090 | Other HVAC Sys. & Equipment | N/A | | – | – | – | |
| **D40 Fire Protection** | | | | | | | |
| 4010 | Sprinklers | Sprinklers, light hazard | | S.F. Floor | 2.54 | 2.54 | 1.3% |
| 4020 | Standpipes | Standpipe | | S.F. Floor | 1 | 1 | |
| **D50 Electrical** | | | | | | | |
| 5010 | Electrical Service/Distribution | 400 ampere service, panel board and feeders | | S.F. Floor | 1.46 | 1.46 | 13.2% |
| 5020 | Lighting & Branch Wiring | High efficiency fluorescent fixtures, receptacles, switches, A.C. and misc. power | | S.F. Floor | 32.06 | 32.06 | |
| 5030 | Communications & Security | Addressable alarm systems and emergency lighting | | S.F. Floor | 1.28 | 1.28 | |
| 5090 | Other Electrical Systems | Emergency generator, 15 kW | | S.F. Floor | .09 | .09 | |
| **E. EQUIPMENT & FURNISHINGS** | | | | | | | |
| 1010 | Commercial Equipment | N/A | | – | – | – | 19.5 % |
| 1020 | Institutional Equipment | N/A | | – | – | – | |
| 1030 | Vehicular Equipment | N/A | | – | – | – | |
| 1090 | Other Equipment | Swimming pool | | S.F. Floor | 52 | 51.58 | |
| **F. SPECIAL CONSTRUCTION** | | | | | | | |
| 1020 | Integrated Construction | N/A | | – | – | – | 0.0 % |
| 1040 | Special Facilities | N/A | | – | – | – | |
| **G. BUILDING SITEWORK** | **N/A** | | | | | | |
| | | | | | **Sub-Total** | 265.04 | **100%** |
| | CONTRACTOR FEES (General Requirements: 10%, Overhead: 5%, Profit: 10%) | | | | *25%* | 66.26 | |
| | ARCHITECT FEES | | | | *8%* | 26.50 | |
| | | | | | **Total Building Cost** | **357.80** | |

# Telephone Exchange

## Costs per square foot of floor area

| Exterior Wall | S.F. Area | 2000 | 3000 | 4000 | 5000 | 6000 | 7000 | 8000 | 9000 | 10000 |
|---|---|---|---|---|---|---|---|---|---|---|
| | L.F. Perimeter | 180 | 220 | 260 | 286 | 320 | 353 | 368 | 397 | 425 |
| Face Brick and Concrete Block | Rigid Steel | 292.55 | 259.70 | 243.30 | 229.85 | 222.55 | 217.15 | 210.20 | 206.80 | 203.95 |
| | Bearing Walls | 280.20 | 250.60 | 235.85 | 223.30 | 216.65 | 211.80 | 205.15 | 202.05 | 199.40 |
| Limestone and Concrete Block | Rigid Steel | 328.45 | 291.10 | 272.50 | 256.35 | 247.90 | 241.70 | 233.00 | 229.05 | 225.65 |
| | Bearing Walls | 327.85 | 287.25 | 267.00 | 249.90 | 240.75 | 234.05 | 225.05 | 220.75 | 217.20 |
| Decorative Concrete Block | Rigid Steel | 275.50 | 245.85 | 231.05 | 219.00 | 212.45 | 207.65 | 201.50 | 198.45 | 195.95 |
| | Bearing Walls | 269.05 | 239.35 | 224.50 | 212.50 | 205.95 | 201.10 | 195.00 | 191.95 | 189.40 |
| Perimeter Adj., Add or Deduct | Per 100 L.F. | 65.30 | 43.55 | 32.75 | 26.15 | 21.80 | 18.70 | 16.30 | 14.50 | 13.10 |
| Story Hgt. Adj., Add or Deduct | Per 1 Ft. | 7.60 | 6.15 | 5.50 | 4.80 | 4.45 | 4.20 | 3.85 | 3.70 | 3.60 |
| ***For Basement**, add $60.80 per square foot of basement area* | | | | | | | | | | |

*The above costs were calculated using the basic specifications shown on the facing page. These costs should be adjusted where necessary for design alternatives and owner's requirements.*

## Common additives

| Description | Unit | $ Cost |
|---|---|---|
| Emergency Lighting, 25 watt, battery operated | | |
| Lead battery | Ea. | 360 |
| Nickel cadmium | Ea. | 585 |
| Smoke Detectors | | |
| Ceiling type | Ea. | 300 |
| Duct type | Ea. | 615 |
| Emergency Generators, complete system, gas | | |
| 15 kw | Ea. | 16,500 |
| 85 kw | Ea. | 46,300 |
| 170 kw | Ea. | 106,000 |
| Diesel, 50 kw | Ea. | 25,700 |
| 150 kw | Ea. | 35,200 |
| 350 kw | Ea. | 98,000 |

**Model costs calculated for a 1 story building with 12′ story height and 5,000 square feet of floor area**

# Telephone Exchange

| | | | | Unit | Unit Cost | Cost Per S.F. | % Of Sub-Total |
|---|---|---|---|---|---|---|---|
| **A. SUBSTRUCTURE** | | | | | | | |
| 1010 | Standard Foundations | Poured concrete; strip and spread footings; 4′ foundation wall | | S.F. Ground | 9.85 | 9.85 | 10.8% |
| 1020 | Special Foundations | N/A | | — | — | — | |
| 1030 | Slab on Grade | 4″ reinforced concrete with vapor barrier and granular base | | S.F. Slab | 7.22 | 7.22 | |
| 2010 | Basement Excavation | Site preparation for slab and trench for foundation wall and footing | | S.F. Ground | .66 | .83 | |
| 2020 | Basement Walls | N/A | | — | — | — | |
| **B. SHELL** | | | | | | | |
| **B10 Superstructure** | | | | | | | |
| 1010 | Floor Construction | Steel column fireproofing | | S.F. Floor | 1.05 | 1.05 | 8.9% |
| 1020 | Roof Construction | Metal deck, open web steel joists, beams, columns | | S.F. Roof | 13.70 | 13.70 | |
| **B20 Exterior Enclosure** | | | | | | | |
| 2010 | Exterior Walls | Face brick with concrete block backup | *80% of wall* | S.F. Wall | 40.67 | 22.33 | 25.6% |
| 2020 | Exterior Windows | Outward projecting steel | *20% of wall* | Each | 2495 | 17.12 | |
| 2030 | Exterior Doors | Single aluminum glass with transom | | Each | 7175 | 2.89 | |
| **B30 Roofing** | | | | | | | |
| 3010 | Roof Coverings | Built-up tar and gravel with flashing; perlite/EPS composite insulation | | S.F. Roof | 9.47 | 9.47 | 5.7% |
| 3020 | Roof Openings | N/A | | — | — | — | |
| **C. INTERIORS** | | | | | | | |
| 1010 | Partitions | Double layer gypsum board on metal studs | *15 S.F. Floor/L.F. Partition* | S.F. Partition | 7.92 | 5.28 | 21.0% |
| 1020 | Interior Doors | Single leaf hollow metal | *150 S.F. Floor/Door* | Each | 1159 | 7.73 | |
| 1030 | Fittings | Toilet partitions | | S.F. Floor | 2.12 | 2.12 | |
| 2010 | Stair Construction | N/A | | — | — | — | |
| 3010 | Wall Finishes | Paint | | S.F. Surface | 2.54 | 3.38 | |
| 3020 | Floor Finishes | 90% carpet, 10% terrazzo | | S.F. Floor | 6.72 | 6.72 | |
| 3030 | Ceiling Finishes | Fiberglass board on exposed grid system, suspended | | S.F. Ceiling | 9.48 | 9.48 | |
| **D. SERVICES** | | | | | | | |
| **D10 Conveying** | | | | | | | |
| 1010 | Elevators & Lifts | N/A | | — | — | — | 0.0 % |
| 1020 | Escalators & Moving Walks | N/A | | — | — | — | |
| **D20 Plumbing** | | | | | | | |
| 2010 | Plumbing Fixtures | Kitchen, toilet and service fixtures, supply and drainage | *1 Fixture/715 S.F. Floor* | Each | 5741 | 8.03 | 8.1% |
| 2020 | Domestic Water Distribution | Gas fired water heater | | S.F. Floor | 2.83 | 2.83 | |
| 2040 | Rain Water Drainage | Roof drains | | S.F. Roof | 2.55 | 2.55 | |
| **D30 HVAC** | | | | | | | |
| 3010 | Energy Supply | N/A | | — | — | — | 6.1 % |
| 3020 | Heat Generating Systems | Included in D3050 | | — | — | — | |
| 3030 | Cooling Generating Systems | N/A | | — | — | — | |
| 3050 | Terminal & Package Units | Single zone unit, gas heating, electric cooling | | S.F. Floor | 10.06 | 10.06 | |
| 3090 | Other HVAC Sys. & Equipment | N/A | | — | — | — | |
| **D40 Fire Protection** | | | | | | | |
| 4010 | Sprinklers | Wet pipe sprinkler system | | S.F. Floor | 7.37 | 7.37 | 6.6% |
| 4020 | Standpipes | Standpipe | | S.F. Floor | 3.55 | 3.55 | |
| **D50 Electrical** | | | | | | | |
| 5010 | Electrical Service/Distribution | 200 ampere service, panel board and feeders | | S.F. Floor | 2.42 | 2.42 | 7.3% |
| 5020 | Lighting & Branch Wiring | High efficiency fluorescent fixtures, receptacles, switches, A.C. and misc. power | | S.F. Floor | 6.57 | 6.57 | |
| 5030 | Communications & Security | Addressable alarm systems and emergency lighting | | S.F. Floor | 2.93 | 2.93 | |
| 5090 | Other Electrical Systems | Emergency generator, 15 kW | | S.F. Floor | .17 | .17 | |
| **E. EQUIPMENT & FURNISHINGS** | | | | | | | |
| 1010 | Commercial Equipment | N/A | | — | — | — | 0.0 % |
| 1020 | Institutional Equipment | N/A | | — | — | — | |
| 1030 | Vehicular Equipment | N/A | | — | — | — | |
| 1090 | Other Equipment | N/A | | — | — | — | |
| **F. SPECIAL CONSTRUCTION** | | | | | | | |
| 1020 | Integrated Construction | N/A | | — | — | — | 0.0 % |
| 1040 | Special Facilities | N/A | | — | — | — | |
| **G. BUILDING SITEWORK** | | **N/A** | | | | | |
| | | | | | **Sub-Total** | 165.65 | **100%** |
| | CONTRACTOR FEES (General Requirements: 10%, Overhead: 5%, Profit: 10%) | | | | *25%* | 41.42 | |
| | ARCHITECT FEES | | | | *11%* | 22.78 | |
| | | | | | **Total Building Cost** | **229.85** | |

## Costs per square foot of floor area

| Exterior Wall | S.F. Area | 5000 | 6500 | 8000 | 9500 | 11000 | 14000 | 17500 | 21000 | 24000 |
|---|---|---|---|---|---|---|---|---|---|---|
| | L.F. Perimeter | 300 | 360 | 386 | 396 | 435 | 510 | 550 | 620 | 680 |
| Face Brick and Concrete Block | Steel Joists | 220.10 | 212.05 | 202.65 | 194.50 | **191.25** | 186.65 | 180.50 | 177.85 | 176.20 |
| | Wood Joists | 211.75 | 204.05 | 195.35 | 187.75 | 184.65 | 180.30 | 174.60 | 172.10 | 170.55 |
| Stone and Concrete Block | Steel Joists | 229.60 | 220.80 | 210.30 | 201.10 | 197.55 | 192.40 | 185.45 | 182.50 | 180.70 |
| | Wood Joists | 221.25 | 212.85 | 203.00 | 194.30 | 190.95 | 186.10 | 179.55 | 176.80 | 175.05 |
| Brick Veneer | Wood Frame | 206.85 | 199.50 | 191.40 | 184.30 | 181.40 | 177.30 | 171.95 | 169.65 | 168.25 |
| E.I.F.S. | Wood Frame | 203.60 | 196.50 | 188.75 | 182.05 | 179.25 | 175.35 | 170.30 | 168.10 | 166.70 |
| Perimeter Adj., Add or Deduct | Per 100 L.F. | 20.45 | 15.70 | 12.80 | 10.75 | 9.30 | 7.25 | 5.85 | 4.90 | 4.25 |
| Story Hgt. Adj., Add or Deduct | Per 1 Ft. | 3.60 | 3.30 | 2.90 | 2.45 | 2.35 | 2.15 | 1.85 | 1.75 | 1.70 |
| ***For Basement**, add $ 50.05 per square foot of basement area* | | | | | | | | | | |

*The above costs were calculated using the basic specifications shown on the facing page. These costs should be adjusted where necessary for design alternatives and owner's requirements.*

## Common additives

| Description | Unit | $ Cost |
|---|---|---|
| Directory Boards, Plastic, glass covered | | |
| 30" x 20" | Ea. | 705 |
| 36" x 48" | Ea. | 1475 |
| Aluminum, 24" x 18" | Ea. | 705 |
| 36" x 24" | Ea. | 985 |
| 48" x 32" | Ea. | 1975 |
| 48" x 60" | Ea. | 2650 |
| Emergency Lighting, 25 watt, battery operated | | |
| Lead battery | Ea. | 360 |
| Nickel cadmium | Ea. | 585 |
| Flagpoles, Complete | | |
| Aluminum, 20' high | Ea. | 2050 |
| 40' high | Ea. | 5275 |
| 70' high | Ea. | 14,300 |
| Fiberglass, 23' high | Ea. | 3025 |
| 39'-5" high | Ea. | 3725 |
| 59' high | Ea. | 12,300 |
| Safe, Office type, 1 hour rating | | |
| 30" x 18" x 18" | Ea. | 1900 |
| 60" x 36" x 18", double door | Ea. | 8625 |

| Description | Unit | $ Cost |
|---|---|---|
| Smoke Detectors | | |
| Ceiling type | Ea. | 300 |
| Duct type | Ea. | 615 |
| Vault Front, Door & frame | | |
| 1 Hour test, 32" x 78" | Opng. | 7450 |
| 2 Hour test, 32" door | Opng. | 7450 |
| 40" door | Opng. | 7925 |
| 4 Hour test, 32" door | Opng. | 7425 |
| 40" door | Opng. | 7625 |
| Time lock movement; two movement | Ea. | 2050 |



**Important: See the Reference Section for Location Factors.**

## Model costs calculated for a 1 story building with 12′ story height and 11,000 square feet of floor area

# Town Hall, 1 Story

| | | | | Unit | Unit Cost | Cost Per S.F. | % Of Sub-Total |
|---|---|---|---|---|---|---|---|
| **A. SUBSTRUCTURE** | | | | | | | |
| 1010 | Standard Foundations | Poured concrete; strip and spread footings; 4′ foundation wall | | S.F. Ground | 6.75 | 6.75 | |
| 1020 | Special Foundations | N/A | | — | — | — | |
| 1030 | Slab on Grade | 4″ reinforced concrete with vapor barrier and granular base | | S.F. Slab | 7.22 | 7.22 | 10.3% |
| 2010 | Basement Excavation | Site preparation for slab and trench for foundation wall and footing | | S.F. Ground | .38 | .42 | |
| 2020 | Basement Walls | N/A | | — | — | — | |
| **B. SHELL** | | | | | | | |
| | **B10 Superstructure** | | | | | | |
| 1010 | Floor Construction | Steel column fireproofing | | S.F. Floor | .36 | .36 | 8.4% |
| 1020 | Roof Construction | Metal deck, open web steel joists, beams, interior columns | | S.F. Roof | 11.41 | 11.41 | |
| | **B20 Exterior Enclosure** | | | | | | |
| 2010 | Exterior Walls | Face brick with concrete block backup | *70% of wall* | S.F. Wall | 40.64 | 13.50 | |
| 2020 | Exterior Windows | Metal outward projecting | *30% of wall* | Each | 839 | 5.19 | 14.6% |
| 2030 | Exterior Doors | Metal and glass with transom | | Each | 4950 | 1.80 | |
| | **B30 Roofing** | | | | | | |
| 3010 | Roof Coverings | Built-up tar and gravel with flashing; perlite/EPS composite insulation | | S.F. Roof | 9.05 | 9.05 | 6.4% |
| 3020 | Roof Openings | N/A | | — | — | — | |
| **C. INTERIORS** | | | | | | | |
| 1010 | Partitions | Gypsum board on metal studs | *20 S.F. Floor/L.F. Partition* | S.F. Partition | 11.90 | 5.95 | |
| 1020 | Interior Doors | Wood solid core | *200 S.F. Floor/Door* | Each | 1231 | 6.16 | |
| 1030 | Fittings | Toilet partitions | | S.F. Floor | .58 | .58 | |
| 2010 | Stair Construction | N/A | | — | — | — | 23.3% |
| 3010 | Wall Finishes | 90% paint, 10% ceramic tile | | S.F. Surface | 1.77 | 1.77 | |
| 3020 | Floor Finishes | 70% carpet tile, 15% terrazzo, 15% vinyl composition tile | | S.F. Floor | 9.30 | 9.30 | |
| 3030 | Ceiling Finishes | Mineral fiber tile on concealed zee bars | | S.F. Ceiling | 9 | 9 | |
| **D. SERVICES** | | | | | | | |
| | **D10 Conveying** | | | | | | |
| 1010 | Elevators & Lifts | N/A | | — | — | — | 0.0 % |
| 1020 | Escalators & Moving Walks | N/A | | — | — | — | |
| | **D20 Plumbing** | | | | | | |
| 2010 | Plumbing Fixtures | Kitchen, toilet and service fixtures, supply and drainage | *1 Fixture/500 S.F. Floor* | Each | 3685 | 7.37 | |
| 2020 | Domestic Water Distribution | Gas fired water heater | | S.F. Floor | 2.31 | 2.31 | 9.0% |
| 2040 | Rain Water Drainage | Roof drains | | S.F. Roof | 2.99 | 2.99 | |
| | **D30 HVAC** | | | | | | |
| 3010 | Energy Supply | N/A | | — | — | — | |
| 3020 | Heat Generating Systems | Included in D3050 | | — | — | — | |
| 3030 | Cooling Generating Systems | N/A | | — | — | — | 8.1 % |
| 3050 | Terminal & Package Units | Multizone unit, gas heating, electric cooling | | S.F. Floor | 11.40 | 11.40 | |
| 3090 | Other HVAC Sys. & Equipment | N/A | | — | — | — | |
| | **D40 Fire Protection** | | | | | | |
| 4010 | Sprinklers | Wet pipe sprinkler system | | S.F. Floor | 5.07 | 5.07 | 4.6% |
| 4020 | Standpipes | Standpipe, wet, Class III | | S.F. Floor | 1.34 | 1.34 | |
| | **D50 Electrical** | | | | | | |
| 5010 | Electrical Service/Distribution | 400 ampere service, panel board and feeders | | S.F. Floor | 2.55 | 2.55 | |
| 5020 | Lighting & Branch Wiring | High efficiency fluorescent fixtures, receptacles, switches, A.C. and misc. power | | S.F. Floor | 15.01 | 15.01 | 15.3% |
| 5030 | Communications & Security | Addressable alarm systems, internet wiring, and emergency lighting | | S.F. Floor | 3.71 | 3.71 | |
| 5090 | Other Electrical Systems | Emergency generator, 15 kW | | S.F. Floor | .15 | .15 | |
| **E. EQUIPMENT & FURNISHINGS** | | | | | | | |
| 1010 | Commercial Equipment | N/A | | — | — | — | |
| 1020 | Institutional Equipment | N/A | | — | — | — | 0.0 % |
| 1030 | Vehicular Equipment | N/A | | — | — | — | |
| 1090 | Other Equipment | N/A | | — | — | — | |
| **F. SPECIAL CONSTRUCTION** | | | | | | | |
| 1020 | Integrated Construction | N/A | | — | — | — | 0.0 % |
| 1040 | Special Facilities | N/A | | — | — | — | |
| **G. BUILDING SITEWORK** | **N/A** | | | | | | |
| | | | | | **Sub-Total** | 140.36 | **100%** |
| | CONTRACTOR FEES (General Requirements: 10%, Overhead: 5%, Profit: 10%) | | | | *25%* | 35.10 | |
| | ARCHITECT FEES | | | | *9%* | 15.79 | |
| | | | | | **Total Building Cost** | **191.25** | |

## Costs per square foot of floor area

| Exterior Wall | S.F. Area | 8000 | 10000 | 12000 | 15000 | 18000 | 24000 | 28000 | 35000 | 40000 |
|---|---|---|---|---|---|---|---|---|---|---|
| | L.F. Perimeter | 206 | 233 | 260 | 300 | 320 | 360 | 393 | 451 | 493 |
| Face Brick and Concrete Block | Rigid Steel | 282.25 | 268.55 | 259.35 | 250.05 | 241.15 | 230.05 | 225.85 | 220.80 | 218.35 |
| | Reinforced Concrete | 288.30 | 274.55 | 265.35 | 256.10 | 247.20 | 236.05 | 231.85 | 226.85 | 224.35 |
| Stone and Concrete Block | Rigid Steel | 294.55 | 279.60 | 269.65 | 259.60 | **249.60** | 237.20 | 232.55 | 226.95 | 224.15 |
| | Reinforced Concrete | 300.55 | 285.60 | 275.65 | 265.60 | 255.65 | 243.20 | 238.55 | 233.00 | 230.20 |
| Limestone and Concrete Block | Rigid Steel | 310.40 | 293.75 | 282.60 | 271.30 | 259.80 | 245.35 | 240.00 | 233.55 | 230.40 |
| | Reinforced Concrete | 319.10 | 302.40 | 291.30 | 280.05 | 268.50 | 254.05 | 248.70 | 242.25 | 239.10 |
| Perimeter Adj., Add or Deduct | Per 100 L.F. | 30.80 | 24.60 | 20.55 | 16.40 | 13.70 | 10.25 | 8.80 | 7.05 | 6.15 |
| Story Hgt. Adj., Add or Deduct | Per 1 Ft. | 4.60 | 4.10 | 3.85 | 3.60 | 3.20 | 2.65 | 2.55 | 2.35 | 2.20 |
| ***For Basement**, add $48.75 per square foot of basement area* | | | | | | | | | | |

*The above costs were calculated using the basic specifications shown on the facing page. These costs should be adjusted where necessary for design alternatives and owner's requirements.*

## Common additives

| Description | Unit | $ Cost |
|---|---|---|
| Directory Boards, Plastic, glass covered | | |
| 30" x 20" | Ea. | 705 |
| 36" x 48" | Ea. | 1475 |
| Aluminum, 24" x 18" | Ea. | 705 |
| 36" x 24" | Ea. | 985 |
| 48" x 32" | Ea. | 1975 |
| 48" x 60" | Ea. | 2650 |
| Elevators, Hydraulic passenger, 2 stops | | |
| 1500# capacity | Ea. | 86,500 |
| 2500# capacity | Ea. | 90,500 |
| 3500# capacity | Ea. | 96,000 |
| Additional stop, add | Ea. | 9875 |
| Emergency Lighting, 25 watt, battery operated | | |
| Lead battery | Ea. | 360 |
| Nickel cadmium | Ea. | 585 |

| Description | Unit | $ Cost |
|---|---|---|
| Flagpoles, Complete | | |
| Aluminum, 20' high | Ea. | 2050 |
| 40' high | Ea. | 5275 |
| 70' high | Ea. | 14,300 |
| Fiberglass, 23' high | Ea. | 3025 |
| 39'-5" high | Ea. | 3725 |
| 59' high | Ea. | 12,300 |
| Safe, Office type, 1 hour rating | | |
| 30" x 18" x 18" | Ea. | 1900 |
| 60" x 36" x 18", double door | Ea. | 8625 |
| Smoke Detectors | | |
| Ceiling type | Ea. | 300 |
| Duct type | Ea. | 615 |
| Vault Front, Door & frame | | |
| 1 Hour test, 32" x 78" | Opng. | 7450 |
| 2 Hour test, 32" door | Opng. | 7450 |
| 40" door | Opng. | 7925 |
| 4 Hour test, 32" door | Opng. | 7425 |
| 40" door | Opng. | 7625 |
| Time lock movement; two movement | Ea. | 2050 |



**Important: See the Reference Section for Location Factors.**

## Model costs calculated for a 3 story building with 12′ story height and 18,000 square feet of floor area

# Town Hall, 2-3 Story

| | | | | Unit | Unit Cost | Cost Per S.F. | % Of Sub-Total |
|---|---|---|---|---|---|---|---|
| **A. SUBSTRUCTURE** | | | | | | | |
| 1010 | Standard Foundations | Poured concrete; strip and spread footings; 4′ foundation wall | | S.F. Ground | 12.09 | 4.03 | 3.7% |
| 1020 | Special Foundations | N/A | | — | — | — | |
| 1030 | Slab on Grade | 4″ reinforced concrete with vapor barrier and granular base | | S.F. Slab | 7.22 | 2.41 | |
| 2010 | Basement Excavation | Site preparation for slab and trench for foundation wall and footing | | S.F. Ground | .66 | .33 | |
| 2020 | Basement Walls | N/A | | — | — | — | |
| **B. SHELL** | | | | | | | |
| **B10 Superstructure** | | | | | | | |
| 1010 | Floor Construction | Open web steel joists, slab form, concrete, wide flange steel columns | | S.F. Floor | 37.10 | 24.73 | 15.8% |
| 1020 | Roof Construction | Metal deck, open web steel joists, beams, interior columns | | S.F. Roof | 12.45 | 4.15 | |
| **B20 Exterior Enclosure** | | | | | | | |
| 2010 | Exterior Walls | Stone with concrete block backup | *70% of wall* | S.F. Wall | 55 | 24.42 | 17.9% |
| 2020 | Exterior Windows | Metal outward projecting | *10% of wall* | Each | 839 | 7.01 | |
| 2030 | Exterior Doors | Metal and glass with transoms | | Each | 4670 | 1.28 | |
| **B30 Roofing** | | | | | | | |
| 3010 | Roof Coverings | Built-up tar and gravel with flashing; perlite/EPS composite insulation | | S.F. Roof | 9.90 | 3.30 | 1.8% |
| 3020 | Roof Openings | N/A | | — | — | — | |
| **C. INTERIORS** | | | | | | | |
| 1010 | Partitions | Gypsum board on metal studs | *20 S.F. Floor/L.F. Partition* | S.F. Partition | 13.30 | 6.65 | 22.8% |
| 1020 | Interior Doors | Wood solid core | *200 S.F. Floor/Door* | Each | 1231 | 6.16 | |
| 1030 | Fittings | Toilet partitions | | S.F. Floor | .36 | .36 | |
| 2010 | Stair Construction | Concrete filled metal pan | | Flight | 19,225 | 8.54 | |
| 3010 | Wall Finishes | 90% paint, 10% ceramic tile | | S.F. Surface | 1.77 | 1.77 | |
| 3020 | Floor Finishes | 70% carpet tile, 15% terrazzo, 15% vinyl composition tile | | S.F. Floor | 9.30 | 9.30 | |
| 3030 | Ceiling Finishes | Mineral fiber tile on concealed zee bars | | S.F. Ceiling | 9 | 9 | |
| **D. SERVICES** | | | | | | | |
| **D10 Conveying** | | | | | | | |
| 1010 | Elevators & Lifts | Two hydraulic elevators | | Each | 147,240 | 16.36 | 8.9% |
| 1020 | Escalators & Moving Walks | N/A | | — | — | — | |
| **D20 Plumbing** | | | | | | | |
| 2010 | Plumbing Fixtures | Toilet and service fixtures, supply and drainage | *1 Fixture/1385 S.F. Floor* | Each | 9820 | 7.09 | 4.8% |
| 2020 | Domestic Water Distribution | Gas fired water heater | | S.F. Floor | .76 | .76 | |
| 2040 | Rain Water Drainage | Roof drains | | S.F. Roof | 3.09 | 1.03 | |
| **D30 HVAC** | | | | | | | |
| 3010 | Energy Supply | N/A | | — | — | — | 6.2 % |
| 3020 | Heat Generating Systems | Included in D3050 | | — | — | — | |
| 3030 | Cooling Generating Systems | N/A | | — | — | — | |
| 3050 | Terminal & Package Units | Multizone unit, gas heating, electric cooling | | S.F. Floor | 11.40 | 11.40 | |
| 3090 | Other HVAC Sys. & Equipment | N/A | | — | — | — | |
| **D40 Fire Protection** | | | | | | | |
| 4010 | Sprinklers | Sprinklers, light hazard | | S.F. Floor | 4.82 | 4.82 | 5.8% |
| 4020 | Standpipes | Standpipe, wet, Class III | | S.F. Floor | 5.88 | 5.88 | |
| **D50 Electrical** | | | | | | | |
| 5010 | Electrical Service/Distribution | 400 ampere service, panel board and feeders | | S.F. Floor | 2.20 | 2.20 | 12.2% |
| 5020 | Lighting & Branch Wiring | High efficiency fluorescent fixtures, receptacles, switches, A.C. and misc. power | | S.F. Floor | 15.88 | 15.88 | |
| 5030 | Communications & Security | Addressable alarm systems, internet wiring, and emergency lighting | | S.F. Floor | 4.17 | 4.17 | |
| 5090 | Other Electrical Systems | Emergency generator, 15 kW | | S.F. Floor | .18 | .18 | |
| **E. EQUIPMENT & FURNISHINGS** | | | | | | | |
| 1010 | Commercial Equipment | N/A | | — | — | — | 0.0 % |
| 1020 | Institutional Equipment | N/A | | — | — | — | |
| 1030 | Vehicular Equipment | N/A | | — | — | — | |
| 1090 | Other Equipment | N/A | | — | — | — | |
| **F. SPECIAL CONSTRUCTION** | | | | | | | |
| 1020 | Integrated Construction | N/A | | — | — | — | 0.0 % |
| 1040 | Special Facilities | N/A | | — | — | — | |
| **G. BUILDING SITEWORK** | | **N/A** | | | | | |
| | | | | | **Sub-Total** | 183.21 | **100%** |
| | CONTRACTOR FEES (General Requirements: 10%, Overhead: 5%, Profit: 10%) | | | | *25%* | 45.78 | |
| | ARCHITECT FEES | | | | *9%* | 20.61 | |
| | | | | | **Total Building Cost** | **249.60** | |

# Veterinary Hospital

## Costs per square foot of floor area

| Exterior Wall | S.F. Area | 3500 | 5000 | 7500 | 9000 | 11000 | 12500 | 15000 | 20000 | 25000 |
|---|---|---|---|---|---|---|---|---|---|---|
| | L.F. Perimeter | 240 | 290 | 350 | 390 | 430 | 460 | 510 | 580 | 650 |
| E.I.F.S. | Wood Truss | 235.50 | 223.30 | 212.00 | 208.45 | 204.50 | 202.45 | 199.90 | 195.85 | 193.35 |
| | Steel Joists | 247.80 | 234.95 | 223.05 | 219.35 | 215.25 | 213.00 | 210.30 | 206.00 | 203.35 |
| Wood Clapboard | Wood Truss | 242.95 | 230.55 | 219.10 | 215.55 | 211.65 | 209.50 | 206.90 | 202.75 | 200.25 |
| Brick Veneer | Wood Truss | 256.90 | 242.40 | 228.65 | 224.35 | 219.55 | 217.00 | 213.80 | 208.65 | 205.55 |
| Face Brick and Concrete Block | Wood Truss | 259.15 | 243.65 | 228.80 | 224.30 | 219.10 | 216.25 | 212.80 | 207.25 | 203.85 |
| Tilt-up Concrete Panels | Steel Joists | 241.25 | 229.50 | 218.70 | 215.35 | 211.70 | 209.70 | 207.25 | 203.45 | 201.10 |
| Perimeter Adj., Add or Deduct | Per 100 L.F. | 16.45 | 11.45 | 7.65 | 6.35 | 5.25 | 4.60 | 3.85 | 2.85 | 2.35 |
| Story Hgt. Adj., Add or Deduct | Per 1 Ft. | 2.00 | 1.65 | 1.35 | 1.30 | 1.10 | 1.05 | 0.90 | 0.80 | 0.75 |
| ***For Basement**, add $ 52.65 per square foot of basement area* | | | | | | | | | | |

*The above costs were calculated using the basic specifications shown on the facing page. These costs should be adjusted where necessary for design alternatives and owner's requirements.*

## Common additives

| Description | Unit | $ Cost |
|---|---|---|
| Closed circuit surveillance, one station | | |
| Camera and monitor | Ea. | 1250 |
| For additional camera stations, add | Ea. | 475 |
| Directory boards, plastic, glass covered | | |
| 30" x 20" | Ea. | 705 |
| 36" x 48" | Ea. | 1475 |
| Aluminum, 24" x 18" | Ea. | 705 |
| 36" x 24" | Ea. | 985 |
| 48" x 32" | Ea. | 1975 |
| 48" x 60" | Ea. | 2650 |
| Electronic, wall mounted | S.F. | 1175 |
| Free standing | S.F. | 1625 |
| Kennel fencing | | |
| Kennel fencing, 1-1/2" mesh, 6' long, 3'-6" wide, 6'-2" high | Ea. | 915 |
| 12' long | Ea. | 1175 |
| Top covers, 1-1/2" mesh, 6' long | Ea. | 259 |
| 12' long | Ea. | 370 |

| Description | Unit | $ Cost |
|---|---|---|
| Kennel doors | | |
| 2 way, swinging type, 13" x 19" opening | Opng. | 231 |
| 17" x 29" opening | Opng. | 273 |
| 9" x 9" opening, electronic with accessories | Opng. | 310 |



**Important: See the Reference Section for Location Factors.**

## Model costs calculated for a 1 story building with 12′ story height and 7,500 square feet of floor area

# Veterinary Hospital

| | | | | Unit | Unit Cost | Cost Per S.F. | % Of Sub-Total |
|---|---|---|---|---|---|---|---|
| **A. SUBSTRUCTURE** | | | | | | | |
| 1010 | Standard Foundations | Poured concrete; strip and spread footings; 4′ foundation wall | | S.F. Ground | 7.97 | 7.97 | |
| 1020 | Special Foundations | N/A | | — | — | — | |
| 1030 | Slab on Grade | 4″ and 5″ reinforced concrete with vapor barrier and granular base | | S.F. Slab | 7.22 | 7.22 | 10.2% |
| 2010 | Basement Excavation | Site preparation for slab and trench for foundation wall and footing | | S.F. Ground | .66 | 1.24 | |
| 2020 | Basement Walls | N/A | | — | — | — | |
| **B. SHELL** | | | | | | | |
| | **B10 Superstructure** | | | | | | |
| 1010 | Floor Construction | 6 x 6 wood columns | | S.F. Floor | .36 | .36 | 8.6% |
| 1020 | Roof Construction | Wood roof truss with plywood sheathing | | S.F. Roof | 13.43 | 13.43 | |
| | **B20 Exterior Enclosure** | | | | | | |
| 2010 | Exterior Walls | Cedar bevel siding on wood studs, insulated | *85% of wall* | S.F. Wall | 18.80 | 8.95 | |
| 2020 | Exterior Windows | Wood double hung and awning | *15% of wall* | Each | 1599 | 5.20 | 11.0% |
| 2030 | Exterior Doors | Aluminum and glass | | Each | 4467 | 3.57 | |
| | **B30 Roofing** | | | | | | |
| 3010 | Roof Coverings | Ashphalt shingles with flashing (pitched); al. gutters and downspouts | | S.F. Roof | 7.99 | 7.99 | 5.0% |
| 3020 | Roof Openings | N/A | | — | — | — | |
| **C. INTERIORS** | | | | | | | |
| 1010 | Partitions | Gypsum board on wood studs | *8 S.F. Floor/L.F. Partition* | S.F. Partition | 7 | 8.75 | |
| 1020 | Interior Doors | Solid core wood | *180 S.F. Floor/Door* | Each | 965 | 2.68 | |
| 1030 | Fittings | Lockers | | S.F. Floor | .70 | .70 | |
| 2010 | Stair Construction | N/A | | — | — | — | 17.6% |
| 3010 | Wall Finishes | Paint on drywall | | S.F. Surface | 1.15 | 2.87 | |
| 3020 | Floor Finishes | 90% vinyl composition tile, 5% ceramic tile, 5% sealed concrete | | S.F. Floor | 3.58 | 3.58 | |
| 3030 | Ceiling Finishes | 90% acoustic tile, 10% gypsum board | | S.F. Ceiling | 9.75 | 9.75 | |
| **D. SERVICES** | | | | | | | |
| | **D10 Conveying** | | | | | | |
| 1010 | Elevators & Lifts | N/A | | — | — | — | 0.0 % |
| 1020 | Escalators & Moving Walks | N/A | | — | — | — | |
| | **D20 Plumbing** | | | | | | |
| 2010 | Plumbing Fixtures | Toilet and service fixtures, supply and drainage | *1 Fixture/1075 S.F. Floor* | Each | 2492 | 4.45 | |
| 2020 | Domestic Water Distribution | Electric water heater | | S.F. Floor | 1.69 | 1.69 | 3.8% |
| 2040 | Rain Water Drainage | N/A | | — | — | — | |
| | **D30 HVAC** | | | | | | |
| 3010 | Energy Supply | N/A | | — | — | — | |
| 3020 | Heat Generating Systems | N/A | | — | — | — | |
| 3030 | Cooling Generating Systems | N/A | | — | — | — | 4.6 % |
| 3050 | Terminal & Package Units | Split system with air cooled condensing units | | S.F. Floor | 7.34 | 7.34 | |
| 3090 | Other HVAC Sys. & Equipment | N/A | | — | — | — | |
| | **D40 Fire Protection** | | | | | | |
| 4010 | Sprinklers | Wet pipe sprinkler system | | S.F. Floor | 5.07 | 5.07 | 3.2% |
| 4020 | Standpipes | N/A | | — | — | — | |
| | **D50 Electrical** | | | | | | |
| 5010 | Electrical Service/Distribution | 800 ampere service, panel board and feeders | | S.F. Floor | 9.82 | 9.82 | |
| 5020 | Lighting & Branch Wiring | High efficiency fluorescent fixtures, receptacles, switches, A.C. and misc. power | | S.F. Floor | 18 | 18 | 20.7% |
| 5030 | Communications & Security | Addressable alarm systems, internet wiring, and emergency lighting | | S.F. Floor | 5.49 | 5.49 | |
| 5090 | Other Electrical Systems | Emergency generator, 100 kW | | S.F. Floor | .06 | .06 | |
| **E. EQUIPMENT & FURNISHINGS** | | | | | | | |
| 1010 | Commercial Equipment | N/A | | — | — | — | |
| 1020 | Institutional Equipment | Eye wash station | | S.F. Floor | 22.25 | 22.25 | 13.8 % |
| 1030 | Vehicular Equipment | N/A | | — | — | — | |
| 1090 | Other Equipment | Countertop, plastic laminate | | S.F. Floor | | | |
| **F. SPECIAL CONSTRUCTION & DEMOLITION** | | | | | | | |
| 1020 | Integrated Construction | N/A | | — | — | — | 0.0 % |
| 1040 | Special Facilities | N/A | | — | — | — | |
| **G. BUILDING SITEWORK** | **N/A** | | | | | | |
| | | | | | **Sub-Total** | 160.82 | **100%** |
| | CONTRACTOR FEES (General Requirements: 10%, Overhead: 5%, Profit: 10%) | | | | *25%* | 40.19 | |
| | ARCHITECT FEES | | | | *9%* | 18.09 | |
| | | | | | **Total Building Cost** | **219.10** | |

## Costs per square foot of floor area

| Exterior Wall | S.F. Area | 10000 | 15000 | 20000 | 25000 | 30000 | 35000 | 40000 | 50000 | 60000 |
|---|---|---|---|---|---|---|---|---|---|---|
| | L.F. Perimeter | 410 | 500 | 600 | 640 | 700 | 766 | 833 | 966 | 1000 |
| Metal Panel | Rigid Steel | 164.05 | 151.20 | 145.40 | 138.85 | 135.35 | 133.05 | 131.35 | 129.00 | 125.30 |
| Pre-Engineered Metal Building | Rigid Steel | 157.80 | 144.30 | 138.25 | 131.35 | 127.75 | 125.30 | 123.50 | 121.05 | 117.15 |
| E.I.F.S. | Rigid Steel | 162.10 | 149.65 | 143.95 | 137.60 | 134.25 | 132.00 | 130.40 | 128.05 | 124.50 |
| Brick Veneer | Reinforced Concrete | 215.50 | 194.25 | 184.85 | 173.55 | **167.60** | 163.70 | 160.90 | 156.90 | 150.35 |
| Precast Concrete | Reinforced Concrete | 248.25 | 220.55 | 208.30 | 193.25 | 185.40 | 180.30 | 176.60 | 171.30 | 162.50 |
| Tilt-up Concrete Panels | Reinforced Concrete | 192.50 | 175.60 | 168.05 | 159.20 | 154.50 | 151.45 | 149.20 | 146.05 | 141.00 |
| Perimeter Adj., Add or Deduct | Per 100 L.F. | 12.55 | 8.35 | 6.25 | 4.95 | 4.10 | 3.60 | 3.15 | 2.50 | 2.10 |
| Story Hgt. Adj., Add or Deduct | Per 1 Ft. | 1.50 | 1.25 | 1.10 | 0.95 | 0.90 | 0.85 | 0.80 | 0.70 | 0.65 |
| ***For Basement**, add $46.85 per square foot of basement area* | | | | | | | | | | |

*The above costs were calculated using the basic specifications shown on the facing page. These costs should be adjusted where necessary for design alternatives and owner's requirements.*

## Common additives

| Description | Unit | $ Cost |
|---|---|---|
| Dock Leveler, 10 ton cap. | | |
| 6′ x 8′ | Ea. | 8025 |
| 7′ x 8′ | Ea. | 9675 |
| Emergency Lighting, 25 watt, battery operated | | |
| Lead battery | Ea. | 360 |
| Nickel cadmium | Ea. | 585 |
| Fence, Chain link, 6′ high | | |
| 9 ga. wire | L.F. | 33.50 |
| 6 ga. wire | L.F. | 41 |
| Gate | Ea. | 485 |
| Flagpoles, Complete | | |
| Aluminum, 20′ high | Ea. | 2050 |
| 40′ high | Ea. | 5275 |
| 70′ high | Ea. | 14,300 |
| Fiberglass, 23′ high | Ea. | 3025 |
| 39′-5″ high | Ea. | 3725 |
| 59′ high | Ea. | 12,300 |
| Paving, Bituminous | | |
| Wearing course plus base course | S.Y. | 9.85 |
| Sidewalks, Concrete 4″ thick | S.F. | 6.40 |

| Description | Unit | $ Cost |
|---|---|---|
| Sound System | | |
| Amplifier, 250 watts | Ea. | 2425 |
| Speaker, ceiling or wall | Ea. | 320 |
| Trumpet | Ea. | 580 |
| Yard Lighting, 20′ aluminum pole with 400 watt high pressure sodium fixture. | Ea. | 3200 |



**Important: See the Reference Section for Location Factors.**

# Model costs calculated for a 1 story building with 24′ story height and 30,000 square feet of floor area

# Warehouse

| | | | | Unit | Unit Cost | Cost Per S.F. | % Of Sub-Total |
|---|---|---|---|---|---|---|---|
| **A. SUBSTRUCTURE** | | | | | | | |
| 1010 | Standard Foundations | Poured concrete; strip and spread footings; 4′ foundation wall | | S.F. Ground | 4.53 | 4.53 | |
| 1020 | Special Foundations | N/A | | — | — | — | |
| 1030 | Slab on Grade | 5″ reinforced concrete | | S.F. Slab | 7.95 | 7.95 | 10.1% |
| 2010 | Basement Excavation | Site preparation for slab and trench for foundation wall and footing | | S.F. Ground | .22 | .22 | |
| 2020 | Basement Walls | N/A | | — | — | — | |
| **B. SHELL** | | | | | | | |
| **B10 Superstructure** | | | | | | | |
| 1010 | Floor Construction | Cast in place concrete columns, beams, and slab, fireproofed | | S.F. Floor | 87 | 8.69 | 23.1% |
| 1020 | Roof Construction | Precast double T with 2″ topping | | S.F. Roof | 20.23 | 20.23 | |
| **B20 Exterior Enclosure** | | | | | | | |
| 2010 | Exterior Walls | Face brick with concrete block back up | *98% of wall* | S.F. Wall | 48.36 | 26.54 | |
| 2020 | Exterior Windows | Aluminum horizontal sliding | *2% of wall* | Each | 1552 | 1.16 | 23.6% |
| 2030 | Exterior Doors | Aluminum and glass entry doors, hollow steel doors, overhead doors | | Each | 5123 | 1.89 | |
| **B30 Roofing** | | | | | | | |
| 3010 | Roof Coverings | Single ply membrane, stone ballast, rigid insulation | | S.F. Roof | 10.05 | 10.05 | 8.6% |
| 3020 | Roof Openings | Roof and smoke hatches | | S.F. Roof | .73 | .73 | |
| **C. INTERIORS** | | | | | | | |
| 1010 | Partitions | Concrete block partitions, gypsum board on metal stud | *100 S.F. Floor/L.F. Partition* | S.F. Partition | 20.50 | 1.64 | |
| 1020 | Interior Doors | Single leaf wood hollow core doors, metal doors | *2500 S.F. Floor/Door* | Each | 1159 | .46 | |
| 1030 | Fittings | N/A | | — | — | — | |
| 2010 | Stair Construction | Steel grate type with rails | | Flight | 15,150 | 1.01 | 6.0% |
| 3010 | Wall Finishes | Paint | | S.F. Surface | 5.25 | .84 | |
| 3020 | Floor Finishes | 90% hardener, 10% vinyl composition tile | | S.F. Floor | 2.65 | 2.65 | |
| 3030 | Ceiling Finishes | Acoustic ceiling tiles on suspended channel grid | | S.F. Ceiling | 9 | .91 | |
| **D. SERVICES** | | | | | | | |
| **D10 Conveying** | | | | | | | |
| 1010 | Elevators & Lifts | N/A | | — | — | — | 0.0 % |
| 1020 | Escalators & Moving Walks | N/A | | — | — | — | |
| **D20 Plumbing** | | | | | | | |
| 2010 | Plumbing Fixtures | Restroom and service fixtures, supply and drainage | *1 Fixture/2500 S.F. Floor* | Each | 2050 | .82 | |
| 2020 | Domestic Water Distribution | Gas fired water heater | | S.F. Floor | .28 | .28 | 1.5% |
| 2040 | Rain Water Drainage | Roof drains | | S.F. Roof | .76 | .76 | |
| **D30 HVAC** | | | | | | | |
| 3010 | Energy Supply | N/A | | — | — | — | |
| 3020 | Heat Generating Systems | Ventilation with heat system | | Each | 166,100 | 5.98 | |
| 3030 | Cooling Generating Systems | N/A | | — | — | — | 5.6 % |
| 3050 | Terminal & Package Units | Single zone unit gas heating, electric cooling | | S.F. Floor | 1.03 | 1.03 | |
| 3090 | Other HVAC Sys. & Equipment | N/A | | — | — | — | |
| **D40 Fire Protection** | | | | | | | |
| 4010 | Sprinklers | Wet pipe sprinkler system, ordinary hazard | | S.F. Floor | 6.25 | 6.25 | 5.6% |
| 4020 | Standpipes | Standpipe | | S.F. Floor | .80 | .80 | |
| **D50 Electrical** | | | | | | | |
| 5010 | Electrical Service/Distribution | 200 ampere service, panel board and feeders | | S.F. Floor | .69 | .69 | |
| 5020 | Lighting & Branch Wiring | Fluorescent fixtures, receptacles, switches, A.C. and misc. power | | S.F. Floor | 6.53 | 6.53 | 8.4% |
| 5030 | Communications & Security | Addressable alarm system | | S.F. Floor | 3.26 | 3.26 | |
| 5090 | Other Electrical Systems | N/A | | — | — | — | |
| **E. EQUIPMENT & FURNISHINGS** | | | | | | | |
| 1010 | Commercial Equipment | N/A | | — | — | — | |
| 1020 | Institutional Equipment | N/A | | — | — | — | 1.7 % |
| 1030 | Vehicular Equipment | Dock boards and levelers | | S.F. Floor | 2.13 | 2.13 | |
| 1090 | Other Equipment | N/A | | — | — | — | |
| **F. SPECIAL CONSTRUCTION** | | | | | | | |
| 1020 | Integrated Construction | Shipping and receiving air curtain | | S.F. Floor | 7.28 | 7.28 | 5.8% |
| 1040 | Special Facilities | N/A | | — | — | — | |
| **G. BUILDING SITEWORK** | | **N/A** | | | | | |
| | | | | | **Sub-Total** | 125.31 | **100%** |
| | CONTRACTOR FEES (General Requirements: 10%, Overhead: 5%, Profit: 10%) | | | | *25%* | 31.33 | |
| | ARCHITECT FEES | | | | *7%* | 10.96 | |
| | | | | | **Total Building Cost** | **167.60** | |

## Costs per square foot of floor area

| Exterior Wall | S.F. Area | 2000 | 3000 | 5000 | 8000 | 12000 | 20000 | 30000 | 50000 | 100000 |
|---|---|---|---|---|---|---|---|---|---|---|
| | L.F. Perimeter | 180 | 220 | 300 | 420 | 580 | 900 | 1300 | 2100 | 4100 |
| Concrete Block | Rigid Steel | 141.55 | 125.35 | 112.35 | 105.00 | 100.95 | 97.70 | 96.05 | 94.75 | 93.75 |
| | Reinforced Concrete | 154.35 | 139.30 | 127.30 | 120.55 | 116.75 | 113.75 | 112.25 | 111.05 | 110.15 |
| Metal Sandwich Panel | Rigid Steel | 139.40 | 123.55 | 110.90 | 103.75 | 99.75 | 96.65 | 95.05 | 93.75 | 92.75 |
| Tilt-up Concrete Panels | Reinforced Concrete | 144.45 | 128.45 | 115.65 | 108.50 | 104.50 | 101.30 | 99.65 | 98.45 | 97.45 |
| Precast Concrete | Rigid Steel | 171.40 | 149.60 | 132.20 | 122.35 | 116.90 | 112.60 | 110.40 | 108.65 | 107.30 |
| | Reinforced Concrete | 211.95 | 188.55 | 169.85 | 159.30 | 153.45 | 148.75 | 146.45 | 144.55 | 143.10 |
| Perimeter Adj., Add or Deduct | Per 100 L.F. | 27.85 | 18.50 | 11.10 | 6.95 | 4.65 | 2.80 | 1.90 | 1.10 | 0.60 |
| Story Hgt. Adj., Add or Deduct | Per 1 Ft. | 1.85 | 1.45 | 1.15 | 1.05 | 0.95 | 0.90 | 0.85 | 0.90 | 0.80 |
| **Basement**—Not Applicable | | | | | | | | | | |

*The above costs were calculated using the basic specifications shown on the facing page. These costs should be adjusted where necessary for design alternatives and owner's requirements.*

## Common additives

| Description | Unit | $ Cost |
|---|---|---|
| Dock Leveler, 10 ton cap. | | |
| 6′ x 8′ | Ea. | 8025 |
| 7′ x 8′ | Ea. | 9675 |
| Emergency Lighting, 25 watt, battery operated | | |
| Lead battery | Ea. | 360 |
| Nickel cadmium | Ea. | 585 |
| Fence, Chain link, 6′ high | | |
| 9 ga. wire | L.F. | 33.50 |
| 6 ga. wire | L.F. | 41 |
| Gate | Ea. | 485 |
| Flagpoles, Complete | | |
| Aluminum, 20′ high | Ea. | 2050 |
| 40′ high | Ea. | 5275 |
| 70′ high | Ea. | 14,300 |
| Fiberglass, 23′ high | Ea. | 3025 |
| 39′-5″ high | Ea. | 3725 |
| 59′ high | Ea. | 12,300 |
| Paving, Bituminous | | |
| Wearing course plus base course | S.Y. | 9.85 |
| Sidewalks, Concrete 4″ thick | S.F. | 6.40 |

| Description | Unit | $ Cost |
|---|---|---|
| Sound System | | |
| Amplifier, 250 watts | Ea. | 2425 |
| Speaker, ceiling or wall | Ea. | 320 |
| Trumpet | Ea. | 580 |
| Yard Lighting, 20′ aluminum pole with 400 watt high pressure sodium fixture | Ea. | 3200 |

## Model costs calculated for a 1 story building with 12′ story height and 20,000 square feet of floor area

# Warehouse Self Storage

| | | | | Unit | Unit Cost | Cost Per S.F. | % Of Sub-Total |
|---|---|---|---|---|---|---|---|
| **A. SUBSTRUCTURE** | | | | | | | |
| 1010 | Standard Foundations | Poured concrete; strip and spread footings; 4′ foundation wall | | S.F. Ground | 8.17 | 8.17 | |
| 1020 | Special Foundations | N/A | | — | — | — | |
| 1030 | Slab on Grade | 4″ reinforced concrete with vapor barrier and granular base | | S.F. Slab | 9.01 | 9.01 | 24.6% |
| 2010 | Basement Excavation | Site preparation for slab and trench for foundation wall and footing | | S.F. Ground | .38 | .76 | |
| 2020 | Basement Walls | N/A | | — | — | — | |
| **B. SHELL** | | | | | | | |
| | **B10 Superstructure** | | | | | | |
| 1010 | Floor Construction | Steel column fireproofing | | S.F. Floor | .92 | .92 | 13.9% |
| 1020 | Roof Construction | Metal deck, open web steel joists, beams, columns | | S.F. Roof | 9.21 | 9.21 | |
| | **B20 Exterior Enclosure** | | | | | | |
| 2010 | Exterior Walls | Concrete block | *53% of wall* | S.F. Wall | 28.30 | 8.10 | |
| 2020 | Exterior Windows | Aluminum projecting | *1% of wall* | Each | 1465 | .15 | 24.5% |
| 2030 | Exterior Doors | Steel overhead, hollow metal | *46% of wall* | Each | 2390 | 9.68 | |
| | **B30 Roofing** | | | | | | |
| 3010 | Roof Coverings | Metal panel roof; perlite/EPS composite insulation | | S.F. Roof | 9.40 | 9.40 | 12.9% |
| 3020 | Roof Openings | N/A | | — | — | — | |
| **C. INTERIORS** | | | | | | | |
| 1010 | Partitions | Metal panels on metal studs | *11 S.F. Floor/L.F. Partition* | S.F. Partition | 3.98 | 4.34 | |
| 1020 | Interior Doors | Single leaf hollow metal | *20,000 S.F. Floor/Door* | Each | 500 | .05 | |
| 1030 | Fittings | N/A | | — | — | — | |
| 2010 | Stair Construction | N/A | | — | — | — | 6.0% |
| 3010 | Wall Finishes | N/A | | — | — | — | |
| 3020 | Floor Finishes | N/A | | — | — | — | |
| 3030 | Ceiling Finishes | N/A | | — | — | — | |
| **D. SERVICES** | | | | | | | |
| | **D10 Conveying** | | | | | | |
| 1010 | Elevators & Lifts | N/A | | — | — | — | 0.0 % |
| 1020 | Escalators & Moving Walks | N/A | | — | — | — | |
| | **D20 Plumbing** | | | | | | |
| 2010 | Plumbing Fixtures | Toilet and service fixtures, supply and drainage | *1 Fixture/10,000 S.F. Floor* | Each | 3400 | .34 | |
| 2020 | Domestic Water Distribution | Gas fired water heater | | S.F. Floor | .45 | .45 | 2.2% |
| 2040 | Rain Water Drainage | Roof drain | | S.F. Roof | .84 | .84 | |
| | **D30 HVAC** | | | | | | |
| 3010 | Energy Supply | N/A | | — | — | — | |
| 3020 | Heat Generating Systems | N/A | | — | — | — | |
| 3030 | Cooling Generating Systems | N/A | | — | — | — | 1.8 % |
| 3050 | Terminal & Package Units | Single zone rooftop unit | | S.F. Floor | 1.30 | 1.30 | |
| 3090 | Other HVAC Sys. & Equipment | N/A | | — | — | — | |
| | **D40 Fire Protection** | | | | | | |
| 4010 | Sprinklers | N/A | | — | — | — | 0.0 % |
| 4020 | Standpipes | N/A | | — | — | — | |
| | **D50 Electrical** | | | | | | |
| 5010 | Electrical Service/Distribution | 60 ampere service, panel board and feeders | | S.F. Floor | .55 | .55 | |
| 5020 | Lighting & Branch Wiring | High bay fixtures, receptacles, switches and misc. power | | S.F. Floor | 8.29 | 8.29 | 14.1% |
| 5030 | Communications & Security | Addressable alarm systems | | S.F. Floor | 1.48 | 1.48 | |
| 5090 | Other Electrical Systems | N/A | | — | — | — | |
| **E. EQUIPMENT & FURNISHINGS** | | | | | | | |
| 1010 | Commercial Equipment | N/A | | — | — | — | |
| 1020 | Institutional Equipment | N/A | | — | — | — | 0.0 % |
| 1030 | Vehicular Equipment | N/A | | — | — | — | |
| 1090 | Other Equipment | N/A | | — | — | — | |
| **F. SPECIAL CONSTRUCTION** | | | | | | | |
| 1020 | Integrated Construction | N/A | | — | — | — | 0.0 % |
| 1040 | Special Facilities | N/A | | — | — | — | |
| **G. BUILDING SITEWORK** | **N/A** | | | | | | |
| | | | | | **Sub-Total** | 73.04 | **100%** |
| | CONTRACTOR FEES (General Requirements: 10%, Overhead: 5%, Profit: 10%) | | | | *25%* | 18.27 | |
| | ARCHITECT FEES | | | | *7%* | 6.39 | |
| | | | | | **Total Building Cost** | **97.70** | |

Deterioration occurs within the structure itself and is determined by the observation of both materials and equipment.

**Curable** deterioration can be remedied either by maintenance, repair or replacement, within prudent economic limits.

**Incurable** deterioration that has progressed to the point of actually affecting the structural integrity of the structure, making repair or replacement not economically feasible.

## *Actual Versus Observed Age*

The observed age of a structure refers to the age that the structure appears to be. Periodic maintenance, remodeling, and renovation all tend to reduce the amount of deterioration that has taken place, thereby decreasing the observed age. Actual age, on the other hand, relates solely to the year that the structure was built.

The Depreciation Table shown here relates to the observed age.

**Obsolescence** arises from conditions either occurring within the structure (functional) or caused by factors outside the limits of the structure (economic).

**Functional obsolescence** is any inadequacy caused by outmoded design, dated construction materials, or oversized or undersized areas, all of which cause excessive operation costs.

**Incurable** is so costly as not to economically justify the capital expenditure required to correct the deficiency.

**Economic obsolescence** is caused by factors outside the limits of the structure. The prime causes of economic obsolescence are:

- zoning and environmental laws
- government legislation
- negative neighborhood influences
- business climate
- proximity to transportation facilities

## Depreciation Table Commercial/Industrial/Institutional

| | Building Material | | |
|---|---|---|---|
| Observed Age (Years) | Frame | Masonry On Wood | Masonry On Masonry Or Steel |
| 1 | 1% | 0% | 0% |
| 2 | 2 | 1 | 0 |
| 3 | 3 | 2 | 1 |
| 4 | 4 | 3 | 2 |
| 5 | 6 | 5 | 3 |
| 10 | 20 | 15 | 8 |
| 15 | 25 | 20 | 15 |
| 20 | 30 | 25 | 20 |
| 25 | 35 | 30 | 25 |
| 30 | 40 | 35 | 30 |
| 35 | 45 | 40 | 35 |
| 40 | 50 | 45 | 40 |
| 45 | 55 | 50 | 45 |
| 50 | 60 | 55 | 50 |
| 55 | 65 | 60 | 55 |
| 60 | 70 | 65 | 60 |

# Green Commercial/Industrial/ Institutional Section

## *Table of Contents*

## Costs per square foot of floor area

| Exterior Wall | S.F. Area | 2000 | 2700 | 3400 | 4100 | 4800 | 5500 | 6200 | 6900 | 7600 |
|---|---|---|---|---|---|---|---|---|---|---|
| | L.F. Perimeter | 180 | 208 | 236 | 256 | 280 | 303 | 317 | 337 | 357 |
| Face Brick and Concrete Block | Rigid Steel | 385.60 | 358.25 | 342.20 | 328.40 | 320.10 | 313.50 | 306.05 | 301.50 | 297.75 |
| | Reinforced Concrete | 408.15 | 380.80 | 364.70 | **350.95** | 342.60 | 335.95 | 328.55 | 324.00 | 320.25 |
| Precast Concrete | Rigid Steel | 385.75 | 355.90 | 338.35 | 323.25 | 314.10 | 306.80 | 298.65 | 293.60 | 289.60 |
| | Reinforced Concrete | 425.60 | 395.75 | 378.20 | 363.10 | 353.95 | 346.70 | 338.50 | 333.50 | 329.40 |
| Limestone and Concrete Block | Rigid Steel | 410.40 | 379.80 | 361.85 | 346.35 | 336.90 | 329.50 | 321.10 | 315.95 | 311.80 |
| | Reinforced Concrete | 430.70 | 400.10 | 382.15 | 366.65 | 357.20 | 349.80 | 341.40 | 336.25 | 332.10 |

| | | | | | | | | | | |
|---|---|---|---|---|---|---|---|---|---|---|
| Perimeter Adj., Add or Deduct | Per 100 L.F. | 82.90 | 61.50 | 48.80 | 40.45 | 34.50 | 30.15 | 26.70 | 24.00 | 21.85 |
| Story Hgt. Adj., Add or Deduct | Per 1 Ft. | 8.15 | 7.00 | 6.35 | 5.75 | 5.35 | 4.95 | 4.65 | 4.40 | 4.30 |

***For Basement**, add $56.30 per square foot of basement area*

*The above costs were calculated using the basic specifications shown on the facing page. These costs should be adjusted where necessary for design alternatives and owner's requirements.*

## Common additives

| Description | Unit | $ Cost |
|---|---|---|
| Bulletproof Teller Window, 44" x 60" | Ea. | 6150 |
| 60" x 48" | Ea. | 9775 |
| Closed Circuit Surveillance, one station, camera & monitor | Ea. | 1250 |
| For additional camera stations, add | Ea. | 475 |
| Counters, complete, dr & frame, 3' x 6'-8", bullet resist stl with vision panel | Ea. | 5625 - 10,800 |
| Drive-up Window, drawer & micr., not incl. glass | Ea. | 6325 - 9850 |
| Night Depository | Ea. | 2650 - 5750 |
| Package Receiver, painted | Ea. | 4875 |
| Stainless steel | Ea. | 2525 |
| Partitions, bullet resistant to 8' high | L.F. | 415 - 660 |
| Pneumatic Tube Systems, 2 station | Ea. | 41,900 |
| With TV viewer | Ea. | 77,000 |
| Service Windows, pass thru, steel, 24" x 36" | Ea. | 6050 |
| 48" x 48" | Ea. | 8625 |
| Twenty-four Hour Teller, automatic deposit cash & memo | Ea. | 12,900 |
| Vault Front, door & frame, 2 hour test, 32" door | Opng. | 7450 |
| 4 hour test, 40" door | Opng. | 7625 |
| Time lock, two movement, add | Ea. | 2050 |

| Description | Unit | $ Cost |
|---|---|---|
| Commissioning Fees, sustainable commercial construction | S.F. | 0.24 - 3.04 |
| Energy Modelling Fees, banks to 10,000 SF | Ea. | 11,000 |
| Green Bldg Cert Fees for comm construction project reg | Project | 1200 |
| Photovoltaic Pwr Sys, grid connected, 20 kW (~2400 SF), roof | Ea. | 92,200 |
| Green Roofs, 6" soil depth, w/treated wd edging & sedum mats | S.F. | 28.30 |
| 10" Soil depth, with treated wood edging & sedum mats | S.F. | 30.65 |
| Greywater Recovery Systems, prepackaged comm, 1530 gal | Ea. | 38,355 |
| Rainwater Harvest Sys, prepckged comm, 10,000 gal, sys contrller | Ea. | 44,975 |
| 20,000 gal. w/system controller | Ea. | 73,350 |
| 30,000 gal. w/system controller | Ea. | 108,025 |
| Solar Domestic HW, closed loop, add-on sys, ext heat exchanger | Ea. | 13,550 |
| Draindown, hot water system, 120 gal tank | Ea. | 16,700 |



**Important: See the Reference Section for Location Factors.**

## Model costs calculated for a 1 story building with 14′ story height and 4,100 square feet of floor area

## G Bank

| | | | | Unit | Unit Cost | Cost Per S.F. | % Of Sub-Total |
|---|---|---|---|---|---|---|---|
| **A. SUBSTRUCTURE** | | | | | | | |
| 1010 | Standard Foundations | Poured concrete; strip and spread footings | | S.F. Ground | 6.11 | 6.11 | |
| 1020 | Special Foundations | N/A | | — | — | — | |
| 1030 | Slab on Grade | 4″ reinforced concrete with recycled vapor barrier and granular base | | S.F. Slab | 7.32 | 7.32 | 9.0% |
| 2010 | Basement Excavation | Site preparation for slab and trench for foundation wall and footing | | S.F. Ground | .38 | .38 | |
| 2020 | Basement Walls | 4′ Foundation wall | | L.F. Wall | 121 | 9.07 | |
| **B. SHELL** | | | | | | | |
| | **B10 Superstructure** | | | | | | |
| 1010 | Floor Construction | Cast-in-place columns | | L.F. Column | 7.83 | 7.83 | 11.8% |
| 1020 | Roof Construction | Cast-in-place concrete flat plate | | S.F. Roof | 22.10 | 22.10 | |
| | **B20 Exterior Enclosure** | | | | | | |
| 2010 | Exterior Walls | Face brick with concrete block backup | *80% of wall* | S.F. Wall | 48.35 | 33.81 | |
| 2020 | Exterior Windows | Horizontal aluminum sliding | *20% of wall* | Each | 1677 | 19.54 | 22.3% |
| 2030 | Exterior Doors | Double aluminum and glass and hollow metal, low VOC paint | | Each | 6185 | 3.02 | |
| | **B30 Roofing** | | | | | | |
| 3010 | Roof Coverings | Single-ply TPO membrane, 60 mils, heat welded seams w/4″ thk. R20 insul. | | S.F. Roof | 12.66 | 12.66 | 5.0% |
| 3020 | Roof Openings | N/A | | — | — | — | |
| **C. INTERIORS** | | | | | | | |
| 1010 | Partitions | Gypsum board on metal studs w/sound attenuation | *20 SF of Flr./LF Part.* | S.F. Partition | 15.36 | 7.68 | |
| 1020 | Interior Doors | Single leaf hollow metal, low VOC paint | *200 S.F. Floor/Door* | Each | 1159 | 5.80 | |
| 1030 | Fittings | N/A | | — | — | — | |
| 2010 | Stair Construction | N/A | | — | — | — | 12.4% |
| 3010 | Wall Finishes | 50% vinyl wall covering, 50% paint, low VOC | | S.F. Surface | 2.62 | 2.62 | |
| 3020 | Floor Finishes | 50% carpet tile, 40% vinyl composition tile, recycled, 10% quarry tile | | S.F. Floor | 6.39 | 6.39 | |
| 3030 | Ceiling Finishes | Mineral fiber tile on concealed zee bars | | S.F. Ceiling | 9 | 9 | |
| **D. SERVICES** | | | | | | | |
| | **D10 Conveying** | | | | | | |
| 1010 | Elevators & Lifts | N/A | | — | — | — | 0.0 % |
| 1020 | Escalators & Moving Walks | N/A | | — | — | — | |
| | **D20 Plumbing** | | | | | | |
| 2010 | Plumbing Fixtures | Toilet low flow, auto sensor and service fixt., supply and drainage | *1 Fixt./580 SF Flr.* | Each | 8074 | 13.92 | |
| 2020 | Domestic Water Distribution | Tankless, on demand water heaters, natural gas/propane | | S.F. Floor | 1.51 | 1.51 | 7.0% |
| 2040 | Rain Water Drainage | Roof drains | | S.F. Roof | 2.30 | 2.30 | |
| | **D30 HVAC** | | | | | | |
| 3010 | Energy Supply | N/A | | — | — | — | |
| 3020 | Heat Generating Systems | Included in D3050 | | — | — | — | |
| 3040 | Distribution Systems | Enthalpy heat recovery packages | | Each | 17,075 | 4.17 | 5.6 % |
| 3050 | Terminal & Package Units | Single zone rooftop air conditioner | | S.F. Floor | 10.08 | 10.08 | |
| 3090 | Other HVAC Sys. & Equipment | N/A | | — | — | — | |
| | **D40 Fire Protection** | | | | | | |
| 4010 | Sprinklers | Wet pipe sprinkler system | | S.F. Floor | 6.60 | 6.60 | 4.6% |
| 4020 | Standpipes | Standpipe | | S.F. Floor | 5.06 | 5.06 | |
| | **D50 Electrical** | | | | | | |
| 5010 | Electrical Service/Distribution | 200 ampere service, panel board and feeders | | S.F. Floor | 1.90 | 1.90 | |
| 5020 | Lighting & Branch Wiring | LED fixtures, daylt. dimming & ltg. on/off control, receptacles, switches, A.C. | | S.F. Floor | 13.59 | 13.59 | 13.2% |
| 5030 | Communications & Security | Alarm systems, internet/phone wiring, and security television | | S.F. Floor | 12.68 | 12.68 | |
| 5090 | Other Electrical Systems | Emergency generator, 15 kW, UPS, energy monitoring systems | | S.F. Floor | 5.18 | 5.18 | |
| **E. EQUIPMENT & FURNISHINGS** | | | | | | | |
| 1010 | Commercial Equipment | Automatic teller, drive up window, night depository | | S.F. Floor | 5.30 | 5.30 | |
| 1020 | Institutional Equipment | Closed circuit TV monitoring system | | S.F. Floor | 3.25 | 3.25 | 4.0% |
| 1090 | Other Equipment | Waste handling recycling tilt truck | | S.F. Floor | 1.55 | 1.55 | |
| 2020 | Moveable Furnishings | No smoking signage | | S.F. Floor | .03 | .03 | |
| **F. SPECIAL CONSTRUCTION** | | | | | | | |
| 1020 | Integrated Construction | N/A | | — | — | — | 4.9 % |
| 1040 | Special Facilities | Security vault door | | S.F. Floor | 12.49 | 12.49 | |
| **G. BUILDING SITEWORK** | | **N/A** | | | | | |
| | | | | | **Sub-Total** | 252.94 | **100%** |
| | CONTRACTOR FEES (General Requirements: 10%, Overhead: 5%, Profit: 10%) | | | | *25%* | 63.23 | |
| | ARCHITECT FEES | | | | *11%* | 34.78 | |
| | | | | | **Total Building Cost** | **350.95** | |

# G.120 G College, Classroom, 2-3 Story

## Costs per square foot of floor area

| Exterior Wall | S.F. Area | 15000 | 20000 | 28000 | 38000 | 50000 | 65000 | 85000 | 100000 | 150000 |
|---|---|---|---|---|---|---|---|---|---|---|
| | L.F. Perimeter | 350 | 400 | 480 | 550 | 630 | 660 | 750 | 825 | 1035 |
| Face Brick and Concrete Block | Rigid Steel | 314.85 | 299.00 | 285.35 | 274.20 | 266.40 | 257.70 | 252.50 | 250.30 | 245.15 |
| | Bearing Walls | 304.30 | 288.05 | 274.20 | 262.70 | 254.70 | 245.80 | 240.45 | 238.20 | 232.90 |
| Decorative Concrete Block | Rigid Steel | 305.00 | 290.50 | 278.10 | 268.05 | 261.05 | 253.40 | 248.75 | 246.80 | 242.15 |
| | Bearing Walls | 292.10 | 277.30 | 264.60 | 254.30 | **247.15** | 239.25 | 234.45 | 232.50 | 227.70 |
| Stucco and Concrete Block | Rigid Steel | 322.45 | 305.50 | 290.90 | 278.95 | 270.50 | 261.00 | 255.40 | 252.95 | 247.35 |
| | Bearing Walls | 311.95 | 294.60 | 279.75 | 267.45 | 258.80 | 249.15 | 243.35 | 240.90 | 235.15 |
| Perimeter Adj., Add or Deduct | Per 100 L.F. | 18.85 | 14.05 | 10.10 | 7.40 | 5.65 | 4.35 | 3.35 | 2.75 | 1.85 |
| Story Hgt. Adj., Add or Deduct | Per 1 Ft. | 3.50 | 2.95 | 2.55 | 2.15 | 1.85 | 1.50 | 1.35 | 1.20 | 1.00 |
| ***For Basement**, add $60.35 per square foot of basement area* | | | | | | | | | | |

*The above costs were calculated using the basic specifications shown on the facing page. These costs should be adjusted where necessary for design alternatives and owner's requirements.*

## Common additives

| Description | Unit | $ Cost |
|---|---|---|
| Clock System, 20 room | Ea. | 23,000 |
| 50 room | Ea. | 55,000 |
| Elevators, hydraulic passenger, 2 stops, 2000# capacity | Ea. | 87,500 |
| 3500# capacity | Ea. | 96,000 |
| Additional stop, add | Ea. | 9875 |
| Seating, auditorium chair, all veneer | Ea. | 480 |
| Veneer back, padded seat | Ea. | 430 |
| Upholstered, spring seat | Ea. | 385 |
| Classroom, movable chair & desk | Set | 81 - 171 |
| Lecture hall, pedestal type | Ea. | 385 - 775 |
| Sound System, amplifier, 250 watts | Ea. | 2425 |
| Speaker, ceiling or wall | Ea. | 320 |
| Trumpet | Ea. | 580 |
| TV Antenna, Master system, 30 outlet | Outlet | 370 |
| 100 outlet | Outlet | 395 |

| Description | Unit | $ Cost |
|---|---|---|
| Commissioning Fees, sustainable institutional construction | S.F. | 0.58 - 2.47 |
| Energy Modelling Fees, academic buildings to 10,000 SF | Ea. | 9000 |
| Greater than 10,000 SF add | S.F. | 0.20 |
| Green Bldg Cert Fees for school construction project reg | Project | 1200 |
| Photovoltaic Pwr Sys, grid connected, 20 kW (~2400 SF), roof | Ea. | 92,200 |
| Green Roofs, 6" soil depth, w/treated wd edging & sedum mats | S.F. | 28.30 |
| 10" Soil depth, with treated wood edging & sedum mats | S.F. | 30.65 |
| Greywater Recovery Systems, prepackaged comm, 3060 gal. | Ea. | 70,415 |
| 4590 gal. | Ea. | 88,275 |
| Rainwater Harvest Sys, prepckged comm, 10,000 gal, sys contrller | Ea. | 44,975 |
| 20,000 gal. w/system controller | Ea. | 73,350 |
| 30,000 gal. w/system controller | Ea. | 108,025 |
| Solar Domestic HW, closed loop, add-on sys, ext heat exchanger | Ea. | 13,550 |
| Drainback, hot water system, 120 gal tank | Ea. | 16,425 |
| Draindown, hot water system, 120 gal tank | Ea. | 16,700 |

## Model costs calculated for a 2 story building with 12′ story height and 50,000 square feet of floor area

# G College, Classroom, 2-3 Story

| | | | | Unit | Unit Cost | Cost Per S.F. | % Of Sub-Total |
|---|---|---|---|---|---|---|---|
| **A. SUBSTRUCTURE** | | | | | | | |
| 1010 | Standard Foundations | Poured concrete; strip and spread footings | | S.F. Ground | 1.84 | .92 | 3.8% |
| 1020 | Special Foundations | N/A | | — | — | — | |
| 1030 | Slab on Grade | 4″ reinforced concrete with vapor barrier and granular base | | S.F. Slab | 7.32 | 3.66 | |
| 2010 | Basement Excavation | Site preparation for slab and trench for foundation wall and footing | | S.F. Ground | .37 | .19 | |
| 2020 | Basement Walls | 4′ Foundation wall | | L.F. Wall | 229 | 2.34 | |
| **B. SHELL** | | | | | | | |
| | **B10 Superstructure** | | | | | | |
| 1010 | Floor Construction | Open web steel joists, slab form, concrete | | S.F. Floor | 25.10 | 12.55 | 10.2% |
| 1020 | Roof Construction | Metal deck on open web steel joists, columns | | S.F. Roof | 12.70 | 6.35 | |
| | **B20 Exterior Enclosure** | | | | | | |
| 2010 | Exterior Walls | Decorative concrete block | *65% of wall* | S.F. Wall | 27.93 | 5.49 | 7.1% |
| 2020 | Exterior Windows | Window wall | *35% of wall* | Each | 66 | 6.48 | |
| 2030 | Exterior Doors | Double glass and aluminum with transom | | Each | 9150 | 1.10 | |
| | **B30 Roofing** | | | | | | |
| 3010 | Roof Coverings | Built-up tar and gravel with flashing; perlite/EPS composite insulation | | S.F. Roof | 10.34 | 5.17 | 2.8% |
| 3020 | Roof Openings | N/A | | — | — | — | |
| **C. INTERIORS** | | | | | | | |
| 1010 | Partitions | Concrete block | *20 SF Flr./LF Part.* | S.F. Partition | 26.14 | 13.07 | 25.1% |
| 1020 | Interior Doors | Single leaf hollow metal | *200 S.F. Floor/Door* | Each | 1159 | 5.80 | |
| 1030 | Fittings | Chalkboards, counters, cabinets | | S.F. Floor | 5.99 | 5.99 | |
| 2010 | Stair Construction | Concrete filled metal pan | | Flight | 19,225 | 3.85 | |
| 3010 | Wall Finishes | 95% paint, 5% ceramic tile | | S.F. Surface | 4.77 | 4.77 | |
| 3020 | Floor Finishes | 70% vinyl composition tile, 25% carpet, 5% ceramic tile | | S.F. Floor | 3.92 | 3.92 | |
| 3030 | Ceiling Finishes | Mineral fiber tile on concealed zee bars | | S.F. Ceiling | 9 | 9 | |
| **D. SERVICES** | | | | | | | |
| | **D10 Conveying** | | | | | | |
| 1010 | Elevators & Lifts | Two hydraulic passenger elevators | | Each | 107,000 | 4.28 | 2.3% |
| 1020 | Escalators & Moving Walks | N/A | | — | — | — | |
| | **D20 Plumbing** | | | | | | |
| 2010 | Plumbing Fixtures | Toilet, low flow, auto sensor & service fixt., supply & drain. | *1 Fixt./455 SF Flr.* | Each | 11,530 | 25.34 | 14.8% |
| 2020 | Domestic Water Distribution | Oil fired hot water heater | | S.F. Floor | 1.28 | 1.28 | |
| 2040 | Rain Water Drainage | Roof drains | | S.F. Roof | 1.58 | .79 | |
| | **D30 HVAC** | | | | | | |
| 3010 | Energy Supply | N/A | | — | — | — | 12.9 % |
| 3020 | Heat Generating Systems | Included in D3050 | | — | — | — | |
| 3040 | Distribution Systems | Enthalpy heat recovery packages | | Each | 42,375 | 2.54 | |
| 3050 | Terminal & Package Units | Multizone unit, gas heating, electric cooling, SEER 14 | | S.F. Floor | 21.25 | 21.25 | |
| 3090 | Other HVAC Sys. & Equipment | N/A | | — | — | — | |
| | **D40 Fire Protection** | | | | | | |
| 4010 | Sprinklers | Sprinklers, light hazard | | S.F. Floor | 4.57 | 4.57 | 2.8% |
| 4020 | Standpipes | Standpipe, dry, Class III | | S.F. Floor | .57 | .57 | |
| | **D50 Electrical** | | | | | | |
| 5010 | Electrical Service/Distribution | 2000 ampere service, panel board and feeders | | S.F. Floor | 4.56 | 4.56 | 18.1% |
| 5020 | Lighting & Branch Wiring | LED fixtures, receptacles, switches, A.C. & misc. power | | S.F. Floor | 17.78 | 17.78 | |
| 5030 | Communications & Security | Addressable alarm sys., internet wiring, comm. sys. & emerg. ltg. | | S.F. Floor | 9.10 | 9.10 | |
| 5090 | Other Electrical Systems | Emergency generator, 100 kW | | S.F. Floor | 1.92 | 1.92 | |
| **E. EQUIPMENT & FURNISHINGS** | | | | | | | |
| 1010 | Commercial Equipment | N/A | | — | — | — | 0.1 % |
| 1020 | Institutional Equipment | N/A | | — | — | — | |
| 1090 | Other Equipment | Waste handling recycling tilt truck | | S.F. Floor | .13 | .13 | |
| 2020 | Moveable Furnishings | No smoking signage | | S.F. Floor | | | |
| **F. SPECIAL CONSTRUCTION** | | | | | | | |
| 1020 | Integrated Construction | N/A | | — | — | — | 0.0 % |
| 1040 | Special Facilities | N/A | | — | — | — | |
| **G. BUILDING SITEWORK** | **N/A** | | | | | | |
| | | | | | **Sub-Total** | 184.76 | **100%** |
| | CONTRACTOR FEES (General Requirements: 10%, Overhead: 5%, Profit: 10%) | | | | *25%* | 46.22 | |
| | ARCHITECT FEES | | | | *7%* | 16.17 | |
| | | | | | **Total Building Cost** | **247.15** | |

## Costs per square foot of floor area

| Exterior Wall | S.F. Area | 10000 | 15000 | 25000 | 40000 | 55000 | 70000 | 80000 | 90000 | 100000 |
|---|---|---|---|---|---|---|---|---|---|---|
| | L.F. Perimeter | 260 | 320 | 400 | 476 | 575 | 628 | 684 | 721 | 772 |
| Face Brick and Concrete Block | Reinforced Concrete | 336.80 | 318.35 | 299.15 | 285.50 | 280.40 | 275.70 | 274.30 | 272.60 | 271.65 |
| | Rigid Steel | 350.95 | 332.40 | 313.25 | 299.65 | 294.50 | 289.85 | 288.40 | 286.70 | 285.70 |
| Decorative Concrete Block | Reinforced Concrete | 316.35 | 301.55 | 286.50 | 276.15 | 272.15 | 268.65 | 267.55 | 266.30 | 265.50 |
| | Rigid Steel | 330.45 | 315.65 | 300.65 | 290.25 | 286.25 | 282.75 | 281.65 | 280.40 | 279.60 |
| Precast Concrete | Reinforced Concrete | 363.75 | 340.40 | 315.70 | 297.80 | 291.20 | 285.05 | 283.10 | 280.90 | 279.60 |
| | Rigid Steel | 377.85 | 354.55 | 329.80 | 311.95 | 305.30 | 299.15 | 297.20 | 295.05 | 293.75 |
| Perimeter Adj., Add or Deduct | Per 100 L.F. | 26.80 | 17.80 | 10.70 | 6.70 | 4.85 | 3.85 | 3.35 | 2.95 | 2.65 |
| Story Hgt. Adj., Add or Deduct | Per 1 Ft. | 5.10 | 4.15 | 3.05 | 2.35 | 2.10 | 1.80 | 1.60 | 1.55 | 1.45 |
| ***For Basement**, add $58.75 per square foot of basement area* | | | | | | | | | | |

*The above costs were calculated using the basic specifications shown on the facing page. These costs should be adjusted where necessary for design alternatives and owner's requirements.*

## Common additives

| Description | Unit | $ Cost |
|---|---|---|
| Closed Circuit Surveillance, one station, camera & monitor | Ea. | 1250 |
| For additional camera stations, add | Ea. | 475 |
| Elevators, hydraulic passenger, 2 stops, 3500# capacity | Ea. | 96,000 |
| Additional stop, add | Ea. | 9875 |
| Furniture | Student | 2800 - 5350 |
| Intercom System, 25 station capacity | | |
| Master station | Ea. | 3175 |
| Intercom outlets | Ea. | 228 |
| Kitchen Equipment | | |
| Broiler | Ea. | 4425 |
| Coffee urn, twin 6 gallon | Ea. | 4075 |
| Cooler, 6 ft. long | Ea. | 4525 |
| Dishwasher, 10-12 racks per hr. | Ea. | 42,900 |
| Food warmer | Ea. | 720 |
| Freezer, 44 C.F., reach-in | Ea. | 3600 |
| Ice cube maker, 50 lb. per day | Ea. | 2525 |
| Range with 1 oven | Ea. | 2050 |
| Laundry Equipment, dryer, 30 lb. capacity | Ea. | 2200 |
| Washer, commercial | Ea. | 2000 |
| TV Antenna, Master system, 30 outlet | Outlet | 370 |
| 100 outlet | Outlet | 395 |

| Description | Unit | $ Cost |
|---|---|---|
| Commissioning Fees, sustainable institutional construction | S.F. | 0.58 - 2.47 |
| Energy Modelling Fees, academic buildings to 10,000 SF | Ea. | 9000 |
| Greater than 10,000 SF add | S.F. | 0.20 |
| Green Bldg Cert Fees for school construction project reg | Project | 1200 |
| Photovoltaic Pwr Sys, grid connected, 20 kW (~2400 SF), roof | Ea. | 92,200 |
| Green Roofs, 6" soil depth, w/treated wd edging & sedum mats | S.F. | 28.30 |
| 10" Soil depth, with treated wood edging & sedum mats | S.F. | 30.65 |
| Greywater Recovery Systems, prepackaged comm, 3060 gal. | Ea. | 70,415 |
| 4590 gal. | Ea. | 88,275 |
| Rainwater Harvest Sys, prepckged comm, 30,000 gal, sys contrller | Ea. | 108,025 |
| Solar Domestic HW, closed loop, add-on sys, ext heat exchanger | Ea. | 13,550 |
| Drainback, hot water system, 120 gal tank | Ea. | 16,425 |
| Draindown, hot water system, 120 gal tank | Ea. | 16,700 |



**Important: See the Reference Section for Location Factors.**

## Model costs calculated for a 3 story building with 12′ story height and 25,000 square feet of floor area

## G College, Dormitory, 2-3 Story

| | | | | Unit | Unit Cost | Cost Per S.F. | % Of Sub-Total |
|---|---|---|---|---|---|---|---|
| **A. SUBSTRUCTURE** | | | | | | | |
| 1010 | Standard Foundations | Poured concrete; strip and spread footings | | S.F. Ground | 8.94 | 2.98 | 3.3% |
| 1020 | Special Foundations | N/A | | — | — | — | |
| 1030 | Slab on Grade | 4″ reinforced concrete with recycled vapor barrier and granular base | | S.F. Slab | 7.32 | 2.44 | |
| 2010 | Basement Excavation | Site preparation for slab and trench for foundation wall and footing | | S.F. Ground | .22 | .07 | |
| 2020 | Basement Walls | 4′ Foundation wall | | L.F. Wall | 121 | 1.93 | |
| **B. SHELL** | | | | | | | |
| **B10 Superstructure** | | | | | | | |
| 1010 | Floor Construction | Concrete flat plate | | S.F. Floor | 34.26 | 22.84 | 13.1% |
| 1020 | Roof Construction | Concrete flat plate | | S.F. Roof | 19.14 | 6.38 | |
| **B20 Exterior Enclosure** | | | | | | | |
| 2010 | Exterior Walls | Face brick with concrete block backup | *80% of wall* | S.F. Wall | 48.35 | 22.28 | 13.0% |
| 2020 | Exterior Windows | Aluminum horizontal sliding | *20% of wall* | Each | 839 | 4.21 | |
| 2030 | Exterior Doors | Double glass & aluminum doors | | Each | 10,800 | 2.59 | |
| **B30 Roofing** | | | | | | | |
| 3010 | Roof Coverings | Single-ply TPO membrane, heat welded w/R-20 insul. | | S.F. Roof | 11.73 | 3.91 | 1.7% |
| 3020 | Roof Openings | N/A | | — | — | — | |
| **C. INTERIORS** | | | | | | | |
| 1010 | Partitions | Gypsum board on metal studs, CMU w/foamed-in insul. | *9 SF Flr./LF Part.* | S.F. Partition | 10.22 | 11.35 | 20.0% |
| 1020 | Interior Doors | Single leaf wood, low VOC paint | *90 S.F. Floor/Door* | Each | 1231 | 13.68 | |
| 1030 | Fittings | Closet shelving, mirrors, bathroom accessories | | S.F. Floor | 4.58 | 4.58 | |
| 2010 | Stair Construction | Cast in place concrete | | Flight | 6725 | 3.49 | |
| 3010 | Wall Finishes | 95% paint, low VOC paint, 5% ceramic tile | | S.F. Surface | 2.18 | 4.84 | |
| 3020 | Floor Finishes | 80% carpet tile, 10% vinyl comp. tile, recycled content, 10% ceramic tile | | S.F. Floor | 5.21 | 5.21 | |
| 3030 | Ceiling Finishes | 90% paint, low VOC, 10% suspended fiberglass board | | S.F. Ceiling | 1.60 | 1.60 | |
| **D. SERVICES** | | | | | | | |
| **D10 Conveying** | | | | | | | |
| 1010 | Elevators & Lifts | One hydraulic passenger elevator | | Each | 145,250 | 5.81 | 2.6% |
| 1020 | Escalators & Moving Walks | N/A | | — | — | — | |
| **D20 Plumbing** | | | | | | | |
| 2010 | Plumbing Fixtures | Toilet, low flow, auto sensor, & service fixt., supply & drain. | *1 Fixt./455 SF Flr.* | Each | 16,102 | 35.39 | 17.0% |
| 2020 | Domestic Water Distribution | Electric, point-of-use water heater | | S.F. Floor | 1.99 | 1.99 | |
| 2040 | Rain Water Drainage | Roof drains | | S.F. Roof | 2.04 | .68 | |
| **D30 HVAC** | | | | | | | |
| 3010 | Energy Supply | N/A | | — | — | — | 6.7 % |
| 3020 | Heat Generating Systems | Included in D3050 | | — | — | — | |
| 3040 | Distribution Systems | Enthalpy heat recovery packages | | Each | 35,150 | 1.41 | |
| 3050 | Terminal & Package Units | Rooftop multizone unit system, SEER 14 | | S.F. Floor | 13.65 | 13.65 | |
| 3090 | Other HVAC Sys. & Equipment | N/A | | — | — | — | |
| **D40 Fire Protection** | | | | | | | |
| 4010 | Sprinklers | Wet pipe sprinkler system | | S.F. Floor | 4.39 | 4.39 | 2.6% |
| 4020 | Standpipes | Standpipe, dry, Class III | | S.F. Floor | 1.44 | 1.44 | |
| **D50 Electrical** | | | | | | | |
| 5010 | Electrical Service/Distribution | 800 ampere service, panel board and feeders | | S.F. Floor | 2.22 | 2.22 | 17.9% |
| 5020 | Lighting & Branch Wiring | LED fixtures, daylt. dim., ltg. on/off, recept., switches, and A.C. power | | S.F. Floor | 23.62 | 23.62 | |
| 5030 | Communications & Security | Alarm sys., internet & phone wiring, comm. sys. and emergency ltg. | | S.F. Floor | 12.97 | 12.97 | |
| 5090 | Other Electrical Systems | Emergency generator, 7.5 kW, energy monitoring systems | | S.F. Floor | 1.28 | 1.28 | |
| **E. EQUIPMENT & FURNISHINGS** | | | | | | | |
| 1010 | Commercial Equipment | N/A | | — | — | — | 2.0 % |
| 1020 | Institutional Equipment | N/A | | — | — | — | |
| 1090 | Other Equipment | Waste handling recycling tilt truck | | S.F. Floor | .26 | .26 | |
| 2020 | Moveable Furnishings | Dormitory furniture, no smoking signage | | S.F. Floor | 4.16 | 4.16 | |
| **F. SPECIAL CONSTRUCTION** | | | | | | | |
| 1020 | Integrated Construction | N/A | | — | — | — | 0.0 % |
| 1040 | Special Facilities | N/A | | — | — | — | |
| **G. BUILDING SITEWORK** | **N/A** | | | | | | |
| | | | | **Sub-Total** | | 223.65 | **100%** |
| | CONTRACTOR FEES (General Requirements: 10%, Overhead: 5%, Profit: 10%) | | | | *25%* | 55.93 | |
| | ARCHITECT FEES | | | | *7%* | 19.57 | |
| | | | | **Total Building Cost** | | **299.15** | |

## Costs per square foot of floor area

| Exterior Wall | S.F. Area | 20000 | 35000 | 45000 | 65000 | 85000 | 110000 | 135000 | 160000 | 200000 |
|---|---|---|---|---|---|---|---|---|---|---|
| | L.F. Perimeter | 260 | 340 | 400 | 440 | 500 | 540 | 560 | 590 | 640 |
| Face Brick and Concrete Block | Reinforced Concrete | 344.45 | 317.10 | 309.90 | 294.25 | 287.45 | 280.45 | 275.15 | 271.80 | 268.25 |
| | Rigid Steel | 361.75 | 334.35 | 327.15 | 311.50 | 304.70 | 297.70 | 292.35 | 289.05 | 285.50 |
| Decorative Concrete Block | Reinforced Concrete | 326.20 | 303.40 | 297.45 | 284.70 | 279.20 | 273.55 | 269.25 | 266.60 | 263.75 |
| | Rigid Steel | 343.45 | 320.70 | 314.65 | 302.00 | 296.40 | 290.75 | 286.55 | 283.85 | 281.00 |
| Precast Concrete | Reinforced Concrete | 353.60 | 323.90 | 316.15 | 299.00 | 291.55 | 283.90 | 278.00 | 274.35 | 270.45 |
| | Rigid Steel | 370.80 | 341.15 | 333.35 | 316.25 | 308.85 | 301.10 | 295.25 | 291.65 | 287.75 |
| Perimeter Adj., Add or Deduct | Per 100 L.F. | 32.10 | 18.30 | 14.25 | 9.85 | 7.55 | 5.80 | 4.70 | 4.00 | 3.20 |
| Story Hgt. Adj., Add or Deduct | Per 1 Ft. | 6.50 | 4.85 | 4.45 | 3.40 | 2.95 | 2.45 | 2.05 | 1.85 | 1.60 |
| ***For Basement**, add $58.75 per square foot of basement area* | | | | | | | | | | |

*The above costs were calculated using the basic specifications shown on the facing page. These costs should be adjusted where necessary for design alternatives and owner's requirements.*

## Common additives

| Description | Unit | $ Cost |
|---|---|---|
| Closed Circuit Surveillance, one station, camera & monitor | Ea. | 1250 |
| For additional camera stations, add | Ea. | 475 |
| Elevators, electric passenger, 5 stops, 3500# capacity | Ea. | 220,500 |
| Additional stop, add | Ea. | 12,600 |
| Furniture | Student | 2800 - 5350 |
| Intercom System, 25 station capacity | | |
| Master station | Ea. | 3175 |
| Intercom outlets | Ea. | 228 |
| Kitchen Equipment | | |
| Broiler | Ea. | 4425 |
| Coffee urn, twin, 6 gallon | Ea. | 4075 |
| Cooler, 6 ft. long | Ea. | 4525 |
| Dishwasher, 10-12 racks per hr. | Ea. | 42,900 |
| Food warmer | Ea. | 720 |
| Freezer, 44 C.F., reach-in | Ea. | 3600 |
| Ice cube maker, 50 lb. per day | Ea. | 2525 |
| Range with 1 oven | Ea. | 2050 |
| Laundry Equipment, dryer, 30 lb. capacity | Ea. | 2200 |
| Washer, commercial | Ea. | 2000 |
| TV Antenna, Master system, 30 outlet | Outlet | 370 |
| 100 outlet | Outlet | 395 |

| Description | Unit | $ Cost |
|---|---|---|
| Commissioning Fees, sustainable institutional construction | S.F. | 0.58 - 2.47 |
| Energy Modelling Fees, academic buildings to 10,000 SF | Ea. | 9000 |
| Greater than 10,000 SF add | S.F. | 0.20 |
| Green Bldg Cert Fees for school construction project reg | Project | 1200 |
| Photovoltaic Pwr Sys, grid connected, 20 kW (~2400 SF), roof | Ea. | 92,200 |
| Green Roofs, 6" soil depth, w/treated wd edging & sedum mats | S.F. | 28.30 |
| 10" Soil depth, with treated wood edging & sedum mats | S.F. | 30.65 |
| Greywater Recovery Systems, prepackaged comm, 3060 gal. | Ea. | 70,415 |
| 4590 gal. | Ea. | 88,275 |
| Rainwater Harvest Sys, prepckged comm, 30,000 gal, sys contrller | Ea. | 108,025 |
| Solar Domestic HW, closed loop, add-on sys, ext heat exchanger | Ea. | 13,550 |
| Drainback, hot water system, 120 gal tank | Ea. | 16,425 |
| Draindown, hot water system, 120 gal tank | Ea. | 16,700 |



**Important: See the Reference Section for Location Factors.**

**Model costs calculated for a 6 story building with 12′ story height and 85,000 square feet of floor area**

# G College, Dormitory, 4-8 Story

| | | | | Unit | Unit Cost | Cost Per S.F. | % Of Sub-Total |
|---|---|---|---|---|---|---|---|
| **A. SUBSTRUCTURE** | | | | | | | |
| 1010 | Standard Foundations | Poured concrete; strip and spread footings | | S.F. Ground | 13.14 | 2.19 | 2.0% |
| 1020 | Special Foundations | N/A | | – | – | – | |
| 1030 | Slab on Grade | 4″ reinforced concrete with recycled vapor barrier and granular base | | S.F. Slab | 7.32 | 1.22 | |
| 2010 | Basement Excavation | Site preparation for slab and trench for foundation wall and footing | | S.F. Ground | .37 | .06 | |
| 2020 | Basement Walls | 4′ foundation wall | | L.F. Wall | 229 | .99 | |
| **B. SHELL** | | | | | | | |
| | **B10 Superstructure** | | | | | | |
| 1010 | Floor Construction | Concrete slab with metal deck and beams | | S.F. Floor | 38.92 | 32.43 | 16.9% |
| 1020 | Roof Construction | Concrete slab with metal deck and beams | | S.F. Roof | 29.58 | 4.93 | |
| | **B20 Exterior Enclosure** | | | | | | |
| 2010 | Exterior Walls | Decorative concrete block | *80% of wall* | S.F. Wall | 30.10 | 10.20 | 8.8% |
| 2020 | Exterior Windows | Aluminum horizontal sliding | *20% of wall* | Each | 1552 | 8.76 | |
| 2030 | Exterior Doors | Double glass & aluminum doors | | Each | 5994 | .56 | |
| | **B30 Roofing** | | | | | | |
| 3010 | Roof Coverings | Single-ply TPO membrane, 60 mils, heat welded seams w/R-20 insul. | | S.F. Roof | 10.92 | 1.82 | 0.8% |
| 3020 | Roof Openings | N/A | | – | – | – | |
| **C. INTERIORS** | | | | | | | |
| 1010 | Partitions | Concrete block w/foamed-in insulation | *9 SF Floor/LF Part.* | S.F. Partition | 14.20 | 15.78 | 22.9% |
| 1020 | Interior Doors | Single leaf wood, low VOC paint | *90 S.F. Floor/Door* | Each | 1231 | 13.68 | |
| 1030 | Fittings | Closet shelving, mirrors, bathroom accessories | | S.F. Floor | 3.75 | 3.75 | |
| 2010 | Stair Construction | Concrete filled metal pan | | Flight | 19,225 | 4.07 | |
| 3010 | Wall Finishes | 95% paint, low VOC, 5% ceramic tile | | S.F. Surface | 2.99 | 6.65 | |
| 3020 | Floor Finishes | 80% carpet tile, 10% vinyl comp. tile, recycled, 10% ceramic tile | | S.F. Floor | 5.21 | 5.21 | |
| 3030 | Ceiling Finishes | Mineral fiber tile on concealed zee bars, paint | | S.F. Ceiling | 1.60 | 1.60 | |
| **D. SERVICES** | | | | | | | |
| | **D10 Conveying** | | | | | | |
| 1010 | Elevators & Lifts | Four geared passenger elevators | | Each | 304,938 | 14.35 | 6.5% |
| 1020 | Escalators & Moving Walks | N/A | | – | – | – | |
| | **D20 Plumbing** | | | | | | |
| 2010 | Plumbing Fixtures | Toilet, low flow, auto sensor, & service fixt., supply & drain. | *1 Fixt./390 SF Flr.* | Each | 13,603 | 34.88 | 16.5% |
| 2020 | Domestic Water Distribution | Electric water heater, point-of-use, energy saver | | S.F. Floor | 1.10 | 1.10 | |
| 2040 | Rain Water Drainage | Roof drains | | S.F. Roof | 3.06 | .51 | |
| | **D30 HVAC** | | | | | | |
| 3010 | Energy Supply | N/A | | – | – | – | 6.3 % |
| 3020 | Heat Generating Systems | N/A | | – | – | – | |
| 3040 | Distribution Systems | Enthalpy heat recovery packages | | Each | 35,150 | .41 | |
| 3050 | Terminal & Package Units | Multizone rooftop air conditioner, SEER 14 | | S.F. Floor | 13.65 | 13.65 | |
| 3090 | Other HVAC Sys. & Equipment | N/A | | – | – | – | |
| | **D40 Fire Protection** | | | | | | |
| 4010 | Sprinklers | Sprinklers, light hazard | | S.F. Floor | 4.33 | 4.33 | 2.4% |
| 4020 | Standpipes | Standpipe, dry, Class III | | S.F. Floor | 1.03 | 1.03 | |
| | **D50 Electrical** | | | | | | |
| 5010 | Electrical Service/Distribution | 1200 ampere service, panel board and feeders | | S.F. Floor | 1.17 | 1.17 | 15.3% |
| 5020 | Lighting & Branch Wiring | LED fixtures, daylt. dim., ltg. on/off, recept. switches, and A.C. power | | S.F. Floor | 22.32 | 22.32 | |
| 5030 | Communications & Security | Alarm systems, internet & phone wiring, comm. systems and emerg. ltg. | | S.F. Floor | 9.48 | 9.48 | |
| 5090 | Other Electrical Systems | Emergency generator, 30 kW, energy monitoring systems | | S.F. Floor | 1.03 | 1.03 | |
| **E. EQUIPMENT & FURNISHINGS** | | | | | | | |
| 1010 | Commercial Equipment | N/A | | – | – | – | 1.6 % |
| 1020 | Institutional Equipment | N/A | | – | – | – | |
| 1090 | Other Equipment | Waste handling recycling tilt truck | | S.F. Floor | .08 | .08 | |
| 2020 | Moveable Furnishings | Built-in dormitory furnishings, no smoking signage | | S.F. Floor | 3.39 | 3.39 | |
| **F. SPECIAL CONSTRUCTION** | | | | | | | |
| 1020 | Integrated Construction | N/A | | – | – | – | 0.0 % |
| 1040 | Special Facilities | N/A | | – | – | – | |
| **G. BUILDING SITEWORK** | **N/A** | | | | | | |
| | | | | | **Sub-Total** | 221.63 | **100%** |
| | CONTRACTOR FEES (General Requirements: 10%, Overhead: 5%, Profit: 10%) | | | | *25%* | 55.38 | |
| | ARCHITECT FEES | | | | *7%* | 19.39 | |
| | | | | | **Total Building Cost** | **296.40** | |

## Costs per square foot of floor area

| Exterior Wall | S.F. Area | 12000 | 20000 | 28000 | 37000 | 45000 | 57000 | 68000 | 80000 | 92000 |
|---|---|---|---|---|---|---|---|---|---|---|
| | L.F. Perimeter | 470 | 600 | 698 | 793 | 900 | 1000 | 1075 | 1180 | 1275 |
| Face Brick and Concrete Block | Rigid Steel | 443.05 | 370.65 | 337.30 | 316.25 | 305.65 | 293.15 | 285.10 | 279.45 | 275.10 |
| | Bearing Walls | 436.45 | 364.00 | 330.70 | 309.65 | **299.00** | 286.50 | 278.50 | 272.85 | 268.45 |
| Decorative Concrete Block | Rigid Steel | 434.20 | 363.80 | 331.65 | 311.40 | 301.10 | 289.15 | 281.55 | 276.10 | 271.95 |
| | Bearing Walls | 427.90 | 357.55 | 325.35 | 305.10 | 294.85 | 282.90 | 275.25 | 269.85 | 265.65 |
| Stucco and Concrete Block | Rigid Steel | 450.70 | 376.45 | 342.20 | 320.45 | 309.60 | 296.60 | 288.25 | 282.35 | 277.80 |
| | Bearing Walls | 444.40 | 370.15 | 335.85 | 314.15 | 303.25 | 290.30 | 281.90 | 276.05 | 271.45 |
| Perimeter Adj., Add or Deduct | Per 100 L.F. | 16.20 | 9.65 | 6.95 | 5.25 | 4.30 | 3.45 | 2.85 | 2.45 | 2.10 |
| Story Hgt. Adj., Add or Deduct | Per 1 Ft. | 2.90 | 2.20 | 1.85 | 1.65 | 1.50 | 1.30 | 1.20 | 1.10 | 1.00 |

***For Basement**, add $38.00 per square foot of basement area*

*The above costs were calculated using the basic specifications shown on the facing page. These costs should be adjusted where necessary for design alternatives and owner's requirements.*

## Common additives

| Description | Unit | $ Cost |
|---|---|---|
| Cabinets, Base, door units, metal | L.F. | 2875 |
| Drawer units | L.F. | 1075 |
| Tall storage cabinets, open | L.F. | 475 |
| With doors | L.F. | 1125 |
| Wall, metal 12-1/2" deep, open | L.F. | 284 |
| With doors | L.F. | 425 |
| Countertops, not incl. base cabinets, acid proof | S.F. | 148 - 143 |
| Stainless steel | S.F. | 95 |
| Fume Hood, Not incl. ductwork | L.F. | 1250 - 3050 |
| Ductwork | Hood | 7700 - 11,400 |
| Glassware Washer, Distilled water rinse | Ea. | 10,100 - 21,800 |
| Seating, auditorium chair, veneer back, padded seat | Ea. | 430 |
| Upholstered, spring seat | Ea. | 385 |
| Classroom, movable chair & desk | Set | 81 - 171 |
| Lecture hall, pedestal type | Ea. | 385 - 775 |
| Safety Equipment, Eye wash, hand held | Ea. | 460 |
| Deluge shower | Ea. | 325 |
| Tables, acid resist. top, drawers | L.F. | 266 |
| Titration Unit, Four 2000 ml reservoirs | Ea. | 8275 |

| Description | Unit | $ Cost |
|---|---|---|
| Commissioning Fees, sustainable institutional construction | S.F. | 0.58 - 2.47 |
| Energy Modelling Fees, academic buildings to 10,000 SF | Ea. | 9000 |
| Greater than 10,000 SF add | S.F. | 0.20 |
| Green Bldg Cert Fees for school construction project reg | Project | 1200 |
| Photovoltaic Pwr Sys, grid connected, 20 kW (~2400 SF), roof | Ea. | 92,200 |
| Green Roofs, 6" soil depth, w/treated wd edging & sedum mats | S.F. | 28.30 |
| 10" Soil depth, with treated wood edging & sedum mats | S.F. | 30.65 |
| Greywater Recovery Systems, prepackaged comm, 3060 gal. | Ea. | 70,415 |
| 4590 gal. | Ea. | 88,275 |
| Rainwater Harvest Sys, prepckged comm, 30,000 gal, sys contrller | Ea. | 108,025 |
| Solar Domestic HW, closed loop, add-on sys, ext heat exchanger | Ea. | 13,550 |
| Drainback, hot water system, 120 gal tank | Ea. | 16,425 |
| Draindown, hot water system, 120 gal tank | Ea. | 16,700 |



**Important: See the Reference Section for Location Factors.**

## Model costs calculated for a 1 story building with 12′ story height and 45,000 square feet of floor area

# G College, Laboratory

| | | | | Unit | Unit Cost | Cost Per S.F. | % Of Sub-Total |
|---|---|---|---|---|---|---|---|
| **A. SUBSTRUCTURE** | | | | | | | |
| 1010 | Standard Foundations | Poured concrete; strip and spread footings | | S.F. Ground | 4.56 | 4.56 | 9.9% |
| 1020 | Special Foundations | N/A | | — | — | — | |
| 1030 | Slab on Grade | 4″ reinforced concrete with recycled vapor barrier and granular base | | S.F. Slab | 7.32 | 7.32 | |
| 2010 | Basement Excavation | Site preparation for slab and trench for foundation wall and footing | | S.F. Ground | .22 | .22 | |
| 2020 | Basement Walls | 4′ foundation wall | | L.F. Wall | 229 | 9.42 | |
| **B. SHELL** | | | | | | | |
| | **B10 Superstructure** | | | | | | |
| 1010 | Floor Construction | Metal deck on open web steel joists | *(5680 S.F.)* | S.F. Floor | 3.27 | 3.27 | 5.2% |
| 1020 | Roof Construction | Metal deck on open web steel joists | | S.F. Roof | 8.14 | 8.14 | |
| | **B20 Exterior Enclosure** | | | | | | |
| 2010 | Exterior Walls | Face brick with concrete block backup | *75% of wall* | S.F. Wall | 48.33 | 8.70 | 7.3% |
| 2020 | Exterior Windows | Window wall | *25% of wall* | Each | 66 | 3.68 | |
| 2030 | Exterior Doors | Glass and metal doors and entrances with transom | | Each | 7785 | 3.46 | |
| | **B30 Roofing** | | | | | | |
| 3010 | Roof Coverings | Single-ply TPO membrane, 60 mils, heat welded w/R-20 insul. | | S.F. Roof | 10.01 | 10.01 | 4.9% |
| 3020 | Roof Openings | Skylight | | S.F. Roof | .74 | .74 | |
| **C. INTERIORS** | | | | | | | |
| 1010 | Partitions | Concrete block, foamed-in insulation | *10 SF Flr./LF Part.* | S.F. Partition | 16.35 | 16.35 | 19.1% |
| 1020 | Interior Doors | Single leaf-kalamein fire doors, low VOC paint | *820 S.F. Floor/Door* | Each | 2060 | 2.51 | |
| 1030 | Fittings | Lockers | | S.F. Floor | .06 | .06 | |
| 2010 | Stair Construction | N/A | | — | — | — | |
| 3010 | Wall Finishes | 60% paint, low VOC, 40% epoxy coating | | S.F. Surface | 3.12 | 6.24 | |
| 3020 | Floor Finishes | 60% epoxy, 20% carpet, 20% vinyl composition tile, recycled content | | S.F. Floor | 7.35 | 7.35 | |
| 3030 | Ceiling Finishes | Mineral fiber tile on concealed zee runners | | S.F. Ceiling | 9 | 9 | |
| **D. SERVICES** | | | | | | | |
| | **D10 Conveying** | | | | | | |
| 1010 | Elevators & Lifts | N/A | | — | — | — | 0.0 % |
| 1020 | Escalators & Moving Walks | N/A | | — | — | — | |
| | **D20 Plumbing** | | | | | | |
| 2010 | Plumbing Fixtures | Toilet, low flow, auto sensor & service fixt., supply & drain. | *1 Fixt./260 SF Flr.* | Each | 11,110 | 42.73 | 21.2% |
| 2020 | Domestic Water Distribution | Electric, point-of-use water heater | | S.F. Floor | 2.52 | 2.52 | |
| 2040 | Rain Water Drainage | Roof drains | | S.F. Roof | .87 | .87 | |
| | **D30 HVAC** | | | | | | |
| 3010 | Energy Supply | N/A | | — | — | — | 10.2 % |
| 3020 | Heat Generating Systems | Included in D3050 | | — | — | — | |
| 3040 | Distribution Systems | Enthalpy heat recovery packages | | Each | 42,375 | .95 | |
| 3050 | Terminal & Package Units | Multizone rooftop air conditioner, SEER 14 | | S.F. Floor | 21.25 | 21.25 | |
| 3090 | Other HVAC Sys. & Equipment | N/A | | — | — | — | |
| | **D40 Fire Protection** | | | | | | |
| 4010 | Sprinklers | Sprinklers, light hazard | | S.F. Floor | 4.46 | 4.46 | 2.3% |
| 4020 | Standpipes | Standpipe, wet, Class III | | S.F. Floor | .54 | .54 | |
| | **D50 Electrical** | | | | | | |
| 5010 | Electrical Service/Distribution | 1000 ampere service, panel board and feeders | | S.F. Floor | 1.91 | 1.91 | 18.0% |
| 5020 | Lighting & Branch Wiring | LED fixtures, daylt. dim., ltg. on/off, recept., switches, & A.C. power | | S.F. Floor | 32.15 | 32.15 | |
| 5030 | Communications & Security | Addressable alarm systems, internet wiring, & emergency lighting | | S.F. Floor | 4.09 | 4.09 | |
| 5090 | Other Electrical Systems | Emergency generator, 11.5 kW, UPS, and energy monitoring systems | | S.F. Floor | .93 | .93 | |
| **E. EQUIPMENT & FURNISHINGS** | | | | | | | |
| 1010 | Commercial Equipment | N/A | | — | — | — | 1.9 % |
| 1020 | Institutional Equipment | Cabinets, fume hoods, lockers, glassware washer | | S.F. Floor | 3.86 | 3.86 | |
| 1090 | Other Equipment | Waste handling recycling tilt truck | | S.F. Floor | .15 | .15 | |
| 2020 | Moveable Furnishings | No smoking signage | | S.F. Floor | .03 | .03 | |
| **F. SPECIAL CONSTRUCTION** | | | | | | | |
| 1020 | Integrated Construction | N/A | | — | — | — | 0.0 % |
| 1040 | Special Facilities | N/A | | — | — | — | |
| **G. BUILDING SITEWORK** | **N/A** | | | | | | |
| | | | | | **Sub-Total** | 217.47 | **100%** |
| | CONTRACTOR FEES (General Requirements: 10%, Overhead: 5%, Profit: 10%) | | | | *25%* | 54.35 | |
| | ARCHITECT FEES | | | | *10%* | 27.18 | |
| | | | | | **Total Building Cost** | **299** | |

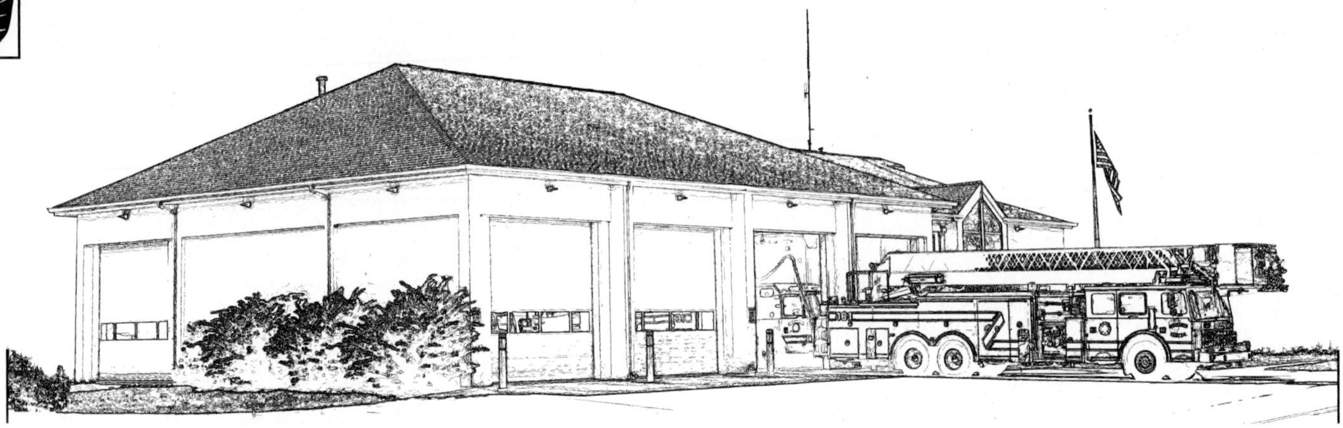

## Costs per square foot of floor area

| Exterior Wall | S.F. Area | 4000 | 4500 | 5000 | 5500 | 6000 | 6500 | 7000 | 7500 | 8000 |
|---|---|---|---|---|---|---|---|---|---|---|
| | L.F. Perimeter | 260 | 280 | 300 | 310 | 320 | 336 | 353 | 370 | 386 |
| Face Brick and Concrete Block | Steel Joists | 284.65 | 279.05 | 274.55 | 268.30 | **263.30** | 260.20 | 257.70 | 255.65 | 253.50 |
| | Bearing Walls | 277.00 | 271.40 | 266.90 | 260.70 | 255.65 | 252.55 | 250.10 | 248.00 | 245.90 |
| Decorative Concrete Block | Steel Joists | 265.85 | 261.00 | 257.15 | 252.00 | 247.80 | 245.15 | 243.10 | 241.30 | 239.50 |
| | Bearing Walls | 259.95 | 255.10 | 251.30 | 246.20 | 241.90 | 239.35 | 237.25 | 235.40 | 233.65 |
| Limestone and Concrete Block | Steel Joists | 299.55 | 293.25 | 288.30 | 281.30 | 275.45 | 272.00 | 269.25 | 266.90 | 264.60 |
| | Bearing Walls | 293.65 | 287.40 | 282.45 | 275.40 | 269.65 | 266.15 | 263.35 | 261.05 | 258.70 |
| Perimeter Adj., Add or Deduct | Per 100 L.F. | 33.25 | 29.45 | 26.50 | 24.25 | 22.10 | 20.40 | 18.95 | 17.70 | 16.60 |
| Story Hgt. Adj., Add or Deduct | Per 1 Ft. | 4.45 | 4.20 | 4.10 | 3.90 | 3.60 | 3.50 | 3.45 | 3.35 | 3.35 |

***For Basement**, add $64.40 per square foot of basement area*

*The above costs were calculated using the basic specifications shown on the facing page. These costs should be adjusted where necessary for design alternatives and owner's requirements.*

## Common additives

| Description | Unit | $ Cost |
|---|---|---|
| Appliances, cooking range, 30" free standing | | |
| 1 oven | Ea. | 885 - 1300 |
| 2 oven | Ea. | 3975 - 5050 |
| Microwave oven | Ea. | 375 - 895 |
| Compactor, residential, 4-1 compaction | Ea. | 1600 - 1875 |
| Dishwasher, built-in, 2 cycles | Ea. | 965 - 1900 |
| 4 cycles | Ea. | 1150 - 1700 |
| Garbage disposer, sink type | Ea. | 300 - 445 |
| Hood for range, 2 speed, vented, 30" wide | Ea. | 425 - 1750 |
| Refrigerator, no frost 10-12 C.F. | Ea. | 1000 - 855 |
| 14-16 C.F. | Ea. | 905 - 1050 |
| 18-20 C.F. | Ea. | 960 - 1100 |
| Lockers, Steel, single tier, 60" or 72" | Opng. | 285 - 520 |
| Locker bench, lam. maple top only | L.F. | 148 |
| Pedestals, steel pipe | Ea. | 87 |
| Sound System, amplifier, 250 watts | Ea. | 2425 |
| Speaker, ceiling or wall | Ea. | 320 |
| Trumpet | Ea. | 580 |

| Description | Unit | $ Cost |
|---|---|---|
| Commissioning Fees, sustainable commercial construction | S.F. | 0.24 - 3.04 |
| Energy Modelling Fees, Fire Stations to 10,000 SF | Ea. | 11,000 |
| Green Bldg Cert Fees for comm construction project reg | Project | 1200 |
| Photovoltaic Pwr Sys, grid connected, 20 kW (~2400 SF), roof | Ea. | 92,200 |
| Green Roofs, 6" soil depth, w/treated wd edging & sedum mats | S.F. | 28.30 |
| 10" Soil depth, with treated wood edging & sedum mats | S.F. | 30.65 |
| Greywater Recovery Systems, prepackaged comm, 3060 gal. | Ea. | 70,415 |
| 4590 gal. | Ea. | 88,275 |
| Rainwater Harvest Sys, prepckged comm, 10,000 gal, sys contrller | Ea. | 44,975 |
| 20,000 gal. w/system controller | Ea. | 73,350 |
| 30,000 gal. w/system controller | Ea. | 108,025 |
| Solar Domestic HW, closed loop, add-on sys, ext heat exchanger | Ea. | 13,550 |
| Drainback, hot water system, 120 gal tank | Ea. | 16,425 |

## Model costs calculated for a 1 story building with 14' story height and 6,000 square feet of floor area

# G Fire Station, 1 Story

| | | | | Unit | Unit Cost | Cost Per S.F. | % Of Sub-Total |
|---|---|---|---|---|---|---|---|
| **A. SUBSTRUCTURE** | | | | | | | |
| 1010 | Standard Foundations | Poured concrete; strip and spread footings | | S.F. Ground | 4.86 | 4.86 | 11.1% |
| 1020 | Special Foundations | N/A | | — | — | — | |
| 1030 | Slab on Grade | 6" reinforced concrete with recycled vapor barrier and granular base | | S.F. Slab | 9.63 | 9.63 | |
| 2010 | Basement Excavation | Site preparation for slab and trench for foundation wall and footing | | S.F. Ground | .66 | .66 | |
| 2020 | Basement Walls | 4' foundation wall | | L.F. Wall | 121 | 6.45 | |
| **B. SHELL** | | | | | | | |
| | **B10 Superstructure** | | | | | | |
| 1010 | Floor Construction | N/A | | — | — | — | 7.5 % |
| 1020 | Roof Construction | Metal deck, open web steel joists, beams on columns | | S.F. Roof | 14.63 | 14.63 | |
| | **B20 Exterior Enclosure** | | | | | | |
| 2010 | Exterior Walls | Face brick with concrete block backup | *75% of wall* | S.F. Wall | 48.36 | 27.08 | 20.7% |
| 2020 | Exterior Windows | Aluminum insulated glass | *10% of wall* | Each | 2490 | 5.81 | |
| 2030 | Exterior Doors | Single aluminum and glass, overhead, hollow metal, low VOC paint | *15% of wall* | S.F. Door | 4852 | 7.50 | |
| | **B30 Roofing** | | | | | | |
| 3010 | Roof Coverings | Single-ply TPO membrane, 60 mil, with flashing, R-20 insulation and roof edges | | S.F. Roof | 12.08 | 12.08 | 6.4% |
| 3020 | Roof Openings | Skylights, roof hatches | | S.F. Roof | .36 | .36 | |
| **C. INTERIORS** | | | | | | | |
| 1010 | Partitions | Concrete block w/foamed-in insulation | *17 S.F. Floor/LF Part.* | S.F. Partition | 12.63 | 7.43 | 10.7% |
| 1020 | Interior Doors | Single leaf hollow metal, low VOC paint | *500 S.F. Floor/Door* | Each | 1159 | 2.32 | |
| 1030 | Fittings | Toilet partitions | | S.F. Floor | .89 | .89 | |
| 2010 | Stair Construction | N/A | | — | — | — | |
| 3010 | Wall Finishes | Paint, low VOC | | S.F. Surface | 2.58 | 3.04 | |
| 3020 | Floor Finishes | 50% vinyl tile with recycled content, 50% paint, low VOC | | S.F. Floor | 2.62 | 2.62 | |
| 3030 | Ceiling Finishes | Mineral board acoustic ceiling tiles, concealed grid, suspended | *50% of area* | S.F. Ceiling | 4.50 | 4.51 | |
| **D. SERVICES** | | | | | | | |
| | **D10 Conveying** | | | | | | |
| 1010 | Elevators & Lifts | N/A | | — | — | — | 0.0 % |
| 1020 | Escalators & Moving Walks | N/A | | — | — | — | |
| | **D20 Plumbing** | | | | | | |
| 2010 | Plumbing Fixtures | Kitchen, toilet, low flow, auto sensor & service fixt., supply & drain. | *1 Fixt./375 SF Flr.* | Each | 6360 | 16.96 | 11.2% |
| 2020 | Domestic Water Distribution | Water heater, tankless, on-demand, natural gas/propane | | S.F. Floor | 3.09 | 3.09 | |
| 2040 | Rain Water Drainage | Roof drains | | S.F. Roof | 1.80 | 1.80 | |
| | **D30 HVAC** | | | | | | |
| 3010 | Energy Supply | N/A | | — | — | — | 13.3 % |
| 3020 | Heat Generating Systems | Included in D3050 | | — | — | — | |
| 3040 | Distribution Systems | Enthalpy heat recovery packages | | Each | 17,075 | 2.85 | |
| 3050 | Terminal & Package Units | Multizone rooftop air conditioner, SEER 14 | | S.F. Floor | 23.16 | 23.16 | |
| 3090 | Other HVAC Sys. & Equipment | N/A | | — | — | — | |
| | **D40 Fire Protection** | | | | | | |
| 4010 | Sprinklers | Wet pipe sprinkler system | | S.F. Floor | 6.60 | 6.60 | 4.7% |
| 4020 | Standpipes | Standpipe, wet, Class III | | S.F. Floor | 2.47 | 2.47 | |
| | **D50 Electrical** | | | | | | |
| 5010 | Electrical Service/Distribution | 200 ampere service, panel board and feeders | | S.F. Floor | 1.66 | 1.66 | 13.9% |
| 5020 | Lighting & Branch Wiring | LED fixt., daylt. dimming & ltg. on/off control, receptacles, switches, A.C. & misc. pwr. | | S.F. Floor | 18.30 | 18.30 | |
| 5030 | Communications & Security | Addressable alarm systems | | S.F. Floor | 1.83 | 1.83 | |
| 5090 | Other Electrical Systems | Energy monitoring systems | | S.F. Floor | 5.33 | 5.33 | |
| **E. EQUIPMENT & FURNISHINGS** | | | | | | | |
| 1010 | Commercial Equipment | N/A | | — | — | — | 0.6 % |
| 1020 | Institutional Equipment | N/A | | — | — | — | |
| 1090 | Other Equipment | Waste handling recycling tilt truck | | S.F. Floor | 1.07 | 1.07 | |
| 2020 | Moveable Furnishings | No smoking signage | | S.F. Floor | .03 | .03 | |
| **F. SPECIAL CONSTRUCTION** | | | | | | | |
| 1020 | Integrated Construction | N/A | | — | — | — | 0.0 % |
| 1040 | Special Facilities | N/A | | — | — | — | |
| **G. BUILDING SITEWORK** | **N/A** | | | | | | |
| | | | | | **Sub-Total** | 195.02 | **100%** |
| | CONTRACTOR FEES (General Requirements: 10%, Overhead: 5%, Profit: 10%) | | | | *25%* | 48.78 | |
| | ARCHITECT FEES | | | | *8%* | 19.50 | |
| | | | | | **Total Building Cost** | **263.30** | |

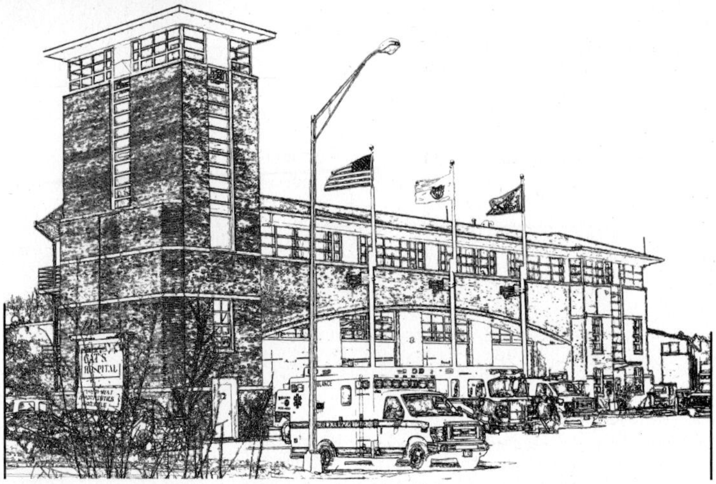

## Costs per square foot of floor area

| Exterior Wall | S.F. Area | 6000 | 7000 | 8000 | 9000 | 10000 | 11000 | 12000 | 13000 | 14000 |
|---|---|---|---|---|---|---|---|---|---|---|
| | L.F. Perimeter | 220 | 240 | 260 | 280 | 286 | 303 | 320 | 336 | 353 |
| Face Brick and Concrete Block | Steel Joists | 287.25 | 279.05 | 273.10 | 268.25 | 261.60 | 258.20 | 255.35 | 252.80 | 250.75 |
| | Precast Concrete | 299.20 | 291.15 | 285.20 | 280.50 | 273.85 | 270.45 | 267.70 | 265.15 | 263.10 |
| Decorative Concrete Block | Steel Joists | 258.55 | 251.60 | 246.45 | 242.35 | **236.80** | 233.90 | 231.50 | 229.30 | 227.55 |
| | Precast Concrete | 281.85 | 274.95 | 269.80 | 265.75 | 260.30 | 257.45 | 255.05 | 252.90 | 251.15 |
| Limestone and Concrete Block | Steel Joists | 304.00 | 294.80 | 287.95 | 282.55 | 274.70 | 270.80 | 267.60 | 264.65 | 262.30 |
| | Precast Concrete | 316.00 | 306.90 | 300.10 | 294.70 | 286.95 | 283.10 | 279.85 | 276.95 | 274.65 |
| Perimeter Adj., Add or Deduct | Per 100 L.F. | 35.40 | 30.50 | 26.60 | 23.70 | 21.30 | 19.35 | 17.70 | 16.40 | 15.20 |
| Story Hgt. Adj., Add or Deduct | Per 1 Ft. | 4.55 | 4.35 | 4.05 | 3.95 | 3.60 | 3.50 | 3.30 | 3.20 | 3.15 |

***For Basement**, add $62.50 per square foot of basement area*

*The above costs were calculated using the basic specifications shown on the facing page. These costs should be adjusted where necessary for design alternatives and owner's requirements.*

## Common additives

| Description | Unit | $ Cost |
|---|---|---|
| Appliances | | |
| Cooking range, 30" free standing | | |
| 1 oven | Ea. | 885 - 1300 |
| 2 oven | Ea. | 3975 - 5050 |
| Microwave oven | Ea. | 375 - 895 |
| Compactor, residential, 4-1 compaction | Ea. | 1600 - 1875 |
| Dishwasher, built-in, 2 cycles | Ea. | 965 - 1900 |
| 4 cycles | Ea. | 1150 - 1700 |
| Garbage diposer, sink type | Ea. | 300 - 445 |
| Hood for range, 2 speed, vented, 30" wide | Ea. | 425 - 1750 |
| Refrigerator, no frost 10-12 C.F. | Ea. | 1000 - 855 |
| 14-16 C.F. | Ea. | 905 - 1050 |
| 18-20 C.F. | Ea. | 960 - 1100 |
| Elevators, hydraulic passenger, 2 stops, 2500# capacity | Ea. | 90,500 |
| 3500# capacity | Ea. | 96,000 |
| Lockers, Steel, single tier, 60" or 72" | Opng. | 285 - 520 |
| Locker bench, lam. maple top only | L.F. | 148 |
| Pedestals, steel pipe | Ea. | 87 |
| Sound System, amplifier, 250 watts | Ea. | 2425 |
| Speaker, ceiling or wall | Ea. | 320 |
| Trumpet | Ea. | 580 |

| Description | Unit | $ Cost |
|---|---|---|
| Commissioning Fees, sustainable commercial construction | S.F. | 0.24 - 3.04 |
| Energy Modelling Fees, Fire Stations to 10,000 SF | Ea. | 11,000 |
| Greater than 10,000 SF add | S.F. | 0.04 |
| Green Bldg Cert Fees for comm construction project reg | Project | 1200 |
| Photovoltaic Pwr Sys, grid connected, 20 kW (~2400 SF), roof | Ea. | 92,200 |
| Green Roofs, 6" soil depth, w/treated wd edging & sedum mats | S.F. | 28.30 |
| 10" Soil depth, with treated wood edging & sedum mats | S.F. | 30.65 |
| Greywater Recovery Systems, prepackaged comm, 3060 gal. | Ea. | 70,415 |
| 4590 gal. | Ea. | 88,275 |
| Rainwater Harvest Sys, prepckged comm, 10,000 gal, sys contrller | Ea. | 44,975 |
| 20,000 gal. w/system controller | Ea. | 73,350 |
| 30,000 gal. w/system controller | Ea. | 108,025 |
| Solar Domestic HW, closed loop, add-on sys, ext heat exchanger | Ea. | 13,550 |
| Drainback, hot water system, 120 gal tank | Ea. | 16,425 |



**Important: See the Reference Section for Location Factors.**

## Model costs calculated for a 2 story building with 14′ story height and 10,000 square feet of floor area

# G Fire Station, 2 Story

| | | | | Unit | Unit Cost | Cost Per S.F. | % Of Sub-Total |
|---|---|---|---|---|---|---|---|
| **A. SUBSTRUCTURE** | | | | | | | |
| 1010 | Standard Foundations | Poured concrete; strip and spread footings | | S.F. Ground | 4.56 | 2.28 | 6.4% |
| 1020 | Special Foundations | N/A | | — | — | — | |
| 1030 | Slab on Grade | 6″ reinforced concrete with recycled vapor barrier and granular base | | S.F. Slab | 9.63 | 4.82 | |
| 2010 | Basement Excavation | Site preparation for slab and trench for foundation wall and footing | | S.F. Ground | .66 | .33 | |
| 2020 | Basement Walls | 4′ foundation wall with insulation | | L.F. Wall | 134 | 3.82 | |
| **B. SHELL** | | | | | | | |
| | **B10 Superstructure** | | | | | | |
| 1010 | Floor Construction | Open web steel joists, slab form, concrete | | S.F. Floor | 21.30 | 10.65 | 8.4% |
| 1020 | Roof Construction | Metal deck on open web steel joists | | S.F. Roof | 8.16 | 4.08 | |
| | **B20 Exterior Enclosure** | | | | | | |
| 2010 | Exterior Walls | Decorative concrete block, insul. | *75% of wall* | S.F. Wall | 31.65 | 19.01 | 15.9% |
| 2020 | Exterior Windows | Aluminum insulated glass | *10% of wall* | Each | 839 | 2.92 | |
| 2030 | Exterior Doors | Single aluminum and glass, steel overhead, hollow metal, low VOC paint | *15% of wall* | S.F. Door | 3543 | 5.97 | |
| | **B30 Roofing** | | | | | | |
| 3010 | Roof Coverings | Single-ply TPO, 60 mils, heat welded seams w/R-20 insul. | | S.F. Roof | 12.36 | 6.18 | 3.5% |
| 3020 | Roof Openings | N/A | | — | — | — | |
| **C. INTERIORS** | | | | | | | |
| 1010 | Partitions | Concrete block, foamed-in insul. | *10 SF Floor/LF Part.* | S.F. Partition | 12.63 | 7.43 | 16.7% |
| 1020 | Interior Doors | Single leaf hollow metal, low VOC paint | *500 S.F. Floor/Door* | Each | 2060 | 4.12 | |
| 1030 | Fittings | Toilet partitions | | S.F. Floor | .80 | .80 | |
| 2010 | Stair Construction | Concrete filled metal pan | | Flight | 22,275 | 4.46 | |
| 3010 | Wall Finishes | Paint, low VOC | | S.F. Surface | 4.34 | 5.10 | |
| 3020 | Floor Finishes | 50% vinyl tile, (recycled content) 50% paint (low VOC) | | S.F. Floor | 2.62 | 2.62 | |
| 3030 | Ceiling Finishes | Fiberglass board on exposed grid, suspended | *50% of area* | S.F. Ceiling | 4.74 | 4.75 | |
| **D. SERVICES** | | | | | | | |
| | **D10 Conveying** | | | | | | |
| 1010 | Elevators & Lifts | One hydraulic passenger elevator | | Each | 107,000 | 10.70 | 6.1% |
| 1020 | Escalators & Moving Walks | N/A | | — | — | — | |
| | **D20 Plumbing** | | | | | | |
| 2010 | Plumbing Fixtures | Kitchen, toilet low flow, auto sensor & service fixt., supply & drain. | *1 Fixt./400 SF Flr.* | Each | 6228 | 15.57 | 10.2% |
| 2020 | Domestic Water Distribution | Gas fired tankless water heater | | S.F. Floor | 1.25 | 1.25 | |
| 2040 | Rain Water Drainage | Roof drains | | S.F. Roof | 2.16 | 1.08 | |
| | **D30 HVAC** | | | | | | |
| 3010 | Energy Supply | N/A | | — | — | — | 14.2 % |
| 3020 | Heat Generating Systems | Included in D3050 | | — | — | — | |
| 3040 | Distribution Systems | Enthalpy heat recovery packages | | Each | 17,075 | 1.71 | |
| 3050 | Terminal & Package Units | Multizone rooftop air conditioner, SEER 14 | | S.F. Floor | 23.16 | 23.16 | |
| 3090 | Other HVAC Sys. & Equipment | N/A | | — | — | — | |
| | **D40 Fire Protection** | | | | | | |
| 4010 | Sprinklers | Wet pipe sprinkler system | | S.F. Floor | 5.47 | 5.47 | 4.6% |
| 4020 | Standpipes | Standpipe, wet, Class III | | S.F. Floor | 2.56 | 2.56 | |
| | **D50 Electrical** | | | | | | |
| 5010 | Electrical Service/Distribution | 400 ampere service, panel board and feeders | | S.F. Floor | 1.41 | 1.41 | 13.8% |
| 5020 | Lighting & Branch Wiring | LED fixt., daylt. dimming & ltg. on/off control., receptacles, switches, A.C. and misc. pwr. | | S.F. Floor | 18.59 | 18.59 | |
| 5030 | Communications & Security | Addressable alarm systems and emergency lighting | | S.F. Floor | 1.53 | 1.53 | |
| 5090 | Other Electrical Systems | Emergency generator, 15 kW, and energy monitoring systems | | S.F. Floor | 2.69 | 2.69 | |
| **E. EQUIPMENT & FURNISHINGS** | | | | | | | |
| 1010 | Commercial Equipment | N/A | | — | — | — | 0.2 % |
| 1020 | Institutional Equipment | N/A | | — | — | — | |
| 1090 | Other Equipment | Waste handling recycling tilt truck | | S.F. Floor | .33 | .33 | |
| 2020 | Moveable Furnishings | No smoking signage | | S.F. Floor | .02 | .02 | |
| **F. SPECIAL CONSTRUCTION** | | | | | | | |
| 1020 | Integrated Construction | N/A | | — | — | — | 0.0 % |
| 1040 | Special Facilities | N/A | | — | — | — | |
| **G. BUILDING SITEWORK** | **N/A** | | | | | | |
| | | | | | **Sub-Total** | 175.41 | **100%** |
| | CONTRACTOR FEES (General Requirements: 10%, Overhead: 5%, Profit: 10%) | | | | *25%* | 43.85 | |
| | ARCHITECT FEES | | | | *8%* | 17.54 | |
| | | | | | **Total Building Cost** | **236.80** | |

## Costs per square foot of floor area

| Exterior Wall | S.F. Area | 4000 | 6000 | 8000 | 10000 | 12000 | 14000 | 16000 | 18000 | 20000 |
|---|---|---|---|---|---|---|---|---|---|---|
| | L.F. Perimeter | 260 | 320 | 384 | 424 | 460 | 484 | 510 | 540 | 576 |
| Wood Board and Batten | Wood Frame | 227.75 | 211.95 | 204.40 | 197.90 | 193.35 | 189.45 | 186.65 | 184.60 | 183.10 |
| Brick Veneer | Wood Frame | 239.05 | 221.60 | 213.35 | 206.15 | 201.00 | 196.50 | 193.35 | 191.05 | 189.45 |
| Aluminum Clapboard | Wood Frame | 220.70 | 206.60 | 199.80 | 194.15 | 190.20 | 186.75 | 184.30 | 182.60 | 181.30 |
| Face Brick and Concrete Block | Wood Truss | 257.35 | 237.60 | 228.25 | 219.95 | 214.00 | 208.80 | 205.05 | 202.35 | 200.55 |
| Limestone and Concrete Block | Wood Truss | 275.60 | 252.55 | 241.70 | 231.75 | 224.75 | 218.45 | 213.95 | 210.80 | 208.60 |
| Stucco and Concrete Block | Wood Truss | 270.80 | 248.25 | 237.55 | 227.90 | 220.95 | 214.80 | 210.45 | 207.30 | 205.20 |
| Perimeter Adj., Add or Deduct | Per 100 L.F. | 20.05 | 13.35 | 10.00 | 8.05 | 6.70 | 5.65 | 5.00 | 4.40 | 4.10 |
| Story Hgt. Adj., Add or Deduct | Per 1 Ft. | 2.65 | 2.15 | 1.95 | 1.75 | 1.60 | 1.35 | 1.25 | 1.15 | 1.20 |
| ***For Basement**, add $53.00 per square foot of basement area* | | | | | | | | | | |

*The above costs were calculated using the basic specifications shown on the facing page. These costs should be adjusted where necessary for design alternatives and owner's requirements.*

## Common additives

| Description | Unit | $ Cost |
|---|---|---|
| Autopsy Table, standard | Ea. | 10,300 |
| Deluxe | Ea. | 4925 |
| Directory Boards, plastic, glass covered, 30″ x 20″ | Ea. | 705 |
| 36″ x 48″ | Ea. | 1475 |
| Aluminum, 24″ x 18″ | Ea. | 705 |
| 36″ x 24″ | Ea. | 985 |
| 48″ x 32″ | Ea. | 1975 |
| Mortuary Refrigerator, end operated | | |
| Two capacity | Ea. | 6750 |
| Six capacity | Ea. | 14,900 |
| Planters, precast concrete, 48″ diam., 24″ high | Ea. | 745 |
| 7″ diam., 36″ high | Ea. | 2175 |
| Fiberglass, 36″ diam., 24″ high | Ea. | 565 |
| 60″ diam., 24″ high | Ea. | 1225 |

| Description | Unit | $ Cost |
|---|---|---|
| Commissioning Fees, sustainable commercial construction | S.F. | 0.24 - 3.04 |
| Energy Modelling Fees, commercial buildings to 10,000 SF | Ea. | 11,000 |
| Greater than 10,000 SF add | S.F. | 0.04 |
| Green Bldg Cert Fees for comm construction project reg | Project | 1200 |
| Photovoltaic Pwr Sys, grid connected, 20 kW (~2400 SF), roof | Ea. | 92,200 |
| Green Roofs, 6″ soil depth, w/treated wd edging & sedum mats | S.F. | 28.30 |
| 10″ Soil depth, with treated wood edging & sedum mats | S.F. | 30.65 |
| Greywater Recovery Systems, prepackaged comm, 3060 gal. | Ea. | 70,415 |
| 4590 gal. | Ea. | 88,275 |
| Rainwater Harvest Sys, prepckged comm, 10,000 gal, sys contrller | Ea. | 44,975 |
| 20,000 gal. w/system controller | Ea. | 73,350 |
| 30,000 gal. w/system controller | Ea. | 108,025 |
| Solar Domestic HW, closed loop, add-on sys, ext heat exchanger | Ea. | 13,550 |
| Drainback, hot water system, 120 gal tank | Ea. | 16,425 |
| Draindown, hot water system, 120 gal tank | Ea. | 16,700 |



**Important: See the Reference Section for Location Factors.**

# Model costs calculated for a 1 story building with 12′ story height and 10,000 square feet of floor area

# G Funeral Home

| | | | | Unit | Unit Cost | Cost Per S.F. | % Of Sub-Total |
|---|---|---|---|---|---|---|---|
| **A. SUBSTRUCTURE** | | | | | | | |
| 1010 | Standard Foundations | Poured concrete; strip and spread footings | | S.F. Ground | 2.66 | 2.66 | 10.6% |
| 1020 | Special Foundations | N/A | | — | — | — | |
| 1030 | Slab on Grade | 4″ reinforced concrete with recycled plastic vapor barrier and granular base | | S.F. Slab | 7.32 | 7.32 | |
| 2010 | Basement Excavation | Site preparation for slab and trench for foundation wall and footing | | S.F. Ground | .38 | .38 | |
| 2020 | Basement Walls | 4′ foundation wall | | L.F. Wall | 108 | 5.03 | |
| **B. SHELL** | | | | | | | |
| | **B10 Superstructure** | | | | | | |
| 1010 | Floor Construction | N/A | | — | — | — | 4.5 % |
| 1020 | Roof Construction | Plywood on wood truss | | S.F. Roof | 6.59 | 6.59 | |
| | **B20 Exterior Enclosure** | | | | | | |
| 2010 | Exterior Walls | 1″ x 4″ vertical T & G redwood siding on 2x6 wood studs with insul. | *90% of wall* | S.F. Wall | 24.65 | 11.29 | 11.7% |
| 2020 | Exterior Windows | Double hung wood | *10% of wall* | Each | 670 | 2.84 | |
| 2030 | Exterior Doors | Wood swinging double doors, single leaf hollow metal, low VOC paint | | Each | 4795 | 2.88 | |
| | **B30 Roofing** | | | | | | |
| 3010 | Roof Coverings | Single ply membrane, TPO, 45 mil, fully adhered; polyisocyanurate sheets | | S.F. Roof | 8.67 | 8.67 | 6.0% |
| 3020 | Roof Openings | N/A | | — | — | — | |
| **C. INTERIORS** | | | | | | | |
| 1010 | Partitions | Gypsum board on wood studs with sound deadening board | *15 SF Flr./LF Part.* | S.F. Partition | 12.39 | 6.61 | 26.1% |
| 1020 | Interior Doors | Single leaf wood, low VOC paint | *150 S.F. Floor/Door* | Each | 1231 | 8.21 | |
| 1030 | Fittings | N/A | | — | — | — | |
| 2010 | Stair Construction | N/A | | — | — | — | |
| 3010 | Wall Finishes | 50% wallpaper, 25% wood paneling, 25% paint (low VOC) | | S.F. Surface | 3.95 | 4.21 | |
| 3020 | Floor Finishes | 70% carpet tile, 30% ceramic tile | | S.F. Floor | 9.41 | 9.41 | |
| 3030 | Ceiling Finishes | Fiberglass board on exposed grid, suspended | | S.F. Ceiling | 9.48 | 9.48 | |
| **D. SERVICES** | | | | | | | |
| | **D10 Conveying** | | | | | | |
| 1010 | Elevators & Lifts | N/A | | — | — | — | 0.0 % |
| 1020 | Escalators & Moving Walks | N/A | | — | — | — | |
| | **D20 Plumbing** | | | | | | |
| 2010 | Plumbing Fixtures | Toilets, low flow, auto sensor, urinals & service fixt., supply & drain. | *1 Fixt./770 SF Flr.* | Each | 5074 | 6.59 | 6.1% |
| 2020 | Domestic Water Distribution | Electric water heater, point-of-use | | S.F. Floor | .72 | .72 | |
| 2040 | Rain Water Drainage | Roof drain | | S.F. Roof | 1.50 | 1.50 | |
| | **D30 HVAC** | | | | | | |
| 3010 | Energy Supply | N/A | | — | — | — | 17.4 % |
| 3020 | Heat Generating Systems | Included in D3050 | | — | — | — | |
| 3040 | Distribution Systems | Enthalpy heat recovery packages | | Each | 42,375 | 4.24 | |
| 3050 | Terminal & Package Units | Multizone rooftop air conditioner, SEER 14 | | S.F. Floor | 21 | 21 | |
| 3090 | Other HVAC Sys. & Equipment | N/A | | — | — | — | |
| | **D40 Fire Protection** | | | | | | |
| 4010 | Sprinklers | Wet pipe sprinkler system | | S.F. Floor | 5.07 | 5.07 | 4.5% |
| 4020 | Standpipes | Standpipe, wet, Class III | | S.F. Floor | 1.48 | 1.48 | |
| | **D50 Electrical** | | | | | | |
| 5010 | Electrical Service/Distribution | 400 ampere service, panel board and feeders | | S.F. Floor | 1.87 | 1.87 | 12.7% |
| 5020 | Lighting & Branch Wiring | LED light fixtures, daylt. dimming control & ltg. on/off sys., recept., switches, & A.C. power | | S.F. Floor | 12.55 | 12.55 | |
| 5030 | Communications & Security | Addressable alarm systems | | S.F. Floor | 1.53 | 1.53 | |
| 5090 | Other Electrical Systems | Emergency generator, 15 kW and energy monitoring systems | | S.F. Floor | 2.47 | 2.47 | |
| **E. EQUIPMENT & FURNISHINGS** | | | | | | | |
| 1010 | Commercial Equipment | N/A | | — | — | — | 0.5 % |
| 1020 | Institutional Equipment | N/A | | — | — | — | |
| 1090 | Other Equipment | Waste handling recycling tilt truck | | S.F. Floor | .64 | .64 | |
| 2020 | Moveable Furnishings | No smoking signage | | S.F. Floor | .03 | .03 | |
| **F. SPECIAL CONSTRUCTION** | | | | | | | |
| 1020 | Integrated Construction | N/A | | — | — | — | 0.0 % |
| 1040 | Special Facilities | N/A | | — | — | — | |
| **G. BUILDING SITEWORK** | **N/A** | | | | | | |
| | | | | | **Sub-Total** | 145.27 | **100%** |
| | CONTRACTOR FEES (General Requirements: 10%, Overhead: 5%, Profit: 10%) | | | | *25%* | 36.29 | |
| | ARCHITECT FEES | | | | *9%* | 16.34 | |
| | | | | | **Total Building Cost** | **197.90** | |

## Costs per square foot of floor area

| Exterior Wall | S.F. Area | 7000 | 10000 | 13000 | 16000 | 19000 | 22000 | 25000 | 28000 | 31000 |
|---|---|---|---|---|---|---|---|---|---|---|
| | L.F. Perimeter | 240 | 300 | 336 | 386 | 411 | 435 | 472 | 510 | 524 |
| Face Brick and Concrete Block | Reinforced Concrete | 276.95 | 262.90 | 250.70 | 245.25 | 238.35 | **233.15** | 230.50 | 228.50 | 225.00 |
| | Rigid Steel | 271.25 | 257.15 | 244.95 | 239.55 | 232.65 | 227.45 | 224.80 | 222.80 | 219.30 |
| Limestone and Concrete Block | Reinforced Concrete | 301.70 | 283.70 | 268.25 | 261.30 | 252.55 | 245.95 | 242.60 | 240.00 | 235.55 |
| | Rigid Steel | 293.40 | 276.55 | 261.70 | 255.15 | 246.65 | 240.25 | 237.00 | 234.60 | 230.20 |
| Precast Concrete | Reinforced Concrete | 311.90 | 292.65 | 275.95 | 268.45 | 258.95 | 251.85 | 248.20 | 245.45 | 240.60 |
| | Rigid Steel | 306.20 | 286.95 | 270.20 | 262.80 | 253.25 | 246.15 | 242.55 | 239.75 | 234.90 |
| Perimeter Adj., Add or Deduct | Per 100 L.F. | 34.75 | 24.30 | 18.75 | 15.25 | 12.85 | 11.10 | 9.75 | 8.70 | 7.90 |
| Story Hgt. Adj., Add or Deduct | Per 1 Ft. | 5.25 | 4.60 | 3.95 | 3.70 | 3.35 | 3.05 | 2.95 | 2.85 | 2.60 |
| ***For Basement**, add $79.10 per square foot of basement area* | | | | | | | | | | |

*The above costs were calculated using the basic specifications shown on the facing page. These costs should be adjusted where necessary for design alternatives and owner's requirements.*

## Common additives

| Description | Unit | $ Cost |
|---|---|---|
| Carrels Hardwood | Ea. | 395 - 2350 |
| Closed Circuit Surveillance, one station, camera and monitor | Ea. | 1250 |
| For additional camera stations, add | Ea. | 475 |
| Elevators, hydraulic passenger, 2 stops, 1500# capacity | Ea. | 86,500 |
| 2500# capacity | Ea. | 90,500 |
| 3500# capacity | Ea. | 96,000 |
| Library Furnishings, bookshelf, 90" high, 10" shelf double face | L.F. | 300 |
| Single face | L.F. | 191 |
| Charging desk, built-in with counter | | |
| Plastic laminated top | L.F. | 710 |
| Reading table, laminated | | |
| Top 60" x 36" | Ea. | 500 |

| Description | Unit | $ Cost |
|---|---|---|
| Commissioning Fees, sustainable institutional construction | S.F. | 0.58 - 2.47 |
| Energy Modelling Fees, commercial buildings to 10,000 SF | Ea. | 11,000 |
| Greater than 10,000 SF add | S.F. | 0.04 |
| Green Bldg Cert Fees for comm construction project reg | Project | 1200 |
| Photovoltaic Pwr Sys, grid connected, 20 kW (~2400 SF), roof | Ea. | 92,200 |
| Green Roofs, 6" soil depth, w/treated wd edging & sedum mats | S.F. | 28.30 |
| 10" Soil depth, with treated wood edging & sedum mats | S.F. | 30.65 |
| Greywater Recovery Systems, prepackaged comm, 3060 gal. | Ea. | 70,415 |
| 4590 gal. | Ea. | 88,275 |
| Rainwater Harvest Sys, prepckged comm, 10,000 gal, sys contrller | Ea. | 44,975 |
| 20,000 gal. w/system controller | Ea. | 73,350 |
| 30,000 gal. w/system controller | Ea. | 108,025 |
| Solar Domestic HW, closed loop, add-on sys, ext heat exchanger | Ea. | 13,550 |
| Drainback, hot water system, 120 gal tank | Ea. | 16,425 |
| Draindown, hot water system, 120 gal tank | Ea. | 16,700 |



**Important: See the Reference Section for Location Factors.**

## Model costs calculated for a 2 story building with 14′ story height and 22,000 square feet of floor area

## G Library

| | | | | Unit | Unit Cost | Cost Per S.F. | % Of Sub-Total |
|---|---|---|---|---|---|---|---|
| **A. SUBSTRUCTURE** | | | | | | | |
| 1010 | Standard Foundations | Poured concrete; strip and spread footings | | S.F. Ground | 5.56 | 2.78 | |
| 1020 | Special Foundations | N/A | | – | – | – | |
| 1030 | Slab on Grade | 4″ reinforced concrete with recycled vapor barrier and granular base | | S.F. Slab | 7.32 | 3.66 | 5.2% |
| 2010 | Basement Excavation | Site preparation for slab and trench for foundation wall and footing | | S.F. Ground | .38 | .19 | |
| 2020 | Basement Walls | 4′ foundation wall | | L.F. Wall | 121 | 2.39 | |
| **B. SHELL** | | | | | | | |
| | **B10 Superstructure** | | | | | | |
| 1010 | Floor Construction | Concrete waffle slab | | S.F. Floor | 40.62 | 20.31 | 20.6% |
| 1020 | Roof Construction | Concrete waffle slab | | S.F. Roof | 30.60 | 15.30 | |
| | **B20 Exterior Enclosure** | | | | | | |
| 2010 | Exterior Walls | Face brick with concrete block backup | *90% of wall* | S.F. Wall | 47.50 | 23.67 | |
| 2020 | Exterior Windows | Window wall | *10% of wall* | Each | 88 | 4.86 | 17.0% |
| 2030 | Exterior Doors | Double aluminum and glass, single leaf hollow metal, low VOC paint | | Each | 9150 | .83 | |
| | **B30 Roofing** | | | | | | |
| 3010 | Roof Coverings | Single-ply TPO membrane, 60 mil, heat welded w/R-20 insulation | | S.F. Roof | 10.78 | 5.39 | 3.2% |
| 3020 | Roof Openings | Roof hatches | | S.F. Roof | .18 | .09 | |
| **C. INTERIORS** | | | | | | | |
| 1010 | Partitions | Gypsum board on metal studs w/sound attenuation insul. | *30 SF Flr./LF Part.* | S.F. Partition | 16.73 | 6.69 | |
| 1020 | Interior Doors | Single leaf wood, low VOC paint | *300 S.F. Floor/Door* | Each | 1231 | 4.10 | |
| 1030 | Fittings | N/A | | – | – | – | |
| 2010 | Stair Construction | Concrete filled metal pan | | Flight | 11,950 | 1.09 | 15.6% |
| 3010 | Wall Finishes | Paint, low VOC | | S.F. Surface | 2.08 | 1.66 | |
| 3020 | Floor Finishes | 50% carpet tile, 50% vinyl composition tile, recycled content | | S.F. Floor | 4.39 | 4.39 | |
| 3030 | Ceiling Finishes | Mineral fiber on concealed zee bars | | S.F. Ceiling | 9 | 9 | |
| **D. SERVICES** | | | | | | | |
| | **D10 Conveying** | | | | | | |
| 1010 | Elevators & Lifts | One hydraulic passenger elevator | | Each | 111,100 | 5.05 | 2.9% |
| 1020 | Escalators & Moving Walks | N/A | | – | – | – | |
| | **D20 Plumbing** | | | | | | |
| 2010 | Plumbing Fixtures | Toilet, low flow, auto sensor & service fixt., supply & drain. | *1 Fixt./1835 SF.Flr.* | Each | 11,726 | 6.39 | |
| 2020 | Domestic Water Distribution | Tankless, on demand water heater, gas/propane | | S.F. Floor | .84 | .84 | 4.7% |
| 2040 | Rain Water Drainage | Roof drains | | S.F. Roof | 1.80 | .90 | |
| | **D30 HVAC** | | | | | | |
| 3010 | Energy Supply | N/A | | – | – | – | |
| 3020 | Heat Generating Systems | Included in D3050 | | – | – | – | |
| 3040 | Distribution Systems | Enthalpy heat recovery packages | | Each | 42,375 | 1.92 | 13.8 % |
| 3050 | Terminal & Package Units | Multizone rooftop air conditioner, SEER 14 | | S.F. Floor | 21.90 | 21.90 | |
| 3090 | Other HVAC Sys. & Equipment | N/A | | – | – | – | |
| | **D40 Fire Protection** | | | | | | |
| 4010 | Sprinklers | Wet pipe sprinkler system | | S.F. Floor | 4.57 | 4.57 | 3.6% |
| 4020 | Standpipes | Standpipe | | S.F. Floor | 1.62 | 1.62 | |
| | **D50 Electrical** | | | | | | |
| 5010 | Electrical Service/Distribution | 400 ampere service, panel board and feeders | | S.F. Floor | .70 | .70 | |
| 5020 | Lighting & Branch Wiring | LED fixtures, daylt. dim., ltg. on/off, recept., switches, and A.C. power | | S.F. Floor | 18.14 | 18.14 | 13.2% |
| 5030 | Communications & Security | Addressable alarm systems, internet wiring, and emergency lighting | | S.F. Floor | 2.58 | 2.58 | |
| 5090 | Other Electrical Systems | Emergency generator, 7.5 kW, UPS, energy monitoring systems | | S.F. Floor | 1.42 | 1.42 | |
| **E. EQUIPMENT & FURNISHINGS** | | | | | | | |
| 1010 | Commercial Equipment | N/A | | – | – | – | |
| 1020 | Institutional Equipment | N/A | | – | – | – | 0.2 % |
| 1090 | Other Equipment | Waste handling recycling tilt truck | | S.F. Floor | .29 | .29 | |
| 2020 | Moveable Furnishings | No smoking signage | | S.F. Floor | | | |
| **F. SPECIAL CONSTRUCTION** | | | | | | | |
| 1020 | Integrated Construction | N/A | | – | – | – | 0.0 % |
| 1040 | Special Facilities | N/A | | – | – | – | |
| **G. BUILDING SITEWORK** | **N/A** | | | | | | |
| | | | | | **Sub-Total** | 172.72 | **100%** |
| | CONTRACTOR FEES (General Requirements: 10%, Overhead: 5%, Profit: 10%) | | | | *25%* | 43.16 | |
| | ARCHITECT FEES | | | | *8%* | 17.27 | |
| | | | | | **Total Building Cost** | **233.15** | |

## Costs per square foot of floor area

| Exterior Wall | S.F. Area | 4000 | 5500 | 7000 | 8500 | 10000 | 11500 | 13000 | 14500 | 16000 |
|---|---|---|---|---|---|---|---|---|---|---|
| | L.F. Perimeter | 280 | 320 | 380 | 440 | 453 | 503 | 510 | 522 | 560 |
| Face Brick and Concrete Block | Steel Joists | 349.90 | 335.10 | 329.60 | 325.95 | 318.75 | 316.60 | 311.70 | 308.10 | 306.85 |
| | Wood Truss | 349.35 | 334.55 | **329.00** | 325.40 | 318.15 | 316.05 | 311.15 | 307.55 | 306.35 |
| Stucco and Concrete Block | Steel Joists | 357.70 | 341.05 | 334.90 | 330.90 | 322.65 | 320.25 | 314.65 | 310.55 | 309.10 |
| | Wood Truss | 360.35 | 343.70 | 337.55 | 333.55 | 325.30 | 322.95 | 317.30 | 313.20 | 311.85 |
| Brick Veneer | Wood Truss | 338.90 | 325.70 | 320.55 | 317.30 | 310.95 | 309.00 | 304.60 | 301.50 | 300.35 |
| Wood Clapboard | Wood Frame | 326.90 | 315.90 | 311.60 | 308.80 | 303.70 | 302.00 | 298.55 | 296.00 | 295.05 |
| Perimeter Adj., Add or Deduct | Per 100 L.F. | 24.85 | 18.20 | 14.20 | 11.70 | 10.00 | 8.70 | 7.70 | 6.90 | 6.25 |
| Story Hgt. Adj., Add or Deduct | Per 1 Ft. | 5.00 | 4.20 | 3.85 | 3.70 | 3.25 | 3.15 | 2.80 | 2.60 | 2.55 |
| ***For Basement**, add $51.55 per square foot of basement area* | | | | | | | | | | |

*The above costs were calculated using the basic specifications shown on the facing page. These costs should be adjusted where necessary for design alternatives and owner's requirements.*

## Common additives

| Description | Unit | $ Cost |
|---|---|---|
| Cabinets, hospital, base, laminated plastic | L.F. | 575 |
| Counter top, laminated plastic | L.F. | 99.50 |
| Nurses station, door type , laminated plastic | L.F. | 645 |
| Wall cabinets, laminated plastic | L.F. | 420 |
| Directory Boards, plastic, glass covered, 30" x 20" | Ea. | 705 |
| 36" x 48" | Ea. | 1475 |
| Aluminum, 36" x 24" | Ea. | 985 |
| 48" x 32" | Ea. | 1975 |
| Heat Therapy Unit, humidified, 26" x 78" x 28" | Ea. | 395 |
| Tables, examining, vinyl top, with base cabinets | Ea. | 1850 - 6025 |
| Utensil Washer, Sanitizer | Ea. | 8650 |
| X-Ray, Mobile | Ea. | 16,200 - 48,400 |

| Description | Unit | $ Cost |
|---|---|---|
| Commissioning Fees, sustainable commercial construction | S.F. | 0.24 - 3.04 |
| Energy Modelling Fees, commercial buildings to 10,000 SF | Ea. | 11,000 |
| Greater than 10,000 SF add | S.F. | 0.04 |
| Green Bldg Cert Fees for comm construction project reg | Project | 1200 |
| Photovoltaic Pwr Sys, grid connected, 20 kW (~2400 SF), roof | Ea. | 92,200 |
| Green Roofs, 6" soil depth, w/treated wd edging & sedum mats | S.F. | 28.30 |
| 10" Soil depth, with treated wood edging & sedum mats | S.F. | 30.65 |
| Greywater Recovery Systems, prepackaged comm, 3060 gal. | Ea. | 70,415 |
| 4590 gal. | Ea. | 88,275 |
| Rainwater Harvest Sys, prepckged comm, 10,000 gal, sys contrller | Ea. | 44,975 |
| 20,000 gal. w/system controller | Ea. | 73,350 |
| 30,000 gal. w/system controller | Ea. | 108,025 |
| Solar Domestic HW, closed loop, add-on sys, ext heat exchanger | Ea. | 13,550 |
| Drainback, hot water system, 120 gal tank | Ea. | 16,425 |
| Draindown, hot water system, 120 gal tank | Ea. | 16,700 |



**Important: See the Reference Section for Location Factors.**

## Model costs calculated for a 1 story building with 10′ story height and 7,000 square feet of floor area

# G Medical Office, 1 Story

| | | | | Unit | Unit Cost | Cost Per S.F. | % Of Sub-Total |
|---|---|---|---|---|---|---|---|
| **A. SUBSTRUCTURE** | | | | | | | |
| 1010 | Standard Foundations | Poured concrete; strip and spread footings | | S.F. Ground | 3.10 | 3.10 | |
| 1020 | Special Foundations | N/A | | — | — | — | |
| 1030 | Slab on Grade | 4″ reinforced concrete with recycled vapor barrier and granular base | | S.F. Slab | 7.32 | 7.32 | 7.2% |
| 2010 | Basement Excavation | Site preparation for slab and trench for foundation wall and footing | | S.F. Ground | .38 | .38 | |
| 2020 | Basement Walls | 4′ foundation wall | | L.F. Wall | 121 | 6.57 | |
| **B. SHELL** | | | | | | | |
| | **B10 Superstructure** | | | | | | |
| 1010 | Floor Construction | N/A | | — | — | — | 5.4 % |
| 1020 | Roof Construction | Plywood on wood trusses | | S.F. Roof | 13.03 | 13.03 | |
| | **B20 Exterior Enclosure** | | | | | | |
| 2010 | Exterior Walls | Face brick with concrete block backup | *70% of wall* | S.F. Wall | 54 | 20.42 | |
| 2020 | Exterior Windows | Wood double hung | *30% of wall* | Each | 850 | 8.14 | 14.3% |
| 2030 | Exterior Doors | Aluminum and glass doors and entrance with transoms | | Each | 3430 | 5.88 | |
| | **B30 Roofing** | | | | | | |
| 3010 | Roof Coverings | Asphalt shingles with flashing (Pitched); rigid fiber glass insulation, gutters | | S.F. Roof | 4.42 | 4.42 | 1.8% |
| 3020 | Roof Openings | N/A | | — | — | — | |
| **C. INTERIORS** | | | | | | | |
| 1010 | Partitions | Gypsum bd. & sound deadening bd. on wood studs w/insul. | *6 SF Flr./LF Part.* | S.F. Partition | 12.29 | 16.39 | |
| 1020 | Interior Doors | Single leaf wood, low VOC paint | *60 S.F. Floor/Door* | Each | 1231 | 20.52 | |
| 1030 | Fittings | N/A | | — | — | — | |
| 2010 | Stair Construction | N/A | | — | — | — | 23.9% |
| 3010 | Wall Finishes | 50% paint, low VOC, 50% vinyl wall covering | | S.F. Surface | 2.63 | 7 | |
| 3020 | Floor Finishes | 50% carpet tile, 50% vinyl composition tile, recycled content | | S.F. Floor | 4.03 | 4.03 | |
| 3030 | Ceiling Finishes | Mineral fiber tile on concealed zee bars | | S.F. Ceiling | 9.67 | 9.67 | |
| **D. SERVICES** | | | | | | | |
| | **D10 Conveying** | | | | | | |
| 1010 | Elevators & Lifts | N/A | | — | — | — | 0.0 % |
| 1020 | Escalators & Moving Walks | N/A | | — | — | — | |
| | **D20 Plumbing** | | | | | | |
| 2010 | Plumbing Fixtures | Toilet, low flow, auto sensor, exam room & service fixt., supply & drain. | *1 Fixt./195 SF Flr.* | Each | 6533 | 33.50 | |
| 2020 | Domestic Water Distribution | Gas fired tankless water heater | | S.F. Floor | 3.84 | 3.84 | 16.1% |
| 2040 | Rain Water Drainage | Roof drains | | S.F. Roof | 1.44 | 1.44 | |
| | **D30 HVAC** | | | | | | |
| 3010 | Energy Supply | N/A | | — | — | — | |
| 3020 | Heat Generating Systems | Included in D3050 | | — | — | — | |
| 3040 | Distribution Systems | Enthalpy heat recovery packages | | Each | 15,575 | 2.22 | 7.0 % |
| 3050 | Terminal & Package Units | Multizone rooftop air conditioner, SEER 14 | | S.F. Floor | 14.75 | 14.75 | |
| 3090 | Other HVAC Sys. & Equipment | N/A | | — | — | — | |
| | **D40 Fire Protection** | | | | | | |
| 4010 | Sprinklers | Wet pipe sprinkler system | | S.F. Floor | 6.60 | 6.60 | 3.6% |
| 4020 | Standpipes | Standpipe | | S.F. Floor | 2.11 | 2.11 | |
| | **D50 Electrical** | | | | | | |
| 5010 | Electrical Service/Distribution | 200 ampere service, panel board and feeders | | S.F. Floor | 1.62 | 1.62 | |
| 5020 | Lighting & Branch Wiring | LED fixtures, daylt. dim., ltg. on/off, recept., switches, and A.C. power | | S.F. Floor | 16.21 | 16.21 | 13.1% |
| 5030 | Communications & Security | Alarm systems, internet & phone wiring, intercom system, & emerg. ltg. | | S.F. Floor | 9.98 | 9.98 | |
| 5090 | Other Electrical Systems | Emergency generator, 7.5 kW, and energy monitoring systems | | S.F. Floor | 3.86 | 3.86 | |
| **E. EQUIPMENT & FURNISHINGS** | | | | | | | |
| 1010 | Commercial Equipment | N/A | | — | — | — | |
| 1020 | Institutional Equipment | Exam room casework and countertops | | S.F. Floor | 17.47 | 17.47 | 7.6 % |
| 1090 | Other Equipment | Waste handling recycling tilt truck | | S.F. Floor | .91 | .91 | |
| 2020 | Moveable Furnishings | No smoking signage | | S.F. Floor | .09 | .09 | |
| **F. SPECIAL CONSTRUCTION** | | | | | | | |
| 1020 | Integrated Construction | N/A | | — | — | — | 0.0 % |
| 1040 | Special Facilities | N/A | | — | — | — | |
| **G. BUILDING SITEWORK** | | **N/A** | | | | | |
| | | | | | **Sub-Total** | 241.47 | **100%** |
| | CONTRACTOR FEES (General Requirements: 10%, Overhead: 5%, Profit: 10%) | | | | 25% | 60.36 | |
| | ARCHITECT FEES | | | | 9% | 27.17 | |
| | | | | | **Total Building Cost** | **329** | |

## Costs per square foot of floor area

| Exterior Wall | S.F. Area | 4000 | 5500 | 7000 | 8500 | 10000 | 11500 | 13000 | 14500 | 16000 |
|---|---|---|---|---|---|---|---|---|---|---|
| | L.F. Perimeter | 180 | 210 | 240 | 270 | 286 | 311 | 336 | 361 | 386 |
| Face Brick and Concrete Block | Steel Joists | 409.15 | 390.60 | 379.90 | 373.10 | 365.20 | 361.10 | 357.95 | 355.40 | 353.40 |
| | Wood Joists | 419.25 | 400.70 | 390.10 | 383.20 | 375.30 | 371.20 | 368.10 | 365.55 | 363.50 |
| Stucco and Concrete Block | Steel Joists | 387.00 | 371.80 | 363.10 | 357.55 | 351.15 | 347.80 | 345.25 | 343.15 | 341.50 |
| | Wood Joists | 397.15 | 381.95 | 373.25 | 367.65 | 361.30 | 357.95 | 355.35 | 353.25 | 351.70 |
| Brick Veneer | Wood Frame | 406.95 | 390.25 | 380.70 | 374.55 | 367.50 | 363.80 | 361.00 | 358.75 | 356.90 |
| Wood Clapboard | Wood Frame | 399.60 | 384.05 | 375.05 | 369.40 | 362.85 | 359.35 | 356.80 | 354.65 | 353.00 |
| Perimeter Adj., Add or Deduct | Per 100 L.F. | 55.25 | 40.10 | 31.60 | 25.95 | 22.10 | 19.25 | 17.00 | 15.25 | 13.80 |
| Story Hgt. Adj., Add or Deduct | Per 1 Ft. | 8.45 | 7.15 | 6.45 | 5.95 | 5.40 | 5.10 | 4.85 | 4.70 | 4.55 |
| ***For Basement**, add $ 57.20 per square foot of basement area* | | | | | | | | | | |

*The above costs were calculated using the basic specifications shown on the facing page. These costs should be adjusted where necessary for design alternatives and owner's requirements.*

## Common additives

| Description | Unit | $ Cost |
|---|---|---|
| Cabinets, hospital, base, laminated plastic | L.F. | 575 |
| Counter top, laminated plastic | L.F. | 99.50 |
| Nurses station, door type , laminated plastic | L.F. | 645 |
| Wall cabinets, laminated plastic | L.F. | 420 |
| Elevators, hydraulic passenger, 2 stops, 2500# capacity | Ea. | 90,500 |
| 3500# capacity | Ea. | 96,000 |
| Directory Boards, plastic, glass covered, 30" x 20" | Ea. | 705 |
| 36" x 48" | Ea. | 1475 |
| Aluminum, 36" x 24" | Ea. | 985 |
| 48" x 32" | Ea. | 1975 |
| Heat Therapy Unit, humidified, 26" x 78" x 28" | Ea. | 395 |
| Tables, examining, vinyl top, with base cabinets | Ea. | 1850 - 6025 |
| Utensil Washer, Sanitizer | Ea. | 8650 |
| X-Ray, Mobile | Ea. | 16,200 - 48,400 |

| Description | Unit | $ Cost |
|---|---|---|
| Commissioning Fees, sustainable commercial construction | S.F. | 0.24 - 3.04 |
| Energy Modelling Fees, commercial buildings to 10,000 SF | Ea. | 11,000 |
| Greater than 10,000 SF add | S.F. | 0.04 |
| Green Bldg Cert Fees for comm construction project reg | Project | 1200 |
| Photovoltaic Pwr Sys, grid connected, 20 kW (~2400 SF), roof | Ea. | 92,200 |
| Green Roofs, 6" soil depth, w/treated wd edging & sedum mats | S.F. | 28.30 |
| 10" Soil depth, with treated wood edging & sedum mats | S.F. | 30.65 |
| Greywater Recovery Systems, prepackaged comm, 3060 gal. | Ea. | 70,415 |
| 4590 gal. | Ea. | 88,275 |
| Rainwater Harvest Sys, prepckged comm, 10,000 gal, sys contrller | Ea. | 44,975 |
| 20,000 gal. w/system controller | Ea. | 73,350 |
| 30,000 gal. w/system controller | Ea. | 108,025 |
| Solar Domestic HW, closed loop, add-on sys, ext heat exchanger | Ea. | 13,550 |
| Drainback, hot water system, 120 gal tank | Ea. | 16,425 |
| Draindown, hot water system, 120 gal tank | Ea. | 16,700 |



**Important: See the Reference Section for Location Factors.**

## Model costs calculated for a 2 story building with 10′ story height and 7,000 square feet of floor area

# G Medical Office, 2 Story

| | | | | Unit | Unit Cost | Cost Per S.F. | % Of Sub-Total |
|---|---|---|---|---|---|---|---|
| **A. SUBSTRUCTURE** | | | | | | | |
| 1010 | Standard Foundations | Poured concrete; strip and spread footings | | S.F. Ground | 4.94 | 2.47 | 4.0% |
| 1020 | Special Foundations | N/A | | — | — | — | |
| 1030 | Slab on Grade | 4″ reinforced concrete with vapor barrier and granular base | | S.F. Slab | 7.32 | 3.66 | |
| 2010 | Basement Excavation | Site preparation for slab and trench for foundation wall and footing | | S.F. Ground | .66 | .33 | |
| 2020 | Basement Walls | 4′ foundation wall | | L.F. Wall | 121 | 4.15 | |
| **B. SHELL** | | | | | | | |
| | **B10 Superstructure** | | | | | | |
| 1010 | Floor Construction | Open web steel joists, slab form, concrete, columns | | S.F. Floor | 17.18 | 8.59 | 4.8% |
| 1020 | Roof Construction | Metal deck, open web steel joists, beams, columns | | S.F. Roof | 8.60 | 4.30 | |
| | **B20 Exterior Enclosure** | | | | | | |
| 2010 | Exterior Walls | Stucco on concrete block | | S.F. Wall | 22.60 | 10.85 | 13.0% |
| 2020 | Exterior Windows | Outward projecting metal | *30% of wall* | Each | 1552 | 21.29 | |
| 2030 | Exterior Doors | Aluminum and glass doors with transoms | | Each | 9150 | 2.61 | |
| | **B30 Roofing** | | | | | | |
| 3010 | Roof Coverings | Built-up tar and gravel with flashing; perlite/EPS composite insulation | | S.F. Roof | 12.24 | 6.12 | 2.4% |
| 3020 | Roof Openings | Roof hatches | | S.F. Roof | .58 | .29 | |
| **C. INTERIORS** | | | | | | | |
| 1010 | Partitions | Gypsum bd. & acous. insul. on metal studs | *6 SF Floor/LF Part.* | S.F. Partition | 10.25 | 13.66 | 22.3% |
| 1020 | Interior Doors | Single leaf wood | *60 S.F. Floor/Door* | Each | 1231 | 20.52 | |
| 1030 | Fittings | N/A | | — | — | — | |
| 2010 | Stair Construction | Concrete filled metal pan | | Flight | 16,075 | 4.60 | |
| 3010 | Wall Finishes | 45% paint, 50% vinyl wall coating, 5% ceramic tile | | S.F. Surface | 2.63 | 7 | |
| 3020 | Floor Finishes | 50% carpet, 50% vinyl composition tile | | S.F. Floor | 4.03 | 4.03 | |
| 3030 | Ceiling Finishes | Mineral fiber tile on concealed zee bars | | S.F. Ceiling | 9.67 | 9.67 | |
| **D. SERVICES** | | | | | | | |
| | **D10 Conveying** | | | | | | |
| 1010 | Elevators & Lifts | One hydraulic hospital elevator | | Each | 141,960 | 20.28 | 7.6% |
| 1020 | Escalators & Moving Walks | N/A | | — | — | — | |
| | **D20 Plumbing** | | | | | | |
| 2010 | Plumbing Fixtures | Toilet, exam room & service fixt., supply & drain. | *1 Fixt./160 SF Flr.* | Each | 6379 | 39.87 | 17.0% |
| 2020 | Domestic Water Distribution | Gas fired water heater | | S.F. Floor | 3.84 | 3.84 | |
| 2040 | Rain Water Drainage | Roof drains | | S.F. Roof | 3.04 | 1.52 | |
| | **D30 HVAC** | | | | | | |
| 3010 | Energy Supply | N/A | | — | — | — | 6.4 % |
| 3020 | Heat Generating Systems | Included in D3050 | | — | — | — | |
| 3040 | Distribution Systems | Enthalpy heat recovery packages | | Each | 15,575 | 2.22 | |
| 3050 | Terminal & Package Units | Multizone rooftop air conditioner, SEER 14 | | S.F. Floor | 14.75 | 14.75 | |
| 3090 | Other HVAC Sys. & Equipment | N/A | | — | — | — | |
| | **D40 Fire Protection** | | | | | | |
| 4010 | Sprinklers | Wet pipe sprinkler system | | S.F. Floor | 5.47 | 5.47 | 3.3% |
| 4020 | Standpipes | Standpipe | | S.F. Floor | 3.26 | 3.26 | |
| | **D50 Electrical** | | | | | | |
| 5010 | Electrical Service/Distribution | 400 ampere service, panel board and feeders | | S.F. Floor | 2.06 | 2.06 | 12.5% |
| 5020 | Lighting & Branch Wiring | LED fixtures, receptacles, switches, A.C. and misc. power | | S.F. Floor | 17.20 | 17.20 | |
| 5030 | Communications & Security | Alarm system, internet & phone wiring, intercom system, & emergency ltg. | | S.F. Floor | 9.98 | 9.98 | |
| 5090 | Other Electrical Systems | Emergency generator, 7.5 kW | | S.F. Floor | 3.95 | 3.95 | |
| **E. EQUIPMENT & FURNISHINGS** | | | | | | | |
| 1010 | Commercial Equipment | N/A | | — | — | — | 6.7 % |
| 1020 | Institutional Equipment | Exam room casework and contertops | | S.F. Floor | 17.47 | 17.47 | |
| 1090 | Other Equipment | Waste handling recycling tilt truck | | S.F. Floor | .47 | .47 | |
| 2020 | Moveable Furnishings | No smoking signage | | S.F. Floor | .01 | .01 | |
| **F. SPECIAL CONSTRUCTION** | | | | | | | |
| 1020 | Integrated Construction | N/A | | — | — | — | 0.0 % |
| 1040 | Special Facilities | N/A | | — | — | — | |
| **G. BUILDING SITEWORK** | | **N/A** | | | | | |
| | | | | | **Sub-Total** | 266.49 | **100%** |
| | CONTRACTOR FEES (General Requirements: 10%, Overhead: 5%, Profit: 10%) | | | | 25% | 66.63 | |
| | ARCHITECT FEES | | | | 9% | 29.98 | |
| | | | | | **Total Building Cost** | **363.10** | |

# G Motel, 1 Story

## Costs per square foot of floor area

| Exterior Wall | S.F. Area | 2000 | 3000 | 4000 | 6000 | 8000 | 10000 | 12000 | 14000 | 16000 |
|---|---|---|---|---|---|---|---|---|---|---|
| | L.F. Perimeter | 240 | 260 | 280 | 380 | 480 | 560 | 580 | 660 | 740 |
| Brick Veneer | Wood Frame | 314.00 | 277.40 | 259.20 | 249.30 | **244.40** | 239.75 | 232.50 | 230.85 | 229.60 |
| Aluminum Clapboard | Wood Frame | 291.80 | 261.40 | 246.25 | 237.60 | 233.30 | 229.45 | 223.50 | 222.10 | 221.10 |
| Wood Clapboard | Wood Frame | 290.70 | 260.60 | 245.60 | 237.00 | 232.80 | 228.95 | 223.10 | 221.70 | 220.65 |
| Wood Shingles | Wood Frame | 299.10 | 266.65 | 250.45 | 241.40 | 236.90 | 232.85 | 226.45 | 225.00 | 223.85 |
| Precast Concrete | Wood Truss | 294.15 | 263.10 | 247.60 | 238.80 | 234.45 | 230.50 | 224.45 | 223.05 | 221.95 |
| Face Brick and Concrete Block | Wood Truss | 330.60 | 289.40 | 268.85 | 258.05 | 252.65 | 247.50 | 239.15 | 237.35 | 236.00 |
| Perimeter Adj., Add or Deduct | Per 100 L.F. | 42.15 | 28.10 | 21.00 | 14.05 | 10.55 | 8.45 | 6.95 | 5.95 | 5.30 |
| Story Hgt. Adj., Add or Deduct | Per 1 Ft. | 6.60 | 4.80 | 3.80 | 3.45 | 3.30 | 3.05 | 2.60 | 2.55 | 2.55 |

***For Basement**, add $39.35 per square foot of basement area*

*The above costs were calculated using the basic specifications shown on the facing page. These costs should be adjusted where necessary for design alternatives and owner's requirements.*

## Common additives

| Description | Unit | $ Cost |
|---|---|---|
| Closed Circuit Surveillance, one station, camera & monitor | Ea. | 1250 |
| For additional camera stations, add | Ea. | 475 |
| Laundry Equipment, dryer, gas, 30 lb. capacity | Ea. | 2200 |
| Washer, commercial | Ea. | 2000 |
| Sauna, prefabricated, complete, 6' x 9' | Ea. | 10,500 |
| 8' x 8' | Ea. | 13,500 |
| Swimming Pools, Complete, gunite | S.F. | 127 - 158 |
| TV Antenna, Master system, 12 outlet | Outlet | 284 |
| 30 outlet | Outlet | 370 |
| 100 outlet | Outlet | 395 |

| Description | Unit | $ Cost |
|---|---|---|
| Commissioning Fees, sustainable commercial construction | S.F. | 0.24 - 3.04 |
| Energy Modelling Fees, commercial buildings to 10,000 SF | Ea. | 11,000 |
| Greater than 10,000 SF add | S.F. | 0.04 |
| Green Bldg Cert Fees for comm construction project reg | Project | 1200 |
| Photovoltaic Pwr Sys, grid connected, 20 kW (~2400 SF), roof | Ea. | 92,200 |
| Green Roofs, 6" soil depth, w/treated wd edging & sedum mats | S.F. | 28.30 |
| 10" Soil depth, with treated wood edging & sedum mats | S.F. | 30.65 |
| Greywater Recovery Systems, prepackaged comm, 3060 gal. | Ea. | 70,415 |
| 4590 gal. | Ea. | 88,275 |
| Rainwater Harvest Sys, prepckged comm, 10,000 gal, sys contrller | Ea. | 44,975 |
| 20,000 gal. w/system controller | Ea. | 73,350 |
| 30,000 gal. w/system controller | Ea. | 108,025 |
| Solar Domestic HW, closed loop, add-on sys, ext heat exchanger | Ea. | 13,550 |
| Drainback, hot water system, 120 gal tank | Ea. | 16,425 |
| Draindown, hot water system, 120 gal tank | Ea. | 16,700 |



**Important: See the Reference Section for Location Factors.**

## Model costs calculated for a 1 story building with 9′ story height and 8,000 square feet of floor area

# G Motel, 1 Story

| | | | | Unit | Unit Cost | Cost Per S.F. | % Of Sub-Total |
|---|---|---|---|---|---|---|---|
| **A. SUBSTRUCTURE** | | | | | | | |
| 1010 | Standard Foundations | Poured concrete; strip and spread footings | | S.F. Ground | 4.68 | 4.68 | |
| 1020 | Special Foundations | N/A | | — | — | — | |
| 1030 | Slab on Grade | 4″ reinforced concrete with recycled vapor barrier and granular base | | S.F. Slab | 7.32 | 7.32 | 12.2% |
| 2010 | Basement Excavation | Site preparation for slab and trench for foundation wall and footing | | S.F. Ground | .38 | .38 | |
| 2020 | Basement Walls | 4′ foundation wall | | L.F. Wall | 121 | 9.95 | |
| **B. SHELL** | | | | | | | |
| **B10 Superstructure** | | | | | | | |
| 1010 | Floor Construction | N/A | | — | — | — | 7.1 % |
| 1020 | Roof Construction | Plywood on wood trusses | | S.F. Roof | 13.03 | 13.03 | |
| **B20 Exterior Enclosure** | | | | | | | |
| 2010 | Exterior Walls | Face brick on wood studs with sheathing, insulation and paper | *80% of wall* | S.F. Wall | 34 | 14.69 | |
| 2020 | Exterior Windows | Wood double hung | *20% of wall* | Each | 670 | 5.16 | 16.0% |
| 2030 | Exterior Doors | Wood solid core | | Each | 3430 | 9.44 | |
| **B30 Roofing** | | | | | | | |
| 3010 | Roof Coverings | Asphalt strip shingles, 210-235 lbs/Sq., R-10 insul. & weather barrier-recycled | | S.F. Roof | 11.57 | 11.57 | 6.3% |
| 3020 | Roof Openings | N/A | | — | — | — | |
| **C. INTERIORS** | | | | | | | |
| 1010 | Partitions | Gypsum bd. and sound deadening bd. on wood studs | *9 SF Flr./LF Part.* | S.F. Partition | 13.13 | 11.67 | |
| 1020 | Interior Doors | Single leaf hollow core wood, low VOC paint | *300 S.F. Floor/Door* | Each | 825 | 2.75 | |
| 1030 | Fittings | N/A | | — | — | — | |
| 2010 | Stair Construction | N/A | | — | — | — | 15.7% |
| 3010 | Wall Finishes | 90% paint, low VOC, 10% ceramic tile | | S.F. Surface | 1.74 | 3.09 | |
| 3020 | Floor Finishes | 85% carpet tile, 15% ceramic tile | | S.F. Floor | 5.62 | 5.62 | |
| 3030 | Ceiling Finishes | Painted gypsum board on furring, low VOC paint | | S.F. Ceiling | 5.52 | 5.52 | |
| **D. SERVICES** | | | | | | | |
| **D10 Conveying** | | | | | | | |
| 1010 | Elevators & Lifts | N/A | | — | — | — | 0.0 % |
| 1020 | Escalators & Moving Walks | N/A | | — | — | — | |
| **D20 Plumbing** | | | | | | | |
| 2010 | Plumbing Fixtures | Toilet, low flow, auto sensor, & service fixt., supply & drainage | *1 Fixt./90 SF Flr.* | Each | 3159 | 35.10 | |
| 2020 | Domestic Water Distribution | Gas fired tankless water heater | | S.F. Floor | .57 | .57 | 20.6% |
| 2040 | Rain Water Drainage | Roof Drains | | S.F. Roof | 2.06 | 2.06 | |
| **D30 HVAC** | | | | | | | |
| 3010 | Energy Supply | N/A | | — | — | — | |
| 3020 | Heat Generating Systems | Included in D3050 | | — | — | — | |
| 3030 | Cooling Generating Systems | N/A | | — | — | — | 5.4 % |
| 3050 | Terminal & Package Units | Through the wall electric heating and cooling units | | S.F. Floor | 9.82 | 9.82 | |
| 3090 | Other HVAC Sys. & Equipment | N/A | | — | — | — | |
| **D40 Fire Protection** | | | | | | | |
| 4010 | Sprinklers | Wet pipe sprinkler system | | S.F. Floor | 6.60 | 6.60 | 4.6% |
| 4020 | Standpipes | Standpipe, wet, Class III | | S.F. Floor | 1.85 | 1.85 | |
| **D50 Electrical** | | | | | | | |
| 5010 | Electrical Service/Distribution | 200 ampere service, panel board and feeders | | S.F. Floor | 1.63 | 1.63 | |
| 5020 | Lighting & Branch Wiring | LED fixt., daylit. dim., ltg. on/off control, recept., switches and misc. pwr. | | S.F. Floor | 12.71 | 12.71 | 11.0% |
| 5030 | Communications & Security | Addressable alarm systems | | S.F. Floor | 2.92 | 2.92 | |
| 5090 | Other Electrical Systems | Emergency generator, 7.5 kW, and energy monitoring systems | | S.F. Floor | 2.75 | 2.75 | |
| **E. EQUIPMENT & FURNISHINGS** | | | | | | | |
| 1010 | Commercial Equipment | Laundry equipment | | S.F. Floor | .90 | .90 | |
| 1020 | Institutional Equipment | N/A | | — | — | — | 1.0% |
| 1090 | Other Equipment | Waste handling recycling tilt truck | | S.F. Floor | .80 | .80 | |
| 2020 | Moveable Furnishings | No smoking signage | | S.F. Floor | .14 | .14 | |
| **F. SPECIAL CONSTRUCTION** | | | | | | | |
| 1020 | Integrated Construction | N/A | | — | — | — | 0.0 % |
| 1040 | Special Facilities | N/A | | — | — | — | |
| **G. BUILDING SITEWORK** | **N/A** | | | | | | |
| | | | | | **Sub-Total** | 182.72 | **100%** |
| | CONTRACTOR FEES (General Requirements: 10%, Overhead: 5%, Profit: 10%) | | | | *25%* | 45.69 | |
| | ARCHITECT FEES | | | | *7%* | 15.99 | |
| | | | | | **Total Building Cost** | **244.40** | |

For customer support on your Square Foot Costs with RSMeans data, call 800.448.8182.

## Costs per square foot of floor area

| Exterior Wall | S.F. Area | 25000 | 37000 | 49000 | 61000 | 73000 | 81000 | 88000 | 96000 | 104000 |
|---|---|---|---|---|---|---|---|---|---|---|
| | L.F. Perimeter | 433 | 593 | 606 | 720 | 835 | 911 | 978 | 1054 | 1074 |
| Decorative Concrete Block | Wood Joists | 257.75 | 251.50 | 241.80 | 239.50 | 238.00 | 237.25 | 236.65 | 236.10 | 234.45 |
| | Precast Concrete | 270.45 | 264.25 | 254.45 | 252.20 | 250.70 | 249.90 | 249.35 | 248.80 | 247.15 |
| Stucco and Concrete Block | Wood Joists | 257.65 | 251.25 | 241.20 | 238.90 | 237.40 | 236.55 | 236.05 | 235.45 | 233.75 |
| | Precast Concrete | 271.95 | 265.60 | 255.60 | 253.25 | 251.70 | 250.95 | 250.35 | 249.80 | 248.05 |
| Wood Clapboard | Wood Frame | 252.50 | 246.55 | 237.55 | 235.35 | 234.00 | 233.25 | 232.70 | 232.20 | 230.70 |
| Brick Veneer | Wood Frame | 258.25 | 251.90 | 241.70 | 239.35 | 237.80 | 237.05 | 236.45 | 235.90 | 234.15 |
| Perimeter Adj., Add or Deduct | Per 100 L.F. | 8.70 | 5.90 | 4.40 | 3.55 | 3.00 | 2.70 | 2.50 | 2.25 | 2.05 |
| Story Hgt. Adj., Add or Deduct | Per 1 Ft. | 3.25 | 3.00 | 2.30 | 2.20 | 2.15 | 2.05 | 2.10 | 2.05 | 1.95 |
| ***For Basement**, add $51.60 per square foot of basement area* | | | | | | | | | | |

*The above costs were calculated using the basic specifications shown on the facing page. These costs should be adjusted where necessary for design alternatives and owner's requirements.*

## Common additives

| Description | Unit | $ Cost |
|---|---|---|
| Closed Circuit Surveillance, one station, camera & monitor | Ea. | 1250 |
| For additional camera station, add | Ea. | 475 |
| Elevators, hydraulic passenger, 2 stops, 2500# capacity | Ea. | 90,500 |
| 3500# capacity | Ea. | 96,000 |
| Additional stop, add | Ea. | 9875 |
| Laundry Equipment, dryer, gas, 30 lb. capacity | Ea. | 2200 |
| Washer, commercial | Ea. | 2000 |
| Sauna, prefabricated, complete, 6′ x 9′ | Ea. | 10,500 |
| 8′ x 8′ | Ea. | 13,500 |
| Swimming Pools, Complete, gunite | S.F. | 127 - 158 |
| TV Antenna, Master system, 12 outlet | Outlet | 284 |
| 30 outlet | Outlet | 370 |
| 100 outlet | Outlet | 395 |

| Description | Unit | $ Cost |
|---|---|---|
| Commissioning Fees, sustainable commercial construction | S.F. | 0.24 - 3.04 |
| Energy Modelling Fees, commercial buildings to 10,000 SF | Ea. | 11,000 |
| Greater than 10,000 SF add | S.F. | 0.04 |
| Green Bldg Cert Fees for comm construction project reg | Project | 1200 |
| Photovoltaic Pwr Sys, grid connected, 20 kW (~2400 SF), roof | Ea. | 92,200 |
| Green Roofs, 6″ soil depth, w/treated wd edging & sedum mats | S.F. | 28.30 |
| 10″ Soil depth, with treated wood edging & sedum mats | S.F. | 30.65 |
| Greywater Recovery Systems, prepackaged comm, 3060 gal. | Ea. | 70,415 |
| 4590 gal. | Ea. | 88,275 |
| Rainwater Harvest Sys, prepckged comm, 10,000 gal, sys contrller | Ea. | 44,975 |
| 20,000 gal. w/system controller | Ea. | 73,350 |
| 30,000 gal. w/system controller | Ea. | 108,025 |
| Solar Domestic HW, closed loop, add-on sys, ext heat exchanger | Ea. | 13,550 |
| Drainback, hot water system, 120 gal tank | Ea. | 16,425 |
| Draindown, hot water system, 120 gal tank | Ea. | 16,700 |



**Important: See the Reference Section for Location Factors.**

# Model costs calculated for a 3 story building with 9' story height and 49,000 square feet of floor area

# G Motel, 2-3 Story

| | | | | Unit | Unit Cost | Cost Per S.F. | % Of Sub-Total |
|---|---|---|---|---|---|---|---|
| **A. SUBSTRUCTURE** | | | | | | | |
| 1010 | Standard Foundations | Poured concrete; strip and spread footings | | S.F. Ground | 2.16 | .72 | 3.2% |
| 1020 | Special Foundations | N/A | | — | — | — | |
| 1030 | Slab on Grade | 4" reinforced concrete with recycled vapor barrier and granular base | | S.F. Slab | 7.32 | 2.44 | |
| 2010 | Basement Excavation | Site preparation for slab and trench for foundation wall and footing | | S.F. Ground | .22 | .07 | |
| 2020 | Basement Walls | 4' foundation wall | | L.F. Wall | 121 | 2.99 | |
| **B. SHELL** | | | | | | | |
| | **B10 Superstructure** | | | | | | |
| 1010 | Floor Construction | Precast concrete plank | | S.F. Floor | 15.54 | 10.36 | 7.7% |
| 1020 | Roof Construction | Precast concrete plank | | S.F. Roof | 13.29 | 4.43 | |
| | **B20 Exterior Enclosure** | | | | | | |
| 2010 | Exterior Walls | Decorative concrete block | *85% of wall* | S.F. Wall | 30.09 | 8.54 | 13.6% |
| 2020 | Exterior Windows | Aluminum sliding | *15% of wall* | Each | 1677 | 5.60 | |
| 2030 | Exterior Doors | Aluminum and glass doors and entrance with transom | | Each | 3597 | 11.90 | |
| | **B30 Roofing** | | | | | | |
| 3010 | Roof Coverings | Single-ply TPO membrane, 60 mils w/R-20 insul. | | S.F. Roof | 11.31 | 3.77 | 2.0% |
| 3020 | Roof Openings | Roof hatches | | S.F. Roof | .24 | .08 | |
| **C. INTERIORS** | | | | | | | |
| 1010 | Partitions | Concrete block w/foamed-in insul. | *7 SF Flr./LF Part.* | S.F. Partition | 25.69 | 29.36 | 31.1% |
| 1020 | Interior Doors | Wood hollow core, low VOC paint | *70 S.F. Floor/Door* | Each | 825 | 11.78 | |
| 1030 | Fittings | N/A | | — | — | — | |
| 2010 | Stair Construction | Concrete filled metal pan | | Flight | 16,075 | 3.94 | |
| 3010 | Wall Finishes | 90% paint, low VOC, 10% ceramic tile | | S.F. Surface | 1.74 | 3.98 | |
| 3020 | Floor Finishes | 85% carpet tile, 5% vinyl composition tile, recycled content, 10% ceramic tile | | S.F. Floor | 5.62 | 5.62 | |
| 3030 | Ceiling Finishes | Textured finish | | S.F. Ceiling | 5.11 | 5.11 | |
| **D. SERVICES** | | | | | | | |
| | **D10 Conveying** | | | | | | |
| 1010 | Elevators & Lifts | Two hydraulic passenger elevators | | Each | 137,935 | 5.63 | 2.9% |
| 1020 | Escalators & Moving Walks | N/A | | — | — | — | |
| | **D20 Plumbing** | | | | | | |
| 2010 | Plumbing Fixtures | Toilet, low flow, auto sensor & service fixtures, supply & drain. | *1 Fixt./180 SF Flr.* | Each | 7474 | 41.52 | 22.1% |
| 2020 | Domestic Water Distribution | Gas fired, tankless water heater | | S.F. Floor | .40 | .40 | |
| 2040 | Rain Water Drainage | Roof drains | | S.F. Roof | 1.83 | .61 | |
| | **D30 HVAC** | | | | | | |
| 3010 | Energy Supply | N/A | | — | — | — | 4.6 % |
| 3020 | Heat Generating Systems | Included in D3050 | | — | — | — | |
| 3030 | Cooling Generating Systems | N/A | | — | — | — | |
| 3050 | Terminal & Package Units | Through the wall electric heating and cooling units | | S.F. Floor | 8.86 | 8.86 | |
| 3090 | Other HVAC Sys. & Equipment | N/A | | — | — | — | |
| | **D40 Fire Protection** | | | | | | |
| 4010 | Sprinklers | Sprinklers, wet, light hazard | | S.F. Floor | 4.39 | 4.39 | 2.5% |
| 4020 | Standpipes | Standpipe, wet, Class III | | S.F. Floor | .43 | .43 | |
| | **D50 Electrical** | | | | | | |
| 5010 | Electrical Service/Distribution | 800 ampere service, panel board and feeders | | S.F. Floor | 1.78 | 1.78 | 10.0% |
| 5020 | Lighting & Branch Wiring | LED fixtures, daylt. dim., ltg. on/off, recept., switches and misc. power | | S.F. Floor | 13.87 | 13.87 | |
| 5030 | Communications & Security | Addressable alarm systems and emergency lighting | | S.F. Floor | 2.30 | 2.30 | |
| 5090 | Other Electrical Systems | Emergency generator, 7.5 kW, energy monitoring systems | | S.F. Floor | 1.20 | 1.20 | |
| **E. EQUIPMENT & FURNISHINGS** | | | | | | | |
| 1010 | Commercial Equipment | Commercial laundry equipment | | S.F. Floor | .29 | .29 | 0.2% |
| 1020 | Institutional Equipment | N/A | | — | — | — | |
| 1090 | Other Equipment | Waste handling recycling tilt truck | | S.F. Floor | .06 | .06 | |
| 2020 | Moveable Furnishings | No smoking signage | | S.F. Floor | .01 | .01 | |
| **F. SPECIAL CONSTRUCTION** | | | | | | | |
| 1020 | Integrated Construction | N/A | | — | — | — | 0.0 % |
| 1040 | Special Facilities | N/A | | — | — | — | |
| **G. BUILDING SITEWORK** | | **N/A** | | | | | |
| | | | | | **Sub-Total** | 192.04 | **100%** |
| | CONTRACTOR FEES (General Requirements: 10%, Overhead: 5%, Profit: 10%) | | | | *25%* | 48.01 | |
| | ARCHITECT FEES | | | | *6%* | 14.40 | |
| | | | | | **Total Building Cost** | **254.45** | |

# G Office, 1 Story

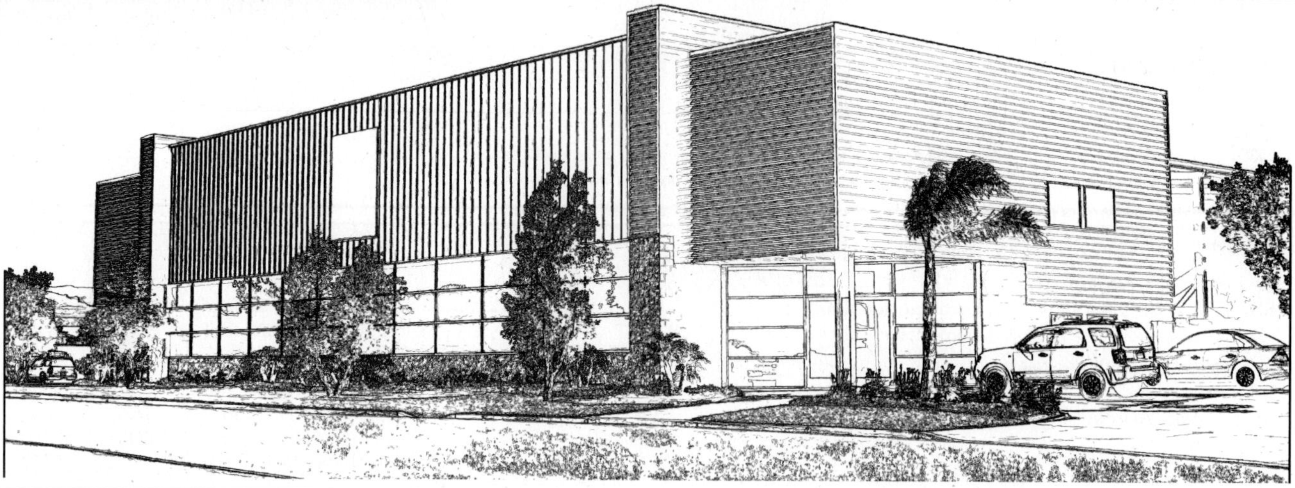

## Costs per square foot of floor area

| Exterior Wall | S.F. Area | 2000 | 3000 | 5000 | 7000 | 9000 | 12000 | 15000 | 20000 | 25000 |
|---|---|---|---|---|---|---|---|---|---|---|
| | L.F. Perimeter | 220 | 260 | 320 | 360 | 420 | 480 | 520 | 640 | 700 |
| Wood Clapboard | Wood Truss | 288.10 | 260.05 | 234.60 | 221.55 | 215.90 | 209.15 | 204.05 | 201.00 | 197.35 |
| Brick Veneer | Wood Truss | 297.85 | 267.55 | 239.95 | 225.60 | 219.55 | 212.10 | 206.50 | 203.15 | 199.15 |
| Face Brick and Concrete Block | Wood Truss | 319.25 | 284.60 | 252.75 | 236.05 | 229.15 | 220.45 | 213.90 | 210.10 | 205.25 |
| | Steel Roof Deck | 342.15 | 305.00 | 270.80 | 252.90 | 245.45 | 236.05 | 228.95 | 224.95 | 219.75 |
| E.I.F.S. and Metal Studs | Steel Roof Deck | 312.75 | 283.20 | 256.30 | **242.50** | 236.60 | 229.40 | 223.95 | 220.80 | 216.90 |
| Tilt-up Concrete Panels | Steel Roof Deck | 325.95 | 293.95 | 264.65 | 249.45 | 243.10 | 235.15 | 229.20 | 225.75 | 221.40 |
| Perimeter Adj., Add or Deduct | Per 100 L.F. | 38.40 | 25.60 | 15.40 | 10.90 | 8.55 | 6.40 | 5.10 | 3.85 | 3.00 |
| Story Hgt. Adj., Add or Deduct | Per 1 Ft. | 4.80 | 3.80 | 2.80 | 2.20 | 2.05 | 1.75 | 1.45 | 1.35 | 1.20 |
| ***For Basement**, add $54.30 per square foot of basement area* | | | | | | | | | | |

*The above costs were calculated using the basic specifications shown on the facing page. These costs should be adjusted where necessary for design alternatives and owner's requirements.*

## Common additives

| Description | Unit | $ Cost |
|---|---|---|
| Closed Circuit Surveillance, one station, camera & monitor | Ea. | 1250 |
| For additional camera stations, add | Ea. | 475 |
| Directory boards, plastic, glass covered, 30" x 20" | Ea. | 705 |
| 36" x 48" | Ea. | 1475 |
| Aluminum, 36" x 24" | Ea. | 985 |
| 48" x 32" | Ea. | 1975 |
| Electronic, wall mounted | S.F. | 1175 |
| Pedestal access flr sys w/PLAM cover, comp rm, | | |
| Less than 6000 SF | S.F. | 8.80 |
| Greater than 6000 SF | S.F. | 8.65 |
| Office, greater than 6000 S.F. | S.F. | 11.95 |
| Uninterruptible power supply, 15 kVA/12.75 kW | kW | 1.35 |

| Description | Unit | $ Cost |
|---|---|---|
| Commissioning Fees, sustainable commercial construction | S.F. | 0.24 - 3.04 |
| Energy Modelling Fees, commercial buildings to 10,000 SF | Ea. | 11,000 |
| Greater than 10,000 SF add | S.F. | 0.04 |
| Green Bldg Cert Fees for comm construction project reg | Project | 1200 |
| Photovoltaic Pwr Sys, grid connected, 20 kW (~2400 SF), roof | Ea. | 92,200 |
| Green Roofs, 6" soil depth, w/treated wd edging & sedum mats | S.F. | 28.30 |
| 10" Soil depth, with treated wood edging & sedum mats | S.F. | 30.65 |
| Greywater Recovery Systems, prepackaged comm, 3060 gal. | Ea. | 70,415 |
| 4590 gal. | Ea. | 88,275 |
| Rainwater Harvest Sys, prepckged comm, 10,000 gal, sys contrller | Ea. | 44,975 |
| 20,000 gal. w/system controller | Ea. | 73,350 |
| 30,000 gal. w/system controller | Ea. | 108,025 |
| Solar Domestic HW, closed loop, add-on sys, ext heat exchanger | Ea. | 13,550 |
| Drainback, hot water system, 120 gal tank | Ea. | 16,425 |
| Draindown, hot water system, 120 gal tank | Ea. | 16,700 |



**Important: See the Reference Section for Location Factors.**

## Model costs calculated for a 1 story building with 12′ story height and 7,000 square feet of floor area

## G Office, 1 Story

| | | | | Unit | Unit Cost | Cost Per S.F. | % Of Sub-Total |
|---|---|---|---|---|---|---|---|
| **A. SUBSTRUCTURE** | | | | | | | |
| 1010 | Standard Foundations | Poured concrete; strip and spread footings | | S.F. Ground | 4.07 | 4.07 | 10.1% |
| 1020 | Special Foundations | N/A | | — | — | — | |
| 1030 | Slab on Grade | 4″ reinforced concrete with recycled vapor barrier and granular base | | S.F. Slab | 7.32 | 7.32 | |
| 2010 | Basement Excavation | Site preparation for slab and trench for foundation wall and footing | | S.F. Ground | .38 | .38 | |
| 2020 | Basement Walls | 4′ foundation wall | | L.F. Wall | 229 | 6.54 | |
| **B. SHELL** | | | | | | | |
| | **B10 Superstructure** | | | | | | |
| 1010 | Floor Construction | N/A | | — | — | — | 8.1 % |
| 1020 | Roof Construction | Steel joists, girders & deck on columns | | S.F. Roof | 14.69 | 14.69 | |
| | **B20 Exterior Enclosure** | | | | | | |
| 2010 | Exterior Walls | E.I.F.S. on metal studs | | S.F. Wall | 22.30 | 11.01 | 11.3% |
| 2020 | Exterior Windows | Aluminum outward projecting | *20% of wall* | Each | 839 | 4.50 | |
| 2030 | Exterior Doors | Aluminum and glass, hollow metal | | Each | 5748 | 4.92 | |
| | **B30 Roofing** | | | | | | |
| 3010 | Roof Coverings | Single-ply TPO membrane, 45 mils, heat welded seams w/R-20 insul. | | S.F. Roof | 18.88 | 18.88 | 10.6% |
| 3020 | Roof Openings | Roof hatch | | S.F. Roof | .30 | .30 | |
| **C. INTERIORS** | | | | | | | |
| 1010 | Partitions | Gyp. bd. on mtl. studs w/sound attenuation | *20 SF Flr/LF Part.* | S.F. Partition | 13.40 | 6.70 | 17.0% |
| 1020 | Interior Doors | Single leaf hollow metal, low VOC paint | *200 S.F. Floor/Door* | Each | 1159 | 5.80 | |
| 1030 | Fittings | Toilet partitions | | S.F. Floor | 1.51 | 1.51 | |
| 2010 | Stair Construction | N/A | | — | — | — | |
| 3010 | Wall Finishes | 60% vinyl wall covering, 40% paint, low VOC | | S.F. Surface | 2.94 | 2.94 | |
| 3020 | Floor Finishes | 60% carpet tile, 30% vinyl composition tile, recycled content, 10% ceramic tile | | S.F. Floor | 4.86 | 4.86 | |
| 3030 | Ceiling Finishes | Mineral fiber tile on concealed zee bars | | S.F. Ceiling | 9 | 9 | |
| **D. SERVICES** | | | | | | | |
| | **D10 Conveying** | | | | | | |
| 1010 | Elevators & Lifts | N/A | | — | — | — | 0.0 % |
| 1020 | Escalators & Moving Walks | N/A | | — | — | — | |
| | **D20 Plumbing** | | | | | | |
| 2010 | Plumbing Fixtures | Toilet, low flow, auto sensor, & service fixt., supply & drain. | *1 Fixt./1320 SF Flr.* | Each | 13,649 | 10.34 | 7.1% |
| 2020 | Domestic Water Distribution | Tankless, on-demand water heater, gas/propane | | S.F. Floor | 1.32 | 1.32 | |
| 2040 | Rain Water Drainage | Roof drains | | S.F. Roof | 1.25 | 1.25 | |
| | **D30 HVAC** | | | | | | |
| 3010 | Energy Supply | N/A | | — | — | — | 12.5 % |
| 3020 | Heat Generating Systems | Included in D3050 | | — | — | — | |
| 3040 | Distribution Systems | Enthalpy heat recovery packages | | Each | 11,450 | 1.64 | |
| 3050 | Terminal & Package Units | Multizone rooftop air conditioner, SEER 14 | | S.F. Floor | 21.05 | 21.05 | |
| 3090 | Other HVAC Sys. & Equipment | N/A | | — | — | — | |
| | **D40 Fire Protection** | | | | | | |
| 4010 | Sprinklers | Sprinkler system, light hazard | | S.F. Floor | 5.07 | 5.07 | 4.2% |
| 4020 | Standpipes | Standpipes and hose systems | | S.F. Floor | 2.54 | 2.54 | |
| | **D50 Electrical** | | | | | | |
| 5010 | Electrical Service/Distribution | 400 ampere service, panel board and feeders | | S.F. Floor | 2.62 | 2.62 | 18.6% |
| 5020 | Lighting & Branch Wiring | LED fixtures, daylt. dim., ltg. on/off, recept., switches, and A.C. power | | S.F. Floor | 19.43 | 19.43 | |
| 5030 | Communications & Security | Addressable alarm systems, internet and phone wiring, and emergency lighting | | S.F. Floor | 8.52 | 8.52 | |
| 5090 | Other Electrical Systems | Emergency generator, 7.5 kW, energy monitoring systems | | S.F. Floor | 3.13 | 3.13 | |
| **E. EQUIPMENT & FURNISHINGS** | | | | | | | |
| 1010 | Commercial Equipment | N/A | | — | — | — | 0.5 % |
| 1020 | Institutional Equipment | N/A | | — | — | — | |
| 1090 | Other Equipment | Waste handling recycling tilt truck | | S.F. Floor | .91 | .91 | |
| 2020 | Moveable Furnishings | No smoking signage | | S.F. Floor | .04 | .04 | |
| **F. SPECIAL CONSTRUCTION** | | | | | | | |
| 1020 | Integrated Construction | N/A | | — | — | — | 0.0 % |
| 1040 | Special Facilities | N/A | | — | — | — | |
| **G. BUILDING SITEWORK** | **N/A** | | | | | | |
| | | | | | **Sub-Total** | 181.28 | **100%** |
| | CONTRACTOR FEES (General Requirements: 10%, Overhead: 5%, Profit: 10%) | | | | *25%* | 45.36 | |
| | ARCHITECT FEES | | | | *7%* | 15.86 | |
| | | | | | **Total Building Cost** | **242.50** | |

# G Office, 2-4 Story

## Costs per square foot of floor area

| Exterior Wall | S.F. Area | 5000 | 8000 | 12000 | 16000 | 20000 | 35000 | 50000 | 65000 | 80000 |
|---|---|---|---|---|---|---|---|---|---|---|
| | L.F. Perimeter | 220 | 260 | 310 | 330 | 360 | 440 | 550 | 600 | 675 |
| Face Brick and Concrete Block | Wood Joists | 344.45 | 300.75 | 275.65 | 257.95 | 248.70 | 230.30 | 224.55 | 218.90 | 216.25 |
| | Steel Joists | 347.30 | 303.60 | 278.50 | 260.85 | 251.60 | 233.15 | 227.40 | 221.80 | 219.15 |
| Curtain Wall | Rigid Steel | 390.25 | 337.20 | 306.65 | 284.70 | 273.35 | 250.50 | 243.45 | 236.40 | 233.10 |
| | Reinforced Concrete | 395.35 | 342.20 | 311.75 | 289.80 | **278.40** | 255.55 | 248.50 | 241.45 | 238.20 |
| Wood Clapboard | Wood Frame | 289.50 | 255.90 | 236.75 | 223.60 | 216.70 | 203.05 | 198.70 | 194.60 | 192.75 |
| Brick Veneer | Wood Frame | 304.00 | 266.60 | 245.20 | 230.40 | 222.60 | 207.20 | 202.35 | 197.70 | 195.50 |
| Perimeter Adj., Add or Deduct | Per 100 L.F. | 55.30 | 34.55 | 23.00 | 17.30 | 13.85 | 7.90 | 5.50 | 4.30 | 3.50 |
| Story Hgt. Adj., Add or Deduct | Per 1 Ft. | 9.00 | 6.60 | 5.25 | 4.20 | 3.65 | 2.55 | 2.20 | 1.90 | 1.75 |
| ***For Basement**, add $60.75 per square foot of basement area* | | | | | | | | | | |

*The above costs were calculated using the basic specifications shown on the facing page. These costs should be adjusted where necessary for design alternatives and owner's requirements.*

## Common additives

| Description | Unit | $ Cost |
|---|---|---|
| Closed Circuit Surveillance, one station, camera and monitor | Ea. | 1250 |
| For additional camera stations, add | Ea. | 475 |
| Directory Boards, plastic, glass covered, 30" x 20" | Ea. | 705 |
| 36" x 48" | Ea. | 1475 |
| Aluminum, 36" x 24" | Ea. | 985 |
| 48" x 32" | Ea. | 1975 |
| Electronic, wall mounted | S.F. | 1175 |
| Escalators, 10' rise, 32" wide, glass balustrade | Ea. | 174,500 |
| 48" wide, glass balustrade | Ea. | 182,500 |
| Pedestal access flr sys w/PLAM cover, comp rm, | | |
| Less than 6000 SF | S.F. | 8.80 |
| Greater than 6000 SF | S.F. | 8.65 |
| Office, greater than 6000 S.F. | S.F. | 11.95 |
| Uninterruptible power supply, 15 kVA/12.75 kW | kW | 1.35 |

| Description | Unit | $ Cost |
|---|---|---|
| Commissioning Fees, sustainable commercial construction | S.F. | 0.24 - 3.04 |
| Energy Modelling Fees, commercial buildings to 10,000 SF | Ea. | 11,000 |
| Greater than 10,000 SF add | S.F. | 0.04 |
| Green Bldg Cert Fees for comm construction project reg | Project | 1200 |
| Photovoltaic Pwr Sys, grid connected, 20 kW (~2400 SF), roof | Ea. | 92,200 |
| Green Roofs, 6" soil depth, w/treated wd edging & sedum mats | S.F. | 28.30 |
| 10" Soil depth, with treated wood edging & sedum mats | S.F. | 30.65 |
| Greywater Recovery Systems, prepackaged comm, 3060 gal. | Ea. | 70,415 |
| 4590 gal. | Ea. | 88,275 |
| Rainwater Harvest Sys, prepckged comm, 10,000 gal, sys contrller | Ea. | 44,975 |
| 20,000 gal. w/system controller | Ea. | 73,350 |
| 30,000 gal. w/system controller | Ea. | 108,025 |
| Solar Domestic HW, closed loop, add-on sys, ext heat exchanger | Ea. | 13,550 |
| Drainback, hot water system, 120 gal tank | Ea. | 16,425 |
| Draindown, hot water system, 120 gal tank | Ea. | 16,700 |



**Important: See the Reference Section for Location Factors.**

**Model costs calculated for a 3 story building with 12′ story height and 20,000 square feet of floor area**

# G Office, 2-4 Story

| | | | | Unit | Unit Cost | Cost Per S.F. | % Of Sub-Total |
|---|---|---|---|---|---|---|---|
| **A. SUBSTRUCTURE** | | | | | | | |
| 1010 | Standard Foundations | Poured concrete; strip and spread footings | | S.F. Ground | 10.77 | 3.59 | 4.2% |
| 1020 | Special Foundations | N/A | | — | — | — | |
| 1030 | Slab on Grade | 4" reinforced concrete with vapor barrier and granular base | | S.F. Slab | 7.32 | 2.44 | |
| 2010 | Basement Excavation | Site preparation for slab and trench for foundation wall and footing | | S.F. Ground | .38 | .13 | |
| 2020 | Basement Walls | 4′ foundation wall | | L.F. Wall | 229 | 2.56 | |
| **B. SHELL** | | | | | | | |
| | **B10 Superstructure** | | | | | | |
| 1010 | Floor Construction | Open web steel joists, slab form, concrete, columns | | S.F. Floor | 32.64 | 21.76 | 13.8% |
| 1020 | Roof Construction | Metal deck, open web steel joists, columns | | S.F. Roof | 20.91 | 6.97 | |
| | **B20 Exterior Enclosure** | | | | | | |
| 2010 | Exterior Walls | Face brick with concrete block backup | *80% of wall* | S.F. Wall | | | 20.4% |
| 2020 | Exterior Windows | Aluminum outward projecting | *20% of wall* | Each | 79 | 40.79 | |
| 2030 | Exterior Doors | Aluminum and glass, hollow metal | | Each | 5748 | 1.73 | |
| | **B30 Roofing** | | | | | | |
| 3010 | Roof Coverings | Built-up tar and gravel with flashing; perlite/EPS composite | | S.F. Roof | 12.54 | 4.18 | 2.0% |
| 3020 | Roof Openings | N/A | | — | — | — | |
| **C. INTERIORS** | | | | | | | |
| 1010 | Partitions | Gypsum board on metal studs | *20 S.F. Floor/L.F. Partition* | S.F. Partition | 13.38 | 5.35 | 17.4% |
| 1020 | Interior Doors | Single leaf hollow metal | *200 S.F. Floor/Door* | Each | 1159 | 5.80 | |
| 1030 | Fittings | Toilet partitions | | S.F. Floor | 3.18 | 3.18 | |
| 2010 | Stair Construction | Concrete filled metal pan | | Flight | 16,075 | 5.63 | |
| 3010 | Wall Finishes | 60% vinyl wall covering, 40% paint | | S.F. Surface | 2.95 | 2.36 | |
| 3020 | Floor Finishes | 60% carpet, 30% vinyl composition tile, 10% ceramic tile | | S.F. Floor | 4.86 | 4.86 | |
| 3030 | Ceiling Finishes | Mineral fiber tile on concealed zee bars | | S.F. Ceiling | 9 | 9 | |
| **D. SERVICES** | | | | | | | |
| | **D10 Conveying** | | | | | | |
| 1010 | Elevators & Lifts | Two hydraulic passenger elevators | | Each | 147,200 | 14.72 | 7.1% |
| 1020 | Escalators & Moving Walks | N/A | | — | — | — | |
| | **D20 Plumbing** | | | | | | |
| 2010 | Plumbing Fixtures | Toilet and service fixtures, supply and drainage | *1 Fixture/1320 S.F. Floor* | Each | 8395 | 6.36 | 3.6% |
| 2020 | Domestic Water Distribution | Gas fired water heater | | S.F. Floor | .31 | .31 | |
| 2040 | Rain Water Drainage | Roof drains | | S.F. Roof | 2.55 | .85 | |
| | **D30 HVAC** | | | | | | |
| 3010 | Energy Supply | N/A | | — | — | — | 9.8 % |
| 3020 | Heat Generating Systems | Included in D3030 | | — | — | — | |
| 3040 | Distribution Systems | Enthalpy heat recovery packages | | Each | 20,225 | 3.03 | |
| 3050 | Terminal & Package Units | Multizone rooftop air conditioner | | S.F. Floor | 17.30 | 17.30 | |
| 3090 | Other HVAC Sys. & Equipment | N/A | | — | — | — | |
| | **D40 Fire Protection** | | | | | | |
| 4010 | Sprinklers | N/A | | — | — | — | 3.4 % |
| 4020 | Standpipes | Standpipes and hose systems | | S.F. Floor | 1.68 | 1.68 | |
| | **D50 Electrical** | | | | | | |
| 5010 | Electrical Service/Distribution | 1000 ampere service, panel board and feeders | | S.F. Floor | 4.15 | 4.15 | 18.2% |
| 5020 | Lighting & Branch Wiring | Fluorescent fixtures, receptacles, switches, A.C. and misc. power | | S.F. Floor | 20.39 | 20.39 | |
| 5030 | Communications & Security | Alarm systems and emergency lighting | | S.F. Floor | 11.73 | 11.73 | |
| 5090 | Other Electrical Systems | Emergency generator, 7.5 kW | | S.F. Floor | 1.56 | 1.56 | |
| **E. EQUIPMENT & FURNISHINGS** | | | | | | | |
| 1010 | Commercial Equipment | N/A | | — | — | — | 0.2 % |
| 1020 | Institutional Equipment | N/A | | — | — | — | |
| 1090 | Other Equipment | Waste handling recycling tilt truck | | S.F. Floor | .32 | .32 | |
| 2020 | Moveable Furnishings | No smoking signage | | S.F. Floor | .01 | .01 | |
| **F. SPECIAL CONSTRUCTION** | | | | | | | |
| 1020 | Integrated Construction | N/A | | — | — | — | 0.0 % |
| 1040 | Special Facilities | N/A | | — | — | — | |
| **G. BUILDING SITEWORK** | **N/A** | | | | | | |
| | | | | | **Sub-Total** | 208.14 | **100%** |
| | CONTRACTOR FEES (General Requirements: 10%, Overhead: 5%, Profit: 10%) | | | | *25%* | 52.05 | |
| | ARCHITECT FEES | | | | *7%* | 18.21 | |
| | | | | | **Total Building Cost** | **278.40** | |

# G Office, 5-10 Story

## Costs per square foot of floor area

| Exterior Wall | S.F. Area | 20000 | 40000 | 60000 | 80000 | 100000 | 150000 | 200000 | 250000 | 300000 |
|---|---|---|---|---|---|---|---|---|---|---|
| | L.F. Perimeter | 260 | 360 | 400 | 420 | 460 | 520 | 650 | 720 | 800 |
| Precast Concrete | Rigid Steel | 366.70 | 305.70 | 272.30 | **252.35** | 243.05 | 227.05 | 223.60 | 218.50 | 215.45 |
| | Reinforced Concrete | 365.45 | 304.45 | 271.00 | 251.10 | 241.80 | 225.80 | 222.35 | 217.15 | 214.20 |
| Face Brick and Concrete Block | Rigid Steel | 310.75 | 266.95 | 243.60 | 229.75 | 223.20 | 212.15 | 209.60 | 206.10 | 203.95 |
| | Reinforced Concrete | 309.45 | 265.70 | 242.35 | 228.50 | 221.95 | 210.90 | 208.35 | 204.80 | 202.70 |
| Limestone and Concrete Block | Rigid Steel | 341.40 | 288.20 | 259.30 | 242.15 | 234.05 | 220.30 | 217.30 | 212.85 | 210.20 |
| | Reinforced Concrete | 340.15 | 286.95 | 258.05 | 240.90 | 232.80 | 219.05 | 216.05 | 211.60 | 208.95 |
| Perimeter Adj., Add or Deduct | Per 100 L.F. | 65.25 | 32.60 | 21.75 | 16.35 | 13.00 | 8.65 | 6.55 | 5.15 | 4.30 |
| Story Hgt. Adj., Add or Deduct | Per 1 Ft. | 13.75 | 9.55 | 7.00 | 5.55 | 4.80 | 3.65 | 3.45 | 3.05 | 2.80 |
| ***For Basement**, add $65.60 per square foot of basement area* | | | | | | | | | | |

*The above costs were calculated using the basic specifications shown on the facing page. These costs should be adjusted where necessary for design alternatives and owner's requirements.*

## Common additives

| Description | Unit | $ Cost |
|---|---|---|
| Closed Circuit Surveillance, one station, camera and monitor | Ea. | 1250 |
| For additional camera stations, add | Ea. | 475 |
| Directory Boards, plastic, glass covered, 30" x 20" | Ea. | 705 |
| 36" x 48" | Ea. | 1475 |
| Aluminum, 36" x 24" | Ea. | 985 |
| 48" x 32" | Ea. | 1975 |
| Electronic, wall mounted | S.F. | 1175 |
| Escalators, 10' rise, 32" wide, glass balustrade | Ea. | 174,500 |
| 48" wide, glass balustrade | Ea. | 182,500 |
| Pedestal access flr sys w/PLAM cover, comp rm, | | |
| Less than 6000 SF | S.F. | 8.80 |
| Greater than 6000 SF | S.F. | 8.65 |
| Office, greater than 6000 S.F. | S.F. | 11.95 |
| Uninterruptible power supply, 15 kVA/12.75 kW | kW | 1.35 |

| Description | Unit | $ Cost |
|---|---|---|
| Commissioning Fees, sustainable commercial construction | S.F. | 0.24 - 3.04 |
| Energy Modelling Fees, commercial buildings to 10,000 SF | Ea. | 11,000 |
| Greater than 10,000 SF add | S.F. | 0.04 |
| Green Bldg Cert Fees for comm construction project reg | Project | 1200 |
| Photovoltaic Pwr Sys, grid connected, 20 kW (~2400 SF), roof | Ea. | 92,200 |
| Green Roofs, 6" soil depth, w/treated wd edging & sedum mats | S.F. | 28.30 |
| 10" Soil depth, with treated wood edging & sedum mats | S.F. | 30.65 |
| Greywater Recovery Systems, prepackaged comm, 3060 gal. | Ea. | 70,415 |
| 4590 gal. | Ea. | 88,275 |
| Rainwater Harvest Sys, prepckged comm, 10,000 gal, sys contrller | Ea. | 44,975 |
| 20,000 gal. w/system controller | Ea. | 73,350 |
| 30,000 gal. w/system controller | Ea. | 108,025 |
| Solar Domestic HW, closed loop, add-on sys, ext heat exchanger | Ea. | 13,550 |
| Drainback, hot water system, 120 gal tank | Ea. | 16,425 |
| Draindown, hot water system, 120 gal tank | Ea. | 16,700 |

## Model costs calculated for a 8 story building with 12′ story height and 80,000 square feet of floor area

# G Office, 5-10 Story

| | | | | Unit | Unit Cost | Cost Per S.F. | % Of Sub-Total |
|---|---|---|---|---|---|---|---|
| **A. SUBSTRUCTURE** | | | | | | | |
| 1010 | Standard Foundations | Poured concrete; strip and spread footings | | S.F. Ground | 17.28 | 2.16 | |
| 1020 | Special Foundations | N/A | | — | — | — | |
| 1030 | Slab on Grade | 4″ reinforced concrete with recycled vapor barrier and granular base | | S.F. Slab | 7.32 | .92 | 2.1% |
| 2010 | Basement Excavation | Site preparation for slab and trench for foundation wall and footing | | S.F. Ground | .38 | .05 | |
| 2020 | Basement Walls | 4′ foundation wall | | L.F. Wall | 121 | .81 | |
| **B. SHELL** | | | | | | | |
| | **B10 Superstructure** | | | | | | |
| 1010 | Floor Construction | Concrete slab with metal deck and beams | | S.F. Floor | 32.25 | 28.22 | 15.5% |
| 1020 | Roof Construction | Metal deck, open web steel joists, interior columns | | S.F. Roof | 9.76 | 1.22 | |
| | **B20 Exterior Enclosure** | | | | | | |
| 2010 | Exterior Walls | Precast concrete panels | *80% of wall* | S.F. Wall | 91 | 36.55 | |
| 2020 | Exterior Windows | Vertical pivoted steel | *20% of wall* | Each | 1677 | 11.27 | 25.3% |
| 2030 | Exterior Doors | Double aluminum and glass doors and entrance with transoms | | Each | 6878 | .43 | |
| | **B30 Roofing** | | | | | | |
| 3010 | Roof Coverings | Single-ply TPO membrane, 60 mils, welded seams w/R-20 insul. | | S.F. Roof | 10.80 | 1.35 | 0.7% |
| 3020 | Roof Openings | N/A | | — | — | — | |
| **C. INTERIORS** | | | | | | | |
| 1010 | Partitions | Gypsum board on metal studs w/sound attenuation | *30 SF Flr./LF Part.* | S.F. Partition | 14.73 | 4.91 | |
| 1020 | Interior Doors | Single leaf hollow metal, low VOC paint | *400 S.F. Floor/Door* | Each | 1159 | 2.90 | |
| 1030 | Fittings | Toilet Partitions | | S.F. Floor | 2.12 | 2.12 | |
| 2010 | Stair Construction | Concrete filled metal pan | | Flight | 16,075 | 3.42 | 15.3% |
| 3010 | Wall Finishes | 60% vinyl wall covering, 40% paint, low VOC paint | | S.F. Surface | 2.96 | 1.97 | |
| 3020 | Floor Finishes | 60% carpet tile, 30% vinyl composition tile, recycled content, 10% ceramic tile | | S.F. Floor | 4.86 | 4.86 | |
| 3030 | Ceiling Finishes | Mineral fiber tile on concealed zee bars | | S.F. Ceiling | 9 | 9 | |
| **D. SERVICES** | | | | | | | |
| | **D10 Conveying** | | | | | | |
| 1010 | Elevators & Lifts | Four geared passenger elevators | | Each | 370,600 | 18.53 | 9.7% |
| 1020 | Escalators & Moving Walks | N/A | | — | — | — | |
| | **D20 Plumbing** | | | | | | |
| 2010 | Plumbing Fixtures | Toilet, low flow, auto sensor, & service fixt., supply & drain. | *1 Fixt./1370 SF Flr.* | Each | 6124 | 4.47 | |
| 2020 | Domestic Water Distribution | Gas fired tankless water heater | | S.F. Floor | .54 | .54 | 2.9% |
| 2040 | Rain Water Drainage | Roof drains | | S.F. Roof | 3.52 | .44 | |
| | **D30 HVAC** | | | | | | |
| 3010 | Energy Supply | N/A | | — | — | — | |
| 3020 | Heat Generating Systems | Included in D3050 | | — | — | — | |
| 3040 | Distribution Systems | Enthalpy heat recovery packages | | Each | 42,375 | 2.12 | 10.3 % |
| 3050 | Terminal & Package Units | Multizone rooftop air conditioner, SEER 14 | | S.F. Floor | 17.50 | 17.50 | |
| 3090 | Other HVAC Sys. & Equipment | N/A | | — | — | — | |
| | **D40 Fire Protection** | | | | | | |
| 4010 | Sprinklers | Wet pipe sprinkler system | | S.F. Floor | 4.33 | 4.33 | 3.2% |
| 4020 | Standpipes | Standpipes and hose systems | | S.F. Floor | 1.83 | 1.83 | |
| | **D50 Electrical** | | | | | | |
| 5010 | Electrical Service/Distribution | 1600 ampere service, panel board and feeders | | S.F. Floor | 1.62 | 1.62 | |
| 5020 | Lighting & Branch Wiring | LED fixtures, daylt. dim., ltg. on/off, recept., switches, and A.C. power | | S.F. Floor | 18.73 | 18.73 | 15.0% |
| 5030 | Communications & Security | Addressable alarm systems, internet and phone wiring, emergency lighting | | S.F. Floor | 6.70 | 6.70 | |
| 5090 | Other Electrical Systems | Emergency generator, 100 kW, UPS, energy monitoring systems | | S.F. Floor | 1.45 | 1.45 | |
| **E. EQUIPMENT & FURNISHINGS** | | | | | | | |
| 1010 | Commercial Equipment | N/A | | — | — | — | |
| 1020 | Institutional Equipment | N/A | | — | — | — | 0.0 % |
| 1090 | Other Equipment | Waste handling recycling tilt truck | | S.F. Floor | .04 | .04 | |
| 2020 | Moveable Furnishings | No smoking signage | | S.F. Floor | | | |
| **F. SPECIAL CONSTRUCTION** | | | | | | | |
| 1020 | Integrated Construction | N/A | | — | — | — | 0.0 % |
| 1040 | Special Facilities | N/A | | — | — | — | |
| **G. BUILDING SITEWORK** | **N/A** | | | | | | |
| | | | | | **Sub-Total** | 190.46 | **100%** |
| | CONTRACTOR FEES (General Requirements: 10%, Overhead: 5%, Profit: 10%) | | | | *25%* | 47.61 | |
| | ARCHITECT FEES | | | | *6%* | 14.28 | |
| | | | | | **Total Building Cost** | **252.35** | |

## Costs per square foot of floor area

| Exterior Wall | S.F. Area | 120000 | 145000 | 170000 | 200000 | 230000 | 260000 | 400000 | 600000 | 800000 |
|---|---|---|---|---|---|---|---|---|---|---|
| | L.F. Perimeter | 420 | 450 | 470 | 490 | 510 | 530 | 650 | 800 | 900 |
| Curtain Wall | Rigid Steel | 264.65 | 253.75 | 244.85 | 236.65 | 230.60 | **225.95** | 214.85 | 207.25 | 202.10 |
| | Reinforced Concrete | 254.20 | 243.55 | 234.80 | 226.70 | 220.70 | 216.15 | 205.30 | 197.75 | 192.65 |
| Face Brick and Concrete Block | Rigid Steel | 232.80 | 225.55 | 219.75 | 214.35 | 210.45 | 207.40 | 200.10 | 195.10 | 191.85 |
| | Reinforced Concrete | 222.40 | 215.30 | 209.65 | 204.40 | 200.55 | 197.65 | 190.50 | 185.65 | 182.45 |
| Precast Concrete | Rigid Steel | 246.70 | 237.80 | 230.70 | 224.10 | 219.20 | 215.45 | 206.55 | 200.40 | 196.30 |
| | Reinforced Concrete | 236.30 | 227.65 | 220.65 | 214.15 | 209.40 | 205.70 | 197.00 | 190.95 | 186.95 |
| Perimeter Adj., Add or Deduct | Per 100 L.F. | 18.15 | 15.05 | 12.90 | 10.95 | 9.55 | 8.40 | 5.50 | 3.60 | 2.70 |
| Story Hgt. Adj., Add or Deduct | Per 1 Ft. | 7.35 | 6.55 | 5.80 | 5.15 | 4.65 | 4.25 | 3.45 | 2.75 | 2.30 |
| ***For Basement**, add $65.50 per square foot of basement area* | | | | | | | | | | |

*The above costs were calculated using the basic specifications shown on the facing page. These costs should be adjusted where necessary for design alternatives and owner's requirements.*

## Common additives

| Description | Unit | $ Cost |
|---|---|---|
| Closed Circuit Surveillance, one station, camera and monitor | Ea. | 1250 |
| For additional camera stations, add | Ea. | 475 |
| Directory Boards, plastic, glass covered, 30" x 20" | Ea. | 705 |
| 36" x 48" | Ea. | 1475 |
| Aluminum, 36" x 24" | Ea. | 985 |
| 48" x 32" | Ea. | 1975 |
| Electronic, wall mounted | S.F. | 1175 |
| Escalators, 10' rise, 32" wide, glass balustrade | Ea. | 174,500 |
| 48" wide, glass balustrade | Ea. | 182,500 |
| Pedestal access flr sys w/PLAM cover, comp rm, | | |
| Less than 6000 SF | S.F. | 8.80 |
| Greater than 6000 SF | S.F. | 8.65 |
| Office, greater than 6000 S.F. | S.F. | 11.95 |
| Uninterruptible power supply, 15 kVA/12.75 kW | kW | 1.35 |

| Description | Unit | $ Cost |
|---|---|---|
| Commissioning Fees, sustainable commercial construction | S.F. | 0.24 - 3.04 |
| Energy Modelling Fees, commercial buildings to 10,000 SF | Ea. | 11,000 |
| Greater than 10,000 SF add | S.F. | 0.04 |
| Green Bldg Cert Fees for comm construction project reg | Project | 1200 |
| Photovoltaic Pwr Sys, grid connected, 20 kW (~2400 SF), roof | Ea. | 92,200 |
| Green Roofs, 6" soil depth, w/treated wd edging & sedum mats | S.F. | 28.30 |
| 10" Soil depth, with treated wood edging & sedum mats | S.F. | 30.65 |
| Greywater Recovery Systems, prepackaged comm, 3060 gal. | Ea. | 70,415 |
| 4590 gal. | Ea. | 88,275 |
| Rainwater Harvest Sys, prepckged comm, 10,000 gal, sys contrller | Ea. | 44,975 |
| 20,000 gal. w/system controller | Ea. | 73,350 |
| 30,000 gal. w/system controller | Ea. | 108,025 |
| Solar Domestic HW, closed loop, add-on sys, ext heat exchanger | Ea. | 13,550 |
| Drainback, hot water system, 120 gal tank | Ea. | 16,425 |
| Draindown, hot water system, 120 gal tank | Ea. | 16,700 |



**Important: See the Reference Section for Location Factors.**

## Model costs calculated for a 16 story building with 10′ story height and 260,000 square feet of floor area

# G Office, 11-20 Story

| | | | | Unit | Unit Cost | Cost Per S.F. | % Of Sub-Total |
|---|---|---|---|---|---|---|---|
| **A. SUBSTRUCTURE** | | | | | | | |
| 1010 | Standard Foundations | CIP concrete pile caps | | S.F. Ground | 14.24 | .89 | |
| 1020 | Special Foundations | Steel H-piles, concrete grade beams | | S.F. Ground | 73 | 4.54 | |
| 1030 | Slab on Grade | 4″ reinforced concrete with recycled vapor barrier and granular base | | S.F. Slab | 7.32 | .46 | 3.8% |
| 2010 | Basement Excavation | Site preparation for slab, piles and grade beams | | S.F. Ground | .38 | .02 | |
| 2020 | Basement Walls | 4′ foundation wall | | L.F. Wall | 121 | .59 | |
| **B. SHELL** | | | | | | | |
| | **B10 Superstructure** | | | | | | |
| 1010 | Floor Construction | Concrete slab, metal deck, beams | | S.F. Floor | 36.62 | 34.33 | 20.6% |
| 1020 | Roof Construction | Metal deck, open web steel joists, beams, columns | | S.F. Roof | 11.52 | .72 | |
| | **B20 Exterior Enclosure** | | | | | | |
| 2010 | Exterior Walls | N/A | | — | — | — | |
| 2020 | Exterior Windows | Double glazed heat absorbing, tinted plate glass wall panels | *100% of wall* | Each | 102 | 30.77 | 18.7 % |
| 2030 | Exterior Doors | Double aluminum & glass doors | | Each | 10,682 | 1.15 | |
| | **B30 Roofing** | | | | | | |
| 3010 | Roof Coverings | Single ply membrane, fully adhered; perlite/EPS R-20 insulation | | S.F. Roof | 10.56 | .66 | 0.4% |
| 3020 | Roof Openings | N/A | | — | — | — | |
| **C. INTERIORS** | | | | | | | |
| 1010 | Partitions | Gypsum board on metal studs, sound attenuation | *30 SF Flr./LF Part.* | S.F. Partition | 16.20 | 4.32 | |
| 1020 | Interior Doors | Single leaf hollow metal, low VOC paint | *400 S.F. Floor/Door* | Each | 1159 | 2.90 | |
| 1030 | Fittings | Toilet partitions | | S.F. Floor | 1.22 | 1.22 | |
| 2010 | Stair Construction | Concrete filled metal pan | | Flight | 19,225 | 2.58 | 15.8% |
| 3010 | Wall Finishes | 60% vinyl wall covering, 40% paint, low VOC | | S.F. Surface | 2.93 | 1.56 | |
| 3020 | Floor Finishes | 60% carpet tile, 30% vinyl composition tile, recycled content, 10% ceramic tile | | S.F. Floor | 5.29 | 5.29 | |
| 3030 | Ceiling Finishes | Mineral fiber tile on concealed zee bars | | S.F. Ceiling | 9 | 9 | |
| **D. SERVICES** | | | | | | | |
| | **D10 Conveying** | | | | | | |
| 1010 | Elevators & Lifts | Four geared passenger elevators | | Each | 578,500 | 8.90 | 5.2% |
| 1020 | Escalators & Moving Walks | N/A | | — | — | — | |
| | **D20 Plumbing** | | | | | | |
| 2010 | Plumbing Fixtures | Toilet, low flow, auto sensor, & service fixt., supply & drain. | *1 Fixt./1345 SF Flr.* | Each | 9375 | 6.97 | |
| 2020 | Domestic Water Distribution | Gas fired, tankless water heater | | S.F. Floor | .24 | .24 | 4.4% |
| 2040 | Rain Water Drainage | Roof drains | | S.F. Roof | 4.32 | .27 | |
| | **D30 HVAC** | | | | | | |
| 3010 | Energy Supply | N/A | | — | — | — | |
| 3020 | Heat Generating Systems | N/A | | — | — | — | |
| 3040 | Distribution Systems | Enthalpy heat recovery packages | | Each | 42,375 | 1.79 | 11.3 % |
| 3050 | Terminal & Package Units | Multizone rooftop air conditioner | | S.F. Floor | 17.50 | 17.50 | |
| 3090 | Other HVAC Sys. & Equipment | N/A | | — | — | — | |
| | **D40 Fire Protection** | | | | | | |
| 4010 | Sprinklers | Sprinkler system, light hazard | | S.F. Floor | 4.21 | 4.21 | 3.0% |
| 4020 | Standpipes | Standpipes and hose systems | | S.F. Floor | .90 | .90 | |
| | **D50 Electrical** | | | | | | |
| 5010 | Electrical Service/Distribution | 2400 ampere service, panel board and feeders | | S.F. Floor | 1.05 | 1.05 | |
| 5020 | Lighting & Branch Wiring | LED fixtures, daylt. dim., ltg. on/off, recept., switches, and A.C. power | | S.F. Floor | 19.75 | 19.75 | 16.8% |
| 5030 | Communications & Security | Addressable alarm systems, internet & phone wiring, emergency ltg. | | S.F. Floor | 7.09 | 7.09 | |
| 5090 | Other Electrical Systems | Emergency generator, 200 kW, UPS, energy monitoring systems | | S.F. Floor | .82 | .82 | |
| **E. EQUIPMENT & FURNISHINGS** | | | | | | | |
| 1010 | Commercial Equipment | N/A | | — | — | — | |
| 1020 | Institutional Equipment | N/A | | — | — | — | 0.0 % |
| 1090 | Other Equipment | Waste handling recycling tilt truck | | S.F. Floor | .01 | .01 | |
| 2020 | Moveable Furnishings | No smoking signage | | S.F. Floor | | | |
| **F. SPECIAL CONSTRUCTION** | | | | | | | |
| 1020 | Integrated Construction | N/A | | — | — | — | 0.0 % |
| 1040 | Special Facilities | N/A | | — | — | — | |
| **G. BUILDING SITEWORK** | **N/A** | | | | | | |
| | | | | | **Sub-Total** | 170.50 | **100%** |
| | CONTRACTOR FEES (General Requirements: 10%, Overhead: 5%, Profit: 10%) | | | | *25%* | 42.66 | |
| | ARCHITECT FEES | | | | *6%* | 12.79 | |
| | | | | | **Total Building Cost** | **225.95** | |

## Costs per square foot of floor area

| Exterior Wall | S.F. Area | 7000 | 9000 | 11000 | 13000 | 15000 | 17000 | 19000 | 21000 | 23000 |
|---|---|---|---|---|---|---|---|---|---|---|
| | L.F. Perimeter | 240 | 280 | 303 | 325 | 354 | 372 | 397 | 422 | 447 |
| Limestone and Concrete Block | Bearing Walls | 337.05 | 318.10 | 301.45 | 289.75 | 282.40 | 274.95 | 270.15 | 266.30 | 263.10 |
| | Reinforced Concrete | 365.70 | 346.75 | 330.00 | 318.35 | 311.00 | 303.60 | 298.80 | 294.90 | 291.70 |
| Face Brick and Concrete Block | Bearing Walls | 316.30 | 299.25 | 284.70 | 274.55 | 268.10 | 261.70 | 257.50 | 254.15 | 251.35 |
| | Reinforced Concrete | 344.95 | 327.90 | 313.35 | 303.20 | 296.75 | 290.35 | 286.15 | 282.75 | 279.95 |
| Decorative Concrete Block | Bearing Walls | 301.35 | 285.65 | 272.70 | 263.70 | 257.80 | 252.15 | 248.35 | 245.35 | 242.80 |
| | Reinforced Concrete | 329.95 | 314.30 | 301.35 | 292.30 | 286.40 | 280.75 | 277.00 | 273.95 | 271.45 |
| Perimeter Adj., Add or Deduct | Per 100 L.F. | 42.60 | 33.10 | 27.05 | 22.80 | 19.90 | 17.50 | 15.70 | 14.25 | 12.90 |
| Story Hgt. Adj., Add or Deduct | Per 1 Ft. | 7.35 | 6.70 | 5.85 | 5.35 | 5.10 | 4.70 | 4.50 | 4.30 | 4.15 |
| ***For Basement**, add $51.55 per square foot of basement area* | | | | | | | | | | |

*The above costs were calculated using the basic specifications shown on the facing page. These costs should be adjusted where necessary for design alternatives and owner's requirements.*

## Common additives

| Description | Unit | $ Cost |
|---|---|---|
| Cells Prefabricated, 5'-6' x 7'-8", 7'-8' high | Ea. | 12,600 |
| Elevators, hydraulic passenger, 2 stops, 2500# capacity | Ea. | 90,500 |
| 3500# capacity | Ea. | 96,000 |
| Lockers, Steel, Single tier, 60" to 72" | Opng. | 285 - 520 |
| Locker bench, lam. maple top only | L.F. | 148 |
| Pedestals, steel pipe | Ea. | 87 |
| Safe, Office type, 1 hr rating, 60"x36"x18", double door | Ea. | 8625 |
| Shooting Range, incl. bullet traps, | | |
| Target provisions & controls, excl. struct shell | Ea. | 65,500 |
| Sound System, amplifier, 250 watts | Ea. | 2425 |
| Speaker, ceiling or wall | Ea. | 320 |
| Trumpet | Ea. | 580 |

| Description | Unit | $ Cost |
|---|---|---|
| Commissioning Fees, sustainable commercial construction | S.F. | 0.24 - 3.04 |
| Energy Modelling Fees, commercial buildings to 10,000 SF | Ea. | 11,000 |
| Greater than 10,000 SF add | S.F. | 0.04 |
| Green Bldg Cert Fees for comm construction project reg | Project | 1200 |
| Photovoltaic Pwr Sys, grid connected, 20 kW (~2400 SF), roof | Ea. | 92,200 |
| Green Roofs, 6" soil depth, w/treated wd edging & sedum mats | S.F. | 28.30 |
| 10" Soil depth, with treated wood edging & sedum mats | S.F. | 30.65 |
| Greywater Recovery Systems, prepackaged comm, 3060 gal. | Ea. | 70,415 |
| 4590 gal. | Ea. | 88,275 |
| Rainwater Harvest Sys, prepckged comm, 10,000 gal, sys contrller | Ea. | 44,975 |
| 20,000 gal. w/system controller | Ea. | 73,350 |
| 30,000 gal. w/system controller | Ea. | 108,025 |
| Solar Domestic HW, closed loop, add-on sys, ext heat exchanger | Ea. | 13,550 |
| Drainback, hot water system, 120 gal tank | Ea. | 16,425 |
| Draindown, hot water system, 120 gal tank | Ea. | 16,700 |



**Important: See the Reference Section for Location Factors.**

# Model costs calculated for a 2 story building with 12′ story height and 11,000 square feet of floor area

# G Police Station

| | | | Unit | Unit Cost | Cost Per S.F. | % Of Sub-Total |
|---|---|---|---|---|---|---|
| **A. SUBSTRUCTURE** | | | | | | |
| 1010 | Standard Foundations | Poured concrete; strip and spread footings | S.F. Ground | 4.16 | 2.08 | 4.7% |
| 1020 | Special Foundations | N/A | — | — | — | |
| 1030 | Slab on Grade | 4″ reinforced concrete with recycled vapor barrier and granular base | S.F. Slab | 7.32 | 3.66 | |
| 2010 | Basement Excavation | Site preparation for slab and trench for foundation wall and footing | S.F. Ground | .38 | .19 | |
| 2020 | Basement Walls | 4′ foundation wall | L.F. Wall | 121 | 4.43 | |
| **B. SHELL** | | | | | | |
| | **B10 Superstructure** | | | | | |
| 1010 | Floor Construction | Open web steel joists, slab form, concrete | S.F. Floor | 17.76 | 8.88 | 5.6% |
| 1020 | Roof Construction | Metal deck on open web steel joists | S.F. Roof | 6.96 | 3.48 | |
| | **B20 Exterior Enclosure** | | | | | |
| 2010 | Exterior Walls | Limestone with concrete block backup *80% of wall* | S.F. Wall | 71 | 37.81 | 24.7% |
| 2020 | Exterior Windows | Metal horizontal sliding *20% of wall* | Each | 1552 | 13.68 | |
| 2030 | Exterior Doors | Hollow metal | Each | 4369 | 3.18 | |
| | **B30 Roofing** | | | | | |
| 3010 | Roof Coverings | Single-ply TPO membrane, 60 mils, heat welded w/R-20 insul. | S.F. Roof | 12.22 | 6.11 | 2.8% |
| 3020 | Roof Openings | N/A | — | — | — | |
| **C. INTERIORS** | | | | | | |
| 1010 | Partitions | Concrete block w/foamed-in insul. *20 SF Flr./LF Part.* | S.F. Partition | 12.64 | 6.32 | 15.0% |
| 1020 | Interior Doors | Single leaf kalamein fire door, low VOC paint *200 S.F. Floor/Door* | Each | 1159 | 5.80 | |
| 1030 | Fittings | Toilet partitions | S.F. Floor | 1.49 | 1.49 | |
| 2010 | Stair Construction | Concrete filled metal pan | Flight | 19,225 | 3.49 | |
| 3010 | Wall Finishes | 90% paint, low VOC, 10% ceramic tile | S.F. Surface | 2.90 | 2.90 | |
| 3020 | Floor Finishes | 70% vinyl composition tile, recycled content, 20% carpet tile, 10% ceramic tile | S.F. Floor | 4.29 | 4.29 | |
| 3030 | Ceiling Finishes | Mineral fiber tile on concealed zee bars | S.F. Ceiling | 9 | 9 | |
| **D. SERVICES** | | | | | | |
| | **D10 Conveying** | | | | | |
| 1010 | Elevators & Lifts | One hydraulic passenger elevator | Each | 107,030 | 9.73 | 4.4% |
| 1020 | Escalators & Moving Walks | N/A | — | — | — | |
| | **D20 Plumbing** | | | | | |
| 2010 | Plumbing Fixtures | Toilet, low flow, auto sensor, & service fixt., supply & drainage *1 Fixt./580 SF Flr.* | Each | 8062 | 13.90 | 8.5% |
| 2020 | Domestic Water Distribution | Electric water heater, point-of-use, energy saver | S.F. Floor | 1.94 | 1.94 | |
| 2040 | Rain Water Drainage | Roof drains | S.F. Roof | 5.90 | 2.95 | |
| | **D30 HVAC** | | | | | |
| 3010 | Energy Supply | N/A | — | — | — | 10.2 % |
| 3020 | Heat Generating Systems | N/A | — | — | — | |
| 3040 | Distribution Systems | Enthalpy heat recovery packages | Each | 17,075 | 1.56 | |
| 3050 | Terminal & Package Units | Multizone rooftop air conditioner, SEER 14 | S.F. Floor | 21.05 | 21.05 | |
| 3090 | Other HVAC Sys. & Equipment | N/A | — | — | — | |
| | **D40 Fire Protection** | | | | | |
| 4010 | Sprinklers | Wet pipe sprinkler system | S.F. Floor | 5.47 | 5.47 | 3.3% |
| 4020 | Standpipes | Standpipe | S.F. Floor | 1.79 | 1.79 | |
| | **D50 Electrical** | | | | | |
| 5010 | Electrical Service/Distribution | 400 ampere service, panel board and feeders | S.F. Floor | 1.27 | 1.27 | 13.2% |
| 5020 | Lighting & Branch Wiring | LED fixtures, daylt. dim., ltg. on/off cntrl., recept., switches, & A.C. pwr. | S.F. Floor | 16.29 | 16.29 | |
| 5030 | Communications & Security | Addressable alarm systems, internet wiring, intercom &emergency ltg. | S.F. Floor | 9.39 | 9.39 | |
| 5090 | Other Electrical Systems | Emergency generator, 15 kW, energy monitoring systems | S.F. Floor | 2.14 | 2.14 | |
| **E. EQUIPMENT & FURNISHINGS** | | | | | | |
| 1020 | Institutional Equipment | Lockers, detention rooms, cells, gasoline dispensers | S.F. Floor | 13.29 | 13.29 | 7.6% |
| 1030 | Vehicular Equipment | Gasoline dispenser system | S.F. Floor | 2.85 | 2.85 | |
| 1090 | Other Equipment | Waste handling recycling tilt truck | S.F. Floor | .58 | .58 | |
| 2020 | Moveable Furnishings | No smoking signage | S.F. Floor | .04 | .04 | |
| **F. SPECIAL CONSTRUCTION** | | | | | | |
| 1020 | Integrated Construction | N/A | — | — | — | 0.0 % |
| 1040 | Special Facilities | N/A | — | — | — | |
| **G. BUILDING SITEWORK** | | **N/A** | | | | |
| | | | | **Sub-Total** | 221.21 | **100%** |
| | CONTRACTOR FEES (General Requirements: 10%, Overhead: 5%, Profit: 10%) | | | 25% | 55.35 | |
| | ARCHITECT FEES | | | 9% | 24.89 | |
| | | | | **Total Building Cost** | **301.45** | |

## Costs per square foot of floor area

| Exterior Wall | S.F. Area | 2000 | 2800 | 3500 | 4200 | 5000 | 5800 | 6500 | 7200 | 8000 |
|---|---|---|---|---|---|---|---|---|---|---|
| | L.F. Perimeter | 180 | 212 | 240 | 268 | 300 | 314 | 336 | 344 | 368 |
| Wood Clapboard | Wood Frame | 359.70 | 340.85 | 331.35 | 325.00 | **320.00** | 313.65 | 310.80 | 306.75 | 304.60 |
| Brick Veneer | Wood Frame | 375.40 | 354.00 | 343.30 | 336.15 | 330.50 | 323.10 | 319.80 | 315.10 | 312.60 |
| Face Brick and Concrete Block | Wood Joists | 389.90 | 366.20 | 354.35 | 346.40 | 340.20 | 331.85 | 328.15 | 322.80 | 320.00 |
| | Steel Joists | 374.65 | 350.90 | 339.10 | 331.20 | 324.90 | 316.55 | 312.90 | 307.55 | 304.75 |
| Stucco and Concrete Block | Wood Joists | 377.60 | 356.35 | 345.80 | 338.75 | 333.10 | 325.85 | 322.55 | 317.90 | 315.35 |
| | Steel Joists | 358.90 | 337.65 | 327.05 | 319.95 | 314.40 | 307.10 | 303.80 | 299.15 | 296.65 |
| Perimeter Adj., Add or Deduct | Per 100 L.F. | 42.25 | 30.15 | 24.15 | 20.15 | 16.90 | 14.60 | 13.05 | 11.75 | 10.55 |
| Story Hgt. Adj., Add or Deduct | Per 1 Ft. | 4.40 | 3.65 | 3.35 | 3.15 | 2.95 | 2.70 | 2.50 | 2.35 | 2.20 |

*For Basement, add $58.75 per square foot of basement area*

*The above costs were calculated using the basic specifications shown on the facing page. These costs should be adjusted where necessary for design alternatives and owner's requirements.*

## Common additives

| Description | Unit | $ Cost |
|---|---|---|
| Bar, Front Bar | L.F. | 490 |
| Back bar | L.F. | 395 |
| Booth, Upholstered, custom straight | L.F. | 281 - 1500 |
| "L" or "U" shaped | L.F. | 291 - 490 |
| Fireplace, brick, excl. chimney or foundation, 30"x29" opening | Ea. | 3750 |
| Chimney, standard brick, single flue, 16" x 20" | V.L.F. | 161 |
| 2 Flue, 20" x 24" | V.L.F. | 247 |
| Kitchen Equipment | | |
| Broiler | Ea. | 4425 |
| Coffee urn, twin 6 gallon | Ea. | 4075 |
| Cooler, 6 ft. long | Ea. | 4525 |
| Dishwasher, 10-12 racks per hr. | Ea. | 42,900 |
| Food warmer, counter, 1.2 KW | Ea. | 720 |
| Freezer, 44 C.F., reach-in | Ea. | 3600 |
| Ice cube maker, 50 lb. per day | Ea. | 2525 |
| Range with 1 oven | Ea. | 2050 |
| Refrigerators, prefabricated, walk-in, 7'-6" high, 6' x 6' | S.F. | 141 |
| 10' x 10' | S.F. | 110 |
| 12' x 14' | S.F. | 96 |
| 12' x 20' | S.F. | 139 |

| Description | Unit | $ Cost |
|---|---|---|
| Commissioning Fees, sustainable commercial construction | S.F. | 0.24 - 3.04 |
| Energy Modelling Fees, commercial buildings to 10,000 SF | Ea. | 11,000 |
| Greater than 10,000 SF add | S.F. | 0.04 |
| Green Bldg Cert Fees for comm construction project reg | Project | 1200 |
| Photovoltaic Pwr Sys, grid connected, 20 kW (~2400 SF), roof | Ea. | 92,200 |
| Green Roofs, 6" soil depth, w/treated wd edging & sedum mats | S.F. | 28.30 |
| 10" Soil depth, with treated wood edging & sedum mats | S.F. | 30.65 |
| Greywater Recovery Systems, prepackaged comm, 3060 gal. | Ea. | 70,415 |
| 4590 gal. | Ea. | 88,275 |
| Rainwater Harvest Sys, prepckged comm, 10,000 gal, sys contrller | Ea. | 44,975 |
| 20,000 gal. w/system controller | Ea. | 73,350 |
| 30,000 gal. w/system controller | Ea. | 108,025 |
| Solar Domestic HW, closed loop, add-on sys, ext heat exchanger | Ea. | 13,550 |
| Drainback, hot water system, 120 gal tank | Ea. | 16,425 |
| Draindown, hot water system, 120 gal tank | Ea. | 16,700 |

## Model costs calculated for a 1 story building with 12′ story height and 5,000 square feet of floor area

# G Restaurant

| | | | | Unit | Unit Cost | Cost Per S.F. | % Of Sub-Total |
|---|---|---|---|---|---|---|---|
| **A. SUBSTRUCTURE** | | | | | | | |
| 1010 | Standard Foundations | Poured concrete; strip and spread footings | | S.F. Ground | 3.83 | 3.83 | 8.0% |
| 1020 | Special Foundations | N/A | | — | — | — | |
| 1030 | Slab on Grade | 4″ reinforced concrete with recycled vapor barrier and granular base | | S.F. Slab | 7.32 | 7.32 | |
| 2010 | Basement Excavation | Site preparation for slab and trench for foundation wall and footing | | S.F. Ground | .66 | .66 | |
| 2020 | Basement Walls | 4′ foundation wall | | L.F. Wall | 121 | 7.26 | |
| **B. SHELL** | | | | | | | |
| | **B10 Superstructure** | | | | | | |
| 1010 | Floor Construction | Wood columns | | S.F. Floor | 1.98 | 1.98 | 6.9% |
| 1020 | Roof Construction | Plywood on wood truss (pitched) | | S.F. Roof | 14.57 | 14.57 | |
| | **B20 Exterior Enclosure** | | | | | | |
| 2010 | Exterior Walls | Cedar siding on wood studs with insulation | *70% of wall* | S.F. Wall | 23.19 | 11.69 | 14.6% |
| 2020 | Exterior Windows | Storefront windows | *30% of wall* | Each | 69 | 13.95 | |
| 2030 | Exterior Doors | Aluminum and glass doors and entrance with transom | | Each | 9279 | 9.30 | |
| | **B30 Roofing** | | | | | | |
| 3010 | Roof Coverings | Cedar shingles with flashing (pitched); rigid fiberglass insulation | | S.F. Roof | 11.84 | 11.84 | 5.0% |
| 3020 | Roof Openings | Skylights | | S.F. Roof | .12 | .12 | |
| **C. INTERIORS** | | | | | | | |
| 1010 | Partitions | Gypsum board on wood studs | *25 SF Floor/LF Part.* | S.F. Partition | 15.40 | 6.16 | 14.3% |
| 1020 | Interior Doors | Hollow core wood, low VOC paint | *250 S.F. Floor/Door* | Each | 825 | 3.30 | |
| 1030 | Fittings | Toilet partitions | | S.F. Floor | 2.12 | 2.12 | |
| 2010 | Stair Construction | N/A | | — | — | — | |
| 3010 | Wall Finishes | 75% paint, low VOC, 25% ceramic tile | | S.F. Surface | 2.95 | 2.36 | |
| 3020 | Floor Finishes | 65% carpet, 35% quarry tile | | S.F. Floor | 11.39 | 11.39 | |
| 3030 | Ceiling Finishes | Mineral fiber tile on concealed zee bars | | S.F. Ceiling | 9 | 9 | |
| **D. SERVICES** | | | | | | | |
| | **D10 Conveying** | | | | | | |
| 1010 | Elevators & Lifts | N/A | | — | — | — | 0.0 % |
| 1020 | Escalators & Moving Walks | N/A | | — | — | — | |
| | **D20 Plumbing** | | | | | | |
| 2010 | Plumbing Fixtures | Kitchen, toilet, low flow, auto sensor, & service fixt., supply & drain. | *1 Fixt./335 SF Flr.* | Each | 5378 | 15.15 | 8.9% |
| 2020 | Domestic Water Distribution | Tankless, on-demand water heater gas/propane | | S.F. Floor | 3.89 | 3.89 | |
| 2040 | Rain Water Drainage | Roof drains | | S.F. Roof | 2.32 | 2.32 | |
| | **D30 HVAC** | | | | | | |
| 3010 | Energy Supply | N/A | | — | — | — | 23.3 % |
| 3020 | Heat Generating Systems | Included in D3050 | | — | — | — | |
| 3040 | Distribution Systems | Enthalpy heat recovery packages and kitchen exhaust/make-up air system | | Each | 52,900 | 10.58 | |
| 3050 | Terminal & Package Units | Multizone rooftop air conditioner, SEER 14 | | S.F. Floor | 45.10 | 45.10 | |
| 3090 | Other HVAC Sys. & Equipment | N/A | | — | — | — | |
| | **D40 Fire Protection** | | | | | | |
| 4010 | Sprinklers | Sprinklers, light hazard and ordinary hazard kitchen | | S.F. Floor | 13.28 | 13.28 | 7.0% |
| 4020 | Standpipes | Standpipe | | S.F. Floor | 3.55 | 3.55 | |
| | **D50 Electrical** | | | | | | |
| 5010 | Electrical Service/Distribution | 400 ampere service, panel board and feeders | | S.F. Floor | 2.96 | 2.96 | 11.4% |
| 5020 | Lighting & Branch Wiring | LED fixtures, daylt. dim., ltg. on/off, receptacles, switches, and A.C. power | | S.F. Floor | 16.11 | 16.11 | |
| 5030 | Communications & Security | Addressable alarm systems and emergency lighting | | S.F. Floor | 3.72 | 3.72 | |
| 5090 | Other Electrical Systems | Emergency generator, 15 kW and energy monitoring systems | | S.F. Floor | 4.42 | 4.42 | |
| **E. EQUIPMENT & FURNISHINGS** | | | | | | | |
| 1010 | Commercial Equipment | N/A | | — | — | — | 0.6 % |
| 1020 | Institutional Equipment | N/A | | — | — | — | |
| 1090 | Other Equipment | Waste handling recycling tilt truck | | S.F. Floor | 1.28 | 1.28 | |
| 2020 | Moveable Furnishings | No smoking signage | | S.F. Floor | .06 | .06 | |
| **F. SPECIAL CONSTRUCTION** | | | | | | | |
| 1020 | Integrated Construction | N/A | | — | — | — | 0.0 % |
| 1040 | Special Facilities | N/A | | — | — | — | |
| **G. BUILDING SITEWORK** | | **N/A** | | | | | |
| | | | | | **Sub-Total** | 239.27 | **100%** |
| | CONTRACTOR FEES (General Requirements: 10%, Overhead: 5%, Profit: 10%) | | | | *25%* | 59.79 | |
| | ARCHITECT FEES | | | | *7%* | 20.94 | |
| | | | | | **Total Building Cost** | **320** | |

## Costs per square foot of floor area

| Exterior Wall | S.F. Area | 25000 | 30000 | 35000 | 40000 | 45000 | 50000 | 55000 | 60000 | 65000 |
|---|---|---|---|---|---|---|---|---|---|---|
| | L.F. Perimeter | 900 | 1050 | 1200 | 1350 | 1510 | 1650 | 1800 | 1970 | 2100 |
| Face Brick and Concrete Block | Rigid Steel | 251.90 | 249.10 | 247.00 | 245.55 | 244.70 | 243.35 | 242.60 | 242.55 | 241.50 |
| | Bearing Walls | 240.95 | 238.45 | 236.60 | 235.25 | **234.60** | 233.30 | 232.65 | 232.65 | 231.65 |
| Stucco and Concrete Block | Rigid Steel | 244.00 | 241.45 | 239.50 | 238.15 | 237.35 | 236.15 | 235.40 | 235.30 | 234.40 |
| | Bearing Walls | 235.00 | 232.40 | 230.45 | 229.10 | 228.30 | 227.10 | 226.40 | 226.30 | 225.35 |
| Decorative Concrete Block | Rigid Steel | 243.50 | 240.85 | 239.00 | 237.60 | 236.85 | 235.65 | 234.95 | 234.85 | 233.90 |
| | Bearing Walls | 234.45 | 231.85 | 230.00 | 228.60 | 227.80 | 226.65 | 225.90 | 225.80 | 224.85 |
| Perimeter Adj., Add or Deduct | Per 100 L.F. | 6.40 | 5.30 | 4.60 | 3.95 | 3.50 | 3.25 | 2.95 | 2.60 | 2.45 |
| Story Hgt. Adj., Add or Deduct | Per 1 Ft. | 2.35 | 2.25 | 2.25 | 2.15 | 2.15 | 2.15 | 2.10 | 2.05 | 2.05 |

***For Basement**, add $43.50 per square foot of basement area*

*The above costs were calculated using the basic specifications shown on the facing page. These costs should be adjusted where necessary for design alternatives and owner's requirements.*

## Common additives

| Description | Unit | $ Cost |
|---|---|---|
| Bleachers, Telescoping, manual, 16-20 tier | Seat | 261 - 550 |
| 21-30 tier | Seat | 390 - 605 |
| For power operation, add | Seat | 1000 - 1875 |
| Carrels Hardwood | Ea. | 395 - 2350 |
| Clock System, 20 room | Ea. | 23,000 |
| 50 room | Ea. | 55,000 |
| Kitchen Equipment | | |
| Broiler | Ea. | 4425 |
| Cooler, 6 ft. long, reach-in | Ea. | 4525 |
| Dishwasher, 10-12 racks per hr. | Ea. | 42,900 |
| Food warmer, counter, 1.2 KW | Ea. | 720 |
| Freezer, 44 C.F., reach-in | Ea. | 3600 |
| Ice cube maker, 50 lb. per day | Ea. | 2525 |
| Range with 1 oven | Ea. | 2050 |
| Lockers, Steel, single tier, 60" to 72" | Opng. | 285 - 520 |
| 2 tier, 60" to 72" total | Opng. | 216 - 265 |
| Locker bench, lam. maple top only | L.F. | 148 |
| Pedestals, steel pipe | Ea. | 87 |
| Seating, auditorium chair, veneer back, padded seat | Ea. | 430 |
| Classroom, movable chair & desk | Set | 81 - 171 |
| Lecture hall, pedestal type | Ea. | 385 - 775 |

| Description | Unit | $ Cost |
|---|---|---|
| Sound System, amplifier, 250 watts | Ea. | 2425 |
| Speaker, ceiling or wall | Ea. | 320 |
| Commissioning Fees, sustainable institutional construction | S.F. | 0.58 - 2.47 |
| Energy Modelling Fees, academic buildings to 10,000 SF | Ea. | 9000 |
| Greater than 10,000 SF add | S.F. | 0.20 |
| Green Bldg Cert Fees for school construction project reg | Project | 1200 |
| Photovoltaic Pwr Sys, grid connected, 20 kW (~2400 SF), roof | Ea. | 92,200 |
| Green Roofs, 6" soil depth, w/treated wd edging & sedum mats | S.F. | 28.30 |
| 10" Soil depth, with treated wood edging & sedum mats | S.F. | 30.65 |
| Greywater Recovery Systems, prepackaged comm, 3060 gal. | Ea. | 70,415 |
| 4590 gal. | Ea. | 88,275 |
| Rainwater Harvest Sys, prepckged comm, 10,000 gal, sys contrller | Ea. | 44,975 |
| 20,000 gal. w/system controller | Ea. | 73,350 |
| 30,000 gal. w/system controller | Ea. | 108,025 |
| Solar Domestic HW, closed loop, add-on sys, ext heat exchanger | Ea. | 13,550 |
| Drainback, hot water system, 120 gal tank | Ea. | 16,425 |
| Draindown, hot water system, 120 gal tank | Ea. | 16,700 |

# Model costs calculated for a 1 story building with 15′ story height and 45,000 square feet of floor area

# G School, Elementary

| | | | | Unit | Unit Cost | Cost Per S.F. | % Of Sub-Total |
|---|---|---|---|---|---|---|---|
| **A. SUBSTRUCTURE** | | | | | | | |
| 1010 | Standard Foundations | Poured concrete; strip and spread footings | | S.F. Ground | 7.26 | 7.26 | 12.4% |
| 1020 | Special Foundations | N/A | | – | – | – | |
| 1030 | Slab on Grade | 4″ reinforced concrete with recycled vapor barrier and granular base | | S.F. Slab | 7.32 | 7.32 | |
| 2010 | Basement Excavation | Site preparation for slab and trench for foundation wall and footing | | S.F. Ground | .22 | .22 | |
| 2020 | Basement Walls | 4′ foundation wall | | L.F. Wall | 121 | 6.90 | |
| **B. SHELL** | | | | | | | |
| | **B10 Superstructure** | | | | | | |
| 1010 | Floor Construction | N/A | | – | – | – | 3.7 % |
| 1020 | Roof Construction | Metal deck on open web steel joists | | S.F. Roof | 6.43 | 6.43 | |
| | **B20 Exterior Enclosure** | | | | | | |
| 2010 | Exterior Walls | Face brick with concrete block backup | *70% of wall* | S.F. Wall | 48.36 | 17.04 | 13.5% |
| 2020 | Exterior Windows | Steel outward projecting | *25% of wall* | Each | 839 | 5.51 | |
| 2030 | Exterior Doors | Metal and glass | *5% of wall* | Each | 6310 | 1.13 | |
| | **B30 Roofing** | | | | | | |
| 3010 | Roof Coverings | Single-ply TPO membrane, 60 mils, w/flashing; polyiso. insulation | | S.F. Roof | 15.42 | 15.42 | 8.8% |
| 3020 | Roof Openings | N/A | | – | – | – | |
| **C. INTERIORS** | | | | | | | |
| 1010 | Partitions | Concrete block w/foamed-in insul. | *20 SF Flr./LF Part.* | S.F. Partition | 13.90 | 6.95 | 18.4% |
| 1020 | Interior Doors | Single leaf kalamein fire doors, low VOC paint | *700 S.F. Floor/Door* | Each | 1159 | 1.65 | |
| 1030 | Fittings | Toilet partitions | | S.F. Floor | 2.69 | 2.69 | |
| 2010 | Stair Construction | N/A | | – | – | – | |
| 3010 | Wall Finishes | 75% paint, low VOC, 15% glazed coating, 10% ceramic tile | | S.F. Surface | 5.41 | 5.41 | |
| 3020 | Floor Finishes | 65% vinyl composition tile, recycled content, 25% carpet tile, 10% terrazzo | | S.F. Floor | 6.61 | 6.61 | |
| 3030 | Ceiling Finishes | Mineral fiber tile on concealed zee bars | | S.F. Ceiling | 9 | 9 | |
| **D. SERVICES** | | | | | | | |
| | **D10 Conveying** | | | | | | |
| 1010 | Elevators & Lifts | N/A | | – | – | – | 0.0 % |
| 1020 | Escalators & Moving Walks | N/A | | – | – | – | |
| | **D20 Plumbing** | | | | | | |
| 2010 | Plumbing Fixtures | Kitchen, toilet, low flow, auto sensor, & service fixt., supply & drain. | *1 Fixt./625 SF Flr.* | Each | 12,463 | 19.94 | 12.6% |
| 2020 | Domestic Water Distribution | Gas fired, tankless water heater | | S.F. Floor | .23 | .23 | |
| 2040 | Rain Water Drainage | Roof drains | | S.F. Roof | 1.90 | 1.90 | |
| | **D30 HVAC** | | | | | | |
| 3010 | Energy Supply | N/A | | – | – | – | 12.6 % |
| 3020 | Heat Generating Systems | N/A | | – | – | – | |
| 3040 | Distribution Systems | Enthalpy heat recovery packages | | Each | 35,150 | .79 | |
| 3050 | Terminal & Package Units | Multizone rooftop air conditioner | | S.F. Floor | 21.25 | 21.25 | |
| 3090 | Other HVAC Sys. & Equipment | N/A | | – | – | – | |
| | **D40 Fire Protection** | | | | | | |
| 4010 | Sprinklers | Sprinklers, light hazard | | S.F. Floor | 4.46 | 4.46 | 3.0% |
| 4020 | Standpipes | Standpipe | | S.F. Floor | .72 | .72 | |
| | **D50 Electrical** | | | | | | |
| 5010 | Electrical Service/Distribution | 800 ampere service, panel board and feeders | | S.F. Floor | 1.17 | 1.17 | 15.0% |
| 5020 | Lighting & Branch Wiring | LED fixtures, daylt. dim., ltg. on/off, recept., switches, and A.C. power | | S.F. Floor | 17.44 | 17.44 | |
| 5030 | Communications & Security | Addressable alarm systems, internet wiring, comm. systems & emerg. ltg. | | S.F. Floor | 6.53 | 6.53 | |
| 5090 | Other Electrical Systems | Emergency generator, 15 kW, energy monitoring systems | | S.F. Floor | 1.20 | 1.20 | |
| **E. EQUIPMENT & FURNISHINGS** | | | | | | | |
| 1010 | Commercial Equipment | N/A | | – | – | – | 0.1 % |
| 1020 | Institutional Equipment | Chalkboards | | S.F. Floor | .11 | .11 | |
| 1090 | Other Equipment | Waste handling recycling tilt truck | | S.F. Floor | .08 | .08 | |
| 2020 | Moveable Furnishings | No smoking signage | | S.F. Floor | .01 | .01 | |
| **F. SPECIAL CONSTRUCTION** | | | | | | | |
| 1020 | Integrated Construction | N/A | | – | – | – | 0.0 % |
| 1040 | Special Facilities | N/A | | – | – | – | |
| **G. BUILDING SITEWORK** | | **N/A** | | | | | |
| | | | | | **Sub-Total** | 175.37 | **100%** |
| | CONTRACTOR FEES (General Requirements: 10%, Overhead: 5%, Profit: 10%) | | | | *25%* | 43.89 | |
| | ARCHITECT FEES | | | | *7%* | 15.34 | |
| | | | | | **Total Building Cost** | **234.60** | |

## Costs per square foot of floor area

| Exterior Wall | S.F. Area | 50000 | 70000 | 90000 | 110000 | 130000 | 150000 | 170000 | 190000 | 210000 |
|---|---|---|---|---|---|---|---|---|---|---|
| | L.F. Perimeter | 850 | 1140 | 1420 | 1700 | 1980 | 2280 | 2560 | 2840 | 3120 |
| Face Brick and Concrete Block | Rigid Steel | 232.85 | 228.90 | 226.25 | 224.60 | 223.55 | 223.10 | 222.45 | 221.95 | 221.45 |
| | Reinforced Concrete | 239.45 | 235.40 | 232.85 | 231.15 | **230.10** | 229.65 | 229.00 | 228.45 | 228.00 |
| Decorative Concrete Block | Rigid Steel | 224.30 | 220.75 | 218.35 | 216.85 | 215.90 | 215.45 | 214.85 | 214.45 | 214.05 |
| | Reinforced Concrete | 230.85 | 227.25 | 224.90 | 223.45 | 222.40 | 222.05 | 221.45 | 220.95 | 220.55 |
| Limestone and Concrete Block | Rigid Steel | 244.70 | 240.25 | 237.30 | 235.40 | 234.15 | 233.70 | 232.90 | 232.30 | 231.85 |
| | Reinforced Concrete | 257.95 | 253.50 | 250.55 | 248.65 | 247.40 | 246.95 | 246.15 | 245.55 | 245.10 |
| Perimeter Adj., Add or Deduct | Per 100 L.F. | 6.05 | 4.30 | 3.35 | 2.80 | 2.30 | 2.00 | 1.75 | 1.55 | 1.45 |
| Story Hgt. Adj., Add or Deduct | Per 1 Ft. | 3.00 | 2.90 | 2.85 | 2.75 | 2.75 | 2.75 | 2.65 | 2.60 | 2.65 |

***For Basement**, add $56.90 per square foot of basement area*

*The above costs were calculated using the basic specifications shown on the facing page. These costs should be adjusted where necessary for design alternatives and owner's requirements.*

## Common additives

| Description | Unit | $ Cost |
|---|---|---|
| Bleachers, Telescoping, manual, 16-20 tier | Seat | 261 - 550 |
| 21-30 tier | Seat | 390 - 605 |
| For power operation, add | Seat | 1000 - 1875 |
| Carrels Hardwood | Ea. | 395 - 2350 |
| Clock System, 20 room | Ea. | 23,000 |
| 50 room | Ea. | 55,000 |
| Elevators, hydraulic passenger, 2 stops, 2500# capacity | Ea. | 90,500 |
| 3500# capacity | Ea. | 96,000 |
| Kitchen Equipment | | |
| Broiler | Ea. | 4425 |
| Cooler, 6 ft. long, reach-in | Ea. | 4525 |
| Dishwasher, 10-12 racks per hr. | Ea. | 42,900 |
| Food warmer, counter, 1.2 KW | Ea. | 720 |
| Freezer, 44 C.F., reach-in | Ea. | 3600 |
| Lockers, Steel, single tier, 60" or 72" | Opng. | 285 - 520 |
| 2 tier, 60" or 72" total | Opng. | 216 - 265 |
| Locker bench, lam. maple top only | L.F. | 148 |
| Pedestals, steel pipe | Ea. | 87 |
| Seat, auditorium chair, veneer back, padded seat | Ea. | 430 |
| Classroom, movable chair & desk | Set | 81 - 171 |
| Lecture hall, pedestal type | Ea. | 385 - 775 |

| Description | Unit | $ Cost |
|---|---|---|
| Sound System, amplifier, 250 watts | Ea. | 2425 |
| Speaker, ceiling or wall | Ea. | 320 |
| Commissioning Fees, sustainable institutional construction | S.F. | 0.58 - 2.47 |
| Energy Modelling Fees, academic buildings to 10,000 SF | Ea. | 9000 |
| Greater than 10,000 SF add | S.F. | 0.20 |
| Green Bldg Cert Fees for school construction project reg | Project | 1200 |
| Photovoltaic Pwr Sys, grid connected, 20 kW (~2400 SF), roof | Ea. | 92,200 |
| Green Roofs, 6" soil depth, w/treated wd edging & sedum mats | S.F. | 28.30 |
| 10" Soil depth, with treated wood edging & sedum mats | S.F. | 30.65 |
| Greywater Recovery Systems, prepackaged comm, 3060 gal. | Ea. | 70,415 |
| 4590 gal. | Ea. | 88,275 |
| Rainwater Harvest Sys, prepckged comm, 10,000 gal, sys contrller | Ea. | 44,975 |
| 20,000 gal. w/system controller | Ea. | 73,350 |
| 30,000 gal. w/system controller | Ea. | 108,025 |
| Solar Domestic HW, closed loop, add-on sys, ext heat exchanger | Ea. | 13,550 |
| Drainback, hot water system, 120 gal tank | Ea. | 16,425 |
| Draindown, hot water system, 120 gal tank | Ea. | 16,700 |



**Important: See the Reference Section for Location Factors.**

## Model costs calculated for a 2 story building with 15′ story height and 130,000 square feet of floor area

# G School, High, 2-3 Story

| | | | | Unit | Unit Cost | Cost Per S.F. | % Of Sub-Total |
|---|---|---|---|---|---|---|---|
| **A. SUBSTRUCTURE** | | | | | | | |
| 1010 | Standard Foundations | Poured concrete; strip and spread footings | | S.F. Ground | 3.88 | 1.94 | 4.4% |
| 1020 | Special Foundations | N/A | | — | — | — | |
| 1030 | Slab on Grade | 4″ reinforced concrete with recycled vapor barrier and granular base | | S.F. Slab | 7.32 | 3.66 | |
| 2010 | Basement Excavation | Site preparation for slab and trench for foundation wall and footing | | S.F. Ground | .22 | .11 | |
| 2020 | Basement Walls | 4′ foundation wall | | L.F. Wall | 121 | 1.84 | |
| **B. SHELL** | | | | | | | |
| | **B10 Superstructure** | | | | | | |
| 1010 | Floor Construction | Concrete slab without drop panel, concrete columns | | S.F. Floor | 30.28 | 15.14 | 15.0% |
| 1020 | Roof Construction | Concrete slab without drop panel | | S.F. Roof | 21.32 | 10.66 | |
| | **B20 Exterior Enclosure** | | | | | | |
| 2010 | Exterior Walls | Face brick with concrete block backup | *75% of wall* | S.F. Wall | 48.32 | 16.56 | 17.1% |
| 2020 | Exterior Windows | Window wall | *25% of wall* | Each | 104 | 11.89 | |
| 2030 | Exterior Doors | Metal and glass | | Each | 3982 | .90 | |
| | **B30 Roofing** | | | | | | |
| 3010 | Roof Coverings | Single-ply TPO membrane and standing seam metal; polyiso. insulation | | S.F. Roof | 18.04 | 9.02 | 5.3% |
| 3020 | Roof Openings | Roof hatches | | S.F. Roof | .26 | .13 | |
| **C. INTERIORS** | | | | | | | |
| 1010 | Partitions | Concrete block w/foamed-in insul. | *25 SF Flr./LF Part.* | S.F. Partition | 16.88 | 8.10 | 18.6% |
| 1020 | Interior Doors | Single leaf kalamein fire doors, low VOC paint | *700 S.F. Floor/Door* | Each | 1159 | 1.65 | |
| 1030 | Fittings | Toilet partitions, chalkboards | | S.F. Floor | 2.16 | 2.16 | |
| 2010 | Stair Construction | Concrete filled metal pan | | Flight | 16,075 | .74 | |
| 3010 | Wall Finishes | 75% paint, low VOC. 15% glazed coating, 10% ceramic tile | | S.F. Surface | 3.91 | 3.75 | |
| 3020 | Floor Finishes | 70% vinyl comp. tile, recycled content, 20% carpet tile, 10% terrazzo | | S.F. Floor | 6.51 | 6.51 | |
| 3030 | Ceiling Finishes | Mineral fiber tile on concealed zee bars | | S.F. Ceiling | 9 | 9 | |
| **D. SERVICES** | | | | | | | |
| | **D10 Conveying** | | | | | | |
| 1010 | Elevators & Lifts | One hydraulic passenger elevator | | Each | 107,900 | .83 | 0.5% |
| 1020 | Escalators & Moving Walks | N/A | | — | — | — | |
| | **D20 Plumbing** | | | | | | |
| 2010 | Plumbing Fixtures | Kitchen, toilet, low flow, auto sensor & service fixt., supply & drain. | *1 Fixt./860 SF Flr.* | Each | 7086 | 8.24 | 5.7% |
| 2020 | Domestic Water Distribution | Gas fired, tankless water heater | | S.F. Floor | .42 | .42 | |
| 2040 | Rain Water Drainage | Roof drains | | S.F. Roof | 2.16 | 1.08 | |
| | **D30 HVAC** | | | | | | |
| 3010 | Energy Supply | N/A | | — | — | — | 12.8 % |
| 3020 | Heat Generating Systems | N/A | | — | — | — | |
| 3040 | Distribution Systems | Enthalpy heat recovery packages | | Each | 35,150 | .81 | |
| 3050 | Terminal & Package Units | Multizone rooftop air conditioner, SEER 14 | | S.F. Floor | 21.25 | 21.25 | |
| 3090 | Other HVAC Sys. & Equipment | N/A | | — | — | — | |
| | **D40 Fire Protection** | | | | | | |
| 4010 | Sprinklers | Sprinklers, light hazard | | S.F. Floor | 3.88 | 3.88 | 2.6% |
| 4020 | Standpipes | Standpipe, wet, Class III | | S.F. Floor | .58 | .58 | |
| | **D50 Electrical** | | | | | | |
| 5010 | Electrical Service/Distribution | 2000 ampere service, panel board and feeders | | S.F. Floor | 1.26 | 1.26 | 15.6% |
| 5020 | Lighting & Branch Wiring | LED fixtures, daylt. dim., ltg. on/off, recept., switches, and A.C. power | | S.F. Floor | 18.61 | 18.61 | |
| 5030 | Communications & Security | Addressable alarm systems, internet wiring, comm. systems and emerg. ltg. | | S.F. Floor | 5.97 | 5.97 | |
| 5090 | Other Electrical Systems | Emergency generator, 250 kW, and energy monitoring systems | | S.F. Floor | 1.01 | 1.01 | |
| **E. EQUIPMENT & FURNISHINGS** | | | | | | | |
| 1010 | Commercial Equipment | N/A | | — | — | — | 2.5 % |
| 1020 | Institutional Equipment | Laboratory casework and counters | | S.F. Floor | 3.10 | 3.10 | |
| 1090 | Other Equipment | Waste handlg. recyc. tilt truck, built-in athletic equip., bleachers & backstp. | | S.F. Floor | 1.11 | 1.11 | |
| 2020 | Moveable Furnishings | No smoking signage | | S.F. Floor | .01 | .01 | |
| **F. SPECIAL CONSTRUCTION** | | | | | | | |
| 1020 | Integrated Construction | N/A | | — | — | — | 0.0 % |
| 1040 | Special Facilities | N/A | | — | — | — | |
| **G. BUILDING SITEWORK** | **N/A** | | | | | | |
| | | | | | **Sub-Total** | 172.02 | **100%** |
| | CONTRACTOR FEES (General Requirements: 10%, Overhead: 5%, Profit: 10%) | | | | *25%* | 43.03 | |
| | ARCHITECT FEES | | | | *7%* | 15.05 | |
| | | | | | **Total Building Cost** | **230.10** | |

## Costs per square foot of floor area

| Exterior Wall | S.F. Area | 50000 | 65000 | 80000 | 95000 | 110000 | 125000 | 140000 | 155000 | 170000 |
|---|---|---|---|---|---|---|---|---|---|---|
| | L.F. Perimeter | 850 | 1060 | 1280 | 1490 | 1700 | 1920 | 2140 | 2340 | 2560 |
| Face Brick and Concrete Block | Rigid Steel | 244.80 | 241.75 | 240.15 | 238.80 | **237.80** | 237.30 | 236.90 | 236.15 | 235.95 |
| | Bearing Walls | 235.05 | 232.00 | 230.35 | 229.00 | 228.05 | 227.55 | 227.10 | 226.40 | 226.20 |
| Stone and Concrete Block | Rigid Steel | 255.05 | 251.60 | 249.85 | 248.30 | 247.15 | 246.60 | 246.15 | 245.35 | 245.10 |
| | Bearing Walls | 245.35 | 241.85 | 240.10 | 238.50 | 237.40 | 236.85 | 236.40 | 235.60 | 235.35 |
| Decorative Concrete Block | Rigid Steel | 236.25 | 233.55 | 232.10 | 230.90 | 230.05 | 229.55 | 229.20 | 228.60 | 228.35 |
| | Bearing Walls | 226.75 | 224.05 | 222.60 | 221.45 | 220.55 | 220.10 | 219.70 | 219.10 | 218.90 |
| Perimeter Adj., Add or Deduct | Per 100 L.F. | 5.55 | 4.25 | 3.50 | 2.95 | 2.60 | 2.20 | 2.00 | 1.85 | 1.70 |
| Story Hgt. Adj., Add or Deduct | Per 1 Ft. | 2.70 | 2.65 | 2.65 | 2.55 | 2.55 | 2.50 | 2.50 | 2.45 | 2.40 |
| ***For Basement**, add $59.20 per square foot of basement area* | | | | | | | | | | |

*The above costs were calculated using the basic specifications shown on the facing page. These costs should be adjusted where necessary for design alternatives and owner's requirements.*

## Common additives

| Description | Unit | $ Cost |
|---|---|---|
| Bleachers, Telescoping, manual, 16-20 tier | Seat | 261 - 550 |
| 21-30 tier | Seat | 390 - 605 |
| For power operation, add | Seat | 1000 - 1875 |
| Carrels Hardwood | Ea. | 395 - 2350 |
| Clock System, 20 room | Ea. | 23,000 |
| 50 room | Ea. | 55,000 |
| Elevators, hydraulic passenger, 2 stops, 2500# capacity | Ea. | 90,500 |
| 3500# capacity | Ea. | 96,000 |
| Kitchen Equipment | | |
| Broiler | Ea. | 4425 |
| Cooler, 6 ft. long, reach-in | Ea. | 4525 |
| Dishwasher, 10-12 racks per hr. | Ea. | 42,900 |
| Food warmer, counter, 1.2 KW | Ea. | 720 |
| Freezer, 44 C.F., reach-in | Ea. | 3600 |
| Lockers, Steel, single tier, 60" to 72" | Opng. | 285 - 520 |
| 2 tier, 60" to 72" total | Opng. | 216 - 265 |
| Locker bench, lam. maple top only | L.F. | 148 |
| Pedestals, steel pipe | Ea. | 87 |

| Description | Unit | $ Cost |
|---|---|---|
| Seating, auditorium chair, veneer back, padded seat | Ea. | 430 |
| Upholstered, spring seat | Ea. | 385 |
| Classroom, movable chair & desk | Set | 81 - 171 |
| Lecture hall, pedestal type | Ea. | 385 - 775 |
| Sound System, amplifier, 250 watts | Ea. | 2425 |
| Speaker, ceiling or wall | Ea. | 320 |
| Commissioning Fees, sustainable institutional construction | S.F. | 0.58 - 2.47 |
| Energy Modelling Fees, academic buildings to 10,000 SF | Ea. | 9000 |
| Greater than 10,000 SF add | S.F. | 0.20 |
| Green Bldg Cert Fees for school construction project reg | Project | 1200 |
| Photovoltaic Pwr Sys, grid connected, 20 kW (~2400 SF), roof | Ea. | 92,200 |
| Green Roofs, 6" soil depth, w/treated wd edging & sedum mats | S.F. | 28.30 |
| 10" Soil depth, with treated wood edging & sedum mats | S.F. | 30.65 |
| Greywater Recovery Systems, prepackaged comm, 3060 gal. | Ea. | 70,415 |
| 4590 gal. | Ea. | 88,275 |
| Rainwater Harvest Sys, prepckged comm, 10,000 gal, sys contrller | Ea. | 44,975 |
| 20,000 gal. w/system controller | Ea. | 73,350 |
| 30,000 gal. w/system controller | Ea. | 108,025 |
| Solar Domestic HW, closed loop, add-on sys, ext heat exchanger | Ea. | 13,550 |
| Drainback, hot water system, 120 gal tank | Ea. | 16,425 |
| Draindown, hot water system, 120 gal tank | Ea. | 16,700 |



**Important: See the Reference Section for Location Factors.**

**Model costs calculated for a 2 story building with 15′ story height and 110,000 square feet of floor area**

# G School, Jr High, 2-3 Story

| | | | | Unit | Unit Cost | Cost Per S.F. | % Of Sub-Total |
|---|---|---|---|---|---|---|---|
| **A. SUBSTRUCTURE** | | | | | | | |
| 1010 | Standard Foundations | Poured concrete; strip and spread footings | | S.F. Ground | 3.54 | 1.77 | |
| 1020 | Special Foundations | N/A | | — | — | — | |
| 1030 | Slab on Grade | 4″ reinforced concrete with recycled vapor barrier and granular base | | S.F. Slab | 7.32 | 3.66 | 4.2% |
| 2010 | Basement Excavation | Site preparation for slab and trench for foundation wall and footing | | S.F. Ground | .22 | .11 | |
| 2020 | Basement Walls | 4′ foundation wall | | L.F. Wall | 121 | 1.88 | |
| **B. SHELL** | | | | | | | |
| | **B10 Superstructure** | | | | | | |
| 1010 | Floor Construction | Open web steel joists, slab form, concrete, columns | | S.F. Floor | 39.06 | 19.53 | 15.7% |
| 1020 | Roof Construction | Metal deck, open web steel joists, columns | | S.F. Roof | 16.76 | 8.38 | |
| | **B20 Exterior Enclosure** | | | | | | |
| 2010 | Exterior Walls | Face brick with concrete block backup | *75% of wall* | S.F. Wall | 48.34 | 16.81 | |
| 2020 | Exterior Windows | Window wall | *25% of wall* | Each | 93 | 10.33 | 15.9% |
| 2030 | Exterior Doors | Double aluminum & glass | | Each | 4152 | 1.09 | |
| | **B30 Roofing** | | | | | | |
| 3010 | Roof Coverings | Single-ply TPO membrane & standing seam metal; polyiso. insulation | | S.F. Roof | 18.42 | 9.21 | 5.2% |
| 3020 | Roof Openings | Roof hatches | | S.F. Roof | .12 | .06 | |
| **C. INTERIORS** | | | | | | | |
| 1010 | Partitions | Concrete block w/foamed-in insul. | *20 SF Flr./LF Part.* | S.F. Partition | 14.20 | 8.52 | |
| 1020 | Interior Doors | Single leaf kalamein fire doors, low VOC paint | *750 S.F. Floor/Door* | Each | 1159 | 1.55 | |
| 1030 | Fittings | Toilet partitions, chalkboards | | S.F. Floor | 2.34 | 2.34 | |
| 2010 | Stair Construction | Concrete filled metal pan | | Flight | 16,075 | .88 | 20.9% |
| 3010 | Wall Finishes | 50% paint, low VOC, 40% glazed coatings, 10% ceramic tile | | S.F. Surface | 4.34 | 5.21 | |
| 3020 | Floor Finishes | 50% vinyl comp. tile, recycled content, 30% carpet tile, 20% terrrazzo | | S.F. Floor | 9.70 | 9.70 | |
| 3030 | Ceiling Finishes | Mineral fiberboard on concealed zee bars | | S.F. Ceiling | 9 | 9 | |
| **D. SERVICES** | | | | | | | |
| | **D10 Conveying** | | | | | | |
| 1010 | Elevators & Lifts | One hydraulic passenger elevator | | Each | 106,700 | .97 | 0.5% |
| 1020 | Escalators & Moving Walks | N/A | | — | — | — | |
| | **D20 Plumbing** | | | | | | |
| 2010 | Plumbing Fixtures | Kitchen, toilet, low flow, auto sensor, & service fixt., supply & drain. | *1 Fixt./1170 SF Flr.* | Each | 10,249 | 8.76 | |
| 2020 | Domestic Water Distribution | Gas fired, tankless water heater | | S.F. Floor | .49 | .49 | 5.8% |
| 2040 | Rain Water Drainage | Roof drains | | S.F. Roof | 2.18 | 1.09 | |
| | **D30 HVAC** | | | | | | |
| 3010 | Energy Supply | N/A | | — | — | — | |
| 3020 | Heat Generating Systems | Included in D3050 | | — | — | — | |
| 3040 | Distribution Systems | Enthalpy heat recovery packages | | Each | 42,375 | .77 | 12.4 % |
| 3050 | Terminal & Package Units | Multizone rooftop air conditioner, SEER 14 | | S.F. Floor | 21.25 | 21.25 | |
| 3090 | Other HVAC Sys. & Equipment | N/A | | — | — | — | |
| | **D40 Fire Protection** | | | | | | |
| 4010 | Sprinklers | Sprinklers, light hazard | *10% of area* | S.F. Floor | 3.88 | 3.88 | 2.6% |
| 4020 | Standpipes | Standpipe, wet, Class III | | S.F. Floor | .68 | .68 | |
| | **D50 Electrical** | | | | | | |
| 5010 | Electrical Service/Distribution | 1600 ampere service, panel board and feeders | | S.F. Floor | 1.11 | 1.11 | |
| 5020 | Lighting & Branch Wiring | LED fixtures, daylt. dim., ltg. on/off, recept., switches, and A.C. power | | S.F. Floor | 16.15 | 16.15 | 14.0% |
| 5030 | Communications & Security | Addressable alarm systems, internet wiring, comm. systems and emerg. ltg. | | S.F. Floor | 6.62 | 6.62 | |
| 5090 | Other Electrical Systems | Emergency generator, 100 kW, and energy monitoring systems | | S.F. Floor | .96 | .96 | |
| **E. EQUIPMENT & FURNISHINGS** | | | | | | | |
| 1010 | Commercial Equipment | N/A | | — | — | — | |
| 1020 | Institutional Equipment | Laboratory casework and counters | | S.F. Floor | 3.70 | 3.70 | 2.8 % |
| 1090 | Other Equipment | Waste handlg. recyc. tilt truck, built-in athletic equip., bleachers & backstps. | | S.F. Floor | 1.33 | 1.33 | |
| 2020 | Moveable Furnishings | No smoking signage | | S.F. Floor | .01 | .01 | |
| **F. SPECIAL CONSTRUCTION** | | | | | | | |
| 1020 | Integrated Construction | N/A | | — | — | — | 0.0 % |
| 1040 | Special Facilities | N/A | | — | — | — | |
| **G. BUILDING SITEWORK** | **N/A** | | | | | | |
| | | | | | **Sub-Total** | 177.80 | **100%** |
| | CONTRACTOR FEES (General Requirements: 10%, Overhead: 5%, Profit: 10%) | | | | *25%* | 44.44 | |
| | ARCHITECT FEES | | | | *7%* | 15.56 | |
| | | | | | **Total Building Cost** | **237.80** | |

## Costs per square foot of floor area

| Exterior Wall | S.F. Area | 20000 | 30000 | 40000 | 50000 | 60000 | 70000 | 80000 | 90000 | 100000 |
|---|---|---|---|---|---|---|---|---|---|---|
| | L.F. Perimeter | 440 | 590 | 740 | 900 | 1050 | 1200 | 1360 | 1510 | 1660 |
| Face Brick and Concrete Block | Rigid Steel | 246.75 | 238.10 | 233.75 | 231.65 | 229.75 | 228.50 | 227.90 | 227.10 | 226.45 |
| | Bearing Walls | 238.95 | 230.30 | **225.95** | 223.90 | 222.00 | 220.75 | 220.15 | 219.30 | 218.70 |
| Decorative Concrete Block | Rigid Steel | 230.40 | 223.50 | 220.00 | 218.25 | 216.80 | 215.80 | 215.25 | 214.60 | 214.10 |
| | Bearing Walls | 220.70 | 213.75 | 210.30 | 208.55 | 207.05 | 206.05 | 205.50 | 204.90 | 204.35 |
| Metal Panel and Metal Studs | Rigid Steel | 217.10 | 211.65 | 208.85 | 207.45 | 206.20 | 205.40 | 205.00 | 204.50 | 204.05 |
| Metal Sandwich Panel | Rigid Steel | 248.45 | 239.60 | 235.20 | 233.10 | 231.15 | 229.85 | 229.25 | 228.40 | 227.75 |
| Perimeter Adj., Add or Deduct | Per 100 L.F. | 14.00 | 9.30 | 6.95 | 5.65 | 4.70 | 4.05 | 3.45 | 3.10 | 2.75 |
| Story Hgt. Adj., Add or Deduct | Per 1 Ft. | 3.40 | 3.05 | 2.85 | 2.80 | 2.70 | 2.70 | 2.60 | 2.60 | 2.50 |
| ***For Basement**, add $57.40 per square foot of basement area* | | | | | | | | | | |

*The above costs were calculated using the basic specifications shown on the facing page. These costs should be adjusted where necessary for design alternatives and owner's requirements.*

## Common additives

| Description | Unit | $ Cost |
|---|---|---|
| Carrels Hardwood | Ea. | 395 - 2350 |
| Clock System, 20 room | Ea. | 23,000 |
| 50 room | Ea. | 55,000 |
| Directory Boards, plastic, glass covered, 36" x 48" | Ea. | 1475 |
| Aluminum, 36" x 24" | Ea. | 985 |
| 48" x 60" | Ea. | 2650 |
| Elevators, hydraulic passenger, 2 stops, 2500# capacity | Ea. | 90,500 |
| 3500# capacity | Ea. | 96,000 |
| Seating, auditorium chair, veneer back, padded seat | Ea. | 430 |
| Classroom, movable chair & desk | Set | 81 - 171 |
| Lecture hall, pedestal type | Ea. | 385 - 775 |
| Shops & Workroom, benches, metal | Ea. | 785 |
| Parts bins 6'-3" high, 3' wide, 12" deep, 72 bins | Ea. | 1475 |
| Shelving, metal 1' x 3' | S.F. | 25 |
| Wide span 6' wide x 24" deep | S.F. | 19.85 |

| Description | Unit | $ Cost |
|---|---|---|
| Sound System, amplifier, 250 watts | Ea. | 2425 |
| Speaker, ceiling or wall | Ea. | 320 |
| Commissioning Fees, sustainable institutional construction | S.F. | 0.58 - 2.47 |
| Energy Modelling Fees, academic buildings to 10,000 SF | Ea. | 9000 |
| Greater than 10,000 SF add | S.F. | 0.20 |
| Green Bldg Cert Fees for school construction project reg | Project | 1200 |
| Photovoltaic Pwr Sys, grid connected, 20 kW (~2400 SF), roof | Ea. | 92,200 |
| Green Roofs, 6" soil depth, w/treated wd edging & sedum mats | S.F. | 28.30 |
| 10" Soil depth, with treated wood edging & sedum mats | S.F. | 30.65 |
| Greywater Recovery Systems, prepackaged comm, 3060 gal. | Ea. | 70,415 |
| 4590 gal. | Ea. | 88,275 |
| Rainwater Harvest Sys, prepckged comm, 10,000 gal, sys contrller | Ea. | 44,975 |
| 20,000 gal. w/system controller | Ea. | 73,350 |
| 30,000 gal. w/system controller | Ea. | 108,025 |
| Solar Domestic HW, closed loop, add-on sys, ext heat exchanger | Ea. | 13,550 |
| Drainback, hot water system, 120 gal tank | Ea. | 16,425 |
| Draindown, hot water system, 120 gal tank | Ea. | 16,700 |



**Important: See the Reference Section for Location Factors.**

# Model costs calculated for a 2 story building with 16′ story height and 40,000 square feet of floor area

# G School, Vocational

| | | | Unit | Unit Cost | Cost Per S.F. | % Of Sub-Total |
|---|---|---|---|---|---|---|
| **A. SUBSTRUCTURE** | | | | | | |
| 1010 | Standard Foundations | Poured concrete; strip and spread footings | S.F. Ground | 4 | 2 | 7.8% |
| 1020 | Special Foundations | N/A | — | — | — | |
| 1030 | Slab on Grade | 5″ reinforced concrete with recycled vapor barrier and granular base | S.F. Slab | 17.65 | 8.83 | |
| 2010 | Basement Excavation | Site preparation for slab and trench for foundation wall and footing | S.F. Ground | .22 | .11 | |
| 2020 | Basement Walls | 4′ foundation wall | L.F. Wall | 121 | 2.24 | |
| **B. SHELL** | | | | | | |
| | **B10 Superstructure** | | | | | |
| 1010 | Floor Construction | Open web steel joists, slab form, concrete, beams, columns | S.F. Floor | 26.34 | 13.17 | 10.7% |
| 1020 | Roof Construction | Metal deck, open web steel joists, beams, columns | S.F. Roof | 9.82 | 4.91 | |
| | **B20 Exterior Enclosure** | | | | | |
| 2010 | Exterior Walls | Face brick with concrete block backup *85% of wall* | S.F. Wall | 48.35 | 24.33 | 19.6% |
| 2020 | Exterior Windows | Tubular aluminum framing with insulated glass *15% of wall* | Each | 93 | 7.92 | |
| 2030 | Exterior Doors | Metal and glass doors, low VOC paint | Each | 4479 | .89 | |
| | **B30 Roofing** | | | | | |
| 3010 | Roof Coverings | Single-ply TPO membrane, 60 mils, heat welded seams w/polyiso. insul. | S.F. Roof | 13.56 | 6.78 | 4.2% |
| 3020 | Roof Openings | Roof hatches | S.F. Roof | .70 | .35 | |
| **C. INTERIORS** | | | | | | |
| 1010 | Partitions | Concrete block w/foamed-in insul. *20 SF Flr./LF Part.* | S.F. Partition | 12.62 | 7.57 | 18.7% |
| 1020 | Interior Doors | Single leaf kalamein fire doors, low VOC paint *600 S.F. Floor/Door* | Each | 1159 | 1.94 | |
| 1030 | Fittings | Toilet partitions, chalkboards | S.F. Floor | 2.28 | 2.28 | |
| 2010 | Stair Construction | Concrete filled metal pan | Flight | 16,075 | 1.61 | |
| 3010 | Wall Finishes | 50% paint, low VOC, 40% glazed coating, 10% ceramic tile | S.F. Surface | 5.26 | 6.31 | |
| 3020 | Floor Finishes | 70% vinyl comp. tile, recycled content,20% carpet tile, 10% terrazzo | S.F. Floor | 6.51 | 6.51 | |
| 3030 | Ceiling Finishes | Mineral fiber tile on concealed zee bars *60% of area* | S.F. Ceiling | 5.40 | 5.40 | |
| **D. SERVICES** | | | | | | |
| | **D10 Conveying** | | | | | |
| 1010 | Elevators & Lifts | One hydraulic passenger elevator | Each | 107,200 | 2.68 | 1.6% |
| 1020 | Escalators & Moving Walks | N/A | — | — | — | |
| | **D20 Plumbing** | | | | | |
| 2010 | Plumbing Fixtures | Toilet, low flow, auto sensor, & service fixt., supply & drain. *1 Fixt./700 SF.Flr.* | Each | 4711 | 6.73 | 4.9% |
| 2020 | Domestic Water Distribution | Gas fired, tankless water heater | S.F. Floor | .46 | .46 | |
| 2040 | Rain Water Drainage | Roof drains | S.F. Roof | 2.34 | 1.17 | |
| | **D30 HVAC** | | | | | |
| 3010 | Energy Supply | N/A | — | — | — | 13.1 % |
| 3020 | Heat Generating Systems | N/A | — | — | — | |
| 3040 | Distribution Systems | Enthalpy heat recovery packages | Each | 35,150 | .88 | |
| 3050 | Terminal & Package Units | Multizone rooftop air conditioner, SEER 14 | S.F. Floor | 21.25 | 21.25 | |
| 3090 | Other HVAC Sys. & Equipment | N/A | — | — | — | |
| | **D40 Fire Protection** | | | | | |
| 4010 | Sprinklers | Sprinklers, light hazard | S.F. Floor | 4.57 | 4.57 | 3.6% |
| 4020 | Standpipes | Standpipe, wet, Class III | S.F. Floor | 1.57 | 1.57 | |
| | **D50 Electrical** | | | | | |
| 5010 | Electrical Service/Distribution | 800 ampere service, panel board and feeders | S.F. Floor | 1.31 | 1.31 | 15.5% |
| 5020 | Lighting & Branch Wiring | LED fixtures, daylt. dim., ltg. on/off, recept., switches, and A.C. power | S.F. Floor | 17.33 | 17.33 | |
| 5030 | Communications & Security | Addressable alarm systems, internet wiring, comm. systems & emerg. ltg. | S.F. Floor | 6.18 | 6.18 | |
| 5090 | Other Electrical Systems | Emergency generator, 11.5 kW, and energy monitoring systems | S.F. Floor | 1.41 | 1.41 | |
| **E. EQUIPMENT & FURNISHINGS** | | | | | | |
| 1010 | Commercial Equipment | N/A | — | — | — | 0.2 % |
| 1020 | Institutional Equipment | Stainless steel countertops | S.F. Floor | .10 | .10 | |
| 1090 | Other Equipment | Waste handling recycling tilt truck | S.F. Floor | .16 | .16 | |
| 2020 | Moveable Furnishings | No smoking signage | S.F. Floor | .01 | .01 | |
| **F. SPECIAL CONSTRUCTION** | | | | | | |
| 1020 | Integrated Construction | N/A | — | — | — | 0.0 % |
| 1040 | Special Facilities | N/A | — | — | — | |
| **G. BUILDING SITEWORK** | | **N/A** | | | | |
| | | | | **Sub-Total** | 168.96 | **100%** |
| | CONTRACTOR FEES (General Requirements: 10%, Overhead: 5%, Profit: 10%) | | | 25% | 42.21 | |
| | ARCHITECT FEES | | | 7% | 14.78 | |
| | | | | **Total Building Cost** | **225.95** | |

## Costs per square foot of floor area

| Exterior Wall | S.F. Area | 12000 | 16000 | 20000 | 26000 | 32000 | 38000 | 44000 | 52000 | 60000 |
|---|---|---|---|---|---|---|---|---|---|---|
| | L.F. Perimeter | 450 | 510 | 570 | 650 | 716 | 780 | 840 | 920 | 1020 |
| Face Brick and Concrete Block | Rigid Steel | 230.70 | 216.20 | 207.50 | 198.80 | 192.65 | 188.35 | 185.10 | 181.95 | 180.05 |
| | Bearing Walls | 226.10 | 211.60 | 202.85 | 194.15 | 188.00 | 183.75 | **180.45** | 177.30 | 175.40 |
| Stucco and Concrete Block | Rigid Steel | 218.75 | 206.05 | 198.40 | 190.80 | 185.50 | 181.80 | 179.05 | 176.25 | 174.65 |
| | Bearing Walls | 215.70 | 203.00 | 195.35 | 187.80 | 182.50 | 178.80 | 175.95 | 173.25 | 171.65 |
| Precast Concrete | Rigid Steel | 248.55 | 231.35 | 221.00 | 210.65 | 203.25 | 198.10 | 194.15 | 190.35 | 188.15 |
| Metal Sandwich Panel | Rigid Steel | 227.45 | 213.40 | 204.95 | 196.60 | 190.65 | 186.55 | 183.40 | 180.35 | 178.60 |
| Perimeter Adj., Add or Deduct | Per 100 L.F. | 13.85 | 10.35 | 8.25 | 6.35 | 5.15 | 4.40 | 3.75 | 3.15 | 2.80 |
| Story Hgt. Adj., Add or Deduct | Per 1 Ft. | 2.85 | 2.40 | 2.15 | 1.90 | 1.70 | 1.60 | 1.45 | 1.30 | 1.30 |
| ***For Basement**, add $43.65 per square foot of basement area* | | | | | | | | | | |

*The above costs were calculated using the basic specifications shown on the facing page. These costs should be adjusted where necessary for design alternatives and owner's requirements.*

## Common additives

| Description | Unit | $ Cost |
|---|---|---|
| Check Out Counter, single belt | Ea. | 4225 |
| Scanner, registers, guns & memory 10 lanes | Ea. | 195,500 |
| Power take away | Ea. | 6375 |
| Refrigerators, prefabricated, walk-in, 7'-6" High, 10' x 10' | S.F. | 110 |
| 12' x 14' | S.F. | 96 |
| 12' x 20' | S.F. | 139 |
| Refrigerated Food Cases, dairy, multi deck, 12' long | Ea. | 20,600 |
| Delicatessen case, multi deck, 18 S.F. shelf display | Ea. | 9700 |
| Freezer, glass door upright, 78 C.F. | Ea. | 10,700 |
| Frozen food, chest type, 12' long | Ea. | 8025 |
| Glass door reach in, 5 door | Ea. | 12,200 |
| Island case 12' long, multi deck | Ea. | 12,200 |
| Meat case, 12' long, multi deck | Ea. | 11,700 |
| Produce, 12' long multi deck | Ea. | 9875 |
| Safe, Office type, 1 hr rating, 60"x36"x18", double door | Ea. | 8625 |

| Description | Unit | $ Cost |
|---|---|---|
| Sound System, amplifier, 250 watts | Ea. | 2425 |
| Speaker, ceiling or wall | Ea. | 320 |
| Commissioning Fees, sustainable commercial construction | S.F. | 0.24 - 3.04 |
| Energy Modelling Fees, commercial buildings to 10,000 SF | Ea. | 11,000 |
| Greater than 10,000 SF add | S.F. | 0.04 |
| Green Bldg Cert Fees for comm construction project reg | Project | 1200 |
| Photovoltaic Pwr Sys, grid connected, 20 kW (~2400 SF), roof | Ea. | 92,200 |
| Green Roofs, 6" soil depth, w/treated wd edging & sedum mats | S.F. | 28.30 |
| 10" Soil depth, with treated wood edging & sedum mats | S.F. | 30.65 |
| Greywater Recovery Systems, prepackaged comm, 3060 gal. | Ea. | 70,415 |
| 4590 gal. | Ea. | 88,275 |
| Rainwater Harvest Sys, prepckged comm, 10,000 gal, sys contrller | Ea. | 44,975 |
| 20,000 gal. w/system controller | Ea. | 73,350 |
| 30,000 gal. w/system controller | Ea. | 108,025 |
| Solar Domestic HW, closed loop, add-on sys, ext heat exchanger | Ea. | 13,550 |
| Drainback, hot water system, 120 gal tank | Ea. | 16,425 |
| Draindown, hot water system, 120 gal tank | Ea. | 16,700 |



**Important: See the Reference Section for Location Factors.**

## Model costs calculated for a 1 story building with 18′ story height and 44,000 square feet of floor area

# G Supermarket

| | | | | Unit | Unit Cost | Cost Per S.F. | % Of Sub-Total |
|---|---|---|---|---|---|---|---|
| **A. SUBSTRUCTURE** | | | | | | | |
| 1010 | Standard Foundations | Poured concrete; strip and spread footings | | S.F. Ground | 1.62 | 1.62 | 8.5% |
| 1020 | Special Foundations | N/A | | — | — | — | |
| 1030 | Slab on Grade | 4″ reinforced concrete with recycled vapor barrier and granular base | | S.F. Slab | 7.32 | 7.32 | |
| 2010 | Basement Excavation | Site preparation for slab and trench for foundation wall and footing | | S.F. Ground | .22 | .22 | |
| 2020 | Basement Walls | 4′ foundation wall | | L.F. Wall | 121 | 2.32 | |
| **B. SHELL** | | | | | | | |
| **B10 Superstructure** | | | | | | | |
| 1010 | Floor Construction | N/A | | — | — | — | 8.9 % |
| 1020 | Roof Construction | Metal deck, open web steel joists, beams, interior columns | | S.F. Roof | 11.96 | 11.96 | |
| **B20 Exterior Enclosure** | | | | | | | |
| 2010 | Exterior Walls | Face brick with concrete block backup | *85% of wall* | S.F. Wall | 48.34 | 14.12 | 14.7% |
| 2020 | Exterior Windows | Storefront windows | *15% of wall* | Each | 79 | 4.05 | |
| 2030 | Exterior Doors | Sliding entrance doors with electrical operator, hollow metal | | Each | 6782 | 1.70 | |
| **B30 Roofing** | | | | | | | |
| 3010 | Roof Coverings | Single-ply TPO membrane, 60 mils, heat welded seams w/R-20 insul. | | S.F. Roof | 9.71 | 9.71 | 7.4% |
| 3020 | Roof Openings | Roof hatches | | S.F. Roof | .28 | .28 | |
| **C. INTERIORS** | | | | | | | |
| 1010 | Partitions | 50% CMU w/foamed-in insul., 50% gyp. bd. on mtl. studs | *50 SF Flr./LF Part.* | S.F. Partition | 11.08 | 2.66 | 13.6% |
| 1020 | Interior Doors | Single leaf hollow metal, low VOC paint | *2000 S.F. Floor/Door* | Each | 1159 | .58 | |
| 1030 | Fittings | N/A | | — | — | — | |
| 2010 | Stair Construction | N/A | | — | — | — | |
| 3010 | Wall Finishes | Paint, low VOC | | S.F. Surface | 6.08 | 2.92 | |
| 3020 | Floor Finishes | Vinyl composition tile, recycled content | | S.F. Floor | 3.15 | 3.15 | |
| 3030 | Ceiling Finishes | Mineral fiber tile on concealed zee bars | | S.F. Ceiling | 9 | 9 | |
| **D. SERVICES** | | | | | | | |
| **D10 Conveying** | | | | | | | |
| 1010 | Elevators & Lifts | N/A | | — | — | — | 0.0 % |
| 1020 | Escalators & Moving Walks | N/A | | — | — | — | |
| **D20 Plumbing** | | | | | | | |
| 2010 | Plumbing Fixtures | Toilet, low flow, auto sensor, & service fixt., supply & drain. | *1 Fixt./1820 SF Flr.* | Each | 3640 | 2 | 2.6% |
| 2020 | Domestic Water Distribution | Point of use water heater, electric, energy saver | | S.F. Floor | .32 | .32 | |
| 2040 | Rain Water Drainage | Roof drains | | S.F. Roof | 1.19 | 1.19 | |
| **D30 HVAC** | | | | | | | |
| 3010 | Energy Supply | N/A | | — | — | — | 4.4 % |
| 3020 | Heat Generating Systems | Included in D3050 | | — | — | — | |
| 3040 | Distribution Systems | Enthalpy heat recovery packages | | Each | 35,150 | .88 | |
| 3050 | Terminal & Package Units | Single zone rooftop air conditioner | | S.F. Floor | 5 | 5 | |
| 3090 | Other HVAC Sys. & Equipment | N/A | | — | — | — | |
| **D40 Fire Protection** | | | | | | | |
| 4010 | Sprinklers | Sprinklers, light hazard | | S.F. Floor | 5.07 | 5.07 | 4.5% |
| 4020 | Standpipes | Standpipe | | S.F. Floor | .98 | .98 | |
| **D50 Electrical** | | | | | | | |
| 5010 | Electrical Service/Distribution | 1600 ampere service, panel board and feeders | | S.F. Floor | 2.80 | 2.80 | 35.4% |
| 5020 | Lighting & Branch Wiring | LED fixtures, daylt. dim., ltg. on/off, receptacles, switches, and A.C.power | | S.F. Floor | 39.05 | 39.05 | |
| 5030 | Communications & Security | Addressable alarm systems, partial internet wiring and emergency lighting | | S.F. Floor | 4.65 | 4.65 | |
| 5090 | Other Electrical Systems | Emergency generator, 15 kW and energy monitoring systems | | S.F. Floor | 1.21 | 1.21 | |
| **E. EQUIPMENT & FURNISHINGS** | | | | | | | |
| 1010 | Commercial Equipment | N/A | | — | — | — | 0.1 % |
| 1020 | Institutional Equipment | N/A | | — | — | — | |
| 1090 | Other Equipment | Waste handling recycling tilt truck | | S.F. Floor | .15 | .15 | |
| 2020 | Moveable Furnishings | No smoking signage | | S.F. Floor | .01 | .01 | |
| **F. SPECIAL CONSTRUCTION** | | | | | | | |
| 1020 | Integrated Construction | N/A | | — | — | — | 0.0 % |
| 1040 | Special Facilities | N/A | | — | — | — | |
| **G. BUILDING SITEWORK** | | **N/A** | | | | | |
| | | | | | **Sub-Total** | 134.92 | **100%** |
| | CONTRACTOR FEES (General Requirements: 10%, Overhead: 5%, Profit: 10%) | | | | *25%* | 33.72 | |
| | ARCHITECT FEES | | | | *7%* | 11.81 | |
| | | | | | **Total Building Cost** | **180.45** | |

## Costs per square foot of floor area

| Exterior Wall | S.F. Area | 10000 | 15000 | 20000 | 25000 | 30000 | 35000 | 40000 | 50000 | 60000 |
|---|---|---|---|---|---|---|---|---|---|---|
| | L.F. Perimeter | 410 | 500 | 600 | 640 | 700 | 766 | 833 | 966 | 1000 |
| Tilt-up Concrete Panels | Rigid Steel | 204.05 | 190.05 | 183.60 | 176.85 | 173.15 | 170.70 | 168.90 | 166.40 | 162.65 |
| Face Brick and Concrete Block | Bearing Walls | 229.70 | 209.90 | 200.95 | 190.85 | 185.40 | 181.90 | 179.25 | 175.60 | 169.90 |
| Concrete Block | Rigid Steel | 199.90 | 186.20 | 179.90 | 173.30 | 169.65 | 167.35 | 165.55 | 163.05 | 159.45 |
| | Bearing Walls | 194.60 | 180.90 | 174.60 | 168.00 | 164.40 | 162.05 | 160.25 | 157.75 | 154.20 |
| Metal Panel | Rigid Steel | 201.60 | 187.55 | 181.15 | 174.35 | 170.65 | 168.20 | 166.40 | 163.85 | 160.15 |
| Metal Sandwich Panel | Rigid Steel | 207.30 | 192.20 | 185.30 | 177.95 | 173.90 | 171.30 | 169.30 | 166.50 | 162.50 |
| Perimeter Adj., Add or Deduct | Per 100 L.F. | 12.15 | 8.00 | 6.05 | 4.80 | 4.05 | 3.45 | 3.00 | 2.30 | 2.05 |
| Story Hgt. Adj., Add or Deduct | Per 1 Ft. | 1.45 | 1.15 | 1.05 | 0.85 | 0.80 | 0.75 | 0.75 | 0.60 | 0.55 |
| ***For Basement**, add $48.25 per square foot of basement area* | | | | | | | | | | |

*The above costs were calculated using the basic specifications shown on the facing page. These costs should be adjusted where necessary for design alternatives and owner's requirements.*

## Common additives

| Description | Unit | $ Cost |
|---|---|---|
| Dock Leveler, 10 ton cap., 6′ x 8′ | Ea. | 8025 |
| 7′ x 8′ | Ea. | 9675 |
| Fence, Chain link, 6′ high, 9 ga. wire | L.F. | 33.50 |
| 6 ga. wire | L.F. | 41 |
| Gate | Ea. | 485 |
| Paving, Bituminous, wearing course plus base course | S.Y. | 9.85 |
| Sidewalks, Concrete 4″ thick | S.F. | 6.40 |
| Sound System, amplifier, 250 watts | Ea. | 2425 |
| Speaker, ceiling or wall | Ea. | 320 |
| Yard Lighting, 20′ aluminum pole, 400W, HP sodium fixture | Ea. | 3200 |

| Description | Unit | $ Cost |
|---|---|---|
| Commissioning Fees, sustainable industrial construction | S.F. | 0.20 - 1.06 |
| Energy Modelling Fees, commercial buildings to 10,000 SF | Ea. | 11,000 |
| Greater than 10,000 SF add | S.F. | 0.04 |
| Green Bldg Cert Fees for comm construction project reg | Project | 1200 |
| Photovoltaic Pwr Sys, grid connected, 20 kW (~2400 SF), roof | Ea. | 92,200 |
| Green Roofs, 6″ soil depth, w/treated wd edging & sedum mats | S.F. | 28.30 |
| 10″ Soil depth, with treated wood edging & sedum mats | S.F. | 30.65 |
| Greywater Recovery Systems, prepackaged comm, 3060 gal. | Ea. | 70,415 |
| 4590 gal. | Ea. | 88,275 |
| Rainwater Harvest Sys, prepckged comm, 10,000 gal, sys contrller | Ea. | 44,975 |
| 20,000 gal. w/system controller | Ea. | 73,350 |
| 30,000 gal. w/system controller | Ea. | 108,025 |
| Solar Domestic HW, closed loop, add-on sys, ext heat exchanger | Ea. | 13,550 |
| Drainback, hot water system, 120 gal tank | Ea. | 16,425 |
| Draindown, hot water system, 120 gal tank | Ea. | 16,700 |

## Model costs calculated for a 1 story building with 24′ story height and 30,000 square feet of floor area

# G Warehouse

| | | | | Unit | Unit Cost | Cost Per S.F. | % Of Sub-Total |
|---|---|---|---|---|---|---|---|
| **A. SUBSTRUCTURE** | | | | | | | |
| 1010 | Standard Foundations | Poured concrete; strip and spread footings | | S.F. Ground | 2.09 | 2.09 | 19.2% |
| 1020 | Special Foundations | N/A | | — | — | — | |
| 1030 | Slab on Grade | 5″ reinforced concrete with recycled vapor barrier and granular base | | S.F. Slab | 17.65 | 17.65 | |
| 2010 | Basement Excavation | Site preparation for slab and trench for foundation wall and footing | | S.F. Ground | .22 | .22 | |
| 2020 | Basement Walls | 4′ foundation wall | | L.F. Wall | 121 | 3.67 | |
| **B. SHELL** | | | | | | | |
| | **B10 Superstructure** | | | | | | |
| 1010 | Floor Construction | Mezzanine: open web steel joists, slab form, concrete beams, columns | *10% of area* | S.F. Floor | 2.72 | 2.72 | 10.4% |
| 1020 | Roof Construction | Metal deck, open web steel joists, beams, columns | | S.F. Roof | 10.06 | 10.06 | |
| | **B20 Exterior Enclosure** | | | | | | |
| 2010 | Exterior Walls | Concrete block | *95% of wall* | S.F. Wall | 22.24 | 11.83 | 11.1% |
| 2020 | Exterior Windows | N/A | | — | — | — | |
| 2030 | Exterior Doors | Steel overhead, hollow metal | *5% of wall* | Each | 5094 | 1.87 | |
| | **B30 Roofing** | | | | | | |
| 3010 | Roof Coverings | Single-ply TPO membrane, 60 mils, heat welded w/R-20 insul. | | S.F. Roof | 9.94 | 9.94 | 8.7% |
| 3020 | Roof Openings | Roof hatches and skylight | | S.F. Roof | .73 | .73 | |
| **C. INTERIORS** | | | | | | | |
| 1010 | Partitions | Concrete block w/foamed-in insul. (office and washrooms) | *100 SF Flr./LF Part.* | S.F. Partition | 12.63 | 1.01 | 6.9% |
| 1020 | Interior Doors | Single leaf hollow metal, low VOC paint | *5000 S.F. Floor/Door* | Each | 1159 | .23 | |
| 1030 | Fittings | N/A | | — | — | — | |
| 2010 | Stair Construction | Steel gate with rails | | Flight | 15,150 | 1.01 | |
| 3010 | Wall Finishes | Paint, low VOC | | S.F. Surface | 16.44 | 2.63 | |
| 3020 | Floor Finishes | 90% hardener, 10% vinyl composition tile, recycled content | | S.F. Floor | 2.71 | 2.71 | |
| 3030 | Ceiling Finishes | Suspended mineral tile on zee channels in office area | *10% of area* | S.F. Ceiling | .90 | .91 | |
| **D. SERVICES** | | | | | | | |
| | **D10 Conveying** | | | | | | |
| 1010 | Elevators & Lifts | N/A | | — | — | — | 0.0 % |
| 1020 | Escalators & Moving Walks | N/A | | — | — | — | |
| | **D20 Plumbing** | | | | | | |
| 2010 | Plumbing Fixtures | Toilet, low flow, auto sensor & service fixt., supply & drainage | *1 Fixt./2500 SF Flr.* | Each | 6175 | 2.47 | 4.0% |
| 2020 | Domestic Water Distribution | Tankless, on-demand water heater, gas/propane | | S.F. Floor | .62 | .62 | |
| 2040 | Rain Water Drainage | Roof drains | | S.F. Roof | 1.88 | 1.88 | |
| | **D30 HVAC** | | | | | | |
| 3010 | Energy Supply | N/A | | — | — | — | 5.5 % |
| 3020 | Heat Generating Systems | Ventilation with heat | | Each | 166,100 | 5.98 | |
| 3030 | Cooling Generating Systems | N/A | | — | — | — | |
| 3050 | Terminal & Package Units | Single zone rooftop air conditioner, SEER 14 | | S.F. Floor | .83 | .83 | |
| 3090 | Other HVAC Sys. & Equipment | N/A | | — | — | — | |
| | **D40 Fire Protection** | | | | | | |
| 4010 | Sprinklers | Sprinklers, ordinary hazard | | S.F. Floor | 6.25 | 6.25 | 5.7% |
| 4020 | Standpipes | Standpipe | | S.F. Floor | .80 | .80 | |
| | **D50 Electrical** | | | | | | |
| 5010 | Electrical Service/Distribution | 200 ampere service, panel board and feeders | | S.F. Floor | .37 | .37 | 20.5% |
| 5020 | Lighting & Branch Wiring | LED fixtures, daylt. dim., ltg. on/off, receptacles, switches, and A.C. power | | S.F. Floor | 20.06 | 20.06 | |
| 5030 | Communications & Security | Addressable alarm systems | | S.F. Floor | 3.26 | 3.26 | |
| 5090 | Other Electrical Systems | Energy monitoring systems | | S.F. Floor | 1.46 | 1.46 | |
| **E. EQUIPMENT & FURNISHINGS** | | | | | | | |
| 1010 | Commercial Equipment | N/A | | — | — | — | 1.9 % |
| 1030 | Vehicular Equipment | Dock boards, dock levelers | | S.F. Floor | 2.13 | 2.13 | |
| 1090 | Other Equipment | Waste handling recycling tilt truck | | S.F. Floor | .22 | .22 | |
| 2020 | Moveable Furnishings | No smoking signage | | S.F. Floor | .02 | .02 | |
| **F. SPECIAL CONSTRUCTION** | | | | | | | |
| 1020 | Integrated Construction | Shipping & receiving air curtain | | S.F. Floor | 7.28 | 7.28 | 5.9% |
| 1040 | Special Facilities | N/A | | — | — | — | |
| **G. BUILDING SITEWORK** | | **N/A** | | | | | |
| | | | | | **Sub-Total** | 122.91 | **100%** |
| | CONTRACTOR FEES (General Requirements: 10%, Overhead: 5%, Profit: 10%) | | | | *25%* | 30.74 | |
| | ARCHITECT FEES | | | | *7%* | 10.75 | |
| | | | | | **Total Building Cost** | **164.40** | |

# Assemblies Section

## Table of Contents

## Table of Contents

# Table of Contents

# *Table of Contents*

# Introduction to the Assemblies Section

This section contains the technical description and installed cost of all components used in the commercial/industrial/institutional section. In most cases, there is a graphic of the component to aid in identification.

## All Costs Include:

**Materials** purchased in lot sizes typical of normal construction projects with discounts appropriate to established contractors.

**Installation** work performed by a union labor working under standard conditions at a normal pace.

## Installing Contractor's Overhead & Profit

Standard installing contractor's overhead and profit are included in the assemblies costs.

These assemblies costs contain no provisions for the general contractor's overhead and profit or the architect's fees, nor do they include premiums for labor, materials, or savings, which may be realized under certain economic situations.

The assemblies tables are arranged by physical size (dimensions) of the component wherever possible.

# RSMeans data: Assemblies— How They Work

Assemblies estimating provides a fast and reasonably accurate way to develop construction costs. An assembly is the grouping of individual work items — with appropriate quantities — to provide a cost for a major construction component in a convenient unit of measure.

An assemblies estimate is often used during early stages of design development to compare the cost impact of various design alternatives on total building cost.

Assemblies estimates are also used as an efficient tool to verify construction estimates.

Assemblies estimates do not require a completed design or detailed drawings. Instead, they are based on the general size of the structure and other known parameters of the project. The degree of accuracy of an assemblies estimate is generally within +/- 15%.

Most assemblies consist of three major elements: a graphic, the system components, and the cost data itself. The **graphic** is a visual representation showing the typical appearance of the assembly

## 1 Unique 12-Character Identifier

Our assemblies are identified by a **unique 12-character identifier**. The assemblies are numbered using UNIFORMAT II, ASTM Standard E1557. The first five characters represent this system to level three. The last seven characters represent further breakdown in order to arrange items in understandable groups of similar tasks. Line numbers are consistent across all of our publications, so a line number in any assemblies data set will always refer to the same item.

## 2 Narrative Descriptions

Our assemblies descriptions appear in two formats: narrative and table. **Narrative descriptions** are shown in a hierarchical structure to make them readable. In order to read a complete description, read up through the indents to the top of the section. Include everything that is above and to the left that is not contradicted by information below.

### Narrative Format

**C20 Stairs**

**C2010 Stair Construction**

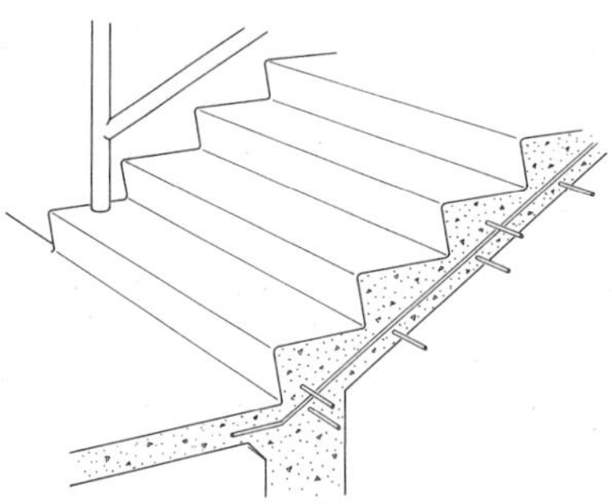

The table below lists the cost per flight for 4'-0" wide stairs. Side walls are not included. Railings are included in the prices.

| C2010 110 | Stairs | COST PER FLIGHT MAT. | INST. | TOTAL |
|---|---|---|---|---|
| 0470 | Stairs, C.I.P. concrete, w/o landing, 12 risers, w/o nosing | 1,800 | 2,850 | 4,650 |
| 0480 | With nosing | 2,700 | 3,100 | 5,800 |
| 0550 | W/landing, 12 risers, w/o nosing | 2,075 | 3,525 | 5,600 |
| 0560 | With nosing | 2,950 | 3,775 | 6,725 |
| 0570 | 16 risers, w/o nosing | 2,525 | 4,425 | 6,950 |
| 0580 | With nosing | 3,725 | 4,750 | 8,475 |
| 0590 | 20 risers, w/o nosing | 3,000 | 5,325 | 8,325 |
| 0600 | With nosing | 4,475 | 5,750 | 10,225 |
| 0610 | 24 risers, w/o nosing | 3,450 | 6,225 | 9,675 |
| 0620 | With nosing | 5,225 | 6,725 | 11,950 |
| 0630 | Steel, grate type w/nosing & rails, 12 risers, w/o landing | 6,050 | 1,350 | 7,400 |
| 0640 | With landing | 8,350 | 1,850 | 10,200 |
| 0660 | 16 risers, with landing | 10,400 | 2,300 | 12,700 |
| 0680 | 20 risers, with landing | 12,400 | 2,750 | 15,150 |
| 0700 | 24 risers, with landing | 14,400 | 3,200 | 17,600 |
| 0701 | | | | |
| 0710 | Metal pan stairs for concrete in-fill, picket rail, 12 risers, w/o landing | 8,050 | 1,350 | 9,400 |
| 0720 | With landing | 10,900 | 2,025 | 12,925 |
| 0740 | 16 risers, with landing | 13,600 | 2,475 | 16,075 |
| 0760 | 20 risers, with landing | 16,300 | 2,925 | 19,225 |
| 0780 | 24 risers, with landing | 18,900 | 3,375 | 22,275 |
| 0790 | Cast iron tread & pipe rail, 12 risers, w/o landing | 8,050 | 1,350 | 9,400 |
| 0800 | With landing | 10,900 | 2,025 | 12,925 |
| 1120 | Wood, prefab box type, oak treads, wood rails 3'-6" wide, 14 risers | 3,425 | 580 | 4,005 |
| 1150 | Prefab basement type, oak treads, wood rails 3'-0" wide, 14 risers | 1,125 | 143 | 1,268 |
| 1151 | Stairs, wood, Parametric, 2 risers includes landing and railing | 345 | 520 | 865 |

For supplemental customizable square foot estimating forms, visit: **RSMeans.com/2023books** in question. It is frequently accompanied by additional explanatory technical information describing the class of items. The **System Components** is a listing of the individual tasks that make up the assembly, including the quantity and unit of measure for each item, along with the cost of material and installation. The **Assemblies data** below lists prices for other similar systems with dimensional and/or size variations.

All of our assemblies costs represent the cost for the installing contractor. An allowance for profit has been added to all material, labor, and equipment rental costs. A markup for labor burdens, including workers' compensation, fixed overhead, and business overhead, is included with installation costs.

The information in RSMeans cost data represents a "national average" cost. This data should be modified to the project location using the **City Cost Indexes** or **Location Factors** tables found in the Reference Section.

## Table Format

**A20 Basement Construction**

**A2020 Basement Walls**

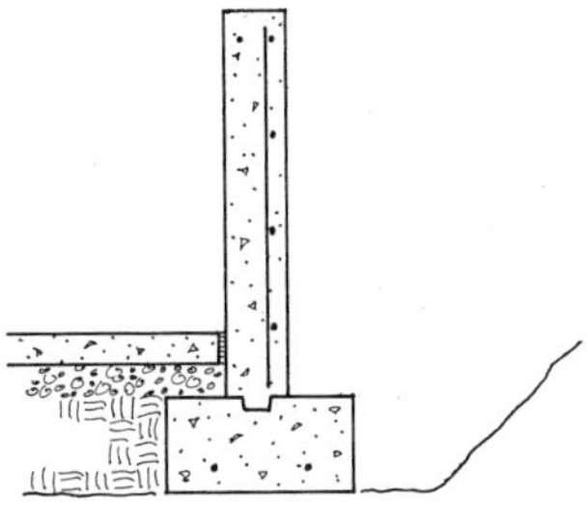

The Foundation Bearing Wall System includes: forms up to 16′ high (four uses); 3,000 p.s.i. concrete placed and vibrated; and form removal with breaking form ties and patching walls. The wall systems list walls from 6″ to 16″ thick and are designed with minimum reinforcement.

Excavation and backfill are not included.

Please see the reference section for further design and cost information.

**A2020 110 Walls, Cast in Place** (3)

| | WALL HEIGHT (FT.) | PLACING METHOD | CONCRETE (C.Y. per L.F.) | REINFORCING (LBS. per L.F.) | WALL THICKNESS (IN.) | COST PER L.F. | | |
|---|---|---|---|---|---|---|---|---|
| | | | | | | MAT. | INST. | TOTAL |
| 5000 | 8′ | direct chute | .148 | 6.6 | 6 | 47.50 | 128 | 175.50 |
| 5020 | | | .199 | 9.6 | 8 | 58.50 | 135 | 193.50 |
| 5040 | (4) | | .250 | 12 | 10 | 69 | 134 | 203 |
| 5061 | | | .296 | 14.39 | 12 | 79 | 137 | 216 |
| 6020 | 10′ | direct chute | .248 | 12 | 8 | 73 | 164 | 237 |
| 6040 | | | .307 | 14.99 | 10 | 85.50 | 167 | 252.50 |
| 6061 | | | .370 | 17.99 | 12 | 98.50 | 171 | 269.50 |
| 7220 | 12′ | pumped | .298 | 14.39 | 8 | 88 | 203 | 291 |
| 7240 | | | .369 | 17.99 | 10 | 103 | 207 | 310 |
| 7260 | | | .444 | 21.59 | 12 | 118 | 213 | 331 |
| 9220 | 16′ | pumped | .397 | 19.19 | 8 | 117 | 270 | 387 |
| 9240 | | | .492 | 23.99 | 10 | 137 | 276 | 413 |
| 9260 | | | .593 | 28.79 | 12 | 158 | 284 | 442 |

### 3 Unit of Measure

All RSMeans data: Assemblies include a typical **Unit of Measure** used for estimating that item. For instance, for continuous footings or foundation walls the unit is linear feet (L.F.). For spread footings the unit is each (Ea.). The estimator needs to take special care that the unit in the data matches the unit in the takeoff. Abbreviations and unit conversions can be found in the Reference Section.

### 4 Table Descriptions

**Table descriptions** work similar to Narrative Descriptions, except that if there is a blank in the column at a particular line number, read up to the description above in the same column.

# RSMeans data: Assemblies—How They Work (Continued)

## Sample Estimate

This sample demonstrates the elements of an estimate, including a tally of the RSMeans data lines. Published assemblies costs include all markups for labor burden and profit for the installing contractor. This estimate adds a summary of the markups applied by a general contractor on the installing contractor's work. These figures represent the total cost to the owner. The location factor with RSMeans data is applied at the bottom of the estimate to adjust the cost of the work to a specific location.

| Project Name: | Interior Fit-out, ABC Office | | | |
|---|---|---|---|---|
| Location: | Anywhere, USA | Date: 1/1/2023 | | STD |
| **Assembly Number** | **Description** | **Qty.** | **Unit** | **Subtotal** |
| 1 C1010 124 1200 | Wood partition, 2 x 4 @ 16" OC w/5/8" FR gypsum board | 560 | S.F. | $3,656.80 |
| C1020 114 1800 | Metal door & frame, flush hollow core, 3'-0" x 7'-0" | 2 | Ea. | $2,370.00 |
| C3010 230 0080 | Painting, brushwork, primer & 2 coats | 1,120 | S.F. | $1,556.80 |
| C3020 410 0140 | Carpet, tufted, nylon, roll goods, 12' wide, 26 oz | 240 | S.F. | $703.20 |
| C3030 210 6000 | Acoustic ceilings, 24" x 48" tile, tee grid suspension | 200 | S.F. | $1,896.00 |
| D5020 125 0560 | Receptacles incl plate, box, conduit, wire, 20 A duplex | 8 | Ea. | $2,844.00 |
| D5020 125 0720 | Light switch incl plate, box, conduit, wire, 20 A single pole | 2 | Ea. | $692.00 |
| D5020 210 0560 | Fluorescent fixtures, recess mounted, 20 per 1000 SF | 200 | S.F. | $3,310.00 |
| | **Assembly Subtotal** | | | **$17,028.80** |
| | **Sales Tax @ 2** | **5 %** | | **$ 425.72** |
| | **General Requirements @ 3** | **7 %** | | **$ 1,192.02** |
| | **Subtotal A** | | | **$18,646.54** |
| | **GC Overhead @ 4** | **5 %** | | **$ 932.33** |
| | **Subtotal B** | | | **$19,578.86** |
| | **GC Profit @ 5** | **5 %** | | **$ 978.94** |
| | **Subtotal C** | | | **$20,557.81** |
| | **Adjusted by Location Factor 6** | **112.5** | | **$ 23,127.53** |
| | **Architects Fee @ 7** | **8 %** | | **$ 1,850.20** |
| | **Contingency @ 8** | **15 %** | | **$ 3,469.13** |
| | **Project Total Cost** | | | **$ 28,446.86** |

This estimate is based on an interactive spreadsheet. You are free to download it and adjust it to your methodology.
A copy of this spreadsheet is available at **RSMeans.com/2023books.**

## 1 Work Performed

The body of the estimate shows the RSMeans data selected, including line numbers, a brief description of each item, its takeoff quantity and unit, and the total installed cost, including the installing contractor's overhead and profit.

## 2 Sales Tax

If the work is subject to state or local sales taxes, the amount must be added to the estimate. In a conceptual estimate, it can be assumed that one half of the total represents material costs. Therefore, apply the sales tax rate to 50% of the assembly subtotal.

## 3 General Requirements

This item covers project-wide needs provided by the general contractor. These items vary by project but may include temporary facilities and utilities, security, testing, project cleanup, etc. In assemblies estimates a percentage is used—typically between 5% and 15% of project cost.

## 4 General Contractor Overhead

This entry represents the general contractor's markup on all work to cover project administration costs.

## 5 General Contractor Profit

This entry represents the General Contractor's profit on all work performed. The value included here can vary widely by project and is influenced by the General Contractor's perception of the project's financial risk and market conditions.

## 6 Location Factor

RSMeans published data are based on national average costs. If necessary, adjust the total cost of the project using a location factor from the "Location Factor" table or the "City Cost Indexes" table found in the Reference Section. Use location factors if the work is general, covering the work of multiple trades. If the work is by a single trade (e.g., masonry), use the more specific data found in the City Cost Indexes.

To adjust costs by location factors, multiply the base cost by the factor and divide by 100.

## 7 Architect's Fee

If appropriate, add the design cost to the project estimate. These fees vary based on project complexity and size. Typical design and engineering fees can be found in the Reference Section.

## 8 Contingency

A factor for contingency may be added to any estimate to represent the cost of unknowns that may occur between the time that the estimate is performed and the time the project is constructed. The amount of the allowance will depend on the stage of design at which the estimate is done, as well as the contractor's assessment of the risk involved.

# Example

Assemblies costs can be used to calculate the cost for each component of a building and, accumulated with appropriate markups, produce a cost for the complete structure. Components from a model building with similar characteristics in conjunction with Assemblies components may be used to calculate costs for a complete structure.

*Example:*

## Outline Specifications

| | |
|---|---|
| **General** | Building size—60' x 100', 8 suspended floors, 12' floor to floor, 4' high parapet above roof, full basement 11'-8" floor to floor, bay size 25' x 30', ceiling heights 9' in office area and 8' in core area. |
| **A Substructure** | Concrete, spread and strip footings, concrete walls waterproofed, 4" slab on grade. |
| **B Shell** | |
| ***B10 Superstructure*** | Columns, wide flange; 3 hr. fire rated; Floors, composite steel frame & deck with concrete slab; Roof, steel beams, open web joists and deck. |
| ***B20 Exterior Enclosure*** | Walls; North, East & West, brick & lightweight concrete block with 2" cavity insulation, 25% window; South, 8" lightweight concrete block insulated, 10% window. Doors, aluminum & glass. Windows, aluminum, 3'-0" x 5'-4", insulating glass. |
| ***B30 Roofing*** | Tar & gravel, 2" rigid insulation, R 12.5. |
| **C Interiors** | Core—6" lightweight concrete block, full height with plaster on exposed faces to ceiling height. |
| | Corridors—1st & 2nd floor; 3-5/8" steel studs with F.R. gypsum board, full height. |
| | Exterior Wall—plaster, ceiling height. |
| | Fittings—Toilet accessories, directory boards. |
| | Doors—hollow metal. |
| | Wall Finishes—lobby, mahogany paneling on furring, remainder plaster & gypsum board, paint. |
| | Floor Finishes—1st floor lobby, corridors & toilet rooms, terrazzo; remainder concrete, tenant developed. 2nd through 8th, toilet rooms, ceramic tile; office & corridor, carpet. |
| | Ceiling Finishes—24" x 48" fiberglass board on Tee grid. |
| **D Services** | |
| ***D10 Conveying*** | 2-2500 lb. capacity, 200 F.P.M. geared elevators, 9 stops. |
| ***D20 Plumbing*** | Fixtures, see sketch. |
| | Roof Drains—2-4" C.I. pipe. |
| ***D30 HVAC*** | Heating—fin tube radiation, forced hot water. |
| | Air Conditioning—chilled water with water cooled condenser. |
| ***D40 Fire Protection*** | Fire Protection—4" standpipe, 9 hose cabinets. |
| ***D50 Electrical*** | Lighting, 1st through 8th, 15 fluorescent fixtures/1000 S.F., 3 Watts/S.F. |
| | Basement, 10 fluorescent fixtures/1000 S.F., 2 Watts/S.F. |
| | Receptacles, 1st through 8th, 16.5/1000 S.F., 2 Watts/S.F. |
| | Basement, 10 receptacles/1000 S.F., 1.2 Watts/S.F. |
| | Air Conditioning, 4 Watts/S.F. |
| | Miscellaneous Connections, 1.2 Watts/S.F. |
| | Elevator Power, 2-10 H.P., 230 volt motors. |
| | Wall Switches, 2/1000 S.F. |
| | Service, panel board & feeder, 2000 Amp. |
| | Fire Detection System, pull stations, signals, smoke and heat detectors. |
| | Emergency Lighting Generator, 30 KW. |
| **E Equipment & Furnishings** | NA. |
| **F Special Construction** | NA. |
| **G Building Sitework** | NA. |

## Front Elevation

## Basement Plan

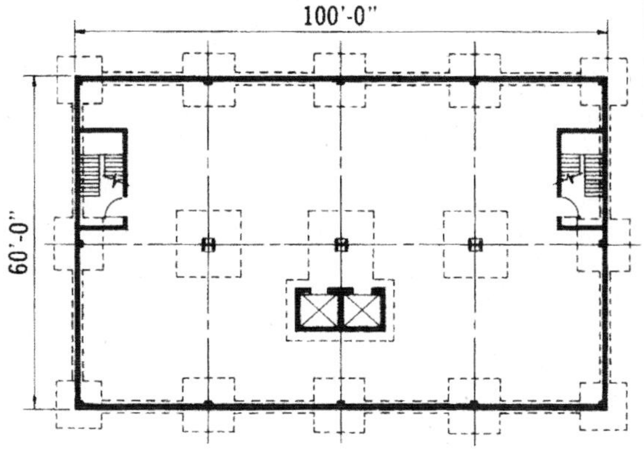


## Ground Floor Plan

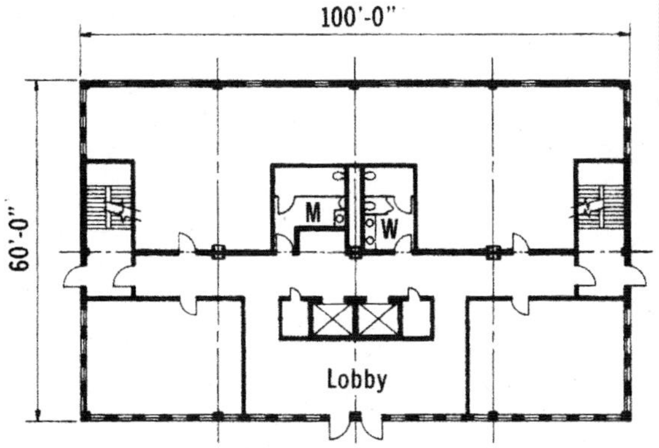


## Typical Floor Plan

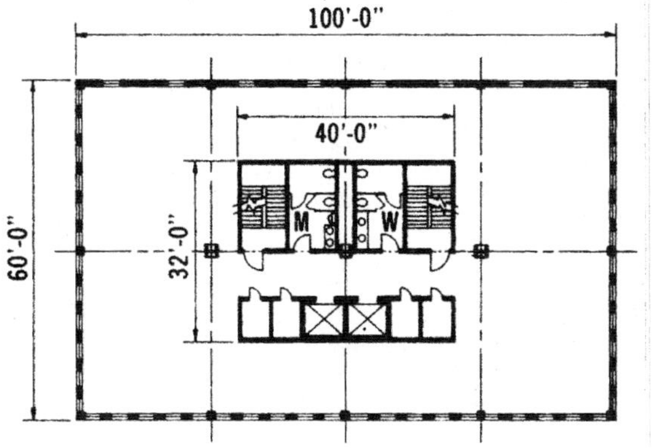

# Example

If spread footing & column sizes are unknown, develop approximate loads as follows. Enter tables with these loads to determine costs.

## Superimposed Load Ranges

| | | | |
|---|---|---|---|
| Apartments & Residential Structures | 65 | to | 75 psf |
| Assembly Areas & Retail Stores | 110 | to | 125 psf |
| Commercial & Manufacturing | 150 | to | 250 psf |
| Offices | 75 | to | 100 psf |

Approximate loads/S.F. for roof & floors.

Roof. Assume 40 psf superimposed load.

Steel joists, beams & deck.

Table B1020 112—Line 3900

| B1010 256 | Composite Beams, Deck & Slab | | | | | | | |
|---|---|---|---|---|---|---|---|---|
| | BAY SIZE (FT.) | SUPERIMPOSED LOAD (P.S.F.) | SLAB THICKNESS (IN.) | TOTAL DEPTH (FT.-IN.) | TOTAL LOAD (P.S.F.) | COST PER S.F. | | |
| | | | | | | MAT. | INST. | TOTAL |
| 3400 | 25x30 | 40 | 5-1/2 | 1 - 11-1/2 | 83 | 17.80 | 7.05 | 24.85 |
| 3600 | | 75 | 5-1/2 | 1 - 11-1/2 | 119 | 19 | 7.10 | 26.10 |
| 3900 | | 125 | 5-1/2 | 1 - 11-1/2 | 170 | 22 | 8 | 30 |
| 4000 | | 200 | 6-1/4 | 2 - 6-1/4 | 252 | 27.50 | 9.15 | 36.65 |

| B1020 112 | Steel Joists, Beams, & Deck on Columns | | | | | | | |
|---|---|---|---|---|---|---|---|---|
| | BAY SIZE (FT.) | SUPERIMPOSED LOAD (P.S.F.) | DEPTH (IN.) | TOTAL LOAD (P.S.F.) | COLUMN ADD | COST PER S.F. | | |
| | | | | | | MAT. | INST. | TOTAL |
| 3500 | 25x30 | 20 | 22 | 40 | | 8.55 | 1.94 | 10.49 |
| 3600 | | | | | columns | 1.50 | .36 | 1.86 |
| 3900 | | 40 | 25 | 60 | | 10.15 | 2.32 | 12.47 |
| 4000 | | | | | columns | 1.79 | .43 | 2.22 |

Floors—Total load, 119 psf.

Interior foundation load.

Roof

[(25' x 30' x 60 psf) + 8 floors x (25' x 30' x 119 psf)] x 1/1000 lb./Kip = 759 Kips

Approximate Footing Loads, Interior footing = 759 Kips

Exterior footing (1/2 bay) 759 k x .6 = 455 Kips

Corner footing (1/4 bay) 759 k x .45 = 342 Kips

*[Factors to convert Interior load to Exterior & Corner loads]*

Approximate average Column load 759 k/2 = 379 Kips

**PRELIMINARY ESTIMATE**

| | | | |
|---|---|---|---|
| PROJECT | **Office Building** | TOTAL SITE AREA | |
| BUILDING TYPE | | OWNER | |
| LOCATION | | ARCHITECT | |
| DATE OF CONSTRUCTION | | ESTIMATED CONSTRUCTION PERIOD | |

BRIEF DESCRIPTION **Building size: 60' x 100' - 8 structural floors - 12' floor to floor**
**4' high parapet above roof, full basement 11' - 8" floor to floor, bay size**
**25' x 30', ceiling heights - 9' in office area + 8' in core area**

| | | | |
|---|---|---|---|
| TYPE OF PLAN | | TYPE OF CONSTRUCTION | |
| QUALITY | | BUILDING CAPACITY | |

| | | |
|---|---|---|
| **Floor** | | |
| Below Grade Levels | | |
| Area | | S.F. |
| Area | | S.F. |
| Total Area | | S.F. |
| Ground Floor | | |
| Area | | S.F. |
| Area | | S.F. |
| Total Area | | S.F. |
| Supported Levels | | |
| Area | | |
| Area | | S.F. |
| Area | | S.F. |
| Area | | S.F. |
| Area | | S.F. |
| Total Area | | S.F. |
| Miscellaneous | | |
| Area | | S.F. |
| Area | | S.F. |
| Area | | S.F. |
| Area | | S.F. |
| Total Area | | S.F. |
| Net Finished Area | | S.F. |
| Net Floor Area | | S.F. |
| Gross Floor Area | **54,000** | S.F. |
| **Roof** | | |
| Total Area | | S.F. |
| Comments | | |
| | | |
| **Volume** | | |
| Depth of Floor System | | |
| Minimum | | In. |
| Maximum | | In. |
| Foundation Wall Height | | Ft. |
| Floor to Floor Height | | Ft. |
| Floor to Ceiling Height | | Ft. |
| Subgrade Volume | | C.F. |
| Above Grade Volume | | C.F. |
| Total Building Volume | **648,000** | C.F. |

| | | | |
|---|---|---|---|
| **Wall Area** | | | |
| Foundation Walls | L.F. | Ht. | S.F. |
| Frost Walls | L.F. | Ht. | S.F. |
| Exterior Closure | | Total | S.F. |
| Comment | | | |
| Fenestration | | % | S.F. |
| | | % | S.F. |
| Exterior Wall | | % | S.F. |
| | | % | S.F. |
| **Site Work** | | | |
| Parking | | S.F. (For | Cars) |
| Access Roads | | L.F. (X | Ft. Wide) |
| Sidewalk | | L.F. (X | Ft. Wide) |
| Landscaping | | S.F. ( | % Unbuilt Site) |
| **Building Codes** | | | |
| City | | Country | |
| National | | Other | |
| **Loading** | | | |
| Roof | psf | Ground Floor | psf |
| Supported Floors | psf | Corridor | psf |
| Balcony | psf | Partition, allow | psf |
| Miscellaneous | | | psf |
| Live Load Reduction | | | |
| Wind | | | |
| Earthquake | | Zone | |
| Comment | | | |
| Soil Type | | | |
| Bearing Capacity | | | K.S.F. |
| Frost Depth | | | Ft. |
| **Frame** | | | |
| Type | | Bay Spacing | |
| Foundation | | | |
| Special | | | |
| Substructure | | | |
| Comment | | | |
| Superstructure, Vertical | | | |
| Fireproofing | | ☐ Columns | Hrs. |
| ☐ Girders | Hrs. | ☐ Beams | Hrs. |
| ☐ Floor | Hrs. | ☐ None | |

| NUMBER | | QTY. | UNIT | TOTAL COST | | COST PER S.F. |
|---|---|---|---|---|---|---|
| | | | | UNIT | TOTAL | |
| A | **SUBSTRUCTURE** | | | | | |
| A1010 210 7900 | Corner Footings 8'-6" SQ. x 27" | 4 | Ea. | 2,687.00 | 10,748 | |
| 8010 | Exterior 9' -6" SQ. x 30" | 8 | | 3,609.50 | 28,876 | |
| 8300 | Interior 12' SQ. | 3 | | 6,583.00 | 19,749 | |
| A1010 110 2700 | Strip 2' Wide x 1' Thick | | | | | |
| | 320 L.F.- [(4 x 8.5) + 8 x 9.5)] = | 210 | L.F. | 57.30 | 12,033 | |
| A2020 110 7260 | Foundation Wall 12' High, 1' Thick | 320 | | 330.20 | 105,664 | |
| A1010 320 2800 | Foundation Waterproofing | 320 | | 27.60 | 8,832 | |
| A1030 120 2240 | 4", non-industrial, reinf. slab on grade | 6000 | S.F. | 7.22 | 43,320 | |
| A2010 110 3440 | Building Excavation + Backfill | 6000 | S.F. | 5.40 | 32,400 | |
| 3500 | (Interpolated ; 12' Between | | | | | |
| 4620 | 8' and 16' ; 6,000 Between | | | | | |
| 4680 | 4,000 and 10,000 S.F. | | | | | |
| | Total | | | | 261,622 | 4.84 |
| B | **SHELL** | | | | | |
| B10 | **Superstructure** | | | | | |
| B1010 208 5800 | Columns: Load 379K Use 400K | | | | | |
| | Exterior 12 x 96' + Interior 3 x 108' | 1476 | V.L.F. | 187.02 | 276,042 | |
| B1010 720 3650 | Column Fireproofing - Interior 4 sides | | | | | |
| 3700 | Exterior 1/2 (Interpolated for 12") | 900 | V.L.F | 48.40 | 43,560 | |
| B1010 256 3600 | Floors: Composite steel + lt. wt. conc. | 48000 | S.F. | 26.10 | 1,252,800 | |
| B1020 112 3900 | Roof: Open web joists, beams + decks | 6000 | S.F. | 12.46 | 74,760 | |
| | | | | | | |
| | Total | | | | 1,647,162 | 30.50 |
| B20 | **Exterior Enclosure** | | | | | |
| B2010 134 1200 | 4" Brick + 6" Block - Insulated | | | | | |
| | 75% NE + W Walls 220' x 100' x .75 | 16500 | S.F. | 38.10 | 628,650 | |
| B2010 110 3410 | 8" Block - Insulated 90% | | | | | |
| | 100' x 100' x .9 | 9000 | S.F. | 15.35 | 138,150 | |
| | | | | | | |
| B2030 110 6950 | Double Aluminum + Glass Door | 1 | Pr. | 9,150.00 | 9,150 | |
| 6300 | Single | 2 | Ea. | 4,725.00 | 9,450 | |
| B2020 106 8800 | Aluminum windows - Insul. glass | | | | | |
| | (5,500 S.F. + 1,000 S.F.)/(3 x 5.33) | 406 | Ea. | 2,759.00 | 1,120,154 | |
| B2010 105 8480 | Precast concrete coping | 320 | L.F. | 33.50 | 10,720 | |
| | Total | | | | 1,916,274 | 35.49 |
| B30 | **Roofing** | | | | | |
| B3010 320 4020 | Insulation: Perlite/Polyisocyanurate | 6000 | S.F. | 2.53 | 15,180 | |
| B3010 105 1400 | Roof: 4 Ply T & G composite | 6000 | | 3.95 | 23,700 | |
| B3010 430 0300 | Flashing: Aluminum - fabric backed | 640 | | 4.28 | 2,739 | |
| B3020 210 0500 | Roof hatch | 1 | Ea. | 2,090.00 | 2,090 | |
| | | | | | | |
| | Total | | | | 43,709 | 0.81 |

| ASSEMBLY NUMBER | | QTY. | UNIT | TOTAL COST UNIT | TOTAL | COST PER S.F. |
|---|---|---|---|---|---|---|
| **C** | **INTERIORS** | | | | | |
| C1010 104 5500 | Core partitions: 6" Lt. Wt. concrete | | | | | |
| | block 288 L.F. x 11.5' x 8 Floors | 26,449 | S.F. | 10.86 | 287,236 | |
| C1010 144 0920 | Plaster: [(196 L.F. x 8') + (144 L.F. x 9')] 8 | | | | | |
| | + Ext. Wall [(320 x 9 x 8 Floors) - 6500] | 39,452 | S.F. | 3.86 | 152,285 | |
| C1010 126 5400 | Corridor partitions 1st + 2nd floors | | | | | |
| | steel studs + F.R. gypsum board | 2,530 | S.F. | 5.65 | 14,295 | |
| C1020 102 2600 | Interior doors | 66 | Ea. | 1,159.00 | 76,494 | |
| | Wall finishes - Lobby: Mahogany w/furring | | | | | |
| C1010 128 0652 | Furring: 150 L.F. x 9' + Ht. | 1,350 | S.F. | 1.99 | 2,687 | |
| C1030 710 0120 | Towel Dispenser | 16 | Ea. | 97.00 | 1,552 | |
| C1030 710 0140 | Grab Bar | 32 | Ea. | 52.00 | 1,664 | |
| C1030 710 0160 | Mirror | 31 | Ea. | 154.00 | 4,774 | |
| C1030 710 0180 | Toilet Tissue Dispenser | 31 | Ea. | 41.90 | 1,299 | |
| C1030 510 0140 | Directory Board | 8 | Ea. | 452.00 | 3,616 | |
| C2010 110 0780 | Stairs: Steel w/conc. fill | 18 | Flt. | 22,262.00 | 400,716 | |
| C3010 230 1662 | Mahogany paneling | 1,350 | S.F. | 6.21 | 8,384 | |
| C3010 230 0080 | Paint, primer + 2 coats finish, on plaster or gyp. board | | | | | |
| | 39,452 + [(220' x 9' x 2) - 1350] + 72 | 42,134 | S.F. | 1.39 | 58,566 | |
| | Floor Finishes | | | | | |
| C3020 410 1100 | 1st floor lobby + terrazzo | 2,175 | S.F. | 24.33 | 52,918 | |
| | Remainder: Concrete - Tenant finished | | | | | |
| C3020 410 0060 | 2nd - 8th: Carpet - 4725 S.F. x 7 | 33,075 | S.F. | 4.90 | 162,068 | |
| C3020 410 1720 | Ceramic Tile - 300 S.F. x 7 | 2,100 | S.F. | 9.66 | 20,286 | |
| C3030 240 2780 | Suspended Ceiling Tiles- 5200 S.F. x 8 | 41,600 | S.F. | 2.28 | 94,848 | |
| C3030 240 3260 | Suspended Ceiling Grid- 5200 S.F. x 8 | 41,600 | S.F. | 2.38 | 99,008 | |
| C1030 110 0700 | Toilet partitions | 31 | Ea. | 1,224.00 | 37,944 | |
| 0760 | Handicapped addition | 16 | Ea. | 161.00 | 2,576 | |
| | | | | | | |
| | Total | | | | 1,483,214 | 27.47 |
| **D** | **SERVICES** | | | | | |
| **D10** | **Conveying** | | | | | |
| | 2 Elevators - 2500# 200'/min. Geared | | | | | |
| D1010 140 1600 | 5 Floors $218,500 | | | | | |
| 1800 | 15 Floors $491,000 | | | | | |
| | Diff. $272,500/10 = 27,250/Flr. | | | | | |
| | $218,500 + (4 x27,250) = $327,500/Ea. | 2 | Ea. | 327,500.00 | 655,000 | |
| | | | | | | |
| | Total | | | | 655,000 | 12.13 |
| **D20** | **Plumbing** | | | | | |
| D2010 310 1600 | Plumbing - Lavatories | 31 | Ea. | 1,885.00 | 58,435 | |
| D2010 440 4340 | -Service Sink | 8 | Ea. | 7,325.00 | 58,600 | |
| D2010 210 2000 | -Urinals | 8 | Ea. | 1,860.00 | 14,880 | |

| ASSEMBLY NUMBER | | QTY. | UNIT | TOTAL COST UNIT | TOTAL | COST PER S.F. |
|---|---|---|---|---|---|---|
| D2010 110 2080 | -Water Closets | 31 | Ea. | 4,175.00 | 129,425 | |
| | Water Control, Waste Vent Piping | 45% | | | 117,603 | |
| D2040 210 4200 | - Roof Drains, 4" C.I. | 2 | Ea. | 2,700.00 | 5,400 | |
| 4240 | - Pipe, 9 Flr. x 12' x 12' Ea. | 216 | L.F. | 43.40 | 9,374 | |
| | Total | | | | 393,717 | 7.29 |
| D30 | HVAC | | | | | |
| D3010 520 2000 | 10,000 S.F. @ $11.11/S.F. Interpolate | | | | | |
| 2040 | 100,000 S.F. @ $5.00/S.F. | 48,000 | S.F. | 6.15 | 295,200 | |
| | Cooling - Chilled Water, Air Cool, Cond. | | | | | |
| D3030 115 3840 | 4,000 S.F. @20.25/S.F. Interpolate | 48,000 | S.F. | 27.85 | 1,336,800 | |
| 4040 | 60,000 S.F. @15.50/S.F. | | | | | |
| | Total | | | | 1,632,000 | 30.22 |
| D40 | Fire Protection | | | | | |
| D4020 310 0560 | Wet Stand Pipe: 4" x 10' 1st floor | 12/10 | Ea. | 14,500.00 | 17,400 | |
| 0580 | Additional Floors: (12'/10 x 8) | 9.6 | Ea. | 3,875.00 | 37,200 | |
| D4020 410 8400 | Cabinet Assembly | 9 | Ea. | 2,285.00 | 20,565 | |
| | Total | | | | 75,165 | 1.39 |
| D50 | Electrical | | | | | |
| D5020 210 0280 | Office Lighting, 15/1000 S.F. - 3 Watts/S.F. | 48,000 | S.F. | 10.95 | 525,600 | |
| 0240 | Basement Lighting, 10/1000 S.F. - 2 Watts/S.F. | 6,000 | S.F. | 7.27 | 43,620 | |
| D5020 110 0640 | Office Receptacles 16.5/1000 S.F. - 2 Watts/S.F. | 48,000 | S.F. | 6.48 | 311,040 | |
| 0560 | Basement Receptacles 10/1000 S.F. - 1.2 Watts/S.F. | 6,000 | S.F. | 4.95 | 29,700 | |
| D5020 140 0280 | Central A.C. - 4 Watts/S.F. | 48,000 | S.F. | 0.82 | 39,360 | |
| D5020 135 0320 | Misc. Connections - 1.2 Watts/S.F. | 48,000 | S.F. | 0.45 | 21,600 | |
| D5020 145 0680 | Elevator Motor Power - 10 H.P. | 2 | Ea. | 3,400.00 | 6,800 | |
| D5020 130 0280 | Wall Switches - 2/1000 S.F. | 54,000 | S.F. | 0.60 | 32,400 | |
| D5010 120 0560 | 2000 Amp Service | 1 | Ea. | 54,100.00 | 54,100 | |
| D5010 240 0400 | Switchgear | 1 | Ea. | 47,000.00 | 47,000 | |
| D5010 230 0560 | Feeder | 50 | L.F. | 814.00 | 40,700 | |
| D5030 910 0400 | Fire Detection System - 50 Detectors | 1 | Ea. | 45,400.00 | 45,400 | |
| D5090 210 0320 | Emergency Generator - 30 kW | 30 | kW | 640.00 | 19,200 | |
| | | | | | | |
| | Total | | | | 1,216,520 | 22.53 |
| E | EQUIPMENT & FURNISHINGS | | | | | |
| | | | | | | |
| | | | | | | |
| G | BUILDING SITEWORK | | | | | |
| | | | | | | |
| | | | | | | |
| | Miscellaneous | | | | | |
| | | | | | | |
| | | | | | | |

## Preliminary Estimate Cost Summary

| | | | |
|---|---|---|---|
| PROJECT: Office Building | TOTAL AREA | 54,000 S.F. | SHEET NO. |
| LOCATION | TOTAL VOLUME | 648,000 C.F. | ESTIMATE NO. |
| ARCHITECT | COST PER S.F. | | DATE |
| OWNER | COST PER C.F. | | NO OF STORIES |
| QUANTITIES BY | EXTENSIONS BY | | CHECKED BY |

| DIV | DESCRIPTION | SUBTOTAL COST | COST/S.F. | PERCENTAGE |
|---|---|---|---|---|
| A | SUBSTRUCTURE | 261,622 | $ 4.84 | |
| B10 | SHELL: SUPERSTRUCTURE | 1,647,162 | $ 30.50 | |
| B20 | SHELL: EXTERIOR ENCLOSURE | 1,916,274 | $ 35.49 | |
| B30 | SHELL: ROOFING | 43,709 | $ 0.81 | |
| C | INTERIORS | 1,483,214 | $ 27.47 | |
| D10 | SERVICES: CONVEYING | 655,000 | $ 12.13 | |
| D20 | SERVICES: PLUMBING | 393,717 | $ 7.29 | |
| D30 | SERVICES: HVAC | 1,632,000 | $ 30.22 | |
| D40 | SERVICES: FIRE PROTECTION | 75,165 | $ 1.39 | |
| D50 | SERVICES: ELECTRICAL | 1,216,520 | $ 22.53 | |
| E | EQUIPMENT & FURNISHINGS | | | |
| F | SPECIAL CONSTRUCTION & DEMO. | | | |
| G | BUILDING SITEWORK | | | |
| | **BUILDING SUBTOTAL** | **$ 9,324,383** | | **$ 9,324,383** |

| | | | |
|---|---|---|---|
| Sales Tax % x Subtotal /2 | N/A | | $ - |
| General Conditions 10 % x Subtotal | | | **$ 932,438** |
| | | Subtotal "A" | **$ 10,256,822** |
| Overhead 5 % x Subtotal "A" | | | **$ 512,841** |
| | | Subtotal "B" | **$ 10,769,663** |
| Profit 10% x Subtotal "B" | | | **$ 1,076,966** |
| | | Subtotal "C" | **$ 11,846,629** |
| Location Factor % x Subtotal "C" | N/A | Localized Cost | |
| Architects Fee 6.5% x Localized Cost = | | | **$ 770,031** |
| Contingency x Localized Cost = | N/A | | $ - |
| | | **Project Total Cost** | **$ 12,616,660** |
| Square Foot Cost $9,081,534/ 54,000 S.F. = | | **S.F. Cost** | **$ 233.64** |
| Cubic Foot Cost $9,081,534/ 648,000 C.F. = | | **C.F. Cost** | **$ 19.47** |

## A1010 Standard Foundations

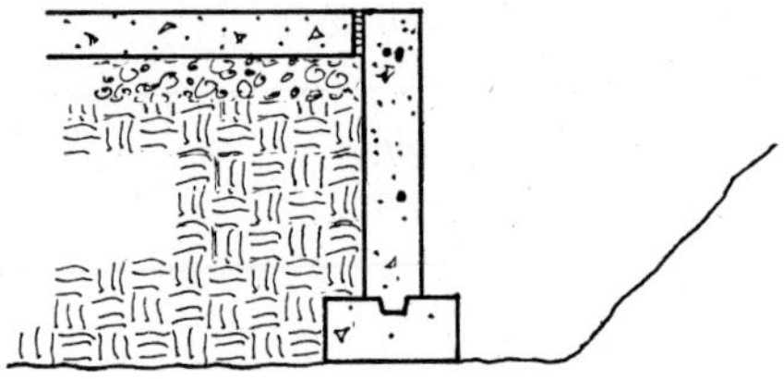

The Foundation Bearing Wall System includes: forms up to 6′ high (four uses); 3,000 p.s.i. concrete placed and vibrated; and form removal with breaking form ties and patching walls. The wall systems list walls from 6″ to 16″ thick and are designed with minimum reinforcement.

Excavation and backfill are not included.

Please see the reference section for further design and cost information.

### A1010 105 Wall Foundations

| | WALL HEIGHT (FT.) | PLACING METHOD | CONCRETE (C.Y. per L.F.) | REINFORCING (LBS. per L.F.) | WALL THICKNESS (IN.) | COST PER L.F. MAT. | INST. | TOTAL |
|---|---|---|---|---|---|---|---|---|
| 1500 | 4′ | direct chute | .074 | 3.3 | 6 | 24 | 64 | 88 |
| 1520 | | | .099 | 4.8 | 8 | 29.50 | 65.50 | 95 |
| 1540 | | | .123 | 6.0 | 10 | 34.50 | 67 | 101.50 |
| 1560 | | | .148 | 7.2 | 12 | 39.50 | 68.50 | 108 |
| 1580 | | | .173 | 8.1 | 14 | 44.50 | 69.50 | 114 |
| 1600 | | | .197 | 9.44 | 16 | 49.50 | 71 | 120.50 |
| 1700 | | pumped | .074 | 3.3 | 6 | 24 | 65.50 | 89.50 |
| 1720 | | | .099 | 4.8 | 8 | 29.50 | 67.50 | 97 |
| 1740 | | | .123 | 6.0 | 10 | 34.50 | 69 | 103.50 |
| 1760 | | | .148 | 7.2 | 12 | 39.50 | 71 | 110.50 |
| 1780 | | | .173 | 8.1 | 14 | 44.50 | 72 | 116.50 |
| 1800 | | | .197 | 9.44 | 16 | 49.50 | 74 | 123.50 |
| 3000 | 6′ | direct chute | .111 | 4.95 | 6 | 35.50 | 96 | 131.50 |
| 3020 | | | .149 | 7.20 | 8 | 44 | 98.50 | 142.50 |
| 3040 | | | .184 | 9.00 | 10 | 51.50 | 100 | 151.50 |
| 3060 | | | .222 | 10.8 | 12 | 59 | 103 | 162 |
| 3080 | | | .260 | 12.15 | 14 | 66.50 | 104 | 170.50 |
| 3100 | | | .300 | 14.39 | 16 | 75.50 | 107 | 182.50 |
| 3200 | | pumped | .111 | 4.95 | 6 | 35.50 | 98 | 133.50 |
| 3220 | | | .149 | 7.20 | 8 | 44 | 101 | 145 |
| 3240 | | | .184 | 9.00 | 10 | 51.50 | 103 | 154.50 |
| 3260 | | | .222 | 10.8 | 12 | 59 | 106 | 165 |
| 3280 | | | .260 | 12.15 | 14 | 66.50 | 108 | 174.50 |
| 3300 | | | .300 | 14.39 | 16 | 75.50 | 111 | 186.50 |

## A1010 Standard Foundations

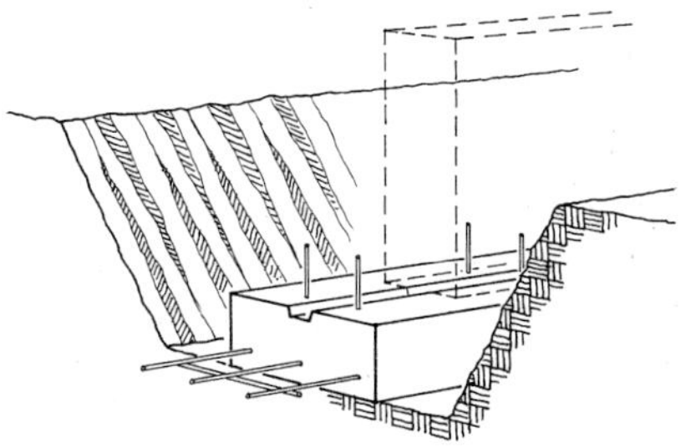

The Strip Footing System includes: excavation; hand trim; all forms needed for footing placement; forms for 2″ x 6″ keyway (four uses); dowels; and 3,000 p.s.i. concrete.

The footing size required varies for different soils. Soil bearing capacities are listed for 3 KSF and 6 KSF. Depths of the system range from 8″ and deeper. Widths range from 16″ and wider. Smaller strip footings may not require reinforcement.

Please see the reference section for further design and cost information.

| A1010 110 | Strip Footings | COST PER L.F. | | |
|---|---|---|---|---|
| | | MAT. | INST. | TOTAL |
| 2100 | Strip footing, load 2.6 KLF, soil capacity 3 KSF, 16″ wide x 8″ deep, plain | 13.55 | 13.25 | 26.80 |
| 2300 | Load 3.9 KLF, soil capacity 3 KSF, 24″ wide x 8″ deep, plain | 16.40 | 14.95 | 31.35 |
| 2500 | Load 5.1 KLF, soil capacity 3 KSF, 24″ wide x 12″ deep, reinf. | 28.50 | 28.50 | 57 |
| 2700 | Load 11.1 KLF, soil capacity 6 KSF, 24″ wide x 12″ deep, reinf. | 28.50 | 28.50 | 57 |
| 2900 | Load 6.8 KLF, soil capacity 3 KSF, 32″ wide x 12″ deep, reinf. | 34 | 31 | 65 |
| 3100 | Load 14.8 KLF, soil capacity 6 KSF, 32″ wide x 12″ deep, reinf. | 34 | 31.50 | 65.50 |
| 3300 | Load 9.3 KLF, soil capacity 3 KSF, 40″ wide x 12″ deep, reinf. | 39 | 33.50 | 72.50 |
| 3500 | Load 18.4 KLF, soil capacity 6 KSF, 40″ wide x 12″ deep, reinf. | 39 | 34 | 73 |
| 4500 | Load 10 KLF, soil capacity 3 KSF, 48″ wide x 16″ deep, reinf. | 54.50 | 42.50 | 97 |
| 4700 | Load 22 KLF, soil capacity 6 KSF, 48″ wide, 16″ deep, reinf. | 55.50 | 43.50 | 99 |
| 5700 | Load 15 KLF, soil capacity 3 KSF, 72″ wide x 20″ deep, reinf. | 91.50 | 60.50 | 152 |
| 5900 | Load 33 KLF, soil capacity 6 KSF, 72″ wide x 20″ deep, reinf. | 96 | 64.50 | 160.50 |

# A1010 Standard Foundations

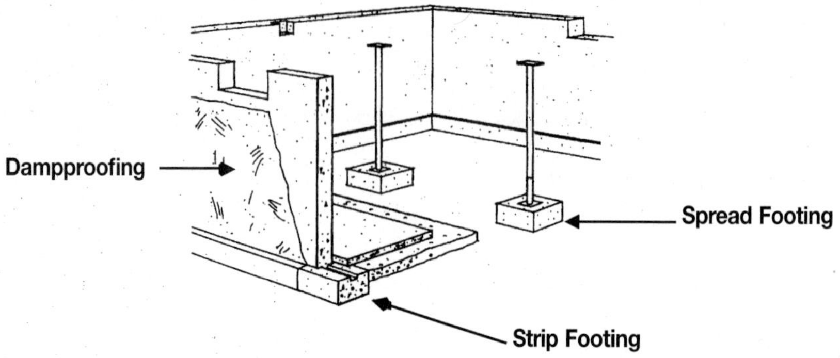


| A1010 210 | Spread Footings | COST EACH | | |
|---|---|---|---|---|
| | | MAT. | INST. | TOTAL |
| 7090 | Spread footings, 3000 psi concrete, chute delivered | | | |
| 7100 | Load 25K, soil capacity 3 KSF, 3′-0″ sq. x 12″ deep | 107 | 150 | 257 |
| 7150 | Load 50K, soil capacity 3 KSF, 4′-6″ sq. x 12″ deep | 217 | 257 | 474 |
| 7200 | Load 50K, soil capacity 6 KSF, 3′-0″ sq. x 12″ deep | 107 | 150 | 257 |
| 7250 | Load 75K, soil capacity 3 KSF, 5′-6″ sq. x 13″ deep | 335 | 365 | 700 |
| 7300 | Load 75K, soil capacity 6 KSF, 4′-0″ sq. x 12″ deep | 178 | 221 | 399 |
| 7350 | Load 100K, soil capacity 3 KSF, 6′-0″ sq. x 14″ deep | 420 | 435 | 855 |
| 7410 | Load 100K, soil capacity 6 KSF, 4′-6″ sq. x 15″ deep | 265 | 305 | 570 |
| 7450 | Load 125K, soil capacity 3 KSF, 7′-0″ sq. x 17″ deep | 660 | 625 | 1,285 |
| 7500 | Load 125K, soil capacity 6 KSF, 5′-0″ sq. x 16″ deep | 335 | 365 | 700 |
| 7550 | Load 150K, soil capacity 3 KSF 7′-6″ sq. x 18″ deep | 790 | 725 | 1,515 |
| 7610 | Load 150K, soil capacity 6 KSF, 5′-6″ sq. x 18″ deep | 445 | 455 | 900 |
| 7650 | Load 200K, soil capacity 3 KSF, 8′-6″ sq. x 20″ deep | 1,100 | 960 | 2,060 |
| 7700 | Load 200K, soil capacity 6 KSF, 6′-0″ sq. x 20″ deep | 575 | 565 | 1,140 |
| 7750 | Load 300K, soil capacity 3 KSF, 10′-6″ sq. x 25″ deep | 2,025 | 1,550 | 3,575 |
| 7810 | Load 300K, soil capacity 6 KSF, 7′-6″ sq. x 25″ deep | 1,075 | 945 | 2,020 |
| 7850 | Load 400K, soil capacity 3 KSF, 12′-6″ sq. x 28″ deep | 3,175 | 2,300 | 5,475 |
| 7900 | Load 400K, soil capacity 6 KSF, 8′-6″ sq. x 27″ deep | 1,475 | 1,225 | 2,700 |
| 8010 | Load 500K, soil capacity 6 KSF, 9′-6″ sq. x 30″ deep | 2,025 | 1,600 | 3,625 |
| 8100 | Load 600K, soil capacity 6 KSF, 10′-6″ sq. x 33″ deep | 2,700 | 2,050 | 4,750 |
| 8200 | Load 700K, soil capacity 6 KSF, 11′-6″ sq. x 36″ deep | 3,450 | 2,500 | 5,950 |
| 8300 | Load 800K, soil capacity 6 KSF, 12′-0″ sq. x 37″ deep | 3,850 | 2,750 | 6,600 |
| 8400 | Load 900K, soil capacity 6 KSF, 13′-0″ sq. x 39″ deep | 4,725 | 3,250 | 7,975 |
| 8500 | Load 1000K, soil capacity 6 KSF, 13′-6″ sq. x 41″ deep | 5,350 | 3,625 | 8,975 |

| A1010 320 | Foundation Dampproofing | COST PER L.F. | | |
|---|---|---|---|---|
| | | MAT. | INST. | TOTAL |
| 1000 | Foundation dampproofing, bituminous, 1 coat, 4′ high | 1 | 5.75 | 6.75 |
| 1400 | 8′ high | 2 | 11.45 | 13.45 |
| 1800 | 12′ high | 3 | 17.75 | 20.75 |
| 2000 | 2 coats, 4′ high | 2.04 | 7.05 | 9.09 |
| 2400 | 8′ high | 4.08 | 14.10 | 18.18 |
| 2800 | 12′ high | 6.10 | 21.50 | 27.60 |
| 3000 | Asphalt with fibers, 1/16″ thick, 4′ high | 2.12 | 7.05 | 9.17 |
| 3400 | 8′ high | 4.24 | 14.10 | 18.34 |
| 3800 | 12′ high | 6.35 | 21.50 | 27.85 |
| 4000 | 1/8″ thick, 4′ high | 3.72 | 8.40 | 12.12 |
| 4400 | 8′ high | 7.45 | 16.85 | 24.30 |
| 4800 | 12′ high | 11.15 | 26 | 37.15 |
| 5000 | Asphalt coated board and mastic, 1/4″ thick, 4′ high | 8.15 | 7.65 | 15.80 |
| 5400 | 8′ high | 16.30 | 15.30 | 31.60 |

## A1010 Standard Foundations

| A1010 320 | Foundation Dampproofing | COST PER L.F. MAT. | INST. | TOTAL |
|---|---|---|---|---|
| 5800 | 12′ high | 24.50 | 23.50 | 48 |
| 6000 | 1/2″ thick, 4′ high | 12.25 | 10.65 | 22.90 |
| 6400 | 8′ high | 24.50 | 21.50 | 46 |
| 6800 | 12′ high | 36.50 | 32.50 | 69 |
| 7000 | Cementitious coating, on walls, 1/8″ thick coating, 4′ high | 3.84 | 10.05 | 13.89 |
| 7400 | 8′ high | 7.70 | 20 | 27.70 |
| 7800 | 12′ high | 11.50 | 30 | 41.50 |
| 8000 | Cementitious/metallic slurry, 4 coat, 1/2″thick, 2′ high | .88 | 10.70 | 11.58 |
| 8400 | 4′ high | 1.76 | 21.50 | 23.26 |
| 8800 | 6′ high | 2.64 | 32 | 34.64 |

## A1030 Slab on Grade

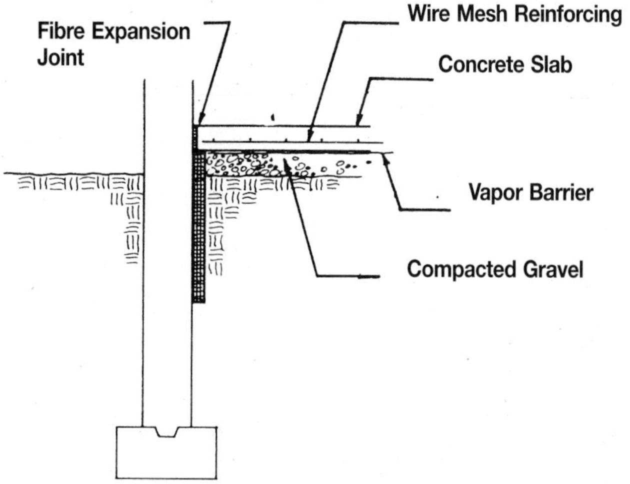


Reinforced Slab on Grade

A Slab on Grade system includes fine grading; 6″ of compacted gravel; vapor barrier; 3500 p.s.i. concrete; bituminous fiber expansion joint; all necessary edge forms
4 uses; steel trowel finish; and sprayed on membrane curing compound. Wire mesh reinforcing used in all reinforced slabs.

Non-industrial slabs are for foot traffic only with negligible abrasion. Light industrial slabs are for pneumatic wheels and light abrasion. Industrial slabs are for solid rubber wheels and moderate abrasion. Heavy industrial slabs are for steel wheels and severe abrasion.

| A1030 120 | Plain & Reinforced | COST PER S.F. | | |
|---|---|---|---|---|
| | | MAT. | INST. | TOTAL |
| 2220 | Slab on grade, 4″ thick, non industrial, non reinforced | 3.05 | 3.44 | 6.49 |
| 2240 | Reinforced | 3.42 | 3.80 | 7.22 |
| 2260 | Light industrial, non reinforced | 3.95 | 4.20 | 8.15 |
| 2280 | Reinforced | 4.37 | 4.64 | 9.01 |
| 2300 | Industrial, non reinforced | 4.84 | 8.65 | 13.49 |
| 2320 | Reinforced | 5.25 | 9.10 | 14.35 |
| 3340 | 5″ thick, non industrial, non reinforced | 3.57 | 3.53 | 7.10 |
| 3360 | Reinforced | 3.98 | 3.97 | 7.95 |
| 3380 | Light industrial, non reinforced | 4.49 | 4.29 | 8.78 |
| 3400 | Reinforced | 4.90 | 4.73 | 9.63 |
| 3420 | Heavy industrial, non reinforced | 6.35 | 10.30 | 16.65 |
| 3440 | Reinforced | 6.90 | 10.80 | 17.70 |
| 4460 | 6″ thick, non industrial, non reinforced | 4.26 | 3.46 | 7.72 |
| 4480 | Reinforced | 5.10 | 4.06 | 9.16 |
| 4500 | Light industrial, non reinforced | 5.20 | 4.22 | 9.42 |
| 4520 | Reinforced | 6.40 | 4.70 | 11.10 |
| 4540 | Heavy industrial, non reinforced | 7.10 | 10.40 | 17.50 |
| 4560 | Reinforced | 7.90 | 11 | 18.90 |
| 5580 | 7″ thick, non industrial, non reinforced | 4.81 | 3.57 | 8.38 |
| 5600 | Reinforced | 5.75 | 4.21 | 9.96 |
| 5620 | Light industrial, non reinforced | 5.75 | 4.33 | 10.08 |
| 5640 | Reinforced | 6.70 | 4.97 | 11.67 |
| 5660 | Heavy industrial, non reinforced | 7.65 | 10.25 | 17.90 |
| 5680 | Reinforced | 8.45 | 10.85 | 19.30 |
| 6700 | 8″ thick, non industrial, non reinforced | 5.35 | 3.64 | 8.99 |
| 6740 | Light industrial, non reinforced | 6.30 | 4.40 | 10.70 |
| 6760 | Reinforced | 7.10 | 4.93 | 12.03 |
| 6780 | Heavy industrial, non reinforced | 8.20 | 10.40 | 18.60 |
| 6800 | Reinforced | 9.30 | 10.95 | 20.25 |

## A2010 Basement Excavation

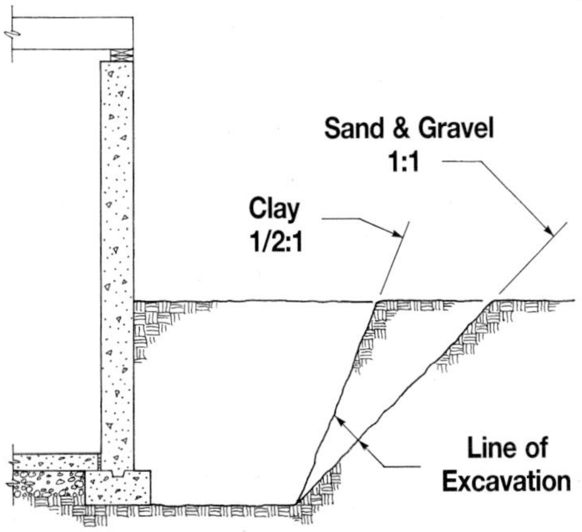


In general, the following items are accounted for in the table below.

Costs:
1) Excavation for building or other structure to depth and extent indicated.
2) Backfill compacted in place
3) Haul of excavated waste
4) Replacement of unsuitable backfill material with bank run gravel.

| A2010 110 | Building Excavation & Backfill | COST PER S.F. | | |
|---|---|---|---|---|
| | | MAT. | INST. | TOTAL |
| 2220 | Excav & fill, 1000 S.F., 4′ sand, gravel, or common earth, on site storage | | 1.25 | 1.25 |
| 2240 | Off site storage | | 1.91 | 1.91 |
| 2260 | Clay excavation, bank run gravel borrow for backfill | 5 | 2.93 | 7.93 |
| 2280 | 8′ deep, sand, gravel, or common earth, on site storage | | 7.60 | 7.60 |
| 2300 | Off site storage | | 17.15 | 17.15 |
| 2320 | Clay excavation, bank run gravel borrow for backfill | 20.50 | 13.75 | 34.25 |
| 2340 | 16′ deep, sand, gravel, or common earth, on site storage | | 20.50 | 20.50 |
| 2350 | Off site storage | | 42 | 42 |
| 2360 | Clay excavation, bank run gravel borrow for backfill | 56 | 35.50 | 91.50 |
| 3380 | 4000 S.F., 4′ deep, sand, gravel, or common earth, on site storage | | .66 | .66 |
| 3400 | Off site storage | | 1.35 | 1.35 |
| 3420 | Clay excavation, bank run gravel borrow for backfill | 2.55 | 1.49 | 4.04 |
| 3440 | 8′ deep, sand, gravel, or common earth, on site storage | | 5.40 | 5.40 |
| 3460 | Off site storage | | 9.65 | 9.65 |
| 3480 | Clay excavation, bank run gravel borrow for backfill | 9.25 | 8.30 | 17.55 |
| 3500 | 16′ deep, sand, gravel, or common earth, on site storage | | 12.90 | 12.90 |
| 3520 | Off site storage | | 26 | 26 |
| 3540 | Clay, excavation, bank run gravel borrow for backfill | 25 | 19.65 | 44.65 |
| 4560 | 10,000 S.F., 4′ deep, sand, gravel, or common earth, on site storage | | .38 | .38 |
| 4580 | Off site storage | | .80 | .80 |
| 4600 | Clay excavation, bank run gravel borrow for backfill | 1.55 | .91 | 2.46 |
| 4620 | 8′ deep, sand, gravel, or common earth, on site storage | | 4.71 | 4.71 |
| 4640 | Off site storage | | 7.25 | 7.25 |
| 4660 | Clay excavation, bank run gravel borrow for backfill | 5.60 | 6.45 | 12.05 |
| 4680 | 16′ deep, sand, gravel, or common earth, on site storage | | 10.60 | 10.60 |
| 4700 | Off site storage | | 18.35 | 18.35 |
| 4720 | Clay excavation, bank run gravel borrow for backfill | 14.85 | 14.75 | 29.60 |
| 5740 | 30,000 S.F., 4′ deep, sand, gravel, or common earth, on site storage | | .22 | .22 |
| 5760 | Off site storage | | .47 | .47 |
| 5780 | Clay excavation, bank run gravel borrow for backfill | .90 | .53 | 1.43 |
| 5860 | 16′ deep, sand, gravel, or common earth, on site storage | | 9.15 | 9.15 |
| 5880 | Off site storage | | 13.35 | 13.35 |
| 5900 | Clay excavation, bank run gravel borrow for backfill | 8.25 | 11.45 | 19.70 |
| 6910 | 100,000 S.F., 4′ deep, sand, gravel, or common earth, on site storage | | .12 | .12 |
| 6940 | 8′ deep, sand, gravel, or common earth, on site storage | | 3.98 | 3.98 |
| 6970 | 16′ deep, sand, gravel, or common earth, on site storage | | 8.35 | 8.35 |
| 6980 | Off site storage | | 10.55 | 10.55 |
| 6990 | Clay excavation, bank run gravel borrow for backfill | 4.45 | 9.55 | 14 |

## A2020 Basement Walls

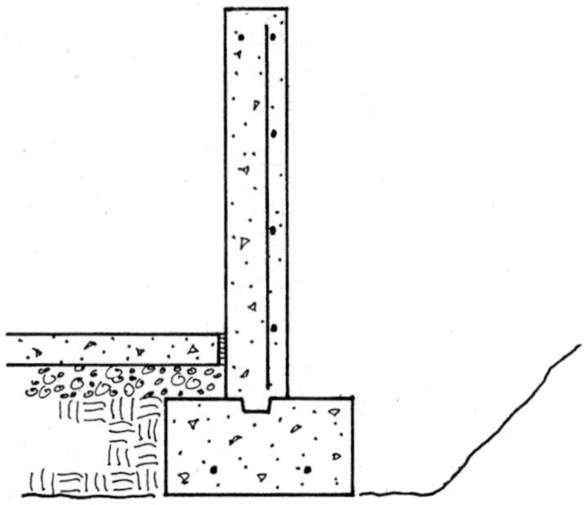

The Foundation Bearing Wall System includes: forms up to 16′ high (four uses); 3,000 p.s.i. concrete placed and vibrated; and form removal with breaking form ties and patching walls. The wall systems list walls from 6″ to 16″ thick and are designed with minimum reinforcement.

Excavation and backfill are not included.

Please see the reference section for further design and cost information.

### A2020 110 Walls, Cast in Place

| | WALL HEIGHT (FT.) | PLACING METHOD | CONCRETE (C.Y. per L.F.) | REINFORCING (LBS. per L.F.) | WALL THICKNESS (IN.) | COST PER L.F. MAT. | INST. | TOTAL |
|---|---|---|---|---|---|---|---|---|
| 5000 | 8′ | direct chute | .148 | 6.6 | 6 | 47.50 | 128 | 175.50 |
| 5020 | | | .199 | 9.6 | 8 | 58.50 | 135 | 193.50 |
| 5040 | | | .250 | 12 | 10 | 69 | 134 | 203 |
| 5061 | | | .296 | 14.39 | 12 | 79 | 137 | 216 |
| 6020 | 10′ | direct chute | .248 | 12 | 8 | 73 | 164 | 237 |
| 6040 | | | .307 | 14.99 | 10 | 85.50 | 167 | 252.50 |
| 6061 | | | .370 | 17.99 | 12 | 98.50 | 171 | 269.50 |
| 7220 | 12′ | pumped | .298 | 14.39 | 8 | 88 | 203 | 291 |
| 7240 | | | .369 | 17.99 | 10 | 103 | 207 | 310 |
| 7260 | | | .444 | 21.59 | 12 | 118 | 213 | 331 |
| 9220 | 16′ | pumped | .397 | 19.19 | 8 | 117 | 270 | 387 |
| 9240 | | | .492 | 23.99 | 10 | 137 | 276 | 413 |
| 9260 | | | .593 | 28.79 | 12 | 158 | 284 | 442 |

## B1010 Floor Construction

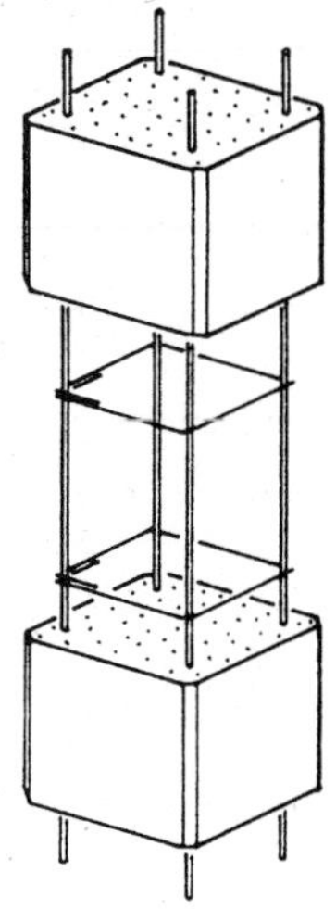

**General:** It is desirable for purposes of consistency and simplicity to maintain constant column sizes throughout building height. To do this, concrete strength may be varied (higher strength concrete at lower stories and lower strength concrete at upper stories), as well as varying the amount of reinforcing.

The table provides probably minimum column sizes with related costs and weight per lineal foot of story height.

### B1010 203 — C.I.P. Column, Square Tied

| | LOAD (KIPS) | STORY HEIGHT (FT.) | COLUMN SIZE (IN.) | COLUMN WEIGHT (P.L.F.) | CONCRETE STRENGTH (PSI) | COST PER V.L.F. | | |
|---|---|---|---|---|---|---|---|---|
| | | | | | | MAT. | INST. | TOTAL |
| 0640 | 100 | 10 | 10 | 96 | 4000 | 17.25 | 59 | 76.25 |
| 0680 | | 12 | 10 | 97 | 4000 | 17.55 | 59.50 | 77.05 |
| 0700 | | 14 | 12 | 142 | 4000 | 23 | 72 | 95 |
| 0840 | 200 | 10 | 12 | 140 | 4000 | 25 | 74.50 | 99.50 |
| 0860 | | 12 | 12 | 142 | 4000 | 25.50 | 75 | 100.50 |
| 0900 | | 14 | 14 | 196 | 4000 | 30 | 83.50 | 113.50 |
| 0920 | 300 | 10 | 14 | 192 | 4000 | 31.50 | 85.50 | 117 |
| 0960 | | 12 | 14 | 194 | 4000 | 32 | 86.50 | 118.50 |
| 0980 | | 14 | 16 | 253 | 4000 | 37 | 95 | 132 |
| 1020 | 400 | 10 | 16 | 248 | 4000 | 39.50 | 98 | 137.50 |
| 1060 | | 12 | 16 | 251 | 4000 | 40 | 99 | 139 |
| 1080 | | 14 | 16 | 253 | 4000 | 41 | 99.50 | 140.50 |
| 1200 | 500 | 10 | 18 | 315 | 4000 | 47 | 109 | 156 |
| 1250 | | 12 | 20 | 394 | 4000 | 56.50 | 124 | 180.50 |
| 1300 | | 14 | 20 | 397 | 4000 | 57.50 | 125 | 182.50 |
| 1350 | 600 | 10 | 20 | 388 | 4000 | 59 | 127 | 186 |
| 1400 | | 12 | 20 | 394 | 4000 | 60 | 128 | 188 |
| 1600 | | 14 | 20 | 397 | 4000 | 61 | 130 | 191 |
| 3400 | 900 | 10 | 24 | 560 | 4000 | 79 | 158 | 237 |
| 3800 | | 12 | 24 | 567 | 4000 | 80.50 | 160 | 240.50 |
| 4000 | | 14 | 24 | 571 | 4000 | 82 | 162 | 244 |
| 7300 | 300 | 10 | 14 | 192 | 6000 | 32 | 85 | 117 |
| 7500 | | 12 | 14 | 194 | 6000 | 32.50 | 85.50 | 118 |
| 7600 | | 14 | 14 | 196 | 6000 | 33 | 86.50 | 119.50 |
| 8000 | 500 | 10 | 16 | 248 | 6000 | 40.50 | 98 | 138.50 |
| 8050 | | 12 | 16 | 251 | 6000 | 41 | 99 | 140 |
| 8100 | | 14 | 16 | 253 | 6000 | 42 | 99.50 | 141.50 |
| 8200 | 600 | 10 | 18 | 315 | 6000 | 46.50 | 110 | 156.50 |
| 8300 | | 12 | 18 | 319 | 6000 | 47.50 | 111 | 158.50 |
| 8400 | | 14 | 18 | 321 | 6000 | 48.50 | 112 | 160.50 |
| 8800 | 800 | 10 | 20 | 388 | 6000 | 58 | 124 | 182 |
| 8900 | | 12 | 20 | 394 | 6000 | 59 | 125 | 184 |
| 9000 | | 14 | 20 | 397 | 6000 | 60.50 | 127 | 187.50 |

## B1010 Floor Construction

### B1010 203 C.I.P. Column, Square Tied

| | LOAD (KIPS) | STORY HEIGHT (FT.) | COLUMN SIZE (IN.) | COLUMN WEIGHT (P.L.F.) | CONCRETE STRENGTH (PSI) | COST PER V.L.F. | | |
|---|---|---|---|---|---|---|---|---|
| | | | | | | MAT. | INST. | TOTAL |
| 9100 | 900 | 10 | 20 | 388 | 6000 | 62.50 | 130 | 192.50 |
| 9300 | | 12 | 20 | 394 | 6000 | 63.50 | 131 | 194.50 |
| 9600 | | 14 | 20 | 397 | 6000 | 65 | 132 | 197 |

### B1010 204 C.I.P. Column, Square Tied-Minimum Reinforcing

| | LOAD (KIPS) | STORY HEIGHT (FT.) | COLUMN SIZE (IN.) | COLUMN WEIGHT (P.L.F.) | CONCRETE STRENGTH (PSI) | COST PER V.L.F. | | |
|---|---|---|---|---|---|---|---|---|
| | | | | | | MAT. | INST. | TOTAL |
| 9913 | 150 | 10-14 | 12 | 135 | 4000 | 21 | 63.50 | 84.50 |
| 9918 | 300 | 10-14 | 16 | 240 | 4000 | 33.50 | 83 | 116.50 |
| 9924 | 500 | 10-14 | 20 | 375 | 4000 | 51 | 117 | 168 |
| 9930 | 700 | 10-14 | 24 | 540 | 4000 | 69.50 | 145 | 214.50 |
| 9936 | 1000 | 10-14 | 28 | 740 | 4000 | 90.50 | 176 | 266.50 |
| 9942 | 1400 | 10-14 | 32 | 965 | 4000 | 106 | 199 | 305 |
| 9948 | 1800 | 10-14 | 36 | 1220 | 4000 | 132 | 232 | 364 |

## B1010 Floor Construction

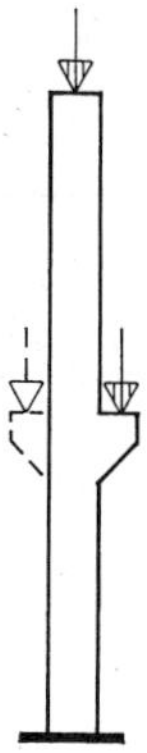

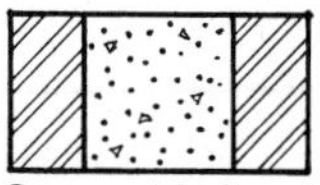

Concentric Load

Eccentric Load

**General:** Data presented here is for plant produced members transported 50 miles to 100 miles to the site and erected.

**Design and pricing assumptions:**
Normal wt. concrete, f'c = 5 KSI

Main reinforcement, fy = 60 KSI
Ties, fy = 40 KSI

Minimum design eccentricity, 0.1t.

Concrete encased structural steel haunches are assumed where practical; otherwise galvanized rebar haunches are assumed.

Base plates are integral with columns.

Foundation anchor bolts, nuts and washers are included in price.

### B1010 206 Tied, Concentric Loaded Precast Concrete Columns

| | LOAD (KIPS) | STORY HEIGHT (FT.) | COLUMN SIZE (IN.) | COLUMN WEIGHT (P.L.F.) | LOAD LEVELS | COST PER V.L.F. | | |
|---|---|---|---|---|---|---|---|---|
| | | | | | | MAT. | INST. | TOTAL |
| 0560 | 100 | 10 | 12x12 | 164 | 2 | 271 | 16.85 | 287.85 |
| 0570 | | 12 | 12x12 | 162 | 2 | 264 | 14.05 | 278.05 |
| 0580 | | 14 | 12x12 | 161 | 2 | 264 | 13.85 | 277.85 |
| 0590 | 150 | 10 | 12x12 | 166 | 3 | 264 | 13.70 | 277.70 |
| 0600 | | 12 | 12x12 | 169 | 3 | 263 | 12.25 | 275.25 |
| 0610 | | 14 | 12x12 | 162 | 3 | 263 | 12.10 | 275.10 |
| 0620 | 200 | 10 | 12x12 | 168 | 4 | 264 | 14.60 | 278.60 |
| 0630 | | 12 | 12x12 | 170 | 4 | 264 | 13.20 | 277.20 |
| 0640 | | 14 | 12x12 | 220 | 4 | 264 | 13.10 | 277.10 |

### B1010 207 Tied, Eccentric Loaded Precast Concrete Columns

| | LOAD (KIPS) | STORY HEIGHT (FT.) | COLUMN SIZE (IN.) | COLUMN WEIGHT (P.L.F.) | LOAD LEVELS | COST PER V.L.F. | | |
|---|---|---|---|---|---|---|---|---|
| | | | | | | MAT. | INST. | TOTAL |
| 1130 | 100 | 10 | 12x12 | 161 | 2 | 259 | 16.85 | 275.85 |
| 1140 | | 12 | 12x12 | 159 | 2 | 259 | 14.05 | 273.05 |
| 1150 | | 14 | 12x12 | 159 | 2 | 258 | 13.85 | 271.85 |
| 1390 | 600 | 10 | 18x18 | 385 | 4 | 380 | 14.60 | 394.60 |
| 1400 | | 12 | 18x18 | 380 | 4 | 380 | 13.20 | 393.20 |
| 1410 | | 14 | 18x18 | 375 | 4 | 380 | 13.10 | 393.10 |
| 1480 | 800 | 10 | 20x20 | 490 | 4 | 340 | 14.60 | 354.60 |
| 1490 | | 12 | 20x20 | 480 | 4 | 340 | 13.20 | 353.20 |
| 1500 | | 14 | 20x20 | 475 | 4 | 340 | 13.10 | 353.10 |

## B1010 Floor Construction

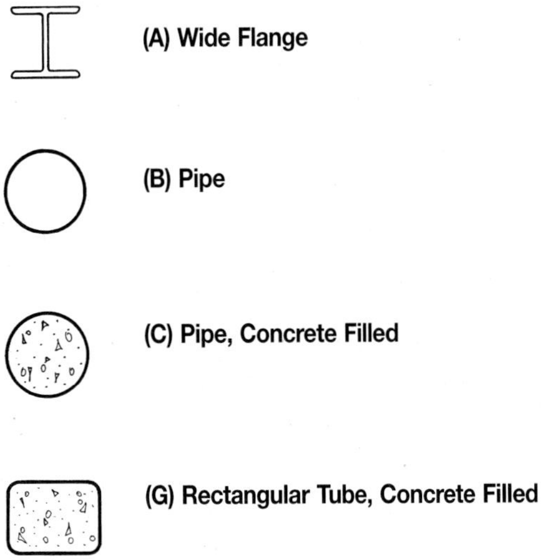


| B1010 208 | Steel Columns | | | | | | | |
|---|---|---|---|---|---|---|---|---|
| | LOAD (KIPS) | UNSUPPORTED HEIGHT (FT.) | WEIGHT (P.L.F.) | SIZE (IN.) | TYPE | COST PER V.L.F. | | |
| | | | | | | MAT. | INST. | TOTAL |
| 1000 | 25 | 10 | 13 | 4 | A | 28.50 | 14 | 42.50 |
| 1020 | | | 7.58 | 3 | B | 16.60 | 14 | 30.60 |
| 1040 | | | 15 | 3-1/2 | C | 20.50 | 14 | 34.50 |
| 1120 | | | 20 | 4x3 | G | 23.50 | 14 | 37.50 |
| 1200 | | 16 | 16 | 5 | A | 32.50 | 10.50 | 43 |
| 1220 | | | 10.79 | 4 | B | 22 | 10.50 | 32.50 |
| 1240 | | | 36 | 5-1/2 | C | 30.50 | 10.50 | 41 |
| 1320 | | | 64 | 8x6 | G | 47.50 | 10.50 | 58 |
| 1600 | 50 | 10 | 16 | 5 | A | 35 | 14 | 49 |
| 1620 | | | 14.62 | 5 | B | 32 | 14 | 46 |
| 1640 | | | 24 | 4-1/2 | C | 24 | 14 | 38 |
| 1720 | | | 28 | 6x3 | G | 31 | 14 | 45 |
| 1800 | | 16 | 24 | 8 | A | 48.50 | 10.50 | 59 |
| 1840 | | | 36 | 5-1/2 | C | 30.50 | 10.50 | 41 |
| 1920 | | | 64 | 8x6 | G | 47.50 | 10.50 | 58 |
| 2000 | | 20 | 28 | 8 | A | 53.50 | 10.50 | 64 |
| 2040 | | | 49 | 6-5/8 | C | 38 | 10.50 | 48.50 |
| 2120 | | | 64 | 8x6 | G | 45 | 10.50 | 55.50 |
| 2200 | 75 | 10 | 20 | 6 | A | 44 | 14 | 58 |
| 2240 | | | 36 | 4-1/2 | C | 60.50 | 14 | 74.50 |
| 2320 | | | 35 | 6x4 | G | 35 | 14 | 49 |
| 2400 | | 16 | 31 | 8 | A | 63 | 10.50 | 73.50 |
| 2440 | | | 49 | 6-5/8 | C | 40 | 10.50 | 50.50 |
| 2520 | | | 64 | 8x6 | G | 47.50 | 10.50 | 58 |
| 2600 | | 20 | 31 | 8 | A | 59.50 | 10.50 | 70 |
| 2640 | | | 81 | 8-5/8 | C | 57 | 10.50 | 67.50 |
| 2720 | | | 64 | 8x6 | G | 45 | 10.50 | 55.50 |
| 2800 | 100 | 10 | 24 | 8 | A | 52.50 | 14 | 66.50 |
| 2840 | | | 35 | 4-1/2 | C | 60.50 | 14 | 74.50 |
| 2920 | | | 46 | 8x4 | G | 43 | 14 | 57 |

## B1010 Floor Construction

### B1010 208 — Steel Columns

| | LOAD (KIPS) | UNSUPPORTED HEIGHT (FT.) | WEIGHT (P.L.F.) | SIZE (IN.) | TYPE | COST PER V.L.F. MAT. | INST. | TOTAL |
|---|---|---|---|---|---|---|---|---|
| 3000 | 100 | 16 | 31 | 8 | A | 63 | 10.50 | 73.50 |
| 3040 | | | 56 | 6-5/8 | C | 59 | 10.50 | 69.50 |
| 3120 | | | 64 | 8x6 | G | 47.50 | 10.50 | 58 |
| 3200 | | 20 | 40 | 8 | A | 76.50 | 10.50 | 87 |
| 3240 | | | 81 | 8-5/8 | C | 57 | 10.50 | 67.50 |
| 3320 | | | 70 | 8x6 | G | 64.50 | 10.50 | 75 |
| 3400 | 125 | 10 | 31 | 8 | A | 68 | 14 | 82 |
| 3440 | | | 81 | 8 | C | 65 | 14 | 79 |
| 3520 | | | 64 | 8x6 | G | 51 | 14 | 65 |
| 3600 | 125 | 16 | 40 | 8 | A | 81 | 10.50 | 91.50 |
| 3640 | | | 81 | 8 | C | 60.50 | 10.50 | 71 |
| 3720 | | | 64 | 8x6 | G | 47.50 | 10.50 | 58 |
| 3800 | | 20 | 48 | 8 | A | 92 | 10.50 | 102.50 |
| 3840 | | | 81 | 8 | C | 57 | 10.50 | 67.50 |
| 3920 | | | 60 | 8x6 | G | 64.50 | 10.50 | 75 |
| 4000 | 150 | 10 | 35 | 8 | A | 76.50 | 14 | 90.50 |
| 4040 | | | 81 | 8-5/8 | C | 65 | 14 | 79 |
| 4120 | | | 64 | 8x6 | G | 51 | 14 | 65 |
| 4200 | | 16 | 45 | 10 | A | 91 | 10.50 | 101.50 |
| 4240 | | | 81 | 8-5/8 | C | 60.50 | 10.50 | 71 |
| 4320 | | | 70 | 8x6 | G | 68 | 10.50 | 78.50 |
| 4400 | | 20 | 49 | 10 | A | 94 | 10.50 | 104.50 |
| 4440 | | | 123 | 10-3/4 | C | 81.50 | 10.50 | 92 |
| 4520 | | | 86 | 10x6 | G | 63.50 | 10.50 | 74 |
| 4600 | 200 | 10 | 45 | 10 | A | 98.50 | 14 | 112.50 |
| 4640 | | | 81 | 8-5/8 | C | 65 | 14 | 79 |
| 4720 | | | 70 | 8x6 | G | 73 | 14 | 87 |
| 4800 | | 16 | 49 | 10 | A | 99.50 | 10.50 | 110 |
| 4840 | | | 123 | 10-3/4 | C | 86 | 10.50 | 96.50 |
| 4920 | | | 85 | 10x6 | G | 79 | 10.50 | 89.50 |
| 5200 | 300 | 10 | 61 | 14 | A | 134 | 14 | 148 |
| 5240 | | | 169 | 12-3/4 | C | 114 | 14 | 128 |
| 5320 | | | 86 | 10x6 | G | 109 | 14 | 123 |
| 5400 | | 16 | 72 | 12 | A | 146 | 10.50 | 156.50 |
| 5440 | | | 169 | 12-3/4 | C | 106 | 10.50 | 116.50 |
| 5600 | | 20 | 79 | 12 | A | 152 | 10.50 | 162.50 |
| 5640 | | | 169 | 12-3/4 | C | 101 | 10.50 | 111.50 |
| 5800 | 400 | 10 | 79 | 12 | A | 173 | 14 | 187 |
| 5840 | | | 178 | 12-3/4 | C | 149 | 14 | 163 |
| 6000 | | 16 | 87 | 12 | A | 176 | 10.50 | 186.50 |
| 6040 | | | 178 | 12-3/4 | C | 138 | 10.50 | 148.50 |
| 6400 | 500 | 10 | 99 | 14 | A | 217 | 14 | 231 |
| 6600 | | 16 | 109 | 14 | A | 221 | 10.50 | 231.50 |
| 6800 | | 20 | 120 | 12 | A | 230 | 10.50 | 240.50 |
| 7000 | 600 | 10 | 120 | 12 | A | 263 | 14 | 277 |
| 7200 | | 16 | 132 | 14 | A | 268 | 10.50 | 278.50 |
| 7400 | | 20 | 132 | 14 | A | 253 | 10.50 | 263.50 |
| 7600 | 700 | 10 | 136 | 12 | A | 298 | 14 | 312 |
| 7800 | | 16 | 145 | 14 | A | 294 | 10.50 | 304.50 |
| 8000 | | 20 | 145 | 14 | A | 278 | 10.50 | 288.50 |
| 8200 | 800 | 10 | 145 | 14 | A | 320 | 14 | 334 |
| 8300 | | 16 | 159 | 14 | A | 320 | 10.50 | 330.50 |
| 8400 | | 20 | 176 | 14 | A | 340 | 10.50 | 350.50 |

## B1010 Floor Construction

### B1010 208 Steel Columns

| | LOAD (KIPS) | UNSUPPORTED HEIGHT (FT.) | WEIGHT (P.L.F.) | SIZE (IN.) | TYPE | COST PER V.L.F. | | |
|---|---|---|---|---|---|---|---|---|
| | | | | | | MAT. | INST. | TOTAL |
| 8800 | 900 | 10 | 159 | 14 | A | 350 | 14 | 364 |
| 8900 | | 16 | 176 | 14 | A | 355 | 10.50 | 365.50 |
| 9000 | | 20 | 193 | 14 | A | 370 | 10.50 | 380.50 |
| 9100 | 1000 | 10 | 176 | 14 | A | 385 | 14 | 399 |
| 9200 | | 16 | 193 | 14 | A | 390 | 10.50 | 400.50 |
| 9300 | | 20 | 211 | 14 | A | 405 | 10.50 | 415.50 |

## B1010 Floor Construction

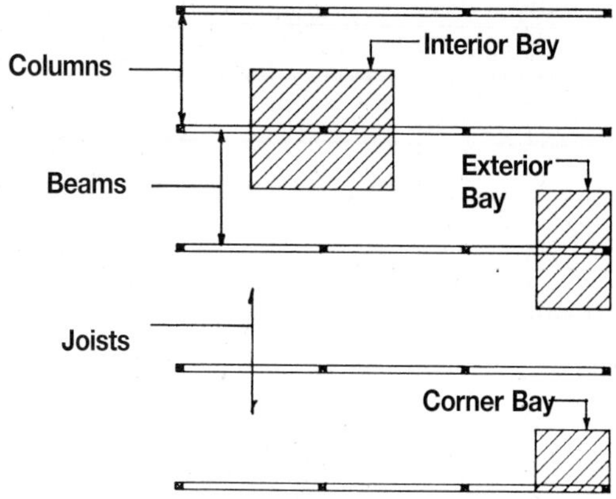


**Description:** Table below lists costs per S.F. of bay size for wood columns of various sizes and unsupported heights and the maximum allowable total load per S.F. per bay size.

### B1010 210 Wood Columns

| | NOMINAL COLUMN SIZE (IN.) | BAY SIZE (FT.) | UNSUPPORTED HEIGHT (FT.) | MATERIAL (BF per M.S.F.) | TOTAL LOAD (P.S.F.) | COST PER S.F. | | |
|---|---|---|---|---|---|---|---|---|
| | | | | | | MAT. | INST. | TOTAL |
| 1000 | 4 x 4 | 10 x 8 | 8 | 133 | 100 | .37 | .31 | .68 |
| 1050 | | | 10 | 167 | 60 | .46 | .39 | .85 |
| 1200 | | 10 x 10 | 8 | 106 | 80 | .29 | .25 | .54 |
| 1250 | | | 10 | 133 | 50 | .37 | .31 | .68 |
| 1400 | | 10 x 15 | 8 | 71 | 50 | .20 | .17 | .37 |
| 1450 | | | 10 | 88 | 30 | .24 | .20 | .44 |
| 1600 | | 15 x 15 | 8 | 47 | 30 | .13 | .11 | .24 |
| 1650 | | | 10 | 59 | 15 | .16 | .14 | .30 |
| 2000 | 6 x 6 | 10 x 15 | 8 | 160 | 230 | .46 | .34 | .80 |
| 2050 | | | 10 | 200 | 210 | .57 | .43 | 1 |
| 2200 | | 15 x 15 | 8 | 107 | 150 | .31 | .23 | .54 |
| 2250 | | | 10 | 133 | 140 | .38 | .29 | .67 |
| 2400 | | 15 x 20 | 8 | 80 | 110 | .23 | .17 | .40 |
| 2450 | | | 10 | 100 | 100 | .29 | .22 | .51 |
| 2500 | | | 12 | 120 | 70 | .34 | .26 | .60 |
| 2600 | | 20 x 20 | 8 | 60 | 80 | .17 | .13 | .30 |
| 2650 | | | 10 | 75 | 70 | .21 | .16 | .37 |
| 2800 | | 20 x 25 | 8 | 48 | 60 | .14 | .10 | .24 |
| 2850 | | | 10 | 60 | 50 | .17 | .13 | .30 |
| 3400 | 8 x 8 | 20 x 20 | 8 | 107 | 160 | .58 | .21 | .79 |
| 3450 | | | 10 | 133 | 160 | .71 | .27 | .98 |
| 3600 | | 20 x 25 | 8 | 85 | 130 | .23 | .20 | .43 |
| 3650 | | | 10 | 107 | 130 | .29 | .25 | .54 |
| 3800 | | 25 x 25 | 8 | 68 | 100 | .16 | .13 | .29 |
| 3850 | | | 10 | 85 | 100 | .21 | .16 | .37 |
| 4200 | 10 x 10 | 20 x 25 | 8 | 133 | 210 | .32 | .25 | .57 |
| 4250 | | | 10 | 167 | 210 | .41 | .31 | .72 |
| 4400 | | 25 x 25 | 8 | 107 | 160 | .26 | .20 | .46 |
| 4450 | | | 10 | 133 | 160 | .32 | .25 | .57 |
| 4700 | 12 x 12 | 20 x 25 | 8 | 192 | 310 | .58 | .34 | .92 |
| 4750 | | | 10 | 240 | 310 | .73 | .42 | 1.15 |
| 4900 | | 25 x 25 | 8 | 154 | 240 | .47 | .27 | .74 |
| 4950 | | | 10 | 192 | 240 | .58 | .34 | .92 |

## B1010 Floor Construction

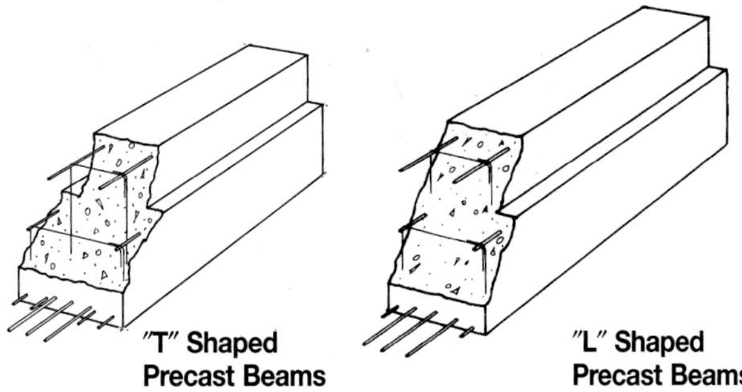


### B1010 214 — "T" Shaped Precast Beams

| | SPAN (FT.) | SUPERIMPOSED LOAD (K.L.F.) | SIZE W X D (IN.) | BEAM WEIGHT (P.L.F.) | TOTAL LOAD (K.L.F.) | COST PER L.F. MAT. | INST. | TOTAL |
|---|---|---|---|---|---|---|---|---|
| 2300 | 15 | 2.8 | 12x16 | 260 | 3.06 | 296 | 24.50 | 320.50 |
| 2500 | | 8.37 | 12x28 | 515 | 8.89 | 370 | 26.50 | 396.50 |
| 8900 | 45 | 3.34 | 12x60 | 1165 | 4.51 | 570 | 15.70 | 585.70 |
| 9900 | | 6.5 | 24x60 | 1915 | 8.42 | 530 | 22 | 552 |

### B1010 215 — "L" Shaped Precast Beams

| | SPAN (FT.) | SUPERIMPOSED LOAD (K.L.F.) | SIZE W X D (IN.) | BEAM WEIGHT (P.L.F.) | TOTAL LOAD (K.L.F.) | COST PER L.F. MAT. | INST. | TOTAL |
|---|---|---|---|---|---|---|---|---|
| 2250 | 15 | 2.58 | 12x16 | 230 | 2.81 | 279 | 24.50 | 303.50 |
| 2400 | | 5.92 | 12x24 | 370 | 6.29 | 294 | 24.50 | 318.50 |
| 4000 | 25 | 2.64 | 12x28 | 435 | 3.08 | 310 | 15.85 | 325.85 |
| 4450 | | 6.44 | 18x36 | 790 | 7.23 | 380 | 18.85 | 398.85 |
| 5300 | 30 | 2.80 | 12x36 | 565 | 3.37 | 355 | 14.30 | 369.30 |
| 6400 | | 8.66 | 24x44 | 1245 | 9.90 | 455 | 20.50 | 475.50 |

## B1010 Floor Construction

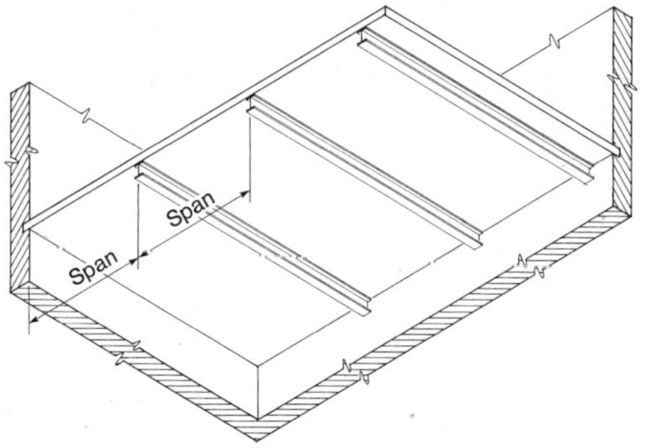


**Cast in Place Floor Slab, One Way**
**General:** Solid concrete slabs of uniform depth reinforced for flexure in one direction and for temperature and shrinkage in the other direction.

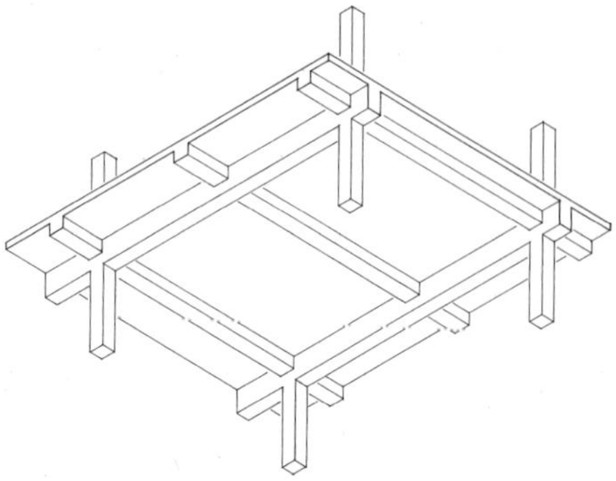

**Cast in Place Beam & Slab, One Way**
**General:** Solid concrete one way slab cast monolithically with reinforced concrete beams and girders.

### B1010 217 Cast in Place Slabs, One Way

| | SLAB DESIGN & SPAN (FT.) | SUPERIMPOSED LOAD (P.S.F.) | THICKNESS (IN.) | TOTAL LOAD (P.S.F.) | | COST PER S.F. | | |
|---|---|---|---|---|---|---|---|---|
| | | | | | | MAT. | INST. | TOTAL |
| 2500 | Single 8 | 40 | 4 | 90 | | 6.35 | 10.05 | 16.40 |
| 2600 | | 75 | 4 | 125 | | 6.45 | 10.95 | 17.40 |
| 2700 | | 125 | 4-1/2 | 181 | | 6.75 | 11.05 | 17.80 |
| 2800 | | 200 | 5 | 262 | | 7.40 | 11.40 | 18.80 |
| 3000 | Single 10 | 40 | 4 | 90 | | 6.65 | 10.85 | 17.50 |
| 3100 | | 75 | 4 | 125 | | 6.65 | 10.85 | 17.50 |
| 3200 | | 125 | 5 | 188 | | 7.35 | 11.15 | 18.50 |
| 3300 | | 200 | 7-1/2 | 293 | | 9.80 | 12.50 | 22.30 |
| 3500 | Single 15 | 40 | 5-1/2 | 90 | | 7.85 | 11.05 | 18.90 |
| 3600 | | 75 | 6-1/2 | 156 | | 8.85 | 11.60 | 20.45 |
| 3700 | | 125 | 7-1/2 | 219 | | 9.55 | 11.85 | 21.40 |
| 3800 | | 200 | 8-1/2 | 306 | | 10.30 | 12.15 | 22.45 |
| 4000 | Single 20 | 40 | 7-1/2 | 115 | | 9.50 | 11.60 | 21.10 |
| 4100 | | 75 | 9 | 200 | | 10.25 | 11.60 | 21.85 |
| 4200 | | 125 | 10 | 250 | | 11.25 | 12.05 | 23.30 |
| 4300 | | 200 | 10 | 324 | | 12.05 | 12.55 | 24.60 |

### B1010 219 Cast in Place Beam & Slab, One Way

| | BAY SIZE (FT.) | SUPERIMPOSED LOAD (P.S.F.) | MINIMUM COL. SIZE (IN.) | SLAB THICKNESS (IN.) | TOTAL LOAD (P.S.F.) | COST PER S.F. | | |
|---|---|---|---|---|---|---|---|---|
| | | | | | | MAT. | INST. | TOTAL |
| 5000 | 20x25 | 40 | 12 | 5-1/2 | 121 | 8.65 | 13.85 | 22.50 |
| 5200 | | 125 | 16 | 5-1/2 | 215 | 10.10 | 15.90 | 26 |
| 5500 | 25x25 | 40 | 12 | 6 | 129 | 9.10 | 13.60 | 22.70 |
| 5700 | | 125 | 18 | 6 | 227 | 11.40 | 16.75 | 28.15 |
| 7500 | 30x35 | 40 | 16 | 8 | 158 | 11.20 | 15.40 | 26.60 |
| 7600 | | 75 | 18 | 8 | 196 | 11.90 | 15.90 | 27.80 |
| 7700 | | 125 | 22 | 8 | 254 | 13.25 | 17.60 | 30.85 |
| 7800 | | 200 | 26 | 8 | 332 | 14.30 | 18.20 | 32.50 |
| 8000 | 35x35 | 40 | 16 | 9 | 169 | 12.40 | 15.85 | 28.25 |
| 8200 | | 75 | 20 | 9 | 213 | 13.40 | 17.30 | 30.70 |
| 8400 | | 125 | 24 | 9 | 272 | 14.65 | 17.90 | 32.55 |
| 8600 | | 200 | 26 | 9 | 355 | 16 | 19.15 | 35.15 |

## B1010 Floor Construction

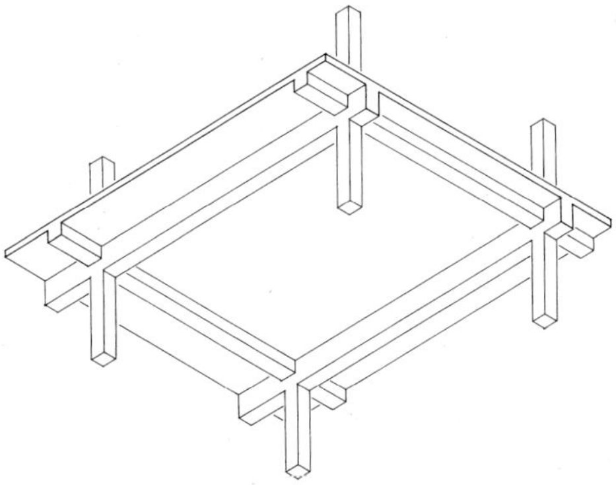

**General:** Solid concrete two way slab cast monolithically with reinforced concrete support beams and girders.

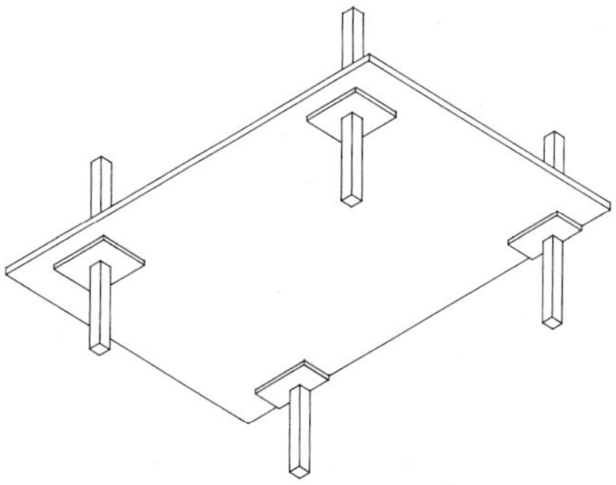

**General:** Flat Slab: Solid uniform depth concrete two way slabs with drop panels at columns and no column capitals.

### B1010 220 — Cast in Place Beam & Slab, Two Way

| | BAY SIZE (FT.) | SUPERIMPOSED LOAD (P.S.F.) | MINIMUM COL. SIZE (IN.) | SLAB THICKNESS (IN.) | TOTAL LOAD (P.S.F.) | COST PER S.F. | | |
|---|---|---|---|---|---|---|---|---|
| | | | | | | MAT. | INST. | TOTAL |
| 4000 | 20 x 25 | 40 | 12 | 7 | 141 | 9.90 | 14 | 23.90 |
| 4300 | | 75 | 14 | 7 | 181 | 11.20 | 15.30 | 26.50 |
| 4500 | | 125 | 16 | 7 | 236 | 11.40 | 15.70 | 27.10 |
| 5100 | 25 x 25 | 40 | 12 | 7-1/2 | 149 | 10.30 | 13.05 | 23.35 |
| 5200 | | 75 | 16 | 7-1/2 | 185 | 11.20 | 15.15 | 26.35 |
| 5300 | | 125 | 18 | 7-1/2 | 250 | 12.10 | 16.45 | 28.55 |
| 7600 | 30 x 35 | 40 | 16 | 10 | 188 | 13.45 | 16 | 29.45 |
| 7700 | | 75 | 18 | 10 | 225 | 14.20 | 16.60 | 30.80 |
| 8000 | | 125 | 22 | 10 | 282 | 15.70 | 17.85 | 33.55 |
| 8500 | 35 x 35 | 40 | 16 | 10-1/2 | 193 | 14.30 | 16.30 | 30.60 |
| 8600 | | 75 | 20 | 10-1/2 | 233 | 15 | 16.90 | 31.90 |
| 9000 | | 125 | 24 | 10-1/2 | 287 | 16.65 | 18.15 | 34.80 |

### B1010 222 — Cast in Place Flat Slab with Drop Panels

| | BAY SIZE (FT.) | SUPERIMPOSED LOAD (P.S.F.) | MINIMUM COL. SIZE (IN.) | SLAB & DROP (IN.) | TOTAL LOAD (P.S.F.) | COST PER S.F. | | |
|---|---|---|---|---|---|---|---|---|
| | | | | | | MAT. | INST. | TOTAL |
| 1960 | 20 x 20 | 40 | 12 | 7 - 3 | 132 | 9 | 11.15 | 20.15 |
| 1980 | | 75 | 16 | 7 - 4 | 168 | 9.50 | 11.40 | 20.90 |
| 2000 | | 125 | 18 | 7 - 6 | 221 | 10.45 | 11.85 | 22.30 |
| 3200 | 25 x 25 | 40 | 12 | 8-1/2 - 5-1/2 | 154 | 10.40 | 11.70 | 22.10 |
| 4000 | | 125 | 20 | 8-1/2 - 8-1/2 | 243 | 11.70 | 12.50 | 24.20 |
| 4400 | | 200 | 24 | 9 - 8-1/2 | 329 | 12.25 | 12.80 | 25.05 |
| 5000 | 25 x 30 | 40 | 14 | 9-1/2 - 7 | 168 | 11.30 | 12.10 | 23.40 |
| 5200 | | 75 | 18 | 9-1/2 - 7 | 203 | 12 | 12.55 | 24.55 |
| 5600 | | 125 | 22 | 9-1/2 - 8 | 256 | 12.50 | 12.85 | 25.35 |
| 6400 | 30 x 30 | 40 | 14 | 10-1/2 - 7-1/2 | 182 | 12.15 | 12.45 | 24.60 |
| 6600 | | 75 | 18 | 10-1/2 - 7-1/2 | 217 | 12.85 | 12.90 | 25.75 |
| 6800 | | 125 | 22 | 10-1/2 - 9 | 269 | 13.40 | 13.20 | 26.60 |
| 7400 | 30 x 35 | 40 | 16 | 11-1/2 - 9 | 196 | 13.15 | 12.90 | 26.05 |
| 7900 | | 75 | 20 | 11-1/2 - 9 | 231 | 13.95 | 13.40 | 27.35 |
| 8000 | | 125 | 24 | 11-1/2 - 11 | 284 | 14.50 | 13.75 | 28.25 |
| 9000 | 35 x 35 | 40 | 16 | 12 - 9 | 202 | 13.50 | 13 | 26.50 |
| 9400 | | 75 | 20 | 12 - 11 | 240 | 14.45 | 13.60 | 28.05 |
| 9600 | | 125 | 24 | 12 - 11 | 290 | 14.90 | 13.85 | 28.75 |

## B1010 Floor Construction

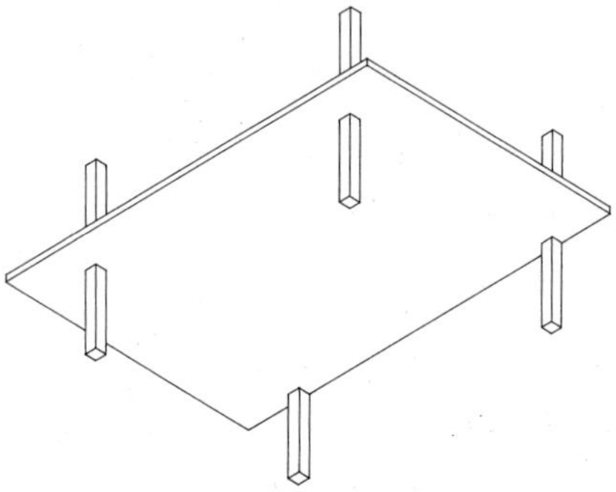

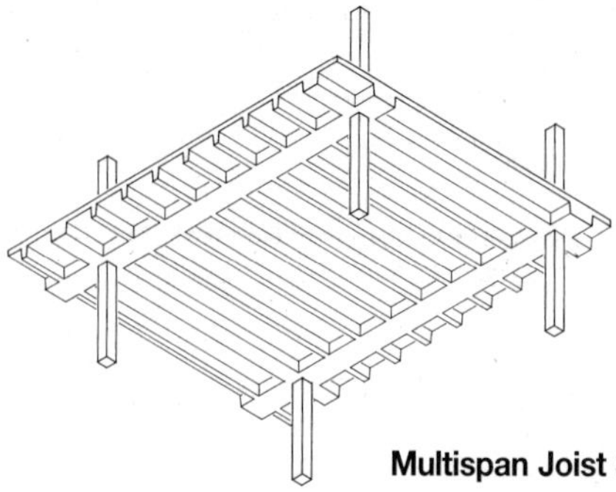

Multispan Joist Slab

**General:** Flat Plates: Solid uniform depth concrete two way slab without drops or interior beams. Primary design limit is shear at columns.

**General:** Combination of thin concrete slab and monolithic ribs at uniform spacing to reduce dead weight and increase rigidity.

### B1010 223 Cast in Place Flat Plate

| | BAY SIZE (FT.) | SUPERIMPOSED LOAD (P.S.F.) | MINIMUM COL. SIZE (IN.) | SLAB THICKNESS (IN.) | TOTAL LOAD (P.S.F.) | COST PER S.F. | | |
|---|---|---|---|---|---|---|---|---|
| | | | | | | MAT. | INST. | TOTAL |
| 3000 | 15 x 20 | 40 | 14 | 7 | 127 | 8.40 | 10.75 | 19.15 |
| 3400 | | 75 | 16 | 7-1/2 | 169 | 8.90 | 10.95 | 19.85 |
| 3600 | | 125 | 22 | 8-1/2 | 231 | 9.70 | 11.30 | 21 |
| 3800 | | 175 | 24 | 8-1/2 | 281 | 9.75 | 11.30 | 21.05 |
| 4200 | 20 x 20 | 40 | 16 | 7 | 127 | 8.40 | 10.75 | 19.15 |
| 4400 | | 75 | 20 | 7-1/2 | 175 | 8.95 | 10.95 | 19.90 |
| 4600 | | 125 | 24 | 8-1/2 | 231 | 9.70 | 11.20 | 20.90 |
| 5000 | | 175 | 24 | 8-1/2 | 281 | 9.80 | 11.30 | 21.10 |
| 5600 | 20 x 25 | 40 | 18 | 8-1/2 | 146 | 9.65 | 11.25 | 20.90 |
| 6000 | | 75 | 20 | 9 | 188 | 9.95 | 11.35 | 21.30 |
| 6400 | | 125 | 26 | 9-1/2 | 244 | 10.70 | 11.70 | 22.40 |
| 6600 | | 175 | 30 | 10 | 300 | 11.10 | 11.85 | 22.95 |
| 7000 | 25 x 25 | 40 | 20 | 9 | 152 | 9.95 | 11.35 | 21.30 |
| 7400 | | 75 | 24 | 9-1/2 | 194 | 10.50 | 11.60 | 22.10 |
| 7600 | | 125 | 30 | 10 | 250 | 11.15 | 11.85 | 23 |

### B1010 226 Cast in Place Multispan Joist Slab

| | BAY SIZE (FT.) | SUPERIMPOSED LOAD (P.S.F.) | MINIMUM COL. SIZE (IN.) | RIB DEPTH (IN.) | TOTAL LOAD (P.S.F.) | COST PER S.F. | | |
|---|---|---|---|---|---|---|---|---|
| | | | | | | MAT. | INST. | TOTAL |
| 2000 | 15 x 15 | 40 | 12 | 8 | 115 | 12.60 | 13.20 | 25.80 |
| 2100 | | 75 | 12 | 8 | 150 | 12.65 | 13.25 | 25.90 |
| 2200 | | 125 | 12 | 8 | 200 | 12.85 | 13.40 | 26.25 |
| 2300 | | 200 | 14 | 8 | 275 | 13.10 | 13.90 | 27 |
| 2600 | 15 x 20 | 40 | 12 | 8 | 115 | 12.80 | 13.20 | 26 |
| 2800 | | 75 | 12 | 8 | 150 | 13.05 | 13.90 | 26.95 |
| 3000 | | 125 | 14 | 8 | 200 | 13.35 | 14.15 | 27.50 |
| 3300 | | 200 | 16 | 8 | 275 | 13.90 | 14.40 | 28.30 |
| 3600 | 20 x 20 | 40 | 12 | 10 | 120 | 13.05 | 13.20 | 26.25 |
| 3900 | | 75 | 14 | 10 | 155 | 13.45 | 13.95 | 27.40 |
| 4000 | | 125 | 16 | 10 | 205 | 13.55 | 14.20 | 27.75 |
| 4100 | | 200 | 18 | 10 | 280 | 14.05 | 14.80 | 28.85 |
| 6200 | 30 x 30 | 40 | 14 | 14 | 131 | 14.20 | 13.85 | 28.05 |
| 6400 | | 75 | 18 | 14 | 166 | 14.45 | 14.25 | 28.70 |
| 6600 | | 125 | 20 | 14 | 216 | 15.25 | 15 | 30.25 |
| 6700 | | 200 | 24 | 16 | 297 | 16.05 | 15.55 | 31.60 |

## B1010 Floor Construction

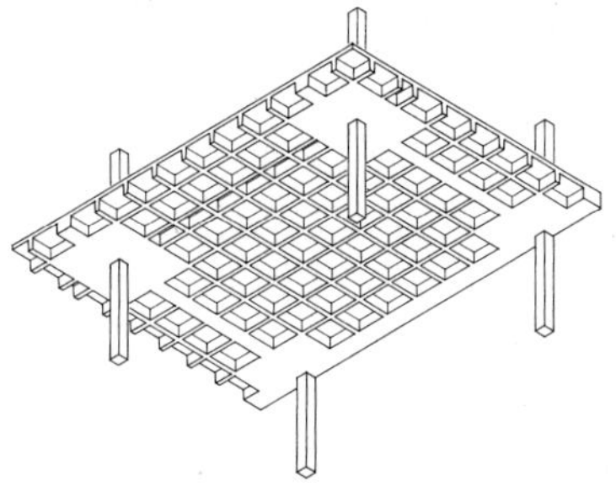

Waffle Slab

| B1010 227 | Cast in Place Waffle Slab | | | | | | | |
|---|---|---|---|---|---|---|---|---|
| | BAY SIZE (FT.) | SUPERIMPOSED LOAD (P.S.F.) | MINIMUM COL. SIZE (IN.) | RIB DEPTH (IN.) | TOTAL LOAD (P.S.F.) | COST PER S.F. | | |
| | | | | | | MAT. | INST. | TOTAL |
| 3900 | 20 x 20 | 40 | 12 | 8 | 144 | 16.55 | 13.25 | 29.80 |
| 4000 | | 75 | 12 | 8 | 179 | 16.75 | 13.40 | 30.15 |
| 4100 | | 125 | 16 | 8 | 229 | 17 | 13.55 | 30.55 |
| 4200 | | 200 | 18 | 8 | 304 | 17.70 | 14 | 31.70 |
| 4400 | 20 x 25 | 40 | 12 | 8 | 146 | 16.80 | 13.35 | 30.15 |
| 4500 | | 75 | 14 | 8 | 181 | 17.10 | 13.50 | 30.60 |
| 4600 | | 125 | 16 | 8 | 231 | 17.35 | 13.70 | 31.05 |
| 4700 | | 200 | 18 | 8 | 306 | 17.95 | 14.05 | 32 |
| 4900 | 25 x 25 | 40 | 12 | 10 | 150 | 17.10 | 13.50 | 30.60 |
| 5000 | | 75 | 16 | 10 | 185 | 17.50 | 13.75 | 31.25 |
| 5300 | | 125 | 18 | 10 | 235 | 17.90 | 14 | 31.90 |
| 5500 | | 200 | 20 | 10 | 310 | 18.25 | 14.25 | 32.50 |
| 5700 | 25 x 30 | 40 | 14 | 10 | 154 | 17.35 | 13.55 | 30.90 |
| 5800 | | 75 | 16 | 10 | 189 | 17.75 | 13.80 | 31.55 |
| 5900 | | 125 | 18 | 10 | 239 | 18.10 | 14.05 | 32.15 |
| 6000 | | 200 | 20 | 12 | 329 | 19.45 | 14.70 | 34.15 |
| 6400 | 30 x 30 | 40 | 14 | 12 | 169 | 18.25 | 13.90 | 32.15 |
| 6500 | | 75 | 18 | 12 | 204 | 18.55 | 14.10 | 32.65 |
| 6600 | | 125 | 20 | 12 | 254 | 18.80 | 14.25 | 33.05 |
| 6700 | | 200 | 24 | 12 | 329 | 20 | 15.05 | 35.05 |
| 6900 | 30 x 35 | 40 | 16 | 12 | 169 | 18.55 | 14.05 | 32.60 |
| 7000 | | 75 | 18 | 12 | 204 | 18.55 | 14.05 | 32.60 |
| 7100 | | 125 | 22 | 12 | 254 | 19.25 | 14.50 | 33.75 |
| 7200 | | 200 | 26 | 14 | 334 | 21 | 15.40 | 36.40 |
| 7400 | 35 x 35 | 40 | 16 | 14 | 174 | 19.35 | 14.45 | 33.80 |
| 7500 | | 75 | 20 | 14 | 209 | 19.70 | 14.65 | 34.35 |
| 7600 | | 125 | 24 | 14 | 259 | 20 | 14.85 | 34.85 |
| 7700 | | 200 | 26 | 16 | 346 | 21 | 15.60 | 36.60 |
| 8000 | 35 x 40 | 40 | 18 | 14 | 176 | 19.75 | 14.65 | 34.40 |
| 8300 | | 75 | 22 | 14 | 211 | 20.50 | 15 | 35.50 |
| 8500 | | 125 | 26 | 16 | 271 | 21 | 15.35 | 36.35 |
| 8750 | | 200 | 30 | 20 | 372 | 22.50 | 16.20 | 38.70 |
| 9200 | 40 x 40 | 40 | 18 | 14 | 176 | 20.50 | 15 | 35.50 |
| 9400 | | 75 | 24 | 14 | 211 | 21 | 15.40 | 36.40 |
| 9500 | | 125 | 26 | 16 | 271 | 21.50 | 15.50 | 37 |
| 9700 | 40 x 45 | 40 | 20 | 16 | 186 | 21 | 15.20 | 36.20 |
| 9800 | | 75 | 24 | 16 | 221 | 21.50 | 15.60 | 37.10 |
| 9900 | | 125 | 28 | 16 | 271 | 22 | 15.80 | 37.80 |

## B1010 Floor Construction

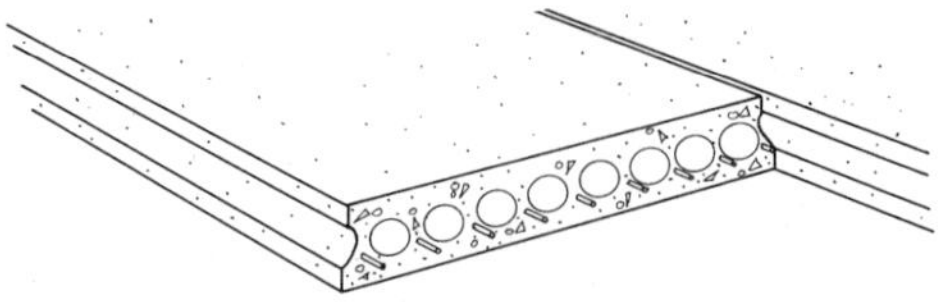

Precast Plank with No Topping

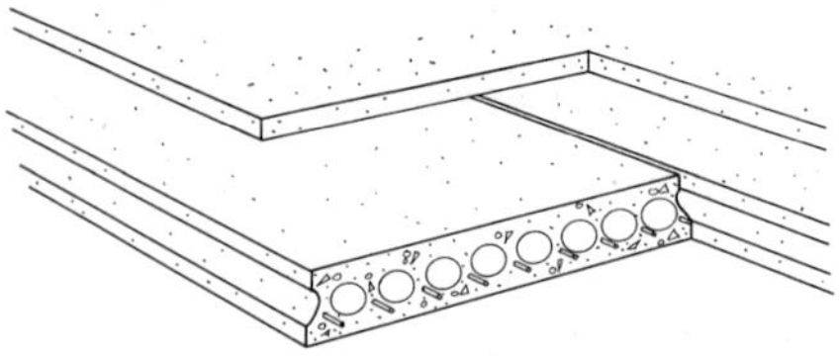

Precast Plank with 2″ Concrete Topping

### B1010 229 Precast Plank with No Topping

| | SPAN (FT.) | SUPERIMPOSED LOAD (P.S.F.) | TOTAL DEPTH (IN.) | DEAD LOAD (P.S.F.) | TOTAL LOAD (P.S.F.) | COST PER S.F. MAT. | INST. | TOTAL |
|---|---|---|---|---|---|---|---|---|
| 0720 | 10 | 40 | 4 | 50 | 90 | 9.60 | 4.12 | 13.72 |
| 0750 | | 75 | 6 | 50 | 125 | 9.75 | 3.54 | 13.29 |
| 0770 | | 100 | 6 | 50 | 150 | 9.75 | 3.54 | 13.29 |
| 0800 | 15 | 40 | 6 | 50 | 90 | 9.75 | 3.54 | 13.29 |
| 0820 | | 75 | 6 | 50 | 125 | 9.75 | 3.54 | 13.29 |
| 0850 | | 100 | 6 | 50 | 150 | 9.75 | 3.54 | 13.29 |
| 0950 | 25 | 40 | 6 | 50 | 90 | 9.75 | 3.54 | 13.29 |
| 0970 | | 75 | 8 | 55 | 130 | 12.45 | 3.09 | 15.54 |
| 1000 | | 100 | 8 | 55 | 155 | 12.45 | 3.09 | 15.54 |
| 1200 | 30 | 40 | 8 | 55 | 95 | 12.45 | 3.09 | 15.54 |
| 1300 | | 75 | 8 | 55 | 130 | 12.45 | 3.09 | 15.54 |
| 1400 | | 100 | 10 | 70 | 170 | 11.35 | 2.75 | 14.10 |
| 1500 | 40 | 40 | 10 | 70 | 110 | 11.35 | 2.75 | 14.10 |
| 1600 | | 75 | 12 | 70 | 145 | 13.35 | 2.47 | 15.82 |
| 1700 | 45 | 40 | 12 | 70 | 110 | 13.35 | 2.47 | 15.82 |

### B1010 230 Precast Plank with 2″ Concrete Topping

| | SPAN (FT.) | SUPERIMPOSED LOAD (P.S.F.) | TOTAL DEPTH (IN.) | DEAD LOAD (P.S.F.) | TOTAL LOAD (P.S.F.) | COST PER S.F. MAT. | INST. | TOTAL |
|---|---|---|---|---|---|---|---|---|
| 2000 | 10 | 40 | 6 | 75 | 115 | 11.35 | 7 | 18.35 |
| 2100 | | 75 | 8 | 75 | 150 | 11.50 | 6.40 | 17.90 |
| 2200 | | 100 | 8 | 75 | 175 | 11.50 | 6.40 | 17.90 |
| 2500 | 15 | 40 | 8 | 75 | 115 | 11.50 | 6.40 | 17.90 |
| 2600 | | 75 | 8 | 75 | 150 | 11.50 | 6.40 | 17.90 |
| 2700 | | 100 | 8 | 75 | 175 | 11.50 | 6.40 | 17.90 |
| 3100 | 25 | 40 | 8 | 75 | 115 | 11.50 | 6.40 | 17.90 |
| 3200 | | 75 | 8 | 75 | 150 | 11.50 | 6.40 | 17.90 |
| 3300 | | 100 | 10 | 80 | 180 | 14.20 | 5.95 | 20.15 |
| 3400 | 30 | 40 | 10 | 80 | 120 | 14.20 | 5.95 | 20.15 |
| 3500 | | 75 | 10 | 80 | 155 | 14.20 | 5.95 | 20.15 |
| 3600 | | 100 | 10 | 80 | 180 | 14.20 | 5.95 | 20.15 |
| 4000 | 40 | 40 | 12 | 95 | 135 | 13.10 | 5.65 | 18.75 |
| 4500 | | 75 | 14 | 95 | 170 | 15.10 | 5.35 | 20.45 |
| 5000 | 45 | 40 | 14 | 95 | 135 | 15.10 | 5.35 | 20.45 |

## B1010 Floor Construction

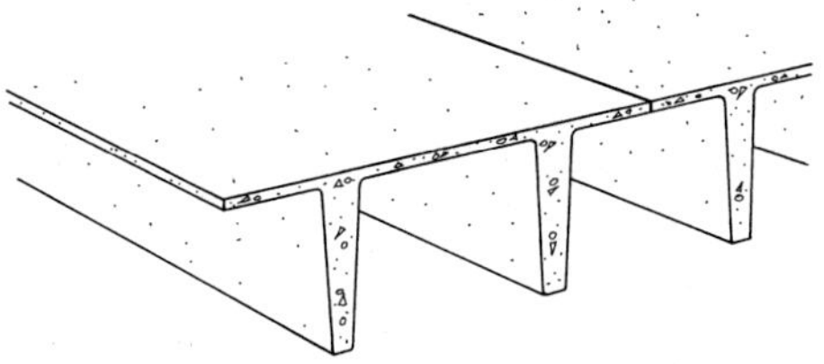

Precast Double "T" Beams with No Topping

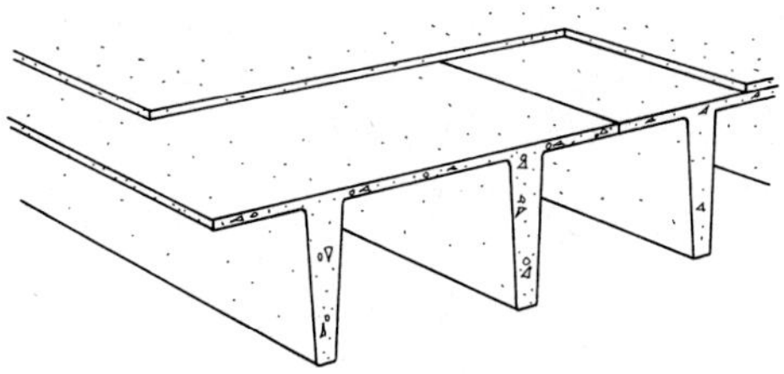

Precast Double "T" Beams with 2″ Topping

Most widely used for moderate span floors and moderate and long span roofs. At shorter spans, they tend to be competitive with hollow core slabs. They are also used as wall panels.

### B1010 234 Precast Double "T" Beams with No Topping

| | SPAN (FT.) | SUPERIMPOSED LOAD (P.S.F.) | DBL. "T" SIZE D (IN.) W (FT.) | CONCRETE "T" TYPE | TOTAL LOAD (P.S.F.) | COST PER S.F. MAT. | COST PER S.F. INST. | COST PER S.F. TOTAL |
|---|---|---|---|---|---|---|---|---|
| 4300 | 50 | 30 | 20x8 | Lt. Wt. | 66 | 13.45 | 1.90 | 15.35 |
| 4400 | | 40 | 20x8 | Lt. Wt. | 76 | 13.50 | 1.71 | 15.21 |
| 4500 | | 50 | 20x8 | Lt. Wt. | 86 | 13.60 | 2.05 | 15.65 |
| 4600 | | 75 | 20x8 | Lt. Wt. | 111 | 13.70 | 2.35 | 16.05 |
| 5600 | 70 | 30 | 32x10 | Lt. Wt. | 78 | 13.45 | 1.30 | 14.75 |
| 5750 | | 40 | 32x10 | Lt. Wt. | 88 | 13.55 | 1.57 | 15.12 |
| 5900 | | 50 | 32x10 | Lt. Wt. | 98 | 13.60 | 1.81 | 15.41 |
| 6000 | | 75 | 32x10 | Lt. Wt. | 123 | 13.75 | 2.20 | 15.95 |
| 6100 | | 100 | 32x10 | Lt. Wt. | 148 | 13.95 | 2.98 | 16.93 |
| 6200 | 80 | 30 | 32x10 | Lt. Wt. | 78 | 13.60 | 1.81 | 15.41 |
| 6300 | | 40 | 32x10 | Lt. Wt. | 88 | 13.75 | 2.19 | 15.94 |
| 6400 | | 50 | 32x10 | Lt. Wt. | 98 | 13.85 | 2.58 | 16.43 |

### B1010 235 Precast Double "T" Beams With 2″ Topping

| | SPAN (FT.) | SUPERIMPOSED LOAD (P.S.F.) | DBL. "T" SIZE D (IN.) W (FT.) | CONCRETE "T" TYPE | TOTAL LOAD (P.S.F.) | COST PER S.F. MAT. | COST PER S.F. INST. | COST PER S.F. TOTAL |
|---|---|---|---|---|---|---|---|---|
| 7100 | 40 | 30 | 18x8 | Reg. Wt. | 120 | 11.95 | 3.90 | 15.85 |
| 7200 | | 40 | 20x8 | Reg. Wt. | 130 | 13.95 | 3.71 | 17.66 |
| 7300 | | 50 | 20x8 | Reg. Wt. | 140 | 14.10 | 4.06 | 18.16 |
| 7400 | | 75 | 20x8 | Reg. Wt. | 165 | 14.10 | 4.21 | 18.31 |
| 7500 | | 100 | 20x8 | Reg. Wt. | 190 | 14.25 | 4.70 | 18.95 |
| 7550 | 50 | 30 | 24x8 | Reg. Wt. | 120 | 14.10 | 3.89 | 17.99 |
| 7600 | | 40 | 24x8 | Reg. Wt. | 130 | 14.10 | 4.01 | 18.11 |
| 7750 | | 50 | 24x8 | Reg. Wt. | 140 | 14.10 | 4.03 | 18.13 |
| 7800 | | 75 | 24x8 | Reg. Wt. | 165 | 14.25 | 4.53 | 18.78 |
| 7900 | | 100 | 32x10 | Reg. Wt. | 189 | 14.10 | 3.72 | 17.82 |

## B1010 Floor Construction

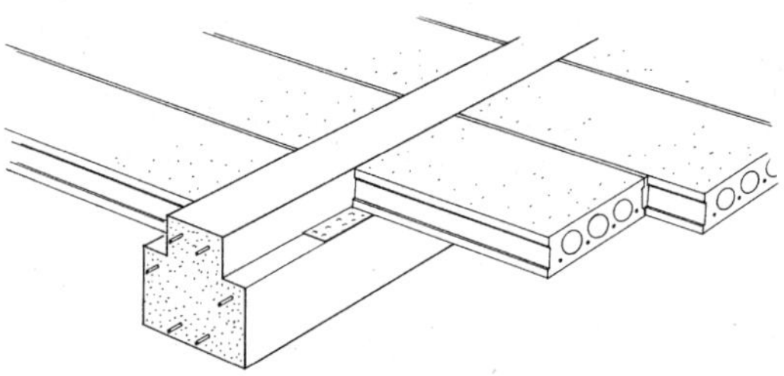

Precast Beam and Plank with No Topping

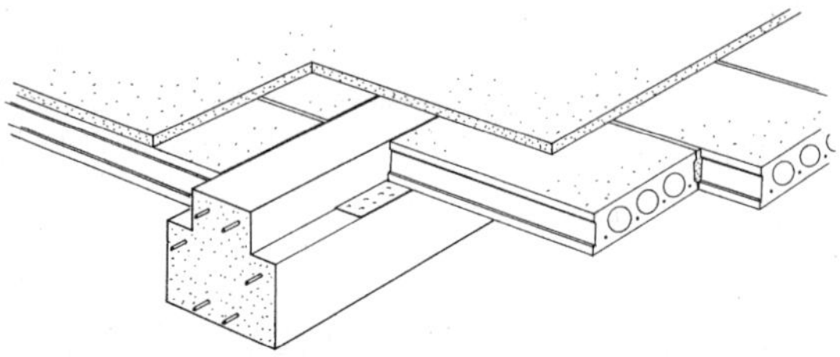

Precast Beam and Plank with 2″ Topping

### B1010 236 Precast Beam & Plank with No Topping

| | BAY SIZE (FT.) | SUPERIMPOSED LOAD (P.S.F.) | PLANK THICKNESS (IN.) | TOTAL DEPTH (IN.) | TOTAL LOAD (P.S.F.) | COST PER S.F. | | |
|---|---|---|---|---|---|---|---|---|
| | | | | | | MAT. | INST. | TOTAL |
| 6200 | 25x25 | 40 | 8 | 28 | 118 | 35 | 4.12 | 39.12 |
| 6400 | | 75 | 8 | 36 | 158 | 34 | 4.12 | 38.12 |
| 6500 | | 100 | 8 | 36 | 183 | 34 | 4.12 | 38.12 |
| 7000 | 25x30 | 40 | 8 | 36 | 110 | 31 | 3.98 | 34.98 |
| 7200 | | 75 | 10 | 36 | 159 | 31 | 3.65 | 34.65 |
| 7400 | | 100 | 12 | 36 | 188 | 32 | 3.32 | 35.32 |
| 7600 | 30x30 | 40 | 8 | 36 | 121 | 32 | 3.86 | 35.86 |
| 8000 | | 75 | 10 | 44 | 140 | 31.50 | 3.87 | 35.37 |
| 8250 | | 100 | 12 | 52 | 206 | 34.50 | 3.26 | 37.76 |
| 8500 | 30x35 | 40 | 12 | 44 | 135 | 30.50 | 3.16 | 33.66 |
| 8750 | | 75 | 12 | 52 | 176 | 31.50 | 3.15 | 34.65 |
| 9000 | 35x35 | 40 | 12 | 52 | 141 | 31.50 | 3.08 | 34.58 |
| 9250 | | 75 | 12 | 60 | 181 | 33 | 3.08 | 36.08 |
| 9500 | 35x40 | 40 | 12 | 52 | 137 | 31.50 | 3.08 | 34.58 |

### B1010 238 Precast Beam & Plank with 2″ Topping

| | BAY SIZE (FT.) | SUPERIMPOSED LOAD (P.S.F.) | PLANK THICKNESS (IN.) | TOTAL DEPTH (IN.) | TOTAL LOAD (P.S.F.) | COST PER S.F. | | |
|---|---|---|---|---|---|---|---|---|
| | | | | | | MAT. | INST. | TOTAL |
| 4300 | 20x20 | 40 | 6 | 22 | 135 | 36 | 7.40 | 43.40 |
| 4400 | | 75 | 6 | 24 | 173 | 37 | 7.45 | 44.45 |
| 4500 | | 100 | 6 | 28 | 200 | 37.50 | 7.45 | 44.95 |
| 4600 | 20x25 | 40 | 6 | 26 | 134 | 33.50 | 7.25 | 40.75 |
| 5000 | | 75 | 8 | 30 | 177 | 35.50 | 6.70 | 42.20 |
| 5200 | | 100 | 8 | 30 | 202 | 35.50 | 6.70 | 42.20 |
| 5400 | 25x25 | 40 | 6 | 38 | 143 | 34 | 6.90 | 40.90 |
| 5600 | | 75 | 8 | 38 | 183 | 26.50 | 6.55 | 33.05 |
| 6000 | | 100 | 8 | 46 | 216 | 28 | 6 | 34 |
| 6200 | 25x30 | 40 | 8 | 38 | 144 | 32.50 | 6.25 | 38.75 |
| 6400 | | 75 | 10 | 46 | 200 | 32 | 5.90 | 37.90 |
| 6600 | | 100 | 10 | 46 | 225 | 32.50 | 5.90 | 38.40 |
| 7000 | 30x30 | 40 | 8 | 46 | 150 | 34 | 6.15 | 40.15 |
| 7200 | | 75 | 10 | 54 | 181 | 35.50 | 6.15 | 41.65 |
| 7600 | | 100 | 10 | 54 | 231 | 35.50 | 6.15 | 41.65 |
| 7800 | 30x35 | 40 | 10 | 54 | 166 | 31.50 | 5.65 | 37.15 |
| 8000 | | 75 | 12 | 54 | 200 | 33 | 5.35 | 38.35 |

## B1010 Floor Construction

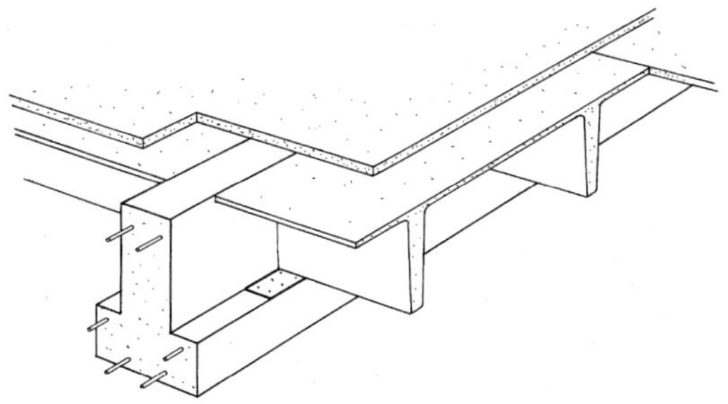

With Topping

**General:** Beams and double tees priced here are for plant produced prestressed members transported to the site and erected.

The 2″ structural topping is applied after the beams and double tees are in place and is reinforced with W.W.F.

### B1010 239 — Precast Double "T" & 2″ Topping on Precast Beams

| | BAY SIZE (FT.) | SUPERIMPOSED LOAD (P.S.F.) | DEPTH (IN.) | | TOTAL LOAD (P.S.F.) | COST PER S.F. MAT. | COST PER S.F. INST. | COST PER S.F. TOTAL |
|---|---|---|---|---|---|---|---|---|
| 3000 | 25x30 | 40 | 38 | | 130 | 33 | 5.25 | 38.25 |
| 3100 | | 75 | 38 | | 168 | 33 | 5.25 | 38.25 |
| 3300 | | 100 | 46 | | 196 | 33 | 5.20 | 38.20 |
| 3600 | 30x30 | 40 | 46 | | 150 | 33.50 | 5.10 | 38.60 |
| 3750 | | 75 | 46 | | 174 | 33.50 | 5.10 | 38.60 |
| 4000 | | 100 | 54 | | 203 | 35.50 | 5.05 | 40.55 |
| 4100 | 30x40 | 40 | 46 | | 136 | 29.50 | 4.58 | 34.08 |
| 4300 | | 75 | 54 | | 173 | 30.50 | 4.54 | 35.04 |
| 4400 | | 100 | 62 | | 204 | 31.50 | 4.56 | 36.06 |
| 4600 | 30x50 | 40 | 54 | | 138 | 27.50 | 4.23 | 31.73 |
| 4800 | | 75 | 54 | | 181 | 26 | 4.28 | 30.28 |
| 5000 | | 100 | 54 | | 219 | 26 | 3.91 | 29.91 |
| 5200 | 30x60 | 40 | 62 | | 151 | 26.50 | 3.84 | 30.34 |
| 5400 | | 75 | 62 | | 192 | 25 | 3.90 | 28.90 |
| 5600 | | 100 | 62 | | 215 | 25 | 3.90 | 28.90 |
| 5800 | 35x40 | 40 | 54 | | 139 | 30.50 | 4.49 | 34.99 |
| 6000 | | 75 | 62 | | 179 | 31.50 | 4.30 | 35.80 |
| 6250 | | 100 | 62 | | 212 | 32 | 4.47 | 36.47 |
| 6500 | 35x50 | 40 | 62 | | 142 | 28.50 | 4.19 | 32.69 |
| 6750 | | 75 | 62 | | 186 | 29 | 4.34 | 33.34 |
| 7300 | | 100 | 62 | | 231 | 27.50 | 3.97 | 31.47 |
| 7600 | 35x60 | 40 | 54 | | 154 | 26.50 | 3.67 | 30.17 |
| 7750 | | 75 | 54 | | 179 | 26.50 | 3.69 | 30.19 |
| 8000 | | 100 | 62 | | 224 | 27 | 3.75 | 30.75 |
| 8250 | 40x40 | 40 | 62 | | 145 | 34 | 4.50 | 38.50 |
| 8400 | | 75 | 62 | | 187 | 31 | 4.52 | 35.52 |
| 8750 | | 100 | 62 | | 223 | 32 | 4.61 | 36.61 |
| 9000 | 40x50 | 40 | 62 | | 151 | 28.50 | 4.23 | 32.73 |
| 9300 | | 75 | 62 | | 193 | 27.50 | 3.11 | 30.61 |
| 9800 | 40x60 | 40 | 62 | | 164 | 31.50 | 2.99 | 34.49 |

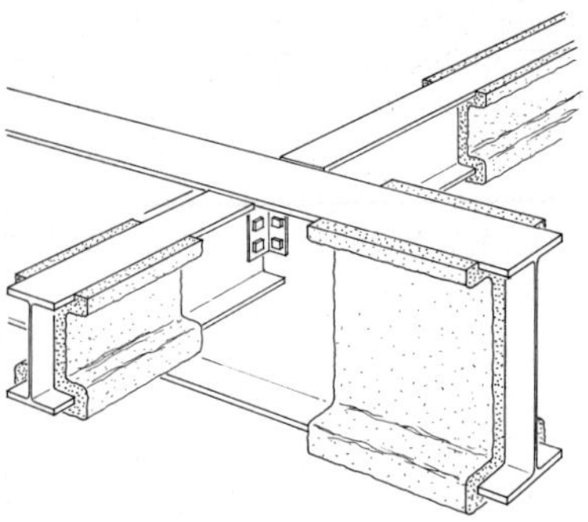

**General:** The following table is based upon structural wide flange (WF) beam and girder framing. Non-composite action is assumed between WF framing and decking. Deck costs not included.

The deck spans the short direction. The steel beams and girders are fireproofed with sprayed fiber fireproofing.

No columns included in price.

## B1010 241 W Shape Beams & Girders

| | BAY SIZE (FT.) BEAM X GIRD | SUPERIMPOSED LOAD (P.S.F.) | STEEL FRAMING DEPTH (IN.) | FIREPROOFING (S.F. PER S.F.) | TOTAL LOAD (P.S.F.) | COST PER S.F. | | |
|---|---|---|---|---|---|---|---|---|
| | | | | | | MAT. | INST. | TOTAL |
| 1350 | 15x20 | 40 | 12 | .535 | 50 | 6.25 | 2.42 | 8.67 |
| 1400 | | 40 | 16 | .65 | 90 | 8.20 | 3.11 | 11.31 |
| 1450 | | 75 | 18 | .694 | 125 | 10.80 | 3.92 | 14.72 |
| 1500 | | 125 | 24 | .796 | 175 | 14.95 | 5.40 | 20.35 |
| 2000 | 20x20 | 40 | 12 | .55 | 50 | 7 | 2.65 | 9.65 |
| 2050 | | 40 | 14 | .579 | 90 | 9.65 | 3.45 | 13.10 |
| 2100 | | 75 | 16 | .672 | 125 | 11.55 | 4.11 | 15.66 |
| 2150 | | 125 | 16 | .714 | 175 | 13.80 | 4.95 | 18.75 |
| 2900 | 20x25 | 40 | 16 | .53 | 50 | 7.75 | 2.84 | 10.59 |
| 2950 | | 40 | 18 | .621 | 96 | 12.25 | 4.26 | 16.51 |
| 3000 | | 75 | 18 | .651 | 131 | 14.10 | 4.84 | 18.94 |
| 3050 | | 125 | 24 | .77 | 200 | 18.65 | 6.50 | 25.15 |
| 5200 | 25x25 | 40 | 18 | .486 | 50 | 8.45 | 3 | 11.45 |
| 5300 | | 40 | 18 | .592 | 96 | 12.60 | 4.33 | 16.93 |
| 5400 | | 75 | 21 | .668 | 131 | 15.25 | 5.20 | 20.45 |
| 5450 | | 125 | 24 | .738 | 191 | 20 | 6.90 | 26.90 |
| 6300 | 25x30 | 40 | 21 | .568 | 50 | 9.60 | 3.43 | 13.03 |
| 6350 | | 40 | 21 | .694 | 90 | 13.05 | 4.57 | 17.62 |
| 6400 | | 75 | 24 | .776 | 125 | 16.80 | 5.75 | 22.55 |
| 6450 | | 125 | 30 | .904 | 175 | 20 | 7.10 | 27.10 |
| 7700 | 30x30 | 40 | 21 | .52 | 50 | 10.35 | 3.59 | 13.94 |
| 7750 | | 40 | 24 | .629 | 103 | 15.95 | 5.35 | 21.30 |
| 7800 | | 75 | 30 | .715 | 138 | 18.95 | 6.30 | 25.25 |
| 7850 | | 125 | 36 | .822 | 206 | 25 | 8.45 | 33.45 |
| 8250 | 30x35 | 40 | 21 | .508 | 50 | 11.80 | 4 | 15.80 |
| 8300 | | 40 | 24 | .651 | 109 | 17.45 | 5.80 | 23.25 |
| 8350 | | 75 | 33 | .732 | 150 | 21 | 7 | 28 |
| 8400 | | 125 | 36 | .802 | 225 | 26.50 | 8.90 | 35.40 |
| 9550 | 35x35 | 40 | 27 | .560 | 50 | 12.20 | 4.18 | 16.38 |
| 9600 | | 40 | 36 | .706 | 109 | 22.50 | 7.30 | 29.80 |
| 9650 | | 75 | 36 | .750 | 150 | 23 | 7.55 | 30.55 |
| 9820 | | 125 | 36 | .797 | 225 | 31 | 10.20 | 41.20 |

## B1010 Floor Construction

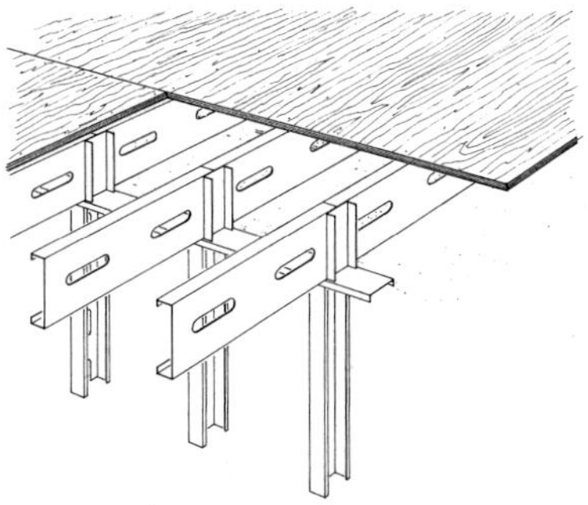

**Description:** Table below lists costs for light gage CEE or PUNCHED DOUBLE joists to suit the span and loading with the minimum thickness subfloor required by the joist spacing.

| B1010 244 | Light Gauge Steel Floor Systems | | | | | | | |
|---|---|---|---|---|---|---|---|---|
| | SPAN (FT.) | SUPERIMPOSED LOAD (P.S.F.) | FRAMING DEPTH (IN.) | FRAMING SPAC. (IN.) | TOTAL LOAD (P.S.F.) | COST PER S.F. | | |
| | | | | | | MAT. | INST. | TOTAL |
| 1500 | 15 | 40 | 8 | 16 | 54 | 5.90 | 2.60 | 8.50 |
| 1550 | | | 8 | 24 | 54 | 6.25 | 2.67 | 8.92 |
| 1600 | | 65 | 10 | 16 | 80 | 7.85 | 3.15 | 11 |
| 1650 | | | 10 | 24 | 80 | 7.80 | 3.09 | 10.89 |
| 1700 | | 75 | 10 | 16 | 90 | 7.85 | 3.15 | 11 |
| 1750 | | | 10 | 24 | 90 | 7.80 | 3.09 | 10.89 |
| 1800 | | 100 | 10 | 16 | 116 | 10.30 | 3.97 | 14.27 |
| 1850 | | | 10 | 24 | 116 | 7.80 | 3.09 | 10.89 |
| 1900 | | 125 | 10 | 16 | 141 | 10.30 | 3.97 | 14.27 |
| 1950 | | | 10 | 24 | 141 | 7.80 | 3.09 | 10.89 |
| 2500 | 20 | 40 | 8 | 16 | 55 | 6.85 | 2.92 | 9.77 |
| 2550 | | | 8 | 24 | 55 | 6.25 | 2.67 | 8.92 |
| 2600 | | 65 | 8 | 16 | 80 | 8 | 3.32 | 11.32 |
| 2650 | | | 10 | 24 | 80 | 7.80 | 3.10 | 10.90 |
| 2700 | | 75 | 10 | 16 | 90 | 7.40 | 3 | 10.40 |
| 2750 | | | 12 | 24 | 90 | 8.75 | 2.71 | 11.46 |
| 2800 | | 100 | 10 | 16 | 115 | 7.40 | 3 | 10.40 |
| 2850 | | | 10 | 24 | 116 | 9.80 | 3.46 | 13.26 |
| 2900 | | 125 | 12 | 16 | 142 | 11.75 | 3.39 | 15.14 |
| 2950 | | | 12 | 24 | 141 | 10.65 | 3.67 | 14.32 |
| 3500 | 25 | 40 | 10 | 16 | 55 | 7.85 | 3.15 | 11 |
| 3550 | | | 10 | 24 | 55 | 7.80 | 3.09 | 10.89 |
| 3600 | | 65 | 10 | 16 | 81 | 10.30 | 3.97 | 14.27 |
| 3650 | | | 12 | 24 | 81 | 9.70 | 2.94 | 12.64 |
| 3700 | | 75 | 12 | 16 | 92 | 11.70 | 3.39 | 15.09 |
| 3750 | | | 12 | 24 | 91 | 10.65 | 3.67 | 14.32 |
| 3800 | | 100 | 12 | 16 | 117 | 13.25 | 3.73 | 16.98 |
| 3850 | | 125 | 12 | 16 | 143 | 14.70 | 4.86 | 19.56 |
| 4500 | 30 | 40 | 12 | 16 | 57 | 11.70 | 3.39 | 15.09 |
| 4550 | | | 12 | 24 | 56 | 9.65 | 2.93 | 12.58 |
| 4600 | | 65 | 12 | 16 | 82 | 13.15 | 3.72 | 16.87 |
| 4650 | | 75 | 12 | 16 | 92 | 13.15 | 3.72 | 16.87 |

## B1010 Floor Construction

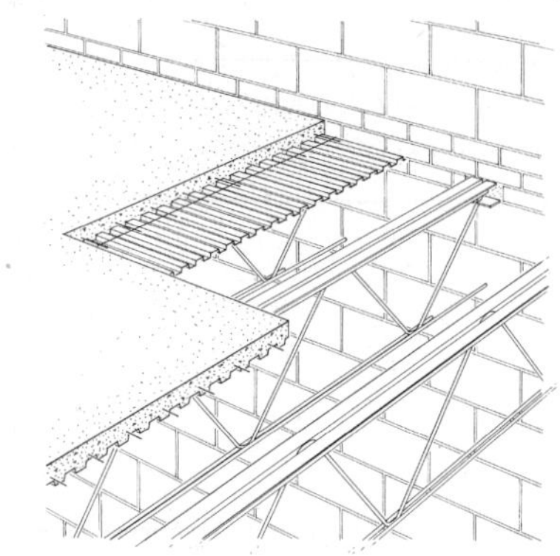

**Description:** The table below lists costs per S.F. for a floor system on bearing walls using open web steel joists, galvanized steel slab form and 2-1/2″ concrete slab reinforced with welded wire fabric. Costs of the bearing walls are not included.

### B1010 246 — Deck & Joists on Bearing Walls

| | SPAN (FT.) | SUPERIMPOSED LOAD (P.S.F.) | JOIST SPACING FT. - IN. | DEPTH (IN.) | TOTAL LOAD (P.S.F.) | COST PER S.F. | | |
|---|---|---|---|---|---|---|---|---|
| | | | | | | MAT. | INST. | TOTAL |
| 1050 | 20 | 40 | 2-0 | 14-1/2 | 83 | 7.85 | 4.67 | 12.52 |
| 1070 | | 65 | 2-0 | 16-1/2 | 109 | 8.40 | 4.96 | 13.36 |
| 1100 | | 75 | 2-0 | 16-1/2 | 119 | 8.40 | 4.96 | 13.36 |
| 1120 | | 100 | 2-0 | 18-1/2 | 145 | 8.45 | 4.98 | 13.43 |
| 1150 | | 125 | 1-9 | 18-1/2 | 170 | 9.10 | 5.30 | 14.40 |
| 1170 | 25 | 40 | 2-0 | 18-1/2 | 84 | 8.45 | 4.98 | 13.43 |
| 1200 | | 65 | 2-0 | 20-1/2 | 109 | 8.65 | 5.10 | 13.75 |
| 1220 | | 75 | 2-0 | 20-1/2 | 119 | 9.20 | 5.30 | 14.50 |
| 1250 | | 100 | 2-0 | 22-1/2 | 145 | 9.30 | 5.35 | 14.65 |
| 1270 | | 125 | 1-9 | 22-1/2 | 170 | 10.40 | 5.90 | 16.30 |
| 1300 | 30 | 40 | 2-0 | 22-1/2 | 84 | 11.20 | 4.81 | 16.01 |
| 1320 | | 65 | 2-0 | 24-1/2 | 110 | 12.15 | 5.05 | 17.20 |
| 1350 | | 75 | 2-0 | 26-1/2 | 121 | 12.60 | 5.15 | 17.75 |
| 1370 | | 100 | 2-0 | 26-1/2 | 146 | 13.45 | 5.35 | 18.80 |
| 1400 | | 125 | 2-0 | 24-1/2 | 172 | 15.85 | 5.90 | 21.75 |
| 1420 | 35 | 40 | 2-0 | 26-1/2 | 85 | 14.95 | 5.70 | 20.65 |
| 1450 | | 65 | 2-0 | 28-1/2 | 111 | 15.50 | 5.80 | 21.30 |
| 1470 | | 75 | 2-0 | 28-1/2 | 121 | 15.50 | 5.80 | 21.30 |
| 1500 | | 100 | 1-11 | 28-1/2 | 147 | 16.85 | 6.10 | 22.95 |
| 1520 | | 125 | 1-8 | 28-1/2 | 172 | 18.60 | 6.50 | 25.10 |
| 1550 | 5/8″ gyp. fireproof. | | | | | | | |
| 1560 | On metal furring, add | | | | | 1.05 | 3.94 | 4.99 |

## B1010 Floor Construction

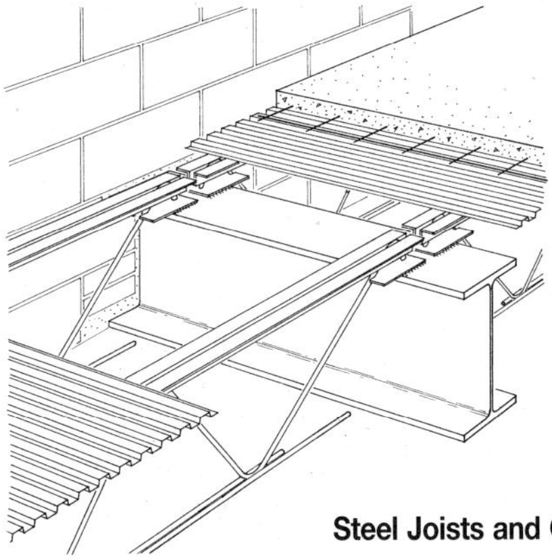

Steel Joists and Concrete Slab on Walls and Beams

The table below lists costs for a floor system on exterior bearing walls and interior columns and beams using open web steel joists, galvanized steel slab form, 2-1/2" concrete slab reinforced with welded wire fabric.

Columns are sized to accommodate one floor plus roof loading but costs for columns are from suspended floor to slab on grade only. Costs of the bearing walls are not included.

| B1010 248 | Steel Joists on Beam & Wall | | | | | | | |
|---|---|---|---|---|---|---|---|---|
| | BAY SIZE (FT.) | SUPERIMPOSED LOAD (P.S.F.) | DEPTH (IN.) | TOTAL LOAD (P.S.F.) | COLUMN ADD | COST PER S.F. | | |
| | | | | | | MAT. | INST. | TOTAL |
| 1720 | 25x25 | 40 | 23 | 84 | | 10.40 | 5.40 | 15.80 |
| 1730 | | | | | columns | .52 | .15 | .67 |
| 1750 | 25x25 | 65 | 29 | 110 | | 10.90 | 5.60 | 16.50 |
| 1760 | | | | | columns | .52 | .15 | .67 |
| 1770 | 25x25 | 75 | 26 | 120 | | 12 | 6.05 | 18.05 |
| 1780 | | | | | columns | .60 | .18 | .78 |
| 1800 | 25x25 | 100 | 29 | 145 | | 13.40 | 6.60 | 20 |
| 1810 | | | | | columns | .60 | .18 | .78 |
| 1820 | 25x25 | 125 | 29 | 170 | | 14.05 | 6.85 | 20.90 |
| 1830 | | | | | columns | .67 | .20 | .87 |
| 2020 | 30x30 | 40 | 29 | 84 | | 13.70 | 5.40 | 19.10 |
| 2030 | | | | | columns | .46 | .14 | .60 |
| 2050 | 30x30 | 65 | 29 | 110 | | 15.45 | 5.85 | 21.30 |
| 2060 | | | | | columns | .46 | .14 | .60 |
| 2070 | 30x30 | 75 | 32 | 120 | | 15.90 | 6 | 21.90 |
| 2080 | | | | | columns | .53 | .16 | .69 |
| 2100 | 30x30 | 100 | 35 | 145 | | 17.55 | 6.40 | 23.95 |
| 2110 | | | | | columns | .62 | .18 | .80 |
| 2120 | 30x30 | 125 | 35 | 172 | | 20.50 | 7.10 | 27.60 |
| 2130 | | | | | columns | .75 | .22 | .97 |
| 2170 | 30x35 | 40 | 29 | 85 | | 15.55 | 5.85 | 21.40 |
| 2180 | | | | | columns | .45 | .13 | .58 |
| 2200 | 30x35 | 65 | 29 | 111 | | 18.65 | 6.60 | 25.25 |
| 2210 | | | | | columns | .51 | .15 | .66 |
| 2220 | 30x35 | 75 | 32 | 121 | | 18.65 | 6.60 | 25.25 |
| 2230 | | | | | columns | .52 | .15 | .67 |
| 2250 | 30x35 | 100 | 35 | 148 | | 18.80 | 6.70 | 25.50 |
| 2260 | | | | | columns | .64 | .19 | .83 |
| 2270 | 30x35 | 125 | 38 | 173 | | 21 | 7.25 | 28.25 |
| 2280 | | | | | columns | .65 | .19 | .84 |
| 2320 | 35x35 | 40 | 32 | 85 | | 15.90 | 6 | 21.90 |
| 2330 | | | | | columns | .46 | .13 | .59 |
| 2350 | 35x35 | 65 | 35 | 111 | | 19.60 | 6.85 | 26.45 |
| 2360 | | | | | columns | .55 | .16 | .71 |
| 2370 | 35x35 | 75 | 35 | 121 | | 19.95 | 6.95 | 26.90 |
| 2380 | | | | | columns | .55 | .16 | .71 |

## B1010 Floor Construction

### B1010 248 Steel Joists on Beam & Wall

| | BAY SIZE (FT.) | SUPERIMPOSED LOAD (P.S.F.) | DEPTH (IN.) | TOTAL LOAD (P.S.F.) | COLUMN ADD | COST PER S.F. | | |
|---|---|---|---|---|---|---|---|---|
| | | | | | | MAT. | INST. | TOTAL |
| 2400 | 35x35 | 100 | 38 | 148 | | 21 | 7.15 | 28.15 |
| 2410 | | | | | columns | .68 | .20 | .88 |
| 2460 | 5/8 gyp. fireproof. | | | | | | | |
| 2475 | On metal furring, add | | | | | 1.05 | 3.94 | 4.99 |

## B1010 Floor Construction

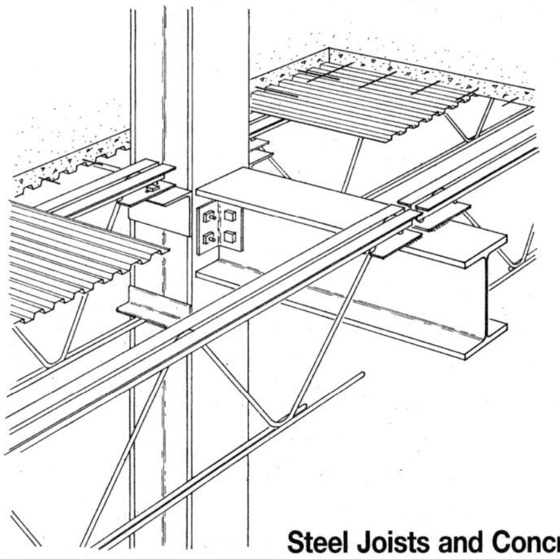

Steel Joists and Concrete Slab on Steel Columns and Beams

The table below lists costs per S.F. for a floor system on steel columns and beams using open web steel joists, galvanized steel slab form, 2-1/2″ concrete slab reinforced with welded wire fabric.

Columns are sized to accommodate one floor plus roof loading but costs for columns are from floor to grade only.

### B1010 250 Steel Joists, Beams & Slab on Columns

| | BAY SIZE (FT.) | SUPERIMPOSED LOAD (P.S.F.) | DEPTH (IN.) | TOTAL LOAD (P.S.F.) | COLUMN ADD | COST PER S.F. | | |
|---|---|---|---|---|---|---|---|---|
| | | | | | | MAT. | INST. | TOTAL |
| 2350 | 15x20 | 40 | 17 | 83 | | 10.75 | 5.45 | 16.20 |
| 2400 | | | | | column | 1.71 | .50 | 2.21 |
| 2450 | 15x20 | 65 | 19 | 108 | | 11.95 | 5.80 | 17.75 |
| 2500 | | | | | column | 1.71 | .50 | 2.21 |
| 2550 | 15x20 | 75 | 19 | 119 | | 12.30 | 6 | 18.30 |
| 2600 | | | | | column | 1.87 | .55 | 2.42 |
| 2650 | 15x20 | 100 | 19 | 144 | | 13.05 | 6.25 | 19.30 |
| 2700 | | | | | column | 1.87 | .55 | 2.42 |
| 2750 | 15x20 | 125 | 19 | 170 | | 13.70 | 6.45 | 20.15 |
| 2800 | | | | | column | 2.49 | .73 | 3.22 |
| 2850 | 20x20 | 40 | 19 | 83 | | 11.75 | 5.70 | 17.45 |
| 2900 | | | | | column | 1.40 | .41 | 1.81 |
| 2950 | 20x20 | 65 | 23 | 109 | | 12.85 | 6.10 | 18.95 |
| 3000 | | | | | column | 1.87 | .55 | 2.42 |
| 3100 | 20x20 | 75 | 26 | 119 | | 13.55 | 6.35 | 19.90 |
| 3200 | | | | | column | 1.87 | .55 | 2.42 |
| 3400 | 20x20 | 100 | 23 | 144 | | 14.05 | 6.50 | 20.55 |
| 3450 | | | | | column | 1.87 | .55 | 2.42 |
| 3500 | 20x20 | 125 | 23 | 170 | | 15.50 | 7.05 | 22.55 |
| 3600 | | | | | column | 2.24 | .66 | 2.90 |
| 3700 | 20x25 | 40 | 44 | 83 | | 12.45 | 6 | 18.45 |
| 3800 | | | | | column | 1.50 | .44 | 1.94 |
| 3900 | 20x25 | 65 | 26 | 110 | | 13.60 | 6.40 | 20 |
| 4000 | | | | | column | 1.50 | .44 | 1.94 |
| 4100 | 20x25 | 75 | 26 | 120 | | 14.15 | 6.65 | 20.80 |
| 4200 | | | | | column | 1.79 | .52 | 2.31 |
| 4300 | 20x25 | 100 | 26 | 145 | | 14.95 | 6.90 | 21.85 |
| 4400 | | | | | column | 1.79 | .52 | 2.31 |
| 4500 | 20x25 | 125 | 29 | 170 | | 16.50 | 7.55 | 24.05 |
| 4600 | | | | | column | 2.09 | .61 | 2.70 |
| 4700 | 25x25 | 40 | 23 | 84 | | 13.55 | 6.30 | 19.85 |
| 4800 | | | | | column | 1.43 | .42 | 1.85 |
| 4900 | 25x25 | 65 | 29 | 110 | | 14.30 | 6.55 | 20.85 |
| 5000 | | | | | column | 1.43 | .42 | 1.85 |
| 5100 | 25x25 | 75 | 26 | 120 | | 15.65 | 7.10 | 22.75 |
| 5200 | | | | | column | 1.67 | .49 | 2.16 |

## B1010 Floor Construction

### B1010 250 Steel Joists, Beams & Slab on Columns

| | BAY SIZE (FT.) | SUPERIMPOSED LOAD (P.S.F.) | DEPTH (IN.) | TOTAL LOAD (P.S.F.) | COLUMN ADD | COST PER S.F. | | |
|---|---|---|---|---|---|---|---|---|
| | | | | | | MAT. | INST. | TOTAL |
| 5300 | 25x25 | 100 | 29 | 145 | | 17.25 | 7.75 | 25 |
| 5400 | | | | | column | 1.67 | .49 | 2.16 |
| 5500 | 25x25 | 125 | 32 | 170 | | 18.25 | 8.05 | 26.30 |
| 5600 | | | | | column | 1.85 | .54 | 2.39 |
| 5700 | 25x30 | 40 | 29 | 84 | | 17.45 | 6.45 | 23.90 |
| 5800 | | | | | column | 1.39 | .41 | 1.80 |
| 5900 | 25x30 | 65 | 29 | 110 | | 18.30 | 6.60 | 24.90 |
| 6000 | | | | | column | 1.39 | .41 | 1.80 |
| 6050 | 25x30 | 75 | 29 | 120 | | 18.55 | 6.75 | 25.30 |
| 6100 | | | | | column | 1.54 | .45 | 1.99 |
| 6150 | 25x30 | 100 | 29 | 145 | | 20 | 7.15 | 27.15 |
| 6200 | | | | | column | 1.54 | .45 | 1.99 |
| 6250 | 25x30 | 125 | 32 | 170 | | 23 | 7.80 | 30.80 |
| 6300 | | | | | column | 1.78 | .52 | 2.30 |
| 6350 | 30x30 | 40 | 29 | 84 | | 17.25 | 6.45 | 23.70 |
| 6400 | | | | | column | 1.29 | .38 | 1.67 |
| 6500 | 30x30 | 65 | 29 | 110 | | 19.55 | 7.05 | 26.60 |
| 6600 | | | | | column | 1.29 | .38 | 1.67 |
| 6700 | 30x30 | 75 | 32 | 120 | | 20 | 7.15 | 27.15 |
| 6800 | | | | | column | 1.48 | .43 | 1.91 |
| 6900 | 30x30 | 100 | 35 | 145 | | 22 | 7.70 | 29.70 |
| 7000 | | | | | column | 1.73 | .51 | 2.24 |
| 7100 | 30x30 | 125 | 35 | 172 | | 25.50 | 8.55 | 34.05 |
| 7200 | | | | | column | 1.92 | .56 | 2.48 |
| 7300 | 30x35 | 40 | 29 | 85 | | 19.55 | 7 | 26.55 |
| 7400 | | | | | column | 1.10 | .32 | 1.42 |
| 7500 | 30x35 | 65 | 29 | 111 | | 23 | 7.85 | 30.85 |
| 7600 | | | | | column | 1.42 | .42 | 1.84 |
| 7700 | 30x35 | 75 | 32 | 121 | | 23 | 7.85 | 30.85 |
| 7800 | | | | | column | 1.45 | .43 | 1.88 |
| 7900 | 30x35 | 100 | 35 | 148 | | 23.50 | 8 | 31.50 |
| 8000 | | | | | column | 1.78 | .52 | 2.30 |
| 8100 | 30x35 | 125 | 38 | 173 | | 26 | 8.65 | 34.65 |
| 8200 | | | | | column | 1.81 | .53 | 2.34 |
| 8300 | 35x35 | 40 | 32 | 85 | | 20 | 7.15 | 27.15 |
| 8400 | | | | | column | 1.27 | .37 | 1.64 |
| 8500 | 35x35 | 65 | 35 | 111 | | 24 | 8.15 | 32.15 |
| 8600 | | | | | column | 1.52 | .45 | 1.97 |
| 9300 | 35x35 | 75 | 38 | 121 | | 24.50 | 8.30 | 32.80 |
| 9400 | | | | | column | 1.52 | .45 | 1.97 |
| 9500 | 35x35 | 100 | 38 | 148 | | 26.50 | 8.80 | 35.30 |
| 9600 | | | | | column | 1.88 | .55 | 2.43 |
| 9750 | 35x35 | 125 | 41 | 173 | | 27 | 9 | 36 |
| 9800 | | | | | column | 1.92 | .56 | 2.48 |
| 9810 | 5/8 gyp. fireproof. | | | | | | | |
| 9815 | On metal furring, add | | | | | 1.05 | 3.94 | 4.99 |

## B1010 Floor Construction

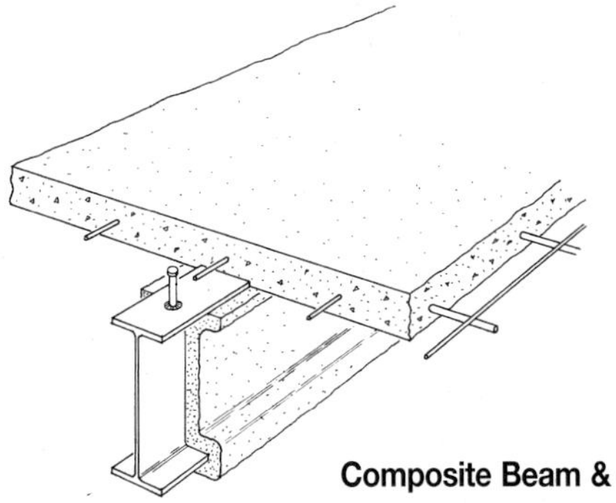

Composite Beam & Cast in Place Slab

**General:** Composite construction of wide flange beams and concrete slabs is most efficiently used when loads are heavy and spans are moderately long. It is stiffer with less deflection than non-composite construction of similar depth and spans.

### B1010 252 Composite Beam & Cast in Place Slab

| | BAY SIZE (FT.) | SUPERIMPOSED LOAD (P.S.F.) | SLAB THICKNESS (IN.) | TOTAL DEPTH (FT.-IN.) | TOTAL LOAD (P.S.F.) | COST PER S.F. | | |
|---|---|---|---|---|---|---|---|---|
| | | | | | | MAT. | INST. | TOTAL |
| 3800 | 20x25 | 40 | 4 | 1 - 8 | 94 | 14.15 | 13.35 | 27.50 |
| 3900 | | 75 | 4 | 1 - 8 | 130 | 16.35 | 14.20 | 30.55 |
| 4000 | | 125 | 4 | 1 - 10 | 181 | 18.90 | 15.15 | 34.05 |
| 4100 | | 200 | 5 | 2 - 2 | 272 | 24.50 | 17.10 | 41.60 |
| 4200 | 25x25 | 40 | 4-1/2 | 1 - 8-1/2 | 99 | 14.75 | 13.50 | 28.25 |
| 4300 | | 75 | 4-1/2 | 1 - 10-1/2 | 136 | 17.65 | 14.60 | 32.25 |
| 4400 | | 125 | 5-1/2 | 2 - 0-1/2 | 200 | 21 | 15.80 | 36.80 |
| 4500 | | 200 | 5-1/2 | 2 - 2-1/2 | 278 | 25.50 | 17.50 | 43 |
| 4600 | 25x30 | 40 | 4-1/2 | 1 - 8-1/2 | 100 | 16.40 | 14.10 | 30.50 |
| 4700 | | 75 | 4-1/2 | 1 - 10-1/2 | 136 | 19.10 | 15.10 | 34.20 |
| 4800 | | 125 | 5-1/2 | 2 - 2-1/2 | 202 | 23.50 | 16.55 | 40.05 |
| 4900 | | 200 | 5-1/2 | 2 - 5-1/2 | 279 | 27.50 | 18.10 | 45.60 |
| 5000 | 30x30 | 40 | 4 | 1 - 8 | 95 | 16.35 | 14.10 | 30.45 |
| 5200 | | 75 | 4 | 2 - 1 | 131 | 18.85 | 14.95 | 33.80 |
| 5400 | | 125 | 4 | 2 - 4 | 183 | 23 | 16.45 | 39.45 |
| 5600 | | 200 | 5 | 2 - 10 | 274 | 29.50 | 18.60 | 48.10 |
| 5800 | 30x35 | 40 | 4 | 2 - 1 | 95 | 17.25 | 14.35 | 31.60 |
| 6000 | | 75 | 4 | 2 - 4 | 139 | 20.50 | 15.50 | 36 |
| 6250 | | 125 | 4 | 2 - 4 | 185 | 26.50 | 17.50 | 44 |
| 6500 | | 200 | 5 | 2 - 11 | 276 | 32.50 | 19.55 | 52.05 |
| 8000 | 35x35 | 40 | 4 | 2 - 1 | 96 | 18.15 | 14.65 | 32.80 |
| 8250 | | 75 | 4 | 2 - 4 | 133 | 21.50 | 15.80 | 37.30 |
| 8500 | | 125 | 4 | 2 - 10 | 185 | 25.50 | 17.25 | 42.75 |
| 8750 | | 200 | 5 | 3 - 5 | 276 | 33 | 19.80 | 52.80 |
| 9000 | 35x40 | 40 | 4 | 2 - 4 | 97 | 20 | 15.30 | 35.30 |
| 9250 | | 75 | 4 | 2 - 4 | 134 | 23.50 | 16.30 | 39.80 |
| 9500 | | 125 | 4 | 2 - 7 | 186 | 28 | 18 | 46 |
| 9750 | | 200 | 5 | 3 - 5 | 278 | 36.50 | 21 | 57.50 |

## B1010 Floor Construction

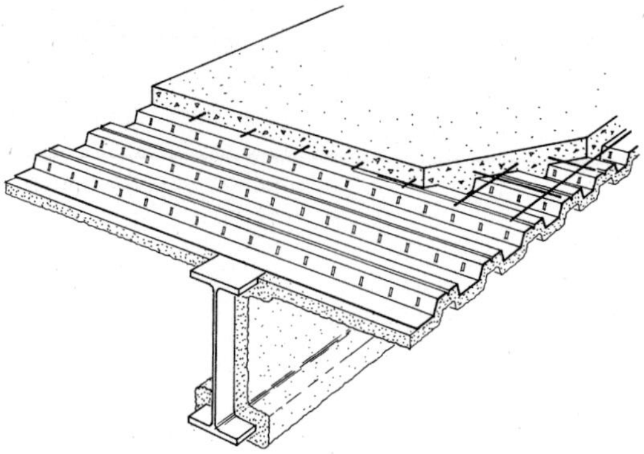

Wide Flange, Composite Deck & Slab

The table below lists costs per S.F. for floors using steel beams and girders, composite steel deck, concrete slab reinforced with W.W.F. and sprayed fiber fireproofing (non- asbestos) on the steel beams and girders and on the steel deck.

### B1010 254 W Shape, Composite Deck, & Slab

| | BAY SIZE (FT.) BEAM X GIRD | SUPERIMPOSED LOAD (P.S.F.) | SLAB THICKNESS (IN.) | TOTAL DEPTH (FT.-IN.) | TOTAL LOAD (P.S.F.) | COST PER S.F. | | |
|---|---|---|---|---|---|---|---|---|
| | | | | | | MAT. | INST. | TOTAL |
| 0540 | 15x20 | 40 | 5 | 1-7 | 89 | 16.35 | 8.05 | 24.40 |
| 0560 | | 75 | 5 | 1-9 | 125 | 17.80 | 8.55 | 26.35 |
| 0580 | | 125 | 5 | 1-11 | 176 | 20.50 | 9.35 | 29.85 |
| 0600 | | 200 | 5 | 2-2 | 254 | 25.50 | 10.70 | 36.20 |
| 0700 | 20x20 | 40 | 5 | 1-9 | 90 | 17.65 | 8.40 | 26.05 |
| 0720 | | 75 | 5 | 1-9 | 126 | 19.80 | 9.10 | 28.90 |
| 0740 | | 125 | 5 | 1-11 | 177 | 22.50 | 9.95 | 32.45 |
| 0760 | | 200 | 5 | 2-5 | 255 | 27 | 11.10 | 38.10 |
| 0780 | 20x25 | 40 | 5 | 1-9 | 90 | 18.45 | 8.35 | 26.80 |
| 0800 | | 75 | 5 | 1-9 | 127 | 22.50 | 9.65 | 32.15 |
| 0820 | | 125 | 5 | 1-11 | 180 | 27.50 | 10.55 | 38.05 |
| 0840 | | 200 | 5 | 2-5 | 256 | 29 | 11.95 | 40.95 |
| 0940 | 25x25 | 40 | 5 | 1-11 | 91 | 20.50 | 9 | 29.50 |
| 0960 | | 75 | 5 | 2-5 | 178 | 23.50 | 9.90 | 33.40 |
| 0980 | | 125 | 5 | 2-5 | 181 | 29.50 | 11.05 | 40.55 |
| 1000 | | 200 | 5-1/2 | 2-8-1/2 | 263 | 31 | 12.85 | 43.85 |
| 1400 | 25x30 | 40 | 5 | 2-5 | 91 | 20 | 9.20 | 29.20 |
| 1500 | | 75 | 5 | 2-5 | 128 | 24.50 | 10.25 | 34.75 |
| 1600 | | 125 | 5 | 2-8 | 180 | 27 | 11.45 | 38.45 |
| 1700 | | 200 | 5 | 2-11 | 259 | 34 | 13.20 | 47.20 |
| 2200 | 30x30 | 40 | 5 | 2-2 | 92 | 22 | 9.80 | 31.80 |
| 2300 | | 75 | 5 | 2-5 | 129 | 25.50 | 10.95 | 36.45 |
| 2400 | | 125 | 5 | 2-11 | 182 | 30 | 12.30 | 42.30 |
| 2500 | | 200 | 5 | 3-2 | 263 | 40.50 | 15.45 | 55.95 |
| 2600 | 30x35 | 40 | 5 | 2-5 | 94 | 24 | 10.40 | 34.40 |
| 2700 | | 75 | 5 | 2-11 | 131 | 27.50 | 11.50 | 39 |
| 2800 | | 125 | 5 | 3-2 | 183 | 32 | 12.95 | 44.95 |
| 2900 | | 200 | 5-1/2 | 3-5-1/2 | 268 | 39.50 | 14.90 | 54.40 |
| 3800 | 35x35 | 40 | 5 | 2-8 | 94 | 25 | 10.40 | 35.40 |
| 3900 | | 75 | 5 | 2-11 | 131 | 29 | 11.55 | 40.55 |
| 4000 | | 125 | 5 | 3-5 | 184 | 34 | 13.25 | 47.25 |
| 4100 | | 200 | 5-1/2 | 3-5-1/2 | 270 | 44.50 | 15.70 | 60.20 |

## B1010 Floor Construction

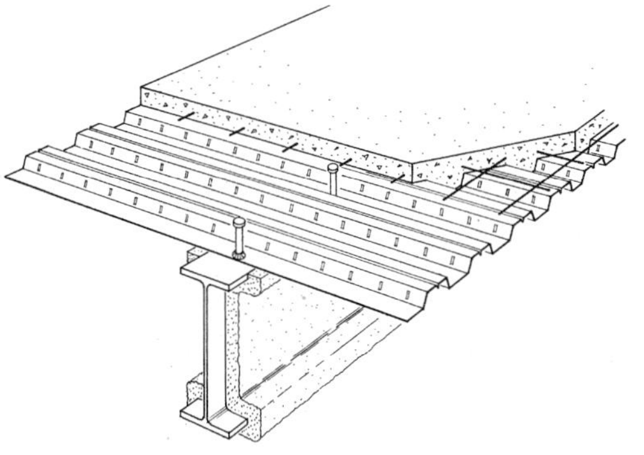

Composite Beam, Deck & Slab

The table below lists costs per S.F. for floors using composite steel beams with welded shear studs, composite steel deck and light weight concrete slab reinforced with W.W.F.

### B1010 256 Composite Beams, Deck & Slab

| | BAY SIZE (FT.) | SUPERIMPOSED LOAD (P.S.F.) | SLAB THICKNESS (IN.) | TOTAL DEPTH (FT.-IN.) | TOTAL LOAD (P.S.F.) | COST PER S.F. | | |
|---|---|---|---|---|---|---|---|---|
| | | | | | | MAT. | INST. | TOTAL |
| 2400 | 20x25 | 40 | 5-1/2 | 1 - 5-1/2 | 80 | 17.15 | 7.45 | 24.60 |
| 2500 | | 75 | 5-1/2 | 1 - 9-1/2 | 115 | 17.70 | 7.45 | 25.15 |
| 2750 | | 125 | 5-1/2 | 1 - 9-1/2 | 167 | 22 | 8.70 | 30.70 |
| 2900 | | 200 | 6-1/4 | 1 - 11-1/2 | 251 | 24.50 | 9.45 | 33.95 |
| 3000 | 25x25 | 40 | 5-1/2 | 1 - 9-1/2 | 82 | 17.55 | 7.10 | 24.65 |
| 3100 | | 75 | 5-1/2 | 1 - 11-1/2 | 118 | 19.25 | 7.20 | 26.45 |
| 3200 | | 125 | 5-1/2 | 2 - 2-1/2 | 169 | 20.50 | 7.75 | 28.25 |
| 3300 | | 200 | 6-1/4 | 2 - 6-1/4 | 252 | 27.50 | 9.10 | 36.60 |
| 3400 | 25x30 | 40 | 5-1/2 | 1 - 11-1/2 | 83 | 17.80 | 7.05 | 24.85 |
| 3600 | | 75 | 5-1/2 | 1 - 11-1/2 | 119 | 19 | 7.10 | 26.10 |
| 3900 | | 125 | 5-1/2 | 1 - 11-1/2 | 170 | 22 | 8 | 30 |
| 4000 | | 200 | 6-1/4 | 2 - 6-1/4 | 252 | 27.50 | 9.15 | 36.65 |
| 4200 | 30x30 | 40 | 5-1/2 | 1 - 11-1/2 | 81 | 17.20 | 7.25 | 24.45 |
| 4400 | | 75 | 5-1/2 | 2 - 2-1/2 | 116 | 18.60 | 7.60 | 26.20 |
| 4500 | | 125 | 5-1/2 | 2 - 5-1/2 | 168 | 22.50 | 8.50 | 31 |
| 4700 | | 200 | 6-1/4 | 2 - 9-1/4 | 252 | 26.50 | 9.90 | 36.40 |
| 4900 | 30x35 | 40 | 5-1/2 | 2 - 2-1/2 | 82 | 17.95 | 7.50 | 25.45 |
| 5100 | | 75 | 5-1/2 | 2 - 5-1/2 | 117 | 19.50 | 7.70 | 27.20 |
| 5300 | | 125 | 5-1/2 | 2 - 5-1/2 | 169 | 23 | 8.70 | 31.70 |
| 5500 | | 200 | 6-1/4 | 2 - 9-1/4 | 254 | 26.50 | 9.90 | 36.40 |
| 5750 | 35x35 | 40 | 5-1/2 | 2 - 5-1/2 | 84 | 19.65 | 7.55 | 27.20 |
| 6000 | | 75 | 5-1/2 | 2 - 5-1/2 | 121 | 22 | 8.05 | 30.05 |
| 7000 | | 125 | 5-1/2 | 2 - 8-1/2 | 170 | 26 | 9.25 | 35.25 |
| 7200 | | 200 | 5-1/2 | 2 - 11-1/2 | 254 | 30.50 | 10.25 | 40.75 |
| 7400 | 35x40 | 40 | 5-1/2 | 2 - 5-1/2 | 85 | 21.50 | 8.10 | 29.60 |
| 7600 | | 75 | 5-1/2 | 2 - 5-1/2 | 121 | 23 | 8.40 | 31.40 |
| 8000 | | 125 | 5-1/2 | 2 - 5-1/2 | 171 | 26.50 | 9.40 | 35.90 |
| 9000 | | 200 | 5-1/2 | 2 - 11-1/2 | 255 | 32.50 | 10.70 | 43.20 |

## B1010 Floor Construction

**Description:** Table B1010 258 lists S.F. costs for steel deck and concrete slabs for various spans.

**Description:** Table B1010 261 lists the S.F. costs for wood joists and a minimum thickness plywood subfloor.

**Description:** Table B1010 264 lists the S.F. costs, total load, and member sizes, for various bay sizes and loading conditions.

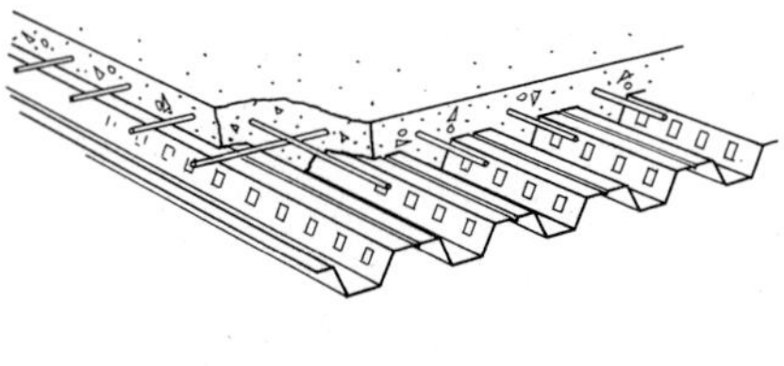

Metal Deck/Concrete Fill

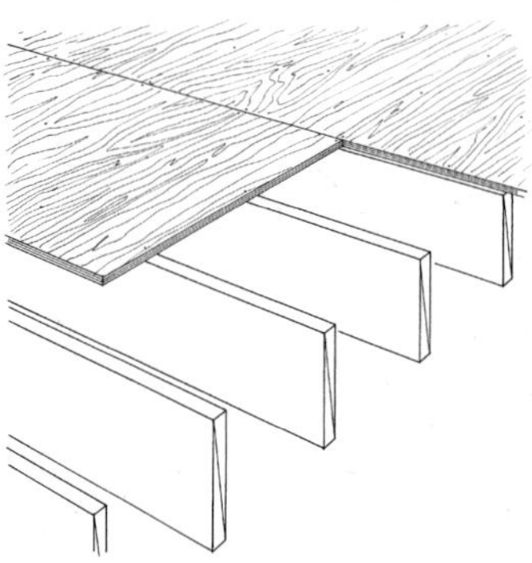

Wood Joist

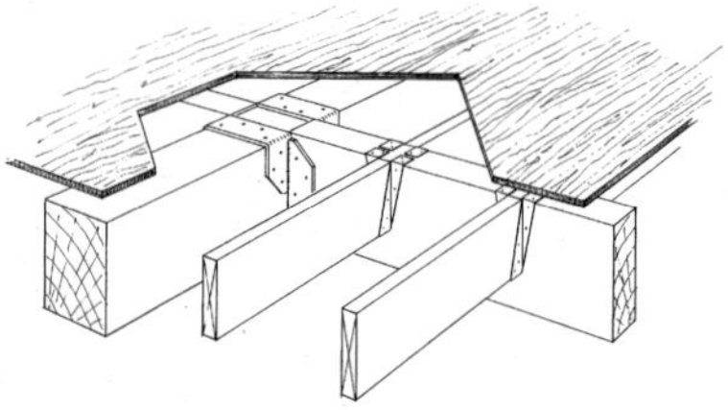

Wood Beam and Joist

### B1010 258 Metal Deck/Concrete Fill

| | SUPERIMPOSED LOAD (P.S.F.) | DECK SPAN (FT.) | DECK GAGE DEPTH | SLAB THICKNESS (IN.) | TOTAL LOAD (P.S.F.) | COST PER S.F. | | |
|---|---|---|---|---|---|---|---|---|
| | | | | | | MAT. | INST. | TOTAL |
| 0900 | 125 | 6 | 22 1-1/2 | 4 | 164 | 5.35 | 3.02 | 8.37 |
| 0920 | | 7 | 20 1-1/2 | 4 | 164 | 6 | 3.20 | 9.20 |
| 0950 | | 8 | 20 1-1/2 | 4 | 165 | 6 | 3.20 | 9.20 |
| 0970 | | 9 | 18 1-1/2 | 4 | 165 | 7.05 | 3.20 | 10.25 |
| 1000 | | 10 | 18 2 | 4 | 165 | 6.30 | 3.34 | 9.64 |
| 1020 | | 11 | 18 3 | 5 | 169 | 7.95 | 3.61 | 11.56 |

### B1010 261 Wood Joist

| | | COST PER S.F. | | |
|---|---|---|---|---|
| | | MAT. | INST. | TOTAL |
| 2900 | 2"x8", 12" O.C. | 4.55 | 2.37 | 6.92 |
| 2905 | 2"x8", 12" O.C. | 5.20 | 2.34 | 7.54 |
| 2950 | 16" O.C. | 3.75 | 2.03 | 5.78 |
| 3000 | 24" O.C. | 3.60 | 1.88 | 5.48 |
| 3300 | 2"x10", 12" O.C. | 5.65 | 2.70 | 8.35 |
| 3350 | 16" O.C. | 4.58 | 2.27 | 6.85 |
| 3400 | 24" O.C. | 4.11 | 2.03 | 6.14 |
| 3700 | 2"x12", 12" O.C. | 6.50 | 2.74 | 9.24 |
| 3750 | 16" O.C. | 5.20 | 2.30 | 7.50 |
| 3800 | 24" O.C. | 4.56 | 2.06 | 6.62 |
| 4100 | 2"x14", 12" O.C. | 9.55 | 2.97 | 12.52 |
| 4150 | 16" O.C. | 7.50 | 2.48 | 9.98 |
| 4200 | 24" O.C. | 6.10 | 2.18 | 8.28 |
| 7101 | Note: Subfloor cost is included in these prices. | | | |

### B1010 264 Wood Beam & Joist

| | BAY SIZE (FT.) | SUPERIMPOSED LOAD (P.S.F.) | GIRDER BEAM (IN.) | JOISTS (IN.) | TOTAL LOAD (P.S.F.) | COST PER S.F. | | |
|---|---|---|---|---|---|---|---|---|
| | | | | | | MAT. | INST. | TOTAL |
| 2000 | 15x15 | 40 | 8 x 12 4 x 12 | 2 x 6 @ 16 | 53 | 9.80 | 4.87 | 14.67 |
| 2050 | | 75 | 8 x 16 4 x 16 | 2 x 8 @ 16 | 90 | 13.15 | 5.20 | 18.35 |
| 2100 | | 125 | 12 x 16 6 x 16 | 2 x 8 @ 12 | 144 | 19.55 | 6.50 | 26.05 |
| 2150 | | 200 | 14 x 22 12 x 16 | 2 x 10 @ 12 | 227 | 33.50 | 8.95 | 42.45 |
| 3000 | 20x20 | 40 | 10 x 14 10 x 12 | 2 x 8 @ 16 | 63 | 15.25 | 4.92 | 20.17 |
| 3050 | | 75 | 12 x 16 8 x 16 | 2 x 10 @ 16 | 102 | 20.50 | 5.85 | 26.35 |
| 3100 | | 125 | 14 x 22 12 x 16 | 2 x 10 @ 12 | 163 | 27.50 | 7.35 | 34.85 |

## B1010 Floor Construction

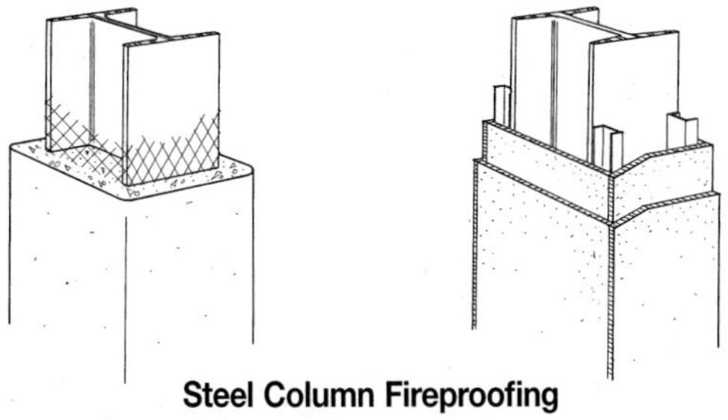


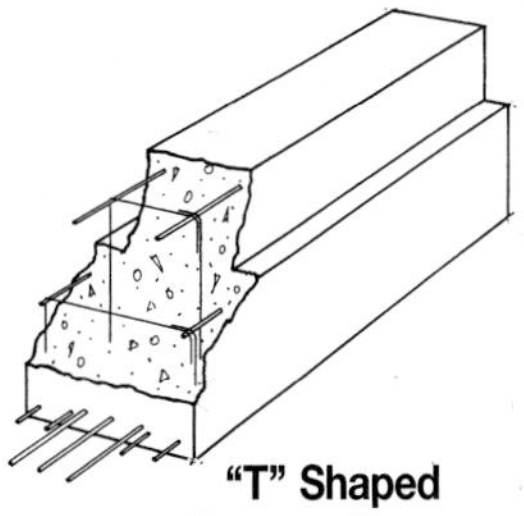


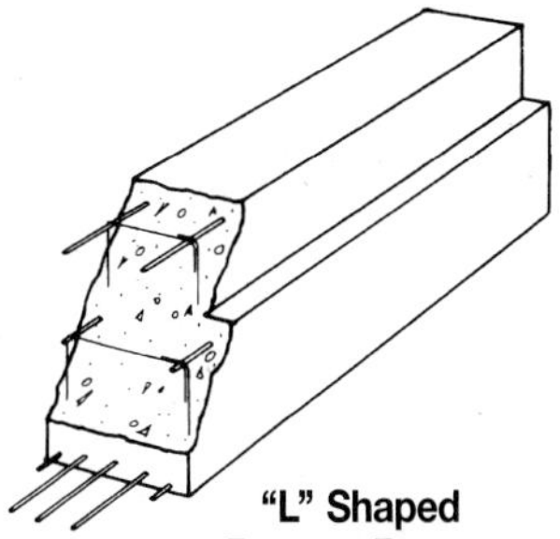


### B1010 720 Steel Column Fireproofing

| | ENCASEMENT SYSTEM | COLUMN SIZE (IN.) | THICKNESS (IN.) | FIRE RATING (HRS.) | WEIGHT (P.L.F.) | COST PER V.L.F. | | |
|---|---|---|---|---|---|---|---|---|
| | | | | | | MAT. | INST. | TOTAL |
| 3000 | Concrete | 8 | 1 | 1 | 110 | 10.70 | 44 | 54.70 |
| 3300 | | 14 | 1 | 1 | 258 | 17.55 | 64.50 | 82.05 |
| 3400 | | | 2 | 3 | 325 | 21 | 72.50 | 93.50 |
| 3450 | Gypsum board | 8 | 1/2 | 2 | 8 | 8.40 | 27 | 35.40 |
| 3550 | 1 layer | 14 | 1/2 | 2 | 18 | 8.75 | 29 | 37.75 |
| 3600 | Gypsum board | 8 | 1 | 3 | 14 | 10.15 | 34.50 | 44.65 |
| 3650 | 1/2" fire rated | 10 | 1 | 3 | 17 | 10.65 | 36.50 | 47.15 |
| 3700 | 2 layers | 14 | 1 | 3 | 22 | 10.90 | 37.50 | 48.40 |
| 3750 | Gypsum board | 8 | 1-1/2 | 3 | 23 | 12.30 | 43.50 | 55.80 |
| 3800 | 1/2" fire rated | 10 | 1-1/2 | 3 | 27 | 13.35 | 48 | 61.35 |
| 3850 | 3 layers | 14 | 1-1/2 | 3 | 35 | 14.40 | 53 | 67.40 |
| 3900 | Sprayed fiber | 8 | 1-1/2 | 2 | 6.3 | 4.47 | 8.75 | 13.22 |
| 3950 | Direct application | | 2 | 3 | 8.3 | 6.15 | 12.05 | 18.20 |
| 4050 | | 10 | 1-1/2 | 2 | 7.9 | 5.40 | 10.55 | 15.95 |
| 4200 | Sprayed fiber | 14 | 1-1/2 | 2 | 10.8 | 6.70 | 13.15 | 19.85 |

## B1020 Roof Construction

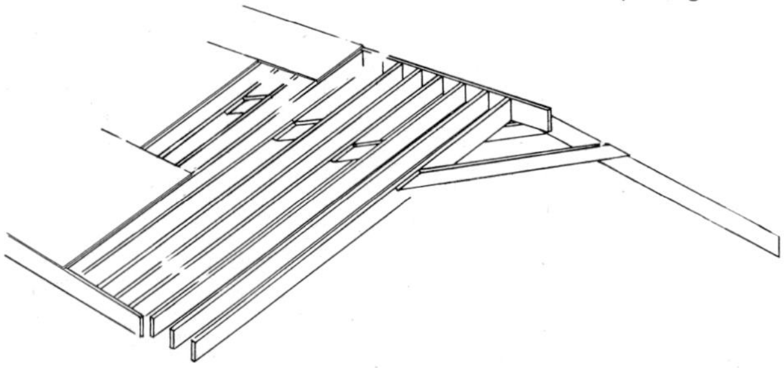

The table below lists prices per S.F. for roof rafters and sheathing by nominal size and spacing. Sheathing is 5/16″ CDX for 12″ and 16″ spacing and 3/8″ CDX for 24″ spacing.

**Factors for Converting Inclined to Horizontal**

| Roof Slope | Approx. Angle | Factor | Roof Slope | Approx. Angle | Factor |
|---|---|---|---|---|---|
| Flat | 0° | 1.000 | 12 in 12 | 45.0° | 1.414 |
| 1 in 12 | 4.8° | 1.003 | 13 in 12 | 47.3° | 1.474 |
| 2 in 12 | 9.5° | 1.014 | 14 in 12 | 49.4° | 1.537 |
| 3 in 12 | 14.0° | 1.031 | 15 in 12 | 51.3° | 1.601 |
| 4 in 12 | 18.4° | 1.054 | 16 in 12 | 53.1° | 1.667 |
| 5 in 12 | 22.6° | 1.083 | 17 in 12 | 54.8° | 1.734 |
| 6 in 12 | 26.6° | 1.118 | 18 in 12 | 56.3° | 1.803 |
| 7 in 12 | 30.3° | 1.158 | 19 in 12 | 57.7° | 1.873 |
| 8 in 12 | 33.7° | 1.202 | 20 in 12 | 59.0° | 1.943 |
| 9 in 12 | 36.9° | 1.250 | 21 in 12 | 60.3° | 2.015 |
| 10 in 12 | 39.8° | 1.302 | 22 in 12 | 61.4° | 2.088 |
| 11 in 12 | 42.5° | 1.357 | 23 in 12 | 62.4° | 2.162 |

| B1020 102 | Wood/Flat or Pitched | COST PER S.F. MAT. | INST. | TOTAL |
|---|---|---|---|---|
| 2500 | Flat rafter, 2″x4″, 12″ O.C. | 2.51 | 2.14 | 4.65 |
| 2550 | 16″ O.C. | 2.18 | 1.83 | 4.01 |
| 2600 | 24″ O.C. | 1.94 | 1.59 | 3.53 |
| 2900 | 2″x6″, 12″ O.C. | 3.40 | 2.15 | 5.55 |
| 2950 | 16″ O.C. | 2.85 | 1.85 | 4.70 |
| 3000 | 24″ O.C. | 2.38 | 1.58 | 3.96 |
| 3300 | 2″x8″, 12″ O.C. | 4.36 | 2.31 | 6.67 |
| 3350 | 16″ O.C. | 3.56 | 1.96 | 5.52 |
| 3355 | 16″ O.C. | 4.01 | 1.97 | 5.98 |
| 3400 | 24″ O.C. | 2.88 | 1.67 | 4.55 |
| 3700 | 2″x10″, 12″ O.C. | 5.45 | 2.63 | 8.08 |
| 3750 | 16″ O.C. | 4.39 | 2.20 | 6.59 |
| 3800 | 24″ O.C. | 3.39 | 1.82 | 5.21 |
| 4100 | 2″x12″, 12″ O.C. | 6.30 | 2.67 | 8.97 |
| 4150 | 16″ O.C. | 5.45 | 2.44 | 7.89 |
| 4200 | 24″ O.C. | 3.83 | 1.85 | 5.68 |
| 4500 | 2″x14″, 12″ O.C. | 9.40 | 3.92 | 13.32 |
| 4550 | 16″ O.C. | 7.35 | 3.18 | 10.53 |
| 4600 | 24″ O.C. | 5.40 | 2.48 | 7.88 |
| 4900 | 3″x6″, 12″ O.C. | 11.10 | 2.27 | 13.37 |
| 4950 | 16″ O.C. | 8.60 | 1.93 | 10.53 |
| 5000 | 24″ O.C. | 6.25 | 1.65 | 7.90 |
| 5300 | 3″x8″, 12″ O.C. | 14.40 | 2.53 | 16.93 |
| 5350 | 16″ O.C. | 11.10 | 2.13 | 13.23 |
| 5400 | 24″ O.C. | 7.90 | 1.77 | 9.67 |
| 5700 | 3″x10″, 12″ O.C. | 17.60 | 2.88 | 20.48 |
| 5750 | 16″ O.C. | 13.50 | 2.39 | 15.89 |
| 5800 | 24″ O.C. | 9.50 | 1.95 | 11.45 |
| 6100 | 3″x12″, 12″ O.C. | 21 | 3.47 | 24.47 |
| 6150 | 16″ O.C. | 16.15 | 2.84 | 18.99 |
| 6200 | 24″ O.C. | 11.25 | 2.24 | 13.49 |
| 7001 | Wood truss, 4 in 12 slope, 24″ O.C., 24′ to 29′ span | 6.60 | 3.72 | 10.32 |
| 7100 | 30′ to 43′ span | 9 | 4.03 | 13.03 |
| 7200 | 44′ to 60′ span | 8.30 | 3.72 | 12.02 |

## B1020 Roof Construction

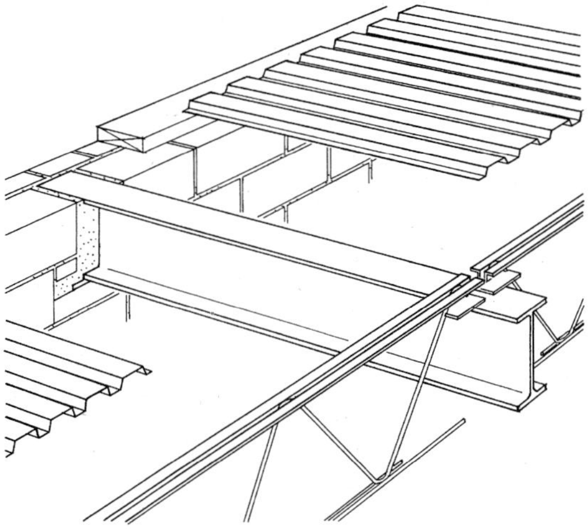

Steel Joists, Beams and Deck on Bearing Walls

The table below lists the cost per S.F. for a roof system with steel columns, beams and deck using open web steel joists and 1-1/2" galvanized metal deck. Perimeter of system is supported on bearing walls.

Fireproofing is not included. Costs/S.F. are based on a building 4 bays long and 4 bays wide.

Column costs are additive. Costs for the bearing walls are not included.

### B1020 108 Steel Joists, Beams & Deck on Columns & Walls

| | BAY SIZE (FT.) | SUPERIMPOSED LOAD (P.S.F.) | DEPTH (IN.) | TOTAL LOAD (P.S.F.) | COLUMN ADD | COST PER S.F. | | |
|---|---|---|---|---|---|---|---|---|
| | | | | | | MAT. | INST. | TOTAL |
| 1800 | 20x20 | 20 | 16 | 40 | | 5.90 | 1.57 | 7.47 |
| 1900 | | | | | columns | .76 | .18 | .94 |
| 2000 | | 30 | 18 | 50 | | 5.90 | 1.57 | 7.47 |
| 2100 | | | | | columns | .76 | .18 | .94 |
| 2200 | | 40 | 18 | 60 | | 6.45 | 1.77 | 8.22 |
| 2300 | | | | | columns | .76 | .18 | .94 |
| 2400 | 20x25 | 20 | 18 | 40 | | 5.85 | 1.62 | 7.47 |
| 2500 | | | | | columns | .60 | .14 | .74 |
| 2600 | | 30 | 18 | 50 | | 6.10 | 1.68 | 7.78 |
| 2700 | | | | | columns | .60 | .14 | .74 |
| 2800 | | 40 | 20 | 60 | | 6.40 | 1.81 | 8.21 |
| 2900 | | | | | columns | .81 | .19 | 1 |
| 3000 | 25x25 | 20 | 18 | 40 | | 6.25 | 1.71 | 7.96 |
| 3100 | | | | | columns | .49 | .12 | .61 |
| 3200 | | 30 | 22 | 50 | | 6.65 | 1.82 | 8.47 |
| 3300 | | | | | columns | .64 | .15 | .79 |
| 3400 | | 40 | 20 | 60 | | 7.25 | 2.02 | 9.27 |
| 3500 | | | | | columns | .64 | .15 | .79 |
| 3600 | 25x30 | 20 | 22 | 40 | | 7.25 | 1.63 | 8.88 |
| 3700 | | | | | columns | .54 | .13 | .67 |
| 3800 | | 30 | 20 | 50 | | 8.15 | 1.84 | 9.99 |
| 3900 | | | | | columns | .54 | .13 | .67 |
| 4000 | | 40 | 25 | 60 | | 8.40 | 1.90 | 10.30 |
| 4100 | | | | | columns | .64 | .15 | .79 |
| 4200 | 30x30 | 20 | 25 | 42 | | 7.85 | 1.77 | 9.62 |
| 4300 | | | | | columns | .45 | .11 | .56 |
| 4400 | | 30 | 22 | 52 | | 8.50 | 1.92 | 10.42 |
| 4500 | | | | | columns | .54 | .13 | .67 |
| 4600 | | 40 | 28 | 62 | | 8.75 | 1.99 | 10.74 |
| 4700 | | | | | columns | .54 | .13 | .67 |

## B1020 Roof Construction

### B1020 108 Steel Joists, Beams & Deck on Columns & Walls

| | BAY SIZE (FT.) | SUPERIMPOSED LOAD (P.S.F.) | DEPTH (IN.) | TOTAL LOAD (P.S.F.) | COLUMN ADD | COST PER S.F. | | |
|---|---|---|---|---|---|---|---|---|
| | | | | | | MAT. | INST. | TOTAL |
| 4800 | 30x35 | 20 | 22 | 42 | | 8.15 | 1.84 | 9.99 |
| 4900 | | | | | columns | .46 | .11 | .57 |
| 5000 | | 30 | 28 | 52 | | 8.55 | 1.94 | 10.49 |
| 5100 | | | | | columns | .46 | .11 | .57 |
| 5200 | | 40 | 25 | 62 | | 9.20 | 2.09 | 11.29 |
| 5300 | | | | | columns | .54 | .13 | .67 |
| 5400 | 35x35 | 20 | 28 | 42 | | 8.20 | 1.86 | 10.06 |
| 5500 | | | | | columns | .39 | .09 | .48 |
| 5600 | | 30 | 25 | 52 | | 9.75 | 2.21 | 11.96 |
| 5700 | | | | | columns | .46 | .11 | .57 |
| 5800 | | 40 | 28 | 62 | | 9.80 | 2.23 | 12.03 |
| 5900 | | | | | columns | .51 | .12 | .63 |

## B1020 Roof Construction

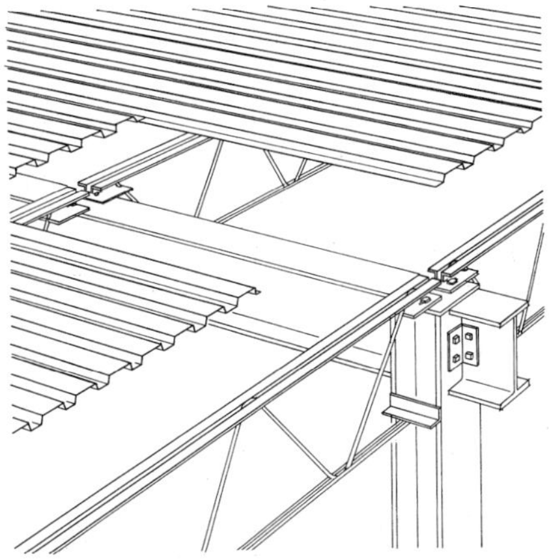

Steel Joists, Beams and Deck on Columns

**Description:** The table below lists the cost per S.F. for a roof system with steel columns, beams, and deck, using open web steel joists and 1-1/2" galvanized metal deck.

Column costs are additive. Fireproofing is not included.

### B1020 112 Steel Joists, Beams, & Deck on Columns

| | BAY SIZE (FT.) | SUPERIMPOSED LOAD (P.S.F.) | DEPTH (IN.) | TOTAL LOAD (P.S.F.) | COLUMN ADD | COST PER S.F. | | |
|---|---|---|---|---|---|---|---|---|
| | | | | | | MAT. | INST. | TOTAL |
| 1100 | 15x20 | 20 | 16 | 40 | | 6.20 | 1.70 | 7.90 |
| 1200 | | | | | columns | 2.80 | .66 | 3.46 |
| 1500 | | 40 | 18 | 60 | | 6.80 | 1.89 | 8.69 |
| 1600 | | | | | columns | 2.80 | .66 | 3.46 |
| 2300 | 20x25 | 20 | 18 | 40 | | 6.90 | 1.91 | 8.81 |
| 2400 | | | | | columns | 1.68 | .40 | 2.08 |
| 2700 | | 40 | 20 | 60 | | 7.60 | 2.15 | 9.75 |
| 2800 | | | | | columns | 2.24 | .53 | 2.77 |
| 2900 | 25x25 | 20 | 18 | 40 | | 7.95 | 2.16 | 10.11 |
| 3000 | | | | | columns | 1.34 | .32 | 1.66 |
| 3100 | | 30 | 22 | 50 | | 8.20 | 2.21 | 10.41 |
| 3200 | | | | | columns | 1.79 | .43 | 2.22 |
| 3300 | | 40 | 20 | 60 | | 9 | 2.48 | 11.48 |
| 3400 | | | | | columns | 1.79 | .43 | 2.22 |
| 3500 | 25x30 | 20 | 22 | 40 | | 8.55 | 1.94 | 10.49 |
| 3600 | | | | | columns | 1.50 | .36 | 1.86 |
| 3900 | | 40 | 25 | 60 | | 10.15 | 2.32 | 12.47 |
| 4000 | | | | | columns | 1.79 | .43 | 2.22 |
| 4100 | 30x30 | 20 | 25 | 42 | | 9.50 | 2.17 | 11.67 |
| 4200 | | | | | columns | 1.25 | .30 | 1.55 |
| 4300 | | 30 | 22 | 52 | | 10.40 | 2.37 | 12.77 |
| 4400 | | | | | columns | 1.50 | .36 | 1.86 |
| 4500 | | 40 | 28 | 62 | | 10.80 | 2.47 | 13.27 |
| 4600 | | | | | columns | 1.50 | .36 | 1.86 |
| 5300 | 35x35 | 20 | 28 | 42 | | 10.35 | 2.36 | 12.71 |
| 5400 | | | | | columns | 1.10 | .26 | 1.36 |
| 5500 | | 30 | 25 | 52 | | 11.40 | 2.61 | 14.01 |
| 5600 | | | | | columns | 1.28 | .30 | 1.58 |
| 5700 | | 40 | 28 | 62 | | 12.20 | 2.80 | 15 |
| 5800 | | | | | columns | 1.42 | .34 | 1.76 |

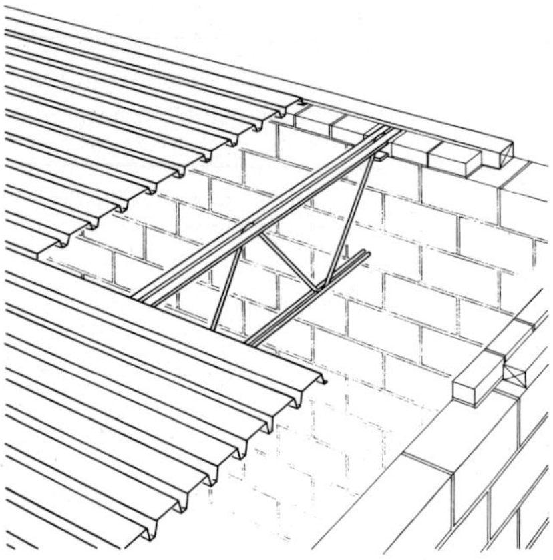

**Description:** The table below lists the cost per S.F. for a roof system using open web steel joists and 1-1/2" galvanized metal deck. The system is assumed supported on bearing walls or other suitable support. Costs for the supports are not included.

### B1020 116 Steel Joists & Deck on Bearing Walls

| | BAY SIZE (FT.) | SUPERIMPOSED LOAD (P.S.F.) | DEPTH (IN.) | TOTAL LOAD (P.S.F.) | | COST PER S.F. | | |
|---|---|---|---|---|---|---|---|---|
| | | | | | | MAT. | INST. | TOTAL |
| 1100 | 20 | 20 | 13-1/2 | 40 | | 4.34 | 1.22 | 5.56 |
| 1200 | | 30 | 15-1/2 | 50 | | 4.40 | 1.25 | 5.65 |
| 1300 | | 40 | 15-1/2 | 60 | | 4.62 | 1.35 | 5.97 |
| 1400 | 25 | 20 | 17-1/2 | 40 | | 4.63 | 1.35 | 5.98 |
| 1500 | | 30 | 17-1/2 | 50 | | 4.89 | 1.47 | 6.36 |
| 1600 | | 40 | 19-1/2 | 60 | | 4.94 | 1.49 | 6.43 |
| 1700 | 30 | 20 | 19-1/2 | 40 | | 4.93 | 1.49 | 6.42 |
| 1800 | | 30 | 21-1/2 | 50 | | 5 | 1.52 | 6.52 |
| 1900 | | 40 | 23-1/2 | 60 | | 5.30 | 1.65 | 6.95 |
| 2000 | 35 | 20 | 23-1/2 | 40 | | 6.15 | 1.37 | 7.52 |
| 2100 | | 30 | 25-1/2 | 50 | | 6.30 | 1.41 | 7.71 |
| 2200 | | 40 | 25-1/2 | 60 | | 6.65 | 1.49 | 8.14 |
| 2300 | 40 | 20 | 25-1/2 | 41 | | 6.75 | 1.51 | 8.26 |
| 2400 | | 30 | 25-1/2 | 51 | | 7.15 | 1.60 | 8.75 |
| 2500 | | 40 | 25-1/2 | 61 | | 7.40 | 1.65 | 9.05 |
| 2600 | 45 | 20 | 27-1/2 | 41 | | 8.05 | 1.80 | 9.85 |
| 2700 | | 30 | 31-1/2 | 51 | | 8.45 | 1.90 | 10.35 |
| 2800 | | 40 | 31-1/2 | 61 | | 8.90 | 2 | 10.90 |
| 2900 | 50 | 20 | 29-1/2 | 42 | | 8.95 | 2.01 | 10.96 |
| 3000 | | 30 | 31-1/2 | 52 | | 9.75 | 2.19 | 11.94 |
| 3100 | | 40 | 31-1/2 | 62 | | 10.30 | 2.32 | 12.62 |
| 3200 | 60 | 20 | 37-1/2 | 42 | | 8.35 | 2.62 | 10.97 |
| 3300 | | 30 | 37-1/2 | 52 | | 9.10 | 2.90 | 12 |
| 3400 | | 40 | 37-1/2 | 62 | | 9.10 | 2.90 | 12 |
| 3500 | 70 | 20 | 41-1/2 | 42 | | 9.10 | 2.90 | 12 |
| 3600 | | 30 | 41-1/2 | 52 | | 9.60 | 3.09 | 12.69 |
| 3700 | | 40 | 41-1/2 | 64 | | 11.40 | 3.76 | 15.16 |
| 3800 | 80 | 20 | 45-1/2 | 44 | | 11.15 | 3.66 | 14.81 |
| 3900 | | 30 | 45-1/2 | 54 | | 11.15 | 3.66 | 14.81 |
| 4000 | | 40 | 45-1/2 | 64 | | 12.15 | 4.05 | 16.20 |
| 4400 | 100 | 20 | 57-1/2 | 44 | | 11.65 | 3.46 | 15.11 |
| 4500 | | 30 | 57-1/2 | 54 | | 13.70 | 4.13 | 17.83 |
| 4600 | | 40 | 57-1/2 | 65 | | 15 | 4.56 | 19.56 |
| 4700 | 125 | 20 | 69-1/2 | 44 | | 13.65 | 4.12 | 17.77 |
| 4800 | | 30 | 69-1/2 | 56 | | 15.70 | 4.80 | 20.50 |
| 4900 | | 40 | 69-1/2 | 67 | | 17.70 | 5.45 | 23.15 |

## B1020 Roof Construction

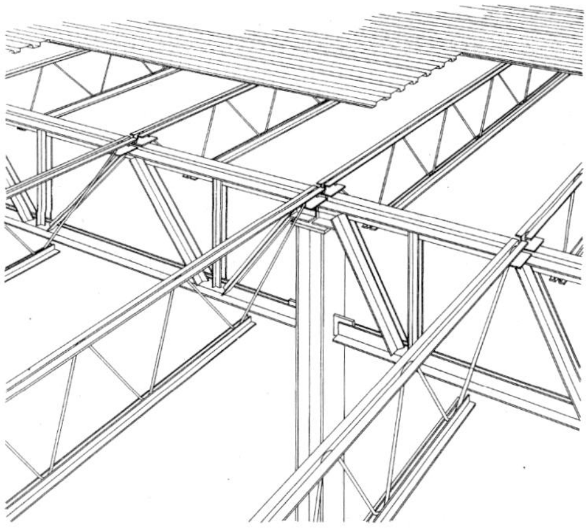

**Description:** The table below lists costs for a roof system supported on exterior bearing walls and interior columns. Costs include bracing, joist girders, open web steel joists and 1-1/2" galvanized metal deck.

Column costs are additive. Fireproofing is not included.

Costs/S.F. are based on a building 4 bays long and 4 bays wide. Costs for bearing walls are not included.

### B1020 120 Steel Joists, Joist Girders & Deck on Columns & Walls

| | BAY SIZE (FT.) GIRD X JOISTS | SUPERIMPOSED LOAD (P.S.F.) | DEPTH (IN.) | TOTAL LOAD (P.S.F.) | COLUMN ADD | COST PER S.F. | | |
|---|---|---|---|---|---|---|---|---|
| | | | | | | MAT. | INST. | TOTAL |
| 2350 | 30x35 | 20 | 32-1/2 | 40 | | 6.55 | 1.68 | 8.23 |
| 2400 | | | | | columns | .46 | .11 | .57 |
| 2550 | | 40 | 36-1/2 | 60 | | 7.25 | 1.87 | 9.12 |
| 2600 | | | | | columns | .54 | .13 | .67 |
| 2650 | 35x30 | 20 | 36-1/2 | 40 | | 6.05 | 1.58 | 7.63 |
| 2700 | | | | | columns | .46 | .11 | .57 |
| 2750 | | 30 | 36-1/2 | 50 | | 6.60 | 1.73 | 8.33 |
| 2800 | | | | | columns | .46 | .11 | .57 |
| 2850 | | 40 | 36-1/2 | 60 | | 8.70 | 2.24 | 10.94 |
| 2900 | | | | | columns | .54 | .13 | .67 |
| 3000 | 35x35 | 20 | 36-1/2 | 40 | | 7 | 2.07 | 9.07 |
| 3050 | | | | | columns | .40 | .09 | .49 |
| 3200 | | 40 | 36-1/2 | 60 | | 7.75 | 2.29 | 10.04 |
| 3250 | | | | | columns | .51 | .12 | .63 |
| 3300 | 35x40 | 20 | 36-1/2 | 40 | | 7.20 | 1.90 | 9.10 |
| 3350 | | | | | columns | .40 | .09 | .49 |
| 3500 | | 40 | 36-1/2 | 60 | | 7.95 | 2.12 | 10.07 |
| 3550 | | | | | columns | .45 | .11 | .56 |
| 3900 | 40x40 | 20 | 40-1/2 | 41 | | 8.25 | 2.16 | 10.41 |
| 3950 | | | | | columns | .39 | .09 | .48 |
| 4100 | | 40 | 40-1/2 | 61 | | 9.15 | 2.35 | 11.50 |
| 4150 | | | | | columns | .39 | .09 | .48 |
| 5100 | 45x50 | 20 | 52-1/2 | 41 | | 9.25 | 2.44 | 11.69 |
| 5150 | | | | | columns | .28 | .07 | .35 |
| 5300 | | 40 | 52-1/2 | 61 | | 11.10 | 2.92 | 14.02 |
| 5350 | | | | | columns | .40 | .09 | .49 |
| 5400 | 50x45 | 20 | 56-1/2 | 41 | | 8.90 | 2.38 | 11.28 |
| 5450 | | | | | columns | .28 | .07 | .35 |
| 5600 | | 40 | 56-1/2 | 61 | | 11.30 | 3 | 14.30 |
| 5650 | | | | | columns | .38 | .09 | .47 |
| 5700 | 50x50 | 20 | 56-1/2 | 42 | | 9.95 | 2.67 | 12.62 |
| 5750 | | | | | columns | .28 | .07 | .35 |
| 5900 | | 40 | 59 | 64 | | 9.40 | 3.28 | 12.68 |
| 5950 | | | | | columns | .40 | .09 | .49 |
| 6300 | 60x50 | 20 | 62-1/2 | 43 | | 10 | 2.72 | 12.72 |
| 6350 | | | | | columns | .45 | .11 | .56 |
| 6500 | | 40 | 71 | 65 | | 9.60 | 3.37 | 12.97 |
| 6550 | | | | | columns | .59 | .14 | .73 |

## B1020 Roof Construction

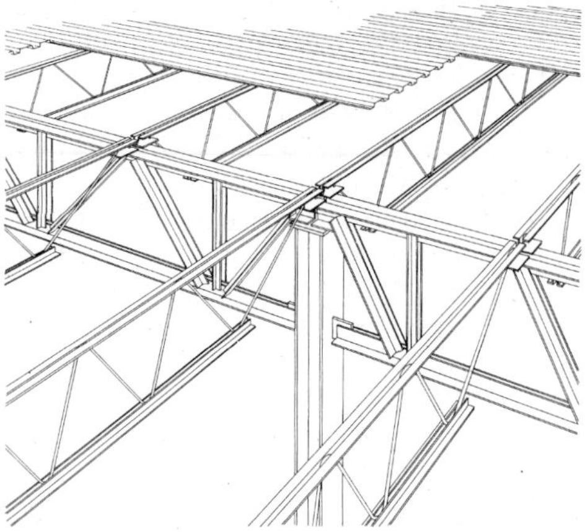

**Description:** The table below lists the cost per S.F. for a roof system supported on columns. Costs include joist girders, open web steel joists and 1-1/2" galvanized metal deck. Column costs are additive.

Fireproofing is not included. Costs/S.F. are based on a building 4 bays long and 4 bays wide.

Costs for wind columns are not included.

### B1020 124 Steel Joists & Joist Girders on Columns

| | BAY SIZE (FT.) GIRD X JOISTS | SUPERIMPOSED LOAD (P.S.F.) | DEPTH (IN.) | TOTAL LOAD (P.S.F.) | COLUMN ADD | COST PER S.F. | | |
|---|---|---|---|---|---|---|---|---|
| | | | | | | MAT. | INST. | TOTAL |
| 2000 | 30x30 | 20 | 17-1/2 | 40 | | 5.75 | 2.02 | 7.77 |
| 2050 | | | | | columns | 1.50 | .35 | 1.85 |
| 2100 | | 30 | 17-1/2 | 50 | | 6.15 | 2.19 | 8.34 |
| 2150 | | | | | columns | 1.50 | .35 | 1.85 |
| 2200 | | 40 | 21-1/2 | 60 | | 6.25 | 2.25 | 8.50 |
| 2250 | | | | | columns | 1.50 | .35 | 1.85 |
| 2300 | 30x35 | 20 | 32-1/2 | 40 | | 6.95 | 1.89 | 8.84 |
| 2350 | | | | | columns | 1.28 | .30 | 1.58 |
| 2500 | | 40 | 36-1/2 | 60 | | 7.70 | 2.10 | 9.80 |
| 2550 | | | | | columns | 1.50 | .35 | 1.85 |
| 3200 | 35x40 | 20 | 36-1/2 | 40 | | 8.85 | 2.57 | 11.42 |
| 3250 | | | | | columns | 1.12 | .26 | 1.38 |
| 3400 | | 40 | 36-1/2 | 60 | | 9.85 | 2.84 | 12.69 |
| 3450 | | | | | columns | 1.24 | .29 | 1.53 |
| 3800 | 40x40 | 20 | 40-1/2 | 41 | | 8.90 | 2.57 | 11.47 |
| 3850 | | | | | columns | 1.09 | .26 | 1.35 |
| 4000 | | 40 | 40-1/2 | 61 | | 9.90 | 2.84 | 12.74 |
| 4050 | | | | | columns | 1.09 | .26 | 1.35 |
| 4100 | 40x45 | 20 | 40-1/2 | 41 | | 9.55 | 2.90 | 12.45 |
| 4150 | | | | | columns | .97 | .23 | 1.20 |
| 4200 | | 30 | 40-1/2 | 51 | | 10.30 | 3.11 | 13.41 |
| 4250 | | | | | columns | .97 | .23 | 1.20 |
| 4300 | | 40 | 40-1/2 | 61 | | 11.40 | 3.39 | 14.79 |
| 4350 | | | | | columns | 1.09 | .26 | 1.35 |
| 5000 | 45x50 | 20 | 52-1/2 | 41 | | 10.10 | 2.95 | 13.05 |
| 5050 | | | | | columns | .77 | .18 | .95 |
| 5200 | | 40 | 52-1/2 | 61 | | 12.20 | 3.51 | 15.71 |
| 5250 | | | | | columns | 1 | .23 | 1.23 |
| 5300 | 50x45 | 20 | 56-1/2 | 41 | | 9.70 | 2.90 | 12.60 |
| 5350 | | | | | columns | .77 | .18 | .95 |
| 5500 | | 40 | 56-1/2 | 61 | | 12.45 | 3.60 | 16.05 |
| 5550 | | | | | columns | 1 | .23 | 1.23 |
| 5600 | 50x50 | 20 | 56-1/2 | 42 | | 10.85 | 3.19 | 14.04 |
| 5650 | | | | | columns | .78 | .18 | .96 |
| 5800 | | 40 | 59 | 64 | | 10.25 | 3.82 | 14.07 |
| 5850 | | | | | columns | 1.10 | .26 | 1.36 |

## B2010 Exterior Walls

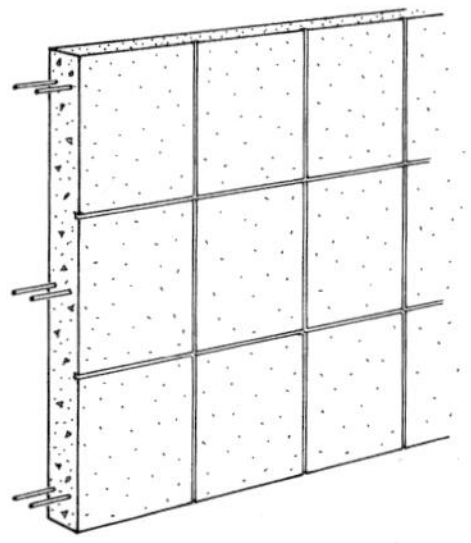

Cast in Place Concrete Wall

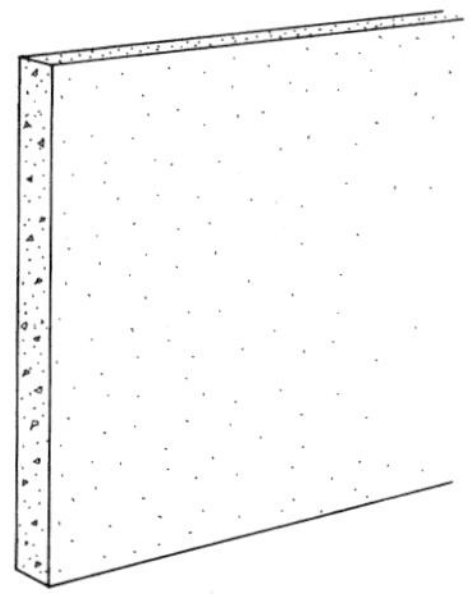

Flat Precast Concrete Wall

Table B2010 101 describes a concrete wall system for exterior closure. There are several types of wall finishes priced from plain finish to a finish with 3/4″ rustication strip.

In Table B2010 103, precast concrete wall panels are either solid or insulated. Prices below are based on delivery within 50 miles of a plant. Small jobs can double the prices below. For large, highly repetitive jobs, deduct up to 15%.

| B2010 101 | Cast In Place Concrete | COST PER S.F. | | |
|---|---|---|---|---|
| | | MAT. | INST. | TOTAL |
| 2100 | Conc wall reinforced, 8′ high, 6″ thick, plain finish, 3000 PSI | 8.90 | 19.90 | 28.80 |
| 2700 | Aged wood liner, 3000 PSI | 10.95 | 22.50 | 33.45 |
| 3000 | Sand blast light 1 side, 3000 PSI | 9.55 | 22.50 | 32.05 |
| 3700 | 3/4″ bevel rustication strip, 3000 PSI | 9 | 21 | 30 |
| 4000 | 8″ thick, plain finish, 3000 PSI | 10.20 | 20.50 | 30.70 |
| 4100 | 4000 PSI | 10.40 | 20.50 | 30.90 |
| 4300 | Rub concrete 1 side, 3000 PSI | 10.20 | 24 | 34.20 |
| 4550 | 8″ thick, aged wood liner, 3000 PSI | 12.25 | 23 | 35.25 |
| 4750 | Sand blast light 1 side, 3000 PSI | 10.85 | 23 | 33.85 |
| 5300 | 3/4″ bevel rustication strip, 3000 PSI | 10.30 | 21.50 | 31.80 |
| 5600 | 10″ thick, plain finish, 3000 PSI | 11.40 | 21 | 32.40 |
| 5900 | Rub concrete 1 side, 3000 PSI | 11.40 | 24.50 | 35.90 |
| 6200 | Aged wood liner, 3000 PSI | 13.45 | 23.50 | 36.95 |
| 6500 | Sand blast light 1 side, 3000 PSI | 12.10 | 23.50 | 35.60 |
| 7100 | 3/4″ bevel rustication strip, 3000 PSI | 11.55 | 22 | 33.55 |
| 7400 | 12″ thick, plain finish, 3000 PSI | 12.85 | 21.50 | 34.35 |
| 7410 | 14′ thick, plain finish, 3000 PSI | 110 | 58.50 | 168.50 |
| 7415 | 24″ thick, plain finish, 3000 PSI | 22 | 25.50 | 47.50 |
| 7700 | Rub concrete 1 side, 3000 PSI | 12.85 | 25 | 37.85 |
| 8000 | Aged wood liner, 3000 PSI | 14.90 | 24 | 38.90 |
| 8300 | Sand blast light 1 side, 3000 PSI | 13.55 | 24 | 37.55 |
| 8900 | 3/4″ bevel rustication strip, 3000 PSI | 13 | 22.50 | 35.50 |

| B2010 102 | Flat Precast Concrete | | | | | | | |
|---|---|---|---|---|---|---|---|---|
| | THICKNESS (IN.) | PANEL SIZE (FT.) | FINISHES | RIGID INSULATION (IN) | TYPE | COST PER S.F. | | |
| | | | | | | MAT. | INST. | TOTAL |
| 3000 | 4 | 5x18 | smooth gray | none | low rise | 20.50 | 9.45 | 29.95 |
| 3050 | | 6x18 | | | | 17.25 | 7.90 | 25.15 |
| 3100 | | 8x20 | | | | 34 | 3.82 | 37.82 |
| 3150 | | 12x20 | | | | 32 | 3.61 | 35.61 |
| 3200 | 6 | 5x18 | smooth gray | 2 | low rise | 22.50 | 10.15 | 32.65 |
| 3250 | | 6x18 | | | | 19 | 8.60 | 27.60 |
| 3300 | | 8x20 | | | | 36.50 | 4.64 | 41.14 |
| 3350 | | 12x20 | | | | 33 | 4.25 | 37.25 |
| 3400 | 8 | 5x18 | smooth gray | 2 | low rise | 47 | 5.85 | 52.85 |
| 3450 | | 6x18 | | | | 44.50 | 5.55 | 50.05 |
| 3500 | | 8x20 | | | | 40.50 | 5.15 | 45.65 |
| 3550 | | 12x20 | | | | 37 | 4.71 | 41.71 |

## B2010 Exterior Walls

### B2010 102 Flat Precast Concrete

| | THICKNESS (IN.) | PANEL SIZE (FT.) | FINISHES | RIGID INSULATION (IN) | TYPE | COST PER S.F. | | |
|---|---|---|---|---|---|---|---|---|
| | | | | | | MAT. | INST. | TOTAL |
| 3600 | 4 | 4x8 | white face | none | low rise | 77.50 | 5.45 | 82.95 |
| 3650 | | 8x8 | | | | 58.50 | 5.95 | 64.45 |
| 3700 | | 10x10 | | | | 51 | 3.59 | 54.59 |
| 3750 | | 20x10 | | | | 46.50 | 3.25 | 49.75 |
| 3800 | 5 | 4x8 | white face | none | low rise | 79.50 | 5.60 | 85.10 |
| 3850 | | 8x8 | | | | 60 | 4.21 | 64.21 |
| 3900 | | 10x10 | | | | 53 | 3.73 | 56.73 |
| 3950 | | 20x20 | | | | 48.50 | 3.41 | 51.91 |
| 4000 | 6 | 4x8 | white face | none | low rise | 82 | 5.80 | 87.80 |
| 4050 | | 8x8 | | | | 62.50 | 4.39 | 66.89 |
| 4100 | | 10x10 | | | | 55 | 3.87 | 58.87 |
| 4150 | | 20x10 | | | | 50.50 | 3.55 | 54.05 |
| 4200 | 6 | 4x8 | white face | 2 | low rise | 84 | 6.55 | 90.55 |
| 4250 | | 8x8 | | | | 64.50 | 5.15 | 69.65 |
| 4300 | | 10x10 | | | | 57 | 4.65 | 61.65 |
| 4350 | | 20x10 | | | | 50.50 | 3.55 | 54.05 |
| 4400 | 7 | 4x8 | white face | none | low rise | 84 | 5.90 | 89.90 |
| 4450 | | 8x8 | | | | 64.50 | 4.55 | 69.05 |
| 4500 | | 10x10 | | | | 58 | 4.07 | 62.07 |
| 4550 | | 20x10 | | | | 53 | 3.73 | 56.73 |
| 4600 | 7 | 4x8 | white face | 2 | low rise | 86 | 6.70 | 92.70 |
| 4650 | | 8x8 | | | | 66.50 | 5.35 | 71.85 |
| 4700 | | 10x10 | | | | 60 | 4.85 | 64.85 |
| 4750 | | 20x10 | | | | 55 | 4.51 | 59.51 |
| 4800 | 8 | 4x8 | white face | none | low rise | 86 | 6.05 | 92.05 |
| 4850 | | 8x8 | | | | 66.50 | 4.66 | 71.16 |
| 4900 | | 10x10 | | | | 59.50 | 4.19 | 63.69 |
| 4950 | | 20x10 | | | | 55 | 3.86 | 58.86 |
| 5000 | 8 | 4x8 | white face | 2 | low rise | 88 | 6.85 | 94.85 |
| 5050 | | 8x8 | | | | 68.50 | 5.45 | 73.95 |
| 5100 | | 10x10 | | | | 69.50 | 5.75 | 75.25 |
| 5150 | | 20x10 | | | | 69.50 | 5.75 | 75.25 |

### B2010 103 Fluted Window or Mullion Precast Concrete

| | THICKNESS (IN.) | PANEL SIZE (FT.) | FINISHES | RIGID INSULATION (IN) | TYPE | COST PER S.F. | | |
|---|---|---|---|---|---|---|---|---|
| | | | | | | MAT. | INST. | TOTAL |
| 5200 | 4 | 4x8 | smooth gray | none | high rise | 47.50 | 21.50 | 69 |
| 5250 | | 8x8 | | | | 34 | 15.45 | 49.45 |
| 5300 | | 10x10 | | | | 65 | 7.30 | 72.30 |
| 5350 | | 20x10 | | | | 57 | 6.40 | 63.40 |
| 5400 | 5 | 4x8 | smooth gray | none | high rise | 48 | 22 | 70 |
| 5450 | | 8x8 | | | | 35 | 16 | 51 |
| 5500 | | 10x10 | | | | 67.50 | 7.60 | 75.10 |
| 5550 | | 20x10 | | | | 60 | 6.75 | 66.75 |
| 5600 | 6 | 4x8 | smooth gray | none | high rise | 49.50 | 22.50 | 72 |
| 5650 | | 8x8 | | | | 36 | 16.55 | 52.55 |
| 5700 | | 10x10 | | | | 69.50 | 7.85 | 77.35 |
| 5750 | | 20x10 | | | | 62 | 6.95 | 68.95 |
| 5800 | 6 | 4x8 | smooth gray | 2 | high rise | 51.50 | 23.50 | 75 |
| 5850 | | 8x8 | | | | 38 | 17.35 | 55.35 |
| 5900 | | 10x10 | | | | 71.50 | 8.60 | 80.10 |
| 5950 | | 20x10 | | | | 64 | 7.75 | 71.75 |

## B2010 Exterior Walls

### B2010 103 Fluted Window or Mullion Precast Concrete

| | THICKNESS (IN.) | PANEL SIZE (FT.) | FINISHES | RIGID INSULATION (IN) | TYPE | COST PER S.F. | | |
|---|---|---|---|---|---|---|---|---|
| | | | | | | MAT. | INST. | TOTAL |
| 6000 | 7 | 4x8 | smooth gray | none | high rise | 50.50 | 23 | 73.50 |
| 6050 | | 8x8 | | | | 37 | 17 | 54 |
| 6100 | | 10x10 | | | | 72.50 | 8.15 | 80.65 |
| 6150 | | 20x10 | | | | 64 | 7.15 | 71.15 |
| 6200 | 7 | 4x8 | smooth gray | 2 | high rise | 52.50 | 24 | 76.50 |
| 6250 | | 8x8 | | | | 39 | 17.80 | 56.80 |
| 6300 | | 10x10 | | | | 74.50 | 8.95 | 83.45 |
| 6350 | | 20x10 | | | | 66 | 7.95 | 73.95 |
| 6400 | 8 | 4x8 | smooth gray | none | high rise | 51 | 23.50 | 74.50 |
| 6450 | | 8x8 | | | | 38 | 17.45 | 55.45 |
| 6500 | | 10x10 | | | | 75 | 8.45 | 83.45 |
| 6550 | | 20x10 | | | | 67 | 7.55 | 74.55 |
| 6600 | 8 | 4x8 | smooth gray | 2 | high rise | 53 | 24 | 77 |
| 6650 | | 8x8 | | | | 40 | 18.25 | 58.25 |
| 6700 | | 10x10 | | | | 77 | 9.20 | 86.20 |
| 6750 | | 20x10 | | | | 69 | 8.30 | 77.30 |

### B2010 104 Ribbed Precast Concrete

| | THICKNESS (IN.) | PANEL SIZE (FT.) | FINISHES | RIGID INSULATION(IN.) | TYPE | COST PER S.F. | | |
|---|---|---|---|---|---|---|---|---|
| | | | | | | MAT. | INST. | TOTAL |
| 6800 | 4 | 4x8 | aggregate | none | high rise | 66.50 | 21.50 | 88 |
| 6850 | | 8x8 | | | | 48.50 | 15.80 | 64.30 |
| 6900 | | 10x10 | | | | 82.50 | 5.70 | 88.20 |
| 6950 | | 20x10 | | | | 73 | 5.05 | 78.05 |
| 7000 | 5 | 4x8 | aggregate | none | high rise | 68 | 22 | 90 |
| 7050 | | 8x8 | | | | 50 | 16.25 | 66.25 |
| 7100 | | 10x10 | | | | 86 | 5.95 | 91.95 |
| 7150 | | 20x10 | | | | 76.50 | 5.30 | 81.80 |
| 7200 | 6 | 4x8 | aggregate | none | high rise | 69 | 22.50 | 91.50 |
| 7250 | | 8x8 | | | | 51.50 | 16.70 | 68.20 |
| 7300 | | 10x10 | | | | 88.50 | 6.15 | 94.65 |
| 7350 | | 20x10 | | | | 79.50 | 5.50 | 85 |
| 7400 | 6 | 4x8 | aggregate | 2 | high rise | 71 | 23 | 94 |
| 7450 | | 8x8 | | | | 53.50 | 17.50 | 71 |
| 7500 | | 10x10 | | | | 90.50 | 6.90 | 97.40 |
| 7550 | | 20x10 | | | | 81.50 | 6.25 | 87.75 |
| 7600 | 7 | 4x8 | aggregate | none | high rise | 71 | 23 | 94 |
| 7650 | | 8x8 | | | | 52.50 | 17.10 | 69.60 |
| 7700 | | 10x10 | | | | 91.50 | 6.35 | 97.85 |
| 7750 | | 20x10 | | | | 81.50 | 5.65 | 87.15 |
| 7800 | 7 | 4x8 | aggregate | 2 | high rise | 73 | 24 | 97 |
| 7850 | | 8x8 | | | | 54.50 | 17.90 | 72.40 |
| 7900 | | 10x10 | | | | 93.50 | 7.10 | 100.60 |
| 7950 | | 20x10 | | | | 83.50 | 6.45 | 89.95 |
| 8000 | 8 | 4x8 | aggregate | none | high rise | 72 | 23.50 | 95.50 |
| 8050 | | 8x8 | | | | 54.50 | 17.60 | 72.10 |
| 8100 | | 10x10 | | | | 94.50 | 6.55 | 101.05 |
| 8150 | | 20x10 | | | | 85.50 | 5.90 | 91.40 |
| 8200 | 8 | 4x8 | aggregate | 2 | high rise | 74 | 24 | 98 |
| 8250 | | 8x8 | | | | 56.50 | 18.40 | 74.90 |
| 8300 | | 10x10 | | | | 97 | 9.15 | 106.15 |
| 8350 | | 20x10 | | | | 87.50 | 6.70 | 94.20 |

## B2010 Exterior Walls

### B2010 105 Precast Concrete Specialties

| | TYPE | SIZE | | | | COST PER L.F. | | |
|---|---|---|---|---|---|---|---|---|
| | | | | | | MAT. | INST. | TOTAL |
| 8400 | Coping, precast | 6" wide | | | | 7.95 | 16.70 | 24.65 |
| 8450 | Stock units | 10" wide | | | | 8.55 | 17.85 | 26.40 |
| 8460 | | 12" wide | | | | 11.55 | 19.25 | 30.80 |
| 8480 | | 14" wide | | | | 12.50 | 21 | 33.50 |
| 8500 | Window sills | 6" wide | | | | 6.35 | 17.85 | 24.20 |
| 8550 | Precast | 10" wide | | | | 7.10 | 21 | 28.10 |
| 8600 | | 14" wide | | | | 9.90 | 25 | 34.90 |
| 8610 | | | | | | | | |

## B2010 Exterior Walls

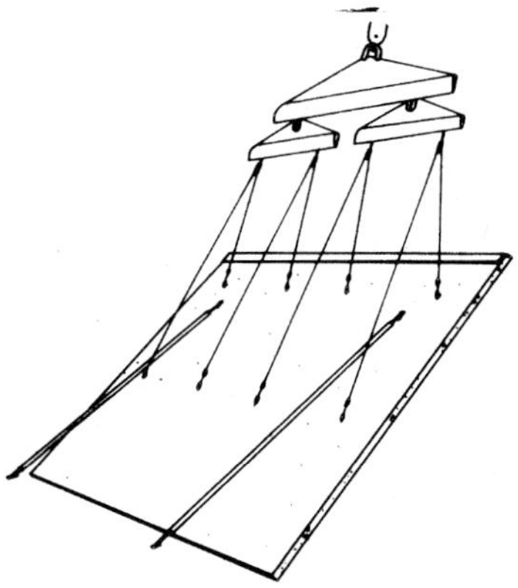

The advantage of tilt up construction is in the low cost of forms and placing of concrete and reinforcing. Tilt up has been used for several types of buildings, including warehouses, stores, offices, and schools. The panels are cast in forms on the ground, or floor slab. Most jobs use 5-1/2" thick solid reinforced concrete panels.

**Design Assumptions:**
Conc. f'c = 3000 psi
Reinf. fy = 60,000

| B2010 106 | Tilt-Up Concrete Panel | COST PER S.F. | | |
|---|---|---|---|---|
| | | MAT. | INST. | TOTAL |
| 3200 | Tilt-up conc panels, broom finish, 5-1/2" thick, 3000 PSI | 6.50 | 7.45 | 13.95 |
| 3250 | 5000 PSI | 6.65 | 7.30 | 13.95 |
| 3300 | 6" thick, 3000 PSI | 7.15 | 7.65 | 14.80 |
| 3350 | 5000 PSI | 7.35 | 7.50 | 14.85 |
| 3400 | 7-1/2" thick, 3000 PSI | 9.20 | 7.90 | 17.10 |
| 3450 | 5000 PSI | 9.45 | 7.80 | 17.25 |
| 3500 | 8" thick, 3000 PSI | 9.85 | 8.10 | 17.95 |
| 3550 | 5000 PSI | 10.10 | 7.95 | 18.05 |
| 3700 | Steel trowel finish, 5-1/2" thick, 3000 PSI | 6.50 | 7.60 | 14.10 |
| 3750 | 5000 PSI | 6.65 | 7.45 | 14.10 |
| 3800 | 6" thick, 3000 PSI | 7.15 | 7.75 | 14.90 |
| 3850 | 5000 PSI | 7.35 | 7.65 | 15 |
| 3900 | 7-1/2" thick, 3000 PSI | 9.20 | 8.05 | 17.25 |
| 3950 | 5000 PSI | 9.45 | 7.90 | 17.35 |
| 4000 | 8" thick, 3000 PSI | 9.85 | 8.25 | 18.10 |
| 4050 | 5000 PSI | 10.30 | 8.25 | 18.55 |
| 4200 | Exp. aggregate finish, 5-1/2" thick, 3000 PSI | 6.90 | 7.60 | 14.50 |
| 4250 | 5000 PSI | 7.05 | 7.50 | 14.55 |
| 4300 | 6" thick, 3000 PSI | 7.55 | 7.80 | 15.35 |
| 4350 | 5000 PSI | 7.75 | 7.65 | 15.40 |
| 4400 | 7-1/2" thick, 3000 PSI | 9.60 | 8.10 | 17.70 |
| 4450 | 5000 PSI | 9.85 | 7.95 | 17.80 |
| 4500 | 8" thick, 3000 PSI | 10.25 | 8.25 | 18.50 |
| 4550 | 5000 PSI | 10.55 | 8.15 | 18.70 |
| 4600 | Exposed aggregate & vert. rustication 5-1/2" thick, 3000 PSI | 11 | 9.45 | 20.45 |
| 4650 | 5000 PSI | 11.15 | 9.30 | 20.45 |
| 4700 | 6" thick, 3000 PSI | 11.65 | 9.60 | 21.25 |
| 4750 | 5000 PSI | 11.80 | 9.50 | 21.30 |
| 4800 | 7-1/2" thick, 3000 PSI | 13.65 | 9.90 | 23.55 |
| 4850 | 5000 PSI | 13.90 | 9.75 | 23.65 |
| 4900 | 8" thick, 3000 PSI | 14.30 | 10.10 | 24.40 |
| 4950 | 5000 PSI | 14.60 | 9.95 | 24.55 |
| 5000 | Vertical rib & light sandblast, 5-1/2" thick, 3000 PSI | 10.30 | 12.35 | 22.65 |
| 5100 | 6" thick, 3000 PSI | 10.95 | 12.55 | 23.50 |
| 5200 | 7-1/2" thick, 3000 PSI | 12.95 | 12.80 | 25.75 |
| 5300 | 8" thick, 3000 PSI | 13.65 | 13 | 26.65 |
| 6000 | Broom finish w/2" polystyrene insulation, 6" thick, 3000 PSI | 7.60 | 9.20 | 16.80 |
| 6100 | Broom finish 2" fiberplank insulation, 6" thick, 3000 PSI | 8.15 | 9.10 | 17.25 |
| 6200 | Exposed aggregate w/2" polystyrene insulation, 6" thick, 3000 PSI | 7.85 | 9.20 | 17.05 |
| 6300 | Exposed aggregate 2" fiberplank insulation, 6" thick, 3000 PSI | 8.40 | 9.10 | 17.50 |

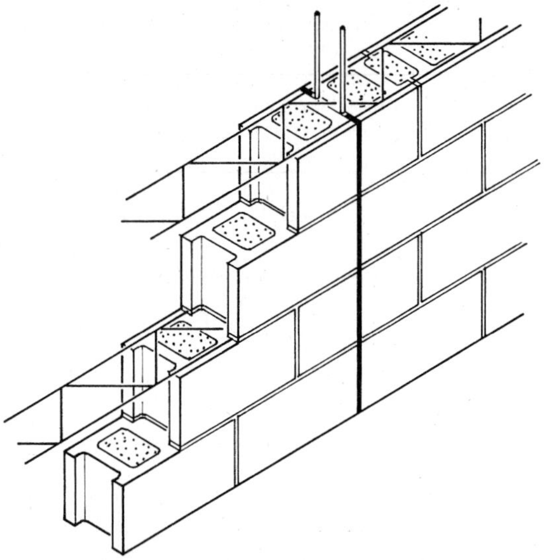

Exterior concrete block walls are defined in the following terms; structural reinforcement, weight, percent solid, size, strength and insulation. Within each of these categories, two to four variations are shown. No costs are included for brick shelf or relieving angles.

### B2010 109 Concrete Block Wall - Regular Weight

| | TYPE | SIZE (IN.) | STRENGTH (P.S.I.) | CORE FILL | | COST PER S.F. MAT. | COST PER S.F. INST. | COST PER S.F. TOTAL |
|---|---|---|---|---|---|---|---|---|
| 1200 | Hollow | 4x8x16 | 2,000 | none | | 2.33 | 7.70 | 10.03 |
| 1250 | | | 4,500 | none | | 3.19 | 7.70 | 10.89 |
| 1400 | | 8x8x16 | 2,000 | perlite | | 4.27 | 9.35 | 13.62 |
| 1410 | | | | styrofoam | | 6.20 | 8.80 | 15 |
| 1440 | | | | none | | 3.38 | 8.80 | 12.18 |
| 1450 | | | 4,500 | perlite | | 5.25 | 9.35 | 14.60 |
| 1460 | | | | styrofoam | | 7.20 | 8.80 | 16 |
| 1490 | | | | none | | 4.36 | 8.80 | 13.16 |
| 2000 | 75% solid | 4x8x16 | 2,000 | none | | 2.79 | 7.75 | 10.54 |
| 2100 | | 6x8x16 | 2,000 | perlite | | 3.75 | 8.60 | 12.35 |
| 2500 | Solid | 4x8x16 | 2,000 | none | | 2.99 | 7.95 | 10.94 |
| 2700 | | 8x8x16 | 2,000 | none | | 4.36 | 9.15 | 13.51 |

### B2010 110 Concrete Block Wall - Lightweight

| | TYPE | SIZE (IN.) | WEIGHT (P.C.F.) | CORE FILL | | COST PER S.F. MAT. | COST PER S.F. INST. | COST PER S.F. TOTAL |
|---|---|---|---|---|---|---|---|---|
| 3100 | Hollow | 8x4x16 | 105 | perlite | | 3.65 | 8.85 | 12.50 |
| 3110 | | | | styrofoam | | 5.60 | 8.30 | 13.90 |
| 3200 | | 4x8x16 | 105 | none | | 2.11 | 7.50 | 9.61 |
| 3250 | | | 85 | none | | 3.09 | 7.35 | 10.44 |
| 3300 | | 6x8x16 | 105 | perlite | | 3.42 | 8.50 | 11.92 |
| 3310 | | | | styrofoam | | 5 | 8.05 | 13.05 |
| 3340 | | | | none | | 2.81 | 8.05 | 10.86 |
| 3400 | | 8x8x16 | 105 | perlite | | 4.78 | 9.15 | 13.93 |
| 3410 | | | | styrofoam | | 6.75 | 8.60 | 15.35 |
| 3440 | | | | none | | 3.89 | 8.60 | 12.49 |
| 3450 | | | 85 | perlite | | 5.35 | 8.95 | 14.30 |
| 4000 | 75% solid | 4x8x16 | 105 | none | | 2.92 | 7.60 | 10.52 |
| 4050 | | | 85 | none | | 3.78 | 7.45 | 11.23 |
| 4100 | | 6x8x16 | 105 | perlite | | 4.25 | 8.40 | 12.65 |
| 4500 | Solid | 4x8x16 | 105 | none | | 3.04 | 7.85 | 10.89 |
| 4700 | | 8x8x16 | 105 | none | | 6.05 | 9.05 | 15.10 |

## B2010 Exterior Walls

### B2010 111 Reinforced Concrete Block Wall - Regular Weight

| | TYPE | SIZE (IN.) | STRENGTH (P.S.I.) | VERT. REINF & GROUT SPACING | | COST PER S.F. | | |
|---|---|---|---|---|---|---|---|---|
| | | | | | | MAT. | INST. | TOTAL |
| 5200 | Hollow | 4x8x16 | 2,000 | #4 @ 48″ | | 2.54 | 8.55 | 11.09 |
| 5300 | | 6x8x16 | 2,000 | #4 @ 48″ | | 3.24 | 9.10 | 12.34 |
| 5330 | | | | #5 @ 32″ | | 3.54 | 9.45 | 12.99 |
| 5340 | | | | #5 @ 16″ | | 4.18 | 10.65 | 14.83 |
| 5350 | | | 4,500 | #4 @ 28″ | | 3.90 | 9.10 | 13 |
| 5390 | | | | #5 @ 16″ | | 4.84 | 10.65 | 15.49 |
| 5400 | | 8x8x16 | 2,000 | #4 @ 48″ | | 3.83 | 9.70 | 13.53 |
| 5430 | | | | #5 @ 32″ | | 4.14 | 10.25 | 14.39 |
| 5440 | | | | #5 @ 16″ | | 4.88 | 11.70 | 16.58 |
| 5450 | | 8x8x16 | 4,500 | #4 @ 48″ | | 4.78 | 9.80 | 14.58 |
| 5490 | | | | #5 @ 16″ | | 5.85 | 11.70 | 17.55 |
| 5500 | | 12x8x16 | 2,000 | #4 @ 48″ | | 5.90 | 12.45 | 18.35 |
| 5540 | | | | #5 @ 16″ | | 7.35 | 14.40 | 21.75 |
| 6100 | 75% solid | 6x8x16 | 2,000 | #4 @ 48″ | | 3.64 | 9.10 | 12.74 |
| 6140 | | | | #5 @ 16″ | | 4.27 | 10.35 | 14.62 |
| 6150 | | | 4,500 | #4 @ 48″ | | 4.51 | 9.10 | 13.61 |
| 6190 | | | | #5 @ 16″ | | 5.15 | 10.35 | 15.50 |
| 6200 | | 8x8x16 | 2,000 | #4 @ 48″ | | 4.25 | 9.80 | 14.05 |
| 6230 | | | | #5 @ 32″ | | 4.48 | 10.15 | 14.63 |
| 6240 | | | | #5 @ 16″ | | 4.91 | 11.30 | 16.21 |
| 6250 | | | 4,500 | #4 @ 48″ | | 5.55 | 9.80 | 15.35 |
| 6280 | | | | #5 @ 32″ | | 5.75 | 10.15 | 15.90 |
| 6290 | | | | #5 @ 16″ | | 6.20 | 11.30 | 17.50 |
| 6500 | Solid-double | 2-4x8x16 | 2,000 | #4 @ 48″ E.W. | | 7.10 | 18 | 25.10 |
| 6530 | Wythe | | | #5 @ 16″ E.W. | | 8.15 | 19.10 | 27.25 |
| 6550 | | | 4,500 | #4 @ 48″ E.W. | | 9.90 | 17.80 | 27.70 |
| 6580 | | | | #5 @ 16″ E.W. | | 10.95 | 18.90 | 29.85 |

### B2010 112 Reinforced Concrete Block Wall - Lightweight

| | TYPE | SIZE (IN.) | WEIGHT (P.C.F.) | VERT REINF. & GROUT SPACING | | COST PER S.F. | | |
|---|---|---|---|---|---|---|---|---|
| | | | | | | MAT. | INST. | TOTAL |
| 7100 | Hollow | 8x4x16 | 105 | #4 @ 48″ | | 3.18 | 9.30 | 12.48 |
| 7140 | | | | #5 @ 16″ | | 4.26 | 11.20 | 15.46 |
| 7150 | | | 85 | #4 @ 48″ | | 5.15 | 9.10 | 14.25 |
| 7190 | | | | #5 @ 16″ | | 6.25 | 11 | 17.25 |
| 7400 | | 8x8x16 | 105 | #4 @ 48″ | | 4.31 | 9.60 | 13.91 |
| 7440 | | | | #5 @ 16″ | | 5.40 | 11.50 | 16.90 |
| 7450 | | 8x8x16 | 85 | #4 @ 48″ | | 4.89 | 9.40 | 14.29 |
| 7490 | | | | #5 @ 16″ | | 5.95 | 11.30 | 17.25 |
| 7800 | | 8x8x24 | 105 | #4 @ 48″ | | 3.40 | 10.35 | 13.75 |
| 7840 | | | | #5 @ 16″ | | 4.48 | 12.25 | 16.73 |
| 7850 | | | 85 | #4 @ 48″ | | 7.30 | 8.80 | 16.10 |
| 7890 | | | | #5 @ 16″ | | 8.40 | 10.70 | 19.10 |
| 8100 | 75% solid | 6x8x16 | 105 | #4 @ 48″ | | 4.14 | 8.90 | 13.04 |
| 8130 | | | | #5 @ 32″ | | 4.36 | 9.15 | 13.51 |
| 8150 | | | 85 | #4 @ 48″ | | 4.88 | 8.70 | 13.58 |
| 8180 | | | | #5 @ 32″ | | 5.10 | 8.95 | 14.05 |
| 8200 | | 8x8x16 | 105 | #4 @ 48″ | | 5.80 | 9.55 | 15.35 |
| 8230 | | | | #5 @ 32″ | | 6.05 | 9.90 | 15.95 |
| 8250 | | | 85 | #4 @ 48″ | | 5.65 | 9.35 | 15 |
| 8280 | | | | #5 @ 32″ | | 5.90 | 9.70 | 15.60 |

## B2010 Exterior Walls

### B2010 112 Reinforced Concrete Block Wall - Lightweight

| | TYPE | SIZE (IN.) | WEIGHT (P.C.F.) | VERT REINF. & GROUT SPACING | | COST PER S.F. | | |
|---|---|---|---|---|---|---|---|---|
| | | | | | | MAT. | INST. | TOTAL |
| 8500 | Solid-double | 2-4x8x16 | 105 | #4 @ 48" | | 7.20 | 17.80 | 25 |
| 8530 | Wythe | | 105 | #5 @ 16" | | 8.25 | 18.90 | 27.15 |
| 8600 | | 2-6x8x16 | 105 | #4 @ 48" | | 8.75 | 19.05 | 27.80 |
| 8630 | | | | #5 @ 16" | | 9.80 | 20 | 29.80 |
| 8650 | | | 85 | #4 @ 48" | | 16.90 | 18.25 | 35.15 |

## B2010 Exterior Walls

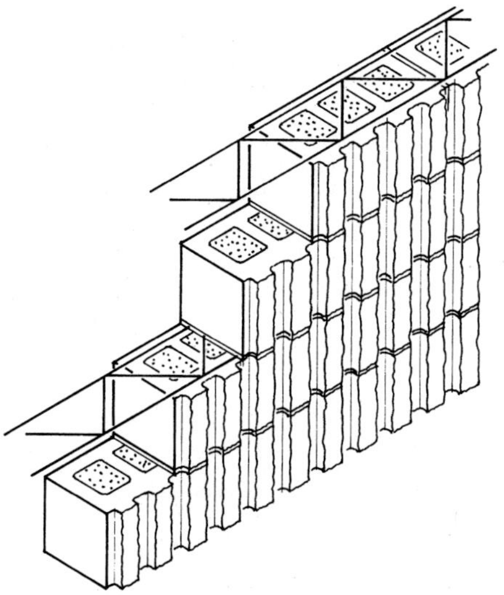

Exterior split ribbed block walls are defined in the following terms; structural reinforcement, weight, percent solid, size, number of ribs and insulation. Within each of these categories two to four variations are shown. No costs are included for brick shelf or relieving angles. Costs include control joints every 20′ and horizontal reinforcing.

### B2010 113 Split Ribbed Block Wall - Regular Weight

| | TYPE | SIZE (IN.) | RIBS | CORE FILL | | COST PER S.F. MAT. | INST. | TOTAL |
|---|---|---|---|---|---|---|---|---|
| 1220 | Hollow | 4x8x16 | 4 | none | | 5.70 | 9.50 | 15.20 |
| 1250 | | | 8 | none | | 6.20 | 9.50 | 15.70 |
| 1280 | | | 16 | none | | 6.70 | 9.65 | 16.35 |
| 1430 | | 8x8x16 | 8 | perlite | | 9.55 | 11.30 | 20.85 |
| 1440 | | | | styrofoam | | 10.85 | 10.75 | 21.60 |
| 1450 | | | | none | | 8.65 | 10.75 | 19.40 |
| 1530 | | 12x8x16 | 8 | perlite | | 11.40 | 15.05 | 26.45 |
| 1540 | | | | styrofoam | | 12.85 | 14 | 26.85 |
| 1550 | | | | none | | 9.90 | 14 | 23.90 |
| 2120 | 75% solid | 4x8x16 | 4 | none | | 7.20 | 9.65 | 16.85 |
| 2150 | | | 8 | none | | 7.85 | 9.65 | 17.50 |
| 2180 | | | 16 | none | | 8.45 | 9.80 | 18.25 |
| 2520 | Solid | 4x8x16 | 4 | none | | 8.20 | 9.80 | 18 |
| 2550 | | | 8 | none | | 9.65 | 9.80 | 19.45 |
| 2580 | | | 16 | none | | 9.65 | 9.95 | 19.60 |

### B2010 115 Reinforced Split Ribbed Block Wall - Regular Weight

| | TYPE | SIZE (IN.) | RIBS | VERT. REINF. & GROUT SPACING | | COST PER S.F. MAT. | INST. | TOTAL |
|---|---|---|---|---|---|---|---|---|
| 5200 | Hollow | 4x8x16 | 4 | #4 @ 48″ | | 5.95 | 10.35 | 16.30 |
| 5230 | | | 8 | #4 @ 48″ | | 6.45 | 10.35 | 16.80 |
| 5260 | | | 16 | #4 @ 48″ | | 6.95 | 10.50 | 17.45 |
| 5430 | | 8x8x16 | 8 | #4 @ 48″ | | 9.05 | 11.75 | 20.80 |
| 5440 | | | | #5 @ 32″ | | 9.40 | 12.20 | 21.60 |
| 5450 | | | | #5 @ 16″ | | 10.15 | 13.65 | 23.80 |
| 5530 | | 12x8x16 | 8 | #4 @ 48″ | | 10.50 | 15.05 | 25.55 |
| 5540 | | | | #5 @ 32″ | | 10.95 | 15.50 | 26.45 |
| 5550 | | | | #5 @ 16″ | | 11.95 | 17 | 28.95 |
| 6230 | 75% solid | 6x8x16 | 8 | #4 @ 48″ | | 9.20 | 11 | 20.20 |
| 6240 | | | | #5 @ 32″ | | 9.45 | 11.25 | 20.70 |
| 6250 | | | | #5 @ 16″ | | 9.85 | 12.25 | 22.10 |
| 6330 | | 8x8x16 | 8 | #4 @ 48″ | | 11.10 | 11.80 | 22.90 |
| 6340 | | | | #5 @ 32″ | | 11.35 | 12.15 | 23.50 |
| 6350 | | | | #5 @ 16″ | | 11.75 | 13.30 | 25.05 |

## B2010 Exterior Walls

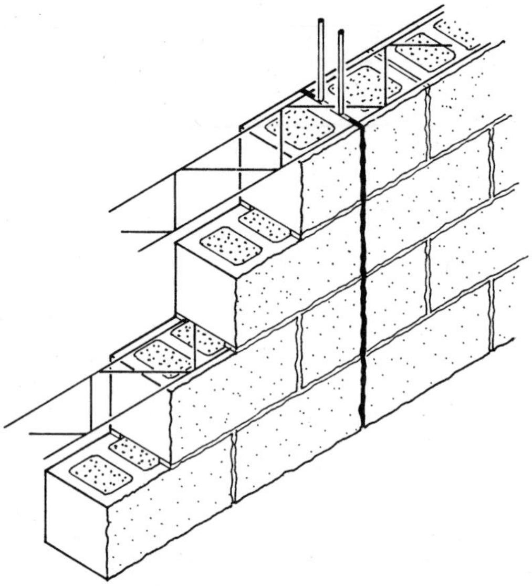

Exterior split face block walls are defined in the following terms; structural reinforcement, weight, percent solid, size, scores and insulation. Within each of these categories two to four variations are shown. No costs are included for brick shelf or relieving angles. Costs include control joints every 20′ and horizontal reinforcing.

### B2010 117 Split Face Block Wall - Regular Weight

| | TYPE | SIZE (IN.) | SCORES | CORE FILL | | COST PER S.F. | | |
|---|---|---|---|---|---|---|---|---|
| | | | | | | MAT. | INST. | TOTAL |
| 1200 | Hollow | 8x4x16 | 0 | perlite | | 8.30 | 12.45 | 20.75 |
| 1210 | | | | styrofoam | | 10.25 | 11.90 | 22.15 |
| 1240 | | | | none | | 7.40 | 11.90 | 19.30 |
| 1250 | | | 1 | perlite | | 8.80 | 12.45 | 21.25 |
| 1260 | | | | styrofoam | | 10.75 | 11.90 | 22.65 |
| 1290 | | | | none | | 7.90 | 11.90 | 19.80 |
| 1300 | | 12x4x16 | 0 | perlite | | 8.95 | 14.15 | 23.10 |
| 1310 | | | | styrofoam | | 10.40 | 13.10 | 23.50 |
| 1340 | | | | none | | 7.45 | 13.10 | 20.55 |
| 1350 | | | 1 | perlite | | 9.45 | 14.15 | 23.60 |
| 1360 | | | | styrofoam | | 10.90 | 13.10 | 24 |
| 1390 | | | | none | | 7.95 | 13.10 | 21.05 |
| 1400 | | 4x8x16 | 0 | none | | 4.58 | 9.35 | 13.93 |
| 1450 | | | 1 | none | | 4.96 | 9.50 | 14.46 |
| 1500 | | 6x8x16 | 0 | perlite | | 5.80 | 10.85 | 16.65 |
| 1510 | | | | styrofoam | | 7.40 | 10.40 | 17.80 |
| 1540 | | | | none | | 5.20 | 10.40 | 15.60 |
| 1550 | | | 1 | perlite | | 6.20 | 11 | 17.20 |
| 1560 | | | | styrofoam | | 7.80 | 10.55 | 18.35 |
| 1590 | | | | none | | 5.60 | 10.55 | 16.15 |
| 1600 | | 8x8x16 | 0 | perlite | | 7.45 | 11.65 | 19.10 |
| 1610 | | | | styrofoam | | 9.40 | 11.10 | 20.50 |
| 1640 | | | | none | | 6.55 | 11.10 | 17.65 |
| 1650 | | 8x8x16 | 1 | perlite | | 8 | 11.85 | 19.85 |
| 1660 | | | | styrofoam | | 9.95 | 11.30 | 21.25 |
| 1690 | | | | none | | 7.10 | 11.30 | 18.40 |
| 1700 | | 12x8x16 | 0 | perlite | | 7.80 | 15.30 | 23.10 |
| 1710 | | | | styrofoam | | 9.25 | 14.25 | 23.50 |
| 1740 | | | | none | | 6.30 | 14.25 | 20.55 |
| 1750 | | | 1 | perlite | | 8.25 | 15.55 | 23.80 |
| 1760 | | | | styrofoam | | 9.70 | 14.50 | 24.20 |
| 1790 | | | | none | | 6.75 | 14.50 | 21.25 |

## B2010 Exterior Walls

### B2010 117 Split Face Block Wall - Regular Weight

| | TYPE | SIZE (IN.) | SCORES | CORE FILL | | COST PER S.F. | | |
|---|---|---|---|---|---|---|---|---|
| | | | | | | MAT. | INST. | TOTAL |
| 1800 | 75% solid | 8x4x16 | 0 | perlite | | 9.45 | 12.40 | 21.85 |
| 1840 | | | | none | | 9 | 12.15 | 21.15 |
| 1850 | | | 1 | perlite | | 10.15 | 12.40 | 22.55 |
| 1890 | | | | none | | 9.70 | 12.15 | 21.85 |
| 2000 | | 4x8x16 | 0 | none | | 5.70 | 9.50 | 15.20 |
| 2050 | | | 1 | none | | 6.20 | 9.65 | 15.85 |
| 2400 | Solid | 8x4x16 | 0 | none | | 10.05 | 12.35 | 22.40 |
| 2450 | | | 1 | none | | 10.85 | 12.35 | 23.20 |
| 2900 | | 12x8x16 | 0 | none | | 8.65 | 14.80 | 23.45 |
| 2950 | | | 1 | none | | 9.35 | 15.05 | 24.40 |

### B2010 119 Reinforced Split Face Block Wall - Regular Weight

| | TYPE | SIZE (IN.) | SCORES | VERT. REINF. & GROUT SPACING | | COST PER S.F. | | |
|---|---|---|---|---|---|---|---|---|
| | | | | | | MAT. | INST. | TOTAL |
| 5200 | Hollow | 8x4x16 | 0 | #4 @ 48″ | | 7.80 | 12.90 | 20.70 |
| 5210 | | | | #5 @ 32″ | | 8.15 | 13.35 | 21.50 |
| 5240 | | | | #5 @ 16″ | | 8.90 | 14.80 | 23.70 |
| 5250 | | | 1 | #4 @ 48″ | | 8.30 | 12.90 | 21.20 |
| 5260 | | | | #5 @ 32″ | | 8.65 | 13.35 | 22 |
| 5290 | | | | #5 @ 16″ | | 9.40 | 14.80 | 24.20 |
| 5700 | | 12x8x16 | 0 | #4 @ 48″ | | 6.90 | 15.30 | 22.20 |
| 5710 | | | | #5 @ 32″ | | 7.35 | 15.75 | 23.10 |
| 5740 | | | | #5 @ 16″ | | 8.35 | 17.25 | 25.60 |
| 5750 | | | 1 | #4 @ 48″ | | 7.35 | 15.55 | 22.90 |
| 5760 | | | | #5 @ 32″ | | 7.80 | 16 | 23.80 |
| 5790 | | | | #5 @ 16″ | | 8.80 | 17.50 | 26.30 |
| 6000 | 75% solid | 8x4x16 | 0 | #4 @ 48″ | | 9.20 | 13 | 22.20 |
| 6010 | | | | #5 @ 32″ | | 9.45 | 13.35 | 22.80 |
| 6040 | | | | #5 @ 16″ | | 9.85 | 14.50 | 24.35 |
| 6050 | | | 1 | #4 @ 48″ | | 9.90 | 13 | 22.90 |
| 6060 | | | | #5 @ 32″ | | 10.15 | 13.35 | 23.50 |
| 6090 | | | | #5 @ 16″ | | 10.55 | 14.50 | 25.05 |
| 6100 | | 12x4x16 | 0 | #4 @ 48″ | | 9.25 | 14.25 | 23.50 |
| 6110 | | | | #5 @ 32″ | | 9.55 | 14.60 | 24.15 |
| 6140 | | | | #5 @ 16″ | | 10.15 | 15.60 | 25.75 |
| 6150 | | | 1 | #4 @ 48″ | | 9.85 | 14.25 | 24.10 |
| 6160 | | | | #5 @ 32″ | | 10.15 | 14.60 | 24.75 |
| 6190 | | | | #5 @ 16″ | | 10.80 | 15.80 | 26.60 |
| 6700 | Solid-double | 2-4x8x16 | 0 | #4 @ 48″ E.W. | | 14.05 | 21.50 | 35.55 |
| 6710 | Wythe | | | #5 @ 32″ E.W. | | 14.45 | 21.50 | 35.95 |
| 6740 | | | | #5 @ 16″ E.W. | | 15.10 | 22.50 | 37.60 |
| 6750 | | | 1 | #4 @ 48″ E.W. | | 15.15 | 21.50 | 36.65 |
| 6760 | | | | #5 @ 32″ E.W. | | 15.55 | 22 | 37.55 |
| 6790 | | | | #5 @ 16″ E.W. | | 16.20 | 23 | 39.20 |
| 6800 | | 2-6x8x16 | 0 | #4 @ 48″ E.W. | | 15.70 | 23.50 | 39.20 |
| 6810 | | | | #5 @ 32″ E.W. | | 16.10 | 23.50 | 39.60 |
| 6840 | | | | #5 @ 16″ E.W. | | 16.75 | 24.50 | 41.25 |
| 6850 | | | 1 | #4 @ 48″ E.W. | | 17 | 24 | 41 |
| 6860 | | | | #5 @ 32″ E.W. | | 17.40 | 24 | 41.40 |
| 6890 | | | | #5 @ 16″ E.W. | | 18.05 | 25 | 43.05 |

## B2010 Exterior Walls

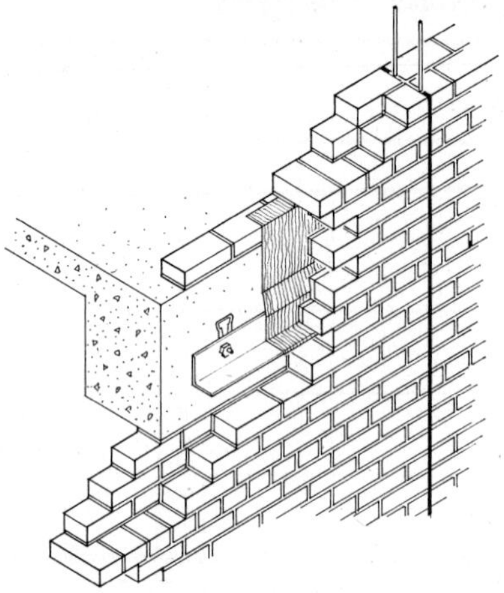

Exterior solid brick walls are defined in the following terms; structural reinforcement, type of brick, thickness, and bond. Nine different types of face bricks are presented, with single wythes shown in four different bonds. Shelf angles are included in system components. These walls do not include ties and as such are not tied to a backup wall.

### B2010 125 Solid Brick Walls - Single Wythe

| | TYPE | THICKNESS (IN.) | BOND | | | COST PER S.F. MAT. | INST. | TOTAL |
|---|---|---|---|---|---|---|---|---|
| 1000 | Common | 4 | running | | | 14.90 | 17.30 | 32.20 |
| 1010 | | | common | | | 18.05 | 19.80 | 37.85 |
| 1050 | | | Flemish | | | 19.95 | 24 | 43.95 |
| 1100 | | | English | | | 22.50 | 25.50 | 48 |
| 1150 | Standard | 4 | running | | | 7.90 | 17.90 | 25.80 |
| 1160 | | | common | | | 9.20 | 20.50 | 29.70 |
| 1200 | | | Flemish | | | 10.10 | 25 | 35.10 |
| 1250 | | | English | | | 11.25 | 26.50 | 37.75 |
| 1300 | Glazed | 4 | running | | | 26.50 | 18.60 | 45.10 |
| 1310 | | | common | | | 31.50 | 21.50 | 53 |
| 1350 | | | Flemish | | | 35 | 26.50 | 61.50 |
| 1400 | | | English | | | 39 | 28 | 67 |
| 1600 | Economy | 4 | running | | | 10 | 13.70 | 23.70 |
| 1610 | | | common | | | 11.65 | 15.70 | 27.35 |
| 1650 | | | Flemish | | | 12.80 | 18.60 | 31.40 |
| 1700 | | | English | | | 25.50 | 19.80 | 45.30 |
| 1900 | Fire | 4-1/2 | running | | | 15.15 | 15.70 | 30.85 |
| 1910 | | | common | | | 17.90 | 17.90 | 35.80 |
| 1950 | | | Flemish | | | 19.75 | 21.50 | 41.25 |
| 2000 | | | English | | | 22 | 23 | 45 |
| 2050 | King | 3-1/2 | running | | | 6 | 14.05 | 20.05 |
| 2060 | | | common | | | 6.85 | 16.15 | 23 |
| 2100 | | | Flemish | | | 8.10 | 19.35 | 27.45 |
| 2150 | | | English | | | 8.90 | 20 | 28.90 |
| 2200 | Roman | 4 | running | | | 11 | 16.15 | 27.15 |
| 2210 | | | common | | | 12.95 | 18.60 | 31.55 |
| 2250 | | | Flemish | | | 14.25 | 22 | 36.25 |
| 2300 | | | English | | | 16 | 24 | 40 |
| 2350 | Norman | 4 | running | | | 8 | 13.40 | 21.40 |
| 2360 | | | common | | | 9.35 | 15.25 | 24.60 |
| 2400 | | | Flemish | | | 21 | 18.25 | 39.25 |
| 2450 | | | English | | | 11.40 | 19.35 | 30.75 |

## B2010 Exterior Walls

### B2010 125 Solid Brick Walls - Single Wythe

| | TYPE | THICKNESS (IN.) | BOND | | | COST PER S.F. MAT. | INST. | TOTAL |
|---|---|---|---|---|---|---|---|---|
| 2500 | Norwegian | 4 | running | | | 6.95 | 11.90 | 18.85 |
| 2510 | | | common | | | 8.05 | 13.55 | 21.60 |
| 2550 | | | Flemish | | | 8.80 | 16.15 | 24.95 |
| 2600 | | | English | | | 9.80 | 17 | 26.80 |

### B2010 126 Solid Brick Walls - Double Wythe

| | TYPE | THICKNESS (IN.) | COLLAR JOINT THICKNESS (IN.) | | | COST PER S.F. MAT. | INST. | TOTAL |
|---|---|---|---|---|---|---|---|---|
| 4100 | Common | 8 | 3/4 | | | 29 | 29 | 58 |
| 4150 | Standard | 8 | 1/2 | | | 14.45 | 30 | 44.45 |
| 4200 | Glazed | 8 | 1/2 | | | 51 | 31 | 82 |
| 4250 | Engineer | 8 | 1/2 | | | 12.05 | 26.50 | 38.55 |
| 4300 | Economy | 8 | 3/4 | | | 18.65 | 23 | 41.65 |
| 4350 | Double | 8 | 3/4 | | | 13.40 | 17.55 | 30.95 |
| 4400 | Fire | 8 | 3/4 | | | 29 | 26.50 | 55.50 |
| 4450 | King | 7 | 3/4 | | | 10.60 | 23.50 | 34.10 |
| 4500 | Roman | 8 | 1 | | | 20.50 | 27.50 | 48 |
| 4550 | Norman | 8 | 3/4 | | | 14.70 | 22.50 | 37.20 |
| 4600 | Norwegian | 8 | 3/4 | | | 12.60 | 19.70 | 32.30 |
| 4650 | Utility | 8 | 3/4 | | | 14.35 | 17 | 31.35 |
| 4700 | Triple | 8 | 3/4 | | | 10.45 | 15.30 | 25.75 |
| 4750 | SCR | 12 | 3/4 | | | 17.20 | 23 | 40.20 |
| 4800 | Norwegian | 12 | 3/4 | | | 14.80 | 20 | 34.80 |

### B2010 127 Reinforced Brick Walls

| | TYPE | THICKNESS (IN.) | WYTHE | REINF. & SPACING | | COST PER S.F. MAT. | INST. | TOTAL |
|---|---|---|---|---|---|---|---|---|
| 7200 | Common | 4″ | 1 | #4 @ 48″vert | | 15.25 | 18 | 33.25 |
| 7220 | | | | #5 @ 32″vert | | 15.45 | 18.20 | 33.65 |
| 7230 | | | | #5 @ 16″vert | | 15.85 | 19 | 34.85 |
| 7700 | King | 9″ | 2 | #4 @ 48″ E.W. | | 11.25 | 24.50 | 35.75 |
| 7720 | | | | #5 @ 32″ E.W. | | 11.65 | 24.50 | 36.15 |
| 7730 | | | | #5 @ 16″ E.W. | | 12.30 | 25.50 | 37.80 |
| 7800 | Common | 10″ | 2 | #4 @ 48″ E.W. | | 30 | 30 | 60 |
| 7820 | | | | #5 @ 32″ E.W. | | 30 | 30.50 | 60.50 |
| 7830 | | | | #5 @ 16″ E.W. | | 31 | 31 | 62 |
| 7900 | Standard | 10″ | 2 | #4 @ 48″ E.W. | | 15.10 | 31 | 46.10 |
| 7920 | | | | #5 @ 32″ E.W. | | 15.50 | 31.50 | 47 |
| 7930 | | | | #5 @ 16″ E.W. | | 16.15 | 32 | 48.15 |
| 8100 | Economy | 10″ | 2 | #4 @ 48″ E.W. | | 19.30 | 24 | 43.30 |
| 8120 | | | | #5 @ 32″ E.W. | | 19.70 | 24 | 43.70 |
| 8130 | | | | #5 @ 16″ E.W. | | 20.50 | 25 | 45.50 |
| 8200 | Double | 10″ | 2 | #4 @ 48″ E.W. | | 18.35 | 19.50 | 37.85 |
| 8220 | | | | #5 @ 32″ E.W. | | 18.75 | 19.70 | 38.45 |
| 8230 | | | | #5 @ 16″ E.W. | | 19.40 | 20.50 | 39.90 |
| 8300 | Fire | 10″ | 2 | #4 @ 48″ E.W. | | 30 | 27.50 | 57.50 |
| 8320 | | | | #5 @ 32″ E.W. | | 30 | 28 | 58 |
| 8330 | | | | #5 @ 16″ E.W. | | 31 | 28.50 | 59.50 |
| 8400 | Roman | 10″ | 2 | #4 @ 48″ E.W. | | 21 | 28.50 | 49.50 |
| 8420 | | | | #5 @ 32″ E.W. | | 21.50 | 29 | 50.50 |
| 8430 | | | | #5 @ 16″ E.W. | | 22.50 | 29.50 | 52 |

## B2010 Exterior Walls

### B2010 127 Reinforced Brick Walls

| | TYPE | THICKNESS (IN.) | WYTHE | REINF. & SPACING | | COST PER S.F. | | |
|---|---|---|---|---|---|---|---|---|
| | | | | | | MAT. | INST. | TOTAL |
| 8500 | Norman | 10" | 2 | #4 @ 48" E.W. | | 15.35 | 23.50 | 38.85 |
| 8520 | | | | #5 @ 32" E.W. | | 15.75 | 23.50 | 39.25 |
| 8530 | | | | #5 @ 16" E.W. | | 16.40 | 24.50 | 40.90 |
| 8600 | Norwegian | 10" | 2 | #4 @ 48" E.W. | | 13.25 | 21 | 34.25 |
| 8620 | | | | #5 @ 32" E.W. | | 13.65 | 21 | 34.65 |
| 8630 | | | | #5 @ 16" E.W. | | 14.30 | 21.50 | 35.80 |
| 8800 | Triple | 10" | 2 | #4 @ 48" E.W. | | 11.10 | 16.40 | 27.50 |
| 8820 | | | | #5 @ 32" E.W. | | 11.50 | 16.60 | 28.10 |
| 8830 | | | | #5 @ 16" E.W. | | 12.15 | 17.35 | 29.50 |

## B2010 Exterior Walls

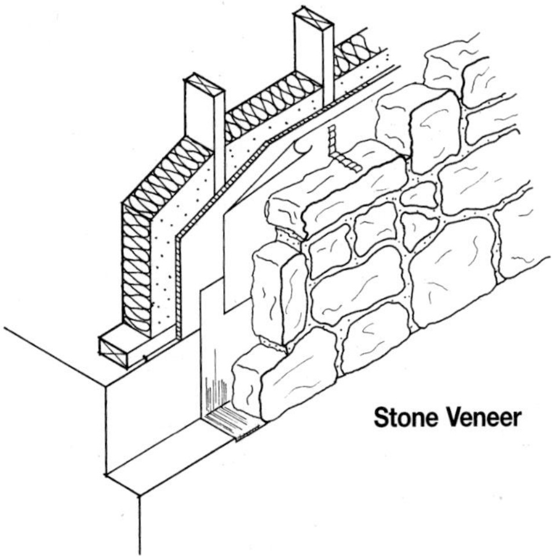


The table below lists costs per S.F. for stone veneer walls on various backup using different stone.

| B2010 128 | Stone Veneer | COST PER S.F. | | |
|---|---|---|---|---|
| | | MAT. | INST. | TOTAL |
| 2000 | Ashlar veneer, 4", 2" x 4" stud backup, 16" O.C., 8' high, low priced stone | 19.15 | 27.50 | 46.65 |
| 2050 | 2" x 6" stud backup, 16" O.C. | 23.50 | 32 | 55.50 |
| 2100 | Metal stud backup, 8' high, 16" O.C. | 20.50 | 28 | 48.50 |
| 2150 | 24" O.C. | 19.90 | 27 | 46.90 |
| 2200 | Conc. block backup, 4" thick | 19.90 | 32.50 | 52.40 |
| 2300 | 6" thick | 20.50 | 33 | 53.50 |
| 2350 | 8" thick | 21 | 33.50 | 54.50 |
| 2400 | 10" thick | 22 | 35.50 | 57.50 |
| 2500 | 12" thick | 23 | 38 | 61 |
| 3100 | High priced stone, wood stud backup, 10' high, 16" O.C. | 25.50 | 31 | 56.50 |
| 3200 | Metal stud backup, 10' high, 16" O.C. | 26.50 | 31.50 | 58 |
| 3250 | 24" O.C. | 26 | 30.50 | 56.50 |
| 3300 | Conc. block backup, 10' high, 4" thick | 26 | 36 | 62 |
| 3350 | 6" thick | 26.50 | 36 | 62.50 |
| 3400 | 8" thick | 28 | 38.50 | 66.50 |
| 3450 | 10" thick | 28 | 39 | 67 |
| 3500 | 12" thick | 29 | 41.50 | 70.50 |
| 4000 | Indiana limestone 2" thk., sawn finish, wood stud backup, 10' high, 16" O.C | 36 | 16.95 | 52.95 |
| 4100 | Metal stud backup, 10' high, 16" O.C. | 40 | 21.50 | 61.50 |
| 4150 | 24" O.C. | 40 | 21.50 | 61.50 |
| 4200 | Conc. block backup, 4" thick | 37 | 22 | 59 |
| 4250 | 6" thick | 37.50 | 22.50 | 60 |
| 4300 | 8" thick | 38 | 23 | 61 |
| 4350 | 10" thick | 39 | 25 | 64 |
| 4400 | 12" thick | 40 | 27.50 | 67.50 |
| 4450 | 2" thick, smooth finish, wood stud backup, 8' high, 16" O.C. | 36 | 16.95 | 52.95 |
| 4550 | Metal stud backup, 8' high, 16" O.C. | 37.50 | 17.10 | 54.60 |
| 4600 | 24" O.C. | 37 | 16.50 | 53.50 |
| 4650 | Conc. block backup, 4" thick | 37 | 22 | 59 |
| 4700 | 6" thick | 37.50 | 22 | 59.50 |
| 4750 | 8" thick | 38 | 23 | 61 |
| 4800 | 10" thick | 39 | 25 | 64 |
| 4850 | 12" thick | 40 | 27.50 | 67.50 |
| 5350 | 4" thick, smooth finish, wood stud backup, 8' high, 16" O.C. | 40 | 16.95 | 56.95 |
| 5450 | Metal stud backup, 8' high, 16" O.C. | 41.50 | 17.30 | 58.80 |
| 5500 | 24" O.C. | 41 | 16.75 | 57.75 |
| 5550 | Conc. block backup, 4" thick | 41 | 22 | 63 |
| 5600 | 6" thick | 41.50 | 22.50 | 64 |

## B2010 Exterior Walls

| B2010 128 | Stone Veneer | COST PER S.F. | | |
|---|---|---|---|---|
| | | MAT. | INST. | TOTAL |
| 5650 | 8" thick | 47 | 28.50 | 75.50 |
| 5700 | 10" thick | 43 | 25 | 68 |
| 5750 | 12" thick | 44 | 27.50 | 71.50 |
| 6000 | Granite, gray or pink, 2" thick, wood stud backup, 8' high, 16" O.C. | 34 | 31 | 65 |
| 6100 | Metal studs, 8' high, 16" O.C. | 35.50 | 31 | 66.50 |
| 6150 | 24" O.C. | 35 | 30.50 | 65.50 |
| 6200 | Conc. block backup, 4" thick | 35 | 36 | 71 |
| 6250 | 6" thick | 35.50 | 36.50 | 72 |
| 6300 | 8" thick | 36 | 37 | 73 |
| 6350 | 10" thick | 37 | 39 | 76 |
| 6400 | 12" thick | 38 | 41 | 79 |
| 6900 | 4" thick, wood stud backup, 8' high, 16" O.C. | 44.50 | 36 | 80.50 |
| 7000 | Metal studs, 8' high, 16" O.C. | 46 | 36 | 82 |
| 7050 | 24" O.C. | 45.50 | 35.50 | 81 |
| 7100 | Conc. block backup, 4" thick | 45.50 | 41 | 86.50 |
| 7150 | 6" thick | 46 | 41.50 | 87.50 |
| 7200 | 8" thick | 46.50 | 42 | 88.50 |
| 7250 | 10" thick | 47.50 | 44 | 91.50 |
| 7300 | 12" thick | 48.50 | 46 | 94.50 |

## B2010 Exterior Walls

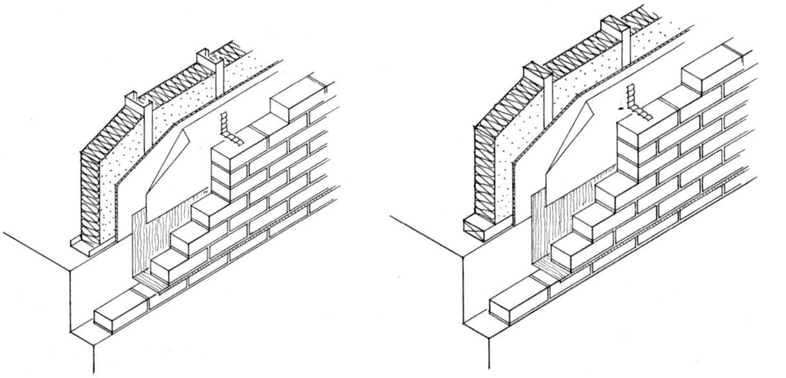

Exterior brick veneer/stud backup walls are defined in the following terms; type of brick and studs, stud spacing and bond. All systems include a brick shelf, ties to the backup and all necessary dampproofing and insulation.

### B2010 129 Brick Veneer/Wood Stud Backup

| | FACE BRICK | STUD BACKUP | STUD SPACING (IN.) | BOND | FACE | COST PER S.F. | | |
|---|---|---|---|---|---|---|---|---|
| | | | | | | MAT. | INST. | TOTAL |
| 1100 | Standard | 2x4-wood | 16 | running | | 11.35 | 21 | 32.35 |
| 1120 | | | | common | | 12.65 | 24 | 36.65 |
| 1140 | | | | Flemish | | 13.55 | 28 | 41.55 |
| 1160 | | | | English | | 14.70 | 29.50 | 44.20 |
| 1400 | | 2x6-wood | 16 | running | | 12.45 | 21 | 33.45 |
| 1420 | | | | common | | 13.50 | 24 | 37.50 |
| 1440 | | | | Flemish | | 14.40 | 28.50 | 42.90 |
| 1460 | | | | English | | 15.55 | 30 | 45.55 |
| 1700 | Glazed | 2x4-wood | 16 | running | | 29.50 | 22 | 51.50 |
| 1720 | | | | common | | 34.50 | 25 | 59.50 |
| 1740 | | | | Flemish | | 38 | 29.50 | 67.50 |
| 1760 | | | | English | | 42 | 31 | 73 |
| 2300 | Engineer | 2x4-wood | 16 | running | | 10.15 | 19 | 29.15 |
| 2320 | | | | common | | 11.20 | 21 | 32.20 |
| 2340 | | | | Flemish | | 11.90 | 25 | 36.90 |
| 2360 | | | | English | | 12.85 | 26 | 38.85 |
| 2900 | Roman | 2x4-wood | 16 | running | | 14.45 | 19.45 | 33.90 |
| 2920 | | | | common | | 16.40 | 22 | 38.40 |
| 2940 | | | | Flemish | | 17.70 | 25.50 | 43.20 |
| 2960 | | | | English | | 19.45 | 27 | 46.45 |
| 4100 | Norwegian | 2x4-wood | 16 | running | | 10.45 | 15.20 | 25.65 |
| 4120 | | | | common | | 11.50 | 16.85 | 28.35 |
| 4140 | | | | Flemish | | 12.25 | 19.45 | 31.70 |
| 4160 | | | | English | | 13.25 | 20.50 | 33.75 |

### B2010 130 Brick Veneer/Metal Stud Backup

| | FACE BRICK | STUD BACKUP | STUD SPACING (IN.) | BOND | FACE | COST PER S.F. | | |
|---|---|---|---|---|---|---|---|---|
| | | | | | | MAT. | INST. | TOTAL |
| 5050 | Standard | 16 ga x 6"LB | 16 | running | | 14.35 | 22 | 36.35 |
| 5100 | | 25ga.x6"NLB | 24 | running | | 10.10 | 20.50 | 30.60 |
| 5120 | | | | common | | 11.40 | 23.50 | 34.90 |
| 5140 | | | | Flemish | | 11.65 | 27 | 38.65 |
| 5160 | | | | English | | 13.45 | 29 | 42.45 |

## B2010 Exterior Walls

### B2010 130 Brick Veneer/Metal Stud Backup

| | FACE BRICK | STUD BACKUP | STUD SPACING (IN.) | BOND | FACE | COST PER S.F. | | |
|---|---|---|---|---|---|---|---|---|
| | | | | | | MAT. | INST. | TOTAL |
| 5200 | Standard | 20ga.x3-5/8"NLB | 16 | running | | 10.85 | 21.50 | 32.35 |
| 5220 | | | | common | | 12.15 | 24.50 | 36.65 |
| 5240 | | | | Flemish | | 13.05 | 28.50 | 41.55 |
| 5260 | | | | English | | 14.20 | 30 | 44.20 |
| 5400 | | 16ga.x3-5/8"LB | 16 | running | | 12.30 | 22 | 34.30 |
| 5420 | | | | common | | 13.60 | 24.50 | 38.10 |
| 5440 | | | | Flemish | | 14.50 | 29 | 43.50 |
| 5460 | | | | English | | 15.65 | 30.50 | 46.15 |
| 5500 | | | 24 | running | | 11.50 | 21.50 | 33 |
| 5520 | | | | common | | 12.80 | 24 | 36.80 |
| 5540 | | | | Flemish | | 13.70 | 28.50 | 42.20 |
| 5560 | | | | English | | 14.85 | 30 | 44.85 |
| 5700 | Glazed | 25ga.x6"NLB | 24 | running | | 28.50 | 21.50 | 50 |
| 5720 | | | | common | | 33.50 | 24.50 | 58 |
| 5740 | | | | Flemish | | 37 | 29 | 66 |
| 5760 | | | | English | | 41 | 30.50 | 71.50 |
| 5800 | | 20ga.x3-5/8"NLB | 24 | running | | 29 | 21.50 | 50.50 |
| 5820 | | | | common | | 34 | 24.50 | 58.50 |
| 5840 | | | | Flemish | | 37.50 | 29.50 | 67 |
| 5860 | | | | English | | 41.50 | 31 | 72.50 |
| 6000 | | 16ga.x3-5/8"LB | 16 | running | | 30.50 | 22.50 | 53 |
| 6020 | | | | common | | 35.50 | 25.50 | 61 |
| 6040 | | | | Flemish | | 39 | 30.50 | 69.50 |
| 6060 | | | | English | | 43 | 32 | 75 |
| 6300 | Engineer | 25ga.x6"NLB | 24 | running | | 8.90 | 18.55 | 27.45 |
| 6320 | | | | common | | 9.95 | 20.50 | 30.45 |
| 6340 | | | | Flemish | | 10.65 | 24.50 | 35.15 |
| 6360 | | | | English | | 11.60 | 25.50 | 37.10 |
| 6400 | | 20ga.x3-5/8"NLB | 16 | running | | 9.65 | 19.40 | 29.05 |
| 6420 | | | | common | | 10.70 | 21.50 | 32.20 |
| 6440 | | | | Flemish | | 11.40 | 25.50 | 36.90 |
| 6460 | | | | English | | 12.35 | 26.50 | 38.85 |
| 6900 | Roman | 25ga.x6"NLB | 24 | running | | 13.20 | 19 | 32.20 |
| 6920 | | | | common | | 15.15 | 21.50 | 36.65 |
| 6940 | | | | Flemish | | 16.45 | 25 | 41.45 |
| 6960 | | | | English | | 18.20 | 26.50 | 44.70 |
| 7000 | | 20ga.x3-5/8"NLB | 16 | running | | 13.95 | 19.85 | 33.80 |
| 7020 | | | | common | | 15.90 | 22.50 | 38.40 |
| 7040 | | | | Flemish | | 17.20 | 26 | 43.20 |
| 7060 | | | | English | | 18.95 | 27.50 | 46.45 |
| 7500 | Norman | 25ga.x6"NLB | 24 | running | | 10.20 | 16.25 | 26.45 |
| 7520 | | | | common | | 11.55 | 18.10 | 29.65 |
| 7540 | | | | Flemish | | 23.50 | 21 | 44.50 |
| 7560 | | | | English | | 13.60 | 22 | 35.60 |
| 7600 | | 20ga.x3-5/8"NLB | 24 | running | | 10.55 | 16.45 | 27 |
| 7620 | | | | common | | 11.90 | 18.30 | 30.20 |
| 7640 | | | | Flemish | | 23.50 | 21.50 | 45 |
| 7660 | | | | English | | 13.95 | 22.50 | 36.45 |
| 8100 | Norwegian | 25ga.x6"NLB | 24 | running | | 9.15 | 14.75 | 23.90 |
| 8120 | | | | common | | 10.25 | 16.40 | 26.65 |
| 8140 | | | | Flemish | | 11 | 19 | 30 |
| 8160 | | | | English | | 12 | 19.85 | 31.85 |

## B2010 Exterior Walls

### B2010 130 Brick Veneer/Metal Stud Backup

| | FACE BRICK | STUD BACKUP | STUD SPACING (IN.) | BOND | FACE | COST PER S.F. | | |
|---|---|---|---|---|---|---|---|---|
| | | | | | | MAT. | INST. | TOTAL |
| 8400 | Norwegian | 16ga.x3-5/8"LB | 16 | running | | 11.40 | 15.90 | 27.30 |
| 8420 | | | | common | | 12.45 | 17.55 | 30 |
| 8440 | | | | Flemish | | 13.20 | 20 | 33.20 |
| 8460 | | | | English | | 14.20 | 21 | 35.20 |

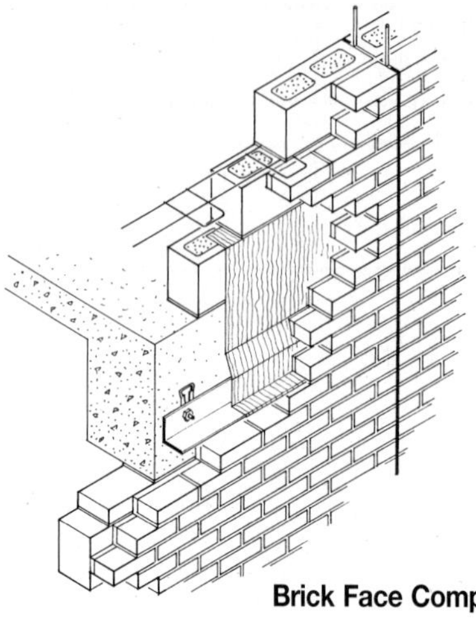

Brick Face Composite Wall

| B2010 132 | Brick Face Composite Wall - Double Wythe | | | | | | | |
|---|---|---|---|---|---|---|---|---|
| | FACE BRICK | BACKUP MASONRY | BACKUP THICKNESS (IN.) | BACKUP CORE FILL | | COST PER S.F. | | |
| | | | | | | MAT. | INST. | TOTAL |
| 1000 | Standard | common brick | 4 | none | | 21.50 | 33 | 54.50 |
| 1040 | | SCR brick | 6 | none | | 15.70 | 29.50 | 45.20 |
| 1080 | | conc. block | 4 | none | | 10.70 | 26.50 | 37.20 |
| 1120 | | | 6 | perlite | | 11.85 | 27.50 | 39.35 |
| 1160 | | | | styrofoam | | 13.45 | 27 | 40.45 |
| 1200 | | | 8 | perlite | | 12.65 | 28 | 40.65 |
| 1240 | | | | styrofoam | | 14.60 | 27.50 | 42.10 |
| 1520 | | glazed block | 4 | none | | 23 | 28 | 51 |
| 1560 | | | 6 | perlite | | 26.50 | 29 | 55.50 |
| 1600 | | | | styrofoam | | 28 | 28.50 | 56.50 |
| 1640 | | | 8 | perlite | | 28.50 | 30 | 58.50 |
| 1680 | | | | styrofoam | | 30.50 | 29.50 | 60 |
| 1720 | | clay tile | 4 | none | | 15.95 | 25.50 | 41.45 |
| 1760 | | | 6 | none | | 19.70 | 26 | 45.70 |
| 1800 | | | 8 | none | | 21 | 27 | 48 |
| 1840 | | glazed tile | 4 | none | | 23.50 | 33.50 | 57 |
| 1880 | | | | | | | | |
| 2000 | Glazed | common brick | 4 | none | | 39.50 | 33.50 | 73 |
| 2040 | | SCR brick | 6 | none | | 34 | 30 | 64 |
| 2080 | | conc. block | 4 | none | | 29 | 27 | 56 |
| 2200 | | | 8 | perlite | | 31 | 28.50 | 59.50 |
| 2240 | | | | styrofoam | | 33 | 28 | 61 |
| 2280 | | L.W. block | 4 | none | | 29 | 27 | 56 |
| 2400 | | | 8 | perlite | | 31.50 | 28.50 | 60 |
| 2520 | | glazed block | 4 | none | | 41.50 | 29 | 70.50 |
| 2560 | | | 6 | perlite | | 45 | 30 | 75 |
| 2600 | | | | styrofoam | | 46.50 | 29.50 | 76 |
| 2640 | | | 8 | perlite | | 47 | 30.50 | 77.50 |
| 2680 | | | | styrofoam | | 49 | 30 | 79 |

## B2010 Exterior Walls

### B2010 132 Brick Face Composite Wall - Double Wythe

| | FACE BRICK | BACKUP MASONRY | BACKUP THICKNESS (IN.) | BACKUP CORE FILL | | COST PER S.F. | | |
|---|---|---|---|---|---|---|---|---|
| | | | | | | MAT. | INST. | TOTAL |
| 2720 | Glazed | clay tile | 4 | none | | 34.50 | 26 | 60.50 |
| 2760 | | | 6 | none | | 38 | 27 | 65 |
| 2800 | | | 8 | none | | 39.50 | 27.50 | 67 |
| 2840 | | glazed tile | 4 | none | | 42 | 34 | 76 |
| 3000 | Engineer | common brick | 4 | none | | 20 | 30.50 | 50.50 |
| 3040 | | SCR brick | 6 | none | | 14.50 | 27 | 41.50 |
| 3080 | | conc. block | 4 | none | | 9.50 | 24 | 33.50 |
| 3200 | | | 8 | perlite | | 11.40 | 26 | 37.40 |
| 3280 | | L.W. block | 4 | none | | 7.60 | 17.15 | 24.75 |
| 3320 | | | 6 | perlite | | 10.60 | 25 | 35.60 |
| 3520 | | glazed block | 4 | none | | 22 | 26 | 48 |
| 3560 | | | 6 | perlite | | 25 | 27 | 52 |
| 3600 | | | | styrofoam | | 27 | 26.50 | 53.50 |
| 3640 | | | 8 | perlite | | 27.50 | 27.50 | 55 |
| 3680 | | | | styrofoam | | 29.50 | 27 | 56.50 |
| 3720 | | clay tile | 4 | none | | 14.75 | 23 | 37.75 |
| 3800 | | | 8 | none | | 19.70 | 25 | 44.70 |
| 3840 | | glazed tile | 4 | none | | 22 | 31.50 | 53.50 |
| 4000 | Roman | common brick | 4 | none | | 24.50 | 31 | 55.50 |
| 4040 | | SCR brick | 6 | none | | 18.80 | 27.50 | 46.30 |
| 4080 | | conc. block | 4 | none | | 13.80 | 24.50 | 38.30 |
| 4120 | | | 6 | perlite | | 14.95 | 25.50 | 40.45 |
| 4200 | | | 8 | perlite | | 15.75 | 26.50 | 42.25 |
| 5000 | Norman | common brick | 4 | none | | 21.50 | 28.50 | 50 |
| 5040 | | SCR brick | 6 | none | | 15.80 | 25 | 40.80 |
| 5280 | | L.W. block | 4 | none | | 10.60 | 21.50 | 32.10 |
| 5320 | | | 6 | perlite | | 11.95 | 23 | 34.95 |
| 5720 | | clay tile | 4 | none | | 16.05 | 21 | 37.05 |
| 5760 | | | 6 | none | | 19.80 | 21.50 | 41.30 |
| 5840 | | glazed tile | 4 | none | | 23.50 | 29 | 52.50 |
| 6000 | Norwegian | common brick | 4 | none | | 20.50 | 27 | 47.50 |
| 6040 | | SCR brick | 6 | none | | 14.75 | 23.50 | 38.25 |
| 6080 | | conc. block | 4 | none | | 9.80 | 20.50 | 30.30 |
| 6120 | | | 6 | perlite | | 10.95 | 21.50 | 32.45 |
| 6160 | | | | styrofoam | | 12.55 | 21 | 33.55 |
| 6200 | | | 8 | perlite | | 11.70 | 22 | 33.70 |
| 6520 | | glazed block | 4 | none | | 22.50 | 22 | 44.50 |
| 6560 | | | 6 | perlite | | 25.50 | 23 | 48.50 |
| 7000 | Utility | common brick | 4 | none | | 21.50 | 25.50 | 47 |
| 7040 | | SCR brick | 6 | none | | 15.65 | 22 | 37.65 |
| 7080 | | conc. block | 4 | none | | 10.65 | 19.05 | 29.70 |
| 7120 | | | 6 | perlite | | 11.80 | 20 | 31.80 |
| 7160 | | | | styrofoam | | 13.40 | 19.60 | 33 |
| 7200 | | | 8 | perlite | | 12.60 | 20.50 | 33.10 |
| 7240 | | | | styrofoam | | 14.55 | 20 | 34.55 |
| 7280 | | L.W. block | 4 | none | | 10.45 | 18.85 | 29.30 |
| 7320 | | | 6 | perlite | | 11.75 | 19.80 | 31.55 |
| 7520 | | glazed block | 4 | none | | 23 | 21 | 44 |
| 7560 | | | 6 | perlite | | 26.50 | 21.50 | 48 |
| 7720 | | clay tile | 4 | none | | 15.90 | 18 | 33.90 |
| 7760 | | | 6 | none | | 19.65 | 18.70 | 38.35 |
| 7840 | | glazed tile | 4 | none | | 23.50 | 26 | 49.50 |

## B2010 Exterior Walls

### B2010 133 Brick Face Composite Wall - Triple Wythe

| | FACE BRICK | MIDDLE WYTHE | INSIDE MASONRY | TOTAL THICKNESS (IN.) | | COST PER S.F. | | |
|---|---|---|---|---|---|---|---|---|
| | | | | | | MAT. | INST. | TOTAL |
| 8000 | Standard | common brick | standard brick | 12 | | 28 | 47 | 75 |
| 8100 | | 4" conc. brick | standard brick | 12 | | 27 | 48.50 | 75.50 |
| 8120 | | 4" conc. brick | common brick | 12 | | 34 | 48 | 82 |
| 8200 | Glazed | common brick | standard brick | 12 | | 46 | 48 | 94 |
| 8300 | | 4" conc. brick | standard brick | 12 | | 45.50 | 49 | 94.50 |
| 8320 | | 4" conc. brick | glazed brick | 12 | | 52.50 | 48.50 | 101 |

## B2010 Exterior Walls

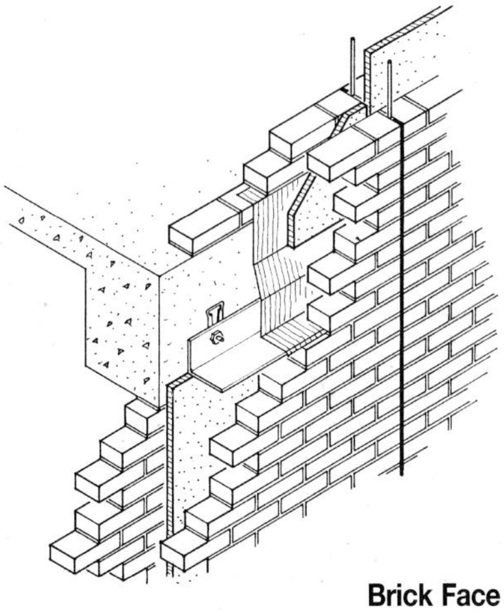

Brick Face Cavity Wall

| B2010 134 | Brick Face Cavity Wall | | | | | | |
|---|---|---|---|---|---|---|---|
| | FACE BRICK | BACKUP MASONRY | TOTAL THICKNESS (IN.) | CAVITY INSULATION | COST PER S.F. | | |
| | | | | | MAT. | INST. | TOTAL |
| 1000 | Standard | 4" common brick | 10 | polystyrene | 21 | 33 | 54 |
| 1020 | | | | none | 21 | 32 | 53 |
| 1040 | | 6" SCR brick | 12 | polystyrene | 15.65 | 29.50 | 45.15 |
| 1060 | | | | none | 15.25 | 28.50 | 43.75 |
| 1080 | | 4" conc. block | 10 | polystyrene | 10.60 | 26.50 | 37.10 |
| 1100 | | | | none | 10.25 | 25.50 | 35.75 |
| 1120 | | 6" conc. block | 12 | polystyrene | 11.20 | 27 | 38.20 |
| 1140 | | | | none | 10.80 | 26 | 36.80 |
| 1160 | | 4" L.W. block | 10 | polystyrene | 10.40 | 26.50 | 36.90 |
| 1180 | | | | none | 10 | 25.50 | 35.50 |
| 1200 | | 6" L.W. block | 12 | polystyrene | 11.10 | 27 | 38.10 |
| 1220 | | | | none | 10.75 | 26 | 36.75 |
| 1240 | | 4" glazed block | 10 | polystyrene | 23 | 28.50 | 51.50 |
| 1260 | | | | none | 22.50 | 27.50 | 50 |
| 1280 | | 6" glazed block | 12 | polystyrene | 23 | 28.50 | 51.50 |
| 1300 | | | | none | 23 | 27.50 | 50.50 |
| 1320 | | 4" clay tile | 10 | polystyrene | 15.85 | 25.50 | 41.35 |
| 1340 | | | | none | 15.45 | 24.50 | 39.95 |
| 1360 | | 4" glazed tile | 10 | polystyrene | 23.50 | 33.50 | 57 |
| 1380 | | | | none | 23 | 32.50 | 55.50 |
| 1500 | Glazed | 4" common brick | 10 | polystyrene | 39.50 | 33.50 | 73 |
| 1520 | | | | none | 39 | 33 | 72 |
| 1580 | | 4" conc. block | 10 | polystyrene | 29 | 27 | 56 |
| 1600 | | | | none | 28.50 | 26.50 | 55 |
| 1660 | | 4" L.W. block | 10 | polystyrene | 28.50 | 27 | 55.50 |
| 1680 | | | | none | 28.50 | 26 | 54.50 |
| 1740 | | 4" glazed block | 10 | polystyrene | 41.50 | 29 | 70.50 |
| 1760 | | | | none | 41 | 28 | 69 |
| 1820 | | 4" clay tile | 10 | polystyrene | 34 | 26 | 60 |
| 1840 | | | | none | 34 | 25.50 | 59.50 |
| 1860 | | 4" glazed tile | 10 | polystyrene | 38 | 27 | 65 |
| 1880 | | | | none | 37.50 | 26 | 63.50 |
| 2000 | Engineer | 4" common brick | 10 | polystyrene | 20 | 31 | 51 |
| 2020 | | | | none | 19.65 | 30 | 49.65 |
| 2080 | | 4" conc. block | 10 | polystyrene | 9.40 | 24.50 | 33.90 |
| 2100 | | | | none | 9 | 23.50 | 32.50 |

## B2010 Exterior Walls

### B2010 134 Brick Face Cavity Wall

| | FACE BRICK | BACKUP MASONRY | TOTAL THICKNESS (IN.) | CAVITY INSULATION | | COST PER S.F. | | |
|---|---|---|---|---|---|---|---|---|
| | | | | | | MAT. | INST. | TOTAL |
| 2160 | Engineer | 4" L.W. block | 10 | polystyrene | | 9.15 | 24 | 33.15 |
| 2180 | | | | none | | 8.80 | 23 | 31.80 |
| 2240 | | 4" glazed block | 10 | polystyrene | | 22 | 26 | 48 |
| 2260 | | | | none | | 21.50 | 25 | 46.50 |
| 2320 | | 4" clay tile | 10 | polystyrene | | 14.65 | 23.50 | 38.15 |
| 2340 | | | | none | | 14.25 | 22.50 | 36.75 |
| 2360 | | 4" glazed tile | 10 | polystyrene | | 22 | 31.50 | 53.50 |
| 2380 | | | | none | | 21.50 | 30.50 | 52 |
| 2500 | Roman | 4" common brick | 10 | polystyrene | | 24.50 | 31 | 55.50 |
| 2520 | | | | none | | 24 | 30.50 | 54.50 |
| 2580 | | 4" conc. block | 10 | polystyrene | | 13.70 | 25 | 38.70 |
| 2600 | | | | none | | 13.35 | 24 | 37.35 |
| 2660 | | 4" L.W. block | 10 | polystyrene | | 13.50 | 24.50 | 38 |
| 2680 | | | | none | | 13.10 | 23.50 | 36.60 |
| 2740 | | 4" glazed block | 10 | polystyrene | | 26 | 26.50 | 52.50 |
| 2760 | | | | none | | 26 | 25.50 | 51.50 |
| 2820 | | 4" clay tile | 10 | polystyrene | | 18.95 | 23.50 | 42.45 |
| 2840 | | | | none | | 18.55 | 23 | 41.55 |
| 2860 | | 4" glazed tile | 10 | polystyrene | | 26.50 | 32 | 58.50 |
| 2880 | | | | none | | 26 | 31 | 57 |
| 3000 | Norman | 4" common brick | 10 | polystyrene | | 21.50 | 28.50 | 50 |
| 3020 | | | | none | | 21 | 27.50 | 48.50 |
| 3080 | | 4" conc. block | 10 | polystyrene | | 10.70 | 22 | 32.70 |
| 3100 | | | | none | | 10.35 | 21 | 31.35 |
| 3160 | | 4" L.W. block | 10 | polystyrene | | 10.50 | 22 | 32.50 |
| 3180 | | | | none | | 10.10 | 21 | 31.10 |
| 3240 | | 4" glazed block | 10 | polystyrene | | 23 | 24 | 47 |
| 3260 | | | | none | | 23 | 23 | 46 |
| 3320 | | 4" clay tile | 10 | polystyrene | | 15.95 | 21 | 36.95 |
| 3340 | | | | none | | 15.55 | 20 | 35.55 |
| 3360 | | 4" glazed tile | 10 | polystyrene | | 23.50 | 29 | 52.50 |
| 3380 | | | | none | | 23 | 28 | 51 |
| 3500 | Norwegian | 4" common brick | 10 | polystyrene | | 20.50 | 27 | 47.50 |
| 3520 | | | | none | | 19.95 | 26 | 45.95 |
| 3580 | | 4" conc. block | 10 | polystyrene | | 9.65 | 20.50 | 30.15 |
| 3600 | | | | none | | 9.30 | 19.65 | 28.95 |
| 3660 | | 4" L.W. block | 10 | polystyrene | | 9.45 | 20.50 | 29.95 |
| 3680 | | | | none | | 9.10 | 19.45 | 28.55 |
| 3740 | | 4" glazed block | 10 | polystyrene | | 22 | 22.50 | 44.50 |
| 3760 | | | | none | | 22 | 21.50 | 43.50 |
| 3820 | | 4" clay tile | 10 | polystyrene | | 14.90 | 19.45 | 34.35 |
| 3840 | | | | none | | 14.55 | 18.60 | 33.15 |
| 3860 | | 4" glazed tile | 10 | polystyrene | | 22.50 | 27.50 | 50 |
| 3880 | | | | none | | 22 | 26.50 | 48.50 |
| 4000 | Utility | 4" common brick | 10 | polystyrene | | 21 | 25.50 | 46.50 |
| 4020 | | | | none | | 21 | 24.50 | 45.50 |
| 4080 | | 4" conc. block | 10 | polystyrene | | 10.55 | 19.10 | 29.65 |
| 4100 | | | | none | | 10.20 | 18.25 | 28.45 |
| 4160 | | 4" L.W. block | 10 | polystyrene | | 10.35 | 18.90 | 29.25 |
| 4180 | | | | none | | 9.95 | 18.05 | 28 |
| 4240 | | 4" glazed block | 10 | polystyrene | | 23 | 21 | 44 |
| 4260 | | | | none | | 22.50 | 20 | 42.50 |

## B2010 Exterior Walls

### B2010 134 — Brick Face Cavity Wall

| | FACE BRICK | BACKUP MASONRY | TOTAL THICKNESS (IN.) | CAVITY INSULATION | | COST PER S.F. | | |
|---|---|---|---|---|---|---|---|---|
| | | | | | | MAT. | INST. | TOTAL |
| 4320 | Utility | 4″ clay tile | 10 | polystyrene | | 15.80 | 18.05 | 33.85 |
| 4340 | | | | none | | 15.40 | 17.20 | 32.60 |
| 4360 | | 4″ glazed tile | 10 | polystyrene | | 23 | 26 | 49 |
| 4380 | | | | none | | 23 | 25.50 | 48.50 |

### B2010 135 — Brick Face Cavity Wall - Insulated Backup

| | FACE BRICK | BACKUP MASONRY | TOTAL THICKNESS (IN.) | BACKUP CORE FILL | | COST PER S.F. | | |
|---|---|---|---|---|---|---|---|---|
| | | | | | | MAT. | INST. | TOTAL |
| 5100 | Standard | 6″ conc. block | 10 | perlite | | 11.40 | 26.50 | 37.90 |
| 5120 | | | | styrofoam | | 13 | 26 | 39 |
| 5180 | | 6″ L.W. block | 10 | perlite | | 11.30 | 26.50 | 37.80 |
| 5200 | | | | styrofoam | | 12.90 | 26 | 38.90 |
| 5260 | | 6″ glazed block | 10 | perlite | | 26 | 28.50 | 54.50 |
| 5280 | | | | styrofoam | | 27.50 | 28 | 55.50 |
| 5340 | | 6″ clay tile | 10 | none | | 19.20 | 25.50 | 44.70 |
| 5360 | | 8″ clay tile | 12 | none | | 20.50 | 26 | 46.50 |
| 5600 | Glazed | 6″ conc. block | 10 | perlite | | 29.50 | 27.50 | 57 |
| 5620 | | | | styrofoam | | 31.50 | 27 | 58.50 |
| 5680 | | 6″ L.W. block | 10 | perlite | | 29.50 | 27 | 56.50 |
| 5700 | | | | styrofoam | | 31.50 | 26.50 | 58 |
| 5760 | | 6″ glazed block | 10 | perlite | | 44.50 | 29 | 73.50 |
| 5780 | | | | styrofoam | | 46 | 28.50 | 74.50 |
| 5840 | | 6″ clay tile | 10 | none | | 37.50 | 26 | 63.50 |
| 5860 | | 8″ clay tile | 8 | none | | 39 | 27 | 66 |
| 6100 | Engineer | 6″ conc. block | 10 | perlite | | 10.20 | 24.50 | 34.70 |
| 6120 | | | | styrofoam | | 11.75 | 24 | 35.75 |
| 6180 | | 6″ L.W. block | 10 | perlite | | 10.10 | 24 | 34.10 |
| 6200 | | | | styrofoam | | 11.70 | 24 | 35.70 |
| 6260 | | 6″ glazed block | 10 | perlite | | 24.50 | 26 | 50.50 |
| 6280 | | | | styrofoam | | 26.50 | 25.50 | 52 |
| 6340 | | 6″ clay tile | 10 | none | | 18 | 23 | 41 |
| 6360 | | 8″ clay tile | 12 | none | | 19.25 | 24 | 43.25 |
| 6600 | Roman | 6″ conc. block | 10 | perlite | | 14.50 | 25 | 39.50 |
| 6620 | | | | styrofoam | | 16.10 | 24.50 | 40.60 |
| 6680 | | 6″ L.W. block | 10 | perlite | | 14.40 | 24.50 | 38.90 |
| 6700 | | | | styrofoam | | 16 | 24 | 40 |
| 6760 | | 6″ glazed block | 10 | perlite | | 29 | 26.50 | 55.50 |
| 6780 | | | | styrofoam | | 30.50 | 26 | 56.50 |
| 6840 | Roman | 6″ clay tile | 10 | none | | 22.50 | 23.50 | 46 |
| 6860 | | 8″ clay tile | 12 | none | | 23.50 | 24.50 | 48 |
| 7100 | Norman | 6″ conc. block | 10 | perlite | | 11.50 | 22 | 33.50 |
| 7120 | | | | styrofoam | | 13.10 | 21.50 | 34.60 |
| 7180 | | 6″ L.W. block | 10 | perlite | | 11.40 | 22 | 33.40 |
| 7200 | | | | styrofoam | | 13 | 21.50 | 34.50 |
| 7260 | | 6″ glazed block | 10 | perlite | | 26 | 24 | 50 |
| 7280 | | | | styrofoam | | 27.50 | 23.50 | 51 |
| 7340 | | 6″ clay tile | 10 | none | | 19.30 | 21 | 40.30 |
| 7360 | | 8″ clay tile | 12 | none | | 20.50 | 21.50 | 42 |
| 7600 | Norwegian | 6″ conc. block | 10 | perlite | | 10.45 | 20.50 | 30.95 |
| 7620 | | | | styrofoam | | 12.05 | 20 | 32.05 |
| 7680 | | 6″ L.W. block | 10 | perlite | | 10.40 | 20.50 | 30.90 |
| 7700 | | | | styrofoam | | 11.95 | 20 | 31.95 |

## B2010 Exterior Walls

### B2010 135 Brick Face Cavity Wall - Insulated Backup

| | FACE BRICK | BACKUP MASONRY | TOTAL THICKNESS (IN.) | BACKUP CORE FILL | | COST PER S.F. | | |
|---|---|---|---|---|---|---|---|---|
| | | | | | | MAT. | INST. | TOTAL |
| 7760 | Norwegian | 6″ glazed block | 10 | perlite | | 25 | 22.50 | 47.50 |
| 7780 | | | | styrofoam | | 26.50 | 22 | 48.50 |
| 7840 | | 6″ clay tile | 10 | none | | 18.30 | 19.30 | 37.60 |
| 7860 | | 8″ clay tile | 12 | none | | 19.55 | 20 | 39.55 |
| 8100 | Utility | 6″ conc. block | 10 | perlite | | 11.35 | 19.20 | 30.55 |
| 8120 | | | | styrofoam | | 12.95 | 18.80 | 31.75 |
| 8180 | | 6″ L.W. block | 10 | perlite | | 11.25 | 19 | 30.25 |
| 8200 | | | | styrofoam | | 12.85 | 18.60 | 31.45 |
| 8220 | | 8″ L.W. block | 12 | perlite | | 12.65 | 19.60 | 32.25 |
| 8240 | | | | styrofoam | | 14.60 | 19.10 | 33.70 |
| 8260 | | 6″ glazed block | 10 | perlite | | 26 | 21 | 47 |
| 8280 | | | | styrofoam | | 27.50 | 20.50 | 48 |
| 8300 | | 8″ glazed block | 12 | perlite | | 28 | 21.50 | 49.50 |
| 8340 | | 6″ clay tile | 10 | none | | 19.15 | 17.90 | 37.05 |
| 8360 | | 8″ clay tile | 12 | none | | 20.50 | 18.80 | 39.30 |

## B2010 Exterior Walls

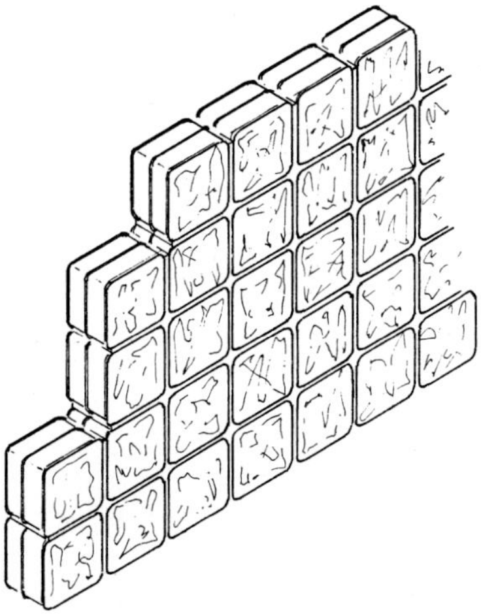

Glass Block

| B2010 140 | Glass Block | COST PER S.F. | | |
|---|---|---|---|---|
| | | MAT. | INST. | TOTAL |
| 2300 | Glass block 4" thick, 6"x6" plain, under 1,000 S.F. | 36.50 | 31 | 67.50 |
| 2400 | 1,000 to 5,000 S.F. | 36 | 26.50 | 62.50 |
| 2500 | Over 5,000 S.F. | 35 | 25 | 60 |
| 2600 | Solar reflective, under 1,000 S.F. | 50.50 | 42.50 | 93 |
| 2700 | 1,000 to 5,000 S.F. | 50 | 36 | 86 |
| 2800 | Over 5,000 S.F. | 48.50 | 34 | 82.50 |
| 3500 | 8"x8" plain, under 1,000 S.F. | 22 | 23 | 45 |
| 3600 | 1,000 to 5,000 S.F. | 21.50 | 20 | 41.50 |
| 3700 | Over 5,000 S.F. | 21 | 18.05 | 39.05 |
| 3800 | Solar reflective, under 1,000 S.F. | 30.50 | 31 | 61.50 |
| 3900 | 1,000 to 5,000 S.F. | 29.50 | 26.50 | 56 |
| 4000 | Over 5,000 S.F. | 29 | 24 | 53 |
| 5000 | 12"x12" plain, under 1,000 S.F. | 28.50 | 21.50 | 50 |
| 5100 | 1,000 to 5,000 S.F. | 28 | 18.05 | 46.05 |
| 5200 | Over 5,000 S.F. | 27.50 | 16.50 | 44 |
| 5300 | Solar reflective, under 1,000 S.F. | 39.50 | 28.50 | 68 |
| 5400 | 1,000 to 5,000 S.F. | 39 | 24 | 63 |
| 5600 | Over 5,000 S.F. | 38 | 22 | 60 |
| 5800 | 3" thinline, 6"x6" plain, under 1,000 S.F. | 31 | 31 | 62 |
| 5900 | Over 5,000 S.F. | 46 | 25 | 71 |
| 6000 | Solar reflective, under 1,000 S.F. | 43 | 42.50 | 85.50 |
| 6100 | Over 5,000 S.F. | 64 | 34 | 98 |
| 6200 | 8"x8" plain, under 1,000 S.F. | 17.50 | 23 | 40.50 |
| 6300 | Over 5,000 S.F. | 26 | 18.05 | 44.05 |
| 6400 | Solar reflective, under 1,000 S.F. | 24.50 | 31 | 55.50 |
| 6500 | Over 5,000 S.F. | 36 | 24 | 60 |

## B2010 Exterior Walls

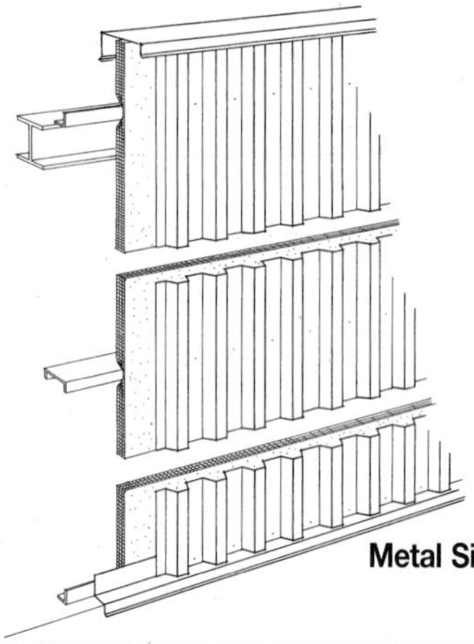


The table below lists costs for metal siding of various descriptions, not including the steel frame, or the structural steel, of a building. Costs are per S.F. including all accessories and insulation.

| B2010 146 | Metal Siding Panel | COST PER S.F. | | |
|---|---|---|---|---|
| | | MAT. | INST. | TOTAL |
| 1400 | Metal siding aluminum panel, corrugated, .024" thick, natural | 4.24 | 5.15 | 9.39 |
| 1450 | Painted | 4.43 | 5.15 | 9.58 |
| 1500 | .032" thick, natural | 9.50 | 5.15 | 14.65 |
| 1550 | Painted | 9.50 | 5.15 | 14.65 |
| 1600 | Ribbed 4" pitch, .032" thick, natural | 4.54 | 5.15 | 9.69 |
| 1650 | Painted | 9.80 | 5.15 | 14.95 |
| 1700 | .040" thick, natural | 4.89 | 5.15 | 10.04 |
| 1750 | Painted | 5.50 | 5.15 | 10.65 |
| 1800 | .050" thick, natural | 5.65 | 5.15 | 10.80 |
| 1850 | Painted | 10.05 | 5.15 | 15.20 |
| 1900 | Ribbed 8" pitch, .032" thick, natural | 4.36 | 4.93 | 9.29 |
| 1950 | Painted | 9.40 | 4.96 | 14.36 |
| 2000 | .040" thick, natural | 4.71 | 4.96 | 9.67 |
| 2050 | Painted | 5.30 | 5 | 10.30 |
| 2100 | .050" thick, natural | 5.40 | 4.99 | 10.39 |
| 2150 | Painted | 9.65 | 5.05 | 14.70 |
| 3000 | Steel, corrugated or ribbed, 29 Ga., .0135" thick, galvanized | 2.11 | 4.67 | 6.78 |
| 3050 | Colored | 3.81 | 4.73 | 8.54 |
| 3100 | 26 Ga., .0179" thick, galvanized | 2.48 | 4.69 | 7.17 |
| 3150 | Colored | 3.49 | 4.75 | 8.24 |
| 3200 | 24 Ga., .0239" thick, galvanized | 3.02 | 4.72 | 7.74 |
| 3250 | Colored | 3.77 | 4.78 | 8.55 |
| 3300 | 22 Ga., .0299" thick, galvanized | 4.18 | 4.74 | 8.92 |
| 3350 | Colored | 4.50 | 4.80 | 9.30 |
| 3400 | 20 Ga., .0359" thick, galvanized | 4.18 | 4.74 | 8.92 |
| 3450 | Colored | 4.76 | 5.10 | 9.86 |
| 4100 | Sandwich panels, factory fab., 1" polystyrene, steel core, 26 Ga., galv. | 6.10 | 7.40 | 13.50 |
| 4200 | Colored, 1 side | 8.25 | 7.40 | 15.65 |
| 4300 | 2 sides | 9.60 | 7.40 | 17 |
| 4400 | 2" polystyrene core, 26 Ga., galvanized | 10.90 | 7.40 | 18.30 |
| 4500 | Colored, 1 side | 9.40 | 7.40 | 16.80 |
| 4600 | 2 sides | 10.75 | 7.40 | 18.15 |
| 4700 | 22 Ga., baked enamel exterior | 13.85 | 7.80 | 21.65 |
| 4800 | Polyvinyl chloride exterior | 14.70 | 7.80 | 22.50 |
| 5100 | Textured aluminum, 4' x 8' x 5/16" plywood backing, single face | 5.70 | 4.51 | 10.21 |
| 5200 | Double face | 4.81 | 4.51 | 9.32 |

## B2010 Exterior Walls

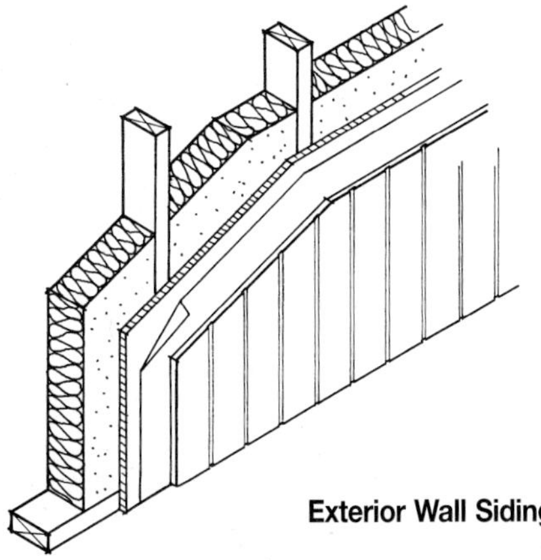

Exterior Wall Siding

The table below lists costs per S.F. for exterior walls with wood siding. A variety of systems are presented using both wood and metal studs at 16″ and 24″ O.C.

| B2010 148 | Panel, Shingle & Lap Siding | COST PER S.F. | | |
|---|---|---|---|---|
| | | MAT. | INST. | TOTAL |
| 1400 | Wood siding w/2″ x 4″ studs, 16″ O.C., insul. wall, 5/8″ text 1-11 fir ply. | 5.30 | 7.15 | 12.45 |
| 1450 | 5/8″ text 1-11 cedar plywood | 7.40 | 6.90 | 14.30 |
| 1500 | 1″ x 4″ vert T.&G. redwood | 13.35 | 8.25 | 21.60 |
| 1600 | 1″ x 8″ vert T.&G. redwood | 16.05 | 7.20 | 23.25 |
| 1650 | 1″ x 5″ rabbetted cedar bev. siding | 9.90 | 7.45 | 17.35 |
| 1700 | 1″ x 6″ cedar drop siding | 10 | 7.50 | 17.50 |
| 1750 | 1″ x 12″ rough sawn cedar | 5.70 | 7.20 | 12.90 |
| 1800 | 1″ x 12″ sawn cedar, 1″ x 4″ battens | 10.45 | 6.75 | 17.20 |
| 1850 | 1″ x 10″ redwood shiplap siding | 10.55 | 6.95 | 17.50 |
| 1900 | 18″ no. 1 red cedar shingles, 5-1/2″ exposed | 10.30 | 9.40 | 19.70 |
| 1950 | 6″ exposed | 9.85 | 9.10 | 18.95 |
| 2000 | 6-1/2″ exposed | 9.40 | 8.80 | 18.20 |
| 2100 | 7″ exposed | 8.95 | 8.50 | 17.45 |
| 2150 | 7-1/2″ exposed | 8.50 | 8.15 | 16.65 |
| 3000 | 8″ wide aluminum siding | 7 | 6.40 | 13.40 |
| 3150 | 8″ plain vinyl siding | 6.30 | 6.50 | 12.80 |
| 3250 | 8″ insulated vinyl siding | 6.80 | 7.20 | 14 |
| 3300 | | | | |
| 3400 | 2″ x 6″ studs, 16″ O.C., insul. wall, w/ 5/8″ text 1-11 fir plywood | 6.40 | 7.35 | 13.75 |
| 3500 | 5/8″ text 1-11 cedar plywood | 8.50 | 7.35 | 15.85 |
| 3600 | 1″ x 4″ vert T.&G. redwood | 14.45 | 8.45 | 22.90 |
| 3700 | 1″ x 8″ vert T.&G. redwood | 17.15 | 7.40 | 24.55 |
| 3800 | 1″ x 5″ rabbetted cedar bev siding | 11 | 7.65 | 18.65 |
| 3900 | 1″ x 6″ cedar drop siding | 11.10 | 7.70 | 18.80 |
| 4000 | 1″ x 12″ rough sawn cedar | 6.80 | 7.40 | 14.20 |
| 4200 | 1″ x 12″ sawn cedar, 1″ x 4″ battens | 11.55 | 6.95 | 18.50 |
| 4500 | 1″ x 10″ redwood shiplap siding | 11.65 | 7.15 | 18.80 |
| 4550 | 18″ no. 1 red cedar shingles, 5-1/2″ exposed | 11.40 | 9.60 | 21 |
| 4600 | 6″ exposed | 10.95 | 9.30 | 20.25 |
| 4650 | 6-1/2″ exposed | 10.50 | 9 | 19.50 |
| 4700 | 7″ exposed | 10.05 | 8.70 | 18.75 |
| 4750 | 7-1/2″ exposed | 9.60 | 8.35 | 17.95 |
| 4800 | 8″ wide aluminum siding | 8.10 | 6.60 | 14.70 |
| 4850 | 8″ plain vinyl siding | 7.70 | 7.15 | 14.85 |
| 4855 | Steel siding | 8.15 | 8.55 | 16.70 |
| 4900 | 8″ insulated vinyl siding | 8.20 | 7.85 | 16.05 |
| 4950 | 8″ fiber cement siding | 6.40 | 8.05 | 14.45 |
| 4955 | Fiber cement panel siding | 6.65 | 6.50 | 13.15 |
| 5000 | 2″ x 6″ studs, 24″ O.C., insul. wall, 5/8″ text 1-11, fir plywood | 5.90 | 6.90 | 12.80 |
| 5050 | 5/8″ text 1-11 cedar plywood | 8 | 6.90 | 14.90 |

## B2010 Exterior Walls

| B2010 148 | Panel, Shingle & Lap Siding | COST PER S.F. | | |
|---|---|---|---|---|
| | | MAT. | INST. | TOTAL |
| 5100 | 1" x 4" vert T.&G. redwood | 15.95 | 12.80 | 28.75 |
| 5150 | 1" x 8" vert T.&G. redwood | 16.65 | 6.95 | 23.60 |
| 5200 | 1" x 5" rabbetted cedar bev siding | 10.50 | 7.20 | 17.70 |
| 5250 | 1" x 6" cedar drop siding | 10.60 | 7.25 | 17.85 |
| 5300 | 1" x 12" rough sawn cedar | 6.30 | 7 | 13.30 |
| 5400 | 1" x 12" sawn cedar, 1" x 4" battens | 11.05 | 6.50 | 17.55 |
| 5450 | 1" x 10" redwood shiplap siding | 11.15 | 6.70 | 17.85 |
| 5500 | 18" no. 1 red cedar shingles, 5-1/2" exposed | 10.90 | 9.20 | 20.10 |
| 5550 | 6" exposed | 10.45 | 8.90 | 19.35 |
| 5650 | 7" exposed | 9.55 | 8.25 | 17.80 |
| 5700 | 7-1/2" exposed | 9.10 | 7.95 | 17.05 |
| 5750 | 8" wide aluminum siding | 7.60 | 6.20 | 13.80 |
| 5800 | 8" plain vinyl siding | 6.90 | 6.30 | 13.20 |
| 5850 | 8" insulated vinyl siding | 7.40 | 7 | 14.40 |
| 5875 | 8" fiber cement siding | 7.60 | 11.95 | 19.55 |
| 5900 | 3-5/8" metal studs, 16 Ga. 16" O.C. insul. wall, 5/8" text 1-11 fir plywood | 6.85 | 7.50 | 14.35 |
| 5950 | 5/8" text 1-11 cedar plywood | 8.95 | 7.50 | 16.45 |
| 6000 | 1" x 4" vert T.&G. redwood | 14.90 | 8.60 | 23.50 |
| 6050 | 1" x 8" vert T.&G. redwood | 17.60 | 7.55 | 25.15 |
| 6100 | 1" x 5" rabbetted cedar bev siding | 11.45 | 7.80 | 19.25 |
| 6150 | 1" x 6" cedar drop siding | 11.55 | 7.85 | 19.40 |
| 6200 | 1" x 12" rough sawn cedar | 7.25 | 7.55 | 14.80 |
| 6250 | 1" x 12" sawn cedar, 1" x 4" battens | 12 | 7.10 | 19.10 |
| 6300 | 1" x 10" redwood shiplap siding | 12.10 | 7.30 | 19.40 |
| 6350 | 18" no. 1 red cedar shingles, 5-1/2" exposed | 11.85 | 9.75 | 21.60 |
| 6500 | 6" exposed | 11.40 | 9.45 | 20.85 |
| 6550 | 6-1/2" exposed | 10.95 | 9.15 | 20.10 |
| 6600 | 7" exposed | 10.50 | 8.85 | 19.35 |
| 6650 | 7-1/2" exposed | 10.50 | 8.60 | 19.10 |
| 6700 | 8" wide aluminum siding | 8.55 | 6.75 | 15.30 |
| 6750 | 8" plain vinyl siding | 7.85 | 6.65 | 14.50 |
| 6755 | Metal siding panel | 8.45 | 8.05 | 16.50 |
| 6800 | 8" insulated vinyl siding | 8.35 | 7.35 | 15.70 |
| 7000 | 3-5/8" metal studs, 16 Ga. 24" O.C. insul wall, 5/8" text 1-11 fir plywood | 6.05 | 6.65 | 12.70 |
| 7050 | 5/8" text 1-11 cedar plywood | 8.15 | 6.65 | 14.80 |
| 7100 | 1" x 4" vert T.&G. redwood | 14.10 | 8 | 22.10 |
| 7150 | 1" x 8" vert T.&G. redwood | 16.80 | 6.95 | 23.75 |
| 7200 | 1" x 5" rabbetted cedar bev siding | 10.65 | 7.20 | 17.85 |
| 7250 | 1" x 6" cedar drop siding | 10.75 | 7.25 | 18 |
| 7300 | 1" x 12" rough sawn cedar | 6.45 | 7 | 13.45 |
| 7350 | 1" x 12" sawn cedar 1" x 4" battens | 11.20 | 6.50 | 17.70 |
| 7400 | 1" x 10" redwood shiplap siding | 11.30 | 6.70 | 18 |
| 7450 | 18" no. 1 red cedar shingles, 5-1/2" exposed | 11.50 | 9.50 | 21 |
| 7500 | 6" exposed | 11.05 | 9.20 | 20.25 |
| 7550 | 6-1/2" exposed | 10.60 | 8.85 | 19.45 |
| 7600 | 7" exposed | 10.15 | 8.55 | 18.70 |
| 7650 | 7-1/2" exposed | 9.25 | 7.95 | 17.20 |
| 7700 | 8" wide aluminum siding | 7.75 | 6.15 | 13.90 |
| 7750 | 8" plain vinyl siding | 7.05 | 6.30 | 13.35 |
| 7800 | 8" insul. vinyl siding | 7.55 | 7 | 14.55 |

## B2010 Exterior Walls

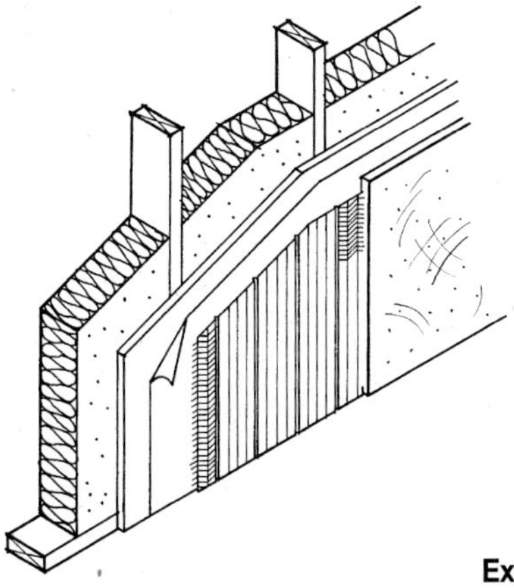

Exterior Stucco Wall

The table below lists costs for some typical stucco walls including all the components as demonstrated in the component block below. Prices are presented for backup walls using wood studs, metal studs and CMU.

| B2010 151 | Stucco Wall | COST PER S.F. | | |
|---|---|---|---|---|
| | | MAT. | INST. | TOTAL |
| 2100 | Cement stucco, 7/8" th., plywood sheathing, stud wall, 2" x 4", 16" O.C. | 5.35 | 11.75 | 17.10 |
| 2200 | 24" O.C. | 5.05 | 11.40 | 16.45 |
| 2300 | 2" x 6", 16" O.C. | 6.45 | 11.95 | 18.40 |
| 2400 | 24" O.C. | 5.95 | 11.50 | 17.45 |
| 2500 | No sheathing, metal lath on stud wall, 2" x 4", 16" O.C. | 3.80 | 10.20 | 14 |
| 2600 | 24" O.C. | 3.49 | 9.85 | 13.34 |
| 2700 | 2" x 6", 16" O.C. | 4.90 | 10.40 | 15.30 |
| 2800 | 24" O.C. | 4.39 | 10 | 14.39 |
| 2900 | 1/2" gypsum sheathing, 3-5/8" metal studs, 16" O.C. | 5.55 | 10.65 | 16.20 |
| 2950 | 24" O.C. | 4.74 | 10.05 | 14.79 |
| 3000 | Cement stucco, 5/8" th., 2 coats on std. CMU block, 8"x 16", 8" thick | 3.96 | 14.30 | 18.26 |
| 3100 | 10" thick | 5.80 | 14.65 | 20.45 |
| 3200 | 12" thick | 5.95 | 16.85 | 22.80 |
| 3300 | Std. light Wt. block 8" x 16", 8" thick | 4.44 | 14.05 | 18.49 |
| 3400 | 10" thick | 4.45 | 14.40 | 18.85 |
| 3500 | 12" thick | 5.20 | 16.55 | 21.75 |
| 3600 | 3 coat stucco, self furring metal lath 3.4 Lb/SY, on 8" x 16", 8" thick | 5.10 | 16.85 | 21.95 |
| 3700 | 10" thick | 5.85 | 15.45 | 21.30 |
| 3800 | 12" thick | 11.75 | 21 | 32.75 |
| 3900 | Lt. Wt. block, 8" thick | 4.50 | 14.85 | 19.35 |
| 4000 | 10" thick | 4.51 | 15.20 | 19.71 |
| 4100 | 12" thick | 5.25 | 17.35 | 22.60 |

| B2010 152 | E.I.F.S. | COST PER S.F. | | |
|---|---|---|---|---|
| | | MAT. | INST. | TOTAL |
| 5100 | E.I.F.S., plywood sheathing, stud wall, 2" x 4", 16" O.C., 1" EPS | 4.20 | 11.70 | 15.90 |
| 5110 | 2" EPS | 5.55 | 11.70 | 17.25 |
| 5120 | 3" EPS | 4.94 | 11.70 | 16.64 |
| 5130 | 4" EPS | 5.30 | 11.70 | 17 |
| 5140 | 2" x 6", 16" O.C., 1" EPS | 5.30 | 11.90 | 17.20 |
| 5150 | 2" EPS | 6.85 | 12.10 | 18.95 |
| 5160 | 3" EPS | 6.05 | 11.90 | 17.95 |
| 5170 | 4" EPS | 6.40 | 11.90 | 18.30 |
| 5180 | Cement board sheathing, 3-5/8" metal studs, 16" O.C., 1" EPS | 5.90 | 14.40 | 20.30 |
| 5190 | 2" EPS | 6.25 | 14.40 | 20.65 |
| 5200 | 3" EPS | 6.65 | 14.40 | 21.05 |
| 5210 | 4" EPS | 8.65 | 14.40 | 23.05 |
| 5220 | 6" metal studs, 16" O.C., 1" EPS | 7.10 | 14.50 | 21.60 |
| 5230 | 2" EPS | 7.65 | 14.65 | 22.30 |

## B2010 Exterior Walls

| B2010 152 | E.I.F.S. | COST PER S.F. | | |
|---|---|---|---|---|
| | | MAT. | INST. | TOTAL |
| 5240 | 3" EPS | 7.85 | 14.50 | 22.35 |
| 5250 | 4" EPS | 9.85 | 14.50 | 24.35 |
| 5252 | E.I.F.S. system, applied existing sheathing | 3.82 | 12.75 | 16.57 |
| 5260 | CMU block, 8" x 8" x 16", 1" EPS | 3.74 | 16.80 | 20.54 |
| 5270 | 2" EPS | 6.45 | 22 | 28.45 |
| 5280 | 3" EPS | 4.48 | 16.80 | 21.28 |
| 5290 | 4" EPS | 5.95 | 18.55 | 24.50 |
| 5300 | 8" x 10" x 16", 1" EPS | 5.55 | 17.15 | 22.70 |
| 5310 | 2" EPS | 6.95 | 17.15 | 24.10 |
| 5320 | 3" EPS | 6.30 | 17.15 | 23.45 |
| 5330 | 4" EPS | 6.70 | 17.15 | 23.85 |
| 5340 | 8" x 12" x 16", 1" EPS | 5.70 | 19.35 | 25.05 |
| 5350 | 2" EPS | 7.10 | 19.35 | 26.45 |
| 5360 | 3" EPS | 6.45 | 19.35 | 25.80 |
| 5370 | 4" EPS | 6.85 | 19.35 | 26.20 |

## B2010 Exterior Walls

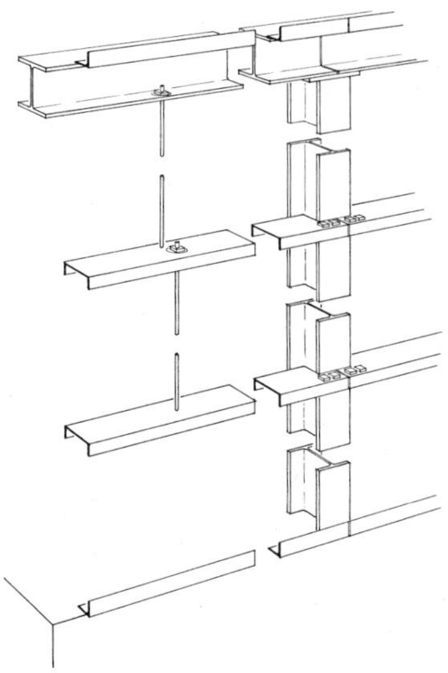

**Description:** The table below lists costs, $/S.F., for channel girts with sag rods and connector angles top and bottom for various column spacings, building heights and wind loads. Additive costs are shown for wind columns.

**How to Use this Table:** Add the cost of girts, sag rods, and angles to the framing costs of steel buildings clad in metal or composition siding. If the column spacing is in excess of the column spacing shown, use intermediate wind columns. Additive costs are shown under "Wind Columns".

### B2010 154 Metal Siding Support

| | BLDG. HEIGHT (FT.) | WIND LOAD (P.S.F.) | COL. SPACING (FT.) | | INTERMEDIATE COLUMNS | COST PER S.F. MAT. | INST. | TOTAL |
|---|---|---|---|---|---|---|---|---|
| 3000 | 18 | 20 | 20 | | | 3 | 4.49 | 7.49 |
| 3100 | | | | | wind cols. | 1.55 | .37 | 1.92 |
| 3200 | | 20 | 25 | | | 3.28 | 4.56 | 7.84 |
| 3300 | | | | | wind cols. | 1.24 | .29 | 1.53 |
| 3400 | | 20 | 30 | | | 3.62 | 4.64 | 8.26 |
| 3500 | | | | | wind cols. | 1.03 | .25 | 1.28 |
| 3600 | | 20 | 35 | | | 3.99 | 4.73 | 8.72 |
| 3700 | | | | | wind cols. | .89 | .21 | 1.10 |
| 3800 | | 30 | 20 | | | 3.32 | 4.57 | 7.89 |
| 3900 | | | | | wind cols. | 1.55 | .37 | 1.92 |
| 4000 | | 30 | 25 | | | 3.62 | 4.64 | 8.26 |
| 4100 | | | | | wind cols. | 1.24 | .29 | 1.53 |
| 4200 | | 30 | 30 | | | 4 | 4.73 | 8.73 |
| 4300 | | | | | wind cols. | 1.40 | .33 | 1.73 |
| 4600 | 30 | 20 | 20 | | | 2.91 | 3.19 | 6.10 |
| 4700 | | | | | wind cols. | 2.19 | .52 | 2.71 |
| 4800 | | 20 | 25 | | | 3.27 | 3.27 | 6.54 |
| 4900 | | | | | wind cols. | 1.75 | .42 | 2.17 |
| 5000 | | 20 | 30 | | | 3.68 | 3.37 | 7.05 |
| 5100 | | | | | wind cols. | 1.72 | .41 | 2.13 |
| 5200 | | 20 | 35 | | | 4.12 | 3.47 | 7.59 |
| 5300 | | | | | wind cols. | 1.71 | .41 | 2.12 |
| 5400 | | 30 | 20 | | | 3.31 | 3.28 | 6.59 |
| 5500 | | | | | wind cols. | 2.59 | .61 | 3.20 |
| 5600 | | 30 | 25 | | | 3.67 | 3.37 | 7.04 |
| 5700 | | | | | wind cols. | 2.47 | .59 | 3.06 |
| 5800 | | 30 | 30 | | | 4.14 | 3.48 | 7.62 |
| 5900 | | | | | wind cols. | 2.32 | .55 | 2.87 |

## B2010 Exterior Walls

| B2010 160 | Pole Barn Exterior Wall | COST PER S.F. | | |
|---|---|---|---|---|
| | | MAT. | INST. | TOTAL |
| 2000 | Pole barn exterior wall, pressure treated pole in concrete, 8′ O.C. | | | |
| 3000 | Steel siding, 8′ eave | 6.75 | 11.90 | 18.65 |
| 3050 | 10′ eave | 6.40 | 10.95 | 17.35 |
| 3100 | 12′ eave | 6.10 | 10 | 16.10 |
| 3150 | 14′ eave | 5.90 | 9.50 | 15.40 |
| 3200 | 16′ eave | 5.75 | 9.05 | 14.80 |
| 4000 | Aluminum siding, 8′ eave | 6.25 | 11.90 | 18.15 |
| 4050 | 10′ eave | 5.85 | 10.80 | 16.65 |
| 4100 | 12′ eave | 5.55 | 10 | 15.55 |
| 4150 | 14′ eave | 5.35 | 9.50 | 14.85 |
| 4200 | 16′ eave | 5.25 | 9.05 | 14.30 |
| 5000 | Wood siding, 8′ eave | 7.35 | 10.40 | 17.75 |
| 5050 | 10′ eave | 6.95 | 9.25 | 16.20 |
| 5100 | 12′ eave | 6.70 | 8.50 | 15.20 |
| 5150 | 14′ eave | 6.50 | 7.95 | 14.45 |
| 5200 | 16′ eave | 6.35 | 7.55 | 13.90 |
| 6000 | Plywood siding, 8′ eave | 5.45 | 10.35 | 15.80 |
| 6050 | 10′ eave | 5.05 | 9.20 | 14.25 |
| 6100 | 12′ eave | 4.79 | 8.45 | 13.24 |
| 6150 | 14′ eave | 4.60 | 7.90 | 12.50 |
| 6200 | 16′ eave | 4.46 | 7.50 | 11.96 |

## B2020 Exterior Windows

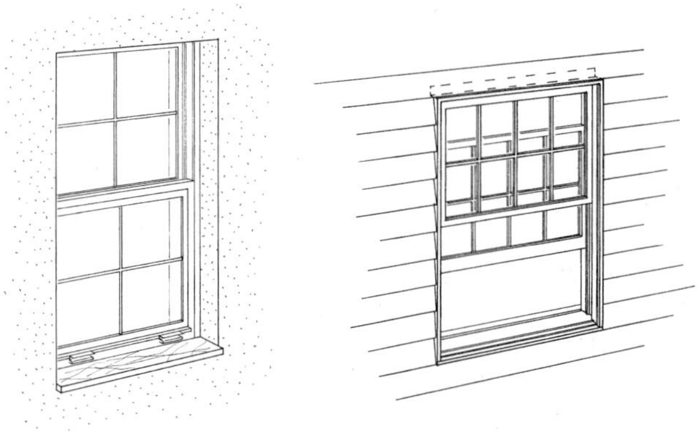

The table below lists window systems by material, type and size. Prices between sizes listed can be interpolated with reasonable accuracy. Prices include frame, hardware, and casing as illustrated in the component block below.

### B2020 102 Wood Windows

| | MATERIAL | TYPE | GLAZING | SIZE | DETAIL | COST PER UNIT | | |
|---|---|---|---|---|---|---|---|---|
| | | | | | | MAT. | INST. | TOTAL |
| 3000 | Wood | double hung | std. glass | 2′-8″ x 4′-6″ | | 485 | 300 | 785 |
| 3050 | | | | 3′-0″ x 5′-6″ | | 455 | 350 | 805 |
| 3100 | | | insul. glass | 2′-8″ x 4′-6″ | | 370 | 300 | 670 |
| 3150 | | | | 3′-0″ x 5′-6″ | | 500 | 350 | 850 |
| 3200 | | sliding | std. glass | 3′-4″ x 2′-7″ | | 530 | 252 | 782 |
| 3250 | | | | 4′-4″ x 3′-3″ | | 535 | 276 | 811 |
| 3300 | | | | 5′-4″ x 6′-0″ | | 680 | 330 | 1,010 |
| 3350 | | | insul. glass | 3′-4″ x 2′-7″ | | 650 | 295 | 945 |
| 3400 | | | | 4′-4″ x 3′-3″ | | 650 | 320 | 970 |
| 3450 | | | | 5′-4″ x 6′-0″ | | 820 | 380 | 1,200 |
| 3500 | | awning | std. glass | 2′-10″ x 1′-9″ | | 380 | 151 | 531 |
| 3600 | | | | 4′-4″ x 2′-8″ | | 570 | 147 | 717 |
| 3700 | | | insul. glass | 2′-10″ x 1′-9″ | | 460 | 175 | 635 |
| 3800 | | | | 4′-4″ x 2′-8″ | | 695 | 161 | 856 |
| 3900 | | casement | std. glass | 1′-10″ x 3′-2″ | 1 lite | 470 | 200 | 670 |
| 3950 | | | | 4′-2″ x 4′-2″ | 2 lite | 835 | 265 | 1,100 |
| 4000 | | | | 5′-11″ x 5′-2″ | 3 lite | 1,375 | 340 | 1,715 |
| 4050 | | | | 7′-11″ x 6′-3″ | 4 lite | 2,000 | 410 | 2,410 |
| 4100 | | | | 9′-11″ x 6′-3″ | 5 lite | 2,600 | 475 | 3,075 |
| 4150 | | | insul. glass | 1′-10″ x 3′-2″ | 1 lite | 470 | 200 | 670 |
| 4200 | | | | 4′-2″ x 4′-2″ | 2 lite | 955 | 265 | 1,220 |
| 4250 | | | | 5′-11″ x 5′-2″ | 3 lite | 1,450 | 340 | 1,790 |
| 4300 | | | | 7′-11″ x 6′-3″ | 4 lite | 2,100 | 410 | 2,510 |
| 4350 | | | | 9′-11″ x 6′-3″ | 5 lite | 2,550 | 475 | 3,025 |
| 4400 | | picture | std. glass | 4′-6″ x 4′-6″ | | 740 | 340 | 1,080 |
| 4450 | | | | 5′-8″ x 4′-6″ | | 830 | 380 | 1,210 |
| 4500 | | picture | insul. glass | 4′-6″ x 4′-6″ | | 900 | 395 | 1,295 |
| 4550 | | | | 5′-8″ x 4′-6″ | | 1,000 | 440 | 1,440 |
| 4600 | | fixed bay | std. glass | 8′ x 5′ | | 2,275 | 625 | 2,900 |
| 4650 | | | | 9′-9″ x 5′-4″ | | 1,625 | 885 | 2,510 |
| 4700 | | | insul. glass | 8′ x 5′ | | 2,875 | 625 | 3,500 |
| 4750 | | | | 9′-9″ x 5′-4″ | | 1,775 | 885 | 2,660 |
| 4800 | | casement bay | std. glass | 8′ x 5′ | | 2,325 | 720 | 3,045 |
| 4850 | | | insul. glass | 8′ x 5′ | | 2,575 | 720 | 3,295 |
| 4900 | | vert. bay | std. glass | 8′ x 5′ | | 2,575 | 720 | 3,295 |
| 4950 | | | insul. glass | 8′ x 5′ | | 2,700 | 720 | 3,420 |

## B2020 Exterior Windows

### B2020 104 Steel Windows

| | MATERIAL | TYPE | GLAZING | SIZE | DETAIL | COST PER UNIT | | |
|---|---|---|---|---|---|---|---|---|
| | | | | | | MAT. | INST. | TOTAL |
| 5000 | Steel | double hung | 1/4" tempered | 2'-8" x 4'-6" | | 1,075 | 229 | 1,304 |
| 5050 | | | | 3'-4" x 5'-6" | | 1,625 | 350 | 1,975 |
| 5100 | | | insul. glass | 2'-8" x 4'-6" | | 1,325 | 264 | 1,589 |
| 5150 | | | | 3'-4" x 5'-6" | | 2,025 | 405 | 2,430 |
| 5200 | | horz. pivoted | std. glass | 2' x 2' | | 325 | 76 | 401 |
| 5250 | | | | 3' x 3' | | 735 | 171 | 906 |
| 5300 | | | | 4' x 4' | | 1,300 | 305 | 1,605 |
| 5350 | | | | 6' x 4' | | 1,950 | 455 | 2,405 |
| 5400 | | | insul. glass | 2' x 2' | | 415 | 88 | 503 |
| 5450 | | | | 3' x 3' | | 930 | 198 | 1,128 |
| 5500 | | | | 4' x 4' | | 1,650 | 350 | 2,000 |
| 5550 | | | | 6' x 4' | | 2,475 | 530 | 3,005 |
| 5600 | | picture window | std. glass | 3' x 3' | | 485 | 171 | 656 |
| 5650 | | | | 6' x 4' | | 1,300 | 455 | 1,755 |
| 5700 | | | insul. glass | 3' x 3' | | 685 | 198 | 883 |
| 5750 | | | | 6' x 4' | | 1,825 | 530 | 2,355 |
| 5800 | | industrial security | std. glass | 2'-9" x 4'-1" | | 985 | 214 | 1,199 |
| 5850 | | | | 4'-1" x 5'-5" | | 1,950 | 420 | 2,370 |
| 5900 | | | insul. glass | 2'-9" x 4'-1" | | 1,225 | 247 | 1,472 |
| 5950 | | | | 4'-1" x 5'-5" | | 2,425 | 485 | 2,910 |
| 6000 | | comm. projected | std. glass | 3'-9" x 5'-5" | | 1,600 | 385 | 1,985 |
| 6050 | | | | 6'-9" x 4'-1" | | 2,175 | 525 | 2,700 |
| 6100 | | | insul. glass | 3'-9" x 5'-5" | | 2,050 | 445 | 2,495 |
| 6150 | | | | 6'-9" x 4'-1" | | 2,775 | 605 | 3,380 |
| 6200 | | casement | std. glass | 4'-2" x 4'-2" | 2 lite | 1,425 | 330 | 1,755 |
| 6250 | | | insul. glass | 4'-2" x 4'-2" | | 1,825 | 380 | 2,205 |
| 6300 | | | std. glass | 5'-11" x 5'-2" | 3 lite | 3,000 | 580 | 3,580 |
| 6350 | | | insul. glass | 5'-11" x 5'-2" | | 3,675 | 675 | 4,350 |

### B2020 106 Aluminum Windows

| | MATERIAL | TYPE | GLAZING | SIZE | DETAIL | COST PER UNIT | | |
|---|---|---|---|---|---|---|---|---|
| | | | | | | MAT. | INST. | TOTAL |
| 6400 | Aluminum | double hung | insul. glass | 3'-0" x 4'-0" | | 685 | 159 | 844 |
| 6450 | | | | 4'-5" x 5'-3" | | 500 | 199 | 699 |
| 6500 | | | insul. glass | 3'-1" x 3'-2" | | 865 | 191 | 1,056 |
| 6550 | | | | 4'-5" x 5'-3" | | 600 | 239 | 839 |
| 6600 | | sliding | std. glass | 3' x 2' | | 630 | 159 | 789 |
| 6650 | | | | 5' x 3' | | 1,375 | 177 | 1,552 |
| 6700 | | | | 8' x 4' | | 2,175 | 265 | 2,440 |
| 6750 | | | | 9' x 5' | | 650 | 400 | 1,050 |
| 6800 | | | insul. glass | 3' x 2' | | 630 | 159 | 789 |
| 6850 | | | | 5' x 3' | | 1,500 | 177 | 1,677 |
| 6900 | | | | 8' x 4' | | 2,225 | 265 | 2,490 |
| 6950 | | | | 9' x 5' | | 995 | 400 | 1,395 |
| 7000 | | single hung | std. glass | 2' x 3' | | 410 | 159 | 569 |
| 7050 | | | | 2'-8" x 6'-8" | | 445 | 199 | 644 |
| 7100 | | | | 3'-4" x 5'-0" | | 380 | 177 | 557 |
| 7150 | | | insul. glass | 2' x 3' | | 320 | 159 | 479 |
| 7200 | | | | 2'-8" x 6'-8" | | 585 | 199 | 784 |
| 7250 | | | | 3'-4" x 5' | | 415 | 177 | 592 |
| 7300 | | double hung | std. glass | 2' x 3' | | 390 | 114 | 504 |
| 7350 | | | | 2'-8" x 6'-8" | | 1,150 | 340 | 1,490 |

## B2020 Exterior Windows

### B2020 106 Aluminum Windows

| | MATERIAL | TYPE | GLAZING | SIZE | DETAIL | COST PER UNIT MAT. | INST. | TOTAL |
|---|---|---|---|---|---|---|---|---|
| 7400 | Aluminum | double hung | | 3'-4" x 5' | | 1,075 | 315 | 1,390 |
| 7450 | | | insul. glass | 2' x 3' | | 520 | 132 | 652 |
| 7500 | | | | 2'-8" x 6'-8" | | 1,550 | 390 | 1,940 |
| 7550 | | | | 3'-4" x 5'-0" | | 1,450 | 365 | 1,815 |
| 7600 | | casement | std. glass | 3'-1" x 3'-2" | | 365 | 186 | 551 |
| 7650 | | | | 4'-5" x 5'-3" | | 885 | 450 | 1,335 |
| 7700 | | | insul. glass | 3'-1" x 3'-2" | | 580 | 215 | 795 |
| 7750 | | | | 4'-5" x 5'-3" | | 1,400 | 520 | 1,920 |
| 7800 | | hinged swing | std. glass | 3' x 4' | | 725 | 229 | 954 |
| 7850 | | | | 4' x 5' | | 1,200 | 380 | 1,580 |
| 7900 | | | insul. glass | 3' x 4' | | 990 | 264 | 1,254 |
| 7950 | | | | 4' x 5' | | 1,650 | 440 | 2,090 |
| 8200 | | picture unit | std. glass | 2'-0" x 3'-0" | | 233 | 114 | 347 |
| 8250 | | | | 2'-8" x 6'-8" | | 690 | 340 | 1,030 |
| 8300 | | | | 3'-4" x 5'-0" | | 650 | 315 | 965 |
| 8350 | | | insul. glass | 2'-0" x 3'-0" | | 365 | 132 | 497 |
| 8400 | | | | 2'-8" x 6'-8" | | 1,075 | 390 | 1,465 |
| 8450 | | | | 3'-4" x 5'-0" | | 1,025 | 365 | 1,390 |
| 8500 | | awning type | std. glass | 3'-0" x 3'-0" | 2 lite | 885 | 114 | 999 |
| 8550 | | | | 3'-0" x 4'-0" | 3 lite | 915 | 159 | 1,074 |
| 8600 | | | | 3'-0" x 5'-4" | 4 lite | 2,325 | 159 | 2,484 |
| 8650 | | | | 4'-0" x 5'-4" | 4 lite | 2,725 | 177 | 2,902 |
| 8700 | | | insul. glass | 3'-0" x 3'-0" | 2 lite | 805 | 114 | 919 |
| 8750 | | | | 3'-0" x 4'-0" | 3 lite | 1,050 | 159 | 1,209 |
| 8800 | | | | 3'-0" x 5'-4" | 4 lite | 2,600 | 159 | 2,759 |
| 8850 | | | | 4'-0" x 5'-4" | 4 lite | 1,025 | 177 | 1,202 |
| 9051 | | | | | | | | |
| 9052 | | | | | | | | |

### B2020 210 Tubular Aluminum Framing

| | | COST/S.F. OPNG. MAT. | INST. | TOTAL |
|---|---|---|---|---|
| 1100 | Alum flush tube frame, for 1/4" glass, 1-3/4"x4", 5'x6'opng, no inter horiz | 18 | 14 | 32 |
| 1150 | One intermediate horizontal | 25 | 16.65 | 41.65 |
| 1200 | Two intermediate horizontals | 31.50 | 19.35 | 50.85 |
| 1250 | 5' x 20' opening, three intermediate horizontals | 16.80 | 11.95 | 28.75 |
| 1400 | 1-3/4" x 4-1/2", 5' x 6' opening, no intermediate horizontals | 20 | 14 | 34 |
| 1450 | One intermediate horizontal | 26.50 | 16.65 | 43.15 |
| 1500 | Two intermediate horizontals | 33 | 19.35 | 52.35 |
| 1550 | 5' x 20' opening, three intermediate horizontals | 18 | 11.95 | 29.95 |
| 1700 | For insulating glass, 2"x4-1/2", 5'x6' opening, no intermediate horizontals | 18.25 | 14.80 | 33.05 |
| 1750 | One intermediate horizontal | 23.50 | 17.60 | 41.10 |
| 1800 | Two intermediate horizontals | 28.50 | 20.50 | 49 |
| 1850 | 5' x 20' opening, three intermediate horizontals | 15.50 | 12.65 | 28.15 |
| 2000 | Thermal break frame, 2-1/4"x4-1/2", 5'x6'opng, no intermediate horizontals | 18.80 | 15 | 33.80 |
| 2050 | One intermediate horizontal | 25 | 18.35 | 43.35 |
| 2100 | Two intermediate horizontals | 31.50 | 21.50 | 53 |
| 2150 | 5' x 20' opening, three intermediate horizontals | 17 | 13.25 | 30.25 |

## B2020 Exterior Windows

The table below lists costs of curtain wall and spandrel panels per S.F. Costs do not include structural framing used to hang the panels.

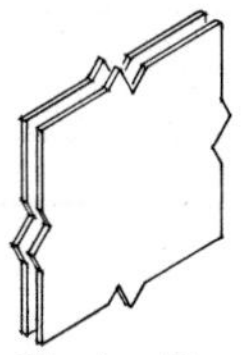

Glazing Panel

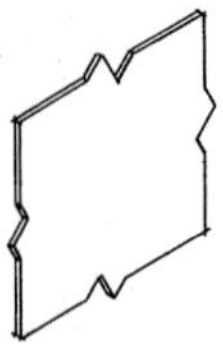

Plate Glass

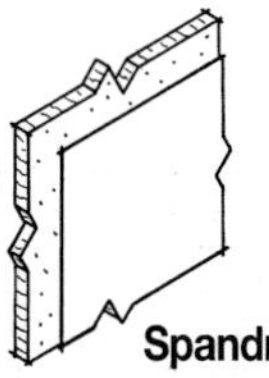

Spandrel Glass

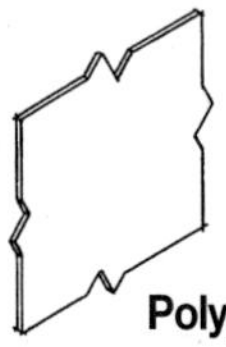

Polycarbonate

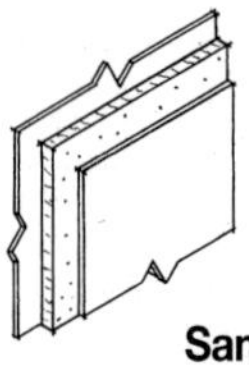

Sandwich Panel

| B2020 220 | Curtain Wall Panels | COST PER S.F. | | |
|---|---|---|---|---|
| | | MAT. | INST. | TOTAL |
| 1000 | Glazing panel, insulating, 1/2″ thick, 2 lites 1/8″ float, clear | 37.50 | 14.05 | 51.55 |
| 1100 | Tinted | 37 | 14.05 | 51.05 |
| 1200 | 5/8″ thick units, 2 lites 3/16″ float, clear | 47 | 14.80 | 61.80 |
| 1300 | Tinted | 21.50 | 14.80 | 36.30 |
| 1400 | 1″ thick units, 2 lites, 1/4″ float, clear | 25.50 | 17.75 | 43.25 |
| 1500 | Tinted | 42 | 17.75 | 59.75 |
| 1600 | Heat reflective film inside | 49 | 15.70 | 64.70 |
| 1700 | Light and heat reflective glass, tinted | 44 | 15.70 | 59.70 |
| 2000 | Plate glass, 1/4″ thick, clear | 12.05 | 11.10 | 23.15 |
| 2050 | Tempered | 15.40 | 11.10 | 26.50 |
| 2100 | Tinted | 11.35 | 11.10 | 22.45 |
| 2200 | 3/8″ thick, clear | 36 | 17.75 | 53.75 |
| 2250 | Tempered | 49.50 | 17.75 | 67.25 |
| 2300 | Tinted | 24 | 17.75 | 41.75 |
| 2400 | 1/2″ thick, clear | 23 | 24 | 47 |
| 2450 | Tempered | 56.50 | 24 | 80.50 |
| 2500 | Tinted | 42.50 | 24 | 66.50 |
| 2600 | 3/4″ thick, clear | 56 | 38 | 94 |
| 2650 | Tempered | 108 | 38 | 146 |
| 3000 | Spandrel glass, panels, 1/4″ plate glass insul w/fiberglass, 1″ thick | 25.50 | 11.10 | 36.60 |
| 3100 | 2″ thick | 27.50 | 11.10 | 38.60 |
| 3200 | Galvanized steel backing, add | 10 | | 10 |
| 3300 | 3/8″ plate glass, 1″ thick | 41 | 11.10 | 52.10 |
| 3400 | 2″ thick | 43 | 11.10 | 54.10 |
| 4000 | Polycarbonate, masked, clear or colored, 1/8″ thick | 4.54 | 7.85 | 12.39 |
| 4100 | 3/16″ thick | 6.85 | 8.10 | 14.95 |
| 4200 | 1/4″ thick | 8.50 | 8.60 | 17.10 |
| 4300 | 3/8″ thick | 15.15 | 8.90 | 24.05 |
| 5000 | Facing panel, textured alum., 4′ x 8′ x 5/16″ plywood backing, sgl face | 5.70 | 4.51 | 10.21 |
| 5100 | Double face | 4.81 | 4.51 | 9.32 |
| 5200 | 4′ x 10′ x 5/16″ plywood backing, single face | 4.36 | 4.51 | 8.87 |
| 5300 | Double face | 5.50 | 4.51 | 10.01 |
| 5400 | 4′ x 12′ x 5/16″ plywood backing, single face | 4.06 | 4.51 | 8.57 |
| 5500 | Sandwich panel, 22 Ga. galv., both sides 2″ insulation, enamel exterior | 13.85 | 7.80 | 21.65 |
| 5600 | Polyvinylidene fluoride exterior finish | 14.70 | 7.80 | 22.50 |
| 5700 | 26 Ga., galv. both sides, 1″ insulation, colored 1 side | 8.25 | 7.40 | 15.65 |
| 5800 | Colored 2 sides | 9.60 | 7.40 | 17 |

## B2030 Exterior Doors

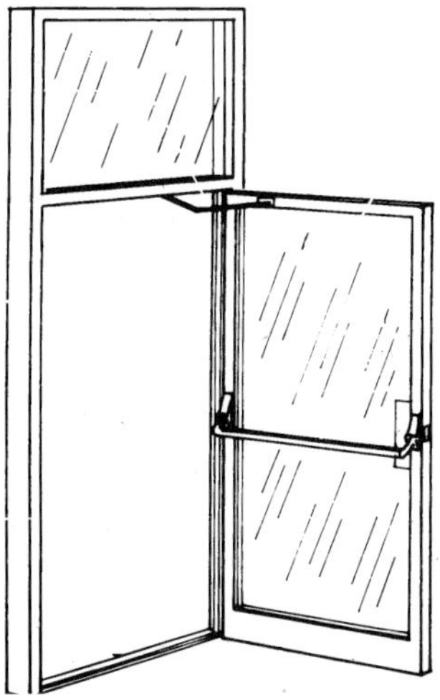

Costs are listed for exterior door systems by material, type and size. Prices between sizes listed can be interpolated with reasonable accuracy. Prices are per opening for a complete door system including frame.

### B2030 110 — Glazed Doors, Steel or Aluminum

| | MATERIAL | TYPE | DOORS | SPECIFICATION | OPENING | COST PER OPNG. MAT. | INST. | TOTAL |
|---|---|---|---|---|---|---|---|---|
| 5600 | St. Stl. & glass | revolving | stock unit | manual oper. | 6′-0″ x 7′-0″ | 58,500 | 10,500 | 69,000 |
| 5650 | | | | auto Cntrls. | 6′-10″ x 7′-0″ | 77,500 | 11,300 | 88,800 |
| 5700 | Bronze | revolving | stock unit | manual oper. | 6′-10″ x 7′-0″ | 57,500 | 21,200 | 78,700 |
| 5750 | | | | auto Cntrls. | 6′-10″ x 7′-0″ | 76,500 | 22,000 | 98,500 |
| 5800 | St. Stl. & glass | balanced | standard | economy | 3′-0″ x 7′-0″ | 13,000 | 1,800 | 14,800 |
| 5850 | | | | premium | 3′-0″ x 7′-0″ | 21,400 | 2,325 | 23,725 |
| 6300 | Alum. & glass | w/o transom | narrow stile | w/panic Hrdwre. | 3′-0″ x 7′-0″ | 3,550 | 1,175 | 4,725 |
| 6350 | | | | dbl. door, Hrdwre. | 6′-0″ x 7′-0″ | 6,900 | 2,000 | 8,900 |
| 6400 | | | wide stile | hdwre. | 3′-0″ x 7′-0″ | 3,750 | 1,175 | 4,925 |
| 6450 | | | | dbl. door, Hdwre. | 6′-0″ x 7′-0″ | 7,350 | 2,375 | 9,725 |
| 6500 | | | full vision | hdwre. | 3′-0″ x 7′-0″ | 5,125 | 1,900 | 7,025 |
| 6550 | | | | dbl. door, Hdwre. | 6′-0″ x 7′-0″ | 8,125 | 2,675 | 10,800 |
| 6600 | | | non-standard | hdwre. | 3′-0″ x 7′-0″ | 3,850 | 1,175 | 5,025 |
| 6650 | | | | dbl. door, Hdwre. | 6′-0″ x 7′-0″ | 7,675 | 2,375 | 10,050 |
| 6700 | | | bronze fin. | hdwre. | 3′-0″ x 7′-0″ | 3,225 | 1,175 | 4,400 |
| 6750 | | | | dbl. door, Hrdwre. | 6′-0″ x 7′-0″ | 6,425 | 2,375 | 8,800 |
| 6800 | | | black fin. | hdwre. | 3′-0″ x 7′-0″ | 3,700 | 1,175 | 4,875 |
| 6850 | | | | dbl. door, Hdwre. | 6′-0″ x 7′-0″ | 7,375 | 2,375 | 9,750 |
| 6900 | | w/transom | narrow stile | hdwre. | 3′-0″ x 10′-0″ | 6,075 | 1,375 | 7,450 |
| 6950 | | | | dbl. door, Hdwre. | 6′-0″ x 10′-0″ | 6,725 | 2,425 | 9,150 |
| 7000 | | | wide stile | hdwre. | 3′-0″ x 10′-0″ | 7,100 | 1,650 | 8,750 |
| 7050 | | | | dbl. door, Hdwre. | 6′-0″ x 10′-0″ | 7,125 | 2,850 | 9,975 |
| 7100 | | | full vision | hdwre. | 3′-0″ x 10′-0″ | 7,850 | 1,825 | 9,675 |
| 7150 | | | | dbl. door, Hdwre. | 6′-0″ x 10′-0″ | 7,550 | 3,150 | 10,700 |
| 7200 | | | non-standard | hdwre. | 3′-0″ x 10′-0″ | 3,975 | 1,275 | 5,250 |
| 7250 | | | | dbl. door, Hdwre. | 6′-0″ x 10′-0″ | 7,950 | 2,575 | 10,525 |
| 7300 | | | bronze fin. | hdwre. | 3′-0″ x 10′-0″ | 3,350 | 1,275 | 4,625 |
| 7350 | | | | dbl. door, Hdwre. | 6′-0″ x 10′-0″ | 6,700 | 2,575 | 9,275 |
| 7400 | | | black fin. | hdwre. | 3′-0″ x 10′-0″ | 3,825 | 1,275 | 5,100 |
| 7450 | | | | dbl. door, Hdwre. | 6′-0″ x 10′-0″ | 7,650 | 2,575 | 10,225 |
| 7500 | | revolving | stock design | minimum | 6′-10″ x 7′-0″ | 45,300 | 4,250 | 49,550 |
| 7550 | | | | average | 6′-0″ x 7′-0″ | 51,500 | 5,300 | 56,800 |

## B2030 Exterior Doors

### B2030 110 Glazed Doors, Steel or Aluminum

| | MATERIAL | TYPE | DOORS | SPECIFICATION | OPENING | COST PER OPNG. MAT. | INST. | TOTAL |
|---|---|---|---|---|---|---|---|---|
| 7600 | Alum. & glass | revolving | stock design | maximum | 6'-10" x 7'-0" | 59,000 | 7,075 | 66,075 |
| 7650 | | | | min., automatic | 6'-10" x 7'-0" | 64,500 | 5,050 | 69,550 |
| 7700 | | | | avg., automatic | 6'-10" x 7'-0" | 70,500 | 6,100 | 76,600 |
| 7750 | | | | max., automatic | 6'-10" x 7'-0" | 78,000 | 7,875 | 85,875 |
| 7800 | | balanced | standard | economy | 3'-0" x 7'-0" | 9,250 | 1,775 | 11,025 |
| 7850 | | | | premium | 3'-0" x 7'-0" | 11,000 | 2,275 | 13,275 |
| 7900 | | mall front | sliding panels | alum. fin. | 16'-0" x 9'-0" | 5,600 | 1,025 | 6,625 |
| 7950 | | | | | 24'-0" x 9'-0" | 7,850 | 1,900 | 9,750 |
| 8000 | | | | bronze fin. | 16'-0" x 9'-0" | 6,525 | 1,200 | 7,725 |
| 8050 | | | | | 24'-0" x 9'-0" | 9,150 | 2,225 | 11,375 |
| 8100 | | | fixed panels | alum. fin. | 48'-0" x 9'-0" | 14,100 | 1,475 | 15,575 |
| 8150 | | | | bronze fin. | 48'-0" x 9'-0" | 16,400 | 1,725 | 18,125 |
| 8200 | | sliding entrance | 5' x 7' door | electric oper. | 12'-0" x 7'-6" | 10,300 | 1,900 | 12,200 |
| 8250 | | sliding patio | temp. glass | economy | 6'-0" x 7'-0" | 1,150 | 350 | 1,500 |
| 8300 | | | temp. glass | economy | 12'-0" x 7'-0" | 4,975 | 465 | 5,440 |
| 8350 | | | | premium | 6'-0" x 7'-0" | 1,725 | 525 | 2,250 |
| 8400 | | | | | 12'-0" x 7'-0" | 7,475 | 700 | 8,175 |

## B2030 Exterior Doors

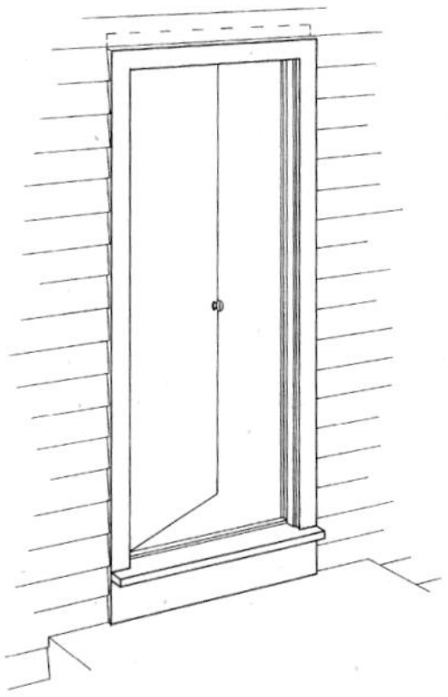

Exterior Door System

The table below lists exterior door systems by material, type and size. Prices between sizes listed can be interpolated with reasonable accuracy. Prices are per opening for a complete door system including frame and required hardware.

Wood doors in this table are designed with wood frames and metal doors with hollow metal frames. Depending upon quality the total material and installation cost of a wood door frame is about the same as a hollow metal frame.

### B2030 210 Wood Doors

| | MATERIAL | TYPE | DOORS | SPECIFICATION | OPENING | COST PER OPNG. | | |
|---|---|---|---|---|---|---|---|---|
| | | | | | | MAT. | INST. | TOTAL |
| 2350 | Birch | solid core | single door | hinged | 2'-6" x 6'-8" | 3,050 | 380 | 3,430 |
| 2400 | | | | | 2'-6" x 7'-0" | 3,050 | 380 | 3,430 |
| 2450 | | | | | 2'-8" x 7'-0" | 3,050 | 380 | 3,430 |
| 2500 | | | | | 3'-0" x 7'-0" | 3,050 | 380 | 3,430 |
| 2550 | | | double door | | 2'-6" x 6'-8" | 5,925 | 695 | 6,620 |
| 2600 | | | | | 2'-6" x 7'-0" | 5,925 | 695 | 6,620 |
| 2650 | | | | | 2'-8" x 7'-0" | 5,925 | 695 | 6,620 |
| 2700 | | | | | 3'-0" x 7'-0" | 5,550 | 610 | 6,160 |
| 2750 | Wood | combination | storm & screen | | 3'-0" x 6'-8" | 495 | 93 | 588 |
| 2800 | | | | | 3'-0" x 7'-0" | 545 | 102 | 647 |
| 2850 | | overhead | panels, H.D. | manual oper. | 8'-0" x 8'-0" | 1,350 | 700 | 2,050 |
| 2900 | | | | | 10'-0" x 10'-0" | 1,950 | 775 | 2,725 |
| 2950 | | | | | 12'-0" x 12'-0" | 2,500 | 930 | 3,430 |
| 3000 | | | | | 14'-0" x 14'-0" | 3,325 | 1,075 | 4,400 |
| 3050 | | | | | 20'-0" x 16'-0" | 8,900 | 2,150 | 11,050 |
| 3100 | | | | electric oper. | 8'-0" x 8'-0" | 2,600 | 1,050 | 3,650 |
| 3150 | | | | | 10'-0" x 10'-0" | 3,200 | 1,125 | 4,325 |
| 3200 | | | | | 12'-0" x 12'-0" | 3,750 | 1,275 | 5,025 |
| 3250 | | | | | 14'-0" x 14'-0" | 4,575 | 1,425 | 6,000 |
| 3300 | | | | | 20'-0" x 16'-0" | 10,200 | 2,850 | 13,050 |

### B2030 220 Steel Doors

| | MATERIAL | TYPE | DOORS | SPECIFICATION | OPENING | COST PER OPNG. | | |
|---|---|---|---|---|---|---|---|---|
| | | | | | | MAT. | INST. | TOTAL |
| 3350 | Steel 18 Ga. | hollow metal | 1 door w/frame | no label | 2'-6" x 7'-0" | 3,075 | 395 | 3,470 |
| 3400 | | | | | 2'-8" x 7'-0" | 3,075 | 395 | 3,470 |
| 3450 | | | | | 3'-0" x 7'-0" | 3,125 | 425 | 3,550 |
| 3500 | | | | | 3'-6" x 7'-0" | 3,725 | 415 | 4,140 |
| 3550 | | hollow metal | 1 door w/frame | no label | 4'-0" x 8'-0" | 4,275 | 415 | 4,690 |
| 3600 | | | 2 doors w/frame | no label | 5'-0" x 7'-0" | 6,150 | 730 | 6,880 |
| 3650 | | | | | 5'-4" x 7'-0" | 6,150 | 730 | 6,880 |
| 3700 | | | | | 6'-0" x 7'-0" | 6,150 | 730 | 6,880 |
| 3750 | | | | | 7'-0" x 7'-0" | 7,400 | 770 | 8,170 |
| 3800 | | | | | 8'-0" x 8'-0" | 8,550 | 770 | 9,320 |

## B2030 Exterior Doors

### B2030 220 Steel Doors

| | MATERIAL | TYPE | DOORS | SPECIFICATION | OPENING | COST PER OPNG. MAT. | INST. | TOTAL |
|---|---|---|---|---|---|---|---|---|
| 3850 | Steel 18 Ga. | hollow metal | 1 door w/frame | "A" label | 2'-6" x 7'-0" | 4,275 | 475 | 4,750 |
| 3900 | | | | | 2'-8" x 7'-0" | 3,675 | 480 | 4,155 |
| 3950 | | | | | 3'-0" x 7'-0" | 3,675 | 480 | 4,155 |
| 4000 | | | | | 3'-6" x 7'-0" | 4,525 | 490 | 5,015 |
| 4050 | | | | | 4'-0" x 8'-0" | 4,675 | 515 | 5,190 |
| 4100 | | | 2 doors w/frame | "A" label | 5'-0" x 7'-0" | 8,325 | 880 | 9,205 |
| 4150 | | | | | 5'-4" x 7'-0" | 7,175 | 890 | 8,065 |
| 4200 | | | | | 6'-0" x 7'-0" | 7,175 | 890 | 8,065 |
| 4250 | | | | | 7'-0" x 7'-0" | 8,875 | 910 | 9,785 |
| 4300 | | | | | 8'-0" x 8'-0" | 8,875 | 910 | 9,785 |
| 4350 | Steel 24 Ga. | overhead | sectional | manual oper. | 8'-0" x 8'-0" | 1,675 | 700 | 2,375 |
| 4400 | | | | | 10'-0" x 10'-0" | 1,950 | 775 | 2,725 |
| 4450 | | | | | 12'-0" x 12'-0" | 2,975 | 930 | 3,905 |
| 4500 | | | | | 20'-0" x 14'-0" | 4,375 | 2,000 | 6,375 |
| 4550 | | | | electric oper. | 8'-0" x 8'-0" | 2,925 | 1,050 | 3,975 |
| 4600 | | | | | 10'-0" x 10'-0" | 3,200 | 1,125 | 4,325 |
| 4650 | | | | | 12'-0" x 12'-0" | 4,225 | 1,275 | 5,500 |
| 4700 | | | | | 20'-0" x 14'-0" | 5,650 | 2,700 | 8,350 |
| 4750 | Steel | overhead | rolling | manual oper. | 8'-0" x 8'-0" | 675 | 995 | 1,670 |
| 4800 | | | | | 10'-0" x 10'-0" | 995 | 1,125 | 2,120 |
| 4850 | | | | | 12'-0" x 12'-0" | 1,375 | 1,325 | 2,700 |
| 4900 | | | | | 14'-0" x 14'-0" | 2,325 | 2,000 | 4,325 |
| 4950 | | | | | 20'-0" x 12'-0" | 3,375 | 1,775 | 5,150 |
| 5000 | | | | | 20'-0" x 16'-0" | 4,225 | 2,650 | 6,875 |
| 5050 | | | | electric oper. | 8'-0" x 8'-0" | 1,875 | 1,325 | 3,200 |
| 5100 | | | | | 10'-0" x 10'-0" | 2,200 | 1,450 | 3,650 |
| 5110 | | | | | 10'-0" x 10'-0" | 3,275 | 2,000 | 5,275 |
| 5150 | | | | | 12'-0" x 12'-0" | 2,575 | 1,650 | 4,225 |
| 5200 | | | | | 14'-0" x 14'-0" | 3,525 | 2,325 | 5,850 |
| 5250 | | | | | 20'-0" x 12'-0" | 4,500 | 2,100 | 6,600 |
| 5300 | | | | | 20'-0" x 16'-0" | 5,350 | 2,975 | 8,325 |
| 5350 | | | | fire rated | 10'-0" x 10'-0" | 3,800 | 1,450 | 5,250 |
| 5400 | | | rolling grille | manual oper. | 10'-0" x 10'-0" | 3,150 | 1,600 | 4,750 |
| 5450 | | | | | 15'-0" x 8'-0" | 4,200 | 2,000 | 6,200 |
| 5500 | | vertical lift | 1 door w/frame | motor operator | 16"-0" x 16"-0" | 27,600 | 9,525 | 37,125 |
| 5550 | | | | | 32'-0" x 24'-0" | 64,000 | 6,350 | 70,350 |

### B2030 230 Aluminum Doors

| | MATERIAL | TYPE | DOORS | SPECIFICATION | OPENING | COST PER OPNG. MAT. | INST. | TOTAL |
|---|---|---|---|---|---|---|---|---|
| 6000 | Aluminum | combination | storm & screen | hinged | 3'-0" x 6'-8" | 385 | 99.50 | 484.50 |
| 6050 | | | | | 3'-0" x 7'-0" | 425 | 109 | 534 |
| 6100 | | overhead | rolling grille | manual oper. | 12'-0" x 12'-0" | 5,175 | 2,800 | 7,975 |
| 6150 | | | | motor oper. | 12'-0" x 12'-0" | 7,000 | 3,125 | 10,125 |
| 6200 | Alum. & Fbrgls. | overhead | heavy duty | manual oper. | 12'-0" x 12'-0" | 2,975 | 930 | 3,905 |
| 6250 | | | | electric oper. | 12'-0" x 12'-0" | 4,225 | 1,275 | 5,500 |

## B3010 Roof Coverings

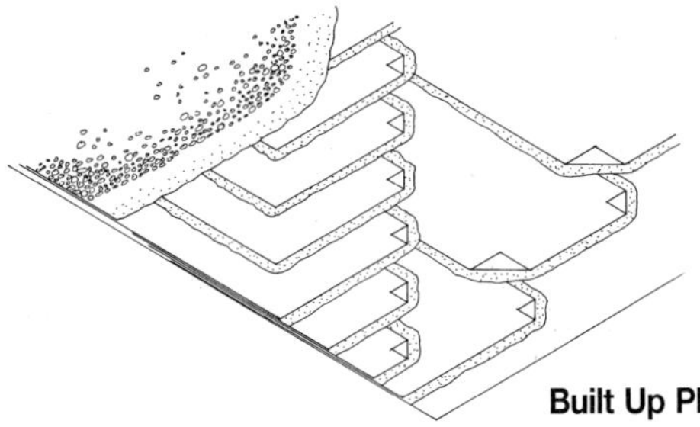


Multiple ply roofing is the most popular covering for minimum pitch roofs.

| B3010 105 | Built-Up | COST PER S.F. | | |
|---|---|---|---|---|
| | | MAT. | INST. | TOTAL |
| 1200 | Asphalt flood coat w/gravel; not incl. insul, flash., nailers | | | |
| 1300 | | | | |
| 1400 | Asphalt base sheets & 3 plies #15 asphalt felt, mopped | 1.65 | 2.30 | 3.95 |
| 1500 | On nailable deck | 1.53 | 2.40 | 3.93 |
| 1600 | 4 plies #15 asphalt felt, mopped | 2.04 | 2.53 | 4.57 |
| 1700 | On nailable deck | 1.79 | 2.66 | 4.45 |
| 1800 | Coated glass base sheet, 2 plies glass (type IV), mopped | 1.65 | 2.30 | 3.95 |
| 1900 | For 3 plies | 1.97 | 2.53 | 4.50 |
| 2000 | On nailable deck | 1.85 | 2.66 | 4.51 |
| 2300 | 4 plies glass fiber felt (type IV), mopped | 2.42 | 2.53 | 4.95 |
| 2400 | On nailable deck | 2.17 | 2.66 | 4.83 |
| 2500 | Organic base sheet & 3 plies #15 organic felt, mopped | 1.52 | 2.55 | 4.07 |
| 2600 | On nailable deck | 1.45 | 2.66 | 4.11 |
| 2700 | 4 plies #15 organic felt, mopped | 1.82 | 2.30 | 4.12 |
| 2750 | | | | |
| 2800 | Asphalt flood coat, smooth surface, not incl. insul, flash., nailers | | | |
| 2900 | Asphalt base sheet & 3 plies #15 asphalt felt, mopped | 1.57 | 2.10 | 3.67 |
| 3000 | On nailable deck | 1.45 | 2.20 | 3.65 |
| 3100 | Coated glass fiber base sheet & 2 plies glass fiber felt, mopped | 1.56 | 2.02 | 3.58 |
| 3200 | On nailable deck | 1.47 | 2.10 | 3.57 |
| 3300 | For 3 plies, mopped | 1.89 | 2.20 | 4.09 |
| 3400 | On nailable deck | 1.76 | 2.30 | 4.06 |
| 3700 | 4 plies glass fiber felt (type IV), mopped | 2.21 | 2.20 | 4.41 |
| 3800 | On nailable deck | 2.09 | 2.30 | 4.39 |
| 3900 | Organic base sheet & 3 plies #15 organic felt, mopped | 1.49 | 2.10 | 3.59 |
| 4000 | On nailable decks | 1.37 | 2.20 | 3.57 |
| 4100 | 4 plies #15 organic felt, mopped | 1.74 | 2.30 | 4.04 |
| 4200 | Coal tar pitch with gravel surfacing | | | |
| 4300 | 4 plies #15 tarred felt, mopped | 2.91 | 2.40 | 5.31 |
| 4400 | 3 plies glass fiber felt (type IV), mopped | 2.41 | 2.66 | 5.07 |
| 4500 | Coated glass fiber base sheets 2 plies glass fiber felt, mopped | 2.52 | 2.66 | 5.18 |
| 4600 | On nailable decks | 2.19 | 2.81 | 5 |
| 4800 | 3 plies glass fiber felt (type IV), mopped | 3.35 | 2.40 | 5.75 |
| 4900 | On nailable decks | 3 | 2.53 | 5.53 |

## B3010 Roof Coverings

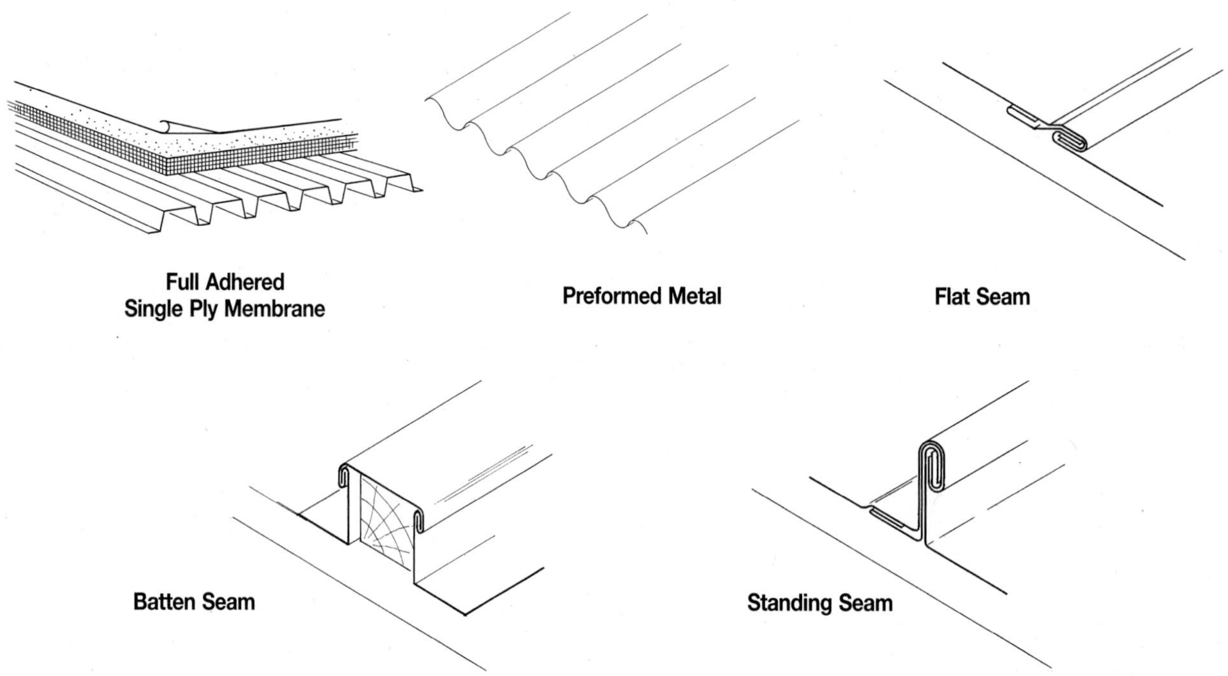


| B3010 120 | Single Ply Membrane | COST PER S.F. | | |
|---|---|---|---|---|
| | | MAT. | INST. | TOTAL |
| 1000 | CSPE (Chlorosulfonated polyethylene), 45 mils, plate attached | 3 | .93 | 3.93 |
| 1100 | Loosely laid with stone ballast | 3 | .93 | 3.93 |
| 2000 | EPDM (Ethylene propylene diene monomer), 45 mils, fully adhered | 1.66 | 1.25 | 2.91 |
| 2100 | Loosely laid with stone ballast | 1.81 | .64 | 2.45 |
| 2200 | Mechanically fastened with batten strips | 1.75 | .93 | 2.68 |
| 3300 | 60 mils, fully adhered | 1.67 | 1.25 | 2.92 |
| 3400 | Loosely laid with stone ballast | 1.83 | .64 | 2.47 |
| 3500 | Mechanically fastened with batten strips | 1.76 | .93 | 2.69 |
| 4000 | Modified bit., SBS modified, granule surface cap sheet, mopped, 150 mils | 1.56 | 2.53 | 4.09 |
| 4100 | Smooth surface cap sheet, mopped, 145 mils | 1.02 | 2.40 | 3.42 |
| 4500 | APP modified, granule surface cap sheet, torched, 180 mils | .90 | 1.62 | 2.52 |
| 4600 | Smooth surface cap sheet, torched, 170 mils | .74 | 1.55 | 2.29 |
| 5000 | PIB (Polyisobutylene), 100 mils, fully adhered with contact cement | 3.10 | 1.25 | 4.35 |
| 5100 | Loosely laid with stone ballast | 2.45 | .64 | 3.09 |
| 5200 | Partially adhered with adhesive | 2.95 | .93 | 3.88 |
| 5300 | Hot asphalt attachment | 2.81 | .93 | 3.74 |
| 6000 | Reinforced PVC, 48 mils, loose laid and ballasted with stone | 1.39 | .64 | 2.03 |
| 6100 | Partially adhered with mechanical fasteners | 1.32 | .93 | 2.25 |
| 6200 | Fully adhered with adhesive | 1.23 | 1.25 | 2.48 |
| 6300 | Reinforced PVC, 60 mils, loose laid and ballasted with stone | 2.60 | .64 | 3.24 |
| 6400 | Partially adhered with mechanical fasteners | 2.53 | .93 | 3.46 |
| 6500 | Fully adhered with adhesive | 2.44 | 1.25 | 3.69 |

| B3010 130 | Preformed Metal Roofing | COST PER S.F. | | |
|---|---|---|---|---|
| | | MAT. | INST. | TOTAL |
| 0200 | Corrugated roofing, aluminum, mill finish, .0175" thick, .272 P.S.F. | 1.58 | 2.35 | 3.93 |
| 0250 | .0215" thick, .334 P.S.F. | 1.53 | 2.35 | 3.88 |
| 0300 | .0240" thick, .412 P.S.F. | 2.21 | 2.35 | 4.56 |
| 0350 | .0320" thick, .552 P.S.F. | 3.60 | 2.35 | 5.95 |

## B3010 Roof Coverings

| B3010 130 | Preformed Metal Roofing | COST PER S.F. | | |
|---|---|---|---|---|
| | | MAT. | INST. | TOTAL |
| 0400 | Painted, .0175" thick, .280 P.S.F. | 1.65 | 2.35 | 4 |
| 0450 | .0215" thick, .344 P.S.F. | 1.51 | 2.35 | 3.86 |
| 0500 | .0240" thick, .426 P.S.F. | 2.53 | 2.35 | 4.88 |
| 0550 | .0320" thick, .569 P.S.F. | 8.85 | 2.35 | 11.20 |
| 0700 | Fiberglass, 6 oz., .375 P.S.F. | 5.25 | 2.82 | 8.07 |
| 0750 | 8 oz., .5 P.S.F. | 5.35 | 2.82 | 8.17 |
| 0900 | Steel, galvanized, 29 ga., .72 P.S.F. | .99 | 2.56 | 3.55 |
| 0930 | 26 ga., .91 P.S.F. | 1.58 | 2.68 | 4.26 |
| 0950 | 24 ga., 1.26 P.S.F. | 1.58 | 2.82 | 4.40 |
| 0970 | 22 ga., 1.45 P.S.F. | 3.52 | 2.97 | 6.49 |
| 1000 | Colored, 28 ga., 1.08 P.S.F. | 1.88 | 2.68 | 4.56 |
| 1050 | 26 ga., 1.43 P.S.F. | 2.50 | 2.82 | 5.32 |

| B3010 135 | Formed Metal | COST PER S.F. | | |
|---|---|---|---|---|
| | | MAT. | INST. | TOTAL |
| 1000 | Batten seam, formed copper roofing, 3" min slope, 16 oz., 1.2 P.S.F. | 35 | 7.80 | 42.80 |
| 1100 | 18 oz., 1.35 P.S.F. | 39 | 8.55 | 47.55 |
| 2000 | Zinc copper alloy, 3" min slope, .020" thick, .88 P.S.F. | 8.75 | 7.15 | 15.90 |
| 3000 | Flat seam, copper, 1/4" min. slope, 16 oz., 1.2 P.S.F. | 25.50 | 7.15 | 32.65 |
| 3100 | 18 oz., 1.35 P.S.F. | 28.50 | 7.45 | 35.95 |
| 5000 | Standing seam, copper, 2-1/2" min. slope, 16 oz., 1.25 P.S.F. | 27.50 | 6.60 | 34.10 |
| 5100 | 18 oz., 1.40 P.S.F. | 31 | 7.15 | 38.15 |
| 6000 | Zinc copper alloy, 2-1/2" min. slope, .020" thick, .87 P.S.F. | 8.35 | 7.15 | 15.50 |
| 6100 | .032" thick, 1.39 P.S.F. | 10.35 | 7.80 | 18.15 |

# B3010 Roof Coverings

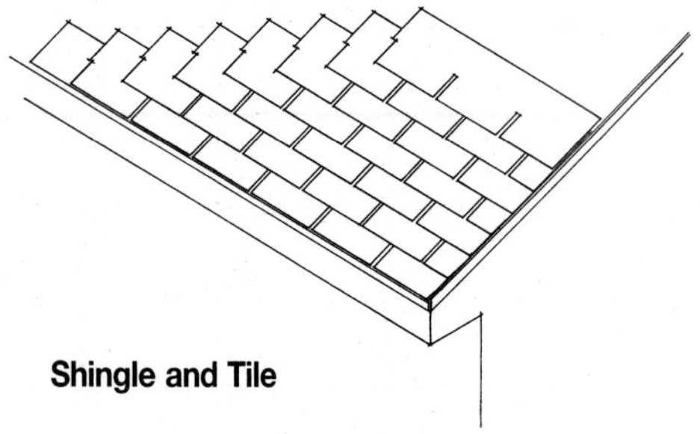

Shingle and Tile

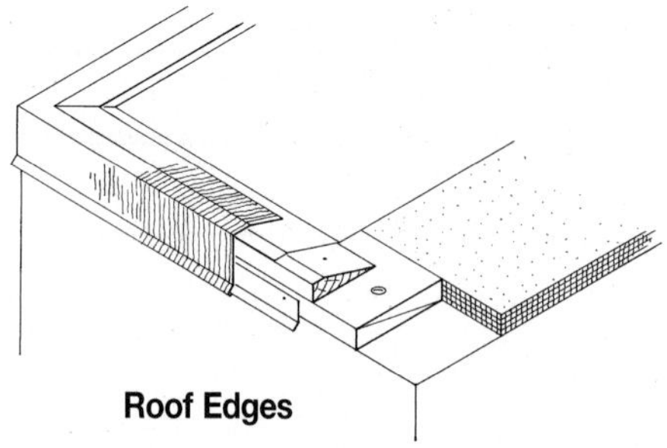

Roof Edges

Shingles and tiles are practical in applications where the roof slope is more than 3-1/2″ per foot of rise. Lines 1100 through 6000 list the various materials and the weight per square foot.

The table below lists the costs for various types of roof perimeter edge treatments.

Roof edge systems include the cost per L.F. for a 2″ x 8″ treated wood nailer fastened at 4′-0″ O.C. and a diagonally cut 4″ x 6″ treated wood cant.

Roof edge and base flashing are assumed to be made from the same material.

| B3010 140 | Shingle & Tile | COST PER S.F. | | |
|---|---|---|---|---|
| | | MAT. | INST. | TOTAL |
| 1095 | Asphalt roofing | | | |
| 1100 | Strip shingles, 4″ slope, inorganic class A 210-235 lb./sq. | 1.18 | 1.41 | 2.59 |
| 1150 | Organic, class C, 235-240 lb./sq. | 1.51 | 1.53 | 3.04 |
| 1200 | Premium laminated multi-layered, class A, 260-300 lb./sq. | 1.94 | 2.11 | 4.05 |
| 1545 | Metal roofing | | | |
| 1550 | Alum., shingles, colors, 3″ min slope, .019″ thick, 0.4 PSF | 3.75 | 1.52 | 5.27 |
| 1850 | Steel, colors, 3″ min slope, 26 gauge, 1.0 PSF | 4.02 | 3.17 | 7.19 |
| 2795 | Slate roofing | | | |
| 2800 | Slate roofing, 4″ min. slope, shingles, 3/16″ thick, 8.0 PSF | 8.25 | 3.97 | 12.22 |
| 3495 | Wood roofing | | | |
| 3500 | 4″ min slope, cedar shingles, 16″ x 5″, 5″ exposure 1.6 PSF | 6.65 | 3.01 | 9.66 |
| 4000 | Shakes, 18″, 8-1/2″ exposure, 2.8 PSF | 5.30 | 3.72 | 9.02 |
| 5095 | Tile roofing | | | |
| 5100 | Aluminum, mission, 3″ min slope, .019″ thick, 0.65 PSF | 8.95 | 2.91 | 11.86 |
| 6000 | Clay tile, flat shingle, interlocking, 15″, 166 pcs/sq, fireflashed blend | 6.25 | 3.47 | 9.72 |

| B3010 320 | Roof Deck Rigid Insulation | COST PER S.F. | | |
|---|---|---|---|---|
| | | MAT. | INST. | TOTAL |
| 0100 | Fiberboard low density | | | |
| 0150 | 1″ thick R2.78 | 1.27 | .87 | 2.14 |
| 0300 | 1 1/2″ thick R4.17 | 1.93 | .87 | 2.80 |
| 0350 | 2″ thick R5.56 | 2.10 | .87 | 2.97 |
| 0370 | Fiberboard high density, 1/2″ thick R1.3 | .64 | .74 | 1.38 |
| 0380 | 1″ thick R2.5 | 2.07 | .87 | 2.94 |
| 0390 | 1 1/2″ thick R3.8 | 3.43 | .87 | 4.30 |
| 0410 | Fiberglass, 3/4″ thick R2.78 | .69 | .74 | 1.43 |
| 0450 | 15/16″ thick R3.70 | 1.49 | .74 | 2.23 |
| 0550 | 1-5/16″ thick R5.26 | 2.43 | .74 | 3.17 |
| 0650 | 2 7/16″ thick R10 | 2.98 | .87 | 3.85 |
| 1510 | Polyisocyanurate 2#/CF density, 1″ thick | 1.34 | .59 | 1.93 |
| 1550 | 1 1/2″ thick | 1.13 | .63 | 1.76 |
| 1600 | 2″ thick | 2.05 | .69 | 2.74 |
| 1650 | 2 1/2″ thick | 2.53 | .71 | 3.24 |
| 1700 | 3″ thick | 2.99 | .74 | 3.73 |
| 1750 | 3 1/2″ thick | 3.44 | .74 | 4.18 |
| 1800 | Tapered for drainage | 1.60 | .59 | 2.19 |

# B3010 Roof Coverings

## B3010 320 Roof Deck Rigid Insulation

| | | COST PER S.F. MAT. | COST PER S.F. INST. | COST PER S.F. TOTAL |
|---|---|---|---|---|
| 1810 | Expanded polystyrene, 1#/CF density, 3/4" thick R2.89 | .49 | .56 | 1.05 |
| 1820 | 2" thick R7.69 | .96 | .63 | 1.59 |
| 1830 | 15 PSI compressive strength, 1" thick, R5 | 1.18 | .56 | 1.74 |
| 1835 | 2" thick R10 | 1.47 | .63 | 2.10 |
| 1840 | 3" thick R15 | 2.73 | .74 | 3.47 |
| 2550 | 40 PSI compressive strength, 1" thick R5 | 1.72 | .56 | 2.28 |
| 2600 | 2" thick R10 | 3.07 | .63 | 3.70 |
| 2650 | 3" thick R15 | 4.35 | .74 | 5.09 |
| 2700 | 4" thick R20 | 5.65 | .74 | 6.39 |
| 2750 | Tapered for drainage | 1.50 | .59 | 2.09 |
| 2810 | 60 PSI compressive strength, 1" thick R5 | 1.64 | .58 | 2.22 |
| 2850 | 2" thick R10 | 2.93 | .65 | 3.58 |
| 2900 | Tapered for drainage | 1.67 | .59 | 2.26 |
| 3050 | Composites with 2" EPS | | | |
| 3060 | 1" Fiberboard | 1.65 | .73 | 2.38 |
| 3070 | 7/16" oriented strand board | 2.26 | .87 | 3.13 |
| 3080 | 1/2" plywood | 3.72 | .87 | 4.59 |
| 3090 | 1" perlite | 1.76 | .87 | 2.63 |
| 4000 | Composites with 1-1/2" polyisocyanurate | | | |
| 4010 | 1" fiberboard | 1.99 | .87 | 2.86 |
| 4020 | 1" perlite | 1.70 | .83 | 2.53 |
| 4030 | 7/16" oriented strand board | 3.90 | .87 | 4.77 |

## B3010 420 Roof Edges

| | EDGE TYPE | DESCRIPTION | SPECIFICATION | FACE HEIGHT | | COST PER L.F. MAT. | COST PER L.F. INST. | COST PER L.F. TOTAL |
|---|---|---|---|---|---|---|---|---|
| 1000 | Aluminum | mill finish | .050" thick | 4" | | 16.15 | 12.90 | 29.05 |
| 1100 | | | | 6" | | 23 | 13.30 | 36.30 |
| 1300 | | duranodic | .050" thick | 4" | | 14.95 | 12.90 | 27.85 |
| 1400 | | | | 6" | | 25.50 | 13.30 | 38.80 |
| 1600 | | painted | .050" thick | 4" | | 16.15 | 12.90 | 29.05 |
| 1700 | | | | 6" | | 23.50 | 13.30 | 36.80 |
| 2000 | Copper | plain | 16 oz. | 4" | | 68 | 12.90 | 80.90 |
| 2100 | | | | 6" | | 80 | 13.30 | 93.30 |
| 2300 | | | 20 oz. | 4" | | 87 | 14.85 | 101.85 |
| 2400 | | | | 6" | | 90.50 | 14.25 | 104.75 |
| 2700 | Sheet Metal | galvanized | 20 Ga. | 4" | | 27 | 15.45 | 42.45 |
| 2800 | | | | 6" | | 26 | 15.45 | 41.45 |
| 3000 | | | 24 Ga. | 4" | | 22 | 12.90 | 34.90 |
| 3100 | | | | 6" | | 21 | 12.90 | 33.90 |

## B3010 430 Flashing

| | MATERIAL | BACKING | SIDES | SPECIFICATION | QUANTITY | COST PER S.F. MAT. | COST PER S.F. INST. | COST PER S.F. TOTAL |
|---|---|---|---|---|---|---|---|---|
| 0040 | Aluminum | none | | .019" | | 7.35 | 4.63 | 11.98 |
| 0050 | | | | .032" | | 7.35 | 4.63 | 11.98 |
| 0300 | | fabric | 2 | .004" | | 2.24 | 2.04 | 4.28 |
| 0400 | | mastic | | .004" | | 2.24 | 2.04 | 4.28 |
| 0700 | Copper | none | | 16 oz. | <500 lbs. | 22 | 5.85 | 27.85 |
| 0800 | | | | 24 oz. | <500 lbs. | 22.50 | 6.40 | 28.90 |
| 3500 | PVC black | none | | .010" | | .39 | 2.36 | 2.75 |
| 3700 | | | | .030" | | .47 | 2.36 | 2.83 |
| 4200 | Neoprene | | | 1/16" | | 1.27 | 2.36 | 3.63 |
| 4500 | Stainless steel | none | | .015" | <500 lbs. | 9.80 | 5.85 | 15.65 |
| 4600 | Copper clad | | | | >2000 lbs. | 9.65 | 4.33 | 13.98 |
| 5000 | Plain | | | 32 ga. | | 5.05 | 4.33 | 9.38 |

## B3010 Roof Coverings

### B3010 610 Gutters

| | SECTION | MATERIAL | THICKNESS | SIZE | FINISH | COST PER L.F. | | |
|---|---|---|---|---|---|---|---|---|
| | | | | | | MAT. | INST. | TOTAL |
| 0050 | Box | aluminum | .027″ | 5″ | enameled | 3.81 | 6.95 | 10.76 |
| 0100 | | | | | mill | 3.57 | 6.95 | 10.52 |
| 0200 | | | .032″ | 5″ | enameled | 4.20 | 6.75 | 10.95 |
| 0500 | | copper | 16 Oz. | 5″ | lead coated | 28 | 6.75 | 34.75 |
| 0600 | | | | | mill | 19.10 | 6.75 | 25.85 |
| 1000 | | steel galv. | 28 Ga. | 5″ | enameled | 4.84 | 6.75 | 11.59 |
| 1200 | | | 26 Ga. | 5″ | mill | 6.55 | 6.75 | 13.30 |
| 1800 | | vinyl | | 4″ | colors | 2.82 | 6.05 | 8.87 |
| 1900 | | | | 5″ | colors | 2.82 | 6.05 | 8.87 |
| 2300 | | hemlock or fir | | 4″x5″ | treated | 23.50 | 7 | 30.50 |
| 3000 | Half round | copper | 16 Oz. | 4″ | lead coated | 26.50 | 6.75 | 33.25 |
| 3100 | | | | | mill | 11.60 | 6.75 | 18.35 |
| 3600 | | steel galv. | 28 Ga. | 5″ | enameled | 4.84 | 6.75 | 11.59 |
| 4102 | | stainless steel | | 5″ | mill | 5.65 | 6.75 | 12.40 |
| 5000 | | vinyl | | 4″ | white | 1.86 | 6.05 | 7.91 |

### B3010 620 Downspouts

| | MATERIALS | SECTION | SIZE | FINISH | THICKNESS | COST PER V.L.F. | | |
|---|---|---|---|---|---|---|---|---|
| | | | | | | MAT. | INST. | TOTAL |
| 0100 | Aluminum | rectangular | 2″x3″ | embossed mill | .020″ | 2.04 | 4.45 | 6.49 |
| 0150 | | | | enameled | .020″ | 2.04 | 4.45 | 6.49 |
| 0250 | | | 3″x4″ | enameled | .024″ | 3.19 | 6.05 | 9.24 |
| 0300 | | round corrugated | 3″ | enameled | .020″ | 7 | 4.45 | 11.45 |
| 0350 | | | 4″ | enameled | .025″ | 12.25 | 6.05 | 18.30 |
| 0500 | Copper | rectangular corr. | 2″x3″ | mill | 16 Oz. | 14.75 | 4.45 | 19.20 |
| 0600 | | smooth | | mill | 16 Oz. | 13.20 | 4.45 | 17.65 |
| 0700 | | rectangular corr. | 3″x4″ | mill | 16 Oz. | 18.75 | 5.85 | 24.60 |
| 1300 | Steel | rectangular corr. | 2″x3″ | galvanized | 28 Ga. | 4.14 | 4.45 | 8.59 |
| 1350 | | | | epoxy coated | 24 Ga. | 7.75 | 4.45 | 12.20 |
| 1400 | | smooth | | galvanized | 28 Ga. | 4.14 | 4.45 | 8.59 |
| 1450 | | rectangular corr. | 3″x4″ | galvanized | 28 Ga. | 5.15 | 5.85 | 11 |
| 1500 | | | | epoxy coated | 24 Ga. | 9.50 | 5.85 | 15.35 |
| 1550 | | smooth | | galvanized | 28 Ga. | 5.15 | 5.85 | 11 |
| 1600 | | round corrugated | 2″ | galvanized | 28 Ga. | 4.60 | 4.45 | 9.05 |
| 1650 | | | 3″ | galvanized | 28 Ga. | 4.60 | 4.45 | 9.05 |
| 1700 | | | 4″ | galvanized | 28 Ga. | 6.25 | 5.85 | 12.10 |
| 1750 | | | 5″ | galvanized | 28 Ga. | 6.85 | 6.50 | 13.35 |
| 2552 | S.S. tubing sch.5 | rectangular | 3″x4″ | mill | | 182 | 5.85 | 187.85 |

### B3010 630 Gravel Stop

| | MATERIALS | SECTION | SIZE | FINISH | THICKNESS | COST PER L.F. | | |
|---|---|---|---|---|---|---|---|---|
| | | | | | | MAT. | INST. | TOTAL |
| 5100 | Aluminum | extruded | 4″ | mill | .050″ | 5.90 | 5.85 | 11.75 |
| 5200 | | | 4″ | duranodic | .050″ | 4.70 | 5.85 | 10.55 |
| 5300 | | | 8″ | mill | .050″ | 15.30 | 6.75 | 22.05 |
| 5400 | | | 8″ | duranodic | .050″ | 15 | 6.75 | 21.75 |
| 6000 | | | 12″-2 pc. | duranodic | .050″ | 17.65 | 8.45 | 26.10 |
| 6100 | Stainless | formed | 6″ | mill | 24 Ga. | 28 | 6.25 | 34.25 |

## B3020 Roof Openings

Roof Hatch

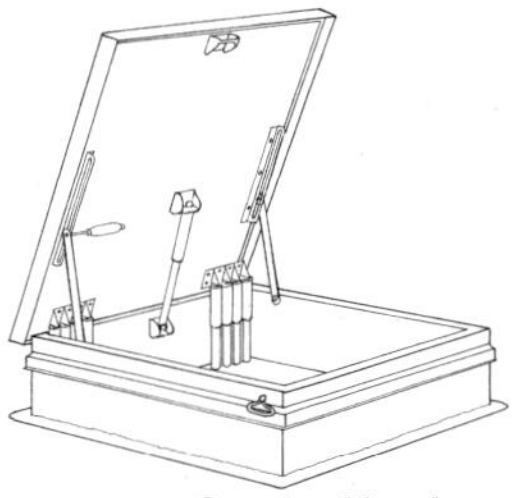

Smoke Hatch

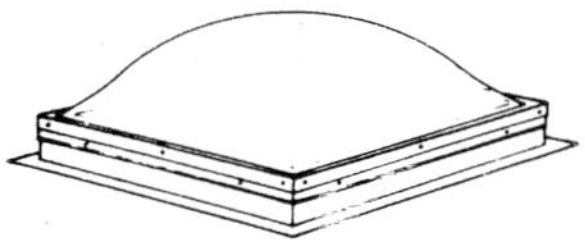

Skylight

| B3020 110 | Skylights | COST PER S.F. | | |
|---|---|---|---|---|
| | | MAT. | INST. | TOTAL |
| 5100 | Skylights, plastic domes, insul curbs, nom. size to 10 S.F., single glaze | 66.50 | 17.60 | 84.10 |
| 5200 | Double glazing | 42.50 | 21.50 | 64 |
| 5300 | 10 S.F. to 20 S.F., single glazing | 39.50 | 7.15 | 46.65 |
| 5400 | Double glazing | 44 | 8.95 | 52.95 |
| 5500 | 20 S.F. to 30 S.F., single glazing | 40.50 | 6.05 | 46.55 |
| 5600 | Double glazing | 61 | 7.15 | 68.15 |
| 5700 | 30 S.F. to 65 S.F., single glazing | 39 | 4.62 | 43.62 |
| 5800 | Double glazing | 57.50 | 6.05 | 63.55 |
| 6000 | Sandwich panels fiberglass, 1-9/16" thick, 2 S.F. to 10 S.F. | 26 | 14.10 | 40.10 |
| 6100 | 10 S.F. to 18 S.F. | 24.50 | 10.65 | 35.15 |
| 6200 | 2-3/4" thick, 25 S.F. to 40 S.F. | 38 | 9.55 | 47.55 |
| 6300 | 40 S.F. to 70 S.F. | 29 | 8.55 | 37.55 |

| B3020 210 | Hatches | COST PER OPNG. | | |
|---|---|---|---|---|
| | | MAT. | INST. | TOTAL |
| 0200 | Roof hatches with curb and 1" fiberglass insulation, 2'-6"x3'-0", aluminum | 1,375 | 282 | 1,657 |
| 0300 | Galvanized steel 165 lbs. | 1,775 | 282 | 2,057 |
| 0400 | Primed steel 164 lbs. | 1,325 | 282 | 1,607 |
| 0500 | 2'-6"x4'-6" aluminum curb and cover, 150 lbs. | 1,775 | 315 | 2,090 |
| 0600 | Galvanized steel 220 lbs. | 2,450 | 315 | 2,765 |
| 0650 | Primed steel 218 lbs. | 1,575 | 315 | 1,890 |
| 0800 | 2'x6"x8'-0" aluminum curb and cover, 260 lbs. | 2,775 | 425 | 3,200 |
| 0900 | Galvanized steel, 360 lbs. | 3,450 | 425 | 3,875 |
| 0950 | Primed steel 358 lbs. | 2,750 | 425 | 3,175 |
| 1200 | For plexiglass panels, add to the above | 895 | | 895 |
| 2100 | Smoke hatches, unlabeled not incl. hand winch operator, 2'-6"x3', galv | 2,150 | 340 | 2,490 |
| 2200 | Plain steel, 160 lbs. | 1,600 | 340 | 1,940 |
| 2400 | 2'-6"x8'-0",galvanized steel, 360 lbs. | 3,775 | 465 | 4,240 |
| 2500 | Plain steel, 350 lbs. | 3,000 | 465 | 3,465 |
| 3000 | 4'-0"x8'-0", double leaf low profile, aluminum cover, 359 lb. | 3,700 | 350 | 4,050 |
| 3100 | Galvanized steel 475 lbs. | 4,075 | 350 | 4,425 |
| 3200 | High profile, aluminum cover, galvanized curb, 361 lbs. | 4,775 | 350 | 5,125 |

## C1010 Partitions

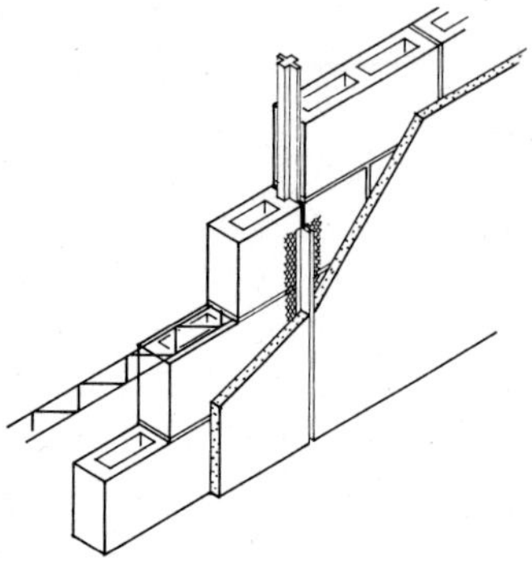

The Concrete Block Partition Systems are defined by weight and type of block, thickness, type of finish and number of sides finished. System components include joint reinforcing on alternate courses and vertical control joints.

### C1010 102 Concrete Block Partitions - Regular Weight

| | TYPE | THICKNESS (IN.) | TYPE FINISH | SIDES FINISHED | | COST PER S.F. MAT. | COST PER S.F. INST. | COST PER S.F. TOTAL |
|---|---|---|---|---|---|---|---|---|
| 1000 | Hollow | 4 | none | 0 | | 2.33 | 7.70 | 10.03 |
| 1010 | | | gyp. plaster 2 coat | 1 | | 2.84 | 11.25 | 14.09 |
| 1020 | | | | 2 | | 3.35 | 14.80 | 18.15 |
| 1200 | | | portland - 3 coat | 1 | | 2.69 | 11.75 | 14.44 |
| 1400 | | | 5/8" drywall | 1 | | 3.11 | 10.35 | 13.46 |
| 1500 | | 6 | none | 0 | | 2.89 | 8.25 | 11.14 |
| 1510 | | | gyp. plaster 2 coat | 1 | | 3.40 | 11.80 | 15.20 |
| 1520 | | | | 2 | | 3.91 | 15.35 | 19.26 |
| 1700 | | | portland - 3 coat | 1 | | 3.25 | 12.30 | 15.55 |
| 1900 | | | 5/8" drywall | 1 | | 3.67 | 10.90 | 14.57 |
| 1910 | | | | 2 | | 4.45 | 13.55 | 18 |
| 2000 | | 8 | none | 0 | | 3.38 | 8.80 | 12.18 |
| 2010 | | | gyp. plaster 2 coat | 1 | | 3.89 | 12.35 | 16.24 |
| 2020 | | | gyp. plaster 2 coat | 2 | | 4.40 | 15.85 | 20.25 |
| 2200 | | | portland - 3 coat | 1 | | 3.74 | 12.85 | 16.59 |
| 2400 | | | 5/8" drywall | 1 | | 4.16 | 11.45 | 15.61 |
| 2410 | | | | 2 | | 4.94 | 14.10 | 19.04 |
| 2500 | | 10 | none | 0 | | 4.45 | 9.20 | 13.65 |
| 2510 | | | gyp. plaster 2 coat | 1 | | 4.95 | 12.75 | 17.70 |
| 2520 | | | | 2 | | 5.45 | 16.25 | 21.70 |
| 2700 | | | portland - 3 coat | 1 | | 4.80 | 13.25 | 18.05 |
| 2900 | | | 5/8" drywall | 1 | | 5.25 | 11.85 | 17.10 |
| 2910 | | | | 2 | | 6 | 14.50 | 20.50 |
| 3000 | Solid | 2 | none | 0 | | 2.10 | 7.60 | 9.70 |
| 3010 | | | gyp. plaster | 1 | | 2.61 | 11.15 | 13.76 |
| 3020 | | | | 2 | | 3.12 | 14.70 | 17.82 |
| 3200 | | | portland - 3 coat | 1 | | 2.46 | 11.65 | 14.11 |
| 3400 | | | 5/8" drywall | 1 | | 2.88 | 10.25 | 13.13 |
| 3410 | | | | 2 | | 3.66 | 12.90 | 16.56 |
| 3500 | | 4 | none | 0 | | 2.99 | 7.95 | 10.94 |
| 3510 | | | gyp. plaster | 1 | | 3.56 | 11.55 | 15.11 |
| 3520 | | | | 2 | | 4.01 | 15.05 | 19.06 |
| 3700 | | | portland - 3 coat | 1 | | 3.35 | 12 | 15.35 |
| 3900 | | | 5/8" drywall | 1 | | 3.77 | 10.60 | 14.37 |
| 3910 | | | | 2 | | 4.55 | 13.25 | 17.80 |

# C1010 Partitions

## C1010 102 Concrete Block Partitions - Regular Weight

| | TYPE | THICKNESS (IN.) | TYPE FINISH | SIDES FINISHED | | COST PER S.F. | | |
|---|---|---|---|---|---|---|---|---|
| | | | | | | MAT. | INST. | TOTAL |
| 4000 | Solid | 6 | none | 0 | | 4.06 | 8.55 | 12.61 |
| 4010 | | | gyp. plaster | 1 | | 4.57 | 12.10 | 16.67 |
| 4020 | | | | 2 | | 5.10 | 15.65 | 20.75 |
| 4200 | | | portland - 3 coat | 1 | | 4.42 | 12.60 | 17.02 |
| 4400 | | | 5/8" drywall | 1 | | 4.84 | 11.20 | 16.04 |
| 4410 | | | | 2 | | 5.60 | 13.85 | 19.45 |

## C1010 104 Concrete Block Partitions - Lightweight

| | TYPE | THICKNESS (IN.) | TYPE FINISH | SIDES FINISHED | | COST PER S.F. | | |
|---|---|---|---|---|---|---|---|---|
| | | | | | | MAT. | INST. | TOTAL |
| 5000 | Hollow | 4 | none | 0 | | 2.11 | 7.50 | 9.61 |
| 5010 | | | gyp. plaster | 1 | | 2.62 | 11.05 | 13.67 |
| 5020 | | | | 2 | | 3.13 | 14.60 | 17.73 |
| 5200 | | | portland - 3 coat | 1 | | 2.47 | 11.55 | 14.02 |
| 5400 | | | 5/8" drywall | 1 | | 2.89 | 10.15 | 13.04 |
| 5410 | | | | 2 | | 3.67 | 12.80 | 16.47 |
| 5500 | | 6 | none | 0 | | 2.81 | 8.05 | 10.86 |
| 5520 | | | gyp. plaster | 2 | | 3.83 | 15.15 | 18.98 |
| 5700 | | | portland - 3 coat | 1 | | 3.17 | 12.10 | 15.27 |
| 5900 | | | 5/8" drywall | 1 | | 3.59 | 10.70 | 14.29 |
| 5910 | | | | 2 | | 4.37 | 13.35 | 17.72 |
| 6000 | | 8 | none | 0 | | 3.89 | 8.60 | 12.49 |
| 6010 | | | gyp. plaster | 1 | | 4.40 | 12.15 | 16.55 |
| 6020 | | | | 2 | | 4.91 | 15.65 | 20.56 |
| 6200 | | | portland - 3 coat | 1 | | 4.25 | 12.65 | 16.90 |
| 6400 | | | 5/8" drywall | 1 | | 4.67 | 11.25 | 15.92 |
| 6410 | | | | 2 | | 5.45 | 13.90 | 19.35 |
| 6500 | | 10 | none | 0 | | 3.91 | 9 | 12.91 |
| 6510 | | | gyp. plaster | 1 | | 4.41 | 12.55 | 16.96 |
| 6520 | | | | 2 | | 4.92 | 16.05 | 20.97 |
| 6700 | | | portland - 3 coat | 1 | | 4.26 | 13.05 | 17.31 |
| 6900 | | | 5/8" drywall | 1 | | 4.69 | 11.65 | 16.34 |
| 6910 | | | | 2 | | 5.45 | 14.30 | 19.75 |
| 7000 | Solid | 4 | none | 0 | | 3.04 | 7.85 | 10.89 |
| 7010 | | | gyp. plaster | 1 | | 3.55 | 11.40 | 14.95 |
| 7020 | | | | 2 | | 4.06 | 14.95 | 19.01 |
| 7200 | | | portland - 3 coat | 1 | | 3.40 | 11.90 | 15.30 |
| 7400 | | | 5/8" drywall | 1 | | 3.82 | 10.50 | 14.32 |
| 7410 | | | | 2 | | 4.60 | 13.15 | 17.75 |
| 7500 | | 6 | none | 0 | | 3.81 | 8.45 | 12.26 |
| 7510 | | | gyp. plaster | 1 | | 4.38 | 12.10 | 16.48 |
| 7520 | | | | 2 | | 4.83 | 15.55 | 20.38 |
| 7700 | | | portland - 3 coat | 1 | | 4.17 | 12.50 | 16.67 |
| 7900 | | | 5/8" drywall | 1 | | 4.59 | 11.10 | 15.69 |
| 7910 | | | | 2 | | 5.35 | 13.75 | 19.10 |
| 8000 | | 8 | none | 0 | | 6.05 | 9.05 | 15.10 |
| 8010 | | | gyp. plaster | 1 | | 6.55 | 12.60 | 19.15 |
| 8020 | | | | 2 | | 7.05 | 16.10 | 23.15 |
| 8200 | | | portland - 3 coat | 1 | | 6.40 | 13.10 | 19.50 |
| 8400 | | | 5/8" drywall | 1 | | 6.80 | 11.70 | 18.50 |
| 8410 | | | | 2 | | 7.60 | 14.35 | 21.95 |

## C1010 Partitions

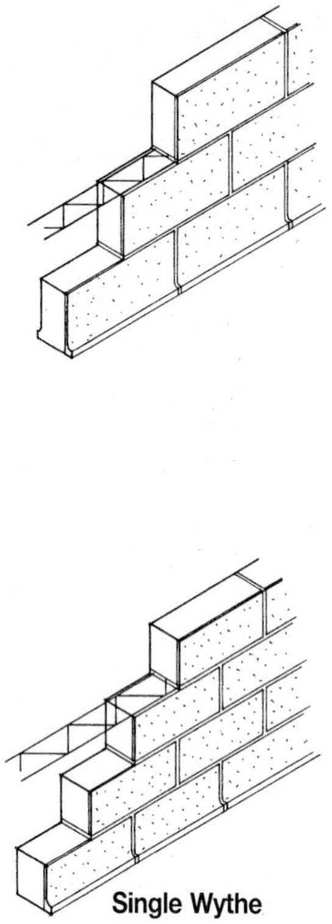

Single Wythe

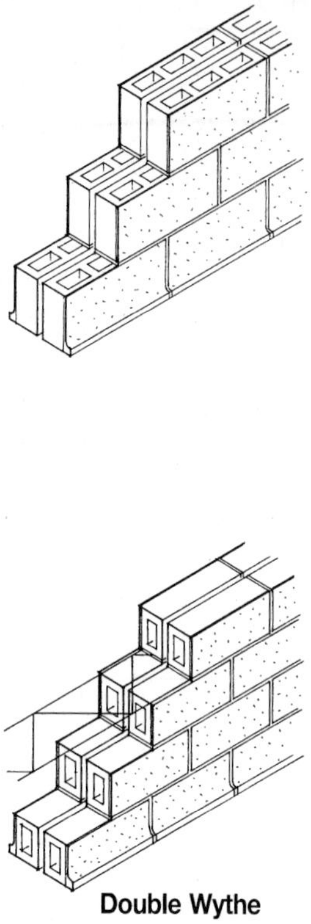

Double Wythe

| C1010 120 | Tile Partitions | COST PER S.F. MAT. | COST PER S.F. INST. | COST PER S.F. TOTAL |
|---|---|---|---|---|
| 1000 | 8W series 8"x16", 4" thick wall, reinf every 2 courses, glazed 1 side | 15.15 | 9.25 | 24.40 |
| 1100 | Glazed 2 sides | 16.15 | 9.85 | 26 |
| 1200 | Glazed 2 sides, using 2 wythes of 2" thick tile | 21.50 | 17.70 | 39.20 |
| 1300 | 6" thick wall, horizontal reinf every 2 courses, glazed 1 side | 35 | 9.70 | 44.70 |
| 1400 | Glazed 2 sides, each face different color, 2" and 4" tile | 26 | 18.10 | 44.10 |
| 1500 | 8" thick wall, glazed 2 sides using 2 wythes of 4" thick tile | 30.50 | 18.50 | 49 |
| 1600 | 10" thick wall, glazed 2 sides using 1 wythe of 4" & 1 wythe of 6" tile | 50 | 18.95 | 68.95 |
| 1700 | Glazed 2 sides cavity wall, using 2 wythes of 4" thick tile | 30.50 | 18.50 | 49 |
| 1800 | 12" thick wall, glazed 2 sides using 2 wythes of 6" thick tile | 70 | 19.40 | 89.40 |
| 1900 | Glazed 2 sides cavity wall, using 2 wythes of 4" thick tile | 30.50 | 18.50 | 49 |
| 2100 | 6T series 5-1/3"x12" tile, 4" thick, non load bearing glazed one side | 14.70 | 14.50 | 29.20 |
| 2200 | Glazed two sides | 19.60 | 16.40 | 36 |
| 2300 | Glazed two sides, using two wythes of 2" thick tile | 22 | 28.50 | 50.50 |
| 2400 | 6" thick, glazed one side | 21 | 15.20 | 36.20 |
| 2500 | Glazed two sides | 25.50 | 17.25 | 42.75 |
| 2600 | Glazed two sides using 2" thick tile and 4" thick tile | 26 | 28.50 | 54.50 |
| 2700 | 8" thick, glazed one side | 25.50 | 17.75 | 43.25 |
| 2800 | Glazed two sides using two wythes of 4" thick tile | 29.50 | 29 | 58.50 |
| 2900 | Glazed two sides using 6" thick tile and 2" thick tile | 32 | 29.50 | 61.50 |
| 3000 | 10" thick cavity wall, glazed two sides using two wythes of 4" tile | 29.50 | 29 | 58.50 |
| 3100 | 12" thick, glazed two sides using 4" thick tile and 8" thick tile | 40 | 32.50 | 72.50 |
| 3200 | 2" thick facing tile, glazed one side, on 6" concrete block | 13.25 | 16.85 | 30.10 |
| 3300 | On 8" concrete block | 13.75 | 17.35 | 31.10 |
| 3400 | On 10" concrete block | 14.80 | 17.70 | 32.50 |

# C10 Interior Construction

## C1010 Partitions

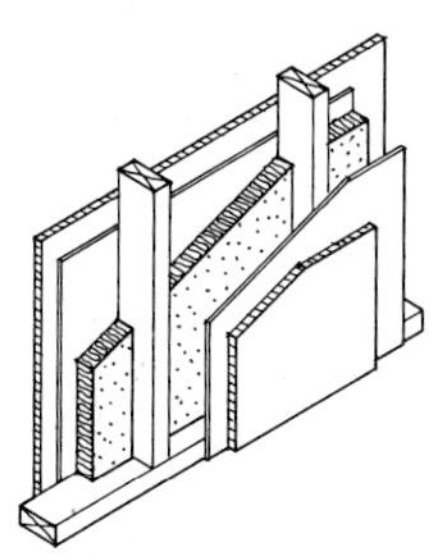

Wood Stud Framing

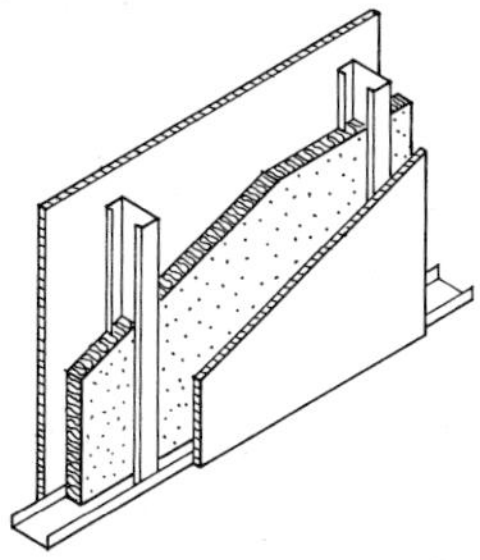

Metal Stud Framing

The Drywall Partitions/Stud Framing Systems are defined by type of drywall and number of layers, type and spacing of stud framing, and treatment on the opposite face. Components include taping and finishing.

Cost differences between regular and fire resistant drywall are negligible, and terminology is interchangeable. In some cases fiberglass insulation is included for additional sound deadening.

### C1010 124 Drywall Partitions/Wood Stud Framing

| | FACE LAYER | BASE LAYER | FRAMING | OPPOSITE FACE | INSULATION | COST PER S.F. | | |
|---|---|---|---|---|---|---|---|---|
| | | | | | | MAT. | INST. | TOTAL |
| 1200 | 5/8″ FR drywall | none | 2 x 4, @ 16″ O.C. | same | 0 | 2.33 | 4.20 | 6.53 |
| 1250 | | | | 5/8″ reg. drywall | 0 | 2.21 | 4.20 | 6.41 |
| 1300 | | | | nothing | 0 | 1.82 | 2.80 | 4.62 |
| 1400 | | 1/4″ SD gypsum | 2 x 4 @ 16″ O.C. | same | 1-1/2″ fiberglass | 4.66 | 6.45 | 11.11 |
| 1425 | | | | | Sound attenuation | 4.04 | 6.55 | 10.59 |
| 1450 | | | | 5/8″ FR drywall | 1-1/2″ fiberglass | 4.22 | 5.70 | 9.92 |
| 1475 | | | | | Sound attenuation | 3.60 | 5.75 | 9.35 |
| 1500 | | | | nothing | 1-1/2″ fiberglass | 3.71 | 4.28 | 7.99 |
| 1600 | | resil. channels | 2 x 4 @ 16″, O.C. | same | 1-1/2″ fiberglass | 4.80 | 8.20 | 13 |
| 1650 | | | | 5/8″ FR drywall | 1-1/2″ fiberglass | 4.29 | 6.55 | 10.84 |
| 1700 | | | | nothing | 1-1/2″ fiberglass | 3.78 | 5.15 | 8.93 |
| 1800 | | 5/8″ FR drywall | 2 x 4 @ 24″ O.C. | same | 0 | 2.92 | 5.30 | 8.22 |
| 1850 | | | | 5/8″ FR drywall | 0 | 2.47 | 4.62 | 7.09 |
| 1900 | | | | nothing | 0 | 1.96 | 3.22 | 5.18 |
| 2200 | | 5/8″ FR drywall | 2 rows-2 x 4 | same | 2″ fiberglass | 5.25 | 7.70 | 12.95 |
| 2250 | | | 16″O.C. | 5/8″ FR drywall | 2″ fiberglass | 4.82 | 7 | 11.82 |
| 2300 | | | | nothing | 2″ fiberglass | 4.31 | 5.60 | 9.91 |
| 2400 | 5/8″ WR drywall | none | 2 x 4, @ 16″ O.C. | same | 0 | 2.89 | 4.20 | 7.09 |
| 2450 | | | | 5/8″ FR drywall | 0 | 2.61 | 4.20 | 6.81 |
| 2500 | | | | nothing | 0 | 2.10 | 2.80 | 4.90 |
| 2600 | | 5/8″ FR drywall | 2 x 4, @ 24″ O.C. | same | 0 | 3.48 | 5.30 | 8.78 |
| 2650 | | | | 5/8″ FR drywall | 0 | 2.75 | 4.62 | 7.37 |
| 2700 | | | | nothing | 0 | 2.24 | 3.22 | 5.46 |
| 2800 | 5/8″ VF drywall | none | 2 x 4, @ 16″ O.C. | same | 0 | 3.59 | 4.50 | 8.09 |
| 2850 | | | | 5/8″ FR drywall | 0 | 2.96 | 4.35 | 7.31 |
| 2900 | | | | nothing | 0 | 2.45 | 2.95 | 5.40 |
| 3000 | | 5/8″ FR drywall | 2 x 4 , 24″ O.C. | same | 0 | 4.18 | 5.60 | 9.78 |
| 3050 | | | | 5/8″ FR drywall | 0 | 3.10 | 4.77 | 7.87 |
| 3100 | | | | nothing | 0 | 2.59 | 3.37 | 5.96 |
| 3200 | 1/2″ reg drywall | 3/8″ reg drywall | 2 x 4, @ 16″ O.C. | same | 0 | 3.05 | 5.60 | 8.65 |
| 3250 | | | | 5/8″ FR drywall | 0 | 2.69 | 4.90 | 7.59 |
| 3300 | | | | nothing | 0 | 2.18 | 3.50 | 5.68 |

### C1010 126 Drywall Partitions/Metal Stud Framing

| | FACE LAYER | BASE LAYER | FRAMING | OPPOSITE FACE | INSULATION | COST PER S.F. | | |
|---|---|---|---|---|---|---|---|---|
| | | | | | | MAT. | INST. | TOTAL |
| 5000 | 5/8″ FR drywall | none | 1-5/8″ @ 16″ O.C. | same | 0 | 2.07 | 4.21 | 6.28 |
| 5010 | | | | 5/8″ reg. drywall | 0 | 1.95 | 4.21 | 6.16 |
| 5020 | | | | nothing | 0 | 1.56 | 2.81 | 4.37 |
| 5030 | | | 2-1/2″″ @ 16″ O.C. | same | 0 | 2 | 4.22 | 6.22 |

### C1010 126 Drywall Partitions/Metal Stud Framing

| | FACE LAYER | BASE LAYER | FRAMING | OPPOSITE FACE | INSULATION | COST PER S.F. | | |
|---|---|---|---|---|---|---|---|---|
| | | | | | | MAT. | INST. | TOTAL |
| 5040 | drywall | | | 5/8" reg. drywall | 0 | 1.88 | 4.22 | 6.10 |
| 5050 | | | | nothing | 0 | 1.49 | 2.82 | 4.31 |
| 5060 | | | 3-5/8" @ 16" O.C. | same | 0 | 2.23 | 4.25 | 6.48 |
| 5070 | | | | 5/8" reg. drywall | 0 | 2.11 | 4.25 | 6.36 |
| 5080 | | | | nothing | 0 | 1.72 | 2.85 | 4.57 |
| 5200 | | | 1-5/8" @ 24" O.C. | same | 0 | 1.79 | 3.72 | 5.51 |
| 5250 | | | | 5/8" reg. drywall | 0 | 1.67 | 3.72 | 5.39 |
| 5300 | | | | nothing | 0 | 1.28 | 2.32 | 3.60 |
| 5310 | | | 2-1/2" @ 24" O.C. | same | 0 | 1.74 | 3.73 | 5.47 |
| 5320 | | | | 5/8" reg. drywall | 0 | 1.62 | 3.73 | 5.35 |
| 5330 | | | | nothing | 0 | 1.23 | 2.33 | 3.56 |
| 5400 | | | 3-5/8" @ 24" O.C. | same | 0 | 1.91 | 3.74 | 5.65 |
| 5450 | | | | 5/8" reg. drywall | 0 | 1.79 | 3.74 | 5.53 |
| 5500 | | | | nothing | 0 | 1.40 | 2.34 | 3.74 |
| 5530 | | 1/4" SD gypsum | 1-5/8" @ 16" O.C. | same | 0 | 2.95 | 5.75 | 8.70 |
| 5535 | | | | 5/8" FR drywall | 0 | 2.07 | 4.21 | 6.28 |
| 5540 | | | | nothing | 0 | 2 | 3.59 | 5.59 |
| 5545 | | | 2-1/2" @ 16" O.C. | same | 0 | 2.88 | 5.80 | 8.68 |
| 5550 | | | | 5/8" FR drywall | 0 | 2 | 4.22 | 6.22 |
| 5555 | | | | nothing | 0 | 1.93 | 3.60 | 5.53 |
| 5560 | | | 3-5/8" @ 16" O.C. | same | 0 | 3.11 | 5.80 | 8.91 |
| 5565 | | | | 5/8" FR drywall | 0 | 2.23 | 4.25 | 6.48 |
| 5570 | | | | nothing | 0 | 2.16 | 3.63 | 5.79 |
| 5600 | | | 1-5/8" @ 24" O.C. | same | 0 | 2.67 | 5.30 | 7.97 |
| 5650 | | | | 5/8" FR drywall | 0 | 2.23 | 4.50 | 6.73 |
| 5700 | | | | nothing | 0 | 1.72 | 3.10 | 4.82 |
| 5800 | | | 2-1/2" @ 24" O.C. | same | 0 | 2.62 | 5.30 | 7.92 |
| 5850 | | | | 5/8" FR drywall | 0 | 2.18 | 4.51 | 6.69 |
| 5900 | | | | nothing | 0 | 1.67 | 3.11 | 4.78 |
| 5910 | | | 3-5/8" @ 24" O.C. | same | 0 | 2.79 | 5.30 | 8.09 |
| 5920 | | | | 5/8" FR drywall | 0 | 2.35 | 4.52 | 6.87 |
| 5930 | | | | nothing | 0 | 1.84 | 3.12 | 4.96 |
| 6000 | | 5/8" FR drywall | 2-1/2" @ 16" O.C. | same | 0 | 2.60 | 6 | 8.60 |
| 6050 | | | | 5/8" FR drywall | 0 | 2.15 | 5.30 | 7.45 |
| 6100 | | | | nothing | 0 | 1.64 | 3.89 | 5.53 |
| 6110 | | | 3-5/8" @ 16" O.C. | same | 0 | 3.13 | 5.65 | 8.78 |
| 6120 | | | | 5/8" FR drywall | 0 | 2.68 | 4.95 | 7.63 |
| 6130 | | | | nothing | 0 | 2.17 | 3.55 | 5.72 |
| 6170 | | | 2-1/2" @ 24" O.C. | same | 0 | 2.64 | 5.15 | 7.79 |
| 6180 | | | | 5/8" FR drywall | 0 | 2.19 | 4.43 | 6.62 |
| 6190 | | | | nothing | 0 | 1.68 | 3.03 | 4.71 |
| 6200 | | | 3-5/8" @ 24" O.C. | same | 0 | 2.81 | 5.15 | 7.96 |
| 6250 | | | | 5/8"FR drywall | 3-1/2" fiberglass | 3.14 | 4.96 | 8.10 |
| 6300 | | | | nothing | 0 | 1.85 | 3.04 | 4.89 |
| 6310 | 5/8" WR drywall | none | 1-5/8" @ 16" O.C. | same | 0 | 2.63 | 4.21 | 6.84 |
| 6320 | | | | 5/8" WR drywall | 0 | 3.36 | 4.91 | 8.27 |
| 6330 | | | | nothing | 0 | 2.57 | 3.51 | 6.08 |
| 6340 | | | 2-1/2" @ 16" O.C. | same | 0 | 4.02 | 5.60 | 9.62 |
| 6350 | | | | 5/8" WR drywall | 0 | 3.29 | 4.92 | 8.21 |
| 6360 | | | | nothing | 0 | 2.50 | 3.52 | 6.02 |
| 6370 | | | 3-5/8" @ 16" O.C. | same | 0 | 4.25 | 5.65 | 9.90 |
| 6380 | | | | 5/8" WR drywall | 0 | 3.52 | 4.95 | 8.47 |
| 6390 | | | | nothing | 0 | 2.73 | 3.55 | 6.28 |

## C1010 Partitions

### C1010 126 Drywall Partitions/Metal Stud Framing

| | FACE LAYER | BASE LAYER | FRAMING | OPPOSITE FACE | INSULATION | COST PER S.F. | | |
|---|---|---|---|---|---|---|---|---|
| | | | | | | MAT. | INST. | TOTAL |
| 6400 | 5/8" WR drywall | none | 1-5/8" @ 24" O.C. | same | 0 | 2.35 | 3.72 | 6.07 |
| 6450 | | | | 5/8" WR drywall | 0 | 2.07 | 3.72 | 5.79 |
| 6500 | | | | nothing | 0 | 1.56 | 2.32 | 3.88 |
| 6510 | | | 2-1/2" @ 24" O.C. | same | 0 | 3.76 | 5.15 | 8.91 |
| 6520 | | | | 5/8" WR drywall | 0 | 2.02 | 3.73 | 5.75 |
| 6530 | | | | nothing | 0 | 1.51 | 2.33 | 3.84 |
| 6600 | | | 3-5/8" @ 24" O.C. | same | 0 | 2.47 | 3.74 | 6.21 |
| 6650 | | | | 5/8" WR drywall | 0 | 2.19 | 3.74 | 5.93 |
| 6700 | | | | nothing | 0 | 1.68 | 2.34 | 4.02 |
| 6800 | | 5/8" FR drywall | 2-1/2" @ 16" O.C. | same | 0 | 3.16 | 6 | 9.16 |
| 6850 | | | | 5/8" FR drywall | 0 | 2.43 | 5.30 | 7.73 |
| 6900 | | | | nothing | 0 | 1.92 | 3.89 | 5.81 |
| 6910 | | | 3-5/8" @ 16" O.C. | same | 0 | 3.69 | 5.65 | 9.34 |
| 6920 | | | | 5/8" FR drywall | 0 | 2.96 | 4.95 | 7.91 |
| 6930 | | | | nothing | 0 | 2.45 | 3.55 | 6 |
| 6940 | | | 2-1/2" @ 24" O.C. | same | 0 | 2.64 | 5.15 | 7.79 |
| 6950 | | | | 5/8" FR drywall | 0 | 2.47 | 4.43 | 6.90 |
| 6960 | | | | nothing | 0 | 1.96 | 3.03 | 4.99 |
| 7000 | | | 3-5/8" @ 24" O.C. | same | 0 | 3.37 | 5.15 | 8.52 |
| 7050 | | | | 5/8"FR drywall | 3-1/2" fiberglass | 3.42 | 4.96 | 8.38 |
| 7100 | | | | nothing | 0 | 2.13 | 3.04 | 5.17 |
| 7110 | 5/8" VF drywall | none | 1-5/8" @ 16" O.C. | same | 0 | 3.33 | 4.51 | 7.84 |
| 7120 | | | | 5/8" FR drywall | 0 | 2.80 | 4.91 | 7.71 |
| 7130 | | | | nothing | 0 | 2.29 | 3.51 | 5.80 |
| 7140 | | | 3-5/8" @ 16" O.C. | same | 0 | 3.69 | 5.65 | 9.34 |
| 7150 | | | | 5/8" FR drywall | 0 | 2.96 | 4.95 | 7.91 |
| 7160 | | | | nothing | 0 | 2.45 | 3.55 | 6 |
| 7200 | 5/8" VF drywall | none | 1-5/8" @ 24" O.C. | same | 0 | 3.05 | 4.02 | 7.07 |
| 7250 | | | | 5/8" FR drywall | 0 | 2.42 | 3.87 | 6.29 |
| 7300 | | | | nothing | 0 | 1.91 | 2.47 | 4.38 |
| 7400 | | | 3-5/8" @ 24" O.C. | same | 0 | 3.17 | 4.04 | 7.21 |
| 7450 | | | | 5/8" FR drywall | 0 | 2.54 | 3.89 | 6.43 |
| 7500 | | | | nothing | 0 | 2.03 | 2.49 | 4.52 |
| 7600 | | 5/8" FR drywall | 2-1/2" @ 16" O.C. | same | 0 | 3.86 | 6.30 | 10.16 |
| 7650 | | | | 5/8" FR drywall | 0 | 2.78 | 5.45 | 8.23 |
| 7700 | | | | nothing | 0 | 2.27 | 4.04 | 6.31 |
| 7710 | | | 3-5/8" @ 16" O.C. | same | 0 | 4.39 | 5.95 | 10.34 |
| 7720 | | | | 5/8" FR drywall | 0 | 3.31 | 5.10 | 8.41 |
| 7730 | | | | nothing | 0 | 2.80 | 3.70 | 6.50 |
| 7740 | | | 2-1/2" @ 24" O.C. | same | 0 | 3.90 | 5.45 | 9.35 |
| 7750 | | | | 5/8" FR drywall | 0 | 2.82 | 4.58 | 7.40 |
| 7760 | | | | nothing | 0 | 2.31 | 3.18 | 5.49 |
| 7800 | | | 3-5/8" @ 24" O.C. | same | 0 | 4.07 | 5.45 | 9.52 |
| 7850 | | | | 5/8"FR drywall | 3-1/2" fiberglass | 3.77 | 5.10 | 8.87 |
| 7900 | | | | nothing | 0 | 2.48 | 3.19 | 5.67 |

## C1010 Partitions

| C1010 128 | Drywall Components | COST PER S.F. MAT. | COST PER S.F. INST. | COST PER S.F. TOTAL |
|---|---|---|---|---|
| 0060 | Metal studs, 24" O.C. including track, load bearing, 20 gage, 2-1/2" | 1.56 | 1.31 | 2.87 |
| 0080 | 3-5/8" | 1.86 | 1.33 | 3.19 |
| 0100 | 4" | 1.68 | 1.36 | 3.04 |
| 0120 | 6" | 2.50 | 1.38 | 3.88 |
| 0140 | Metal studs, 24" O.C. including track, load bearing, 18 gage, 2-1/2" | 1.56 | 1.31 | 2.87 |
| 0160 | 3-5/8" | 1.86 | 1.33 | 3.19 |
| 0180 | 4" | 1.68 | 1.36 | 3.04 |
| 0200 | 6" | 2.50 | 1.38 | 3.88 |
| 0220 | 16 gage, 2-1/2" | 1.81 | 1.49 | 3.30 |
| 0240 | 3-5/8" | 2.15 | 1.52 | 3.67 |
| 0260 | 4" | 2.25 | 1.55 | 3.80 |
| 0280 | 6" | 2.90 | 1.59 | 4.49 |
| 0300 | Non load bearing, 25 gage, 1-5/8" | .77 | .92 | 1.69 |
| 0340 | 3-5/8" | .89 | .94 | 1.83 |
| 0360 | 4" | .66 | .94 | 1.60 |
| 0380 | 6" | .72 | .96 | 1.68 |
| 0400 | 20 gage, 2-1/2" | .50 | 1.16 | 1.66 |
| 0420 | 3-5/8" | 1.08 | 1.18 | 2.26 |
| 0440 | 4" | .87 | 1.18 | 2.05 |
| 0460 | 6" | .93 | 1.20 | 2.13 |
| 0540 | Wood studs including blocking, shoe and double top plate, 2"x4", 12" O.C. | 1.62 | 1.75 | 3.37 |
| 0560 | 16" O.C. | 1.31 | 1.40 | 2.71 |
| 0580 | 24" O.C. | 1 | 1.12 | 2.12 |
| 0600 | 2"x6", 12" O.C. | 2.65 | 2 | 4.65 |
| 0620 | 16" O.C. | 2.15 | 1.55 | 3.70 |
| 0640 | 24" O.C. | 1.64 | 1.22 | 2.86 |
| 0642 | Furring one side only, steel channels, 3/4", 12" O.C. | .55 | 2.90 | 3.45 |
| 0644 | 16" O.C. | .49 | 2.58 | 3.07 |
| 0646 | 24" O.C. | .33 | 1.95 | 2.28 |
| 0647 | 1-1/2" , 12" O.C. | .74 | 3.25 | 3.99 |
| 0648 | 16" O.C. | .66 | 2.84 | 3.50 |
| 0649 | 24" O.C. | .44 | 2.24 | 2.68 |
| 0650 | Wood strips, 1" x 3", on wood, 12" O.C. | .54 | 1.27 | 1.81 |
| 0651 | 16" O.C. | .41 | .95 | 1.36 |
| 0652 | On masonry, 12" O.C. | .58 | 1.41 | 1.99 |
| 0653 | 16" O.C. | .44 | 1.06 | 1.50 |
| 0654 | On concrete, 12" O.C. | .58 | 2.68 | 3.26 |
| 0655 | 16" O.C. | .44 | 2.01 | 2.45 |
| 0665 | Gypsum board, one face only, exterior sheathing, 1/2" | .62 | 1.24 | 1.86 |
| 0680 | Interior, fire resistant, 1/2" | .50 | .70 | 1.20 |
| 0700 | 5/8" | .45 | .70 | 1.15 |
| 0720 | Sound deadening board 1/4" | .44 | .78 | 1.22 |
| 0740 | Standard drywall 3/8" | .42 | .70 | 1.12 |
| 0760 | 1/2" | .39 | .70 | 1.09 |
| 0780 | 5/8" | .33 | .70 | 1.03 |
| 0800 | Tongue & groove coreboard 1" | .85 | 2.91 | 3.76 |
| 0820 | Water resistant, 1/2" | .53 | .70 | 1.23 |
| 0840 | 5/8" | .73 | .70 | 1.43 |
| 0860 | Add for the following:, foil backing | .23 | | .23 |
| 0880 | Fiberglass insulation, 3-1/2" | .78 | .52 | 1.30 |
| 0900 | 6" | .98 | .52 | 1.50 |
| 0920 | Rigid insulation 1" | .96 | .70 | 1.66 |
| 0940 | Resilient furring @ 16" O.C. | .68 | 2.19 | 2.87 |
| 0960 | Taping and finishing | .06 | .70 | .76 |
| 0980 | Texture spray | .04 | .85 | .89 |
| 1000 | Thin coat plaster | .16 | .88 | 1.04 |
| 1050 | Sound wall framing, 2x6 plates, 2x4 staggered studs, 12" O.C. | 2.02 | 1.71 | 3.73 |

## C1010 Partitions

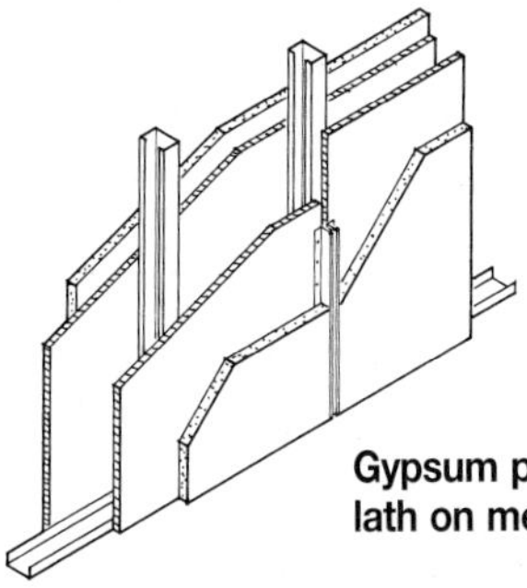

Gypsum plaster and gypsum lath on metal studs.

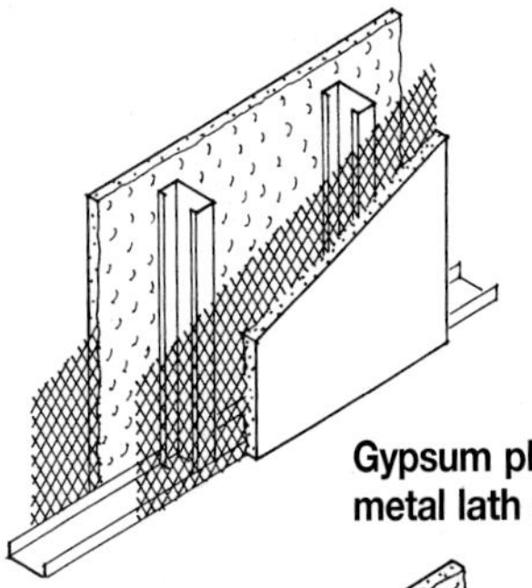

Gypsum plaster and diamond metal lath on metal studs.

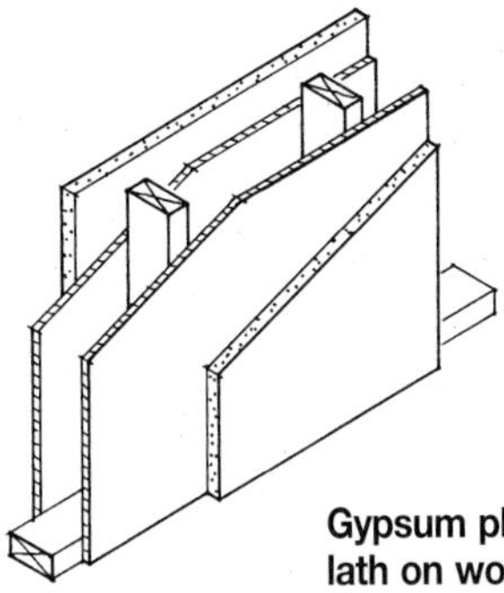

Gypsum plaster and gypsum lath on wood studs.

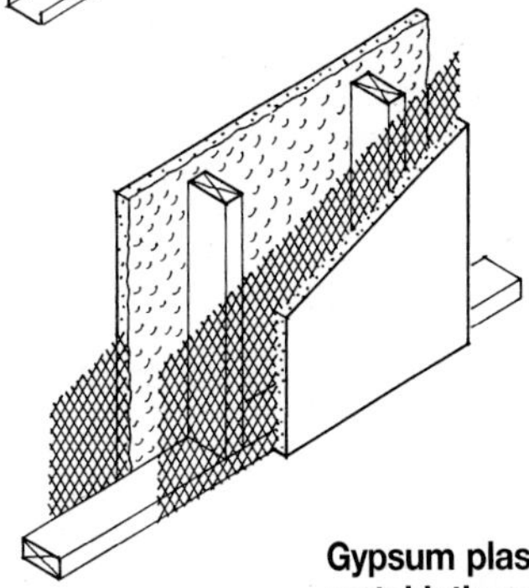

Gypsum plaster and diamond metal lath on wood studs.

### C1010 140 Plaster Partitions/Metal Stud Framing

| | TYPE | FRAMING | LATH | OPPOSITE FACE | | COST PER S.F. | | |
|---|---|---|---|---|---|---|---|---|
| | | | | | | MAT. | INST. | TOTAL |
| 1000 | 2 coat gypsum | 2-1/2" @ 16"O.C. | 3/8" gypsum | same | | 4.18 | 10.40 | 14.58 |
| 1010 | | | | nothing | | 2.66 | 6.05 | 8.71 |
| 1100 | | 3-1/4" @ 24"O.C. | 1/2" gypsum | same | | 3.97 | 10.05 | 14.02 |
| 1110 | | | | nothing | | 2.51 | 5.65 | 8.16 |
| 1500 | 2 coat vermiculite | 2-1/2" @ 16"O.C. | 3/8" gypsum | same | | 3.41 | 11.35 | 14.76 |
| 1510 | | | | nothing | | 2.28 | 6.50 | 8.78 |
| 1600 | | 3-1/4" @ 24"O.C. | 1/2" gypsum | same | | 3.21 | 11 | 14.21 |
| 1610 | | | | nothing | | 2.13 | 6.10 | 8.23 |
| 2000 | 3 coat gypsum | 2-1/2" @ 16"O.C. | 3/8" gypsum | same | | 2.75 | 11.80 | 14.55 |
| 2010 | | | | nothing | | 1.95 | 6.75 | 8.70 |
| 2020 | | | 3.4lb. diamond | same | | 2.97 | 11.80 | 14.77 |
| 2030 | | | | nothing | | 2.06 | 6.75 | 8.81 |
| 2040 | | | 2.75lb. ribbed | same | | 2.91 | 11.80 | 14.71 |
| 2050 | | | | nothing | | 2.03 | 6.75 | 8.78 |
| 2100 | | 3-1/4" @ 24"O.C. | 1/2" gypsum | same | | 2.55 | 11.45 | 14 |
| 2110 | | | | nothing | | 1.80 | 6.30 | 8.10 |
| 2120 | | | 3.4lb. ribbed | same | | 3.14 | 11.45 | 14.59 |
| 2130 | | | | nothing | | 2.09 | 6.30 | 8.39 |
| 3500 | 3 coat gypsum W/med. Keenes | 2-1/2" @ 16"O.C. | 3/8" gypsum | same | | 3.15 | 15.05 | 18.20 |
| 3510 | | | | nothing | | 2.14 | 8.35 | 10.49 |
| 3520 | | | 3.4lb. diamond | same | | 3.37 | 15.05 | 18.42 |
| 3530 | | | | nothing | | 2.25 | 8.35 | 10.60 |
| 3540 | | | 2.75lb. ribbed | same | | 3.31 | 15.05 | 18.36 |
| 3550 | | | | nothing | | 2.23 | 8.35 | 10.58 |
| 3600 | | 3-1/4" @ 24"O.C. | 1/2" gypsum | same | | 2.94 | 14.70 | 17.64 |
| 3610 | | | | nothing | | 2 | 7.95 | 9.95 |
| 3620 | | | 3.4lb. ribbed | same | | 3.53 | 14.70 | 18.23 |

# C1010 Partitions

## C1010 140 Plaster Partitions/Metal Stud Framing

| | TYPE | FRAMING | LATH | OPPOSITE FACE | | COST PER S.F. MAT. | INST. | TOTAL |
|---|---|---|---|---|---|---|---|---|
| 3630 | 3 coat gypsum | 3/4" @ 24"O.C. | 3.4lb ribbed | nothing | | 2.29 | 7.95 | 10.24 |
| 4000 | 3 coat gypsum | 2-1/2" @ 16"O.C. | 3/8" gypsum | same | | 3.15 | 16.65 | 19.80 |
| 4010 | W/hard Keenes | | | nothing | | 2.15 | 9.15 | 11.30 |
| 4020 | | | 3.4lb. diamond | same | | 3.37 | 16.65 | 20.02 |
| 4030 | | | | nothing | | 2.26 | 9.15 | 11.41 |
| 4040 | | | 2.75lb. ribbed | same | | 3.31 | 16.65 | 19.96 |
| 4050 | | | | nothing | | 2.23 | 9.15 | 11.38 |
| 4100 | | 3-1/4" @ 24"O.C. | 1/2" gypsum | same | | 2.95 | 16.30 | 19.25 |
| 4110 | | | | nothing | | 2 | 8.75 | 10.75 |
| 4120 | | | 3.4lb. ribbed | same | | 3.53 | 16.30 | 19.83 |
| 4130 | | | | nothing | | 2.29 | 8.75 | 11.04 |

## C1010 142 Plaster Partitions/Wood Stud Framing

| | TYPE | FRAMING | LATH | OPPOSITE FACE | | COST PER S.F. MAT. | INST. | TOTAL |
|---|---|---|---|---|---|---|---|---|
| 5000 | 2 coat gypsum | 2"x4" @ 16"O.C. | 3/8" gypsum | same | | 4.50 | 10.15 | 14.65 |
| 5010 | | | | nothing | | 2.98 | 5.90 | 8.88 |
| 5100 | | 2"x4" @ 24"O.C. | 1/2" gypsum | same | | 4.08 | 9.95 | 14.03 |
| 5110 | | | | nothing | | 2.62 | 5.65 | 8.27 |
| 5500 | 2 coat vermiculite | 2"x4" @ 16"O.C. | 3/8" gypsum | same | | 3.73 | 11.05 | 14.78 |
| 5510 | | | | nothing | | 2.60 | 6.35 | 8.95 |
| 5600 | | 2"x4" @ 24"O.C. | 1/2" gypsum | same | | 3.31 | 10.90 | 14.21 |
| 5610 | | | | nothing | | 2.24 | 6.15 | 8.39 |
| 6000 | 3 coat gypsum | 2"x4" @ 16"O.C. | 3/8" gypsum | same | | 3.08 | 11.55 | 14.63 |
| 6010 | | | | nothing | | 2.27 | 6.60 | 8.87 |
| 6020 | | | 3.4lb. diamond | same | | 3.30 | 11.65 | 14.95 |
| 6030 | | | | nothing | | 2.38 | 6.65 | 9.03 |
| 6040 | | | 2.75lb. ribbed | same | | 3.20 | 11.70 | 14.90 |
| 6050 | | | | nothing | | 2.34 | 6.70 | 9.04 |
| 6100 | | 2"x4" @ 24"O.C. | 1/2" gypsum | same | | 2.65 | 11.35 | 14 |
| 6110 | | | | nothing | | 1.91 | 6.35 | 8.26 |
| 6120 | | | 3.4lb. ribbed | same | | 2.93 | 11.50 | 14.43 |
| 6130 | | | | nothing | | 2.04 | 6.45 | 8.49 |
| 7500 | 3 coat gypsum | 2"x4" @ 16"O.C. | 3/8" gypsum | same | | 3.47 | 14.80 | 18.27 |
| 7510 | W/med Keenes | | | nothing | | 2.47 | 8.20 | 10.67 |
| 7520 | | | 3.4lb. diamond | same | | 3.69 | 14.90 | 18.59 |
| 7530 | | | | nothing | | 2.58 | 8.30 | 10.88 |
| 7540 | | | 2.75lb. ribbed | same | | 3.60 | 14.95 | 18.55 |
| 7550 | | | | nothing | | 2.54 | 8.30 | 10.84 |
| 7600 | | 2"x4" @ 24"O.C. | 1/2" gypsum | same | | 3.05 | 14.60 | 17.65 |
| 7610 | | | | nothing | | 2.10 | 8 | 10.10 |
| 7620 | | | 3.4lb. ribbed | same | | 3.64 | 14.90 | 18.54 |
| 7630 | | | | nothing | | 2.40 | 8.15 | 10.55 |
| 8000 | 3 coat gypsum | 2"x4" @ 16"O.C. | 3/8" gypsum | same | | 3.47 | 16.40 | 19.87 |
| 8010 | W/hard Keenes | | | nothing | | 2.47 | 9 | 11.47 |
| 8020 | | | 3.4lb. diamond | same | | 3.69 | 16.50 | 20.19 |
| 8030 | | | | nothing | | 2.58 | 9.10 | 11.68 |
| 8040 | | | 2.75lb. ribbed | same | | 3.60 | 16.55 | 20.15 |
| 8050 | | | | nothing | | 2.54 | 9.10 | 11.64 |
| 8100 | | 2"x4" @ 24"O.C. | 1/2" gypsum | same | | 3.05 | 16.20 | 19.25 |
| 8110 | | | | nothing | | 2.10 | 8.80 | 10.90 |
| 8120 | | | 3.4lb. ribbed | same | | 3.64 | 16.50 | 20.14 |
| 8130 | | | | nothing | | 2.40 | 8.95 | 11.35 |

## C1010 Partitions

| C1010 144 | Plaster Partition Components | COST PER S.F. MAT. | COST PER S.F. INST. | COST PER S.F. TOTAL |
|---|---|---|---|---|
| 0060 | Metal studs, 16" O.C., including track, non load bearing, 25 gage, 1-5/8" | .98 | 1.42 | 2.40 |
| 0080 | 2-1/2" | .98 | 1.42 | 2.40 |
| 0100 | 3-1/4" | 1.21 | 1.45 | 2.66 |
| 0120 | 3-5/8" | 1.21 | 1.45 | 2.66 |
| 0140 | 4" | .92 | 1.47 | 2.39 |
| 0160 | 6" | .98 | 1.49 | 2.47 |
| 0180 | Load bearing, 20 gage, 2-1/2" | 2.10 | 1.82 | 3.92 |
| 0200 | 3-5/8" | 2.50 | 1.84 | 4.34 |
| 0220 | 4" | 2.65 | 1.89 | 4.54 |
| 0240 | 6" | 3.35 | 1.91 | 5.26 |
| 0260 | 16 gage 2-1/2" | 2.50 | 2.05 | 4.55 |
| 0280 | 3-5/8" | 2.95 | 2.10 | 5.05 |
| 0300 | 4" | 3.10 | 2.15 | 5.25 |
| 0320 | 6" | 3.95 | 2.20 | 6.15 |
| 0340 | Wood studs, including blocking, shoe and double plate, 2"x4" , 12" O.C. | 1.62 | 1.75 | 3.37 |
| 0360 | 16" O.C. | 1.31 | 1.40 | 2.71 |
| 0380 | 24" O.C. | 1 | 1.12 | 2.12 |
| 0400 | 2"x6" , 12" O.C. | 2.65 | 2 | 4.65 |
| 0420 | 16" O.C. | 2.15 | 1.55 | 3.70 |
| 0440 | 24" O.C. | 1.64 | 1.22 | 2.86 |
| 0460 | Furring one face only, steel channels, 3/4" , 12" O.C. | .55 | 2.90 | 3.45 |
| 0480 | 16" O.C. | .49 | 2.58 | 3.07 |
| 0500 | 24" O.C. | .33 | 1.95 | 2.28 |
| 0520 | 1-1/2" , 12" O.C. | .74 | 3.25 | 3.99 |
| 0540 | 16" O.C. | .66 | 2.84 | 3.50 |
| 0560 | 24"O.C. | .44 | 2.24 | 2.68 |
| 0580 | Wood strips 1"x3", on wood., 12" O.C. | .54 | 1.27 | 1.81 |
| 0600 | 16"O.C. | .41 | .95 | 1.36 |
| 0620 | On masonry, 12" O.C. | .58 | 1.41 | 1.99 |
| 0640 | 16" O.C. | .44 | 1.06 | 1.50 |
| 0660 | On concrete, 12" O.C. | .58 | 2.68 | 3.26 |
| 0680 | 16" O.C. | .44 | 2.01 | 2.45 |
| 0700 | Gypsum lath. plain or perforated, nailed to studs, 3/8" thick | .47 | .89 | 1.36 |
| 0720 | 1/2" thick | .42 | .95 | 1.37 |
| 0740 | Clipped to studs, 3/8" thick | .47 | 1.01 | 1.48 |
| 0760 | 1/2" thick | .42 | 1.08 | 1.50 |
| 0780 | Metal lath, diamond painted, nailed to wood studs, 2.5 lb. | 1.08 | .89 | 1.97 |
| 0800 | 3.4 lb. | .58 | .95 | 1.53 |
| 0820 | Screwed to steel studs, 2.5 lb. | 1.08 | .95 | 2.03 |
| 0840 | 3.4 lb. | .90 | 1.01 | 1.91 |
| 0860 | Rib painted, wired to steel, 2.75 lb | .56 | 1.01 | 1.57 |
| 0880 | 3.4 lb | .71 | 1.08 | 1.79 |
| 0900 | 4.0 lb | .83 | 1.17 | 2 |
| 0910 | | | | |
| 0920 | Gypsum plaster, 2 coats | .50 | 3.35 | 3.85 |
| 0940 | 3 coats | .72 | 4.05 | 4.77 |
| 0960 | Perlite or vermiculite plaster, 2 coats | .66 | 3.82 | 4.48 |
| 0980 | 3 coats | .94 | 4.74 | 5.68 |
| 1000 | Stucco, 3 coats, 1" thick, on wood framing | 1.19 | 6.75 | 7.94 |
| 1020 | On masonry | .36 | 5.25 | 5.61 |
| 1100 | Metal base galvanized and painted 2-1/2" high | .84 | 2.84 | 3.68 |

## C1010 Partitions

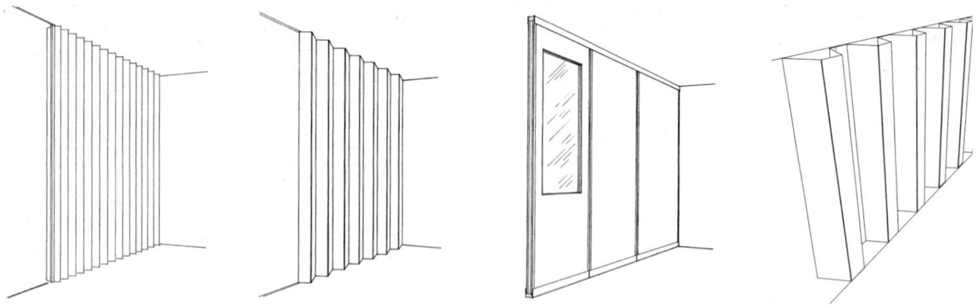

| C1010 205 | Partitions | COST PER S.F. MAT. | COST PER S.F. INST. | COST PER S.F. TOTAL |
|---|---|---|---|---|
| 0360 | Folding accordion, vinyl covered, acoustical, 3 lb. S.F., 17 ft max. hgt | 46 | 13.95 | 59.95 |
| 0380 | 5 lb. per S.F. 27 ft max height | 74.50 | 14.70 | 89.20 |
| 0400 | 5.5 lb. per S.F., 17 ft. max height | 87.50 | 15.50 | 103 |
| 0420 | Commercial, 1.75 lb per S.F., 8 ft. max height | 29.50 | 6.20 | 35.70 |
| 0440 | 2.0 Lb per S.F., 17 ft. max height | 44 | 9.30 | 53.30 |
| 0460 | Industrial, 4.0 lb. per S.F. 27 ft. max height | 66 | 18.60 | 84.60 |
| 0480 | Vinyl clad wood or steel, electric operation 6 psf | 93.50 | 8.75 | 102.25 |
| 0500 | Wood, non acoustic, birch or mahogany | 50 | 4.65 | 54.65 |
| 0560 | Folding leaf, alum framed acoustical 12′ high., 5.5 lb/S.F. standard trim | 82 | 23.50 | 105.50 |
| 0580 | Premium trim | 93.50 | 46.50 | 140 |
| 0600 | 6.5 lb. per S.F., standard trim | 81.50 | 23.50 | 105 |
| 0620 | Premium trim | 104 | 46.50 | 150.50 |
| 0640 | Steel acoustical, 7.5 per S.F., vinyl faced, standard trim | 115 | 23.50 | 138.50 |
| 0660 | Premium trim | 128 | 46.50 | 174.50 |
| 0680 | Wood acoustic type, vinyl faced to 18′ high 6 psf, economy trim | 108 | 23.50 | 131.50 |
| 0700 | Standard trim | 129 | 31 | 160 |
| 0720 | Premium trim | 166 | 46.50 | 212.50 |
| 0740 | Plastic lam. or hardwood faced, standard trim | 111 | 23.50 | 134.50 |
| 0760 | Premium trim | 117 | 46.50 | 163.50 |
| 0780 | Wood, low acoustical type to 12 ft. high 4.5 psf | 80.50 | 28 | 108.50 |
| 0840 | Demountable, trackless wall, cork finish, semi acous, 1-5/8″ th, unsealed | 54 | 4.30 | 58.30 |
| 0860 | Sealed | 65 | 7.35 | 72.35 |
| 0880 | Acoustic, 2″ thick, unsealed | 55.50 | 4.58 | 60.08 |
| 0900 | Sealed | 76.50 | 6.20 | 82.70 |
| 0920 | In-plant modular office system, w/prehung steel door | | | |
| 0940 | 3″ thick honeycomb core panels | | | |
| 0960 | 12′ x 12′, 2 wall | 20.50 | .89 | 21.39 |
| 0970 | 4 wall | 20 | 1.18 | 21.18 |
| 0980 | 16′ x 16′, 2 wall | 21.50 | .63 | 22.13 |
| 0990 | 4 wall | 14 | .63 | 14.63 |
| 1000 | Gypsum, demountable, 3″ to 3-3/4″ thick x 9′ high, vinyl clad | 9.95 | 3.22 | 13.17 |
| 1020 | Fabric clad | 22 | 3.50 | 25.50 |
| 1040 | 1.75 system, vinyl clad hardboard, paper honeycomb core panel | | | |
| 1060 | 1-3/4″ to 2-1/2″ thick x 9′ high | 14.75 | 3.22 | 17.97 |
| 1080 | Unitized gypsum panel system, 2″ to 2-1/2″ thick x 9′ high | | | |
| 1100 | Vinyl clad gypsum | 19 | 3.22 | 22.22 |
| 1120 | Fabric clad gypsum | 31.50 | 3.50 | 35 |
| 1140 | Movable steel walls, modular system | | | |
| 1160 | Unitized panels, 48″ wide x 9′ high | | | |
| 1180 | Baked enamel, pre-finished | 21.50 | 2.61 | 24.11 |
| 1200 | Fabric clad | 31 | 2.78 | 33.78 |
| 1300 | Metal panel partition, load bearing studs, 16 gage, corrugate/ribbed panel, | 6.30 | 5.75 | 12.05 |

## C1020 Interior Doors

| C1020 102 | Special Doors | COST PER OPNG. MAT. | INST. | TOTAL |
|---|---|---|---|---|
| 2500 | Single leaf, wood, 3'-0"x7'-0"x1 3/8", birch, solid core | 970 | 261 | 1,231 |
| 2510 | Hollow core | 575 | 250 | 825 |
| 2530 | Hollow core, lauan | 545 | 250 | 795 |
| 2540 | Louvered pine | 790 | 250 | 1,040 |
| 2550 | Paneled pine | 735 | 250 | 985 |
| 2600 | Hollow metal, comm. quality, flush, 3'-0"x7'-0"x1-3/8" | 885 | 274 | 1,159 |
| 2650 | 3'-0"x10'-0" openings with panel | 1,550 | 355 | 1,905 |
| 2700 | Metal fire, comm. quality, 3'-0"x7'-0"x1-3/8" | 1,775 | 285 | 2,060 |
| 3200 | Double leaf, wood, hollow core, 2 - 3'-0"x7'-0"x1-3/8" | 880 | 475 | 1,355 |
| 3300 | Hollow metal, comm. quality, B label, 2'-3'-0"x7'-0"x1-3/8" | 3,400 | 600 | 4,000 |
| 3400 | 6'-0"x10'-0" opening, with panel | 2,950 | 740 | 3,690 |
| 3500 | Double swing door system, 12'-0"x7'-0", mill finish | 11,700 | 3,650 | 15,350 |
| 3700 | Black finish | 11,800 | 3,775 | 15,575 |
| 3800 | Sliding entrance door and system mill finish | 12,300 | 3,375 | 15,675 |
| 3900 | Bronze finish | 13,400 | 3,625 | 17,025 |
| 4000 | Black finish | 14,000 | 3,775 | 17,775 |
| 4100 | Sliding panel mall front, 16'x9' opening, mill finish | 5,600 | 1,025 | 6,625 |
| 4200 | Bronze finish | 7,275 | 1,325 | 8,600 |
| 4300 | Black finish | 8,950 | 1,650 | 10,600 |
| 4400 | 24'x9' opening mill finish | 7,850 | 1,900 | 9,750 |
| 4500 | Bronze finish | 10,200 | 2,475 | 12,675 |
| 4600 | Black finish | 12,600 | 3,050 | 15,650 |
| 4700 | 48'x9' opening mill finish | 14,100 | 1,475 | 15,575 |
| 4800 | Bronze finish | 18,300 | 1,925 | 20,225 |
| 4900 | Black finish | 22,600 | 2,350 | 24,950 |
| 5000 | Rolling overhead steel door, manual, 8' x 8' high | 675 | 995 | 1,670 |
| 5100 | 10' x 10' high | 995 | 1,125 | 2,120 |
| 5200 | 20' x 10' high | 3,000 | 1,600 | 4,600 |
| 5300 | 12' x 12' high | 1,375 | 1,325 | 2,700 |
| 5400 | Motor operated, 8' x 8' high | 1,875 | 1,325 | 3,200 |
| 5500 | 10' x 10' high | 2,200 | 1,450 | 3,650 |
| 5600 | 20' x 10' high | 4,200 | 1,925 | 6,125 |
| 5700 | 12' x 12' high | 2,575 | 1,650 | 4,225 |
| 5800 | Roll up grille, aluminum, manual, 10' x 10' high, mill finish | 3,600 | 1,950 | 5,550 |
| 5900 | Bronze anodized | 6,550 | 1,950 | 8,500 |
| 6000 | Motor operated, 10' x 10' high, mill finish | 5,425 | 2,250 | 7,675 |
| 6100 | Bronze anodized | 8,375 | 2,250 | 10,625 |
| 6200 | Steel, manual, 10' x 10' high | 3,150 | 1,600 | 4,750 |
| 6300 | 15' x 8' high | 4,200 | 2,000 | 6,200 |
| 6400 | Motor operated, 10' x 10' high | 4,975 | 1,925 | 6,900 |
| 6500 | 15' x 8' high | 6,025 | 2,325 | 8,350 |
| 8970 | Counter door, rolling, 6' high, 14' wide, aluminum | 4,225 | 995 | 5,220 |

## C1030 Fittings

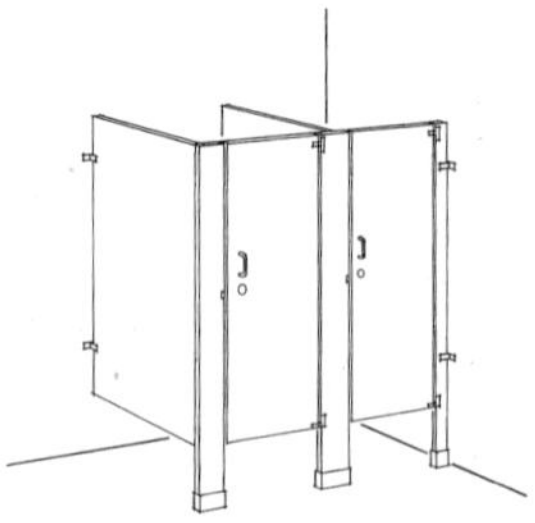

Toilet Units

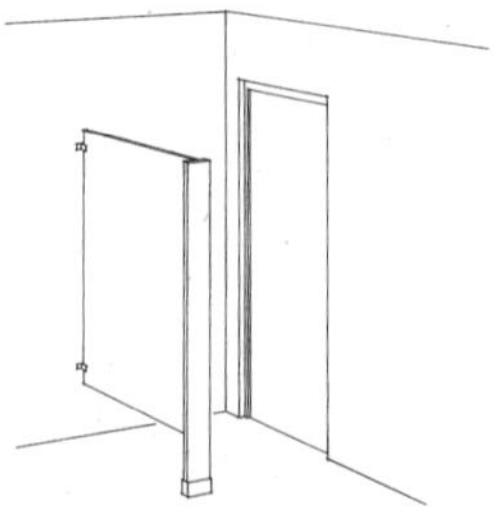

Entrance Screens

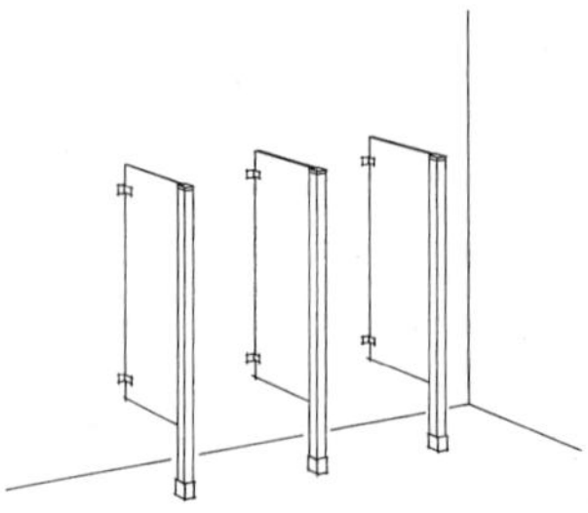

Urinal Screens

| C1030 110 | Toilet Partitions | COST PER UNIT | | |
|---|---|---|---|---|
| | | MAT. | INST. | TOTAL |
| 0380 | Toilet partitions, cubicles, ceiling hung, marble | 2,225 | 685 | 2,910 |
| 0400 | Painted metal | 570 | 350 | 920 |
| 0420 | Plastic laminate | 715 | 350 | 1,065 |
| 0430 | Phenolic | 1,475 | 350 | 1,825 |
| 0440 | Polymer plastic | 440 | 350 | 790 |
| 0460 | Stainless steel | 2,300 | 350 | 2,650 |
| 0480 | Handicap addition | 161 | | 161 |
| 0520 | Floor and ceiling anchored, marble | 2,250 | 550 | 2,800 |
| 0540 | Painted metal | 860 | 279 | 1,139 |
| 0560 | Plastic laminate | 760 | 279 | 1,039 |
| 0570 | Phenolic | 1,525 | 279 | 1,804 |
| 0580 | Polymer plastic | 1,100 | 279 | 1,379 |
| 0600 | Stainless steel | 2,200 | 279 | 2,479 |
| 0620 | Handicap addition | 161 | | 161 |
| 0660 | Floor mounted marble | 1,425 | 455 | 1,880 |
| 0680 | Painted metal | 850 | 199 | 1,049 |
| 0700 | Plastic laminate | 1,025 | 199 | 1,224 |
| 0710 | Phenolic | 1,450 | 199 | 1,649 |
| 0720 | Polymer plastic | 1,025 | 199 | 1,224 |
| 0740 | Stainless steel | 1,375 | 199 | 1,574 |
| 0760 | Handicap addition | 161 | | 161 |
| 0780 | Juvenile deduction | 60.50 | | 60.50 |
| 0820 | Floor mounted with headrail marble | 1,625 | 455 | 2,080 |
| 0840 | Painted metal | 640 | 233 | 873 |
| 0860 | Plastic laminate | 1,100 | 233 | 1,333 |
| 0870 | Phenolic | 1,425 | 233 | 1,658 |
| 0880 | Polymer plastic | 420 | 233 | 653 |
| 0900 | Stainless steel | 1,475 | 233 | 1,708 |
| 0920 | Handicap addition | 263 | | 263 |
| 0960 | Wall hung, painted metal | 680 | 199 | 879 |
| 1020 | Stainless steel | 490 | 199 | 689 |
| 1040 | Handicap addition | 945 | | 945 |
| 1080 | Entrance screens, floor mounted, 54″ high, marble | 975 | 152 | 1,127 |
| 1100 | Painted metal | 286 | 93 | 379 |
| 1140 | Stainless steel | 570 | 93 | 663 |
| 1150 | Polymer plastic | 350 | 233 | 583 |
| 1300 | Urinal screens, floor mounted, 24″ wide, plastic laminate | 256 | 175 | 431 |
| 1320 | Marble | 875 | 209 | 1,084 |
| 1330 | Polymer plastic | 300 | 233 | 533 |
| 1340 | Painted metal | 249 | 175 | 424 |
| 1380 | Stainless steel | 490 | 175 | 665 |
| 1428 | Wall mounted wedge type, painted metal | 185 | 140 | 325 |

## C1030 Fittings

| C1030 110 | Toilet Partitions | COST PER UNIT | | |
|---|---|---|---|---|
| | | MAT. | INST. | TOTAL |
| 1460 | Stainless steel | 845 | 140 | 985 |
| 1500 | Partitions, shower stall, single wall, painted steel, 2'-8" x 2'-8" | 990 | 340 | 1,330 |
| 1510 | Fiberglass, 2'-8" x 2'-8" | 1,950 | 375 | 2,325 |
| 1520 | Double wall, enameled steel, 2'-8" x 2'-8" | 1,850 | 340 | 2,190 |
| 1530 | Stainless steel, 2'-8" x 2'-8" | 2,600 | 340 | 2,940 |
| 1560 | Tub enclosure, sliding panels, tempered glass, aluminum frame | 525 | 425 | 950 |
| 1570 | Chrome/brass frame, clear glass | 1,550 | 565 | 2,115 |

| C1030 310 | Storage Specialties, EACH | COST EACH | | |
|---|---|---|---|---|
| | | MAT. | INST. | TOTAL |
| 0200 | Lockers, steel, 1-tier, 5' to 6' high, per opng, 1 wide, knock down constr. | 224 | 60.50 | 284.50 |
| 0210 | 3 wide | 450 | 70.50 | 520.50 |
| 0220 | 2- tier | 183 | 32.50 | 215.50 |
| 0235 | Two person | 355 | 42.50 | 397.50 |
| 0240 | Duplex | 930 | 42.50 | 972.50 |
| 0245 | Welded, athletic type, ventilated, 1- tier | 395 | 113 | 508 |
| 0600 | Shelving, metal industrial, braced, 3' wide, 1' deep | 61.50 | 13.60 | 75.10 |
| 0610 | 2' deep | 54 | 14.45 | 68.45 |

| C1030 510 | Identifying/Visual Aid Specialties, EACH | COST EACH | | |
|---|---|---|---|---|
| | | MAT. | INST. | TOTAL |
| 0100 | Control boards, magnetic, porcelain finish, framed, 24" x 18" | 209 | 175 | 384 |
| 0110 | 96" x 48" | 1,150 | 279 | 1,429 |
| 0120 | Directory boards, outdoor, black plastic, 36" x 24" | 640 | 700 | 1,340 |
| 0130 | 36" x 36" | 635 | 930 | 1,565 |
| 0140 | Indoor, economy, open faced, 18" x 24" | 253 | 199 | 452 |
| 0510 | Street, reflective alum., dbl. face, 4 way, w/bracket | 59.50 | 46.50 | 106 |
| 0520 | Letters, cast aluminum, 1/2" deep, 4" high | 27.50 | 39 | 66.50 |
| 0530 | 1" deep, 10" high | 71.50 | 39 | 110.50 |
| 0540 | Plaques, cast aluminum, 20" x 30" | 1,725 | 350 | 2,075 |
| 0550 | Cast bronze, 36" x 48" | 9,325 | 700 | 10,025 |

| C1030 520 | Identifying/Visual Aid Specialties, S.F. | COST PER S.F. | | |
|---|---|---|---|---|
| | | MAT. | INST. | TOTAL |
| 0100 | Bulletin board, cork sheets, no frame, 1/4" thick | 3.18 | 4.81 | 7.99 |
| 0120 | Aluminum frame, 1/4" thick, 3' x 5' | 9.80 | 5.85 | 15.65 |
| 0200 | Chalkboards, wall hung, alum, frame & chalktrough | 16.75 | 3.08 | 19.83 |
| 0210 | Wood frame & chalktrough | 22 | 3.32 | 25.32 |
| 0220 | Sliding board, one board with back panel | 101 | 2.98 | 103.98 |
| 0230 | Two boards with back panel | 101 | 2.98 | 103.98 |
| 0240 | Liquid chalk type, alum. frame & chalktrough | 15.95 | 3.08 | 19.03 |
| 0250 | Wood frame & chalktrough | 32.50 | 3.08 | 35.58 |

| C1030 710 | Bath and Toilet Accessories, EACH | COST EACH | | |
|---|---|---|---|---|
| | | MAT. | INST. | TOTAL |
| 0100 | Specialties, bathroom accessories, st. steel, curtain rod, 5' long, 1" diam | 55 | 53.50 | 108.50 |
| 0120 | Dispenser, towel, surface mounted | 53.50 | 43.50 | 97 |
| 0140 | Grab bar, 1-1/4" diam., 12" long | 23 | 29 | 52 |
| 0160 | Mirror, framed with shelf, 18" x 24" | 119 | 35 | 154 |
| 0170 | 72" x 24" | 880 | 116 | 996 |
| 0180 | Toilet tissue dispenser, surface mounted, single roll | 18.40 | 23.50 | 41.90 |
| 0200 | Towel bar, 18" long | 45 | 30.50 | 75.50 |
| 0300 | Medicine cabinets, sliding mirror doors, 20" x 16" x 4-3/4", unlighted | 181 | 99.50 | 280.50 |
| 0310 | 24" x 19" x 8-1/2", lighted | 196 | 140 | 336 |

## C1030 Fittings

| C1030 730 | Bath and Toilet Accessories, L.F. | COST PER L.F. | | |
|---|---|---|---|---|
| | | MAT. | INST. | TOTAL |
| 0100 | Partitions, hospital curtain, ceiling hung, polyester oxford cloth | 33.50 | 6.80 | 40.30 |
| 0110 | Designer oxford cloth | 29 | 8.65 | 37.65 |

| C1030 830 | Fabricated Cabinets, EACH | COST EACH | | |
|---|---|---|---|---|
| | | MAT. | INST. | TOTAL |
| 0110 | Household, base, hardwood, one top drawer & one door below x 12″ wide | 640 | 56.50 | 696.50 |
| 0115 | 24″ wide | 540 | 62.50 | 602.50 |
| 0120 | Four drawer x 24″ wide | 940 | 62.50 | 1,002.50 |
| 0130 | Wall, hardwood, 30″ high with one door x 12″ wide | 125 | 63.50 | 188.50 |
| 0140 | Two doors x 48″ wide | 900 | 76 | 976 |

| C1030 830 | Fabricated Counters, L.F. | COST PER L.F. | | |
|---|---|---|---|---|
| | | MAT. | INST. | TOTAL |
| 0150 | Counter top-laminated plastic, stock, economy | 20.50 | 23.50 | 44 |
| 0160 | Custom-square edge, 7/8″ thick | 18.95 | 52 | 70.95 |
| 0170 | School, counter, wood, 32″ high | 299 | 70 | 369 |
| 0180 | Metal, 84″ high | 675 | 93 | 768 |

| C1030 910 | Other Fittings, EACH | COST EACH | | |
|---|---|---|---|---|
| | | MAT. | INST. | TOTAL |
| 0500 | Mail boxes, horizontal, rear loaded, aluminum, 5″ x 6″ x 15″ deep | 27 | 20.50 | 47.50 |
| 0510 | Front loaded, aluminum, 10″ x 12″ x 15″ deep | 134 | 35 | 169 |
| 0520 | Vertical, front loaded, aluminum, 15″ x 5″ x 6″ deep | 134 | 20.50 | 154.50 |
| 0530 | Bronze, duranodic finish | 107 | 20.50 | 127.50 |
| 0540 | Letter slot, post office | 235 | 87.50 | 322.50 |
| 0550 | Mail counter, window, post office, with grille | 1,925 | 350 | 2,275 |
| 0700 | Turnstiles, one way, 4′ arm, 46″ diam., manual | 2,450 | 279 | 2,729 |
| 0710 | Electric | 5,950 | 1,175 | 7,125 |
| 0720 | 3 arm, 5′-5″ diam. & 7′ high, manual | 9,175 | 1,400 | 10,575 |
| 0730 | Electric | 15,100 | 2,325 | 17,425 |

## C2010 Stair Construction

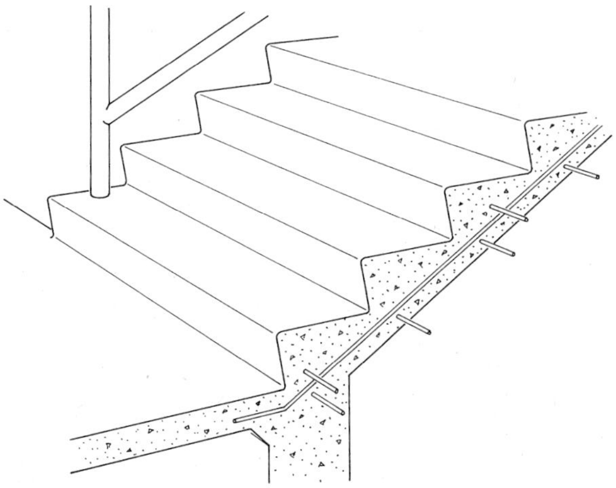

The table below lists the cost per flight for 4′-0″ wide stairs. Side walls are not included. Railings are included in the prices.

| C2010 110 | Stairs | COST PER FLIGHT | | |
|---|---|---|---|---|
| | | MAT. | INST. | TOTAL |
| 0470 | Stairs, C.I.P. concrete, w/o landing, 12 risers, w/o nosing | 1,800 | 2,850 | 4,650 |
| 0480 | With nosing | 2,700 | 3,100 | 5,800 |
| 0550 | W/landing, 12 risers, w/o nosing | 2,075 | 3,525 | 5,600 |
| 0560 | With nosing | 2,950 | 3,775 | 6,725 |
| 0570 | 16 risers, w/o nosing | 2,525 | 4,425 | 6,950 |
| 0580 | With nosing | 3,725 | 4,750 | 8,475 |
| 0590 | 20 risers, w/o nosing | 3,000 | 5,325 | 8,325 |
| 0600 | With nosing | 4,475 | 5,750 | 10,225 |
| 0610 | 24 risers, w/o nosing | 3,450 | 6,225 | 9,675 |
| 0620 | With nosing | 5,225 | 6,725 | 11,950 |
| 0630 | Steel, grate type w/nosing & rails, 12 risers, w/o landing | 6,050 | 1,350 | 7,400 |
| 0640 | With landing | 8,350 | 1,850 | 10,200 |
| 0660 | 16 risers, with landing | 10,400 | 2,300 | 12,700 |
| 0680 | 20 risers, with landing | 12,400 | 2,750 | 15,150 |
| 0700 | 24 risers, with landing | 14,400 | 3,200 | 17,600 |
| 0701 | | | | |
| 0710 | Metal pan stairs for concrete in-fill, picket rail, 12 risers, w/o landing | 8,050 | 1,350 | 9,400 |
| 0720 | With landing | 10,900 | 2,025 | 12,925 |
| 0740 | 16 risers, with landing | 13,600 | 2,475 | 16,075 |
| 0760 | 20 risers, with landing | 16,300 | 2,925 | 19,225 |
| 0780 | 24 risers, with landing | 18,900 | 3,375 | 22,275 |
| 0790 | Cast iron tread & pipe rail, 12 risers, w/o landing | 8,050 | 1,350 | 9,400 |
| 0800 | With landing | 10,900 | 2,025 | 12,925 |
| 1120 | Wood, prefab box type, oak treads, wood rails 3′-6″ wide, 14 risers | 3,425 | 580 | 4,005 |
| 1150 | Prefab basement type, oak treads, wood rails 3′-0″ wide, 14 risers | 1,125 | 143 | 1,268 |
| 1151 | Stairs, wood, Parametric, 2 risers includes landing and railing | 345 | 520 | 865 |

## C3010 Wall Finishes

| C3010 230 | Paint & Covering | COST PER S.F. MAT. | INST. | TOTAL |
|---|---|---|---|---|
| 0060 | Painting, interior on plaster and drywall, brushwork, primer & 1 coat | .13 | .91 | 1.04 |
| 0080 | Primer & 2 coats | .19 | 1.20 | 1.39 |
| 0100 | Primer & 3 coats | .26 | 1.47 | 1.73 |
| 0120 | Walls & ceilings, roller work, primer & 1 coat | .13 | .60 | .73 |
| 0140 | Primer & 2 coats | .19 | .77 | .96 |
| 0160 | Woodwork incl. puttying, brushwork, primer & 1 coat | .13 | 1.31 | 1.44 |
| 0180 | Primer & 2 coats | .19 | 1.73 | 1.92 |
| 0200 | Primer & 3 coats | .26 | 2.35 | 2.61 |
| 0260 | Cabinets and casework, enamel, primer & 1 coat | .14 | 1.47 | 1.61 |
| 0280 | Primer & 2 coats | .20 | 1.81 | 2.01 |
| 0300 | Masonry or concrete, latex, brushwork, primer & 1 coat | .26 | 1.23 | 1.49 |
| 0320 | Primer & 2 coats | .34 | 1.76 | 2.10 |
| 0340 | Addition for block filler | .20 | 1.51 | 1.71 |
| 0380 | Fireproof paints, intumescent, 1/8" thick 3/4 hour | 2.41 | 1.20 | 3.61 |
| 0400 | 3/16" thick 1 hour | 5.35 | 1.81 | 7.16 |
| 0420 | 7/16" thick 2 hour | 6.90 | 4.20 | 11.10 |
| 0440 | 1-1/16" thick 3 hour | 11.30 | 8.40 | 19.70 |
| 0500 | Gratings, primer & 1 coat | .83 | 1.84 | 2.67 |
| 0600 | Pipes over 12" diameter | 1.13 | 5.90 | 7.03 |
| 0700 | Structural steel, brushwork, light framing 300-500 S.F./Ton | .20 | 2.04 | 2.24 |
| 0720 | Heavy framing 50-100 S.F./Ton | .20 | 1.02 | 1.22 |
| 0740 | Spraywork, light framing 300-500 S.F./Ton | .22 | .45 | .67 |
| 0760 | Heavy framing 50-100 S.F./Ton | .22 | .50 | .72 |
| 0800 | Varnish, interior wood trim, no sanding sealer & 1 coat | .22 | 1.47 | 1.69 |
| 0820 | Hardwood floor, no sanding 2 coats | .17 | .31 | .48 |
| 0840 | Wall coatings, acrylic glazed coatings, minimum | .44 | 1.12 | 1.56 |
| 0860 | Maximum | .32 | 1.93 | 2.25 |
| 0880 | Epoxy coatings, solvent based | .55 | 1.12 | 1.67 |
| 0900 | Water based | .13 | 3.46 | 3.59 |
| 0940 | Exposed epoxy aggregate, troweled on, 1/16" to 1/4" aggregate, topping mix | .89 | 2.50 | 3.39 |
| 0960 | Integral mix | 1.94 | 4.53 | 6.47 |
| 0980 | 1/2" to 5/8" aggregate, topping mix | 1.68 | 4.53 | 6.21 |
| 1000 | Integral mix | 2.92 | 7.35 | 10.27 |
| 1020 | 1" aggregate, topping mix | 2.97 | 6.55 | 9.52 |
| 1040 | Integral mix | 4.53 | 10.70 | 15.23 |
| 1060 | Sprayed on, topping mix | .67 | 1.99 | 2.66 |
| 1080 | Water based | 1.46 | 4.06 | 5.52 |
| 1100 | High build epoxy 50 mil, solvent based | .89 | 1.51 | 2.40 |
| 1120 | Water based | 1.22 | 6.20 | 7.42 |
| 1140 | Laminated epoxy with fiberglass solvent based | .99 | 1.99 | 2.98 |
| 1160 | Water based | 1.91 | 4.06 | 5.97 |
| 1180 | Sprayed perlite or vermiculite 1/16" thick, solvent based | .32 | .20 | .52 |
| 1200 | Water based | 1.01 | .92 | 1.93 |
| 1260 | Wall coatings, vinyl plastic, solvent based | .47 | .80 | 1.27 |
| 1280 | Water based | 1.19 | 2.45 | 3.64 |
| 1300 | Urethane on smooth surface, 2 coats, solvent based | .40 | .52 | .92 |
| 1320 | Water based | .73 | .88 | 1.61 |
| 1340 | 3 coats, solvent based | .51 | .70 | 1.21 |
| 1360 | Water based | 1.17 | 1.25 | 2.42 |
| 1380 | Ceramic-like glazed coating, cementitious, solvent based | .57 | 1.34 | 1.91 |
| 1400 | Water based | 1.18 | 1.71 | 2.89 |
| 1420 | Resin base, solvent based | .40 | .92 | 1.32 |
| 1440 | Water based | .78 | 1.78 | 2.56 |
| 1460 | Wall coverings, aluminum foil | 1.19 | 2.18 | 3.37 |
| 1500 | Vinyl backing | 6.35 | 2.50 | 8.85 |
| 1520 | Cork tiles, 12"x12", light or dark, 3/16" thick | 4.48 | 2.50 | 6.98 |
| 1540 | 5/16" thick | 3.75 | 2.55 | 6.30 |
| 1560 | Basketweave, 1/4" thick | 3.45 | 2.50 | 5.95 |

## C3010 Wall Finishes

| C3010 230 | Paint & Covering | COST PER S.F. | | |
|---|---|---|---|---|
| | | MAT. | INST. | TOTAL |
| 1580 | Natural, non-directional, 1/2" thick | 7.30 | 2.50 | 9.80 |
| 1600 | 12"x36", granular, 3/16" thick | 1.50 | 1.56 | 3.06 |
| 1620 | 1" thick | 1.95 | 1.62 | 3.57 |
| 1640 | 12"x12", polyurethane coated, 3/16" thick | 4.72 | 2.50 | 7.22 |
| 1660 | 5/16" thick | 6.75 | 2.55 | 9.30 |
| 1661 | Paneling, prefinished plywood, birch | 1.68 | 3.32 | 5 |
| 1662 | Mahogany, African | 2.72 | 3.49 | 6.21 |
| 1663 | Philippine (lauan) | .62 | 2.79 | 3.41 |
| 1664 | Oak or cherry | 3.54 | 3.49 | 7.03 |
| 1665 | Rosewood | 4.54 | 4.36 | 8.90 |
| 1666 | Teak | 4.82 | 3.49 | 8.31 |
| 1667 | Chestnut | 7.95 | 3.72 | 11.67 |
| 1668 | Pecan | 3.71 | 3.49 | 7.20 |
| 1669 | Walnut | 3.62 | 3.49 | 7.11 |
| 1670 | Wood board, knotty pine, finished | 3.27 | 5.75 | 9.02 |
| 1671 | Rough sawn cedar | 8.65 | 5.75 | 14.40 |
| 1672 | Redwood | 18.80 | 5.75 | 24.55 |
| 1673 | Aromatic cedar | 3.80 | 6.20 | 10 |
| 1680 | Cork wallpaper, paper backed, natural | 1.83 | 1.25 | 3.08 |
| 1700 | Color | 2.38 | 1.25 | 3.63 |
| 1720 | Gypsum based, fabric backed, minimum | 1.68 | .75 | 2.43 |
| 1740 | Average | 1.45 | .83 | 2.28 |
| 1760 | Small quantities | 1.68 | .94 | 2.62 |
| 1780 | Vinyl wall covering, fabric back, light weight | 3.18 | .94 | 4.12 |
| 1800 | Medium weight | 3.04 | 1.25 | 4.29 |
| 1820 | Heavy weight | 2.07 | 1.38 | 3.45 |
| 1840 | Wall paper, double roll, solid pattern, avg. workmanship | .30 | .94 | 1.24 |
| 1860 | Basic pattern, avg. workmanship | .37 | 1.12 | 1.49 |
| 1880 | Basic pattern, quality workmanship | 2.93 | 1.38 | 4.31 |
| 1900 | Grass cloths with lining paper, minimum | 1.40 | 1.50 | 2.90 |
| 1920 | Maximum | 3.82 | 1.71 | 5.53 |
| 1940 | Ceramic tile, thin set, 4-1/4" x 4-1/4" | 2.87 | 6.15 | 9.02 |
| 1942 | | | | |
| 1960 | 12" x 12" | 3.34 | 7.30 | 10.64 |

| C3010 235 | Paint Trim | COST PER L.F. | | |
|---|---|---|---|---|
| | | MAT. | INST. | TOTAL |
| 2040 | Painting, wood trim, to 6" wide, enamel, primer & 1 coat | .14 | .74 | .88 |
| 2060 | Primer & 2 coats | .20 | .93 | 1.13 |
| 2080 | Misc. metal brushwork, ladders | 1.66 | 7.35 | 9.01 |
| 2100 | Pipes, to 4" dia. | .11 | 1.55 | 1.66 |
| 2120 | 6" to 8" dia. | .22 | 3.10 | 3.32 |
| 2140 | 10" to 12" dia. | .89 | 4.63 | 5.52 |
| 2160 | Railings, 2" pipe | .59 | 3.68 | 4.27 |
| 2180 | Handrail, single | .30 | 1.47 | 1.77 |
| 2185 | Caulking & Sealants, Polyurethane, In place, 1 or 2 component, 1/2" X 1/4" | .50 | 2.40 | 2.90 |

## C3020 Floor Finishes

| C3020 410 | Tile & Covering | COST PER S.F. | | |
|---|---|---|---|---|
| | | MAT. | INST. | TOTAL |
| 0060 | Carpet tile, nylon, fusion bonded, 18" x 18" or 24" x 24", 24 oz. | 4 | .90 | 4.90 |
| 0080 | 35 oz. | 4.72 | .90 | 5.62 |
| 0100 | 42 oz. | 2.72 | .90 | 3.62 |
| 0140 | Carpet, tufted, nylon, roll goods, 12' wide, 26 oz. | 1.97 | .96 | 2.93 |
| 0160 | 36 oz. | 4.77 | .96 | 5.73 |
| 0180 | Woven, wool, 36 oz. | 12.20 | 1.03 | 13.23 |
| 0200 | 42 oz. | 13.45 | 1.03 | 14.48 |
| 0220 | Padding, add to above, 2.7 density | .73 | .48 | 1.21 |
| 0240 | 13.0 density | .98 | .48 | 1.46 |
| 0260 | Composition flooring, acrylic, 1/4" thick | 2.21 | 6.85 | 9.06 |
| 0280 | 3/8" thick | 2.95 | 7.90 | 10.85 |
| 0300 | Epoxy, 3/8" thick | 4.09 | 5.25 | 9.34 |
| 0320 | 1/2" thick | 5.50 | 7.25 | 12.75 |
| 0340 | Epoxy terrazzo, granite chips | 7.45 | 7.35 | 14.80 |
| 0360 | Recycled porcelain | 12.65 | 9.80 | 22.45 |
| 0380 | Mastic, hot laid, 1-1/2" thick, minimum | 5.85 | 5.15 | 11 |
| 0400 | Maximum | 7.50 | 6.85 | 14.35 |
| 0420 | Neoprene 1/4" thick, minimum | 5.80 | 6.50 | 12.30 |
| 0440 | Maximum | 6.95 | 8.25 | 15.20 |
| 0460 | Polyacrylate with ground granite 1/4", granite chips | 5.50 | 4.83 | 10.33 |
| 0480 | Recycled porcelain | 8.60 | 7.40 | 16 |
| 0500 | Polyester with colored quartz chips 1/16", minimum | 4.50 | 3.33 | 7.83 |
| 0520 | Maximum | 6.85 | 5.25 | 12.10 |
| 0540 | Polyurethane with vinyl chips, clear | 9.65 | 3.33 | 12.98 |
| 0560 | Pigmented | 13.85 | 4.13 | 17.98 |
| 0600 | Concrete topping, granolithic concrete, 1/2" thick | .45 | 5.65 | 6.10 |
| 0620 | 1" thick | .91 | 5.75 | 6.66 |
| 0640 | 2" thick | 1.82 | 6.65 | 8.47 |
| 0660 | Heavy duty 3/4" thick, minimum | .61 | 8.80 | 9.41 |
| 0680 | Maximum | .96 | 10.40 | 11.36 |
| 0700 | For colors, add to above, minimum | .70 | 2.01 | 2.71 |
| 0720 | Maximum | 1.16 | 2.22 | 3.38 |
| 0740 | Exposed aggregate finish, minimum | .25 | 1.03 | 1.28 |
| 0760 | Maximum | .42 | 1.38 | 1.80 |
| 0780 | Abrasives, .25 P.S.F. add to above, minimum | .50 | .76 | 1.26 |
| 0800 | Maximum | .79 | .76 | 1.55 |
| 0820 | Dust on coloring, add, minimum | .70 | .50 | 1.20 |
| 0840 | Maximum | 1.16 | 1.03 | 2.19 |
| 0860 | Floor coloring using 0.6 psf powdered color, 1/2" integral, minimum | 6.10 | 5.65 | 11.75 |
| 0880 | Maximum | 6.55 | 5.65 | 12.20 |
| 0900 | Dustproofing, add, minimum | .28 | .34 | .62 |
| 0920 | Maximum | 1 | .50 | 1.50 |
| 0930 | Paint | .34 | 1.76 | 2.10 |
| 0940 | Hardeners, metallic add, minimum | .86 | .76 | 1.62 |
| 0960 | Maximum | 2.58 | 1.12 | 3.70 |
| 0980 | Non-metallic, minimum | .23 | .76 | .99 |
| 1000 | Maximum | .68 | 1.12 | 1.80 |
| 1020 | Integral topping and finish, 1:1:2 mix, 3/16" thick | .15 | 3.33 | 3.48 |
| 1040 | 1/2" thick | .41 | 3.50 | 3.91 |
| 1060 | 3/4" thick | .61 | 3.92 | 4.53 |
| 1080 | 1" thick | .81 | 4.44 | 5.25 |
| 1100 | Terrazzo, minimum | 4.71 | 19.60 | 24.31 |
| 1120 | Maximum | 8.75 | 24.50 | 33.25 |
| 1340 | Cork tile, minimum | 4.09 | 2.05 | 6.14 |
| 1360 | Maximum | 7.30 | 2.05 | 9.35 |
| 1380 | Polyethylene, in rolls, minimum | 3.65 | 2.35 | 6 |
| 1400 | Maximum | 8.55 | 2.35 | 10.90 |
| 1420 | Polyurethane, thermoset, minimum | 6.75 | 6.45 | 13.20 |

## C3020 Floor Finishes

| C3020 410 | Tile & Covering | COST PER S.F. MAT. | INST. | TOTAL |
|---|---|---|---|---|
| 1440 | Maximum | 7.05 | 12.95 | 20 |
| 1460 | Rubber, sheet goods, minimum | 1.54 | 5.40 | 6.94 |
| 1480 | Maximum | 2.13 | 7.20 | 9.33 |
| 1500 | Tile, minimum | 7.45 | 1.62 | 9.07 |
| 1520 | Maximum | 4.74 | 2.35 | 7.09 |
| 1580 | Vinyl, composition tile, minimum | .90 | 1.29 | 2.19 |
| 1600 | Maximum | 1.29 | 1.29 | 2.58 |
| 1620 | Vinyl tile, 3/32″, minimum | 1.58 | 1.29 | 2.87 |
| 1640 | Maximum | 1.43 | 1.29 | 2.72 |
| 1660 | Sheet goods, plain pattern/colors | 1.40 | 2.59 | 3.99 |
| 1680 | Intricate pattern/colors | 7.90 | 3.23 | 11.13 |
| 1720 | Tile, ceramic natural clay | 3.31 | 6.35 | 9.66 |
| 1730 | Marble, synthetic 12″x12″x5/8″ | 1.10 | 19.45 | 20.55 |
| 1740 | Ceramic tile, floors, porcelain type, 1 color, color group 2, 1″ x 1″ | 8.05 | 6.35 | 14.40 |
| 1760 | Ceramic flr porcelain 1 color, color group 2 2″ x 2″ epoxy grout | 12.35 | 7.55 | 19.90 |
| 1800 | Quarry tile, mud set, minimum | 12.55 | 8.35 | 20.90 |
| 1820 | Maximum | 12.60 | 10.60 | 23.20 |
| 1840 | Thin set, deduct | | 1.67 | 1.67 |
| 1850 | Tile, natural stone, marble, in mortar bed, 12″ x 12″ x 3/8″ thick | 11.75 | 30.50 | 42.25 |
| 1860 | Terrazzo precast, minimum | 6.25 | 8.60 | 14.85 |
| 1880 | Maximum | 14.95 | 8.60 | 23.55 |
| 1900 | Non-slip, minimum | 33.50 | 21 | 54.50 |
| 1920 | Maximum | 31.50 | 28 | 59.50 |
| 1960 | Stone flooring, polished marble in mortar bed | 15.35 | 30.50 | 45.85 |
| 2020 | Wood block, end grain factory type, natural finish, 2″ thick | 6.05 | 5.60 | 11.65 |
| 2040 | Fir, vertical grain, 1″x4″, no finish, minimum | 6.90 | 2.74 | 9.64 |
| 2060 | Maximum | 6.85 | 2.74 | 9.59 |
| 2080 | Prefinished white oak, prime grade, 2-1/4″ wide | 5.80 | 4.11 | 9.91 |
| 2100 | 3-1/4″ wide | 5.05 | 3.77 | 8.82 |
| 2120 | Maple strip, sanded and finished, minimum | 6.75 | 6 | 12.75 |
| 2140 | Maximum | 10.60 | 6 | 16.60 |
| 2160 | Oak strip, sanded and finished, minimum | 5.60 | 6 | 11.60 |
| 2180 | Maximum | 6.20 | 6 | 12.20 |
| 2200 | Parquetry, sanded and finished, plain pattern | 13.40 | 6.25 | 19.65 |
| 2220 | Intricate pattern | 27 | 8.90 | 35.90 |
| 2260 | Add for sleepers on concrete, treated, 24″ O.C., 1″x2″ | 3.18 | 3.58 | 6.76 |
| 2280 | 1″x3″ | 2.10 | 2.80 | 4.90 |
| 2300 | 2″x4″ | 2.23 | 1.40 | 3.63 |
| 2340 | Underlayment, plywood, 3/8″ thick | 1.68 | .93 | 2.61 |
| 2350 | 1/2″ thick | 2.20 | .96 | 3.16 |
| 2360 | 5/8″ thick | 2.33 | 1 | 3.33 |
| 2370 | 3/4″ thick | 2.85 | 1.07 | 3.92 |
| 2380 | Particle board, 3/8″ thick | .83 | .93 | 1.76 |
| 2390 | 1/2″ thick | .86 | .96 | 1.82 |
| 2400 | 5/8″ thick | .89 | 1 | 1.89 |
| 2410 | 3/4″ thick | .91 | 1.07 | 1.98 |
| 2420 | Hardboard, 4′ x 4′, .215″ thick | 1.23 | .93 | 2.16 |
| 9200 | Vinyl, composition tile, 12″ x 12″ x 1/8″ thick, recycled content | 1.86 | 1.29 | 3.15 |

| C3020 600 | Bases, Curbs & Trim | MAT. | INST. | TOTAL |
|---|---|---|---|---|
| 0050 | 1/8″ vinyl base, 2-1/2″ H, straight or cove, std. colors | 1.34 | 2.05 | 3.39 |
| 0055 | 4″ H | 1.29 | 2.05 | 3.34 |
| 0060 | 6″ H | 3 | 2.05 | 5.05 |
| 0065 | Corners, 2-1/2″ H | 4.97 | 2.05 | 7.02 |
| 0070 | 4″ H | 5.50 | 2.05 | 7.55 |
| 0075 | 6″ H | 5.15 | 2.05 | 7.20 |

## C3020 Floor Finishes

| C3020 600 | Bases, Curbs & Trim | MAT. | INST. | TOTAL |
|---|---|---|---|---|
| 0080 | 1/8" rubber base, 2-1/2" H, straight or cove, std. colors | 1.53 | 2.05 | 3.58 |
| 0085 | 4" H | 1.07 | 2.05 | 3.12 |
| 0090 | 6" H | 3.25 | 2.05 | 5.30 |
| 0095 | Corners, 2-1/2" H | 3.70 | 2.05 | 5.75 |
| 0100 | 4" H | 4.38 | 2.05 | 6.43 |
| 0105 | 6" H | 5.10 | 2.05 | 7.15 |

## C3030 Ceiling Finishes

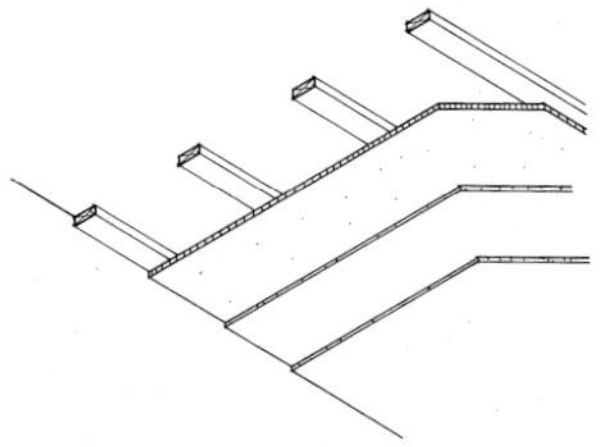

2 Coats of Plaster on Gypsum Lath on Wood Furring

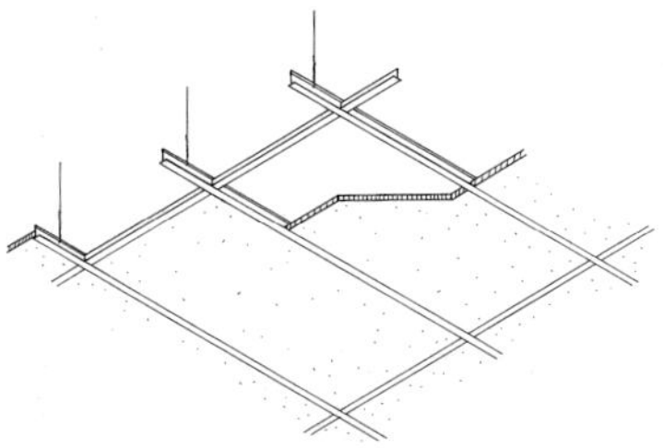

Fiberglass Board on Exposed Suspended Grid System

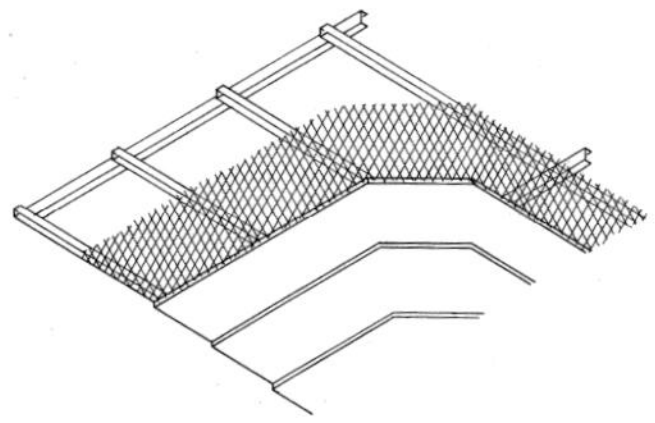

Plaster and Metal Lath on Metal Furring

### C3030 105 Plaster Ceilings

| | TYPE | LATH | FURRING | SUPPORT | | COST PER S.F. | | |
|---|---|---|---|---|---|---|---|---|
| | | | | | | MAT. | INST. | TOTAL |
| 2400 | 2 coat gypsum | 3/8" gypsum | 1"x3" wood, 16" O.C. | wood | | 1.51 | 7.15 | 8.66 |
| 2500 | Painted | | | masonry | | 1.54 | 7.30 | 8.84 |
| 2600 | | | | concrete | | 1.54 | 8.15 | 9.69 |
| 2700 | 3 coat gypsum | 3.4# metal | 1"x3" wood, 16" O.C. | wood | | 1.83 | 7.70 | 9.53 |
| 2800 | Painted | | | masonry | | 1.86 | 7.85 | 9.71 |
| 2900 | | | | concrete | | 1.86 | 8.70 | 10.56 |
| 3000 | 2 coat perlite | 3/8" gypsum | 1"x3" wood, 16" O.C. | wood | | 1.67 | 7.45 | 9.12 |
| 3100 | Painted | | | masonry | | 1.70 | 7.60 | 9.30 |
| 3200 | | | | concrete | | 1.70 | 8.45 | 10.15 |
| 3300 | 3 coat perlite | 3.4# metal | 1"x3" wood, 16" O.C. | wood | | 1.78 | 7.65 | 9.43 |
| 3400 | Painted | | | masonry | | 1.81 | 7.75 | 9.56 |
| 3500 | | | | concrete | | 1.81 | 8.65 | 10.46 |
| 3600 | 2 coat gypsum | 3/8" gypsum | 3/4" CRC, 12" O.C. | 1-1/2" CRC, 48"O.C. | | 1.65 | 8.90 | 10.55 |
| 3700 | Painted | | 3/4" CRC, 16" O.C. | 1-1/2" CRC, 48"O.C. | | 1.59 | 8 | 9.59 |
| 3800 | | | 3/4" CRC, 24" O.C. | 1-1/2" CRC, 48"O.C. | | 1.43 | 7.30 | 8.73 |
| 3900 | 2 coat perlite | 3/8" gypsum | 3/4" CRC, 12" O.C. | 1-1/2" CRC, 48"O.C | | 1.81 | 9.55 | 11.36 |
| 4000 | Painted | | 3/4" CRC, 16" O.C. | 1-1/2" CRC, 48"O.C. | | 1.75 | 8.65 | 10.40 |
| 4100 | | | 3/4" CRC, 24" O.C. | 1-1/2" CRC, 48"O.C. | | 1.59 | 7.90 | 9.49 |
| 4200 | 3 coat gypsum | 3.4# metal | 3/4" CRC, 12" O.C. | 1-1/2" CRC, 36" O.C. | | 2.38 | 11.55 | 13.93 |
| 4300 | Painted | | 3/4" CRC, 16" O.C. | 1-1/2" CRC, 36" O.C. | | 2.32 | 10.65 | 12.97 |
| 4400 | | | 3/4" CRC, 24" O.C. | 1-1/2" CRC, 36" O.C. | | 2.16 | 9.90 | 12.06 |
| 4500 | 3 coat perlite | 3.4# metal | 3/4" CRC, 12" O.C. | 1-1/2" CRC,36" O.C. | | 2.60 | 12.55 | 15.15 |
| 4600 | Painted | | 3/4" CRC, 16" O.C. | 1-1/2" CRC, 36" O.C. | | 2.54 | 11.65 | 14.19 |
| 4700 | | | 3/4" CRC, 24" O.C. | 1-1/2" CRC, 36" O.C. | | 2.38 | 10.95 | 13.33 |

### C3030 110 Drywall Ceilings

| | TYPE | FINISH | FURRING | SUPPORT | | COST PER S.F. | | |
|---|---|---|---|---|---|---|---|---|
| | | | | | | MAT. | INST. | TOTAL |
| 4800 | 1/2" F.R. drywall | painted and textured | 1"x3" wood, 16" O.C. | wood | | 1.14 | 4.39 | 5.53 |
| 4900 | | | | masonry | | 1.17 | 4.54 | 5.71 |
| 5000 | | | | concrete | | 1.17 | 5.40 | 6.57 |
| 5100 | 5/8" F.R. drywall | painted and textured | 1"x3" wood, 16" O.C. | wood | | 1.09 | 4.39 | 5.48 |
| 5200 | | | | masonry | | 1.12 | 4.54 | 5.66 |
| 5300 | | | | concrete | | 1.12 | 5.40 | 6.52 |

# C3030 Ceiling Finishes

## C3030 110 Drywall Ceilings

| | TYPE | FINISH | FURRING | SUPPORT | | COST PER S.F. MAT. | INST. | TOTAL |
|---|---|---|---|---|---|---|---|---|
| 5400 | 1/2" F.R. drywall | painted and textured | 7/8" resil. channels | 24" O.C. | | 1.16 | 4.27 | 5.43 |
| 5500 | | | 1"x2" wood | stud clips | | 1.18 | 4.14 | 5.32 |
| 5602 | | painted | 1-5/8" metal studs | 24" O.C. | | 1.50 | 3.82 | 5.32 |
| 5700 | 5/8" F.R. drywall | painted and textured | 1-5/8"metal studs | 24" O.C. | | 1.45 | 3.82 | 5.27 |
| 5702 | | | | | | | | |

## C3030 140 Plaster Ceiling Components

| | | COST PER S.F. MAT. | INST. | TOTAL |
|---|---|---|---|---|
| 0060 | Plaster, gypsum incl. finish | | | |
| 0080 | 3 coats | .72 | 4.51 | 5.23 |
| 0100 | Perlite, incl. finish, 2 coats | .66 | 4.45 | 5.11 |
| 0120 | 3 coats | .94 | 5.55 | 6.49 |
| 0140 | Thin coat on drywall | .16 | .88 | 1.04 |
| 0200 | Lath, gypsum, 3/8" thick | .47 | 1.24 | 1.71 |
| 0220 | 1/2" thick | .42 | 1.30 | 1.72 |
| 0240 | 5/8" thick | .40 | 1.52 | 1.92 |
| 0260 | Metal, diamond, 2.5 lb. | 1.08 | 1.01 | 2.09 |
| 0280 | 3.4 lb. | .58 | 1.08 | 1.66 |
| 0300 | Flat rib, 2.75 lb. | .56 | 1.01 | 1.57 |
| 0320 | 3.4 lb. | .71 | 1.08 | 1.79 |
| 0440 | Furring, steel channels, 3/4" galvanized , 12" O.C. | .55 | 3.25 | 3.80 |
| 0460 | 16" O.C. | .49 | 2.35 | 2.84 |
| 0480 | 24" O.C. | .33 | 1.62 | 1.95 |
| 0500 | 1-1/2" galvanized , 12" O.C. | .74 | 3.59 | 4.33 |
| 0520 | 16" O.C. | .66 | 2.62 | 3.28 |
| 0540 | 24" O.C. | .44 | 1.75 | 2.19 |
| 0560 | Wood strips, 1"x3", on wood, 12" O.C. | .54 | 1.99 | 2.53 |
| 0580 | 16" O.C. | .41 | 1.49 | 1.90 |
| 0600 | 24" O.C. | .27 | 1 | 1.27 |
| 0620 | On masonry, 12" O.C. | .58 | 2.18 | 2.76 |
| 0640 | 16" O.C. | .44 | 1.64 | 2.08 |
| 0660 | 24" O.C. | .29 | 1.09 | 1.38 |
| 0680 | On concrete, 12" O.C. | .58 | 3.32 | 3.90 |
| 0700 | 16" O.C. | .44 | 2.49 | 2.93 |
| 0720 | 24" O.C. | .29 | 1.66 | 1.95 |
| 0940 | Paint on plaster or drywall, roller work, primer + 1 coat | .13 | .60 | .73 |
| 0960 | Primer + 2 coats | .19 | .77 | .96 |

## C3030 210 Acoustical Ceilings

| | TYPE | TILE | GRID | SUPPORT | | COST PER S.F. MAT. | INST. | TOTAL |
|---|---|---|---|---|---|---|---|---|
| 5800 | 5/8" fiberglass board | 24" x 48" | tee | suspended | | 4.71 | 2.09 | 6.80 |
| 5900 | | 24" x 24" | tee | suspended | | 5.05 | 2.29 | 7.34 |
| 6000 | 3/4" fiberglass board | 24" x 48" | tee | suspended | | 7.35 | 2.13 | 9.48 |
| 6100 | | 24" x 24" | tee | suspended | | 7.70 | 2.33 | 10.03 |
| 6500 | 5/8" mineral fiber | 12" x 12" | 1"x3" wood, 12" O.C. | wood | | 5.35 | 4.32 | 9.67 |
| 6600 | | | | masonry | | 5.35 | 4.51 | 9.86 |
| 6700 | | | | concrete | | 5.35 | 5.65 | 11 |
| 6800 | 3/4" mineral fiber | 12" x 12" | 1"x3" wood, 12" O.C. | wood | | 5.90 | 4.32 | 10.22 |
| 6900 | | | | masonry | | 5.90 | 4.32 | 10.22 |
| 7000 | | | | concrete | | 5.90 | 4.32 | 10.22 |
| 7100 | 3/4"mineral fiber on | 12" x 12" | 25 ga. channels | runners | | 6.50 | 5.45 | 11.95 |
| 7102 | 5/8" F.R. drywall | | | | | | | |

## C3030 Ceiling Finishes

### C3030 210 Acoustical Ceilings

| | TYPE | TILE | GRID | SUPPORT | | COST PER S.F. MAT. | COST PER S.F. INST. | COST PER S.F. TOTAL |
|---|---|---|---|---|---|---|---|---|
| 7200 | 5/8" plastic coated | 12" x 12" | | adhesive backed | | 5.35 | 2.33 | 7.68 |
| 7201 | Mineral fiber | | | | | | | |
| 7202 | | | | | | | | |
| 7300 | 3/4" plastic coated | 12" x 12" | | adhesive backed | | 5.90 | 2.33 | 8.23 |
| 7301 | Mineral fiber | | | | | | | |
| 7302 | | | | | | | | |
| 7400 | 3/4" mineral fiber | 12" x 12" | conceal 2" bar & | suspended | | 3.75 | 5.25 | 9 |
| 7401 | | | channels | | | | | |
| 7402 | | | | | | | | |

### C3030 240 Acoustical Ceiling Components

| | | COST PER S.F. MAT. | COST PER S.F. INST. | COST PER S.F. TOTAL |
|---|---|---|---|---|
| 2480 | Ceiling boards, eggcrate, acrylic, 1/2" x 1/2" x 1/2" cubes | 2.37 | 1.40 | 3.77 |
| 2500 | Polystyrene, 3/8" x 3/8" x 1/2" cubes | 1.91 | 1.37 | 3.28 |
| 2520 | 1/2" x 1/2" x 1/2" cubes | 2.05 | 1.40 | 3.45 |
| 2540 | Fiberglass boards, plain, 5/8" thick | 2.96 | 1.12 | 4.08 |
| 2560 | 3/4" thick | 5.60 | 1.16 | 6.76 |
| 2580 | Grass cloth faced, 3/4" thick | 3.87 | 1.40 | 5.27 |
| 2600 | 1" thick | 8.30 | 1.44 | 9.74 |
| 2620 | Luminous panels, prismatic, acrylic | 4.09 | 1.75 | 5.84 |
| 2640 | Polystyrene | 1.95 | 1.75 | 3.70 |
| 2660 | Flat or ribbed, acrylic | 5.80 | 1.75 | 7.55 |
| 2680 | Polystyrene | 2.89 | 1.75 | 4.64 |
| 2700 | Drop pan, white, acrylic | 7.20 | 1.75 | 8.95 |
| 2720 | Polystyrene | 5.35 | 1.75 | 7.10 |
| 2740 | Mineral fiber boards, 5/8" thick, standard | 1.43 | 1.03 | 2.46 |
| 2760 | Plastic faced | 1.52 | 1.75 | 3.27 |
| 2780 | 2 hour rating | 1.25 | 1.03 | 2.28 |
| 2800 | Perforated aluminum sheets, .024 thick, corrugated painted | 3.28 | 1.42 | 4.70 |
| 2820 | Plain | 5.65 | 1.40 | 7.05 |
| 3080 | Mineral fiber, plastic coated, 12" x 12" or 12" x 24", 5/8" thick | 4.79 | 2.33 | 7.12 |
| 3100 | 3/4" thick | 5.35 | 2.33 | 7.68 |
| 3120 | Fire rated, 3/4" thick, plain faced | 2.16 | 2.33 | 4.49 |
| 3140 | Mylar faced | 1.32 | 2.33 | 3.65 |
| 3160 | Add for ceiling primer | .18 | | .18 |
| 3180 | Add for ceiling cement | .57 | | .57 |
| 3240 | Suspension system, furring, 1" x 3" wood 12" O.C. | .54 | 1.99 | 2.53 |
| 3260 | T bar suspension system, 2' x 4' grid | 1.51 | .87 | 2.38 |
| 3280 | 2' x 2' grid | 1.84 | 1.07 | 2.91 |
| 3300 | Concealed Z bar suspension system 12" module | 1.06 | 1.34 | 2.40 |
| 3320 | Add to above for 1-1/2" carrier channels 4' O.C. | .29 | 1.49 | 1.78 |
| 3340 | Add to above for carrier channels for recessed lighting | .53 | 1.52 | 2.05 |

## D1010 Elevators and Lifts

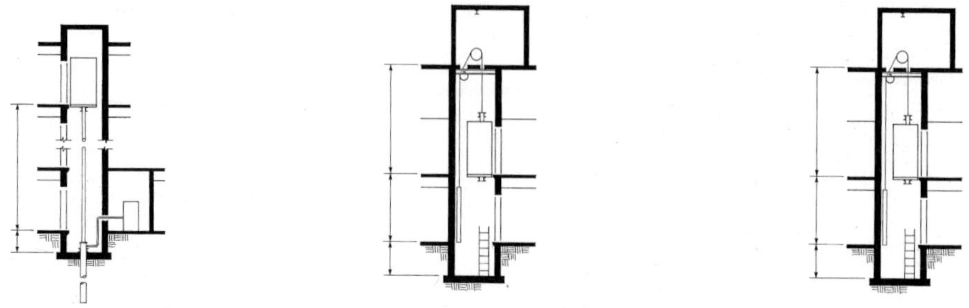

Hydraulic Traction Geared Traction Gearless

| D1010 110 | Hydraulic | COST EACH | | |
|---|---|---|---|---|
| | | MAT. | INST. | TOTAL |
| 1300 | Pass. elev., 1500 lb., 2 Floors, 100 FPM | 63,000 | 23,500 | 86,500 |
| 1400 | 5 Floors, 100 FPM | 105,500 | 62,500 | 168,000 |
| 1600 | 2000 lb., 2 Floors, 100 FPM | 64,000 | 23,500 | 87,500 |
| 1700 | 5 floors, 100 FPM | 107,000 | 62,500 | 169,500 |
| 1900 | 2500 lb., 2 Floors, 100 FPM | 67,000 | 23,500 | 90,500 |
| 2000 | 5 floors, 100 FPM | 109,500 | 62,500 | 172,000 |
| 2200 | 3000 lb., 2 Floors, 100 FPM | 68,500 | 23,500 | 92,000 |
| 2300 | 5 floors, 100 FPM | 111,500 | 62,500 | 174,000 |
| 2500 | 3500 lb., 2 Floors, 100 FPM | 72,500 | 23,500 | 96,000 |
| 2600 | 5 floors, 100 FPM | 115,500 | 62,500 | 178,000 |
| 2800 | 4000 lb., 2 Floors, 100 FPM | 74,500 | 23,500 | 98,000 |
| 2900 | 5 floors, 100 FPM | 117,000 | 62,500 | 179,500 |
| 3100 | 4500 lb., 2 Floors, 100 FPM | 78,000 | 23,500 | 101,500 |
| 3200 | 5 floors, 100 FPM | 121,000 | 62,500 | 183,500 |
| 4000 | Hospital elevators, 3500 lb., 2 Floors, 100 FPM | 108,500 | 23,500 | 132,000 |
| 4100 | 5 floors, 100 FPM | 162,500 | 62,500 | 225,000 |
| 4300 | 4000 lb., 2 Floors, 100 FPM | 108,500 | 23,500 | 132,000 |
| 4400 | 5 floors, 100 FPM | 162,500 | 62,500 | 225,000 |
| 4600 | 4500 lb., 2 Floors, 100 FPM | 118,000 | 23,500 | 141,500 |
| 4800 | 5 floors, 100 FPM | 172,000 | 62,500 | 234,500 |
| 4900 | 5000 lb., 2 Floors, 100 FPM | 122,500 | 23,500 | 146,000 |
| 5000 | 5 floors, 100 FPM | 176,500 | 62,500 | 239,000 |
| 6700 | Freight elevators (Class "B"), 3000 lb., 2 Floors, 50 FPM | 146,500 | 29,900 | 176,400 |
| 6800 | 5 floors, 100 FPM | 228,500 | 78,500 | 307,000 |
| 7000 | 4000 lb., 2 Floors, 50 FPM | 153,000 | 29,900 | 182,900 |
| 7100 | 5 floors, 100 FPM | 234,500 | 78,500 | 313,000 |
| 7500 | 10,000 lb., 2 Floors, 50 FPM | 186,500 | 29,900 | 216,400 |
| 7600 | 5 floors, 100 FPM | 268,500 | 78,500 | 347,000 |
| 8100 | 20,000 lb., 2 Floors, 50 FPM | 225,000 | 29,900 | 254,900 |
| 8200 | 5 Floors, 100 FPM | 306,500 | 78,500 | 385,000 |

| D1010 140 | Traction Geared Elevators | COST EACH | | |
|---|---|---|---|---|
| | | MAT. | INST. | TOTAL |
| 1300 | Passenger, 2000 Lb., 5 floors, 200 FPM | 154,000 | 59,000 | 213,000 |
| 1500 | 15 floors, 350 FPM | 307,500 | 178,000 | 485,500 |
| 1600 | 2500 Lb., 5 floors, 200 FPM | 159,500 | 59,000 | 218,500 |
| 1800 | 15 floors, 350 FPM | 313,000 | 178,000 | 491,000 |
| 2200 | 3500 Lb., 5 floors, 200 FPM | 161,500 | 59,000 | 220,500 |
| 2400 | 15 floors, 350 FPM | 315,000 | 178,000 | 493,000 |
| 2500 | 4000 Lb., 5 floors, 200 FPM | 163,000 | 59,000 | 222,000 |
| 2700 | 15 floors, 350 FPM | 316,500 | 178,000 | 494,500 |

# D1010 Elevators and Lifts

| D1010 140 | Traction Geared Elevators | COST EACH | | |
|---|---|---|---|---|
| | | MAT. | INST. | TOTAL |
| 2800 | 4500 Lb., 5 floors, 200 FPM | 166,500 | 59,000 | 225,500 |
| 3000 | 15 floors, 350 FPM | 320,000 | 178,000 | 498,000 |
| 3100 | 5000 Lb., 5 floors, 200 FPM | 170,000 | 59,000 | 229,000 |
| 3300 | 15 floors, 350 FPM | 323,500 | 178,000 | 501,500 |
| 4000 | Hospital, 3500 Lb., 5 floors, 200 FPM | 167,000 | 59,000 | 226,000 |
| 4200 | 15 floors, 350 FPM | 379,000 | 178,000 | 557,000 |
| 4300 | 4000 Lb., 5 floors, 200 FPM | 167,000 | 59,000 | 226,000 |
| 4500 | 15 floors, 350 FPM | 379,000 | 178,000 | 557,000 |
| 4600 | 4500 Lb., 5 floors, 200 FPM | 174,500 | 59,000 | 233,500 |
| 4800 | 15 floors, 350 FPM | 386,500 | 178,000 | 564,500 |
| 4900 | 5000 Lb., 5 floors, 200 FPM | 177,000 | 59,000 | 236,000 |
| 5100 | 15 floors, 350 FPM | 389,000 | 178,000 | 567,000 |
| 6000 | Freight, 4000 Lb., 5 floors, 50 FPM class 'B' | 188,000 | 61,000 | 249,000 |
| 6200 | 15 floors, 200 FPM class 'B' | 421,500 | 212,000 | 633,500 |
| 6500 | 15 floors, 200 FPM class 'B' | 455,000 | 212,000 | 667,000 |
| 7000 | 10,000 Lb., 5 floors, 50 FPM class 'B' | 259,000 | 61,000 | 320,000 |
| 7200 | 15 floors, 200 FPM class 'B' | 741,500 | 212,000 | 953,500 |
| 8000 | 20,000 Lb., 5 floors, 50 FPM class 'B' | 292,000 | 61,000 | 353,000 |
| 8200 | 15 floors, 200 FPM class 'B' | 774,000 | 212,000 | 986,000 |

| D1010 150 | Traction Gearless Elevators | COST EACH | | |
|---|---|---|---|---|
| | | MAT. | INST. | TOTAL |
| 1700 | Passenger, 2500 Lb., 10 floors, 200 FPM | 330,000 | 153,500 | 483,500 |
| 1900 | 30 floors, 600 FPM | 682,500 | 391,500 | 1,074,000 |
| 2000 | 3000 Lb., 10 floors, 200 FPM | 330,500 | 153,500 | 484,000 |
| 2200 | 30 floors, 600 FPM | 683,000 | 391,500 | 1,074,500 |
| 2300 | 3500 Lb., 10 floors, 200 FPM | 332,500 | 153,500 | 486,000 |
| 2500 | 30 floors, 600 FPM | 685,000 | 391,500 | 1,076,500 |
| 2700 | 50 floors, 800 FPM | 984,500 | 630,000 | 1,614,500 |
| 2800 | 4000 Lb., 10 floors, 200 FPM | 333,500 | 153,500 | 487,000 |
| 3000 | 30 floors, 600 FPM | 686,000 | 391,500 | 1,077,500 |
| 3200 | 50 floors, 800 FPM | 985,500 | 630,000 | 1,615,500 |
| 3300 | 4500 Lb., 10 floors, 200 FPM | 337,000 | 153,500 | 490,500 |
| 3500 | 30 floors, 600 FPM | 689,500 | 391,500 | 1,081,000 |
| 3700 | 50 floors, 800 FPM | 989,000 | 630,000 | 1,619,000 |
| 3800 | 5000 Lb., 10 floors, 200 FPM | 341,000 | 153,500 | 494,500 |
| 4000 | 30 floors, 600 FPM | 693,500 | 391,500 | 1,085,000 |
| 4200 | 50 floors, 800 FPM | 993,000 | 630,000 | 1,623,000 |
| 6000 | Hospital, 3500 Lb., 10 floors, 200 FPM | 366,500 | 153,500 | 520,000 |
| 6200 | 30 floors, 600 FPM | 841,000 | 391,500 | 1,232,500 |
| 6400 | 4000 Lb., 10 floors, 200 FPM | 366,500 | 153,500 | 520,000 |
| 6600 | 30 floors, 600 FPM | 841,000 | 391,500 | 1,232,500 |
| 6800 | 4500 Lb., 10 floors, 200 FPM | 374,500 | 153,500 | 528,000 |
| 7000 | 30 floors, 600 FPM | 849,000 | 391,500 | 1,240,500 |
| 7200 | 5000 Lb., 10 floors, 200 FPM | 376,500 | 153,500 | 530,000 |
| 7400 | 30 floors, 600 FPM | 851,000 | 391,500 | 1,242,500 |

## Minimum Plumbing Fixture Requirements

| Classification | Occupancy | Description | Water |  | Lavatories |  | Bathtubs/Showers | Drinking Fountains | Other |
|---|---|---|---|---|---|---|---|---|---|
|  |  |  | Male | Female | Male | Female |  |  |  |
| Assembly | A-1 | Theaters and other buildings for the performing arts and motion pictures | 1:125 | 1:65 | 1:200 |  |  | 1:500 | 1 Service Sink |
|  | A-2 | Nightclubs, bars, taverns dance halls | 1:40 |  | 1:75 |  |  | 1:500 | 1 Service Sink |
|  |  | Restaurants, banquet halls, food courts | 1:75 |  | 1:200 |  |  | 1:500 | 1 Service Sink |
|  | A-3 | Auditorium w/o permanent seating, art galleries, exhibition halls, museums, lecture halls, libraries, arcades & gymnasiums | 1:125 | 1:65 | 1:200 |  |  | 1:500 | 1 Service Sink |
|  |  | Passenger terminals and transportation facilities | 1:500 |  | 1:750 |  |  | 1:1000 | 1 Service Sink |
|  |  | Places of worship and other religious services | 1:150 | 1:75 | 1:200 |  |  | 1:1000 | 1 Service Sink |
|  | A-4 | Indoor sporting events and activities, coliseums, arenas, skating rinks, pools, and tennis courts | 1:75 for the first 1500, then 1:120 for the remainder | 1:40 for the first 1520, then 1:60 for the remainder | 1:200 | 1:150 |  | 1:1000 | 1 Service Sink |
|  | A-5 | Outdoor sporting events and activities, stadiums, amusement parks, bleachers, grandstands | 1:75 for the first 1500, then 1:120 for the remainder | 1:40 for the first 1520, then 1:60 for the remainder | 1:200 | 1:150 |  | 1:1000 | 1 Service Sink |
| Business | B | Buildings for the transaction of business, professional services, other services involving merchandise, office buildings, banks, light industrial | 1:25 for the first 50, then 1:50 for the remainder |  | 1:40 for the first 80, then 1:80 for the remainder |  |  | 1:100 | 1 Service Sink |
| Educational | E | Educational Facilities | 1:50 |  | 1:50 |  |  | 1:100 | 1 Service Sink |
| Factory and industrial | F-1 and F-2 | Structures in which occupants are engaged in work fabricating, assembly or processing of products or materials | 1:100 |  | 1:100 |  | See *International Plumbing Code* | 1:400 | 1 Service Sink |
| Institutional | I-1 | Residential Care | 1:10 |  | 1:10 |  | 1:8 | 1:100 | 1 Service Sink |
|  | I-2 | Hospitals, ambulatory nursing home care recipient | 1 per room |  | 1 per room |  | 1:15 | 1:100 | 1 Service Sink |
|  |  | Employees, other than residential care | 1:25 |  | 1:35 |  |  | 1:100 |  |
|  |  | Visitors, other than residential care | 1:75 |  | 1:100 |  |  | 1:500 |  |
|  | I-3 | Prisons | 1 per cell |  | 1 per cell |  | 1:15 | 1:100 | 1 Service Sink |
|  |  | Reformatories, detention and correction centers | 1:15 |  | 1:15 |  | 1:15 | 1:100 | 1 Service Sink |
|  |  | Employees | 1:25 |  | 1:35 |  |  | 1:100 |  |
|  | I-4 | Adult and child day care | 1:15 |  | 1:15 |  | 1 | 1:100 | 1 Service Sink |
| Mercantile | M | Retail stores, service stations, shops, salesrooms, markets and shopping centers | 1:500 |  | 1:750 |  |  | 1:1000 | 1 Service Sink |
| Residential | R-1 | Hotels, Motels, boarding houses (transient) | 1 per sleeping unit |  | 1 per sleeping unit |  | 1 per sleeping unit |  | 1 Service Sink |
|  | R-2 | Dormitories, fraternities, sororities and boarding houses (not transient) | 1:10 |  | 1:10 |  | 1:8 | 1:100 | 1 Service Sink |
|  |  | Apartment House | 1 per dwelling unit |  | 1 per dwelling unit |  | 1 per dwelling unit |  | 1 Kitchen sink per dwelling; 1 clothes washer connection per 20 dwellings |
|  | R-3 | 1 and 2 Family Dwellings | 1 per dwelling unit |  | 1:10 |  | 1 per dwelling unit |  | 1 Kitchen sink per dwelling; 1 clothes washer connection per dwelling |
|  | R-3 | Congregate living facilities w/<16 people | 1:10 |  | 1:10 |  | 1:8 | 1:100 | 1 Service Sink |
|  | R-4 | Congregate living facilities w/<16 people | 1:10 |  | 1:10 |  | 1:8 | 1:100 | 1 Service Sink |
| Storage | S-1 and S-2 | Structures for the storage of good, warehouses, storehouses and freight depots, low and moderate hazard | 1:100 |  | 1:100 |  | See *International Plumbing Code* | 1;1000 | 1 Service Sink |

Table 2902.1

Excerpted from the 2012 *International Building Code*, Copyright 2011. Washington, D.C.: International Code Council. Reproduced with permission.

# D20 Plumbing

## D2010 Plumbing Fixtures

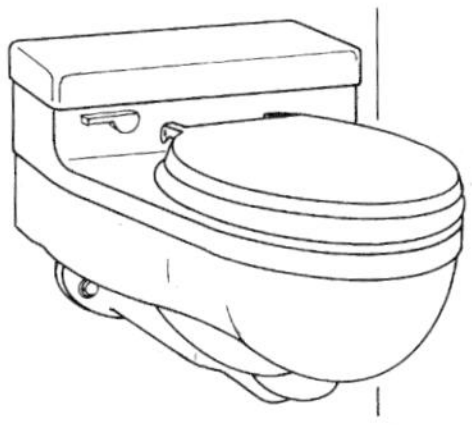

One Piece Wall Hung Water Closet

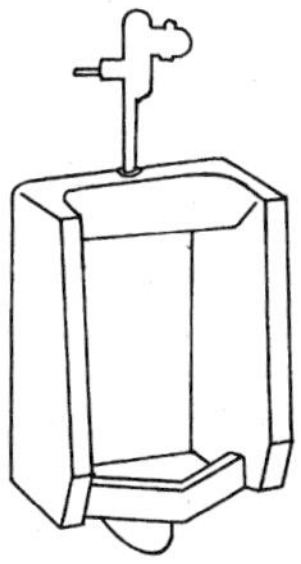

Wall Hung Urinal

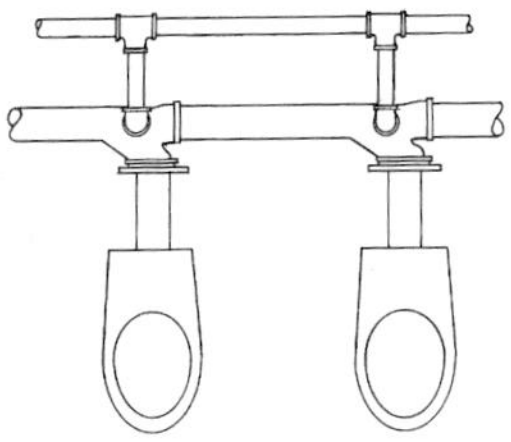

Side By Side Water Closet Group

Floor Mount Water Closet

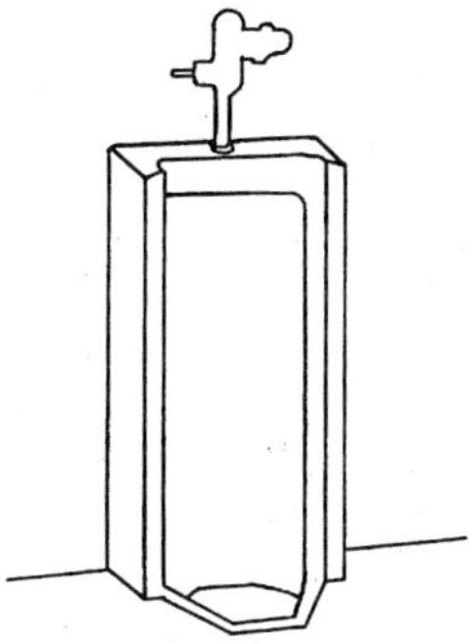

Stall Type Urinal

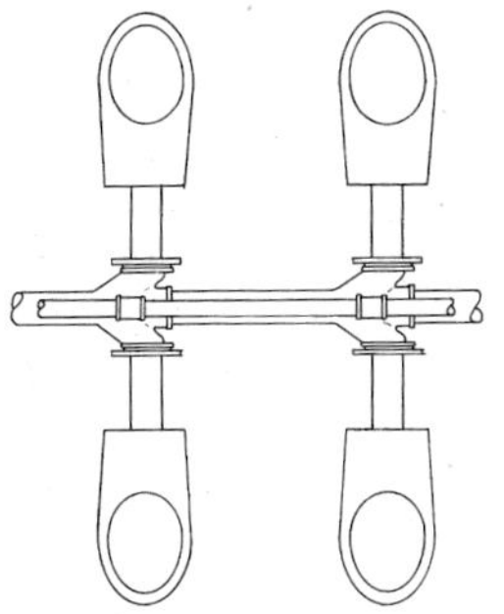

Back to Back Water Closet Group

| D2010 110 | Water Closet Systems | COST EACH | | |
|---|---|---|---|---|
| | | MAT. | INST. | TOTAL |
| 1800 | Water closet, vitreous china | | | |
| 1840 | Tank type, wall hung | | | |
| 1880 | Close coupled two piece | 2,325 | 910 | 3,235 |
| 1920 | Floor mount, one piece | 1,675 | 970 | 2,645 |
| 1960 | One piece low profile | 1,650 | 970 | 2,620 |
| 2000 | Two piece close coupled | 935 | 970 | 1,905 |
| 2040 | Bowl only with flush valve | | | |
| 2080 | Wall hung | 3,150 | 1,025 | 4,175 |
| 2120 | Floor mount | 1,125 | 985 | 2,110 |
| 2122 | | | | |
| 2160 | Floor mount, ADA compliant with 18" high bowl | 1,150 | 1,000 | 2,150 |

| D2010 120 | Water Closets, Group | COST EACH | | |
|---|---|---|---|---|
| | | MAT. | INST. | TOTAL |
| 1760 | Water closets, battery mount, wall hung, side by side, first closet | 3,350 | 1,075 | 4,425 |
| 1800 | Each additional water closet, add | 3,175 | 1,000 | 4,175 |
| 3000 | Back to back, first pair of closets | 5,925 | 1,425 | 7,350 |
| 3100 | Each additional pair of closets, back to back | 5,750 | 1,400 | 7,150 |
| 9000 | Back to back, first pair of closets, auto sensor flush valve, 1.28 gpf | 6,425 | 1,525 | 7,950 |
| 9100 | Ea additional pair of cls, back to back, auto sensor flush valve, 1.28 gpf | 6,175 | 1,425 | 7,600 |

| D2010 210 | Urinal Systems | COST EACH | | |
|---|---|---|---|---|
| | | MAT. | INST. | TOTAL |
| 2000 | Urinal, vitreous china, wall hung | 835 | 1,025 | 1,860 |
| 2001 | Urinal, vitreous china, wall hung | 835 | 1,025 | 1,860 |
| 2040 | Stall type | 2,075 | 1,225 | 3,300 |

## D2010 Plumbing Fixtures

Systems are complete with trim and rough-in (supply, waste and vent) to connect to supply branches and waste mains.

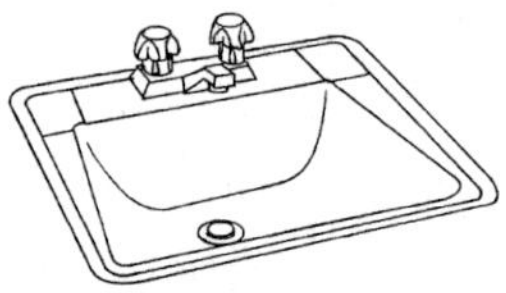

Vanity Top

Wall Hung

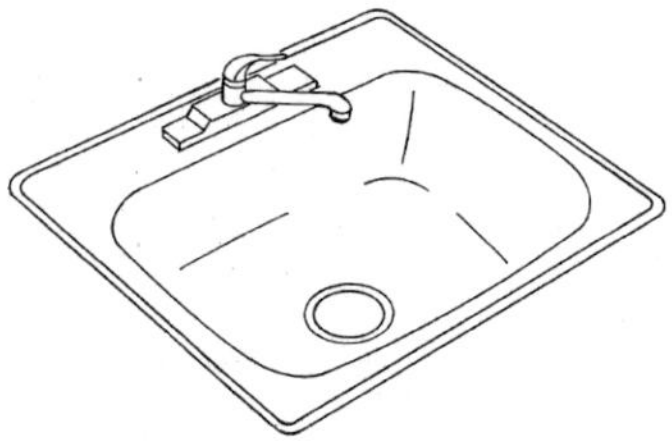

Counter Top Single Bowl

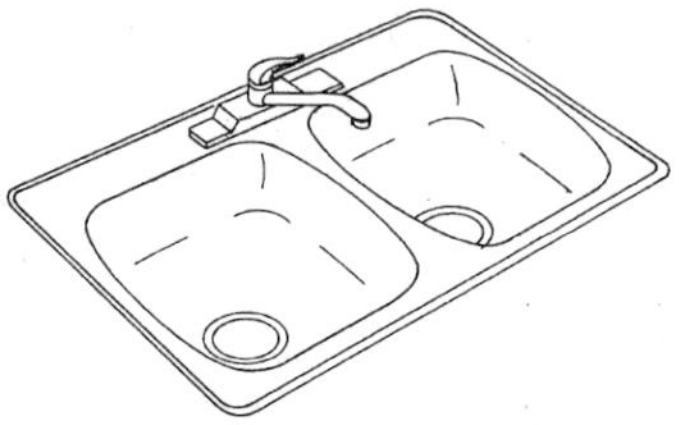

Counter Top Double Bowl

| D2010 310 | Lavatory Systems | COST EACH | | |
|---|---|---|---|---|
| | | MAT. | INST. | TOTAL |
| 1560 | Lavatory w/trim, vanity top, PE on CI, 20″ x 18″, Vanity top by others. | 1,250 | 915 | 2,165 |
| 1600 | 19″ x 16″ oval | 970 | 915 | 1,885 |
| 1640 | 18″ round | 1,600 | 915 | 2,515 |
| 1680 | Cultured marble, 19″ x 17″ | 965 | 915 | 1,880 |
| 1720 | 25″ x 19″ | 1,025 | 915 | 1,940 |
| 1760 | Stainless, self-rimming, 25″ x 22″ | 1,400 | 915 | 2,315 |
| 1800 | 17″ x 22″ | 1,375 | 915 | 2,290 |
| 1840 | Steel enameled, 20″ x 17″ | 1,000 | 940 | 1,940 |
| 1880 | 19″ round | 1,000 | 940 | 1,940 |
| 1920 | Vitreous china, 20″ x 16″ | 1,075 | 960 | 2,035 |
| 1960 | 19″ x 16″ | 1,075 | 960 | 2,035 |
| 2000 | 22″ x 13″ | 1,075 | 960 | 2,035 |
| 2040 | Wall hung, PE on CI, 18″ x 15″ | 1,100 | 1,000 | 2,100 |
| 2080 | 19″ x 17″ | 1,225 | 1,000 | 2,225 |
| 2120 | 20″ x 18″ | 1,050 | 1,000 | 2,050 |
| 2160 | Vitreous china, 18″ x 15″ | 920 | 1,025 | 1,945 |
| 2200 | 19″ x 17″ | 900 | 1,025 | 1,925 |
| 2240 | 24″ x 20″ | 1,025 | 1,025 | 2,050 |
| 2300 | 20″ x 27″, handicap | 1,450 | 1,125 | 2,575 |

| D2010 410 | Kitchen Sink Systems | COST EACH | | |
|---|---|---|---|---|
| | | MAT. | INST. | TOTAL |
| 1720 | Kitchen sink w/trim, countertop, PE on CI, 24″x21″, single bowl | 1,625 | 1,000 | 2,625 |
| 1760 | 30″ x 21″ single bowl | 2,175 | 1,000 | 3,175 |
| 1800 | 32″ x 21″ double bowl | 1,225 | 1,075 | 2,300 |
| 1880 | Stainless steel, 19″ x 18″ single bowl | 1,475 | 1,000 | 2,475 |
| 1920 | 25″ x 22″ single bowl | 1,550 | 1,000 | 2,550 |
| 1960 | 33″ x 22″ double bowl | 1,950 | 1,075 | 3,025 |
| 2000 | 43″ x 22″ double bowl | 2,175 | 1,100 | 3,275 |
| 2040 | 44″ x 22″ triple bowl | 2,050 | 1,150 | 3,200 |
| 2080 | 44″ x 24″ corner double bowl | 1,700 | 1,100 | 2,800 |
| 2120 | Steel, enameled, 24″ x 21″ single bowl | 1,300 | 1,000 | 2,300 |
| 2160 | 32″ x 21″ double bowl | 1,325 | 1,075 | 2,400 |
| 2240 | Raised deck, PE on CI, 32″ x 21″, dual level, double bowl | 1,350 | 1,375 | 2,725 |
| 2280 | 42″ x 21″ dual level, triple bowl | 1,950 | 1,500 | 3,450 |

## D2010 Plumbing Fixtures

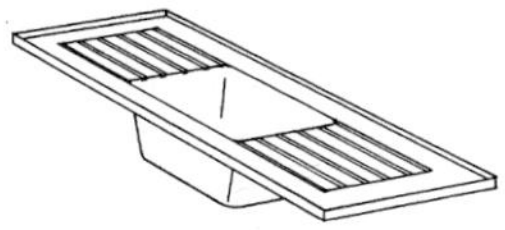

Laboratory Sink

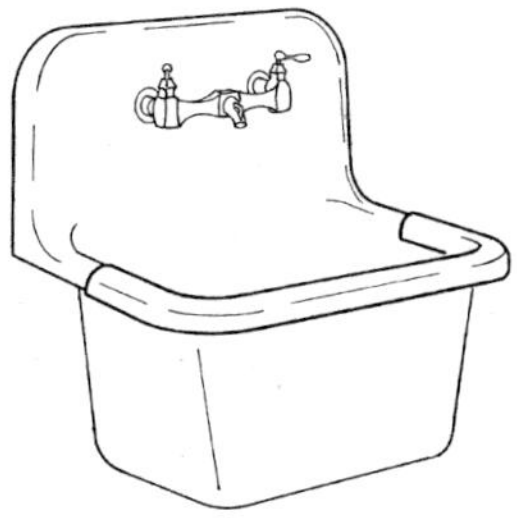

Service Sink

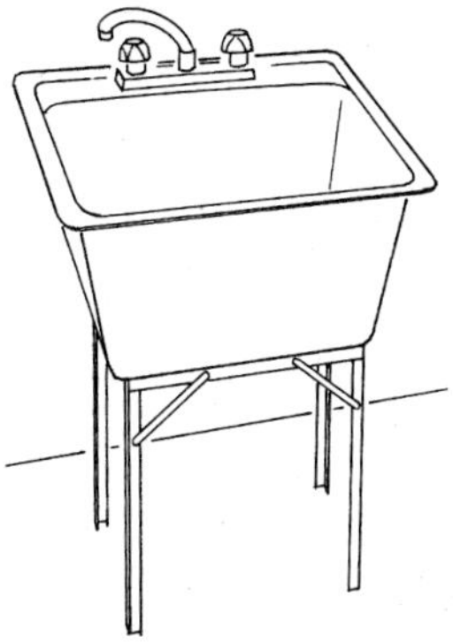

Single Compartment Sink

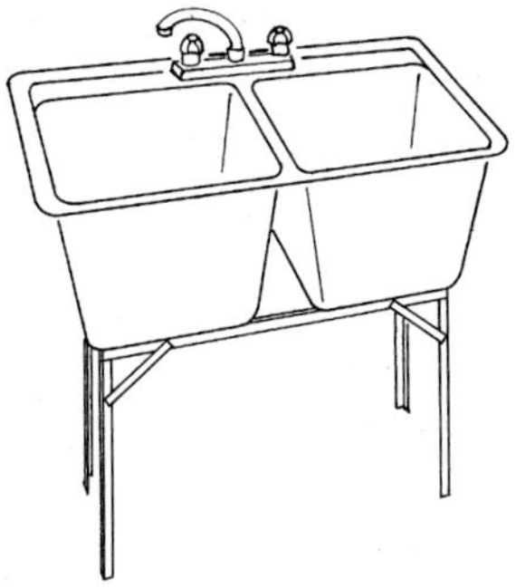

Double Compartment Sink

Systems are complete with trim and rough-in (supply, waste and vent) to connect to supply branches and waste mains.

| D2010 420 | Laundry Sink Systems | COST EACH | | |
|---|---|---|---|---|
| | | MAT. | INST. | TOTAL |
| 1740 | Laundry sink w/trim, PE on CI, black iron frame | | | |
| 1760 | 24" x 20", single compartment | 1,450 | 985 | 2,435 |
| 1840 | 48" x 21" double compartment | 1,700 | 1,075 | 2,775 |
| 1920 | Molded stone, on wall, 22" x 21" single compartment | 935 | 985 | 1,920 |
| 1960 | 45"x 21" double compartment | 1,175 | 1,075 | 2,250 |
| 2040 | Plastic, on wall or legs, 18" x 23" single compartment | 895 | 965 | 1,860 |
| 2080 | 20" x 24" single compartment | 920 | 965 | 1,885 |
| 2120 | 36" x 23" double compartment | 1,000 | 1,025 | 2,025 |
| 2160 | 40" x 24" double compartment | 1,075 | 1,025 | 2,100 |

| D2010 430 | Laboratory Sink Systems | COST EACH | | |
|---|---|---|---|---|
| | | MAT. | INST. | TOTAL |
| 1580 | Laboratory sink w/trim, | | | |
| 1590 | Stainless steel, single bowl, | | | |
| 1600 | Double drainboard, 54" x 24" O.D. | 2,100 | 1,275 | 3,375 |
| 1640 | Single drainboard, 47" x 24"O.D. | 1,675 | 1,275 | 2,950 |
| 1670 | Stainless steel, double bowl, | | | |
| 1680 | 70" x 24" O.D. | 2,275 | 1,275 | 3,550 |
| 1750 | Polyethylene, single bowl, | | | |
| 1760 | Flanged, 14-1/2" x 14-1/2" O.D. | 825 | 1,150 | 1,975 |
| 1800 | 18-1/2" x 18-1/2" O.D. | 960 | 1,150 | 2,110 |
| 1840 | 23-1/2" x 20-1/2" O.D. | 970 | 1,150 | 2,120 |
| 1920 | Polypropylene, cup sink, oval, 7" x 4" O.D. | 745 | 1,025 | 1,770 |
| 1960 | 10" x 4-1/2" O.D. | 785 | 1,025 | 1,810 |
| 1961 | | | | |

| D2010 440 | Service Sink Systems | COST EACH | | |
|---|---|---|---|---|
| | | MAT. | INST. | TOTAL |
| 4260 | Service sink w/trim, PE on CI, corner floor, 28" x 28", w/rim guard | 4,450 | 1,300 | 5,750 |
| 4300 | Wall hung w/rim guard, 22" x 18" | 5,275 | 1,500 | 6,775 |
| 4340 | 24" x 20" | 5,825 | 1,500 | 7,325 |
| 4380 | Vitreous china, wall hung 22" x 20" | 5,300 | 1,500 | 6,800 |
| 4383 | | | | |

# D2010 Plumbing Fixtures

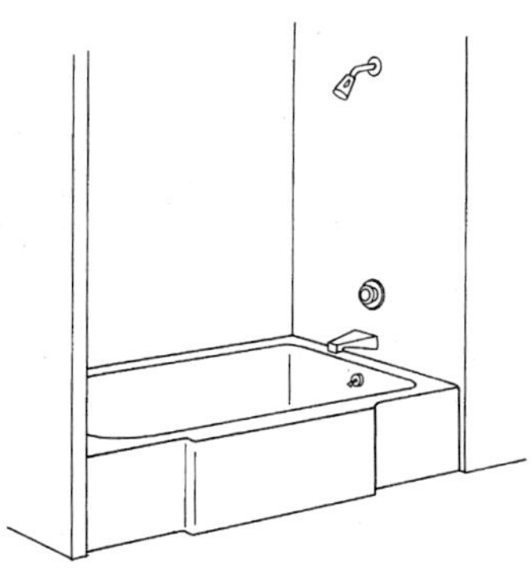

Recessed Bathtub

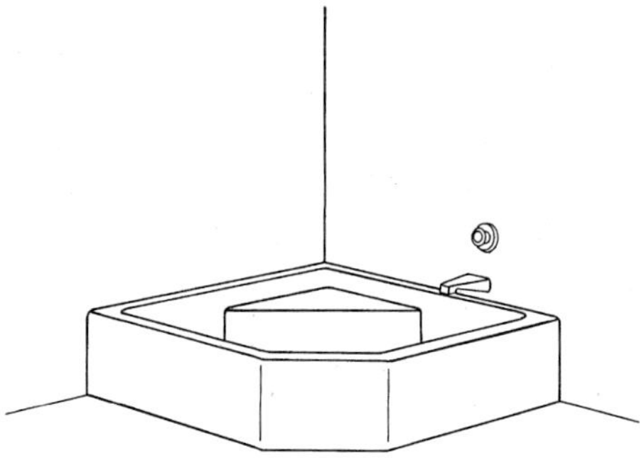

Corner Bathtub

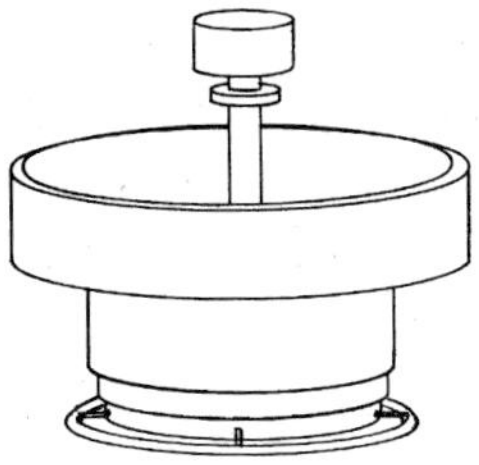

Circular Wash Fountain

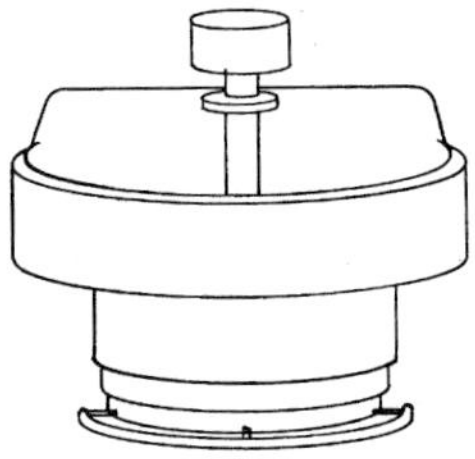

Semi-Circular Wash Fountain

Systems are complete with trim and rough-in (supply, waste and vent) to connect to supply branches and waste mains.

| D2010 510 | Bathtub Systems | COST EACH | | |
|---|---|---|---|---|
| | | MAT. | INST. | TOTAL |
| 2000 | Bathtub, recessed, P.E. on CI., 48″ x 42″ | 5,025 | 1,125 | 6,150 |
| 2040 | 72″ x 36″ | 4,925 | 1,250 | 6,175 |
| 2080 | Mat bottom, 5′ long | 2,950 | 1,100 | 4,050 |
| 2120 | 5′-6″ long | 3,325 | 1,125 | 4,450 |
| 2160 | Corner, 48″ x 42″ | 4,675 | 1,100 | 5,775 |
| 2200 | Formed steel, enameled, 4′-6″ long | 1,825 | 1,025 | 2,850 |

| D2010 610 | Group Wash Fountain Systems | COST EACH | | |
|---|---|---|---|---|
| | | MAT. | INST. | TOTAL |
| 1740 | Group wash fountain, precast terrazzo | | | |
| 1760 | Circular, 36″ diameter | 9,600 | 1,650 | 11,250 |
| 1800 | 54″ diameter | 13,500 | 1,825 | 15,325 |
| 1840 | Semi-circular, 36″ diameter | 8,025 | 1,650 | 9,675 |
| 1880 | 54″ diameter | 13,900 | 1,825 | 15,725 |
| 1960 | Stainless steel, circular, 36″ diameter | 8,575 | 1,550 | 10,125 |
| 2000 | 54″ diameter | 10,500 | 1,700 | 12,200 |
| 2040 | Semi-circular, 36″ diameter | 7,200 | 1,550 | 8,750 |
| 2080 | 54″ diameter | 7,625 | 1,700 | 9,325 |
| 2160 | Thermoplastic, circular, 36″ diameter | 6,275 | 1,250 | 7,525 |
| 2200 | 54″ diameter | 6,050 | 1,450 | 7,500 |
| 2240 | Semi-circular, 36″ diameter | 6,700 | 1,250 | 7,950 |
| 2280 | 54″ diameter | 6,775 | 1,450 | 8,225 |

## D2010 Plumbing Fixtures

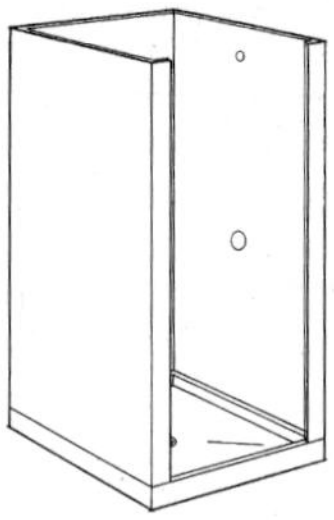

Square Shower Stall

Corner Angle Shower Stall

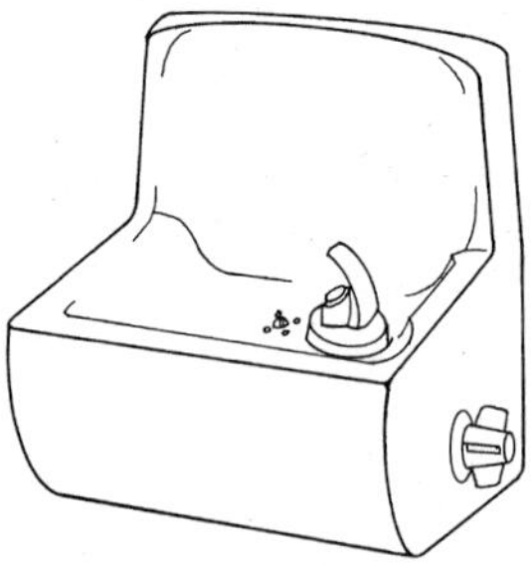

Wall Mounted, Low Back

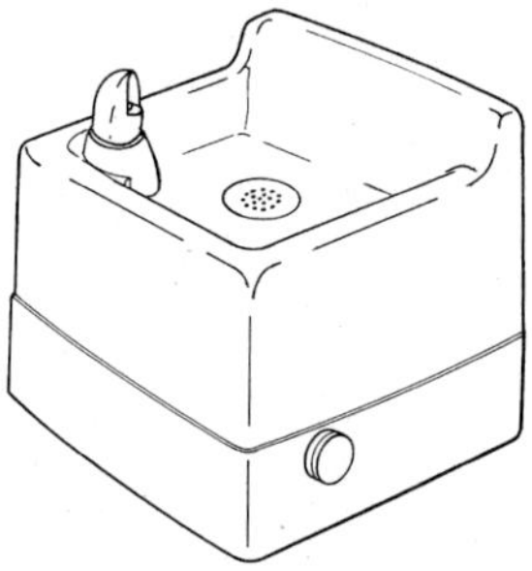

Wall Mounted, No Back

Systems are complete with trim and rough-in (supply, waste and vent) to connect to supply branches and waste mains.

| D2010 710 | Shower Systems | COST EACH | | |
|---|---|---|---|---|
| | | MAT. | INST. | TOTAL |
| 1560 | Shower, stall, baked enamel, molded stone receptor, 30" square | 2,350 | 1,050 | 3,400 |
| 1600 | 32" square | 2,100 | 1,075 | 3,175 |
| 1640 | Terrazzo receptor, 32" square | 2,325 | 1,075 | 3,400 |
| 1680 | 36" square | 2,825 | 1,075 | 3,900 |
| 1720 | 36" corner angle | 3,075 | 445 | 3,520 |
| 1800 | Fiberglass one piece, three walls, 32" square | 1,250 | 1,025 | 2,275 |
| 1840 | 36" square | 1,300 | 1,025 | 2,325 |
| 1880 | Polypropylene, molded stone receptor, 30" square | 1,650 | 1,525 | 3,175 |
| 1920 | 32" square | 1,650 | 1,525 | 3,175 |
| 1960 | Built-in head, arm, bypass, stops and handles | 148 | 395 | 543 |
| 2050 | Shower, stainless steel panels, handicap | | | |
| 2100 | w/fixed and handheld head, control valves, grab bar, and seat | 6,825 | 4,750 | 11,575 |
| 2500 | Shower, group with six heads, thermostatic mix valves & balancing valve | 14,100 | 1,150 | 15,250 |
| 2520 | Five heads | 10,100 | 1,050 | 11,150 |

| D2010 810 | Drinking Fountain Systems | COST EACH | | |
|---|---|---|---|---|
| | | MAT. | INST. | TOTAL |
| 1740 | Drinking fountain, one bubbler, wall mounted | | | |
| 1760 | Non recessed | | | |
| 1800 | Bronze, no back | 2,350 | 605 | 2,955 |
| 1840 | Cast iron, enameled, low back | 2,500 | 605 | 3,105 |
| 1880 | Fiberglass, 12" back | 4,250 | 605 | 4,855 |
| 1920 | Stainless steel, no back | 1,750 | 605 | 2,355 |
| 1960 | Semi-recessed, poly marble | 2,075 | 605 | 2,680 |
| 2040 | Stainless steel | 2,775 | 605 | 3,380 |
| 2080 | Vitreous china | 2,250 | 605 | 2,855 |
| 2120 | Full recessed, poly marble | 3,275 | 605 | 3,880 |
| 2200 | Stainless steel | 2,650 | 605 | 3,255 |
| 2240 | Floor mounted, pedestal type, aluminum | 4,150 | 820 | 4,970 |
| 2320 | Bronze | 4,825 | 820 | 5,645 |
| 2360 | Stainless steel | 3,600 | 820 | 4,420 |

## D2010 Plumbing Fixtures

Wall Hung Water Cooler

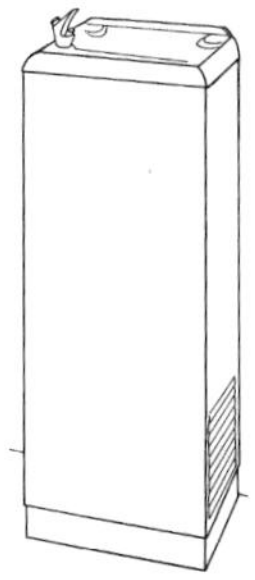

Floor Mounted Water Cooler

Systems are complete with trim and rough-in (supply, waste and vent) to connect to supply branches and waste mains.

| D2010 820 | Water Cooler Systems | COST EACH | | |
|---|---|---|---|---|
| | | MAT. | INST. | TOTAL |
| 1840 | Water cooler, electric, wall hung, 8.2 G.P.H. | 2,025 | 775 | 2,800 |
| 1880 | Dual height, 14.3 G.P.H. | 3,675 | 795 | 4,470 |
| 1920 | Wheelchair type, 7.5 G.P.H. | 2,075 | 775 | 2,850 |
| 1960 | Semi recessed, 8.1 G.P.H. | 1,925 | 775 | 2,700 |
| 2000 | Full recessed, 8 G.P.H. | 3,700 | 830 | 4,530 |
| 2040 | Floor mounted, 14.3 G.P.H. | 2,125 | 675 | 2,800 |
| 2080 | Dual height, 14.3 G.P.H. | 2,525 | 820 | 3,345 |
| 2120 | Refrigerated compartment type, 1.5 G.P.H. | 2,950 | 675 | 3,625 |

## D2010 Plumbing Fixtures

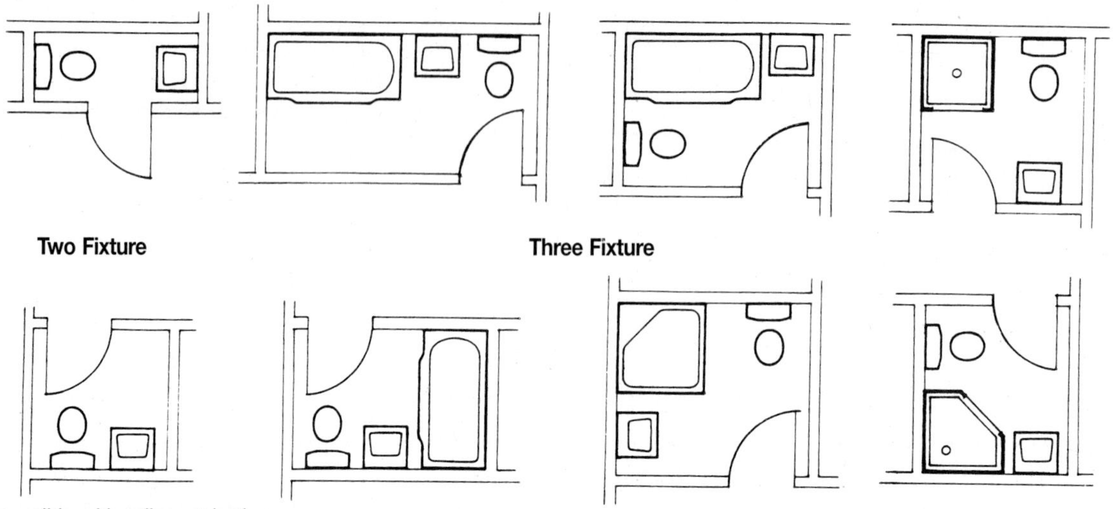


*Common wall is with adjacent bathroom

### D2010 920 Two Fixture Bathroom, Two Wall Plumbing

| | | COST EACH | | |
|---|---|---|---|---|
| | | MAT. | INST. | TOTAL |
| 1180 | Bathroom, lavatory & water closet, 2 wall plumbing, stand alone | 2,400 | 2,500 | 4,900 |
| 1200 | Share common plumbing wall* | 2,100 | 2,175 | 4,275 |

### D2010 922 Two Fixture Bathroom, One Wall Plumbing

| | | COST EACH | | |
|---|---|---|---|---|
| | | MAT. | INST. | TOTAL |
| 2220 | Bathroom, lavatory & water closet, one wall plumbing, stand alone | 2,200 | 2,250 | 4,450 |
| 2240 | Share common plumbing wall* | 1,925 | 1,925 | 3,850 |

### D2010 924 Three Fixture Bathroom, One Wall Plumbing

| | | COST EACH | | |
|---|---|---|---|---|
| | | MAT. | INST. | TOTAL |
| 1150 | Bathroom, three fixture, one wall plumbing | | | |
| 1160 | Lavatory, water closet & bathtub | | | |
| 1170 | Stand alone | 4,550 | 3,025 | 7,575 |
| 1180 | Share common plumbing wall * | 3,875 | 2,125 | 6,000 |

### D2010 926 Three Fixture Bathroom, Two Wall Plumbing

| | | COST EACH | | |
|---|---|---|---|---|
| | | MAT. | INST. | TOTAL |
| 2130 | Bathroom, three fixture, two wall plumbing | | | |
| 2140 | Lavatory, water closet & bathtub | | | |
| 2160 | Stand alone | 4,525 | 2,975 | 7,500 |
| 2180 | Long plumbing wall common * | 4,075 | 2,375 | 6,450 |
| 3610 | Lavatory, bathtub & water closet | | | |
| 3620 | Stand alone | 4,925 | 3,400 | 8,325 |
| 3640 | Long plumbing wall common * | 4,600 | 3,075 | 7,675 |
| 4660 | Water closet, corner bathtub & lavatory | | | |
| 4680 | Stand alone | 6,275 | 3,025 | 9,300 |
| 4700 | Long plumbing wall common * | 5,425 | 2,275 | 7,700 |
| 6100 | Water closet, stall shower & lavatory | | | |
| 6120 | Stand alone | 4,425 | 3,375 | 7,800 |
| 6140 | Long plumbing wall common * | 4,225 | 3,125 | 7,350 |
| 7060 | Lavatory, corner stall shower & water closet | | | |
| 7080 | Stand alone | 5,375 | 3,000 | 8,375 |
| 7100 | Short plumbing wall common * | 4,375 | 2,000 | 6,375 |

## D2010 Plumbing Fixtures

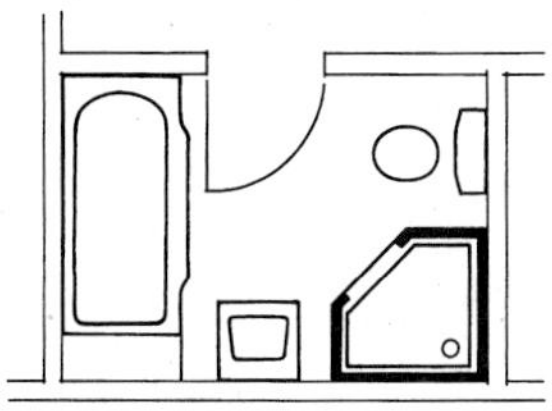

Four Fixture Bathroom Systems consisting of a lavatory, water closet, bathtub, shower and rough-in service piping.

- Prices for plumbing and fixtures only.

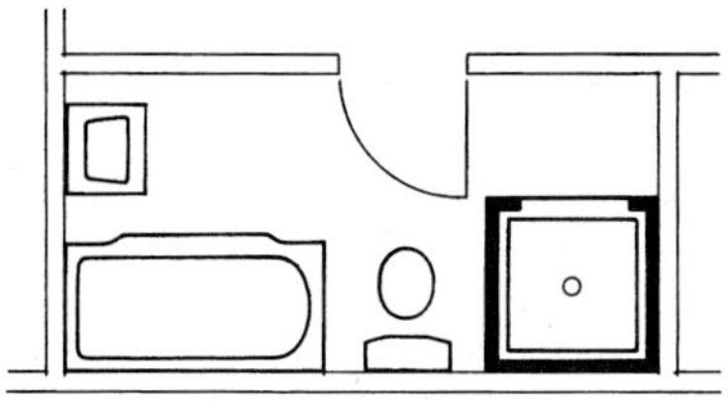

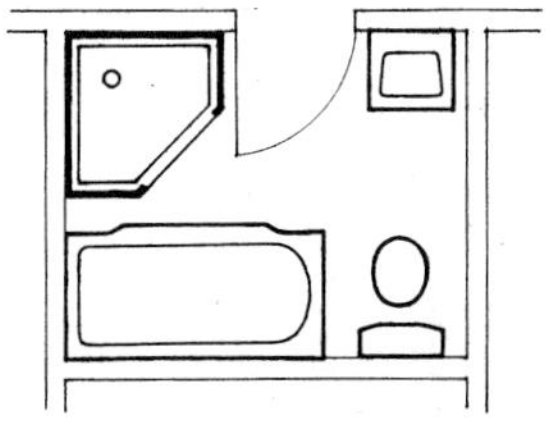

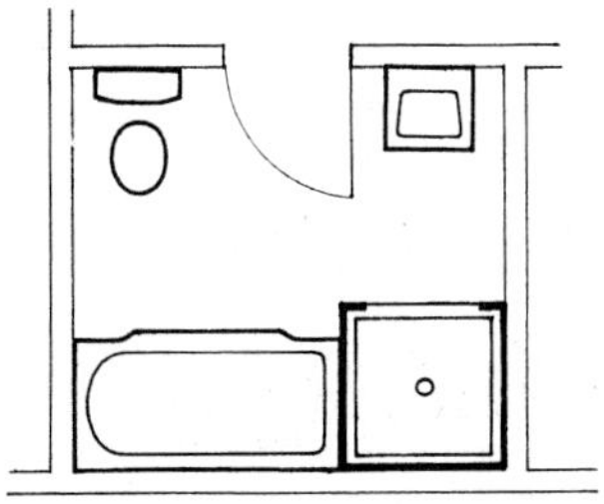

*Common wall is with an adjacent bathroom.

| D2010 928 | Four Fixture Bathroom, Two Wall Plumbing | COST EACH | | |
|---|---|---|---|---|
| | | MAT. | INST. | TOTAL |
| 1140 | Bathroom, four fixture, two wall plumbing | | | |
| 1150 | Bathtub, water closet, stall shower & lavatory | | | |
| 1160 | Stand alone | 6,750 | 4,075 | 10,825 |
| 1180 | Long plumbing wall common * | 5,275 | 2,500 | 7,775 |
| 2260 | Bathtub, lavatory, corner stall shower & water closet | | | |
| 2280 | Stand alone | 7,375 | 3,250 | 10,625 |
| 2320 | Long plumbing wall common * | 6,525 | 2,500 | 9,025 |
| 3620 | Bathtub, stall shower, lavatory & water closet | | | |
| 3640 | Stand alone | 6,750 | 4,075 | 10,825 |
| 3660 | Long plumbing wall (opp. door) common * | 5,900 | 3,325 | 9,225 |

| D2010 930 | Four Fixture Bathroom, Three Wall Plumbing | COST EACH | | |
|---|---|---|---|---|
| | | MAT. | INST. | TOTAL |
| 4680 | Bathroom, four fixture, three wall plumbing | | | |
| 4700 | Bathtub, stall shower, lavatory & water closet | | | |
| 4720 | Stand alone | 8,375 | 4,475 | 12,850 |
| 4760 | Long plumbing wall (opposite door) common * | 8,050 | 4,150 | 12,200 |

## D2010 Plumbing Fixtures

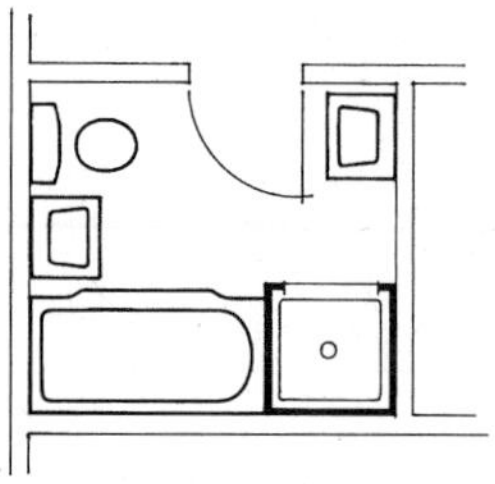

Five Fixture Bathroom Systems consisting of two lavatories, a water closet, bathtub, shower and rough-in service piping.

- Prices for plumbing and fixtures only.

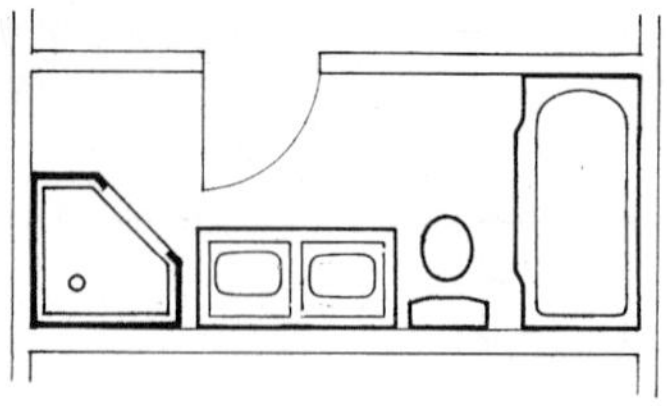

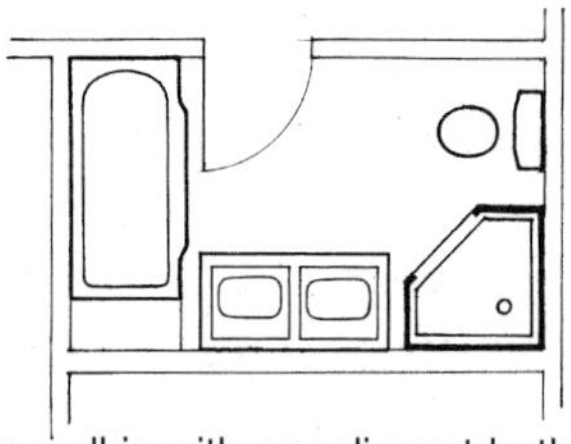

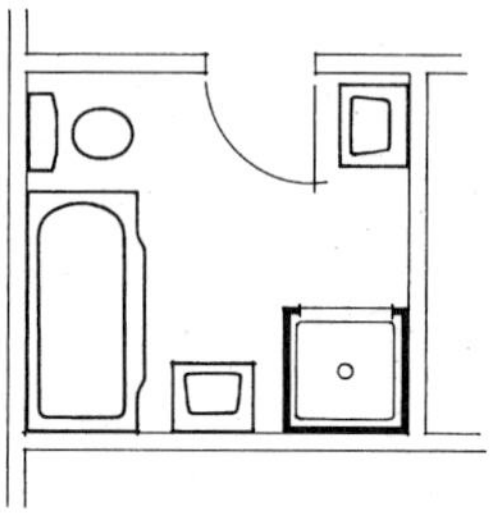

*Common wall is with an adjacent bathroom.

| D2010 932 | Five Fixture Bathroom, Two Wall Plumbing | COST EACH | | |
|---|---|---|---|---|
| | | MAT. | INST. | TOTAL |
| 1320 | Bathroom, five fixture, two wall plumbing | | | |
| 1340 | Bathtub, water closet, stall shower & two lavatories | | | |
| 1360 | Stand alone | 7,800 | 5,200 | 13,000 |
| 1400 | One short plumbing wall common * | 6,950 | 4,450 | 11,400 |

| D2010 934 | Five Fixture Bathroom, Three Wall Plumbing | COST EACH | | |
|---|---|---|---|---|
| | | MAT. | INST. | TOTAL |
| 2360 | Bathroom, five fixture, three wall plumbing | | | |
| 2380 | Water closet, bathtub, two lavatories & stall shower | | | |
| 2400 | Stand alone | 9,050 | 5,225 | 14,275 |
| 2440 | One short plumbing wall common * | 8,200 | 4,475 | 12,675 |

| D2010 936 | Five Fixture Bathroom, One Wall Plumbing | COST EACH | | |
|---|---|---|---|---|
| | | MAT. | INST. | TOTAL |
| 4080 | Bathroom, five fixture, one wall plumbing | | | |
| 4100 | Bathtub, two lavatories, corner stall shower & water closet | | | |
| 4120 | Stand alone | 8,650 | 4,650 | 13,300 |
| 4160 | Share common wall * | 7,250 | 3,025 | 10,275 |

## D2020 Domestic Water Distribution

Installation includes piping and fittings within 10′ of heater. Gas and oil fired heaters require vent piping (not included with these units).

Gas Fired

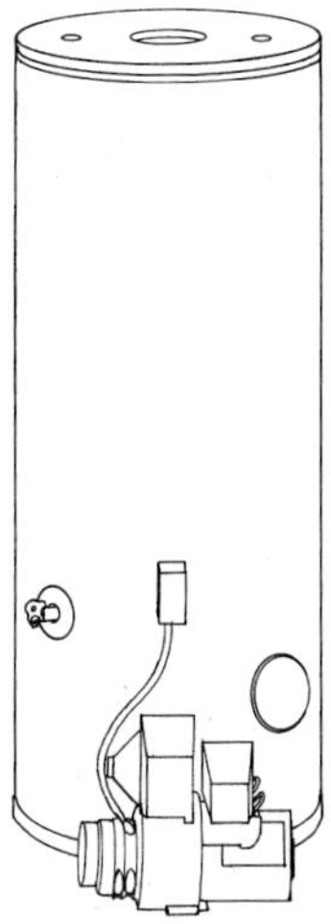

Oil Fired

| D2020 220 | Gas Fired Water Heaters - Residential Systems | COST EACH | | |
|---|---|---|---|---|
| | | MAT. | INST. | TOTAL |
| 2200 | Gas fired water heater, residential, 100°F rise | | | |
| 2260 | 30 gallon tank, 32 GPH | 3,575 | 1,775 | 5,350 |
| 2300 | 40 gallon tank, 32 GPH | 2,325 | 2,000 | 4,325 |
| 2340 | 50 gallon tank, 63 GPH | 2,450 | 2,000 | 4,450 |
| 2380 | 75 gallon tank, 63 GPH | 3,625 | 2,250 | 5,875 |
| 2420 | 100 gallon tank, 63 GPH | 4,925 | 2,350 | 7,275 |
| 2422 | | | | |

| D2020 230 | Oil Fired Water Heaters - Residential Systems | COST EACH | | |
|---|---|---|---|---|
| | | MAT. | INST. | TOTAL |
| 2200 | Oil fired water heater, residential, 100°F rise | | | |
| 2220 | 30 gallon tank, 103 GPH | 2,950 | 1,650 | 4,600 |
| 2260 | 50 gallon tank, 145 GPH | 3,075 | 1,850 | 4,925 |
| 2300 | 70 gallon tank, 164 GPH | 4,525 | 2,100 | 6,625 |
| 2340 | 85 gallon tank, 181 GPH | 11,700 | 2,150 | 13,850 |

## D2020 Domestic Water Distribution

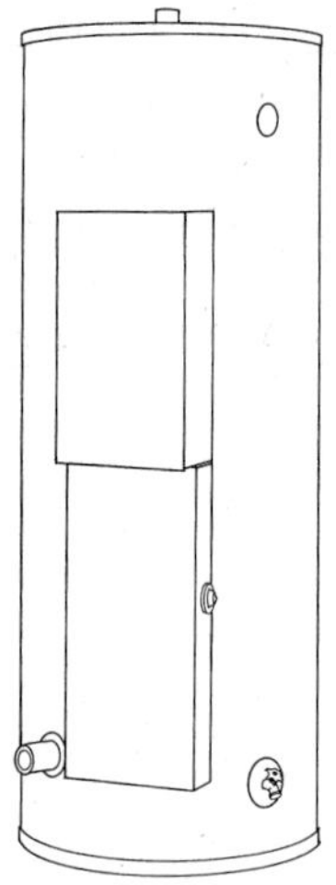

Electric

Systems below include piping and fittings within 10′ of heater. Electric water heaters do not require venting. Gas fired heaters require vent piping (not included in these prices).

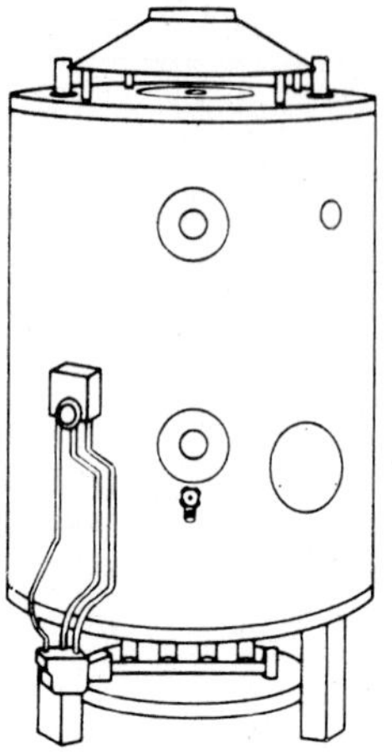

Gas Fired

| D2020 240 | Electric Water Heaters - Commercial Systems | COST EACH | | |
|---|---|---|---|---|
| | | MAT. | INST. | TOTAL |
| 1800 | Electric water heater, commercial, 100°F rise | | | |
| 1820 | 50 gallon tank, 9 KW 37 GPH | 8,250 | 1,500 | 9,750 |
| 1860 | 80 gal, 12 KW 49 GPH | 10,800 | 1,850 | 12,650 |
| 1864 | 50 gal, 9 KW 49 GPH | 9,100 | 1,750 | 10,850 |
| 1900 | 36 KW 147 GPH | 16,100 | 2,000 | 18,100 |
| 1940 | 120 gal, 36 KW 147 GPH | 17,700 | 2,150 | 19,850 |
| 1980 | 150 gal, 120 KW 490 GPH | 56,500 | 2,300 | 58,800 |
| 2020 | 200 gal, 120 KW 490 GPH | 59,000 | 2,375 | 61,375 |
| 2060 | 250 gal, 150 KW 615 GPH | 57,000 | 2,750 | 59,750 |
| 2100 | 300 gal, 180 KW 738 GPH | 86,500 | 2,925 | 89,425 |
| 2140 | 350 gal, 30 KW 123 GPH | 46,300 | 3,125 | 49,425 |
| 2180 | 180 KW 738 GPH | 64,000 | 3,125 | 67,125 |
| 2220 | 500 gal, 30 KW 123 GPH | 72,000 | 3,675 | 75,675 |
| 2260 | 240 KW 984 GPH | 117,000 | 3,675 | 120,675 |
| 2300 | 700 gal, 30 KW 123 GPH | 72,000 | 4,225 | 76,225 |
| 2340 | 300 KW 1230 GPH | 106,000 | 4,225 | 110,225 |
| 2380 | 1000 gal, 60 KW 245 GPH | 88,500 | 5,900 | 94,400 |
| 2420 | 480 KW 1970 GPH | 141,000 | 5,900 | 146,900 |
| 2460 | 1500 gal, 60 KW 245 GPH | 127,500 | 7,275 | 134,775 |
| 2500 | 480 KW 1970 GPH | 173,500 | 7,275 | 180,775 |

| D2020 250 | Gas Fired Water Heaters - Commercial Systems | COST EACH | | |
|---|---|---|---|---|
| | | MAT. | INST. | TOTAL |
| 1760 | Gas fired water heater, commercial, 100°F rise | | | |
| 1780 | 75.5 MBH input, 63 GPH | 6,025 | 2,300 | 8,325 |
| 1820 | 95 MBH input, 86 GPH | 11,700 | 2,300 | 14,000 |
| 1860 | 100 MBH input, 91 GPH | 9,625 | 2,400 | 12,025 |
| 1900 | 115 MBH input, 110 GPH | 7,675 | 2,475 | 10,150 |
| 1980 | 155 MBH input, 150 GPH | 9,175 | 2,775 | 11,950 |
| 2020 | 175 MBH input, 168 GPH | 14,700 | 2,975 | 17,675 |
| 2060 | 200 MBH input, 192 GPH | 15,200 | 3,350 | 18,550 |
| 2100 | 240 MBH input, 230 GPH | 16,200 | 3,650 | 19,850 |
| 2140 | 300 MBH input, 278 GPH | 12,800 | 4,175 | 16,975 |
| 2180 | 390 MBH input, 374 GPH | 14,400 | 4,225 | 18,625 |
| 2220 | 500 MBH input, 480 GPH | 18,600 | 4,550 | 23,150 |
| 2260 | 600 MBH input, 576 GPH | 34,800 | 4,925 | 39,725 |

## D2020 Domestic Water Distribution

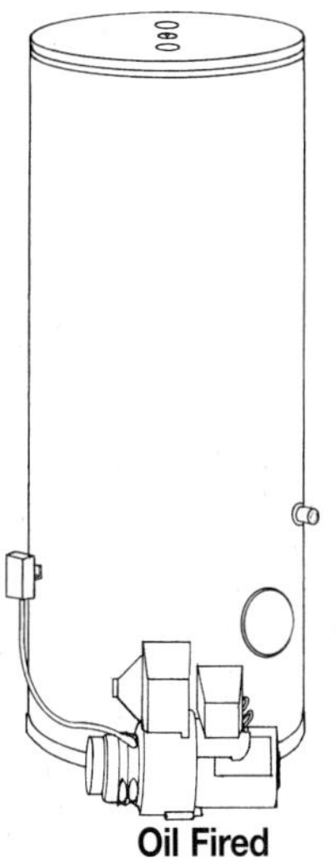

Oil Fired

Oil fired water heater systems include piping and fittings within 10′ of heater. Oil fired heaters require vent piping (not included in these systems).

| D2020 260 | Oil Fired Water Heaters - Commercial Systems | COST EACH | | |
|---|---|---|---|---|
| | | MAT. | INST. | TOTAL |
| 1800 | Oil fired water heater, commercial, 100°F rise | | | |
| 1820 | 140 gal., 140 MBH input, 134 GPH | 27,300 | 1,950 | 29,250 |
| 1900 | 140 gal., 255 MBH input, 247 GPH | 29,900 | 2,450 | 32,350 |
| 1940 | 140 gal., 270 MBH input, 259 GPH | 36,400 | 2,825 | 39,225 |
| 1980 | 140 gal., 400 MBH input, 384 GPH | 37,900 | 3,250 | 41,150 |
| 2060 | 140 gal., 720 MBH input, 691 GPH | 40,200 | 3,375 | 43,575 |
| 2100 | 221 gal., 300 MBH input, 288 GPH | 53,500 | 3,700 | 57,200 |
| 2140 | 221 gal., 600 MBH input, 576 GPH | 68,500 | 3,750 | 72,250 |
| 2180 | 221 gal., 800 MBH input, 768 GPH | 60,000 | 3,875 | 63,875 |
| 2220 | 201 gal., 1000 MBH input, 960 GPH | 61,500 | 3,900 | 65,400 |
| 2260 | 201 gal., 1250 MBH input, 1200 GPH | 63,500 | 4,025 | 67,525 |
| 2300 | 201 gal., 1500 MBH input, 1441 GPH | 68,000 | 4,125 | 72,125 |
| 2340 | 411 gal., 600 MBH input, 576 GPH | 68,500 | 4,225 | 72,725 |
| 2380 | 411 gal., 800 MBH input, 768 GPH | 71,500 | 4,325 | 75,825 |
| 2420 | 411 gal., 1000 MBH input, 960 GPH | 76,000 | 5,000 | 81,000 |
| 2460 | 411 gal., 1250 MBH input, 1200 GPH | 77,500 | 5,125 | 82,625 |
| 2500 | 397 gal., 1500 MBH input, 1441 GPH | 81,500 | 5,300 | 86,800 |
| 2540 | 397 gal., 1750 MBH input, 1681 GPH | 84,000 | 5,475 | 89,475 |

## D2040 Rain Water Drainage

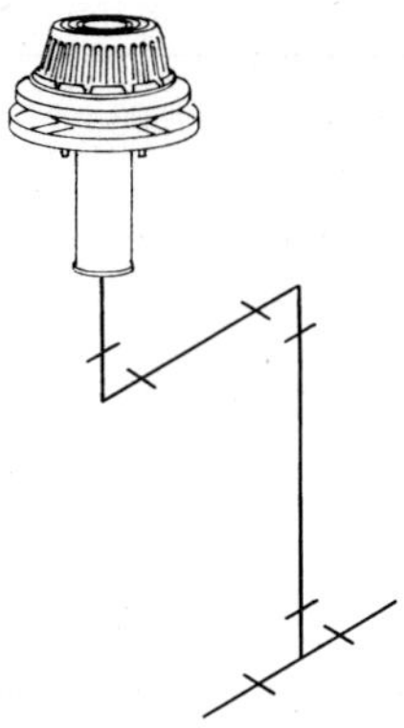

**Design Assumptions:** Vertical conductor size is based on a maximum rate of rainfall of 4″ per hour. To convert roof area to other rates multiply "Max. S.F. Roof Area" shown by four and divide the result by desired local rate. The answer is the local roof area that may be handled by the indicated pipe diameter.

Basic cost is for roof drain, 10′ of vertical leader and 10′ of horizontal, plus connection to the main.

| Pipe Dia. | Max. S.F. Roof Area | Gallons per Min. |
|---|---|---|
| 2″ | 544 | 23 |
| 3″ | 1610 | 67 |
| 4″ | 3460 | 144 |
| 5″ | 6280 | 261 |
| 6″ | 10,200 | 424 |
| 8″ | 22,000 | 913 |

| D2040 210 | Roof Drain Systems | COST EACH | | |
|---|---|---|---|---|
| | | MAT. | INST. | TOTAL |
| 1880 | Roof drain, DWV PVC, 2″ diam., piping, 10′ high | 430 | 860 | 1,290 |
| 1920 | For each additional foot add | 6.70 | 26 | 32.70 |
| 1960 | 3″ diam., 10′ high | 695 | 1,000 | 1,695 |
| 2000 | For each additional foot add | 14.15 | 29 | 43.15 |
| 2040 | 4″ diam., 10′ high | 930 | 1,125 | 2,055 |
| 2080 | For each additional foot add | 19.80 | 32 | 51.80 |
| 2120 | 5″ diam., 10′ high | 2,050 | 1,300 | 3,350 |
| 2160 | For each additional foot add | 34.50 | 36 | 70.50 |
| 2200 | 6″ diam., 10′ high | 2,800 | 1,450 | 4,250 |
| 2240 | For each additional foot add | 52.50 | 39.50 | 92 |
| 2280 | 8″ diam., 10′ high | 5,100 | 2,450 | 7,550 |
| 2320 | For each additional foot add | 76.50 | 50 | 126.50 |
| 3940 | C.I., soil, single hub, service wt., 2″ diam. piping, 10′ high | 745 | 940 | 1,685 |
| 3980 | For each additional foot add | 8.65 | 24.50 | 33.15 |
| 4120 | 3″ diam., 10′ high | 1,075 | 1,025 | 2,100 |
| 4160 | For each additional foot add | 11.95 | 26 | 37.95 |
| 4200 | 4″ diam., 10′ high | 1,600 | 1,100 | 2,700 |
| 4240 | For each additional foot add | 15.40 | 28 | 43.40 |
| 4280 | 5″ diam., 10′ high | 2,325 | 1,225 | 3,550 |
| 4320 | For each additional foot add | 43.50 | 31.50 | 75 |
| 4360 | 6″ diam., 10′ high | 2,375 | 1,325 | 3,700 |
| 4400 | For each additional foot add | 26 | 33 | 59 |
| 4440 | 8″ diam., 10′ high | 4,975 | 2,675 | 7,650 |
| 4480 | For each additional foot add | 50.50 | 55.50 | 106 |
| 6040 | Steel galv. sch 40 threaded, 2″ diam. piping, 10′ high | 1,200 | 910 | 2,110 |
| 6080 | For each additional foot add | 26.50 | 24 | 50.50 |
| 6120 | 3″ diam., 10′ high | 2,400 | 1,325 | 3,725 |
| 6160 | For each additional foot add | 56 | 36 | 92 |
| 6200 | 4″ diam., 10′ high | 3,825 | 1,700 | 5,525 |
| 6240 | For each additional foot add | 84 | 43 | 127 |
| 6280 | 5″ diam., 10′ high | 3,000 | 1,400 | 4,400 |
| 6320 | For each additional foot add | 43 | 42 | 85 |
| 6360 | 6″ diam, 10′ high | 3,825 | 1,825 | 5,650 |
| 6400 | For each additional foot add | 57 | 57.50 | 114.50 |
| 6440 | 8″ diam., 10′ high | 6,875 | 2,625 | 9,500 |
| 6480 | For each additional foot add | 86 | 65 | 151 |

## D2090 Other Plumbing Systems

| D2090 810 | Piping - Installed - Unit Costs | COST PER L.F. MAT. | INST. | TOTAL |
|---|---|---|---|---|
| 0840 | Cast iron, soil, B & S, service weight, 2" diameter | 8.65 | 24.50 | 33.15 |
| 0860 | 3" diameter | 11.95 | 26 | 37.95 |
| 0880 | 4" diameter | 15.40 | 28 | 43.40 |
| 0900 | 5" diameter | 43.50 | 31.50 | 75 |
| 0920 | 6" diameter | 26 | 33 | 59 |
| 0940 | 8" diameter | 50.50 | 55.50 | 106 |
| 0960 | 10" diameter | 94 | 60.50 | 154.50 |
| 0980 | 12" diameter | 335 | 68 | 403 |
| 1040 | No hub, 1-1/2" diameter | 13.50 | 22 | 35.50 |
| 1060 | 2" diameter | 14.05 | 23 | 37.05 |
| 1080 | 3" diameter | 18.95 | 24 | 42.95 |
| 1100 | 4" diameter | 25 | 26.50 | 51.50 |
| 1120 | 5" diameter | 36 | 29 | 65 |
| 1140 | 6" diameter | 42 | 30.50 | 72.50 |
| 1160 | 8" diameter | 83 | 47.50 | 130.50 |
| 1180 | 10" diameter | 132 | 53.50 | 185.50 |
| 1220 | Copper tubing, hard temper, solder, type K, 1/2" diameter | 6 | 11 | 17 |
| 1260 | 3/4" diameter | 8.55 | 11.60 | 20.15 |
| 1280 | 1" diameter | 8.40 | 13 | 21.40 |
| 1300 | 1-1/4" diameter | 11.10 | 15.35 | 26.45 |
| 1320 | 1-1/2" diameter | 14.35 | 17.20 | 31.55 |
| 1340 | 2" diameter | 22 | 21.50 | 43.50 |
| 1360 | 2-1/2" diameter | 63.50 | 26 | 89.50 |
| 1380 | 3" diameter | 49.50 | 28.50 | 78 |
| 1400 | 4" diameter | 93.50 | 40.50 | 134 |
| 1480 | 5" diameter | 173 | 48.50 | 221.50 |
| 1500 | 6" diameter | 270 | 63.50 | 333.50 |
| 1520 | 8" diameter | 400 | 71 | 471 |
| 1560 | Type L, 1/2" diameter | 5.40 | 10.60 | 16 |
| 1600 | 3/4" diameter | 7.05 | 11.30 | 18.35 |
| 1620 | 1" diameter | 6.90 | 12.65 | 19.55 |
| 1640 | 1-1/4" diameter | 9.75 | 14.80 | 24.55 |
| 1660 | 1-1/2" diameter | 12.55 | 16.55 | 29.10 |
| 1680 | 2" diameter | 26.50 | 20.50 | 47 |
| 1700 | 2-1/2" diameter | 32 | 25 | 57 |
| 1720 | 3" diameter | 44 | 27.50 | 71.50 |
| 1740 | 4" diameter | 82.50 | 39.50 | 122 |
| 1760 | 5" diameter | 150 | 45.50 | 195.50 |
| 1780 | 6" diameter | 227 | 60 | 287 |
| 1800 | 8" diameter | 320 | 67 | 387 |
| 1840 | Type M, 1/2" diameter | 4.86 | 10.25 | 15.11 |
| 1880 | 3/4" diameter | 6.15 | 11 | 17.15 |
| 1900 | 1" diameter | 5.80 | 12.30 | 18.10 |
| 1920 | 1-1/4" diameter | 8.70 | 14.35 | 23.05 |
| 1940 | 1-1/2" diameter | 11.65 | 15.90 | 27.55 |
| 1960 | 2" diameter | 18.30 | 19.55 | 37.85 |
| 1980 | 2-1/2" diameter | 30 | 24 | 54 |
| 2000 | 3" diameter | 40 | 26.50 | 66.50 |
| 2020 | 4" diameter | 79 | 38.50 | 117.50 |
| 2060 | 6" diameter | 228 | 57.50 | 285.50 |
| 2080 | 8" diameter | 325 | 63.50 | 388.50 |
| 2120 | Type DWV, 1-1/4" diameter | 10.40 | 14.35 | 24.75 |
| 2160 | 1-1/2" diameter | 13.10 | 15.90 | 29 |
| 2180 | 2" diameter | 18.50 | 19.55 | 38.05 |
| 2200 | 3" diameter | 38.50 | 26.50 | 65 |
| 2220 | 4" diameter | 102 | 38.50 | 140.50 |
| 2240 | 5" diameter | 177 | 43 | 220 |
| 2260 | 6" diameter | 270 | 57.50 | 327.50 |

## D2090 Other Plumbing Systems

| D2090 810 | Piping - Installed - Unit Costs | COST PER L.F. | | |
|---|---|---|---|---|
| | | MAT. | INST. | TOTAL |
| 2280 | 8" diameter | 860 | 63.50 | 923.50 |
| 2800 | Plastic,PVC, DWV, schedule 40, 1-1/4" diameter | 9.35 | 20.50 | 29.85 |
| 2820 | 1-1/2" diameter | 5.25 | 24 | 29.25 |
| 2830 | 2" diameter | 6.70 | 26 | 32.70 |
| 2840 | 3" diameter | 14.15 | 29 | 43.15 |
| 2850 | 4" diameter | 19.80 | 32 | 51.80 |
| 2890 | 6" diameter | 52.50 | 39.50 | 92 |
| 3010 | Pressure pipe 200 PSI, 1/2" diameter | 10.80 | 15.90 | 26.70 |
| 3030 | 3/4" diameter | 10.85 | 16.85 | 27.70 |
| 3040 | 1" diameter | 4 | 18.70 | 22.70 |
| 3050 | 1-1/4" diameter | 5.85 | 20.50 | 26.35 |
| 3060 | 1-1/2" diameter | 5.50 | 24 | 29.50 |
| 3070 | 2" diameter | 7.50 | 26 | 33.50 |
| 3080 | 2-1/2" diameter | 10.85 | 27.50 | 38.35 |
| 3090 | 3" diameter | 12.05 | 29 | 41.05 |
| 3100 | 4" diameter | 16.20 | 32 | 48.20 |
| 3110 | 6" diameter | 32.50 | 39.50 | 72 |
| 3120 | 8" diameter | 64 | 50 | 114 |
| 4000 | Steel, schedule 40, black, threaded, 1/2" diameter | 6.15 | 13.65 | 19.80 |
| 4020 | 3/4" diameter | 7.75 | 14.10 | 21.85 |
| 4030 | 1" diameter | 10.65 | 16.20 | 26.85 |
| 4040 | 1-1/4" diameter | 14.10 | 17.40 | 31.50 |
| 4050 | 1-1/2" diameter | 16.75 | 19.35 | 36.10 |
| 4060 | 2" diameter | 22.50 | 24 | 46.50 |
| 4070 | 2-1/2" diameter | 37 | 31 | 68 |
| 4080 | 3" diameter | 48.50 | 36 | 84.50 |
| 4090 | 4" diameter | 71 | 43 | 114 |
| 4100 | Grooved, 5" diameter | 43 | 42 | 85 |
| 4110 | 6" diameter | 120 | 57.50 | 177.50 |
| 4120 | 8" diameter | 141 | 65 | 206 |
| 4130 | 10" diameter | 196 | 77.50 | 273.50 |
| 4140 | 12" diameter | 224 | 89 | 313 |
| 4200 | Galvanized, threaded, 1/2" diameter | 7.25 | 13.65 | 20.90 |
| 4220 | 3/4" diameter | 9.15 | 14.10 | 23.25 |
| 4230 | 1" diameter | 12.50 | 16.20 | 28.70 |
| 4240 | 1-1/4" diameter | 16.55 | 17.40 | 33.95 |
| 4250 | 1-1/2" diameter | 19.70 | 19.35 | 39.05 |
| 4260 | 2" diameter | 26.50 | 24 | 50.50 |
| 4270 | 2-1/2" diameter | 43 | 31 | 74 |
| 4280 | 3" diameter | 56 | 36 | 92 |
| 4290 | 4" diameter | 84 | 43 | 127 |
| 4300 | Grooved, 5" diameter | 43 | 42 | 85 |
| 4310 | 6" diameter | 57 | 57.50 | 114.50 |
| 4320 | 8" diameter | 86 | 65 | 151 |
| 4330 | 10" diameter | 193 | 77.50 | 270.50 |
| 4340 | 12" diameter | 238 | 89 | 327 |
| 5010 | Flanged, black, 1" diameter | 23.50 | 23 | 46.50 |
| 5020 | 1-1/4" diameter | 29.50 | 25 | 54.50 |
| 5030 | 1-1/2" diameter | 27.50 | 27.50 | 55 |
| 5040 | 2" diameter | 33 | 36 | 69 |
| 5050 | 2-1/2" diameter | 44.50 | 45 | 89.50 |
| 5060 | 3" diameter | 54 | 50.50 | 104.50 |
| 5070 | 4" diameter | 69 | 62 | 131 |
| 5080 | 5" diameter | 52 | 77 | 129 |
| 5090 | 6" diameter | 128 | 99.50 | 227.50 |
| 5100 | 8" diameter | 149 | 131 | 280 |
| 5110 | 10" diameter | 243 | 154 | 397 |
| 5120 | 12" diameter | 291 | 177 | 468 |

## D2090 Other Plumbing Systems

| D2090 810 | Piping - Installed - Unit Costs | COST PER L.F. | | |
|---|---|---|---|---|
| | | MAT. | INST. | TOTAL |
| 5720 | Grooved joints, black, 3/4" diameter | 11.25 | 12.10 | 23.35 |
| 5730 | 1" diameter | 13.40 | 13.65 | 27.05 |
| 5740 | 1-1/4" diameter | 17.65 | 14.80 | 32.45 |
| 5750 | 1-1/2" diameter | 20.50 | 16.85 | 37.35 |
| 5760 | 2" diameter | 26 | 21.50 | 47.50 |
| 5770 | 2-1/2" diameter | 37 | 27 | 64 |
| 5900 | 3" diameter | 46.50 | 31 | 77.50 |
| 5910 | 4" diameter | 66.50 | 34.50 | 101 |
| 5920 | 5" diameter | 43 | 42 | 85 |
| 5930 | 6" diameter | 120 | 57.50 | 177.50 |
| 5940 | 8" diameter | 141 | 65 | 206 |
| 5950 | 10" diameter | 196 | 77.50 | 273.50 |
| 5960 | 12" diameter | 224 | 89 | 313 |

## D3010 Energy Supply

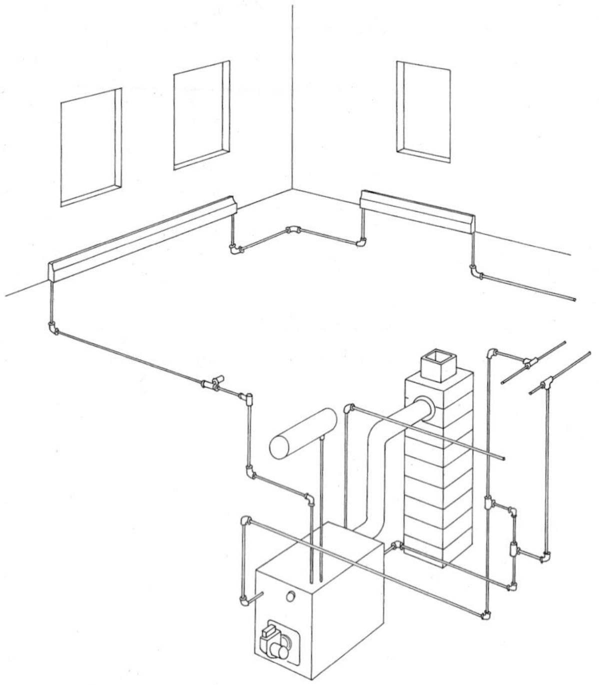

Forced Hot Water Heating System

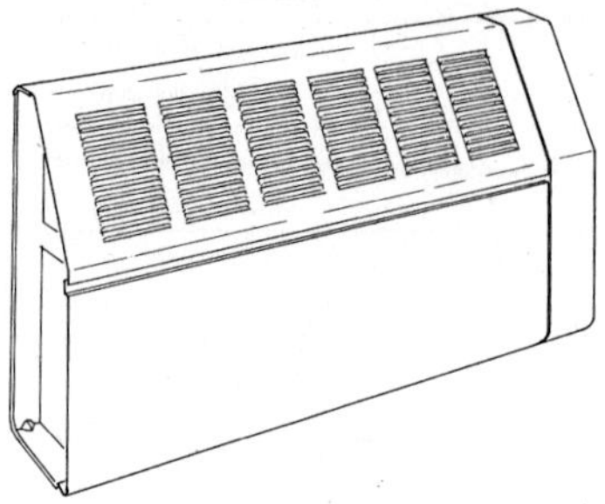

Fin Tube Radiation

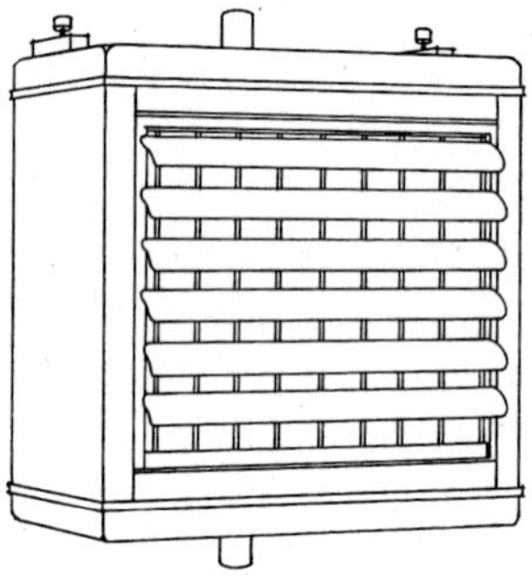

Terminal Unit Heater

| D3010 510 | Apartment Building Heating - Fin Tube Radiation | COST PER S.F. MAT. | COST PER S.F. INST. | COST PER S.F. TOTAL |
|---|---|---|---|---|
| 1740 | Heating systems, fin tube radiation, forced hot water | | | |
| 1760 | 1,000 S.F. area, 10,000 C.F. volume | 10.10 | 8.28 | 18.38 |
| 1800 | 10,000 S.F. area, 100,000 C.F. volume | 4.32 | 4.98 | 9.30 |
| 1840 | 20,000 S.F. area, 200,000 C.F. volume | 4.20 | 5.60 | 9.80 |
| 1880 | 30,000 S.F. area, 300,000 C.F. volume | 4.10 | 5.40 | 9.50 |

| D3010 520 | Commercial Building Heating - Fin Tube Radiation | COST PER S.F. MAT. | COST PER S.F. INST. | COST PER S.F. TOTAL |
|---|---|---|---|---|
| 1940 | Heating systems, fin tube radiation, forced hot water | | | |
| 1960 | 1,000 S.F. bldg, one floor | 27.60 | 18.70 | 46.30 |
| 2000 | 10,000 S.F., 100,000 C.F., total two floors | 7.15 | 7.10 | 14.25 |
| 2040 | **100,000 S.F., 1,000,000 C.F., total three floors** | 2.98 | 3.18 | 6.16 |
| 2080 | 1,000,000 S.F., 10,000,000 C.F., total five floors | 1.68 | 1.69 | 3.37 |

| D3010 530 | Commercial Bldg. Heating - Terminal Unit Heaters | COST PER S.F. MAT. | COST PER S.F. INST. | COST PER S.F. TOTAL |
|---|---|---|---|---|
| 1860 | Heating systems, terminal unit heaters, forced hot water | | | |
| 1880 | 1,000 S.F. bldg., one floor | 28.10 | 17.20 | 45.30 |
| 1920 | 10,000 S.F. bldg., 100,000 C.F. total two floors | 7.05 | 5.90 | 12.95 |
| 1960 | 100,000 S.F. bldg., 1,000,000 C.F. total three floors | 3.39 | 2.91 | 6.30 |
| 2000 | 1,000,000 S.F. bldg., 10,000,000 C.F. total five floors | 2.41 | 1.90 | 4.31 |

# D3020 Heat Generating Systems

**Small Electric Boiler Systems Considerations:**

1. Terminal units are fin tube baseboard radiation rated at 720 BTU/hr with 200° water temperature or 820 BTU/hr steam.
2. Primary use being for residential or smaller supplementary areas, the floor levels are based on 7-1/2″ ceiling heights.
3. All distribution piping is copper for boilers through 205 MBH. All piping for larger systems is steel pipe.

**Large Electric Boiler System Considerations:**

1. Terminal units are all unit heaters of the same size. Quantities are varied to accommodate total requirements.
2. All air is circulated through the heaters a minimum of three times per hour.
3. As the capacities are adequate for commercial use, gross output rating by floor levels are based on 10′ ceiling height.
4. All distribution piping is black steel pipe.

| D3020 102 | Small Heating Systems, Hydronic, Electric Boilers | COST PER S.F. | | |
|---|---|---|---|---|
| | | MAT. | INST. | TOTAL |
| 1100 | Small heating systems, hydronic, electric boilers | | | |
| 1120 | Steam, 1 floor, 1480 S.F., 61 M.B.H. | 9.87 | 11.06 | 20.93 |
| 1160 | 3,000 S.F., 123 M.B.H. | 7.55 | 9.35 | 16.90 |
| 1200 | 5,000 S.F., 205 M.B.H. | 6.65 | 8.60 | 15.25 |
| 1240 | 2 floors, 12,400 S.F., 512 M.B.H. | 6.25 | 8.55 | 14.80 |
| 1280 | 3 floors, 24,800 S.F., 1023 M.B.H. | 6.50 | 8.45 | 14.95 |
| 1320 | 34,750 S.F., 1,433 M.B.H. | 6.05 | 8.20 | 14.25 |
| 1360 | Hot water, 1 floor, 1,000 S.F., 41 M.B.H. | 14.50 | 5.95 | 20.45 |
| 1400 | 2,500 S.F., 103 M.B.H. | 11.15 | 10.65 | 21.80 |
| 1440 | 2 floors, 4,850 S.F., 205 M.B.H. | 11.05 | 12.75 | 23.80 |
| 1480 | 3 floors, 9,700 S.F., 410 M.B.H. | 11.95 | 13.25 | 25.20 |

| D3020 104 | Large Heating Systems, Hydronic, Electric Boilers | COST PER S.F. | | |
|---|---|---|---|---|
| | | MAT. | INST. | TOTAL |
| 1230 | Large heating systems, hydronic, electric boilers | | | |
| 1240 | 9,280 S.F., 135 K.W., 461 M.B.H., 1 floor | 5.95 | 3.70 | 9.65 |
| 1280 | 14,900 S.F., 240 K.W., 820 M.B.H., 2 floors | 8.90 | 6.45 | 15.35 |
| 1320 | 18,600 S.F., 296 K.W., 1,010 M.B.H., 3 floors | 9.10 | 7 | 16.10 |
| 1360 | 26,100 S.F., 420 K.W., 1,432 M.B.H., 4 floors | 8.95 | 6.85 | 15.80 |
| 1400 | 39,100 S.F., 666 K.W., 2,273 M.B.H., 4 floors | 7.65 | 5.75 | 13.40 |
| 1440 | 57,700 S.F., 900 K.W., 3,071 M.B.H., 5 floors | 8 | 5.65 | 13.65 |
| 1480 | 111,700 S.F., 1,800 K.W., 6,148 M.B.H., 6 floors | 7.15 | 4.86 | 12.01 |
| 1520 | 149,000 S.F., 2,400 K.W., 8,191 M.B.H., 8 floors | 7.10 | 4.85 | 11.95 |
| 1560 | 223,300 S.F., 3,600 K.W., 12,283 M.B.H., 14 floors | 7.75 | 5.50 | 13.25 |

## D3020 Heat Generating Systems

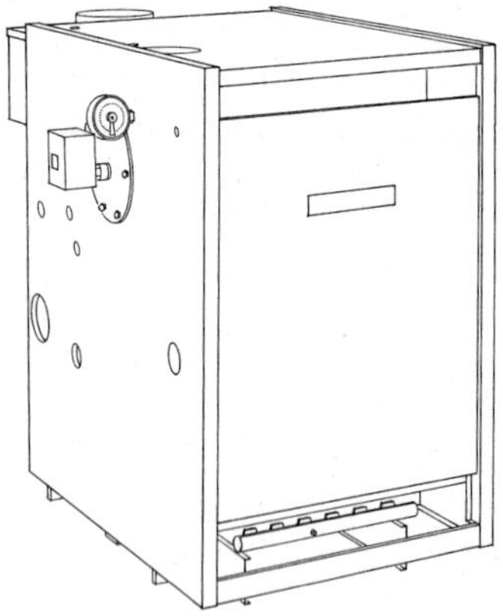

**Boiler Selection:** The maximum allowable working pressures are limited by ASME "Code for Heating Boilers" to 15 PSI for steam and 160 PSI for hot water heating boilers, with a maximum temperature limitation of 250° F. Hot water boilers are generally rated for a working pressure of 30 PSI. High pressure boilers are governed by the ASME "Code for Power Boilers" which is used almost universally for boilers operating over 15 PSIG. High pressure boilers used for a combination of heating/ process loads are usually designed for 150 PSIG.

Boiler ratings are usually indicated as either Gross or Net Output. The Gross Load is equal to the Net Load plus a piping and pickup allowance. When this allowance cannot be determined, divide the gross output rating by 1.25 for a value equal to or greater than the next heat loss requirement of the building.

Table below lists installed cost per boiler and includes insulating jacket, standard controls, burner and safety controls. Costs do not include piping or boiler base pad. Outputs are Gross.

| D3020 106 | Boilers, Hot Water & Steam | COST EACH | | |
|---|---|---|---|---|
| | | MAT. | INST. | TOTAL |
| 0600 | Boiler, electric, steel, hot water, 12 K.W., 41 M.B.H. | 5,675 | 1,825 | 7,500 |
| 0620 | 30 K.W., 103 M.B.H. | 5,950 | 1,975 | 7,925 |
| 0640 | 60 K.W., 205 M.B.H. | 6,775 | 2,150 | 8,925 |
| 0660 | 120 K.W., 410 M.B.H. | 7,500 | 2,625 | 10,125 |
| 0680 | 210 K.W., 716 M.B.H. | 9,025 | 3,925 | 12,950 |
| 0700 | 510 K.W., 1,739 M.B.H. | 26,400 | 7,325 | 33,725 |
| 0720 | 720 K.W., 2,452 M.B.H. | 31,600 | 8,275 | 39,875 |
| 0740 | 1,200 K.W., 4,095 M.B.H. | 40,200 | 9,475 | 49,675 |
| 0760 | 2,100 K.W., 7,167 M.B.H. | 76,000 | 11,900 | 87,900 |
| 0780 | 3,600 K.W., 12,283 M.B.H. | 110,500 | 20,200 | 130,700 |
| 0820 | Steam, 6 K.W., 20.5 M.B.H. | 4,975 | 1,975 | 6,950 |
| 0840 | 24 K.W., 81.8 M.B.H. | 5,700 | 2,150 | 7,850 |
| 0860 | 60 K.W., 205 M.B.H. | 7,875 | 2,350 | 10,225 |
| 0880 | 150 K.W., 512 M.B.H. | 11,400 | 3,625 | 15,025 |
| 0900 | 510 K.W., 1,740 M.B.H. | 35,900 | 8,950 | 44,850 |
| 0920 | 1,080 K.W., 3,685 M.B.H. | 50,500 | 12,900 | 63,400 |
| 0940 | 2,340 K.W., 7,984 M.B.H. | 113,500 | 20,200 | 133,700 |
| 0980 | Gas, cast iron, hot water, 80 M.B.H. | 3,150 | 2,250 | 5,400 |
| 1000 | 100 M.B.H. | 3,100 | 2,450 | 5,550 |
| 1020 | 163 M.B.H. | 3,925 | 3,300 | 7,225 |
| 1040 | 280 M.B.H. | 4,275 | 3,650 | 7,925 |
| 1060 | 544 M.B.H. | 9,600 | 6,475 | 16,075 |
| 1080 | 1,088 M.B.H. | 16,200 | 8,250 | 24,450 |
| 1100 | 2,000 M.B.H. | 27,800 | 12,900 | 40,700 |
| 1120 | 2,856 M.B.H. | 33,900 | 16,500 | 50,400 |
| 1140 | 4,720 M.B.H. | 76,500 | 22,700 | 99,200 |
| 1160 | 6,970 M.B.H. | 142,000 | 37,000 | 179,000 |
| 1180 | For steam systems under 2,856 M.B.H., add 8% | | | |
| 1520 | Oil, cast iron, hot water, 109 M.B.H. | 2,750 | 2,750 | 5,500 |
| 1540 | 173 M.B.H. | 3,500 | 3,300 | 6,800 |
| 1560 | 236 M.B.H. | 4,100 | 3,875 | 7,975 |
| 1580 | 1,084 M.B.H. | 12,900 | 8,775 | 21,675 |
| 1600 | 1,600 M.B.H. | 20,900 | 12,600 | 33,500 |
| 1620 | 2,480 M.B.H. | 23,100 | 16,100 | 39,200 |
| 1640 | 3,550 M.B.H. | 32,500 | 19,300 | 51,800 |
| 1660 | Steam systems same price as hot water | | | |

## D3020 Heat Generating Systems

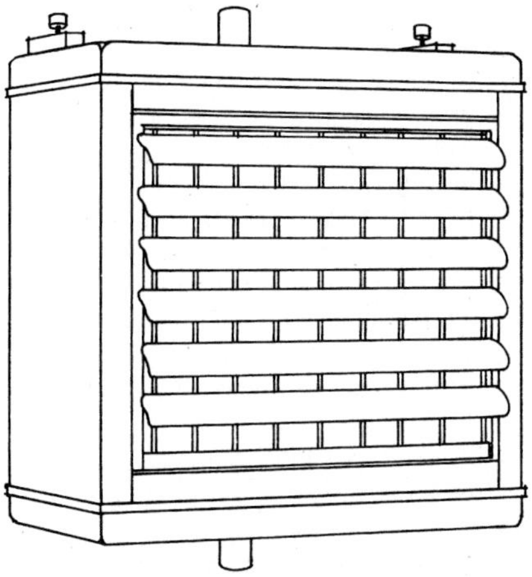

Unit Heater

**Fossil Fuel Boiler System Considerations:**

1. Terminal units are horizontal unit heaters. Quantities are varied to accommodate total heat loss per building.
2. Unit heater selection was determined by their capacity to circulate the building volume a minimum of three times per hour in addition to the BTU output.
3. Systems shown are forced hot water. Steam boilers cost slightly more than hot water boilers. However, this is compensated for by the smaller size or fewer terminal units required with steam.
4. Floor levels are based on 10′ story heights.
5. MBH requirements are gross boiler output.

| D3020 108 | Heating Systems, Unit Heaters | COST PER S.F. | | |
|---|---|---|---|---|
| | | MAT. | INST. | TOTAL |
| 1260 | Heating systems, hydronic, fossil fuel, terminal unit heaters, | | | |
| 1280 | Cast iron boiler, gas, 80 M.B.H., 1,070 S.F. bldg. | 17.46 | 12.24 | 29.70 |
| 1320 | 163 M.B.H., 2,140 S.F. bldg. | 11.70 | 8.65 | 20.35 |
| 1360 | 544 M.B.H., 7,250 S.F. bldg. | 8.55 | 6.10 | 14.65 |
| 1400 | 1,088 M.B.H., 14,500 S.F. bldg. | 7.75 | 5.80 | 13.55 |
| 1440 | 3,264 M.B.H., 43,500 S.F. bldg. | 6.50 | 4.37 | 10.87 |
| 1480 | 5,032 M.B.H., 67,100 S.F. bldg. | 7.20 | 4.49 | 11.69 |
| 1520 | Oil, 109 M.B.H., 1,420 S.F. bldg. | 19.75 | 11.35 | 31.10 |
| 1560 | 235 M.B.H., 3,150 S.F. bldg. | 11.45 | 8.05 | 19.50 |
| 1600 | 940 M.B.H., 12,500 S.F. bldg. | 9.05 | 5.30 | 14.35 |
| 1640 | 1,600 M.B.H., 21,300 S.F. bldg. | 8 | 5.10 | 13.10 |
| 1680 | 2,480 M.B.H., 33,100 S.F. bldg. | 7.35 | 4.58 | 11.93 |
| 1720 | 3,350 M.B.H., 44,500 S.F. bldg. | 7.55 | 4.68 | 12.23 |
| 1760 | Coal, 148 M.B.H., 1,975 S.F. bldg. | 102 | 7.40 | 109.40 |
| 1800 | 300 M.B.H., 4,000 S.F. bldg. | 53 | 5.80 | 58.80 |
| 1840 | 2,360 M.B.H., 31,500 S.F. bldg. | 14.30 | 4.66 | 18.96 |

## D3020 Heat Generating Systems

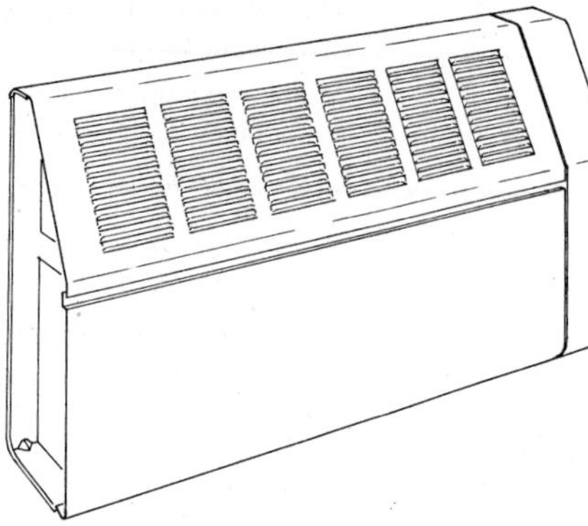

Fin Tube Radiator

**Fossil Fuel Boiler System Considerations:**

1. Terminal units are commercial steel fin tube radiation. Quantities are varied to accommodate total heat loss per building.
2. Systems shown are forced hot water. Steam boilers cost slightly more than hot water boilers. However, this is compensated for by the smaller size or fewer terminal units required with steam.
3. Floor levels are based on 10′ story heights.
4. MBH requirements are gross boiler output.

| D3020 110 | Heating System, Fin Tube Radiation | COST PER S.F. | | |
|---|---|---|---|---|
| | | MAT. | INST. | TOTAL |
| 3230 | Heating systems, hydronic, fossil fuel, fin tube radiation | | | |
| 3240 | Cast iron boiler, gas, 80 MBH, 1,070 S.F. bldg. | 18.36 | 18.27 | 36.63 |
| 3280 | 169 M.B.H., 2,140 S.F. bldg. | 11.60 | 12.10 | 23.70 |
| 3320 | 544 M.B.H., 7,250 S.F. bldg. | 9.75 | 10.35 | 20.10 |
| 3360 | 1,088 M.B.H., 14,500 S.F. bldg. | 9.15 | 10.15 | 19.30 |
| 3400 | 3,264 M.B.H., 43,500 S.F. bldg. | 8.20 | 8.95 | 17.15 |
| 3440 | 5,032 M.B.H., 67,100 S.F. bldg. | 8.95 | 9.10 | 18.05 |
| 3480 | Oil, 109 M.B.H., 1,420 S.F. bldg. | 23.50 | 21 | 44.50 |
| 3520 | 235 M.B.H., 3,150 S.F. bldg. | 12.65 | 12.25 | 24.90 |
| 3560 | 940 M.B.H., 12,500 S.F. bldg. | 10.50 | 9.75 | 20.25 |
| 3600 | 1,600 M.B.H., 21,300 S.F. bldg. | 9.70 | 9.70 | 19.40 |
| 3640 | 2,480 M.B.H., 33,100 S.F. bldg. | 9.05 | 9.20 | 18.25 |
| 3680 | 3,350 M.B.H., 44,500 S.F. bldg. | 9.20 | 9.25 | 18.45 |
| 3720 | Coal, 148 M.B.H., 1,975 S.F. bldg. | 103 | 11.55 | 114.55 |
| 3760 | 300 M.B.H., 4,000 S.F. bldg. | 54 | 9.90 | 63.90 |
| 3800 | 2,360 M.B.H., 31,500 S.F. bldg. | 15.95 | 9.20 | 25.15 |
| 4080 | Steel boiler, oil, 97 M.B.H., 1,300 S.F. bldg. | 17.45 | 17.15 | 34.60 |
| 4120 | 315 M.B.H., 4,550 S.F. bldg. | 8.55 | 8.70 | 17.25 |
| 4160 | 525 M.B.H., 7,000 S.F. bldg. | 12.30 | 10 | 22.30 |
| 4200 | 1,050 M.B.H., 14,000 S.F. bldg. | 11.25 | 10 | 21.25 |
| 4240 | 2,310 M.B.H., 30,800 S.F. bldg. | 10 | 9.25 | 19.25 |
| 4280 | 3,150 M.B.H., 42,000 S.F. bldg. | 9.75 | 9.35 | 19.10 |
| 1010 | 9,000 BTUH cooling, 13,900 BTU heat | 3,825 | 310 | 4,135 |

## D3030 Cooling Generating Systems

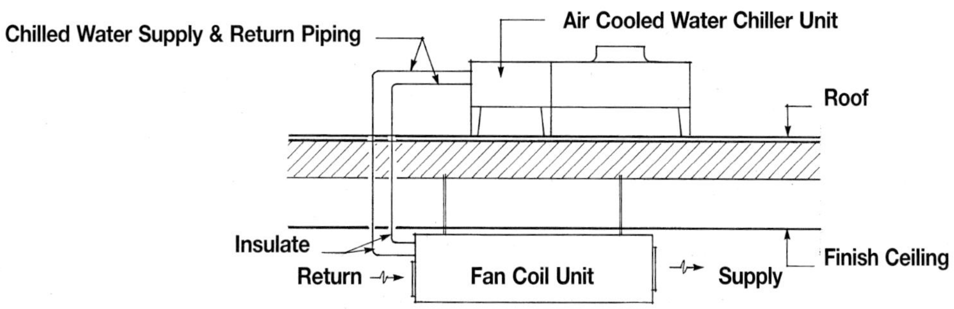


*Cooling requirements would lead to a choice of multiple chillers.

| D3030 110 | Chilled Water, Air Cooled Condenser Systems | COST PER S.F. | | |
|---|---|---|---|---|
| | | MAT. | INST. | TOTAL |
| 1180 | Packaged chiller, air cooled, with fan coil unit | | | |
| 1200 | Apartment corridors, 3,000 S.F., 5.50 ton | 12.87 | 9.51 | 22.38 |
| 1240 | 6,000 S.F., 11.00 ton | 11.35 | 8.40 | 19.75 |
| 1280 | 10,000 S.F., 18.33 ton | 9.15 | 6.35 | 15.50 |
| 1320 | 20,000 S.F., 36.66 ton | 7.15 | 4.59 | 11.74 |
| 1360 | 40,000 S.F., 73.33 ton | 5.55 | 4.59 | 10.14 |
| 1440 | Banks and libraries, 3,000 S.F., 12.50 ton | 18.65 | 12.30 | 30.95 |
| 1480 | 6,000 S.F., 25.00 ton | 16.15 | 9.95 | 26.10 |
| 1520 | 10,000 S.F., 41.66 ton | 12.70 | 6.90 | 19.60 |
| 1560 | 20,000 S.F., 83.33 ton | 9.75 | 6.20 | 15.95 |
| 1600 | 40,000 S.F., 167 ton* | | | |
| 1680 | Bars and taverns, 3,000 S.F., 33.25 ton | 29.50 | 14.35 | 43.85 |
| 1720 | 6,000 S.F., 66.50 ton | 25 | 10.85 | 35.85 |
| 1760 | 10,000 S.F., 110.83 ton | 15.80 | 3.25 | 19.05 |
| 1800 | 20,000 S.F., 220 ton* | | | |
| 1840 | 40,000 S.F., 440 ton* | | | |
| 1920 | Bowling alleys, 3,000 S.F., 17.00 ton | 22 | 13.75 | 35.75 |
| 1960 | 6,000 S.F., 34.00 ton | 17.35 | 9.60 | 26.95 |
| 2000 | 10,000 S.F., 56.66 ton | 14.15 | 6.85 | 21 |
| 2040 | 20,000 S.F., 113.33 ton | 10.65 | 6.25 | 16.90 |
| 2080 | 40,000 S.F., 227 ton* | | | |
| 2160 | Department stores, 3,000 S.F., 8.75 ton | 18.15 | 11.75 | 29.90 |
| 2200 | 6,000 S.F., 17.50 ton | 13.30 | 9 | 22.30 |
| 2240 | 10,000 S.F., 29.17 ton | 10.80 | 6.45 | 17.25 |
| 2280 | 20,000 S.F., 58.33 ton | 8.60 | 4.72 | 13.32 |
| 2320 | 40,000 S.F., 116.66 ton | 6.80 | 4.72 | 11.52 |
| 2400 | Drug stores, 3,000 S.F., 20.00 ton | 24.50 | 14.20 | 38.70 |
| 2440 | 6,000 S.F., 40.00 ton | 19.80 | 10.35 | 30.15 |
| 2480 | 10,000 S.F., 66.66 ton | 15.30 | 8.85 | 24.15 |
| 2520 | 20,000 S.F., 133.33 ton | 12.90 | 6.55 | 19.45 |
| 2560 | 40,000 S.F., 267 ton* | | | |
| 2640 | Factories, 2,000 S.F., 10.00 ton | 17.15 | 11.80 | 28.95 |
| 2680 | 6,000 S.F., 20.00 ton | 14.65 | 9.50 | 24.15 |
| 2720 | 10,000 S.F., 33.33 ton | 11.40 | 6.60 | 18 |
| 2760 | 20,000 S.F., 66.66 ton | 8.45 | 5.90 | 14.35 |
| 2800 | 40,000 S.F., 133.33 ton | 7.45 | 4.83 | 12.28 |
| 2880 | Food supermarkets, 3,000 S.F., 8.50 ton | 17.90 | 11.70 | 29.60 |
| 2920 | 6,000 S.F., 17.00 ton | 13.15 | 8.95 | 22.10 |
| 2960 | 10,000 S.F., 28.33 ton | 10.30 | 6.30 | 16.60 |
| 3000 | 20,000 S.F., 56.66 ton | 8.30 | 4.62 | 12.92 |

## D3030 Cooling Generating Systems

| D3030 110 | Chilled Water, Air Cooled Condenser Systems | COST PER S.F. | | |
|---|---|---|---|---|
| | | MAT. | INST. | TOTAL |
| 3040 | 40,000 S.F., 113.33 ton | 6.45 | 4.73 | 11.18 |
| 3120 | Medical centers, 3,000 S.F., 7.00 ton | 16.75 | 11.40 | 28.15 |
| 3160 | 6,000 S.F., 14.00 ton | 12.25 | 8.70 | 20.95 |
| 3200 | 10,000 S.F., 23.33 ton | 10.15 | 6.60 | 16.75 |
| 3240 | 20,000 S.F., 46.66 ton | 8.15 | 4.82 | 12.97 |
| 3280 | 40,000 S.F., 93.33 ton | 6 | 4.65 | 10.65 |
| 3360 | Offices, 3,000 S.F., 9.50 ton | 16.55 | 11.65 | 28.20 |
| 3400 | 6,000 S.F., 19.00 ton | 14.35 | 9.40 | 23.75 |
| 3440 | 10,000 S.F., 31.66 ton | 11.15 | 6.55 | 17.70 |
| 3480 | 20,000 S.F., 63.33 ton | 8.60 | 6 | 14.60 |
| 3520 | 40,000 S.F., 126.66 ton | 7.40 | 4.88 | 12.28 |
| 3600 | Restaurants, 3,000 S.F., 15.00 ton | 20 | 12.75 | 32.75 |
| 3640 | 6,000 S.F., 30.00 ton | 16.95 | 9.65 | 26.60 |
| 3680 | 10,000 S.F., 50.00 ton | 14 | 7 | 21 |
| 3720 | 20,000 S.F., 100.00 ton | 11.20 | 6.55 | 17.75 |
| 3760 | 40,000 S.F., 200 ton* | | | |
| 3840 | Schools and colleges, 3,000 S.F., 11.50 ton | 18.05 | 12.10 | 30.15 |
| 3880 | 6,000 S.F., 23.00 ton | 15.55 | 9.75 | 25.30 |
| 3920 | 10,000 S.F., 38.33 ton | 12.20 | 6.80 | 19 |
| 3960 | 20,000 S.F., 76.66 ton | 9.70 | 6.25 | 15.95 |
| 4000 | 40,000 S.F., 153 ton* | | | |

# D3030 Cooling Generating Systems

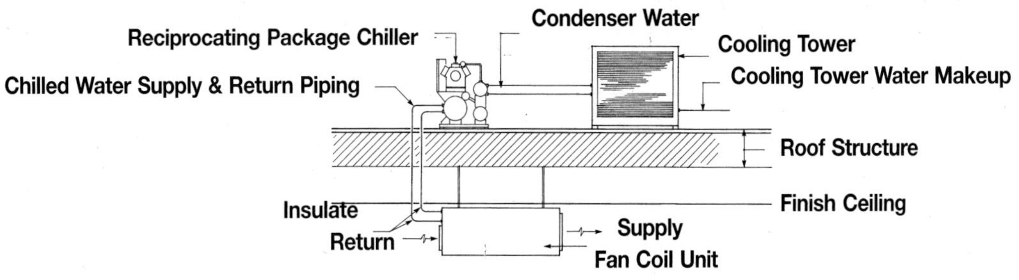


*Cooling requirements would lead to a choice of multiple chillers

| D3030 115 | Chilled Water, Cooling Tower Systems | COST PER S.F. MAT. | COST PER S.F. INST. | COST PER S.F. TOTAL |
|---|---|---|---|---|
| 1300 | Packaged chiller, water cooled, with fan coil unit | | | |
| 1320 | Apartment corridors, 4,000 S.F., 7.33 ton | 16.35 | 12.42 | 28.77 |
| 1360 | 6,000 S.F., 11.00 ton | 11.30 | 8.85 | 20.15 |
| 1400 | 10,000 S.F., 18.33 ton | 9.90 | 6.65 | 16.55 |
| 1440 | 20,000 S.F., 26.66 ton | 7.80 | 4.78 | 12.58 |
| 1480 | 40,000 S.F., 73.33 ton | 5.95 | 4.77 | 10.72 |
| 1520 | 60,000 S.F., 110.00 ton | 5.60 | 5.05 | 10.65 |
| 1600 | Banks and libraries, 4,000 S.F., 16.66 ton | 19.65 | 11.20 | 30.85 |
| 1640 | 6,000 S.F., 25.00 ton | 17.25 | 9.85 | 27.10 |
| 1680 | 10,000 S.F., 41.66 ton | 13.80 | 7.30 | 21.10 |
| 1720 | 20,000 S.F., 83.33 ton | 10.50 | 6.50 | 17 |
| 1760 | 40,000 S.F., 166.66 ton | 14.75 | 8.45 | 23.20 |
| 1800 | 60,000 S.F., 250.00 ton | 15.45 | 8.90 | 24.35 |
| 1880 | Bars and taverns, 4,000 S.F., 44.33 ton | 30.50 | 13.90 | 44.40 |
| 1920 | 6,000 S.F., 66.50 ton | 25 | 14.40 | 39.40 |
| 1960 | 10,000 S.F., 110.83 ton | 21.50 | 11 | 32.50 |
| 2000 | 20,000 S.F., 221.66 ton | 28.50 | 11.45 | 39.95 |
| 2040 | 40,000 S.F., 440 ton* | | | |
| 2080 | 60,000 S.F., 660 ton* | | | |
| 2160 | Bowling alleys, 4,000 S.F., 22.66 ton | 22 | 12.55 | 34.55 |
| 2200 | 6,000 S.F., 34.00 ton | 19.75 | 10.55 | 30.30 |
| 2240 | 10,000 S.F., 56.66 ton | 15.90 | 7.85 | 23.75 |
| 2280 | 20,000 S.F., 113.33 ton | 11.80 | 7.15 | 18.95 |
| 2320 | 40,000 S.F., 226.66 ton | 17.55 | 8.40 | 25.95 |
| 2360 | 60,000 S.F., 340 ton | | | |
| 2440 | Department stores, 4,000 S.F., 11.66 ton | 14.50 | 11.10 | 25.60 |
| 2480 | 6,000 S.F., 17.50 ton | 15.10 | 9.15 | 24.25 |
| 2520 | 10,000 S.F., 29.17 ton | 11.30 | 6.65 | 17.95 |
| 2560 | 20,000 S.F., 58.33 ton | 8.75 | 5.05 | 13.80 |
| 2600 | 40,000 S.F., 116.66 ton | 6.90 | 5.10 | 12 |
| 2640 | 60,000 S.F., 175.00 ton | 13.60 | 8.20 | 21.80 |
| 2720 | Drug stores, 4,000 S.F., 26.66 ton | 24 | 12.60 | 36.60 |
| 2760 | 6,000 S.F., 40.00 ton | 21.50 | 10.75 | 32.25 |
| 2800 | 10,000 S.F., 66.66 ton | 16 | 9.75 | 25.75 |
| 2840 | 20,000 S.F., 133.33 ton | 13.50 | 7.60 | 21.10 |
| 2880 | 40,000 S.F., 266.67 ton | 19.15 | 9.50 | 28.65 |
| 2920 | 60,000 S.F., 400 ton* | | | |
| 3000 | Factories, 4,000 S.F., 13.33 ton | 17.65 | 10.70 | 28.35 |
| 3040 | 6,000 S.F., 20.00 ton | 14.95 | 9.40 | 24.35 |
| 3080 | 10,000 S.F., 33.33 ton | 12.10 | 6.85 | 18.95 |
| 3120 | 20,000 S.F., 66.66 ton | 8.60 | 6.30 | 14.90 |
| 3160 | 40,000 S.F., 133.33 ton | 7.75 | 5.35 | 13.10 |

## D3030 Cooling Generating Systems

| D3030 115 | Chilled Water, Cooling Tower Systems | COST PER S.F. | | |
|---|---|---|---|---|
| | | MAT. | INST. | TOTAL |
| 3200 | 60,000 S.F., 200.00 ton | 14.25 | 8.60 | 22.85 |
| 3280 | Food supermarkets, 4,000 S.F., 11.33 ton | 14.35 | 11.05 | 25.40 |
| 3320 | 6,000 S.F., 17.00 ton | 13.75 | 9.15 | 22.90 |
| 3360 | 10,000 S.F., 28.33 ton | 11.15 | 6.60 | 17.75 |
| 3400 | 20,000 S.F., 56.66 ton | 9 | 5.05 | 14.05 |
| 3440 | 40,000 S.F., 113.33 ton | 6.90 | 5.10 | 12 |
| 3480 | 60,000 S.F., 170.00 ton | 13.55 | 8.20 | 21.75 |
| 3560 | Medical centers, 4.000 S.F., 9.33 ton | 12.85 | 10.15 | 23 |
| 3600 | 6,000 S.F., 14.00 ton | 13.70 | 8.80 | 22.50 |
| 3640 | 10,000 S.F., 23.33 ton | 10.75 | 6.55 | 17.30 |
| 3680 | 20,000 S.F., 46.66 ton | 8.35 | 4.93 | 13.28 |
| 3720 | 40,000 S.F., 93.33 ton | 6.60 | 4.98 | 11.58 |
| 3760 | 60,000 S.F., 140.00 ton | 12.45 | 8.30 | 20.75 |
| 3840 | Offices, 4,000 S.F., 12.66 ton | 17.25 | 10.60 | 27.85 |
| 3880 | 6,000 S.F., 19.00 ton | 15.05 | 9.60 | 24.65 |
| 3920 | 10,000 S.F., 31.66 ton | 12.15 | 6.95 | 19.10 |
| 3960 | 20,000 S.F., 63.33 ton | 8.55 | 6.30 | 14.85 |
| 4000 | 40,000 S.F., 126.66 ton | 12.90 | 8 | 20.90 |
| 4040 | 60,000 S.F., 190.00 ton | 13.90 | 8.50 | 22.40 |
| 4120 | Restaurants, 4,000 S.F., 20.00 ton | 19.95 | 11.65 | 31.60 |
| 4160 | 6,000 S.F., 30.00 ton | 18.10 | 9.90 | 28 |
| 4200 | 10,000 S.F., 50.00 ton | 14.90 | 7.55 | 22.45 |
| 4240 | 20,000 S.F., 100.00 ton | 12 | 7 | 19 |
| 4280 | 40,000 S.F., 200.00 ton | 15.05 | 8.15 | 23.20 |
| 4320 | 60,000 S.F., 300.00 ton | 16.75 | 9.20 | 25.95 |
| 4400 | Schools and colleges, 4,000 S.F., 15.33 ton | 18.85 | 11 | 29.85 |
| 4440 | 6,000 S.F., 23.00 ton | 16.55 | 9.65 | 26.20 |
| 4480 | 10,000 S.F., 38.33 ton | 13.20 | 7.15 | 20.35 |
| 4520 | 20,000 S.F., 76.66 ton | 10.20 | 6.45 | 16.65 |
| 4560 | 40,000 S.F., 153.33 ton | 14.10 | 8.25 | 22.35 |
| 4600 | 60,000 S.F., 230.00 ton | 14.45 | 8.60 | 23.05 |

## D3050 Terminal & Package Units

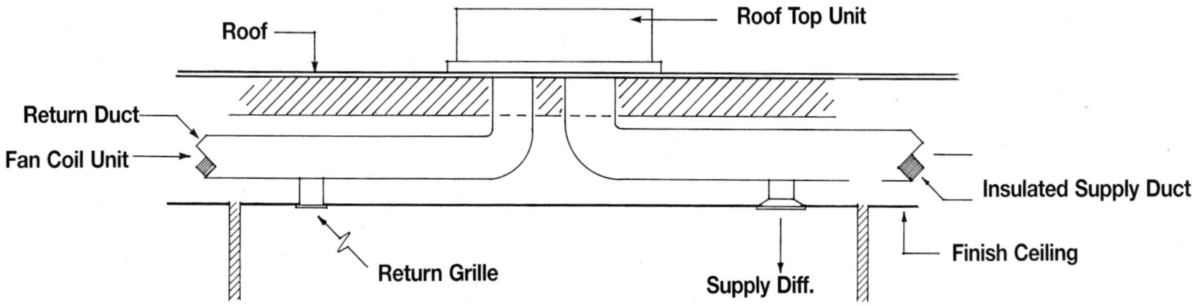


*Above normal capacity

Rooftop, Single Zone System

| D3050 150 | Rooftop Single Zone Unit Systems | COST PER S.F. MAT. | COST PER S.F. INST. | COST PER S.F. TOTAL |
|---|---|---|---|---|
| 1260 | Rooftop, single zone, air conditioner | | | |
| 1280 | Apartment corridors, 500 S.F., .92 ton | 2.65 | 4.95 | 7.60 |
| 1320 | 1,000 S.F., 1.83 ton | 2.62 | 4.92 | 7.54 |
| 1360 | 1,500 S.F., 2.75 ton | 2.52 | 4.06 | 6.58 |
| 1400 | 3,000 S.F., 5.50 ton | 2.49 | 3.91 | 6.40 |
| 1440 | 5,000 S.F., 9.17 ton | 2.39 | 3.55 | 5.94 |
| 1480 | 10,000 S.F., 18.33 ton | 2.36 | 3.34 | 5.70 |
| 1560 | Banks or libraries, 500 S.F., 2.08 ton | 5.95 | 11.20 | 17.15 |
| 1600 | 1,000 S.F., 4.17 ton | 5.75 | 9.25 | 15 |
| 1640 | 1,500 S.F., 6.25 ton | 5.65 | 8.90 | 14.55 |
| 1680 | 3,000 S.F., 12.50 ton | 5.45 | 8.05 | 13.50 |
| 1720 | 5,000 S.F., 20.80 ton | 5.35 | 7.60 | 12.95 |
| 1760 | 10,000 S.F., 41.67 ton | 6.95 | 7.55 | 14.50 |
| 1840 | Bars and taverns, 500 S.F., 5.54 ton | 12.75 | 14.85 | 27.60 |
| 1880 | 1,000 S.F., 11.08 ton | 12.15 | 12.75 | 24.90 |
| 1920 | 1,500 S.F., 16.62 ton | 12.20 | 11.85 | 24.05 |
| 1960 | 3,000 S.F., 33.25 ton | 17.45 | 11.35 | 28.80 |
| 2000 | 5,000 S.F., 55.42 ton | 14.95 | 11.30 | 26.25 |
| 2040 | 10,000 S.F., 110.83 ton* | | | |
| 2080 | Bowling alleys, 500 S.F., 2.83 ton | 7.80 | 12.55 | 20.35 |
| 2120 | 1,000 S.F., 5.67 ton | 7.70 | 12.05 | 19.75 |
| 2160 | 1,500 S.F., 8.50 ton | 7.40 | 11 | 18.40 |
| 2200 | 3,000 S.F., 17.00 ton | 7.45 | 10.55 | 18 |
| 2240 | 5,000 S.F., 28.33 ton | 10.10 | 10.25 | 20.35 |
| 2280 | 10,000 S.F., 56.67 ton | 8.85 | 10.25 | 19.10 |
| 2360 | Department stores, 500 S.F., 1.46 ton | 4.18 | 7.85 | 12.03 |
| 2400 | 1,000 S.F., 2.92 ton | 4.01 | 6.50 | 10.51 |
| 2480 | 3,000 S.F., 8.75 ton | 3.81 | 5.65 | 9.46 |
| 2520 | 5,000 S.F., 14.58 ton | 3.83 | 5.40 | 9.23 |
| 2560 | 10,000 S.F., 29.17 ton | 5.20 | 5.30 | 10.50 |
| 2640 | Drug stores, 500 S.F., 3.33 ton | 9.15 | 14.80 | 23.95 |
| 2680 | 1,000 S.F., 6.67 ton | 9.05 | 14.20 | 23.25 |
| 2720 | 1,500 S.F., 10.00 ton | 8.70 | 12.90 | 21.60 |
| 2760 | 3,000 S.F., 20.00 ton | 8.55 | 12.15 | 20.70 |
| 2800 | 5,000 S.F., 33.33 ton | 11.90 | 12.05 | 23.95 |
| 2840 | 10,000 S.F., 66.67 ton | 10.40 | 12.05 | 22.45 |
| 2920 | Factories, 500 S.F., 1.67 ton | 4.76 | 8.95 | 13.71 |
| 3000 | 1,500 S.F., 5.00 ton | 4.53 | 7.10 | 11.63 |
| 3040 | 3,000 S.F., 10.00 ton | 4.35 | 6.45 | 10.80 |
| 3080 | 5,000 S.F., 16.67 ton | 4.38 | 6.20 | 10.58 |
| 3120 | 10,000 S.F., 33.33 ton | 5.95 | 6.05 | 12 |
| 3200 | Food supermarkets, 500 S.F., 1.42 ton | 4.06 | 7.60 | 11.66 |

## D3050 Terminal & Package Units

| D3050 150 | Rooftop Single Zone Unit Systems | COST PER S.F. | | |
|---|---|---|---|---|
| | | MAT. | INST. | TOTAL |
| 3240 | 1,000 S.F., 2.83 ton | 3.87 | 6.25 | 10.12 |
| 3280 | 1,500 S.F., 4.25 ton | 3.85 | 6.05 | 9.90 |
| 3320 | 3,000 S.F., 8.50 ton | 3.70 | 5.50 | 9.20 |
| 3360 | 5,000 S.F., 14.17 ton | 3.72 | 5.25 | 8.97 |
| 3400 | 10,000 S.F., 28.33 ton | 5.05 | 5.15 | 10.20 |
| 3480 | Medical centers, 500 S.F., 1.17 ton | 3.34 | 6.30 | 9.64 |
| 3520 | 1,000 S.F., 2.33 ton | 3.34 | 6.25 | 9.59 |
| 3560 | 1,500 S.F., 3.50 ton | 3.21 | 5.20 | 8.41 |
| 3640 | 5,000 S.F., 11.67 ton | 3.04 | 4.52 | 7.56 |
| 3680 | 10,000 S.F., 23.33 ton | 3 | 4.25 | 7.25 |
| 3760 | Offices, 500 S.F., 1.58 ton | 4.53 | 8.50 | 13.03 |
| 3800 | 1,000 S.F., 3.17 ton | 4.36 | 7.05 | 11.41 |
| 3840 | 1,500 S.F., 4.75 ton | 4.31 | 6.75 | 11.06 |
| 3880 | 3,000 S.F., 9.50 ton | 4.13 | 6.15 | 10.28 |
| 3920 | 5,000 S.F., 15.83 ton | 4.16 | 5.90 | 10.06 |
| 3960 | 10,000 S.F., 31.67 ton | 5.65 | 5.75 | 11.40 |
| 4000 | Restaurants, 500 S.F., 2.50 ton | 7.15 | 13.45 | 20.60 |
| 4040 | 1,000 S.F., 5.00 ton | 6.80 | 10.65 | 17.45 |
| 4080 | 1,500 S.F., 7.50 ton | 6.55 | 9.70 | 16.25 |
| 4120 | 3,000 S.F., 15.00 ton | 6.55 | 9.30 | 15.85 |
| 4160 | 5,000 S.F., 25.00 ton | 6.45 | 9.10 | 15.55 |
| 4200 | 10,000 S.F., 50.00 ton | 7.80 | 9.05 | 16.85 |
| 4240 | Schools and colleges, 500 S.F., 1.92 ton | 5.50 | 10.30 | 15.80 |
| 4280 | 1,000 S.F., 3.83 ton | 5.25 | 8.50 | 13.75 |
| 4360 | 3,000 S.F., 11.50 ton | 5 | 7.45 | 12.45 |
| 4400 | 5,000 S.F., 19.17 ton | 4.93 | 7 | 11.93 |

## D3050 Terminal & Package Units

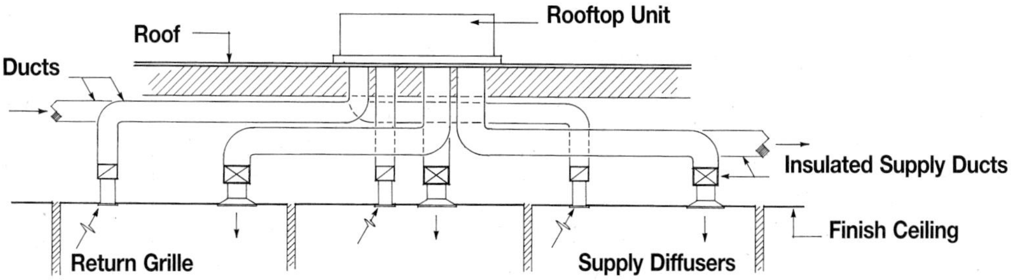


*Note A: Small single zone unit recommended.

*Note B: A combination of multizone units recommended.

| D3050 155 | Rooftop Multizone Unit Systems | COST PER S.F. | | |
|---|---|---|---|---|
| | | MAT. | INST. | TOTAL |
| 1240 | Rooftop, multizone, air conditioner | | | |
| 1260 | Apartment corridors, 1,500 S.F., 2.75 ton. See Note A. | | | |
| 1280 | 3,000 S.F., 5.50 ton | 11.28 | 5.76 | 17.04 |
| 1320 | 10,000 S.F., 18.30 ton | 7.55 | 6.15 | 13.70 |
| 1360 | 15,000 S.F., 27.50 ton | 7.30 | 6.10 | 13.40 |
| 1400 | 20,000 S.F., 36.70 ton | 7.65 | 6.15 | 13.80 |
| 1440 | 25,000 S.F., 45.80 ton | 7.15 | 6.15 | 13.30 |
| 1520 | Banks or libraries, 1,500 S.F., 6.25 ton | 28.50 | 14.50 | 43 |
| 1560 | 3,000 S.F., 12.50 ton | 24 | 14.20 | 38.20 |
| 1600 | 10,000 S.F., 41.67 ton | 16.30 | 14.05 | 30.35 |
| 1640 | 15,000 S.F., 62.50 ton | 12.40 | 13.95 | 26.35 |
| 1680 | 20,000 S.F., 83.33 ton | 12.40 | 13.95 | 26.35 |
| 1720 | 25,000 S.F., 104.00 ton | 12.40 | 13.90 | 26.30 |
| 1800 | Bars and taverns, 1,500 S.F., 16.62 ton | 61 | 21 | 82 |
| 1840 | 3,000 S.F., 33.24 ton | 43 | 20 | 63 |
| 1880 | 10,000 S.F., 110.83 ton | 30 | 20 | 50 |
| 1920 | 15,000 S.F., 165 ton, See Note B. | | | |
| 1960 | 20,000 S.F., 220 ton, See Note B. | | | |
| 2000 | 25,000 S.F., 275 ton, See Note B. | | | |
| 2080 | Bowling alleys, 1,500 S.F., 8.50 ton | 39 | 19.75 | 58.75 |
| 2120 | 3,000 S.F., 17.00 ton | 33 | 19.30 | 52.30 |
| 2160 | 10,000 S.F., 56.70 ton | 22 | 19.10 | 41.10 |
| 2200 | 15,000 S.F., 85.00 ton | 16.85 | 18.95 | 35.80 |
| 2240 | 20,000 S.F., 113.00 ton | 16.85 | 18.85 | 35.70 |
| 2280 | 25,000 S.F., 140.00 ton see Note B. | | | |
| 2360 | Department stores, 1,500 S.F., 4.37 ton, See Note A. | | | |
| 2400 | 3,000 S.F., 8.75 ton | 19.95 | 10.15 | 30.10 |
| 2440 | 10,000 S.F., 29.17 ton | 12.15 | 9.75 | 21.90 |
| 2520 | 20,000 S.F., 58.33 ton | 8.70 | 9.75 | 18.45 |
| 2560 | 25,000 S.F., 72.92 ton | 8.65 | 9.75 | 18.40 |
| 2640 | Drug stores, 1,500 S.F., 10.00 ton | 45.50 | 23 | 68.50 |
| 2680 | 3,000 S.F., 20.00 ton | 27.50 | 22.50 | 50 |
| 2720 | 10,000 S.F., 66.66 ton | 19.85 | 22.50 | 42.35 |
| 2760 | 15,000 S.F., 100.00 ton | 19.90 | 22 | 41.90 |
| 2800 | 20,000 S.F., 135 ton, See Note B. | | | |
| 2840 | 25,000 S.F., 165 ton, See Note B. | | | |
| 2920 | Factories, 1,500 S.F., 5 ton, See Note A. | | | |
| 3000 | 10,000 S.F., 33.33 ton | 13.90 | 11.15 | 25.05 |

## D3050 Terminal & Package Units

| D3050 155 | Rooftop Multizone Unit Systems | COST PER S.F. | | |
|---|---|---|---|---|
| | | MAT. | INST. | TOTAL |
| 3040 | 15,000 S.F., 50.00 ton | 13.05 | 11.20 | 24.25 |
| 3080 | 20,000 S.F., 66.66 ton | 9.95 | 11.15 | 21.10 |
| 3120 | 25,000 S.F., 83.33 ton | 9.90 | 11.15 | 21.05 |
| 3200 | Food supermarkets, 1,500 S.F., 4.25 ton, See Note A. | | | |
| 3240 | 3,000 S.F., 8.50 ton | 19.40 | 9.85 | 29.25 |
| 3280 | 10,000 S.F., 28.33 ton | 11.30 | 9.45 | 20.75 |
| 3320 | 15,000 S.F., 42.50 ton | 11.10 | 9.55 | 20.65 |
| 3360 | 20,000 S.F., 56.67 ton | 8.45 | 9.45 | 17.90 |
| 3400 | 25,000 S.F., 70.83 ton | 8.45 | 9.45 | 17.90 |
| 3480 | Medical centers, 1,500 S.F., 3.5 ton, See Note A. | | | |
| 3520 | 3,000 S.F., 7.00 ton | 15.95 | 8.10 | 24.05 |
| 3560 | 10,000 S.F., 23.33 ton | 9.30 | 7.80 | 17.10 |
| 3600 | 15,000 S.F., 35.00 ton | 9.70 | 7.80 | 17.50 |
| 3640 | 20,000 S.F., 46.66 ton | 9.10 | 7.85 | 16.95 |
| 3680 | 25,000 S.F., 58.33 ton | 6.95 | 7.80 | 14.75 |
| 3760 | Offices, 1,500 S.F., 4.75 ton, See Note A. | | | |
| 3800 | 3,000 S.F., 9.50 ton | 21.50 | 11.05 | 32.55 |
| 3840 | 10,000 S.F., 31.66 ton | 13.20 | 10.60 | 23.80 |
| 3920 | 20,000 S.F., 63.33 ton | 9.45 | 10.60 | 20.05 |
| 3960 | 25,000 S.F., 79.16 ton | 9.40 | 10.60 | 20 |
| 4000 | Restaurants, 1,500 S.F., 7.50 ton | 34 | 17.40 | 51.40 |
| 4040 | 3,000 S.F., 15.00 ton | 29 | 17.05 | 46.05 |
| 4080 | 10,000 S.F., 50.00 ton | 19.55 | 16.85 | 36.40 |
| 4120 | 15,000 S.F., 75.00 ton | 14.90 | 16.70 | 31.60 |
| 4160 | 20,000 S.F., 100.00 ton | 14.90 | 16.70 | 31.60 |
| 4200 | 25,000 S.F., 125 ton, See Note B. | | | |
| 4240 | Schools and colleges, 1,500 S.F., 5.75 ton | 26 | 13.35 | 39.35 |
| 4320 | 10,000 S.F., 38.33 ton | 15 | 12.90 | 27.90 |
| 4360 | 15,000 S.F., 57.50 ton | 11.40 | 12.80 | 24.20 |
| 4400 | 20,000 S.F., 76.66 ton | 11.40 | 12.80 | 24.20 |
| 4440 | 25,000 S.F., 95.83 ton | 11.90 | 12.80 | 24.70 |

## D3050 Terminal & Package Units

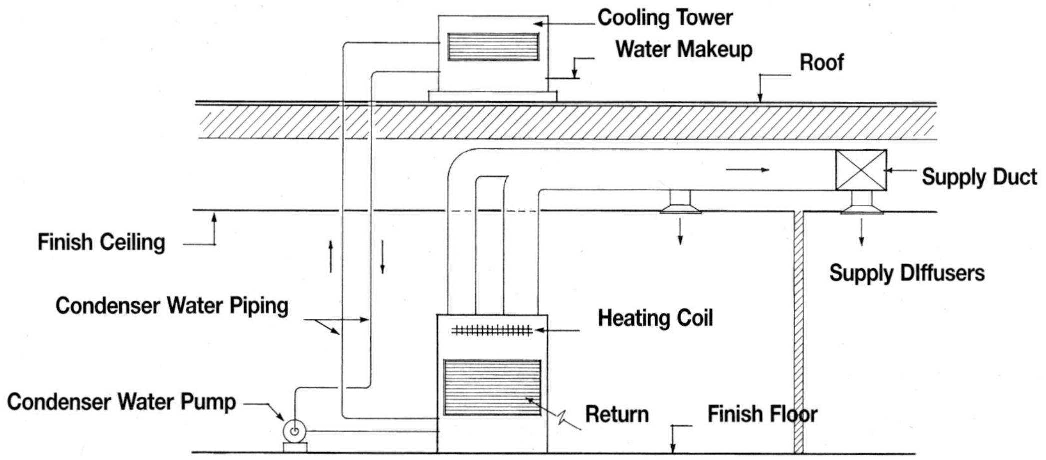


Self-Contained Water Cooled System

| D3050 160 | Self-contained, Water Cooled Unit Systems | COST PER S.F. | | |
|---|---|---|---|---|
| | | MAT. | INST. | TOTAL |
| 1280 | Self-contained, water cooled unit | 3.78 | 4.01 | 7.79 |
| 1300 | Apartment corridors, 500 S.F., .92 ton | 3.80 | 4 | 7.80 |
| 1320 | 1,000 S.F., 1.83 ton | 3.77 | 3.99 | 7.76 |
| 1360 | 3,000 S.F., 5.50 ton | 3.16 | 3.34 | 6.50 |
| 1400 | 5,000 S.F., 9.17 ton | 2.89 | 3.10 | 5.99 |
| 1440 | 10,000 S.F., 18.33 ton | 3.99 | 2.78 | 6.77 |
| 1520 | Banks or libraries, 500 S.F., 2.08 ton | 8.20 | 4.07 | 12.27 |
| 1560 | 1,000 S.F., 4.17 ton | 7.15 | 7.60 | 14.75 |
| 1600 | 3,000 S.F., 12.50 ton | 6.60 | 7.05 | 13.65 |
| 1640 | 5,000 S.F., 20.80 ton | 9.05 | 6.30 | 15.35 |
| 1680 | 10,000 S.F., 41.66 ton | 7.65 | 6.30 | 13.95 |
| 1760 | Bars and taverns, 500 S.F., 5.54 ton | 18 | 6.90 | 24.90 |
| 1800 | 1,000 S.F., 11.08 ton | 16.90 | 12.05 | 28.95 |
| 1840 | 3,000 S.F., 33.25 ton | 21.50 | 9.55 | 31.05 |
| 1880 | 5,000 S.F., 55.42 ton | 18 | 9.95 | 27.95 |
| 1920 | 10,000 S.F., 110.00 ton | 17.40 | 9.80 | 27.20 |
| 2000 | Bowling alleys, 500 S.F., 2.83 ton | 11.15 | 5.55 | 16.70 |
| 2040 | 1,000 S.F., 5.66 ton | 9.75 | 10.35 | 20.10 |
| 2080 | 3,000 S.F., 17.00 ton | 12.35 | 8.60 | 20.95 |
| 2120 | 5,000 S.F., 28.33 ton | 11.20 | 8.30 | 19.50 |
| 2160 | 10,000 S.F., 56.66 ton | 9.45 | 8.50 | 17.95 |
| 2200 | Department stores, 500 S.F., 1.46 ton | 5.75 | 2.86 | 8.61 |
| 2240 | 1,000 S.F., 2.92 ton | 5 | 5.30 | 10.30 |
| 2280 | 3,000 S.F., 8.75 ton | 4.60 | 4.94 | 9.54 |
| 2320 | 5,000 S.F., 14.58 ton | 6.35 | 4.43 | 10.78 |
| 2360 | 10,000 S.F., 29.17 ton | 5.75 | 4.27 | 10.02 |
| 2440 | Drug stores, 500 S.F., 3.33 ton | 13.15 | 6.55 | 19.70 |
| 2480 | 1,000 S.F., 6.66 ton | 11.45 | 12.15 | 23.60 |
| 2520 | 3,000 S.F., 20.00 ton | 14.50 | 10.10 | 24.60 |
| 2560 | 5,000 S.F., 33.33 ton | 15.20 | 10 | 25.20 |
| 2600 | 10,000 S.F., 66.66 ton | 11.10 | 10 | 21.10 |
| 2680 | Factories, 500 S.F., 1.66 ton | 6.55 | 3.26 | 9.81 |
| 2720 | 1,000 S.F., 3.37 ton | 5.80 | 6.15 | 11.95 |
| 2760 | 3,000 S.F., 10.00 ton | 5.25 | 5.65 | 10.90 |
| 2800 | 5,000 S.F., 16.66 ton | 7.25 | 5.05 | 12.30 |
| 2840 | 10,000 S.F., 33.33 ton | 6.60 | 4.88 | 11.48 |

## D3050 Terminal & Package Units

| D3050 160 | Self-contained, Water Cooled Unit Systems | COST PER S.F. | | |
|---|---|---|---|---|
| | | MAT. | INST. | TOTAL |
| 2920 | Food supermarkets, 500 S.F., 1.42 ton | 5.60 | 2.77 | 8.37 |
| 2960 | 1,000 S.F., 2.83 ton | 5.85 | 6.15 | 12 |
| 3000 | 3,000 S.F., 8.50 ton | 4.88 | 5.15 | 10.03 |
| 3040 | 5,000 S.F., 14.17 ton | 4.47 | 4.80 | 9.27 |
| 3080 | 10,000 S.F., 28.33 ton | 5.60 | 4.15 | 9.75 |
| 3160 | Medical centers, 500 S.F., 1.17 ton | 4.60 | 2.28 | 6.88 |
| 3200 | 1,000 S.F., 2.33 ton | 4.81 | 5.10 | 9.91 |
| 3240 | 3,000 S.F., 7.00 ton | 4.02 | 4.26 | 8.28 |
| 3280 | 5,000 S.F., 11.66 ton | 3.68 | 3.95 | 7.63 |
| 3320 | 10,000 S.F., 23.33 ton | 5.10 | 3.54 | 8.64 |
| 3400 | Offices, 500 S.F., 1.58 ton | 6.25 | 3.10 | 9.35 |
| 3440 | 1,000 S.F., 3.17 ton | 6.50 | 6.90 | 13.40 |
| 3480 | 3,000 S.F., 9.50 ton | 5 | 5.35 | 10.35 |
| 3520 | 5,000 S.F., 15.83 ton | 6.90 | 4.81 | 11.71 |
| 3560 | 10,000 S.F., 31.67 ton | 6.25 | 4.63 | 10.88 |
| 3640 | Restaurants, 500 S.F., 2.50 ton | 9.85 | 4.90 | 14.75 |
| 3680 | 1,000 S.F., 5.00 ton | 8.60 | 9.10 | 17.70 |
| 3720 | 3,000 S.F., 15.00 ton | 7.90 | 8.45 | 16.35 |
| 3760 | 5,000 S.F., 25.00 ton | 10.90 | 7.60 | 18.50 |
| 3800 | 10,000 S.F., 50.00 ton | 6.85 | 6.95 | 13.80 |
| 3880 | Schools and colleges, 500 S.F., 1.92 ton | 7.55 | 3.75 | 11.30 |
| 3920 | 1,000 S.F., 3.83 ton | 6.60 | 7 | 13.60 |
| 3960 | 3,000 S.F., 11.50 ton | 6.05 | 6.50 | 12.55 |
| 4000 | 5,000 S.F., 19.17 ton | 8.35 | 5.80 | 14.15 |
| 4040 | 10,000 S.F., 38.33 ton | 7.05 | 5.80 | 12.85 |

## D3050 Terminal & Package Units

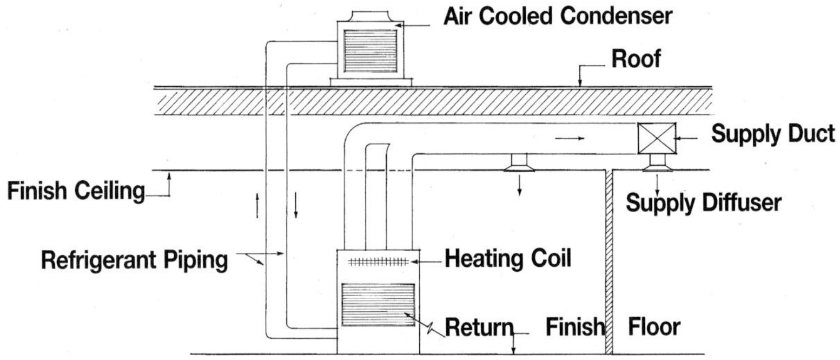


Self-Contained Air Cooled System

| D3050 165 | Self-contained, Air Cooled Unit Systems | COST PER S.F. MAT. | COST PER S.F. INST. | COST PER S.F. TOTAL |
|---|---|---|---|---|
| 1300 | Self-contained, air cooled unit | | | |
| 1320 | Apartment corridors, 500 S.F., .92 ton | 6.25 | 5.10 | 11.35 |
| 1360 | 1,000 S.F., 1.83 ton | 6.15 | 5.05 | 11.20 |
| 1400 | 3,000 S.F., 5.50 ton | 5.40 | 4.73 | 10.13 |
| 1440 | 5,000 S.F., 9.17 ton | 4.68 | 4.50 | 9.18 |
| 1480 | 10,000 S.F., 18.33 ton | 3.94 | 4.13 | 8.07 |
| 1560 | Banks or libraries, 500 S.F., 2.08 ton | 13.55 | 6.50 | 20.05 |
| 1600 | 1,000 S.F., 4.17 ton | 12.25 | 10.75 | 23 |
| 1640 | 3,000 S.F., 12.50 ton | 10.65 | 10.25 | 20.90 |
| 1680 | 5,000 S.F., 20.80 ton | 9.05 | 9.40 | 18.45 |
| 1720 | 10,000 S.F., 41.66 ton | 10 | 9.20 | 19.20 |
| 1800 | Bars and taverns, 500 S.F., 5.54 ton | 30 | 14.15 | 44.15 |
| 1840 | 1,000 S.F., 11.08 ton | 28 | 20.50 | 48.50 |
| 1880 | 3,000 S.F., 33.25 ton | 26.50 | 17.80 | 44.30 |
| 1920 | 5,000 S.F., 55.42 ton | 26.50 | 17.80 | 44.30 |
| 1960 | 10,000 S.F., 110.00 ton | 27 | 17.65 | 44.65 |
| 2040 | Bowling alleys, 500 S.F., 2.83 ton | 18.55 | 8.85 | 27.40 |
| 2080 | 1,000 S.F., 5.66 ton | 16.75 | 14.65 | 31.40 |
| 2120 | 3,000 S.F., 17.00 ton | 12.20 | 12.80 | 25 |
| 2160 | 5,000 S.F., 28.33 ton | 13.75 | 12.50 | 26.25 |
| 2200 | 10,000 S.F., 56.66 ton | 13.80 | 12.50 | 26.30 |
| 2240 | Department stores, 500 S.F., 1.46 ton | 9.55 | 4.56 | 14.11 |
| 2280 | 1,000 S.F., 2.92 ton | 8.60 | 7.55 | 16.15 |
| 2320 | 3,000 S.F., 8.75 ton | 7.45 | 7.15 | 14.60 |
| 2360 | 5,000 S.F., 14.58 ton | 7.45 | 7.15 | 14.60 |
| 2400 | 10,000 S.F., 29.17 ton | 7.10 | 6.45 | 13.55 |
| 2480 | Drug stores, 500 S.F., 3.33 ton | 22 | 10.45 | 32.45 |
| 2520 | 1,000 S.F., 6.66 ton | 19.65 | 17.20 | 36.85 |
| 2560 | 3,000 S.F., 20.00 ton | 14.55 | 15.05 | 29.60 |
| 2600 | 5,000 S.F., 33.33 ton | 16.20 | 14.70 | 30.90 |
| 2640 | 10,000 S.F., 66.66 ton | 16.40 | 14.70 | 31.10 |
| 2720 | Factories, 500 S.F., 1.66 ton | 11.05 | 5.25 | 16.30 |
| 2760 | 1,000 S.F., 3.33 ton | 9.90 | 8.60 | 18.50 |
| 2800 | 3,000 S.F., 10.00 ton | 8.50 | 8.20 | 16.70 |
| 2840 | 5,000 S.F., 16.66 ton | 7.15 | 7.50 | 14.65 |
| 2880 | 10,000 S.F., 33.33 ton | 8.10 | 7.35 | 15.45 |
| 2960 | Food supermarkets, 500 S.F., 1.42 ton | 9.30 | 4.43 | 13.73 |
| 3000 | 1,000 S.F., 2.83 ton | 9.50 | 7.80 | 17.30 |
| 3040 | 3,000 S.F., 8.50 ton | 8.35 | 7.30 | 15.65 |
| 3080 | 5,000 S.F., 14.17 ton | 7.25 | 6.95 | 14.20 |

## D3050 Terminal & Package Units

| D3050 165 | Self-contained, Air Cooled Unit Systems | COST PER S.F. | | |
|---|---|---|---|---|
| | | MAT. | INST. | TOTAL |
| 3120 | 10,000 S.F., 28.33 ton | 6.90 | 6.25 | 13.15 |
| 3200 | Medical centers, 500 S.F., 1.17 ton | 7.70 | 3.66 | 11.36 |
| 3240 | 1,000 S.F., 2.33 ton | 7.90 | 6.45 | 14.35 |
| 3280 | 3,000 S.F., 7.00 ton | 6.90 | 6 | 12.90 |
| 3320 | 5,000 S.F., 16.66 ton | 6 | 5.75 | 11.75 |
| 3360 | 10,000 S.F., 23.33 ton | 5 | 5.25 | 10.25 |
| 3440 | Offices, 500 S.F., 1.58 ton | 10.40 | 4.96 | 15.36 |
| 3480 | 1,000 S.F., 3.16 ton | 10.70 | 8.75 | 19.45 |
| 3520 | 3,000 S.F., 9.50 ton | 8.10 | 7.80 | 15.90 |
| 3560 | 5,000 S.F., 15.83 ton | 6.90 | 7.15 | 14.05 |
| 3600 | 10,000 S.F., 31.66 ton | 7.70 | 7 | 14.70 |
| 3680 | Restaurants, 500 S.F., 2.50 ton | 16.30 | 7.80 | 24.10 |
| 3720 | 1,000 S.F., 5.00 ton | 14.75 | 12.90 | 27.65 |
| 3760 | 3,000 S.F., 15.00 ton | 12.75 | 12.30 | 25.05 |
| 3800 | 5,000 S.F., 25.00 ton | 12.10 | 11 | 23.10 |
| 3840 | 10,000 S.F., 50.00 ton | 12.70 | 11 | 23.70 |
| 3920 | Schools and colleges, 500 S.F., 1.92 ton | 12.55 | 6 | 18.55 |
| 3960 | 1,000 S.F., 3.83 ton | 11.40 | 9.90 | 21.30 |
| 4000 | 3,000 S.F., 11.50 ton | 9.80 | 9.40 | 19.20 |
| 4040 | 5,000 S.F., 19.17 ton | 8.25 | 8.65 | 16.90 |
| 4080 | 10,000 S.F., 38.33 ton | 9.20 | 8.45 | 17.65 |

## D3050 Terminal & Package Units

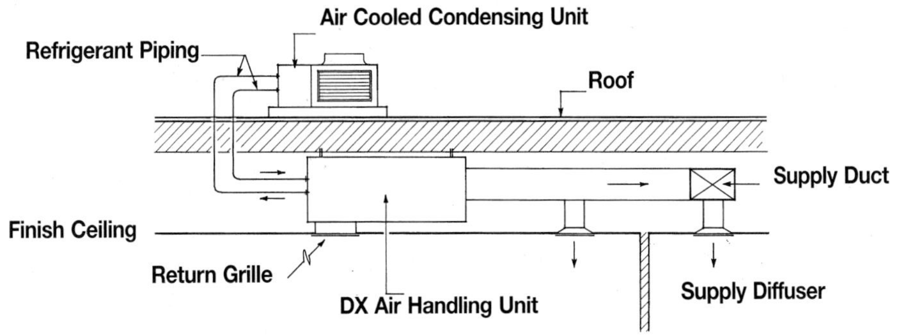


*Cooling requirements would lead to more than one system.

| D3050 170 | Split Systems With Air Cooled Condensing Units | COST PER S.F. | | |
|---|---|---|---|---|
| | | MAT. | INST. | TOTAL |
| 1260 | Split system, air cooled condensing unit | | | |
| 1280 | Apartment corridors, 1,000 S.F., 1.83 ton | 2.80 | 3.20 | 6 |
| 1320 | 2,000 S.F., 3.66 ton | 2.03 | 3.22 | 5.25 |
| 1360 | 5,000 S.F., 9.17 ton | 1.72 | 4.04 | 5.76 |
| 1400 | 10,000 S.F., 18.33 ton | 2.09 | 4.41 | 6.50 |
| 1440 | 20,000 S.F., 36.66 ton | 2.66 | 4.48 | 7.14 |
| 1520 | Banks and libraries, 1,000 S.F., 4.17 ton | 4.63 | 7.35 | 11.98 |
| 1560 | 2,000 S.F., 8.33 ton | 3.91 | 9.20 | 13.11 |
| 1600 | 5,000 S.F., 20.80 ton | 4.74 | 10 | 14.74 |
| 1640 | 10,000 S.F., 41.66 ton | 6.05 | 10.20 | 16.25 |
| 1680 | 20,000 S.F., 83.32 ton | 6.95 | 10.55 | 17.50 |
| 1760 | Bars and taverns, 1,000 S.F., 11.08 ton | 8.85 | 14.45 | 23.30 |
| 1800 | 2,000 S.F., 22.16 ton | 13.05 | 17.30 | 30.35 |
| 1840 | 5,000 S.F., 55.42 ton | 13.35 | 16.20 | 29.55 |
| 1880 | 10,000 S.F., 110.84 ton | 14.85 | 16.85 | 31.70 |
| 1920 | 20,000 S.F., 220 ton* | | | |
| 2000 | Bowling alleys, 1,000 S.F., 5.66 ton | 6.30 | 13.75 | 20.05 |
| 2040 | 2,000 S.F., 11.33 ton | 5.30 | 12.50 | 17.80 |
| 2080 | 5,000 S.F., 28.33 ton | 6.45 | 13.65 | 20.10 |
| 2120 | 10,000 S.F., 56.66 ton | 8.25 | 13.85 | 22.10 |
| 2160 | 20,000 S.F., 113.32 ton | 9.85 | 15 | 24.85 |
| 2320 | Department stores, 1,000 S.F., 2.92 ton | 3.37 | 5.05 | 8.42 |
| 2360 | 2,000 S.F., 5.83 ton | 3.26 | 7.05 | 10.31 |
| 2400 | 5,000 S.F., 14.58 ton | 2.74 | 6.45 | 9.19 |
| 2440 | 10,000 S.F., 29.17 ton | 3.33 | 7 | 10.33 |
| 2480 | 20,000 S.F., 58.33 ton | 4.24 | 7.15 | 11.39 |
| 2560 | Drug stores, 1,000 S.F., 6.66 ton | 7.45 | 16.15 | 23.60 |
| 2600 | 2,000 S.F., 13.32 ton | 6.25 | 14.70 | 20.95 |
| 2640 | 5,000 S.F., 33.33 ton | 9.70 | 16.30 | 26 |
| 2680 | 10,000 S.F., 66.66 ton | 8.70 | 16.95 | 25.65 |
| 2720 | 20,000 S.F., 133.32 ton* | | | |
| 2800 | Factories, 1,000 S.F., 3.33 ton | 3.85 | 5.75 | 9.60 |
| 2840 | 2,000 S.F., 6.66 ton | 3.72 | 8.05 | 11.77 |
| 2880 | 5,000 S.F., 16.66 ton | 3.80 | 8 | 11.80 |
| 2920 | 10,000 S.F., 33.33 ton | 4.84 | 8.15 | 12.99 |
| 2960 | 20,000 S.F., 66.66 ton | 4.35 | 8.50 | 12.85 |
| 3040 | Food supermarkets, 1,000 S.F., 2.83 ton | 3.28 | 4.90 | 8.18 |
| 3080 | 2,000 S.F., 5.66 ton | 3.16 | 6.85 | 10.01 |
| 3120 | 5,000 S.F., 14.66 ton | 2.66 | 6.25 | 8.91 |
| 3160 | 10,000 S.F., 28.33 ton | 3.23 | 6.80 | 10.03 |
| 3200 | 20,000 S.F., 56.66 ton | 4.12 | 6.95 | 11.07 |
| 3280 | Medical centers, 1,000 S.F., 2.33 ton | 2.80 | 3.95 | 6.75 |

## D3050 Terminal & Package Units

| D3050 170 | Split Systems With Air Cooled Condensing Units | COST PER S.F. | | |
|---|---|---|---|---|
| | | MAT. | INST. | TOTAL |
| 3320 | 2,000 S.F., 4.66 ton | 2.60 | 5.65 | 8.25 |
| 3360 | 5,000 S.F., 11.66 ton | 2.19 | 5.15 | 7.34 |
| 3400 | 10,000 S.F., 23.33 ton | 2.66 | 5.60 | 8.26 |
| 3440 | 20,000 S.F., 46.66 ton | 3.39 | 5.70 | 9.09 |
| 3520 | Offices, 1,000 S.F., 3.17 ton | 3.66 | 5.45 | 9.11 |
| 3560 | 2,000 S.F., 6.33 ton | 3.53 | 7.65 | 11.18 |
| 3600 | 5,000 S.F., 15.83 ton | 2.97 | 7 | 9.97 |
| 3601 | Self contained heating and air conditioning, offices, 7,500 S.F., 30 ton | 20.50 | 1.65 | 22.15 |
| 3640 | 10,000 S.F., 31.66 ton | 3.61 | 7.60 | 11.21 |
| 3680 | 20,000 S.F., 63.32 ton | 4.13 | 8.05 | 12.18 |
| 3760 | Restaurants, 1,000 S.F., 5.00 ton | 5.60 | 12.10 | 17.70 |
| 3800 | 2,000 S.F., 10.00 ton | 4.69 | 11.05 | 15.74 |
| 3840 | 5,000 S.F., 25.00 ton | 5.70 | 12.05 | 17.75 |
| 3880 | 10,000 S.F., 50.00 ton | 7.25 | 12.25 | 19.50 |
| 3920 | 20,000 S.F., 100.00 ton | 8.70 | 13.25 | 21.95 |
| 4000 | Schools and colleges, 1,000 S.F., 3.83 ton | 4.26 | 6.75 | 11.01 |
| 4040 | 2,000 S.F., 7.66 ton | 3.60 | 8.45 | 12.05 |
| 4080 | 5,000 S.F., 19.17 ton | 4.37 | 9.20 | 13.57 |
| 4120 | 10,000 S.F., 38.33 ton | 5.55 | 9.35 | 14.90 |
| 8012 | Fan coil A.C., DX w/air cooled condensing unit, 20 ton cooling | 19,400 | 5,000 | 24,400 |

## D3090 Other HVAC Systems/Equip

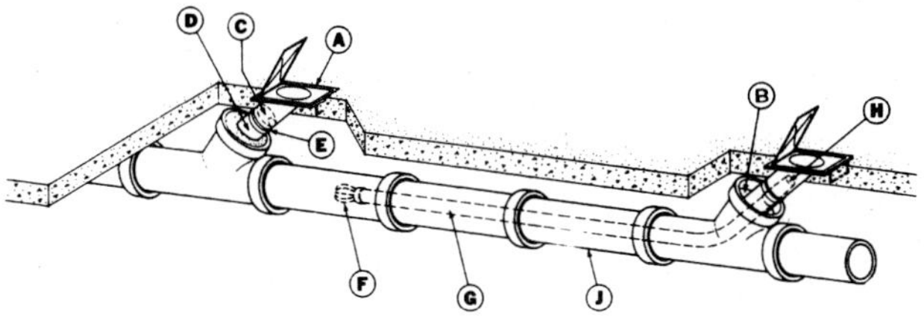


Cast Iron Garage Exhaust System

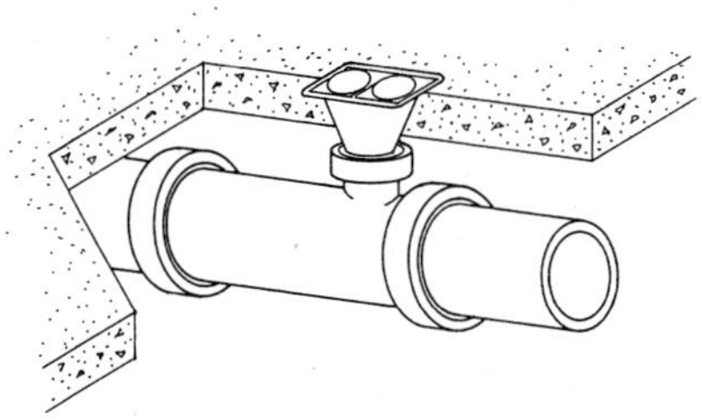

Dual Exhaust System

| D3090 320 | Garage Exhaust Systems | COST PER BAY | | |
|---|---|---|---|---|
| | | MAT. | INST. | TOTAL |
| 1040 | Garage, single 3" exhaust outlet, cars & light trucks, one bay | 5,425 | 2,400 | 7,825 |
| 1060 | Additional bays up to seven bays | 1,150 | 645 | 1,795 |
| 1500 | 4" outlet, trucks, one bay | 5,450 | 2,400 | 7,850 |
| 1520 | Additional bays up to six bays | 1,175 | 645 | 1,820 |
| 1600 | 5" outlet, diesel trucks, one bay | 5,800 | 2,400 | 8,200 |
| 1650 | Additional single bays up to six bays | 1,650 | 760 | 2,410 |
| 1700 | Two adjoining bays | 5,800 | 2,400 | 8,200 |
| 2000 | Dual exhaust, 3" outlets, pair of adjoining bays | 6,550 | 2,975 | 9,525 |
| 2100 | Additional pairs of adjoining bays | 1,800 | 760 | 2,560 |

## Reference - System Classification

### System Classification

Rules for installation of sprinkler systems vary depending on the classification of occupancy falling into one of three categories as follows:

### Light Hazard Occupancy

The protection area allotted per sprinkler should not exceed 225 S.F., with the maximum distance between lines and sprinklers on lines being 15′. The sprinklers do not need to be staggered. Branch lines should not exceed eight sprinklers on either side of a cross main. Each large area requiring more than 100 sprinklers and without a sub-dividing partition should be supplied by feed mains or risers sized for ordinary hazard occupancy.
Maximum system area = 52,000 S.F.

**Included in this group are:**

Churches
Clubs
Educational
Hospitals
Institutional
Libraries
(except large stack rooms)
Museums
Nursing Homes
Offices
Residential
Restaurants
Theaters and Auditoriums
(except stages and prosceniums)
Unused Attics

### Ordinary Hazard Occupancy

The protection area allotted per sprinkler shall not exceed 130 S.F. of noncombustible ceiling and 130 S.F. of combustible ceiling. The maximum allowable distance between sprinkler lines and sprinklers on line is 15′. Sprinklers shall be staggered if the distance between heads exceeds 12′. Branch lines should not exceed eight sprinklers on either side of a cross main.
Maximum system area = 52,000 S.F.

**Included in this group are:**

Group 1
Automotive Parking and Showrooms
Bakeries
Beverage manufacturing
Canneries
Dairy Products Manufacturing/Processing
Electronic Plans
Glass and Glass Products Manufacturing
Laundries
Restaurant Service Areas

Group 2
Cereal Mills
Chemical Plants—Ordinary
Confectionery Products
Distilleries
Dry Cleaners
Feed Mills
Horse Stables
Leather Goods Manufacturing
Libraries—Large Stack Room Areas
Machine Shops
Metal Working
Mercantile
Paper and Pulp Mills
Paper Process Plants
Piers and Wharves
Post Offices
Printing and Publishing
Repair Garages
Stages
Textile Manufacturing
Tire Manufacturing
Tobacco Products Manufacturing
Wood Machining
Wood Product Assembly

### Extra Hazard Occupancy

The protection area allotted per sprinkler shall not exceed 100 S.F. of noncombustible ceiling and 100 S.F. of combustible ceiling. The maximum allowable distance between lines and between sprinklers on lines is 12′. Sprinklers on alternate lines shall be staggered if the distance between sprinklers on lines exceeds 8′. Branch lines should not exceed six sprinklers on either side of a cross main.
Maximum system area:
Design by pipe schedule = 25,000 S.F.
Design by hydraulic calculation = 40,000 S.F.

**Included in this group are:**

Group 1
Aircraft hangars
Combustible Hydraulic Fluid Use Area
Die Casting
Metal Extruding
Plywood/Particle Board Manufacturing
Printing (inks with flash points < 100 degrees F
Rubber Reclaiming, Compounding, Drying, Milling, Vulcanizing
Saw Mills
Textile Picking, Opening, Blending, Garnetting, Carding, Combing of Cotton, Synthetics, Wood Shoddy, or Burlap
Upholstering with Plastic Foams

Group 2
Asphalt Saturating
Flammable Liquids Spraying
Flow Coating
Manufactured/Modular Home Building Assemblies (where finished enclosure is present and has combustible interiors)
Open Oil Quenching
Plastics Processing
Solvent Cleaning
Varnish and Paint Dipping

## Reference - Sprinkler Systems (Automatic)

Sprinkler systems may be classified by type as follows:

1. **Wet Pipe System.** A system employing automatic sprinklers attached to a piping system containing water and connected to a water supply so that water discharges immediately from sprinklers opened by a fire.
2. **Dry Pipe System.** A system employing automatic sprinklers attached to a piping system containing air under pressure, the release of which as from the opening of sprinklers permits the water pressure to open a valve known as a "dry pipe valve". The water then flows into the piping system and out the opened sprinklers.
3. **Pre-Action System.** A system employing automatic sprinklers attached to a piping system containing air that may or may not be under pressure, with a supplemental heat responsive system of generally more sensitive characteristics than the automatic sprinklers themselves, installed in the same areas as the sprinklers; actuation of the heat responsive system, as from a fire, opens a valve which permits water to flow into the sprinkler piping system and to be discharged from any sprinklers which may be open.
4. **Deluge System.** A system employing open sprinklers attached to a piping system connected to a water supply through a valve which is opened by the operation of a heat responsive system installed in the same areas as the sprinklers. When this valve opens, water flows into the piping system and discharges from all sprinklers attached thereto.
5. **Combined Dry Pipe and Pre-Action Sprinkler System.** A system employing automatic sprinklers attached to a piping system containing air under pressure with a supplemental heat responsive system of generally more sensitive characteristics than the automatic sprinklers themselves, installed in the same areas as the sprinklers; operation of the heat responsive system, as from a fire, actuates tripping devices which open dry pipe valves simultaneously and without loss of air pressure in the system. Operation of the heat responsive system also opens approved air exhaust valves at the end of the feed main which facilitates the filling of the system with water which usually precedes the opening of sprinklers. The heat responsive system also serves as an automatic fire alarm system.
6. **Limited Water Supply System.** A system employing automatic sprinklers and conforming to these standards but supplied by a pressure tank of limited capacity.
7. **Chemical Systems.** Systems using halon, carbon dioxide, dry chemical or high expansion foam as selected for special requirements. Agent may extinguish flames by chemically inhibiting flame propagation, suffocate flames by excluding oxygen, interrupting chemical action of oxygen uniting with fuel or sealing and cooling the combustion center.
8. **Firecycle System.** Firecycle is a fixed fire protection sprinkler system utilizing water as its extinguishing agent. It is a time delayed, recycling, preaction type which automatically shuts the water off when heat is reduced below the detector operating temperature and turns the water back on when that temperature is exceeded. The system senses a fire condition through a closed circuit electrical detector system which controls water flow to the fire automatically. Batteries supply up to 90 hour emergency power supply for system operation. The piping system is dry (until water is required) and is monitored with pressurized air. Should any leak in the system piping occur, an alarm will sound, but water will not enter the system until heat is sensed by a firecycle detector.

Area coverage sprinkler systems may be laid out and fed from the supply in any one of several patterns as shown below. It is desirable, if possible, to utilize a central feed and achieve a shorter flow path from the riser to the furthest sprinkler. This permits use of the smallest sizes of pipe possible with resulting savings.



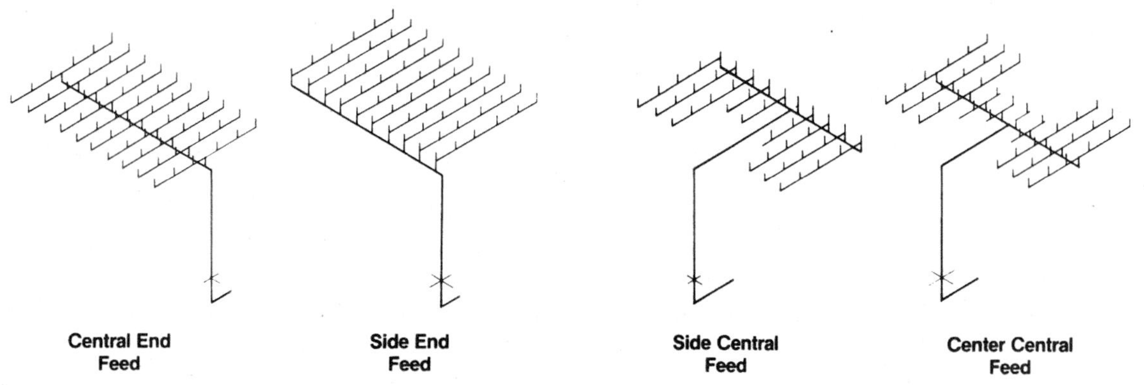

## D4010 Sprinklers

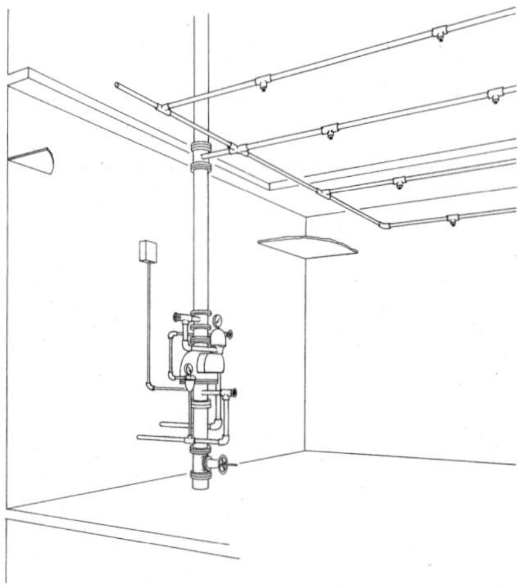

**Dry Pipe System:** A system employing automatic sprinklers attached to a piping system containing air under pressure, the release of which from the opening of sprinklers permits the water pressure to open a valve known as a "dry pipe valve". The water then flows into the piping system and out the opened sprinklers.

All areas are assumed to be open.

| D4010 310 | Dry Pipe Sprinkler Systems | COST PER S.F. | | |
|---|---|---|---|---|
| | | MAT. | INST. | TOTAL |
| 0520 | Dry pipe sprinkler systems, steel, black, sch. 40 pipe | | | |
| 0530 | Light hazard, one floor, 500 S.F. | 18.60 | 8 | 26.60 |
| 0560 | 1000 S.F. | 12.45 | 4.70 | 17.15 |
| 0580 | 2000 S.F. | 10.28 | 4.48 | 14.76 |
| 0600 | 5000 S.F. | 5.10 | 3.16 | 8.26 |
| 0620 | 10,000 S.F. | 3.52 | 2.58 | 6.10 |
| 0640 | 50,000 S.F. | 2.70 | 2.27 | 4.97 |
| 0660 | Each additional floor, 500 S.F. | 3.83 | 3.79 | 7.62 |
| 0680 | 1000 S.F. | 3.40 | 3.09 | 6.49 |
| 0700 | 2000 S.F. | 3.10 | 2.85 | 5.95 |
| 0720 | 5000 S.F. | 2.38 | 2.44 | 4.82 |
| 0740 | 10,000 S.F. | 2.22 | 2.24 | 4.46 |
| 0760 | 50,000 S.F. | 2 | 2 | 4 |
| 1000 | Ordinary hazard, one floor, 500 S.F. | 18.80 | 8.05 | 26.85 |
| 1020 | 1000 S.F. | 12.55 | 4.74 | 17.29 |
| 1040 | 2000 S.F. | 10.40 | 4.95 | 15.35 |
| 1060 | 5000 S.F. | 5.80 | 3.38 | 9.18 |
| 1080 | 10,000 S.F. | 4.49 | 3.37 | 7.86 |
| 1100 | 50,000 S.F. | 3.85 | 3.15 | 7 |
| 1140 | Each additional floor, 500 S.F. | 4.02 | 3.88 | 7.90 |
| 1160 | 1000 S.F. | 3.82 | 3.46 | 7.28 |
| 1180 | 2000 S.F. | 3.55 | 3.14 | 6.69 |
| 1200 | 5000 S.F. | 3.20 | 2.70 | 5.90 |
| 1220 | 10,000 S.F. | 2.83 | 2.63 | 5.46 |
| 1240 | 50,000 S.F. | 2.58 | 2.27 | 4.85 |
| 1500 | Extra hazard, one floor, 500 S.F. | 24.50 | 10.05 | 34.55 |
| 1520 | 1000 S.F. | 17.75 | 7.30 | 25.05 |
| 1540 | 2000 S.F. | 11.30 | 6.30 | 17.60 |
| 1560 | 5000 S.F. | 6.60 | 4.67 | 11.27 |
| 1580 | 10,000 S.F. | 6.70 | 4.42 | 11.12 |
| 1600 | 50,000 S.F. | 7.25 | 4.24 | 11.49 |
| 1660 | Each additional floor, 500 S.F. | 5.90 | 4.79 | 10.69 |
| 1680 | 1000 S.F. | 5.35 | 4.49 | 9.84 |
| 1700 | 2000 S.F. | 4.72 | 4.49 | 9.21 |
| 1720 | 5000 S.F. | 3.98 | 3.93 | 7.91 |
| 1740 | 10,000 S.F. | 4.62 | 3.59 | 8.21 |
| 1760 | 50,000 S.F. | 4.65 | 3.45 | 8.10 |
| 2020 | Grooved steel, black, sch. 40 pipe, light hazard, one floor, 2000 S.F. | 10.30 | 4.12 | 14.42 |

## D4010 Sprinklers

| D4010 310 | Dry Pipe Sprinkler Systems | COST PER S.F. | | |
|---|---|---|---|---|
| | | MAT. | INST. | TOTAL |
| 2060 | 10,000 S.F. | 3.77 | 2.24 | 6.01 |
| 2100 | Each additional floor, 2000 S.F. | 3.44 | 2.31 | 5.75 |
| 2150 | 10,000 S.F. | 2.47 | 1.90 | 4.37 |
| 2200 | Ordinary hazard, one floor, 2000 S.F. | 10.65 | 4.35 | 15 |
| 2250 | 10,000 S.F. | 4.58 | 2.87 | 7.45 |
| 2300 | Each additional floor, 2000 S.F. | 3.78 | 2.54 | 6.32 |
| 2350 | 10,000 S.F. | 3.58 | 2.56 | 6.14 |
| 2400 | Extra hazard, one floor, 2000 S.F. | 11.80 | 5.40 | 17.20 |
| 2450 | 10,000 S.F. | 6.40 | 3.71 | 10.11 |
| 2500 | Each additional floor, 2000 S.F. | 5.35 | 3.72 | 9.07 |
| 2550 | 10,000 S.F. | 4.61 | 3.17 | 7.78 |
| 3050 | Grooved steel, black, sch. 10 pipe, light hazard, one floor, 2000 S.F. | 9.85 | 4.09 | 13.94 |
| 3100 | 10,000 S.F. | 3.40 | 2.21 | 5.61 |
| 3150 | Each additional floor, 2000 S.F. | 3.01 | 2.27 | 5.28 |
| 3200 | 10,000 S.F. | 2.10 | 1.87 | 3.97 |
| 3250 | Ordinary hazard, one floor, 2000 S.F. | 10.25 | 4.32 | 14.57 |
| 3300 | 10,000 S.F. | 3.96 | 2.79 | 6.75 |
| 3350 | Each additional floor, 2000 S.F. | 3.38 | 2.51 | 5.89 |
| 3400 | 10,000 S.F. | 2.74 | 2.47 | 5.21 |
| 3450 | Extra hazard, one floor, 2000 S.F. | 11.50 | 5.40 | 16.90 |
| 3500 | 10,000 S.F. | 5.75 | 3.65 | 9.40 |
| 3550 | Each additional floor, 2000 S.F. | 5 | 3.69 | 8.69 |
| 3600 | 10,000 S.F. | 4.22 | 3.13 | 7.35 |
| 4050 | Copper tubing, type L, light hazard, one floor, 2000 S.F. | 9.95 | 4.12 | 14.07 |
| 4100 | 10,000 S.F. | 3.60 | 2.29 | 5.89 |
| 4150 | Each additional floor, 2000 S.F. | 3.11 | 2.35 | 5.46 |
| 4200 | 10,000 S.F. | 2.31 | 1.96 | 4.27 |
| 4250 | Ordinary hazard, one floor, 2000 S.F. | 10.35 | 4.55 | 14.90 |
| 4300 | 10,000 S.F. | 3.98 | 2.63 | 6.61 |
| 4350 | Each additional floor, 2000 S.F. | 3.79 | 2.66 | 6.45 |
| 4400 | 10,000 S.F. | 2.58 | 2.25 | 4.83 |
| 4450 | Extra hazard, one floor, 2000 S.F. | 11.50 | 5.50 | 17 |
| 4500 | 10,000 S.F. | 7.95 | 3.98 | 11.93 |
| 4550 | Each additional floor, 2000 S.F. | 4.87 | 3.75 | 8.62 |
| 4600 | 10,000 S.F. | 5.50 | 3.41 | 8.91 |
| 5050 | Copper tubing, type L, T-drill system, light hazard, one floor | | | |
| 5060 | 2000 S.F. | 9.80 | 3.88 | 13.68 |
| 5100 | 10,000 S.F. | 3.24 | 1.92 | 5.16 |
| 5150 | Each additional floor, 2000 S.F. | 2.98 | 2.11 | 5.09 |
| 5200 | 10,000 S.F. | 1.95 | 1.59 | 3.54 |
| 5250 | Ordinary hazard, one floor, 2000 S.F. | 9.80 | 3.95 | 13.75 |
| 5300 | 10,000 S.F. | 3.95 | 2.41 | 6.36 |
| 5350 | Each additional floor, 2000 S.F. | 2.95 | 2.14 | 5.09 |
| 5400 | 10,000 S.F. | 2.53 | 1.97 | 4.50 |
| 5450 | Extra hazard, one floor, 2000 S.F. | 10.50 | 4.62 | 15.12 |
| 5500 | 10,000 S.F. | 6.05 | 3.01 | 9.06 |
| 5550 | Each additional floor, 2000 S.F. | 4.02 | 2.93 | 6.95 |
| 5600 | 10,000 S.F. | 3.62 | 2.44 | 6.06 |

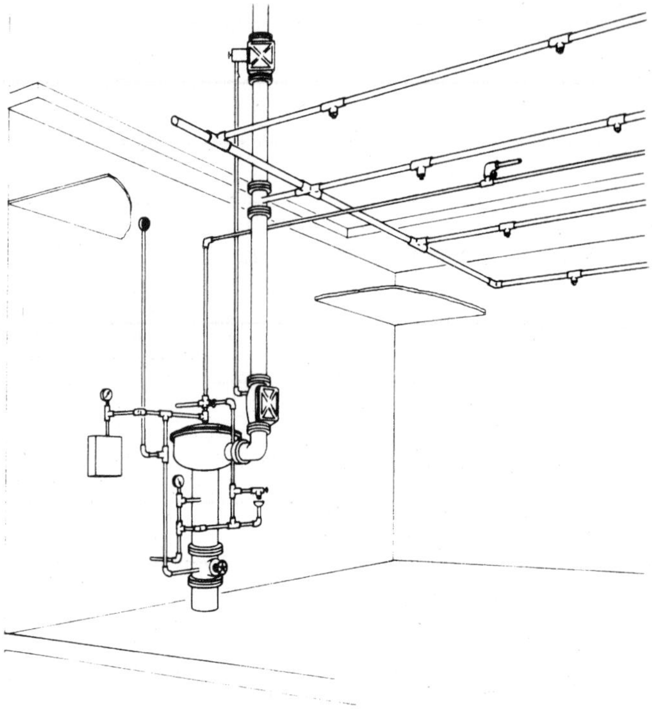

**Preaction System:** A system employing automatic sprinklers attached to a piping system containing air that may or may not be under pressure, with a supplemental heat responsive system of generally more sensitive characteristics than the automatic sprinklers themselves, installed in the same areas as the sprinklers. Actuation of the heat responsive system, as from a fire, opens a valve which permits water to flow into the sprinkler piping system and to be discharged from those sprinklers which were opened by heat from the fire.

All areas are assumed to be opened.

| D4010 350 | Preaction Sprinkler Systems | COST PER S.F. | | |
|---|---|---|---|---|
| | | MAT. | INST. | TOTAL |
| 0520 | Preaction sprinkler systems, steel, black, sch. 40 pipe | | | |
| 0530 | Light hazard, one floor, 500 S.F. | 19.50 | 6.45 | 25.95 |
| 0560 | 1000 S.F. | 11.20 | 4.77 | 15.97 |
| 0580 | 2000 S.F. | 10.72 | 4.48 | 15.20 |
| 0600 | 5000 S.F. | 5.35 | 3.15 | 8.50 |
| 0620 | 10,000 S.F. | 3.72 | 2.57 | 6.29 |
| 0640 | 50,000 S.F. | 2.89 | 2.26 | 5.15 |
| 0660 | Each additional floor, 500 S.F. | 5 | 3.39 | 8.39 |
| 0680 | 1000 S.F. | 3.83 | 3.09 | 6.92 |
| 0700 | 2000 S.F. | 3.53 | 2.85 | 6.38 |
| 0720 | 5000 S.F. | 3.53 | 2.49 | 6.02 |
| 0740 | 10,000 S.F. | 2.91 | 2.27 | 5.18 |
| 0760 | 50,000 S.F. | 2.43 | 2.06 | 4.49 |
| 1000 | Ordinary hazard, one floor, 500 S.F. | 20.50 | 6.95 | 27.45 |
| 1020 | 1000 S.F. | 12.85 | 4.73 | 17.58 |
| 1040 | 2000 S.F. | 11.10 | 4.96 | 16.06 |
| 1060 | 5000 S.F. | 5.90 | 3.36 | 9.26 |
| 1080 | 10,000 S.F. | 4.53 | 3.35 | 7.88 |
| 1100 | 50,000 S.F. | 3.90 | 3.12 | 7.02 |
| 1140 | Each additional floor, 500 S.F. | 5.15 | 3.90 | 9.05 |
| 1160 | 1000 S.F. | 3.81 | 3.12 | 6.93 |
| 1180 | 2000 S.F. | 3.42 | 3.11 | 6.53 |
| 1200 | 5000 S.F. | 3.58 | 2.91 | 6.49 |
| 1220 | 10,000 S.F. | 3.26 | 3.02 | 6.28 |
| 1240 | 50,000 S.F. | 2.94 | 2.67 | 5.61 |
| 1500 | Extra hazard, one floor, 500 S.F. | 29 | 8.95 | 37.95 |
| 1520 | 1000 S.F. | 17.95 | 6.70 | 24.65 |
| 1540 | 2000 S.F. | 11.30 | 6.25 | 17.55 |

## D4010 Sprinklers

| D4010 350 | Preaction Sprinkler Systems | COST PER S.F. MAT. | COST PER S.F. INST. | COST PER S.F. TOTAL |
|---|---|---|---|---|
| 1560 | 5000 S.F. | 7.25 | 5 | 12.25 |
| 1580 | 10,000 S.F. | 6.95 | 4.88 | 11.83 |
| 1600 | 50,000 S.F. | 7.35 | 4.70 | 12.05 |
| 1660 | Each additional floor, 500 S.F. | 6.80 | 4.79 | 11.59 |
| 1680 | 1000 S.F. | 5.60 | 4.49 | 10.09 |
| 1700 | 2000 S.F. | 4.84 | 4.48 | 9.32 |
| 1720 | 5000 S.F. | 4.04 | 3.96 | 8 |
| 1740 | 10,000 S.F. | 4.47 | 3.63 | 8.10 |
| 1760 | 50,000 S.F. | 4.33 | 3.40 | 7.73 |
| 2020 | Grooved steel, black, sch. 40 pipe, light hazard, one floor, 2000 S.F. | 10.70 | 4.11 | 14.81 |
| 2060 | 10,000 S.F. | 3.97 | 2.23 | 6.20 |
| 2100 | Each additional floor of 2000 S.F. | 3.87 | 2.30 | 6.17 |
| 2150 | 10,000 S.F. | 2.68 | 1.89 | 4.57 |
| 2200 | Ordinary hazard, one floor, 2000 S.F. | 10.95 | 4.34 | 15.29 |
| 2250 | 10,000 S.F. | 4.62 | 2.85 | 7.47 |
| 2300 | Each additional floor, 2000 S.F. | 4.08 | 2.53 | 6.61 |
| 2350 | 10,000 S.F. | 3.34 | 2.51 | 5.85 |
| 2400 | Extra hazard, one floor, 2000 S.F. | 11.85 | 5.40 | 17.25 |
| 2450 | 10,000 S.F. | 6.30 | 3.66 | 9.96 |
| 2500 | Each additional floor, 2000 S.F. | 5.35 | 3.68 | 9.03 |
| 2550 | 10,000 S.F. | 4.37 | 3.13 | 7.50 |
| 3050 | Grooved steel, black, sch. 10 pipe light hazard, one floor, 2000 S.F. | 10.30 | 4.08 | 14.38 |
| 3100 | 10,000 S.F. | 3.60 | 2.20 | 5.80 |
| 3150 | Each additional floor, 2000 S.F. | 3.44 | 2.27 | 5.71 |
| 3200 | 10,000 S.F. | 2.31 | 1.86 | 4.17 |
| 3250 | Ordinary hazard, one floor, 2000 S.F. | 10.35 | 4.05 | 14.40 |
| 3300 | 10,000 S.F. | 3.64 | 2.77 | 6.41 |
| 3350 | Each additional floor, 2000 S.F. | 3.67 | 2.50 | 6.17 |
| 3400 | 10,000 S.F. | 2.78 | 2.45 | 5.23 |
| 3450 | Extra hazard, one floor, 2000 S.F. | 11.50 | 5.35 | 16.85 |
| 3500 | 10,000 S.F. | 5.50 | 3.60 | 9.10 |
| 3550 | Each additional floor, 2000 S.F. | 5.05 | 3.66 | 8.71 |
| 3600 | 10,000 S.F. | 3.98 | 3.08 | 7.06 |
| 4050 | Copper tubing, type L, light hazard, one floor, 2000 S.F. | 10.40 | 4.12 | 14.52 |
| 4100 | 10,000 S.F. | 3.81 | 2.28 | 6.09 |
| 4150 | Each additional floor, 2000 S.F. | 3.56 | 2.35 | 5.91 |
| 4200 | 10,000 S.F. | 2.09 | 1.93 | 4.02 |
| 4250 | Ordinary hazard, one floor, 2000 S.F. | 10.50 | 4.50 | 15 |
| 4300 | 10,000 S.F. | 4.02 | 2.61 | 6.63 |
| 4350 | Each additional floor, 2000 S.F. | 3.49 | 2.36 | 5.85 |
| 4400 | 10,000 S.F. | 2.46 | 2.06 | 4.52 |
| 4450 | Extra hazard, one floor, 2000 S.F. | 11.35 | 5.40 | 16.75 |
| 4500 | 10,000 S.F. | 7.60 | 3.92 | 11.52 |
| 4550 | Each additional floor, 2000 S.F. | 4.89 | 3.72 | 8.61 |
| 4600 | 10,000 S.F. | 5.30 | 3.37 | 8.67 |
| 5050 | Copper tubing, type L, T-drill system, light hazard, one floor | | | |
| 5060 | 2000 S.F. | 10.25 | 3.87 | 14.12 |
| 5100 | 10,000 S.F. | 3.45 | 1.91 | 5.36 |
| 5150 | Each additional floor, 2000 S.F. | 3.41 | 2.11 | 5.52 |
| 5200 | 10,000 S.F. | 2.16 | 1.58 | 3.74 |
| 5250 | Ordinary hazard, one floor, 2000 S.F. | 10.10 | 3.94 | 14.04 |
| 5300 | 10,000 S.F. | 3.99 | 2.39 | 6.38 |
| 5350 | Each additional floor, 2000 S.F. | 3.26 | 2.14 | 5.40 |
| 5400 | 10,000 S.F. | 2.71 | 2.05 | 4.76 |
| 5450 | Extra hazard, one floor, 2000 S.F. | 10.50 | 4.58 | 15.08 |
| 5500 | 10,000 S.F. | 5.70 | 2.96 | 8.66 |
| 5550 | Each additional floor, 2000 S.F. | 4.04 | 2.89 | 6.93 |
| 5600 | 10,000 S.F. | 3.39 | 2.40 | 5.79 |

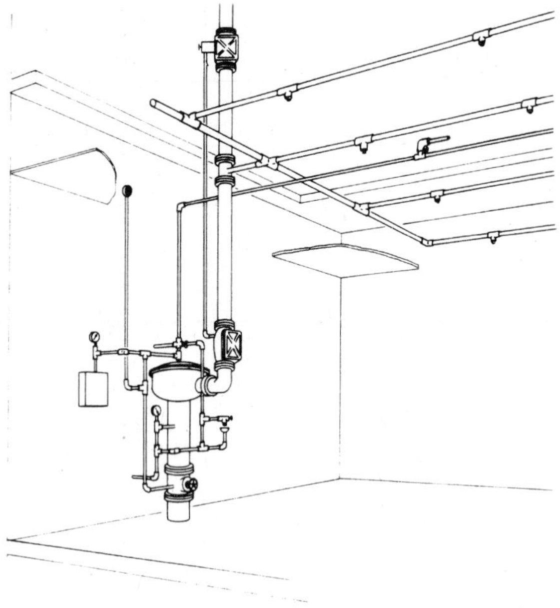

**Deluge System:** A system employing open sprinklers attached to a piping system connected to a water supply through a valve which is opened by the operation of a heat responsive system installed in the same areas as the sprinklers. When this valve opens, water flows into the piping system and discharges from all sprinklers attached thereto.

| D4010 370 | Deluge Sprinkler Systems | COST PER S.F. | | |
|---|---|---|---|---|
| | | MAT. | INST. | TOTAL |
| 0520 | Deluge sprinkler systems, steel, black, sch. 40 pipe | | | |
| 0530 | Light hazard, one floor, 500 S.F. | 61 | 6.50 | 67.50 |
| 0560 | 1000 S.F. | 33.50 | 4.63 | 38.13 |
| 0580 | 2000 S.F. | 22.60 | 4.48 | 27.08 |
| 0600 | 5000 S.F. | 9.80 | 3.16 | 12.96 |
| 0620 | 10,000 S.F. | 5.95 | 2.57 | 8.52 |
| 0640 | 50,000 S.F. | 3.33 | 2.26 | 5.59 |
| 0660 | Each additional floor, 500 S.F. | 4.34 | 3.39 | 7.73 |
| 0680 | 1000 S.F. | 3.83 | 3.09 | 6.92 |
| 0700 | 2000 S.F. | 3.53 | 2.85 | 6.38 |
| 0720 | 5000 S.F. | 2.62 | 2.43 | 5.05 |
| 0740 | 10,000 S.F. | 2.43 | 2.23 | 4.66 |
| 0760 | 50,000 S.F. | 2.41 | 2.06 | 4.47 |
| 1000 | Ordinary hazard, one floor, 500 S.F. | 63.50 | 7.40 | 70.90 |
| 1020 | 1000 S.F. | 33.50 | 4.77 | 38.27 |
| 1040 | 2000 S.F. | 22 | 4.97 | 26.97 |
| 1060 | 5000 S.F. | 10.35 | 3.37 | 13.72 |
| 1080 | 10,000 S.F. | 6.75 | 3.35 | 10.10 |
| 1100 | 50,000 S.F. | 4.38 | 3.17 | 7.55 |
| 1140 | Each additional floor, 500 S.F. | 5.15 | 3.90 | 9.05 |
| 1160 | 1000 S.F. | 3.81 | 3.12 | 6.93 |
| 1180 | 2000 S.F. | 3.42 | 3.11 | 6.53 |
| 1200 | 5000 S.F. | 3.33 | 2.68 | 6.01 |
| 1220 | 10,000 S.F. | 3.12 | 2.66 | 5.78 |
| 1240 | 50,000 S.F. | 2.76 | 2.45 | 5.21 |
| 1500 | Extra hazard, one floor, 500 S.F. | 70.50 | 9.05 | 79.55 |
| 1520 | 1000 S.F. | 39.50 | 6.95 | 46.45 |
| 1540 | 2000 S.F. | 22.50 | 6.25 | 28.75 |
| 1560 | 5000 S.F. | 10.95 | 4.64 | 15.59 |
| 1580 | 10,000 S.F. | 8.75 | 4.47 | 13.22 |
| 1600 | 50,000 S.F. | 8.75 | 4.32 | 13.07 |
| 1660 | Each additional floor, 500 S.F. | 6.80 | 4.79 | 11.59 |

## D4010 Sprinklers

| D4010 370 | Deluge Sprinkler Systems | COST PER S.F. | | |
|---|---|---|---|---|
| | | MAT. | INST. | TOTAL |
| 1680 | 1000 S.F. | 5.60 | 4.49 | 10.09 |
| 1700 | 2000 S.F. | 4.84 | 4.48 | 9.32 |
| 1720 | 5000 S.F. | 4.04 | 3.96 | 8 |
| 1740 | 10,000 S.F. | 4.59 | 3.77 | 8.36 |
| 1760 | 50,000 S.F. | 4.58 | 3.63 | 8.21 |
| 2000 | Grooved steel, black, sch. 40 pipe, light hazard, one floor | | | |
| 2020 | 2000 S.F. | 22 | 4.13 | 26.13 |
| 2060 | 10,000 S.F. | 6.25 | 2.26 | 8.51 |
| 2100 | Each additional floor, 2,000 S.F. | 3.87 | 2.30 | 6.17 |
| 2150 | 10,000 S.F. | 2.68 | 1.89 | 4.57 |
| 2200 | Ordinary hazard, one floor, 2000 S.F. | 10.95 | 4.34 | 15.29 |
| 2250 | 10,000 S.F. | 6.85 | 2.85 | 9.70 |
| 2300 | Each additional floor, 2000 S.F. | 4.08 | 2.53 | 6.61 |
| 2350 | 10,000 S.F. | 3.34 | 2.51 | 5.85 |
| 2400 | Extra hazard, one floor, 2000 S.F. | 23 | 5.40 | 28.40 |
| 2450 | 10,000 S.F. | 8.45 | 3.68 | 12.13 |
| 2500 | Each additional floor, 2000 S.F. | 5.35 | 3.68 | 9.03 |
| 2550 | 10,000 S.F. | 4.37 | 3.13 | 7.50 |
| 3000 | Grooved steel, black, sch. 10 pipe, light hazard, one floor | | | |
| 3050 | 2000 S.F. | 20.50 | 3.93 | 24.43 |
| 3100 | 10,000 S.F. | 5.80 | 2.21 | 8.01 |
| 3150 | Each additional floor, 2000 S.F. | 3.44 | 2.27 | 5.71 |
| 3200 | 10,000 S.F. | 2.31 | 1.86 | 4.17 |
| 3250 | Ordinary hazard, one floor, 2000 S.F. | 21.50 | 4.33 | 25.83 |
| 3300 | 10,000 S.F. | 5.85 | 2.77 | 8.62 |
| 3350 | Each additional floor, 2000 S.F. | 3.67 | 2.50 | 6.17 |
| 3400 | 10,000 S.F. | 2.78 | 2.45 | 5.23 |
| 3450 | Extra hazard, one floor, 2000 S.F. | 22.50 | 5.35 | 27.85 |
| 3500 | 10,000 S.F. | 7.75 | 3.60 | 11.35 |
| 3550 | Each additional floor, 2000 S.F. | 5.05 | 3.66 | 8.71 |
| 3600 | 10,000 S.F. | 3.98 | 3.08 | 7.06 |
| 4000 | Copper tubing, type L, light hazard, one floor | | | |
| 4050 | 2000 S.F. | 21.50 | 4.13 | 25.63 |
| 4100 | 10,000 S.F. | 5.95 | 2.28 | 8.23 |
| 4150 | Each additional floor, 2000 S.F. | 3.54 | 2.35 | 5.89 |
| 4200 | 10,000 S.F. | 2.09 | 1.93 | 4.02 |
| 4250 | Ordinary hazard, one floor, 2000 S.F. | 21.50 | 4.56 | 26.06 |
| 4300 | 10,000 S.F. | 6.40 | 2.67 | 9.07 |
| 4350 | Each additional floor, 2000 S.F. | 3.59 | 2.39 | 5.98 |
| 4400 | 10,000 S.F. | 2.64 | 2.10 | 4.74 |
| 4450 | Extra hazard, one floor, 2000 S.F. | 22.50 | 5.50 | 28 |
| 4500 | 10,000 S.F. | 9.85 | 4.01 | 13.86 |
| 4550 | Each additional floor, 2000 S.F. | 5.05 | 3.78 | 8.83 |
| 4600 | 10,000 S.F. | 5.40 | 3.42 | 8.82 |
| 5000 | Copper tubing, type L, T-drill system, light hazard, one floor | | | |
| 5050 | 2000 S.F. | 21.50 | 3.89 | 25.39 |
| 5100 | 10,000 S.F. | 5.65 | 1.91 | 7.56 |
| 5150 | Each additional floor, 2000 S.F. | 3.37 | 2.14 | 5.51 |
| 5200 | 10,000 S.F. | 2.16 | 1.58 | 3.74 |
| 5250 | Ordinary hazard, one floor, 2000 S.F. | 19.35 | 3.70 | 23.05 |
| 5300 | 10,000 S.F. | 6.20 | 2.39 | 8.59 |
| 5350 | Each additional floor, 2000 S.F. | 3.23 | 2.12 | 5.35 |
| 5400 | 10,000 S.F. | 2.71 | 2.05 | 4.76 |
| 5450 | Extra hazard, one floor, 2000 S.F. | 19.80 | 4.35 | 24.15 |
| 5500 | 10,000 S.F. | 7.90 | 2.96 | 10.86 |
| 5550 | Each additional floor, 2000 S.F. | 4.04 | 2.89 | 6.93 |
| 5600 | 10,000 S.F. | 3.39 | 2.40 | 5.79 |

## D4010 Sprinklers

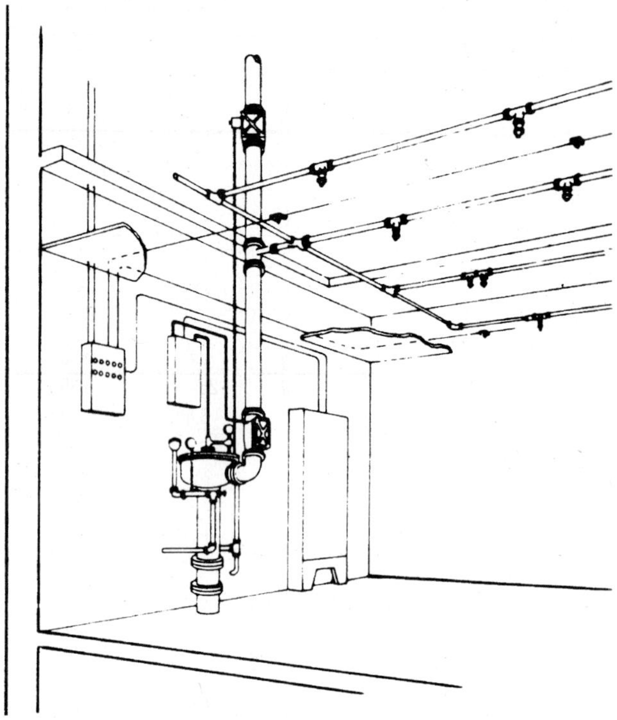

On-off multicycle is a fixed fire protection sprinkler system utilizing water as its extinguishing agent. It is a time delayed, recycling, preaction type which automatically shuts the water off when heat is reduced below the detector operating temperature and turns the water back on when that temperature is exceeded.

The system senses a fire condition through a closed circuit electrical detector system which controls water flow to the fire automatically. Batteries supply up to 90 hours emergency power supply for system operation. The piping system is dry (until water is required) and is monitored with pressurized air. Shouldany leak in the system piping occur, an alarm will sound, but water will not enter the system until heat is sensed by a Firecycle detector.

| D4010 390 | On-off multicycle Sprinkler Systems | COST PER S.F. | | |
|---|---|---|---|---|
| | | MAT. | INST. | TOTAL |
| 0520 | On-off multicycle sprinkler systems, steel, black, sch. 40 pipe | | | |
| 0530 | Light hazard, one floor, 500 S.F. | 80 | 12.35 | 92.35 |
| 0560 | 1000 S.F. | 43 | 7.75 | 50.75 |
| 0580 | 2000 S.F. | 27 | 5.56 | 32.56 |
| 0600 | 5000 S.F. | 11.50 | 3.57 | 15.07 |
| 0620 | 10,000 S.F. | 6.90 | 2.78 | 9.68 |
| 0640 | 50,000 S.F. | 3.60 | 2.30 | 5.90 |
| 0660 | Each additional floor of 500 S.F. | 4.46 | 3.40 | 7.86 |
| 0680 | 1000 S.F. | 3.89 | 3.10 | 6.99 |
| 0700 | 2000 S.F. | 3.14 | 2.83 | 5.97 |
| 0720 | 5000 S.F. | 2.66 | 2.43 | 5.09 |
| 0740 | 10,000 S.F. | 2.56 | 2.24 | 4.80 |
| 0760 | 50,000 S.F. | 2.49 | 2.06 | 4.55 |
| 1000 | Ordinary hazard, one floor, 500 S.F. | 76.50 | 12.50 | 89 |
| 1020 | 1000 S.F. | 43 | 7.65 | 50.65 |
| 1040 | 2000 S.F. | 26 | 5.95 | 31.95 |
| 1060 | 5000 S.F. | 12.05 | 3.77 | 15.82 |
| 1080 | 10,000 S.F. | 7.70 | 3.56 | 11.26 |
| 1100 | 50,000 S.F. | 4.85 | 3.54 | 8.39 |
| 1140 | Each additional floor, 500 S.F. | 5.25 | 3.92 | 9.17 |
| 1160 | 1000 S.F. | 3.87 | 3.13 | 7 |
| 1180 | 2000 S.F. | 3.72 | 2.86 | 6.58 |
| 1200 | 5000 S.F. | 3.37 | 2.69 | 6.06 |
| 1220 | 10,000 S.F. | 3 | 2.61 | 5.61 |
| 1240 | 50,000 S.F. | 2.79 | 2.33 | 5.12 |
| 1500 | Extra hazard, one floor, 500 S.F. | 89 | 14.85 | 103.85 |
| 1520 | 1000 S.F. | 47 | 9.60 | 56.60 |
| 1540 | 2000 S.F. | 26.50 | 7.30 | 33.80 |
| 1560 | 5000 S.F. | 12.65 | 5.05 | 17.70 |
| 1580 | 10,000 S.F. | 9.95 | 5.05 | 15 |

## D4010 Sprinklers

| D4010 390 | On-off multicycle Sprinkler Systems | COST PER S.F. | | |
|---|---|---|---|---|
| | | MAT. | INST. | TOTAL |
| 1600 | 50,000 S.F. | 8.85 | 5.55 | 14.40 |
| 1660 | Each additional floor, 500 S.F. | 6.90 | 4.81 | 11.71 |
| 1680 | 1000 S.F. | 5.65 | 4.50 | 10.15 |
| 1700 | 2000 S.F. | 4.90 | 4.49 | 9.39 |
| 1720 | 5000 S.F. | 4.09 | 3.96 | 8.05 |
| 1740 | 10,000 S.F. | 4.60 | 3.64 | 8.24 |
| 1760 | 50,000 S.F. | 4.58 | 3.51 | 8.09 |
| 2020 | Grooved steel, black, sch. 40 pipe, light hazard, one floor | | | |
| 2030 | 2000 S.F. | 24 | 4.89 | 28.89 |
| 2060 | 10,000 S.F. | 7.85 | 3.38 | 11.23 |
| 2100 | Each additional floor, 2000 S.F. | 3.92 | 2.31 | 6.23 |
| 2150 | 10,000 S.F. | 2.81 | 1.90 | 4.71 |
| 2200 | Ordinary hazard, one floor, 2000 S.F. | 26 | 5.35 | 31.35 |
| 2250 | 10,000 S.F. | 8.40 | 3.23 | 11.63 |
| 2300 | Each additional floor, 2000 S.F. | 4.14 | 2.54 | 6.68 |
| 2350 | 10,000 S.F. | 3.47 | 2.52 | 5.99 |
| 2400 | Extra hazard, one floor, 2000 S.F. | 25 | 6.15 | 31.15 |
| 2450 | 10,000 S.F. | 9.30 | 3.85 | 13.15 |
| 2500 | Each additional floor, 2000 S.F. | 5.40 | 3.69 | 9.09 |
| 2550 | 10,000 S.F. | 4.50 | 3.14 | 7.64 |
| 3050 | Grooved steel, black, sch. 10 pipe, light hazard, one floor, | | | |
| 3060 | 2000 S.F. | 25.50 | 5.10 | 30.60 |
| 3100 | 10,000 S.F. | 6.75 | 2.42 | 9.17 |
| 3150 | Each additional floor, 2000 S.F. | 3.50 | 2.28 | 5.78 |
| 3200 | 10,000 S.F. | 2.44 | 1.87 | 4.31 |
| 3250 | Ordinary hazard, one floor, 2000 S.F. | 26 | 5.35 | 31.35 |
| 3300 | 10,000 S.F. | 7.20 | 3 | 10.20 |
| 3350 | Each additional floor, 2000 S.F. | 3.73 | 2.51 | 6.24 |
| 3400 | 10,000 S.F. | 2.91 | 2.46 | 5.37 |
| 3450 | Extra hazard, one floor, 2000 S.F. | 26.50 | 6.40 | 32.90 |
| 3500 | 10,000 S.F. | 8.65 | 3.79 | 12.44 |
| 3550 | Each additional floor, 2000 S.F. | 5.10 | 3.67 | 8.77 |
| 3600 | 10,000 S.F. | 4.11 | 3.09 | 7.20 |
| 4060 | Copper tubing, type L, light hazard, one floor, 2000 S.F. | 25.50 | 5.15 | 30.65 |
| 4100 | 10,000 S.F. | 6.95 | 2.49 | 9.44 |
| 4150 | Each additional floor, 2000 S.F. | 3.60 | 2.36 | 5.96 |
| 4200 | 10,000 S.F. | 2.64 | 1.96 | 4.60 |
| 4250 | Ordinary hazard, one floor, 2000 S.F. | 25.50 | 5.55 | 31.05 |
| 4300 | 10,000 S.F. | 7.20 | 2.83 | 10.03 |
| 4350 | Each additional floor, 2000 S.F. | 3.55 | 2.37 | 5.92 |
| 4400 | 10,000 S.F. | 2.56 | 2.04 | 4.60 |
| 4450 | Extra hazard, one floor, 2000 S.F. | 26.50 | 6.45 | 32.95 |
| 4500 | 10,000 S.F. | 10.85 | 4.17 | 15.02 |
| 4550 | Each additional floor, 2000 S.F. | 4.94 | 3.73 | 8.67 |
| 4600 | 10,000 S.F. | 5.40 | 3.38 | 8.78 |
| 5060 | Copper tubing, type L, T-drill system, light hazard, one floor 2000 S.F. | 25.50 | 4.90 | 30.40 |
| 5100 | 10,000 S.F. | 6.50 | 2.11 | 8.61 |
| 5150 | Each additional floor, 2000 S.F. | 3.79 | 2.21 | 6 |
| 5200 | 10,000 S.F. | 2.29 | 1.59 | 3.88 |
| 5250 | Ordinary hazard, one floor, 2000 S.F. | 25 | 4.92 | 29.92 |
| 5300 | 10,000 S.F. | 6.90 | 2.55 | 9.45 |
| 5350 | Each additional floor, 2000 S.F. | 3.17 | 2.09 | 5.26 |
| 5400 | 10,000 S.F. | 2.58 | 2.01 | 4.59 |
| 5450 | Extra hazard, one floor, 2000 S.F. | 25.50 | 5.55 | 31.05 |
| 5500 | 10,000 S.F. | 8.70 | 3.09 | 11.79 |
| 5550 | Each additional floor, 2000 S.F. | 3.96 | 2.84 | 6.80 |
| 5600 | 10,000 S.F. | 3.40 | 2.35 | 5.75 |

## D4010 Sprinklers

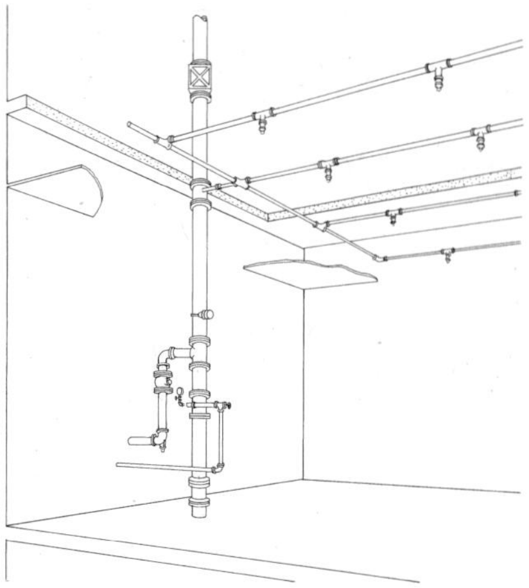

**Wet Pipe System**. A system employing automatic sprinklers attached to a piping system containing water and connected to a water supply so that water discharges immediately from sprinklers opened by heat from a fire.

All areas are assumed to be open.

| D4010 410 | Wet Pipe Sprinkler Systems | COST PER S.F. | | |
|---|---|---|---|---|
| | | MAT. | INST. | TOTAL |
| 0520 | Wet pipe sprinkler systems, steel, black, sch. 40 pipe | | | |
| 0530 | Light hazard, one floor, 500 S.F. | 8.60 | 4.25 | 12.85 |
| 0560 | 1000 S.F. | 7.50 | 3.72 | 11.22 |
| 0581 | 2000 S.F. | | | |
| 0600 | 5000 S.F. | 3.80 | 2.80 | 6.60 |
| 0620 | 10,000 S.F. | 2.69 | 2.38 | 5.07 |
| 0640 | 50,000 S.F. | 2.26 | 2.20 | 4.46 |
| 0660 | Each additional floor, 500 S.F. | 2.72 | 3.40 | 6.12 |
| 0680 | 1000 S.F. | 3.04 | 3.14 | 6.18 |
| 0700 | 2000 S.F. | 2.69 | 2.81 | 5.50 |
| 0720 | 5000 S.F. | 1.94 | 2.40 | 4.34 |
| 0740 | 10,000 S.F. | 1.84 | 2.21 | 4.05 |
| 0760 | 50,000 S.F. | 1.55 | 1.74 | 3.29 |
| 1000 | Ordinary hazard, one floor, 500 S.F. | 9.30 | 4.52 | 13.82 |
| 1020 | 1000 S.F. | 7.45 | 3.64 | 11.09 |
| 1040 | 2000 S.F. | 7.65 | 4.09 | 11.74 |
| 1060 | 5000 S.F. | 4.36 | 3.01 | 7.37 |
| 1080 | 10,000 S.F. | 3.50 | 3.16 | 6.66 |
| 1100 | 50,000 S.F. | 3.23 | 3.03 | 6.26 |
| 1140 | Each additional floor, 500 S.F. | 3.47 | 3.84 | 7.31 |
| 1160 | 1000 S.F. | 2.97 | 3.09 | 6.06 |
| 1180 | 2000 S.F. | 3 | 3.10 | 6.10 |
| 1200 | 5000 S.F. | 2.95 | 2.93 | 5.88 |
| 1220 | 10,000 S.F. | 2.66 | 2.99 | 5.65 |
| 1240 | 50,000 S.F. | 2.40 | 2.65 | 5.05 |
| 1500 | Extra hazard, one floor, 500 S.F. | 14 | 5.85 | 19.85 |
| 1520 | 1000 S.F. | 10.45 | 5.20 | 15.65 |
| 1540 | 2000 S.F. | 8.35 | 5.55 | 13.90 |
| 1560 | 5000 S.F. | 6.20 | 4.95 | 11.15 |
| 1580 | 10,000 S.F. | 5.75 | 4.75 | 10.50 |
| 1600 | 50,000 S.F. | 6.40 | 4.54 | 10.94 |
| 1660 | Each additional floor, 500 S.F. | 5.10 | 4.73 | 9.83 |
| 1680 | 1000 S.F. | 4.74 | 4.46 | 9.20 |
| 1700 | 2000 S.F. | 4 | 4.45 | 8.45 |
| 1720 | 5000 S.F. | 3.37 | 3.93 | 7.30 |
| 1740 | 10,000 S.F. | 3.88 | 3.61 | 7.49 |
| 1760 | 50,000 S.F. | 3.91 | 3.44 | 7.35 |
| 2020 | Grooved steel, black sch. 40 pipe, light hazard, one floor, 2000 S.F. | 7.65 | 3.27 | 10.92 |

## D4010 Sprinklers

| D4010 410 | Wet Pipe Sprinkler Systems | COST PER S.F. MAT. | COST PER S.F. INST. | COST PER S.F. TOTAL |
|---|---|---|---|---|
| 2060 | 10,000 S.F. | 2.94 | 2.05 | 4.99 |
| 2100 | Each additional floor, 2000 S.F. | 3.02 | 2.27 | 5.29 |
| 2150 | 10,000 S.F. | 2.09 | 1.87 | 3.96 |
| 2200 | Ordinary hazard, one floor, 2000 S.F. | 7.90 | 3.49 | 11.39 |
| 2250 | 10,000 S.F. | 3.59 | 2.66 | 6.25 |
| 2300 | Each additional floor, 2000 S.F. | 3.24 | 2.50 | 5.74 |
| 2350 | 10,000 S.F. | 2.75 | 2.49 | 5.24 |
| 2400 | Extra hazard, one floor, 2000 S.F. | 6.95 | 4.28 | 11.23 |
| 2450 | 10,000 S.F. | 4.64 | 3.41 | 8.05 |
| 2500 | Each additional floor, 2000 S.F. | 4.52 | 3.65 | 8.17 |
| 2550 | 10,000 S.F. | 3.78 | 3.10 | 6.88 |
| 3050 | Grooved steel, black sch. 10 pipe, light hazard, one floor, 2000 S.F. | 5.40 | 2.98 | 8.38 |
| 3100 | 10,000 S.F. | 2.57 | 2.02 | 4.59 |
| 3150 | Each additional floor, 2000 S.F. | 2.60 | 2.24 | 4.84 |
| 3200 | 10,000 S.F. | 1.72 | 1.84 | 3.56 |
| 3250 | Ordinary hazard, one floor, 2000 S.F. | 7.50 | 3.46 | 10.96 |
| 3300 | 10,000 S.F. | 2.97 | 2.59 | 5.56 |
| 3350 | Each additional floor, 2000 S.F. | 2.83 | 2.47 | 5.30 |
| 3400 | 10,000 S.F. | 2.19 | 2.43 | 4.62 |
| 3450 | Extra hazard, one floor, 2000 S.F. | 8.45 | 4.51 | 12.96 |
| 3500 | 10,000 S.F. | 4.47 | 3.41 | 7.88 |
| 3550 | Each additional floor, 2000 S.F. | 4.19 | 3.63 | 7.82 |
| 3600 | 10,000 S.F. | 3.39 | 3.06 | 6.45 |
| 4050 | Copper tubing, type L, light hazard, one floor, 2000 S.F. | 7.35 | 3.27 | 10.62 |
| 4100 | 10,000 S.F. | 2.77 | 2.09 | 4.86 |
| 4150 | Each additional floor, 2000 S.F. | 2.70 | 2.32 | 5.02 |
| 4200 | 10,000 S.F. | 1.92 | 1.92 | 3.84 |
| 4250 | Ordinary hazard, one floor, 2000 S.F. | 7.60 | 3.69 | 11.29 |
| 4300 | 10,000 S.F. | 3.25 | 2.48 | 5.73 |
| 4350 | Each additional floor, 2000 S.F. | 3.01 | 2.56 | 5.57 |
| 4400 | 10,000 S.F. | 2.29 | 2.26 | 4.55 |
| 4450 | Extra hazard, one floor, 2000 S.F. | 8.45 | 4.62 | 13.07 |
| 4500 | 10,000 S.F. | 6.70 | 3.80 | 10.50 |
| 4550 | Each additional floor, 2000 S.F. | 4.19 | 3.74 | 7.93 |
| 4600 | 10,000 S.F. | 4.81 | 3.40 | 8.21 |
| 5050 | Copper tubing, type L, T-drill system, light hazard, one floor | | | |
| 5060 | 2000 S.F. | 7.20 | 3.03 | 10.23 |
| 5100 | 10,000 S.F. | 2.42 | 1.72 | 4.14 |
| 5150 | Each additional floor, 2000 S.F. | 2.57 | 2.08 | 4.65 |
| 5200 | 10,000 S.F. | 1.57 | 1.56 | 3.13 |
| 5250 | Ordinary hazard, one floor, 2000 S.F. | 5.20 | 2.84 | 8.04 |
| 5300 | 10,000 S.F. | 2.96 | 2.20 | 5.16 |
| 5350 | Each additional floor, 2000 S.F. | 2.40 | 2.10 | 4.50 |
| 5400 | 10,000 S.F. | 2.12 | 2.03 | 4.15 |
| 5450 | Extra hazard, one floor, 2000 S.F. | 7.45 | 3.74 | 11.19 |
| 5500 | 10,000 S.F. | 4.67 | 2.78 | 7.45 |
| 5550 | Each additional floor, 2000 S.F. | 5.65 | 3.20 | 8.85 |
| 5600 | 10,000 S.F. | 2.79 | 2.37 | 5.16 |

## D4020 Standpipes

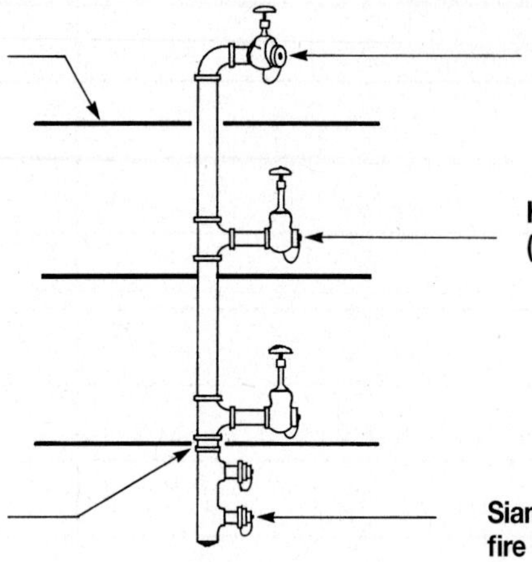


| D4020 310 | Wet Standpipe Risers, Class I | COST PER FLOOR | | |
|---|---|---|---|---|
| | | MAT. | INST. | TOTAL |
| 0550 | Wet standpipe risers, Class I, steel, black, sch. 40, 10′ height | | | |
| 0560 | 4″ diameter pipe, one floor | 10,200 | 4,300 | 14,500 |
| 0580 | Additional floors | 2,550 | 1,325 | 3,875 |
| 0600 | 6″ diameter pipe, one floor | 16,300 | 7,475 | 23,775 |
| 0620 | Additional floors | 4,250 | 2,100 | 6,350 |
| 0640 | 8″ diameter pipe, one floor | 24,200 | 9,025 | 33,225 |
| 0660 | Additional floors | 5,475 | 2,550 | 8,025 |

| D4020 310 | Wet Standpipe Risers, Class II | COST PER FLOOR | | |
|---|---|---|---|---|
| | | MAT. | INST. | TOTAL |
| 1030 | Wet standpipe risers, Class II, steel, black sch. 40, 10′ height | | | |
| 1040 | 2″ diameter pipe, one floor | 4,475 | 1,600 | 6,075 |
| 1060 | Additional floors | 1,275 | 595 | 1,870 |
| 1080 | 2-1/2″ diameter pipe, one floor | 6,025 | 2,250 | 8,275 |
| 1100 | Additional floors | 1,550 | 695 | 2,245 |

| D4020 310 | Wet Standpipe Risers, Class III | COST PER FLOOR | | |
|---|---|---|---|---|
| | | MAT. | INST. | TOTAL |
| 1530 | Wet standpipe risers, Class III, steel, black, sch. 40, 10′ height | | | |
| 1540 | 4″ diameter pipe, one floor | 10,500 | 4,300 | 14,800 |
| 1560 | Additional floors | 2,400 | 1,100 | 3,500 |
| 1580 | 6″ diameter pipe, one floor | 16,600 | 7,475 | 24,075 |
| 1600 | Additional floors | 4,400 | 2,100 | 6,500 |
| 1620 | 8″ diameter pipe, one floor | 24,500 | 9,025 | 33,525 |
| 1640 | Additional floors | 5,625 | 2,550 | 8,175 |

## D4020 Standpipes

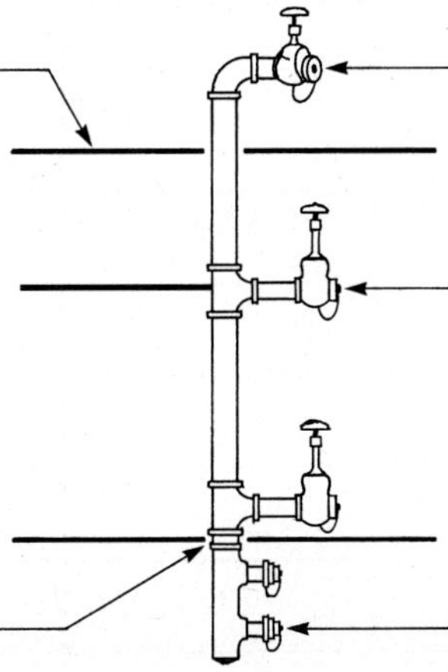


| D4020 330 | Dry Standpipe Risers, Class I | COST PER FLOOR | | |
|---|---|---|---|---|
| | | MAT. | INST. | TOTAL |
| 0530 | Dry standpipe riser, Class I, steel, black, sch. 40, 10′ height | | | |
| 0540 | 4″ diameter pipe, one floor | 5,875 | 3,500 | 9,375 |
| 0560 | Additional floors | 2,375 | 1,250 | 3,625 |
| 0580 | 6″ diameter pipe, one floor | 11,500 | 5,925 | 17,425 |
| 0600 | Additional floors | 4,075 | 2,025 | 6,100 |
| 0620 | 8″ diameter pipe, one floor | 16,700 | 7,200 | 23,900 |
| 0640 | Additional floors | 5,300 | 2,475 | 7,775 |

| D4020 330 | Dry Standpipe Risers, Class II | COST PER FLOOR | | |
|---|---|---|---|---|
| | | MAT. | INST. | TOTAL |
| 1030 | Dry standpipe risers, Class II, steel, black, sch. 40, 10′ height | | | |
| 1040 | 2″ diameter pipe, one floor | 3,250 | 1,600 | 4,850 |
| 1060 | Additional floors | 1,125 | 520 | 1,645 |
| 1080 | 2-1/2″ diameter pipe, one floor | 4,825 | 1,875 | 6,700 |
| 1100 | Additional floors | 1,375 | 625 | 2,000 |

| D4020 330 | Dry Standpipe Risers, Class III | COST PER FLOOR | | |
|---|---|---|---|---|
| | | MAT. | INST. | TOTAL |
| 1530 | Dry standpipe risers, Class III, steel, black, sch. 40, 10′ height | | | |
| 1540 | 4″ diameter pipe, one floor | 5,725 | 3,375 | 9,100 |
| 1560 | Additional floors | 2,250 | 1,125 | 3,375 |
| 1580 | 6″ diameter pipe, one floor | 11,600 | 5,925 | 17,525 |
| 1600 | Additional floors | 4,225 | 2,025 | 6,250 |
| 1620 | 8″ diameter pipe, one floor | 16,900 | 7,200 | 24,100 |
| 1640 | Additional floors | 5,450 | 2,475 | 7,925 |

## D4020 Standpipes

| D4020 410 | Fire Hose Equipment | COST EACH MAT. | COST EACH INST. | COST EACH TOTAL |
|---|---|---|---|---|
| 0100 | Adapters, reducing, 1 piece, FxM, hexagon, cast brass, 2-1/2" x 1-1/2" | 81.50 | | 81.50 |
| 0200 | Pin lug, 1-1/2" x 1" | 50.50 | | 50.50 |
| 0250 | 3" x 2-1/2" | 97.50 | | 97.50 |
| 0300 | For polished chrome, add 75% mat. | | | |
| 0400 | Cabinets, D.S. glass in door, recessed, steel box, not equipped | | | |
| 0500 | Single extinguisher, steel door & frame | 102 | 190 | 292 |
| 0550 | Stainless steel door & frame | 177 | 190 | 367 |
| 0600 | Valve, 2-1/2" angle, steel door & frame | 345 | 127 | 472 |
| 0650 | Aluminum door & frame | 400 | 127 | 527 |
| 0700 | Stainless steel door & frame | 480 | 127 | 607 |
| 0750 | Hose rack assy, 2-1/2" x 1-1/2" valve & 100' hose, steel door & frame | 1,025 | 254 | 1,279 |
| 0800 | Aluminum door & frame | 1,150 | 254 | 1,404 |
| 0850 | Stainless steel door & frame | 1,325 | 254 | 1,579 |
| 0900 | Hose rack assy & extinguisher,2-1/2"x1-1/2" valve & hose,steel door & frame | 440 | 305 | 745 |
| 0950 | Aluminum | 440 | 305 | 745 |
| 1000 | Stainless steel | 700 | 305 | 1,005 |
| 1550 | Compressor, air, dry pipe system, automatic, 200 gal., 3/4 H.P. | 2,025 | 650 | 2,675 |
| 1600 | 520 gal., 1 H.P. | 1,825 | 650 | 2,475 |
| 1650 | Alarm, electric pressure switch (circuit closer) | 168 | 32.50 | 200.50 |
| 2500 | Couplings, hose, rocker lug, cast brass, 1-1/2" | 74 | | 74 |
| 2550 | 2-1/2" | 162 | | 162 |
| 3000 | Escutcheon plate, for angle valves, polished brass, 1-1/2" | 25 | | 25 |
| 3050 | 2-1/2" | 42.50 | | 42.50 |
| 3500 | Fire pump, electric, w/controller, fittings, relief valve | | | |
| 3550 | 4" pump, 30 HP, 500 GPM | 24,800 | 4,725 | 29,525 |
| 3600 | 5" pump, 40 H.P., 1000 G.P.M. | 36,200 | 5,375 | 41,575 |
| 3650 | 5" pump, 100 H.P., 1000 G.P.M. | 40,500 | 5,950 | 46,450 |
| 3700 | For jockey pump system, add | 4,700 | 760 | 5,460 |
| 5000 | Hose, per linear foot, synthetic jacket, lined, | | | |
| 5100 | 300 lb. test, 1-1/2" diameter | 3.64 | .59 | 4.23 |
| 5150 | 2-1/2" diameter | 6.40 | .69 | 7.09 |
| 5200 | 500 lb. test, 1-1/2" diameter | 3.98 | .59 | 4.57 |
| 5250 | 2-1/2" diameter | 6.70 | .69 | 7.39 |
| 5500 | Nozzle, plain stream, polished brass, 1-1/2" x 10" | 64.50 | | 64.50 |
| 5550 | 2-1/2" x 15" x 13/16" or 1-1/2" | 186 | | 186 |
| 5600 | Heavy duty combination adjustable fog and straight stream w/handle 1-1/2" | 745 | | 745 |
| 5650 | 2-1/2" direct connection | 750 | | 750 |
| 6000 | Rack, for 1-1/2" diameter hose 100 ft. long, steel | 129 | 76 | 205 |
| 6050 | Brass | 200 | 76 | 276 |
| 6500 | Reel, steel, for 50 ft. long 1-1/2" diameter hose | 206 | 109 | 315 |
| 6550 | For 75 ft. long 2-1/2" diameter hose | 294 | 109 | 403 |
| 7050 | Siamese, w/plugs & chains, polished brass, sidewalk, 4" x 2-1/2" x 2-1/2" | 965 | 610 | 1,575 |
| 7100 | 6" x 2-1/2" x 2-1/2" | 1,525 | 760 | 2,285 |
| 7200 | Wall type, flush, 4" x 2-1/2" x 2-1/2" | 930 | 305 | 1,235 |
| 7250 | 6" x 2-1/2" x 2-1/2" | 1,200 | 330 | 1,530 |
| 7300 | Projecting, 4" x 2-1/2" x 2-1/2" | 665 | 305 | 970 |
| 7350 | 6" x 2-1/2" x 2-1/2" | 1,100 | 330 | 1,430 |
| 7400 | For chrome plate, add 15% mat. | | | |
| 8000 | Valves, angle, wheel handle, 300 Lb., rough brass, 1-1/2" | 111 | 70.50 | 181.50 |
| 8050 | 2-1/2" | 214 | 121 | 335 |
| 8100 | Combination pressure restricting, 1-1/2" | 145 | 70.50 | 215.50 |
| 8150 | 2-1/2" | 238 | 121 | 359 |
| 8200 | Pressure restricting, adjustable, satin brass, 1-1/2" | 530 | 70.50 | 600.50 |
| 8250 | 2-1/2" | 800 | 121 | 921 |
| 8300 | Hydrolator, vent and drain, rough brass, 1-1/2" | 168 | 70.50 | 238.50 |
| 8350 | 2-1/2" | 168 | 70.50 | 238.50 |
| 8400 | Cabinet assy, incls. adapter, rack, hose, and nozzle | 1,825 | 460 | 2,285 |

## D4090 Other Fire Protection Systems

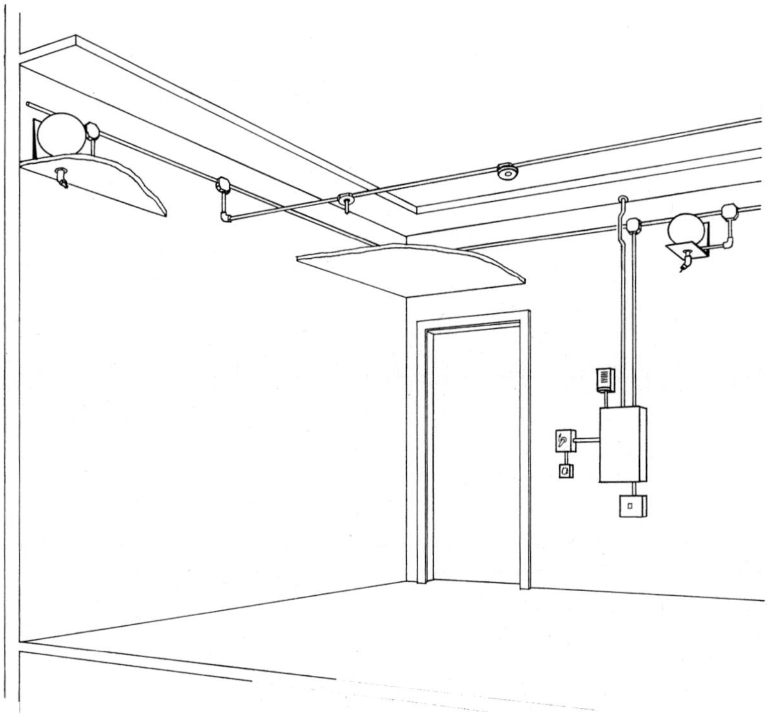

**General:** Automatic fire protection (suppression) systems other than water sprinklers may be desired for special environments, high risk areas, isolated locations or unusual hazards. Some typical applications would include:

1. Paint dip tanks
2. Securities vaults
3. Electronic data processing
4. Tape and data storage
5. Transformer rooms
6. Spray booths
7. Petroleum storage
8. High rack storage

Piping and wiring costs are highly variable and are not included.

| D4090 910 | Fire Suppression Unit Components | COST EACH | | |
|---|---|---|---|---|
| | | MAT. | INST. | TOTAL |
| 0020 | Detectors with brackets | | | |
| 0040 | Fixed temperature heat detector | 48 | 114 | 162 |
| 0060 | Rate of temperature rise detector | 36.50 | 100 | 136.50 |
| 0080 | Ion detector (smoke) detector | 171 | 129 | 300 |
| 0200 | Extinguisher agent | | | |
| 0240 | 200 lb FM200, container | 8,550 | 385 | 8,935 |
| 0280 | 75 lb carbon dioxide cylinder | 1,725 | 258 | 1,983 |
| 0320 | Dispersion nozzle | | | |
| 0340 | FM200 1-1/2" dispersion nozzle | 310 | 61.50 | 371.50 |
| 0380 | Carbon dioxide 3" x 5" dispersion nozzle | 193 | 48 | 241 |
| 0420 | Control station | | | |
| 0440 | Single zone control station with batteries | 1,550 | 800 | 2,350 |
| 0470 | Multizone (4) control station with batteries | 3,750 | 1,600 | 5,350 |
| 0500 | Electric mechanical release | 1,275 | 415 | 1,690 |
| 0550 | Manual pull station | 112 | 143 | 255 |
| 0640 | Battery standby power 10" x 10" x 17" | 570 | 200 | 770 |
| 0740 | Bell signalling device | 62.50 | 100 | 162.50 |
| 0900 | Standard low-rise sprinkler accessory package, 3 story | 3,825 | 2,250 | 6,075 |
| 1000 | Standard mid-rise sprinkler accessory package, 8 story | 7,875 | 4,300 | 12,175 |
| 1100 | Standard high-rise sprinkler accessory package, 16 story | 18,600 | 8,425 | 27,025 |

| D4090 920 | FM200 Systems | COST PER C.F. | | |
|---|---|---|---|---|
| | | MAT. | INST. | TOTAL |
| 0820 | Average FM200 system, minimum | 2.32 | | 2.32 |
| 0840 | Maximum | 4.62 | | 4.62 |

## D5010 Electrical Service/Distribution

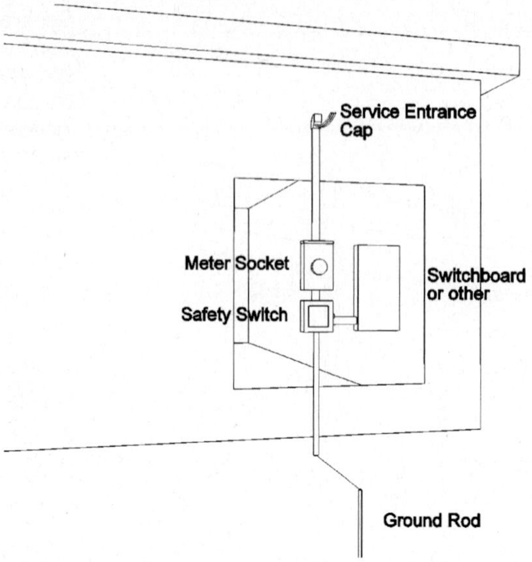


| D5010 120 | Overhead Electric Service, 3 Phase - 4 Wire | COST EACH | | |
|---|---|---|---|---|
| | | MAT. | INST. | TOTAL |
| 0200 | Service installation, includes breakers, metering, 20' conduit & wire | | | |
| 0220 | 3 phase, 4 wire, 120/208 volts, 60 A | 760 | 1,300 | 2,060 |
| 0240 | 100 A | 1,025 | 1,475 | 2,500 |
| 0245 | 100 A w/circuit breaker | 1,750 | 1,825 | 3,575 |
| 0280 | 200 A | 1,925 | 2,025 | 3,950 |
| 0285 | 200 A w/circuit breaker | 3,200 | 2,575 | 5,775 |
| 0320 | 400 A | 3,825 | 4,050 | 7,875 |
| 0325 | 400 A w/circuit breaker | 8,800 | 5,050 | 13,850 |
| 0360 | 600 A | 7,050 | 6,000 | 13,050 |
| 0365 | 600 A, w/switchboard | 12,500 | 7,600 | 20,100 |
| 0400 | 800 A | 13,900 | 7,175 | 21,075 |
| 0405 | 800 A, w/switchboard | 19,400 | 9,000 | 28,400 |
| 0440 | 1000 A | 16,200 | 8,825 | 25,025 |
| 0445 | 1000 A, w/switchboard | 22,800 | 10,800 | 33,600 |
| 0480 | 1200 A | 23,000 | 10,100 | 33,100 |
| 0485 | 1200 A, w/groundfault switchboard | 51,500 | 12,500 | 64,000 |
| 0520 | 1600 A | 28,400 | 13,200 | 41,600 |
| 0525 | 1600 A, w/groundfault switchboard | 59,500 | 15,800 | 75,300 |
| 0560 | 2000 A | 38,100 | 16,000 | 54,100 |
| 0565 | 2000 A, w/groundfault switchboard | 73,500 | 19,700 | 93,200 |
| 0610 | 1 phase, 3 wire, 120/240 volts, 100 A (no safety switch) | 310 | 720 | 1,030 |
| 0615 | 100 A w/load center | 685 | 1,375 | 2,060 |
| 0620 | 200 A | 900 | 990 | 1,890 |
| 0625 | 200 A w/load center | 1,725 | 2,100 | 3,825 |

# D5010 Electrical Service/Distribution

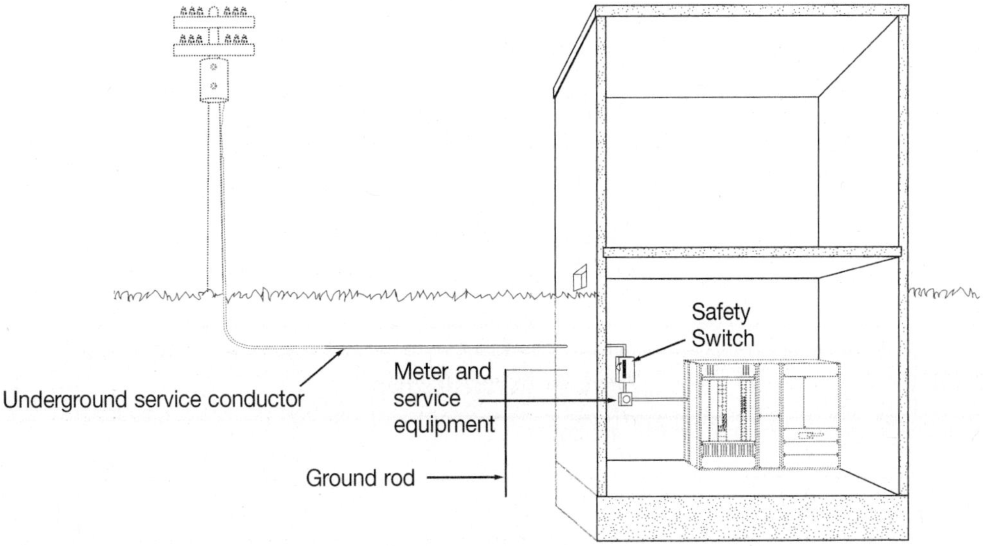


| D5010 130 | Underground Electric Service | COST EACH MAT. | INST. | TOTAL |
|---|---|---|---|---|
| 0950 | Underground electric service including excavation, backfill and compaction | | | |
| 1000 | 3 phase, 4 wire, 277/480 volts, 2000 A | 93,000 | 25,700 | 118,700 |
| 1050 | 2000 A w/groundfault switchboard | 127,000 | 28,500 | 155,500 |
| 1100 | 1600 A | 70,500 | 20,700 | 91,200 |
| 1150 | 1600 A w/groundfault switchboard | 101,500 | 23,300 | 124,800 |
| 1200 | 1200 A | 58,000 | 16,500 | 74,500 |
| 1250 | 1200 A w/groundfault switchboard | 86,500 | 18,900 | 105,400 |
| 1400 | 800 A | 27,500 | 13,700 | 41,200 |
| 1450 | 800 A w/switchboard | 33,000 | 15,500 | 48,500 |
| 1500 | 600 A | 17,200 | 12,600 | 29,800 |
| 1550 | 600 A w/switchboard | 22,700 | 14,200 | 36,900 |
| 1600 | 1 phase, 3 wire, 120/240 volts, 200 A | 5,150 | 4,375 | 9,525 |
| 1650 | 200 A w/load center | 5,950 | 5,475 | 11,425 |
| 1700 | 100 A | 3,800 | 3,575 | 7,375 |
| 1750 | 100 A w/load center | 4,625 | 4,675 | 9,300 |

## D5010 Electrical Service/Distribution

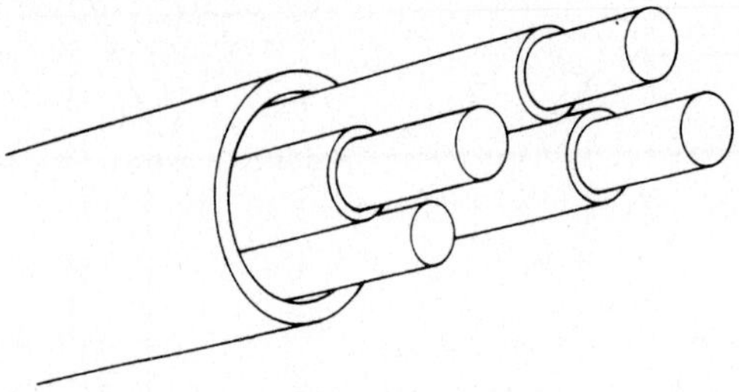

| D5010 230 | Feeder Installation | COST PER L.F. MAT. | COST PER L.F. INST. | COST PER L.F. TOTAL |
|---|---|---|---|---|
| 0200 | Feeder installation 600 V, including RGS conduit and XHHW wire, 60 A | 10.25 | 14.70 | 24.95 |
| 0240 | 100 A | 20 | 19.15 | 39.15 |
| 0280 | 200 A | 39 | 29 | 68 |
| 0320 | 400 A | 78 | 58 | 136 |
| 0360 | 600 A | 158 | 94.50 | 252.50 |
| 0400 | 800 A | 211 | 112 | 323 |
| 0440 | 1000 A | 261 | 147 | 408 |
| 0480 | 1200 A | 315 | 189 | 504 |
| 0520 | 1600 A | 420 | 224 | 644 |
| 0560 | 2000 A | 520 | 294 | 814 |
| 1200 | Branch installation 600 V, including EMT conduit and THW wire, 15 A | 2.10 | 7.15 | 9.25 |
| 1240 | 20 A | 2.39 | 7.65 | 10.04 |
| 1280 | 30 A | 2.89 | 7.90 | 10.79 |
| 1320 | 50 A | 5.95 | 10.95 | 16.90 |
| 1360 | 65 A | 6.70 | 11.65 | 18.35 |
| 1400 | 85 A | 11.20 | 13.55 | 24.75 |
| 1440 | 100 A | 12.15 | 13.80 | 25.95 |
| 1480 | 130 A | 16.45 | 16.15 | 32.60 |
| 1520 | 150 A | 19.85 | 18.50 | 38.35 |
| 1560 | 200 A | 27 | 21 | 48 |

## D5010 Electrical Service/Distribution

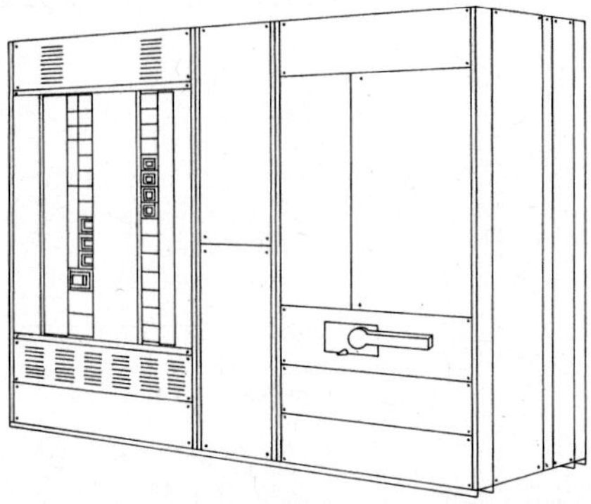

| D5010 240 | Switchgear | COST PER EACH | | |
|---|---|---|---|---|
| | | MAT. | INST. | TOTAL |
| 0190 | Switchgear installation, including switchboard, panels, & circuit breaker | | | |
| 0200 | 120/208 V, 3 phase, 400 A | 9,975 | 3,400 | 13,375 |
| 0240 | 600 A | 13,600 | 3,800 | 17,400 |
| 0280 | 800 A | 15,900 | 4,400 | 20,300 |
| 0300 | 1000 A | 17,700 | 4,875 | 22,575 |
| 0320 | 1200 A | 20,400 | 5,500 | 25,900 |
| 0360 | 1600 A | 33,100 | 6,350 | 39,450 |
| 0400 | 2000 A | 40,100 | 6,900 | 47,000 |
| 0500 | 277/480 V, 3 phase, 400 A | 13,700 | 6,300 | 20,000 |
| 0520 | 600 A | 18,700 | 7,250 | 25,950 |
| 0540 | 800 A | 20,400 | 8,050 | 28,450 |
| 0560 | 1000 A | 23,700 | 8,875 | 32,575 |
| 0580 | 1200 A | 27,500 | 9,950 | 37,450 |
| 0600 | 1600 A | 42,300 | 11,000 | 53,300 |
| 0620 | 2000 A | 53,500 | 12,100 | 65,600 |

## D5010 Electrical Service/Distribution

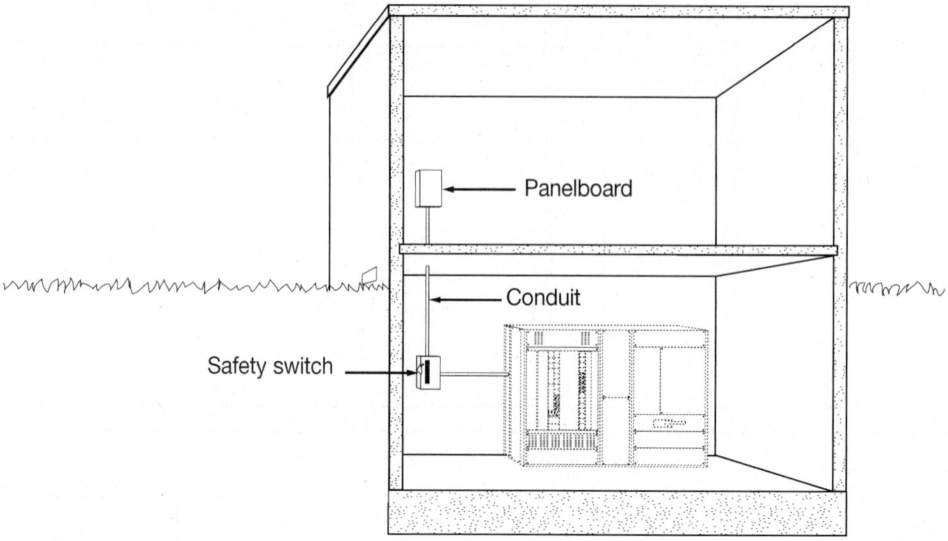


| D5010 250 | Panelboard | COST EACH | | |
|---|---|---|---|---|
| | | MAT. | INST. | TOTAL |
| 0900 | Panelboards, NQOD, 4 wire, 120/208 volts w/conductor & conduit | | | |
| 1000 | 100 A, 0 stories, 0′ horizontal | 2,525 | 4,275 | 6,800 |
| 1020 | 1 story, 25′ horizontal | 3,425 | 2,425 | 5,850 |
| 1040 | 5 stories, 50′ horizontal | 4,825 | 3,875 | 8,700 |
| 1060 | 10 stories, 75′ horizontal | 6,475 | 5,550 | 12,025 |
| 1080 | 225A, 0 stories, 0′ horizontal | 3,050 | 2,225 | 5,275 |
| 2000 | 1 story, 25′ horizontal | 5,075 | 3,550 | 8,625 |
| 2020 | 5 stories, 50′ horizontal | 9,050 | 6,150 | 15,200 |
| 2040 | 10 stories, 75′ horizontal | 13,700 | 9,200 | 22,900 |
| 2060 | 400A, 0 stories, 0′ horizontal | 7,375 | 3,325 | 10,700 |
| 2080 | 1 story, 25′ horizontal | 9,950 | 5,475 | 15,425 |
| 3000 | 5 stories, 50′ horizontal | 15,100 | 9,675 | 24,775 |
| 3020 | 10 stories, 75′ horizontal | 28,000 | 18,900 | 46,900 |
| 3040 | 600 A, 0 stories, 0′ horizontal | 10,800 | 4,000 | 14,800 |
| 3060 | 1 story, 25′ horizontal | 16,400 | 7,500 | 23,900 |
| 3080 | 5 stories, 50′ horizontal | 27,400 | 14,400 | 41,800 |
| 4000 | 10 stories, 75′ horizontal | 55,500 | 28,300 | 83,800 |
| 4010 | Panelboards, NEHB, 4 wire, 277/480 volts w/conductor, conduit, & safety switch | | | |
| 4020 | 100 A, 0 stories, 0′ horizontal, includes safety switch | 6,400 | 2,325 | 8,725 |
| 4040 | 1 story, 25′ horizontal | 7,125 | 3,050 | 10,175 |
| 4060 | 5 stories, 50′ horizontal | 8,525 | 4,500 | 13,025 |
| 4080 | 10 stories, 75′ horizontal | 10,200 | 6,175 | 16,375 |
| 5000 | 225 A, 0 stories, 0′ horizontal | 8,100 | 2,850 | 10,950 |
| 5020 | 1 story, 25′ horizontal | 10,100 | 4,150 | 14,250 |
| 5040 | 5 stories, 50′ horizontal | 14,100 | 6,775 | 20,875 |
| 5060 | 10 stories, 75′ horizontal | 18,700 | 9,800 | 28,500 |
| 5080 | 400 A, 0 stories, 0′ horizontal | 14,400 | 4,375 | 18,775 |
| 6000 | 1 story, 25′ horizontal | 17,000 | 6,500 | 23,500 |
| 6020 | 5 stories, 50′ horizontal | 22,100 | 10,700 | 32,800 |
| 6040 | 10 stories, 75′ horizontal | 35,000 | 20,000 | 55,000 |
| 6060 | 600 A, 0 stories, 0′ horizontal | 19,100 | 5,550 | 24,650 |
| 6080 | 1 story, 25′ horizontal | 24,700 | 9,050 | 33,750 |
| 7000 | 5 stories, 50′ horizontal | 35,700 | 15,900 | 51,600 |
| 7020 | 10 stories, 75′ horizontal | 63,500 | 29,800 | 93,300 |

## D5020 Lighting and Branch Wiring

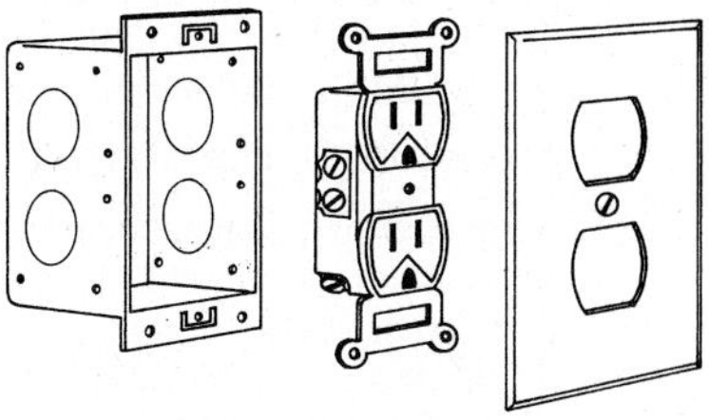

Duplex Wall Receptacle

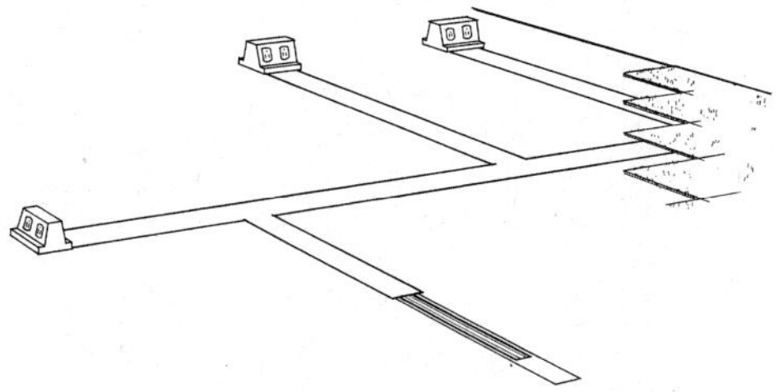

Undercarpet Receptacle System

| D5020 110 | Receptacle (by Wattage) | COST PER S.F. MAT. | COST PER S.F. INST. | COST PER S.F. TOTAL |
|---|---|---|---|---|
| 0190 | Receptacles include plate, box, conduit, wire & transformer when required | | | |
| 0200 | 2.5 per 1000 S.F., .3 watts per S.F. | .68 | 1.79 | 2.47 |
| 0240 | With transformer | .84 | 1.87 | 2.71 |
| 0280 | 4 per 1000 S.F., .5 watts per S.F. | .76 | 2.08 | 2.84 |
| 0320 | With transformer | 1.03 | 2.22 | 3.25 |
| 0360 | 5 per 1000 S.F., .6 watts per S.F. | .21 | .82 | 1.03 |
| 0400 | With transformer | 1.22 | 2.63 | 3.85 |
| 0440 | 8 per 1000 S.F., .9 watts per S.F. | .92 | 2.72 | 3.64 |
| 0480 | With transformer | 1.46 | 3.01 | 4.47 |
| 0520 | 10 per 1000 S.F., 1.2 watts per S.F. | .97 | 2.95 | 3.92 |
| 0560 | With transformer | 1.64 | 3.31 | 4.95 |
| 0600 | 16.5 per 1000 S.F., 2.0 watts per S.F. | 1.11 | 3.69 | 4.80 |
| 0640 | With transformer | 2.21 | 4.27 | 6.48 |
| 0680 | 20 per 1000 S.F., 2.4 watts per S.F. | 1.15 | 4.02 | 5.17 |
| 0720 | With transformer | 2.50 | 4.73 | 7.23 |

| D5020 115 | Receptacles, Floor | COST PER S.F. MAT. | COST PER S.F. INST. | COST PER S.F. TOTAL |
|---|---|---|---|---|
| 0200 | Receptacle systems, underfloor duct, 5′ on center, low density | 8.25 | 3.94 | 12.19 |
| 0240 | High density | 9 | 5.05 | 14.05 |
| 0280 | 7′ on center, low density | 6.55 | 3.38 | 9.93 |
| 0320 | High density | 7.30 | 4.51 | 11.81 |
| 0400 | Poke thru fittings, low density | 2 | 1.92 | 3.92 |
| 0440 | High density | 4 | 3.83 | 7.83 |
| 0520 | Telepoles, using Romex, low density | 2.07 | 1.18 | 3.25 |
| 0560 | High density | 4.14 | 2.37 | 6.51 |
| 0600 | Using EMT, low density | 2.16 | 1.57 | 3.73 |
| 0640 | High density | 4.32 | 3.13 | 7.45 |
| 0720 | Conduit system with floor boxes, low density | 2.22 | 1.34 | 3.56 |
| 0760 | High density | 4.44 | 2.69 | 7.13 |
| 0840 | Undercarpet power system, 3 conductor with 5 conductor feeder, low density | 1.75 | .49 | 2.24 |
| 0880 | High density | 3.49 | .98 | 4.47 |

## D5020 Lighting and Branch Wiring

**Description:** Table D5020 130 includes the cost for switch, plate, box, conduit in slab or EMT exposed and copper wire. Add 20% for exposed conduit.

No power required for switches.

Federal energy guidelines recommend the maximum lighting area controlled per switch shall not exceed 1000 S.F. and that areas over 500 S.F. shall be so controlled that total illumination can be reduced by at least 50%.

| D5020 130 | Wall Switch by Sq. Ft. | COST PER S.F. | | |
|---|---|---|---|---|
| | | MAT. | INST. | TOTAL |
| 0200 | Wall switches, 1.0 per 1000 S.F. | .10 | .29 | .39 |
| 0240 | 1.2 per 1000 S.F. | .10 | .32 | .42 |
| 0280 | 2.0 per 1000 S.F. | .14 | .46 | .60 |
| 0320 | 2.5 per 1000 S.F. | .18 | .58 | .76 |
| 0360 | 5.0 per 1000 S.F. | .39 | 1.24 | 1.63 |
| 0400 | 10.0 per 1000 S.F. | .80 | 2.51 | 3.31 |

| D5020 135 | Miscellaneous Power | COST PER S.F. | | |
|---|---|---|---|---|
| | | MAT. | INST. | TOTAL |
| 0200 | Miscellaneous power, to .5 watts | .06 | .14 | .20 |
| 0240 | .8 watts | .08 | .20 | .28 |
| 0280 | 1 watt | .11 | .27 | .38 |
| 0320 | 1.2 watts | .13 | .32 | .45 |
| 0360 | 1.5 watts | .16 | .37 | .53 |
| 0400 | 1.8 watts | .18 | .43 | .61 |
| 0440 | 2 watts | .21 | .52 | .73 |
| 0480 | 2.5 watts | .26 | .63 | .89 |
| 0520 | 3 watts | .31 | .75 | 1.06 |

| D5020 140 | Central A. C. Power (by Wattage) | COST PER S.F. | | |
|---|---|---|---|---|
| | | MAT. | INST. | TOTAL |
| 0200 | Central air conditioning power, 1 watt | .13 | .31 | .44 |
| 0220 | 2 watts | .15 | .36 | .51 |
| 0240 | 3 watts | .30 | .54 | .84 |
| 0280 | 4 watts | .28 | .54 | .82 |
| 0320 | 6 watts | .55 | .72 | 1.27 |
| 0360 | 8 watts | .69 | .78 | 1.47 |
| 0400 | 10 watts | .97 | .90 | 1.87 |

## D5020 Lighting and Branch Wiring

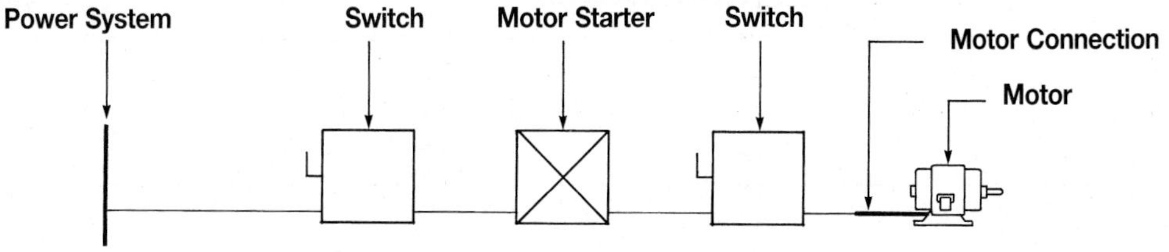


Motor Installation

| D5020 145 | Motor Installation | COST EACH | | |
|---|---|---|---|---|
| | | MAT. | INST. | TOTAL |
| 0200 | Motor installation, single phase, 115V, 1/3 HP motor size | 655 | 1,225 | 1,880 |
| 0240 | 1 HP motor size | 675 | 1,225 | 1,900 |
| 0280 | 2 HP motor size | 750 | 1,300 | 2,050 |
| 0320 | 3 HP motor size | 850 | 1,325 | 2,175 |
| 0360 | 230V, 1 HP motor size | 655 | 1,225 | 1,880 |
| 0400 | 2 HP motor size | 730 | 1,225 | 1,955 |
| 0440 | 3 HP motor size | 800 | 1,325 | 2,125 |
| 0520 | Three phase, 200V, 1-1/2 HP motor size | 700 | 1,350 | 2,050 |
| 0560 | 3 HP motor size | 1,050 | 1,475 | 2,525 |
| 0600 | 5 HP motor size | 870 | 1,650 | 2,520 |
| 0640 | 7-1/2 HP motor size | 930 | 1,675 | 2,605 |
| 0680 | 10 HP motor size | 1,300 | 2,100 | 3,400 |
| 0720 | 15 HP motor size | 1,775 | 2,350 | 4,125 |
| 0760 | 20 HP motor size | 2,325 | 2,700 | 5,025 |
| 0800 | 25 HP motor size | 2,375 | 2,700 | 5,075 |
| 0840 | 30 HP motor size | 3,550 | 3,175 | 6,725 |
| 0880 | 40 HP motor size | 4,600 | 3,750 | 8,350 |
| 0920 | 50 HP motor size | 7,400 | 4,375 | 11,775 |
| 0960 | 60 HP motor size | 7,850 | 4,625 | 12,475 |
| 1000 | 75 HP motor size | 10,500 | 5,300 | 15,800 |
| 1040 | 100 HP motor size | 20,400 | 6,225 | 26,625 |
| 1080 | 125 HP motor size | 21,300 | 6,850 | 28,150 |
| 1120 | 150 HP motor size | 25,400 | 8,050 | 33,450 |
| 1160 | 200 HP motor size | 28,200 | 9,500 | 37,700 |
| 1240 | 230V, 1-1/2 HP motor size | 680 | 1,350 | 2,030 |
| 1280 | 3 HP motor size | 1,025 | 1,450 | 2,475 |
| 1320 | 5 HP motor size | 855 | 1,625 | 2,480 |
| 1360 | 7-1/2 HP motor size | 855 | 1,625 | 2,480 |
| 1400 | 10 HP motor size | 1,250 | 2,000 | 3,250 |
| 1440 | 15 HP motor size | 1,475 | 2,175 | 3,650 |
| 1480 | 20 HP motor size | 2,200 | 2,625 | 4,825 |
| 1520 | 25 HP motor size | 2,325 | 2,700 | 5,025 |
| 1560 | 30 HP motor size | 2,425 | 2,700 | 5,125 |
| 1600 | 40 HP motor size | 4,325 | 3,650 | 7,975 |
| 1640 | 50 HP motor size | 4,775 | 3,875 | 8,650 |
| 1680 | 60 HP motor size | 7,425 | 4,400 | 11,825 |
| 1720 | 75 HP motor size | 9,525 | 4,975 | 14,500 |
| 1760 | 100 HP motor size | 11,400 | 5,550 | 16,950 |
| 1800 | 125 HP motor size | 21,200 | 6,450 | 27,650 |
| 1840 | 150 HP motor size | 22,600 | 7,300 | 29,900 |
| 1880 | 200 HP motor size | 24,800 | 8,125 | 32,925 |
| 1960 | 460V, 2 HP motor size | 915 | 1,350 | 2,265 |
| 2000 | 5 HP motor size | 1,250 | 1,475 | 2,725 |
| 2040 | 10 HP motor size | 985 | 1,625 | 2,610 |
| 2080 | 15 HP motor size | 1,250 | 1,875 | 3,125 |
| 2120 | 20 HP motor size | 1,425 | 2,000 | 3,425 |

## D5020 Lighting and Branch Wiring

| D5020 145 | Motor Installation | COST EACH | | |
|---|---|---|---|---|
| | | MAT. | INST. | TOTAL |
| 2160 | 25 HP motor size | 1,525 | 2,100 | 3,625 |
| 2200 | 30 HP motor size | 1,850 | 2,250 | 4,100 |
| 2240 | 40 HP motor size | 2,475 | 2,425 | 4,900 |
| 2280 | 50 HP motor size | 2,800 | 2,700 | 5,500 |
| 2320 | 60 HP motor size | 3,850 | 3,150 | 7,000 |
| 2360 | 75 HP motor size | 4,775 | 3,475 | 8,250 |
| 2400 | 100 HP motor size | 5,425 | 3,875 | 9,300 |
| 2440 | 125 HP motor size | 8,100 | 4,400 | 12,500 |
| 2480 | 150 HP motor size | 10,700 | 4,950 | 15,650 |
| 2520 | 200 HP motor size | 13,100 | 5,575 | 18,675 |
| 2600 | 575V, 2 HP motor size | 915 | 1,350 | 2,265 |
| 2640 | 5 HP motor size | 1,250 | 1,475 | 2,725 |
| 2680 | 10 HP motor size | 985 | 1,625 | 2,610 |
| 2720 | 20 HP motor size | 1,250 | 1,875 | 3,125 |
| 2760 | 25 HP motor size | 1,425 | 2,000 | 3,425 |
| 2800 | 30 HP motor size | 1,850 | 2,250 | 4,100 |
| 2840 | 50 HP motor size | 2,025 | 2,350 | 4,375 |
| 2880 | 60 HP motor size | 3,775 | 3,125 | 6,900 |
| 2920 | 75 HP motor size | 3,850 | 3,150 | 7,000 |
| 2960 | 100 HP motor size | 4,775 | 3,475 | 8,250 |
| 3000 | 125 HP motor size | 7,700 | 4,325 | 12,025 |
| 3040 | 150 HP motor size | 8,100 | 4,400 | 12,500 |
| 3080 | 200 HP motor size | 11,300 | 5,000 | 16,300 |

| D5020 155 | Motor Feeder | COST PER L.F. | | |
|---|---|---|---|---|
| | | MAT. | INST. | TOTAL |
| 0200 | Motor feeder systems, single phase, feed up to 115V 1HP or 230V 2HP | 3.91 | 9.45 | 13.36 |
| 0240 | 115V 2HP, 230V 3HP | 4.19 | 9.60 | 13.79 |
| 0280 | 115V 3HP | 4.84 | 10 | 14.84 |
| 0360 | Three phase, feed to 200V 3HP, 230V 5HP, 460V 10HP, 575V 10HP | 4.14 | 10.20 | 14.34 |
| 0440 | 200V 5HP, 230V 7.5HP, 460V 15HP, 575V 20HP | 4.56 | 10.40 | 14.96 |
| 0520 | 200V 10HP, 230V 10HP, 460V 30HP, 575V 30HP | 5.55 | 11 | 16.55 |
| 0600 | 200V 15HP, 230V 15HP, 460V 40HP, 575V 50HP | 7.50 | 12.60 | 20.10 |
| 0680 | 200V 20HP, 230V 25HP, 460V 50HP, 575V 60HP | 11.50 | 16 | 27.50 |
| 0760 | 200V 25HP, 230V 30HP, 460V 60HP, 575V 75HP | 12.65 | 16.25 | 28.90 |
| 0840 | 200V 30HP | 14.20 | 16.80 | 31 |
| 0920 | 230V 40HP, 460V 75HP, 575V 100HP | 17.55 | 18.30 | 35.85 |
| 1000 | 200V 40HP | 19.30 | 19.60 | 38.90 |
| 1080 | 230V 50HP, 460V 100HP, 575V 125HP | 24.50 | 21.50 | 46 |
| 1160 | 200V 50HP, 230V 60HP, 460V 125HP, 575V 150HP | 27.50 | 23 | 50.50 |
| 1240 | 200V 60HP, 460V 150HP | 34.50 | 27 | 61.50 |
| 1320 | 230V 75HP, 575V 200HP | 37.50 | 28 | 65.50 |
| 1400 | 200V 75HP | 42 | 28.50 | 70.50 |
| 1480 | 230V 100HP, 460V 200HP | 60.50 | 33.50 | 94 |
| 1560 | 200V 100HP | 83.50 | 41.50 | 125 |
| 1640 | 230V 125HP | 83.50 | 41.50 | 125 |
| 1720 | 200V 125HP, 230V 150HP | 91 | 51.50 | 142.50 |
| 1800 | 200V 150HP | 110 | 56 | 166 |
| 1880 | 200V 200HP | 140 | 59.50 | 199.50 |
| 1960 | 230V 200HP | 144 | 62 | 206 |

## D5020 Lighting and Branch Wiring

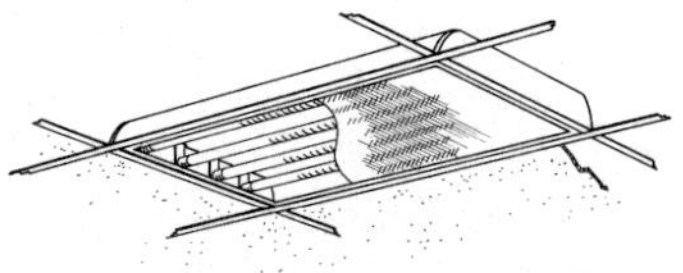

Fluorescent Fixture

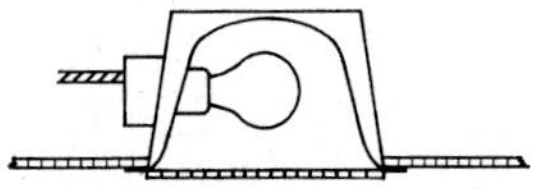

Incandescent Fixture

| D5020 210 | Fluorescent Fixtures (by Wattage) | COST PER S.F. | | |
|---|---|---|---|---|
| | | MAT. | INST. | TOTAL |
| 0190 | Fluorescent fixtures recess mounted in ceiling | | | |
| 0195 | T12, standard 40 watt lamps | | | |
| 0200 | 1 watt per S.F., 20 FC, 5 fixtures @40 watts per 1000 S.F. | 1.34 | 2.34 | 3.68 |
| 0240 | 2 watt per S.F., 40 FC, 10 fixtures @40 watt per 1000 S.F. | 2.66 | 4.61 | 7.27 |
| 0280 | 3 watt per S.F., 60 FC, 15 fixtures @40 watt per 1000 S.F | 4 | 6.95 | 10.95 |
| 0320 | 4 watt per S.F., 80 FC, 20 fixtures @40 watt per 1000 S.F. | 5.35 | 9.25 | 14.60 |
| 0400 | 5 watt per S.F., 100 FC, 25 fixtures @40 watt per 1000 S.F. | 6.70 | 11.55 | 18.25 |
| 0450 | T8, energy saver 32 watt lamps | | | |
| 0500 | 0.8 watt per S.F., 20 FC, 5 fixtures @32 watt per 1000 S.F. | 1.84 | 2.34 | 4.18 |
| 0520 | 1.6 watt per S.F., 40 FC, 10 fixtures @32 watt per 1000 S.F. | 3.65 | 4.61 | 8.26 |
| 0540 | 2.4 watt per S.F., 60 FC, 15 fixtures @ 32 watt per 1000 S.F | 5.50 | 6.95 | 12.45 |
| 0560 | 3.2 watt per S.F., 80 FC, 20 fixtures @32 watt per 1000 S.F. | 7.30 | 9.25 | 16.55 |
| 0580 | 4 watt per S.F., 100 FC, 25 fixtures @32 watt per 1000 S.F. | 9.15 | 11.55 | 20.70 |

| D5020 216 | Incandescent Fixture (by Wattage) | COST PER S.F. | | |
|---|---|---|---|---|
| | | MAT. | INST. | TOTAL |
| 0190 | Incandescent fixture recess mounted, type A | | | |
| 0200 | 1 watt per S.F., 8 FC, 6 fixtures per 1000 S.F. | 1.27 | 1.89 | 3.16 |
| 0240 | 2 watt per S.F., 16 FC, 12 fixtures per 1000 S.F. | 2.54 | 3.79 | 6.33 |
| 0280 | 3 watt per S.F., 24 FC, 18 fixtures, per 1000 S.F. | 3.79 | 5.60 | 9.39 |
| 0320 | 4 watt per S.F., 32 FC, 24 fixtures per 1000 S.F. | 5.05 | 7.50 | 12.55 |
| 0400 | 5 watt per S.F., 40 FC, 30 fixtures per 1000 S.F. | 6.35 | 9.40 | 15.75 |

## D5020 Lighting and Branch Wiring

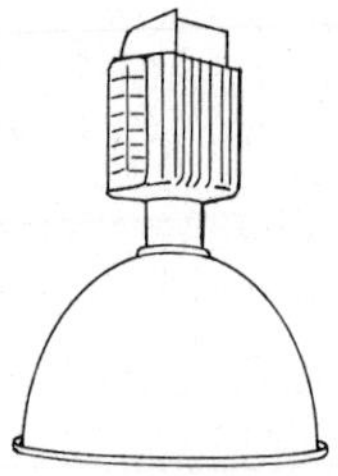

High Bay Fixture

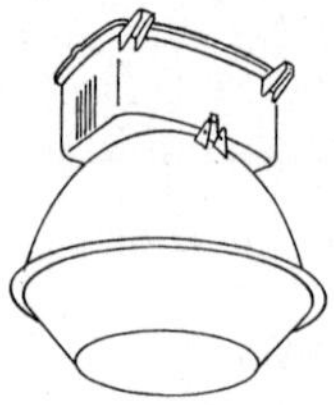

Low Bay Fixture

| D5020 226 | H.I.D. Fixture, High Bay, 16′ (by Wattage) | COST PER S.F. | | |
|---|---|---|---|---|
| | | MAT. | INST. | TOTAL |
| 0190 | High intensity discharge fixture, 16′ above work plane | | | |
| 0240 | 1 watt/S.F., type E, 42 FC, 1 fixture/1000 S.F. | 1.62 | 1.97 | 3.59 |
| 0280 | Type G, 52 FC, 1 fixture/1000 S.F. | 1.62 | 1.97 | 3.59 |
| 0320 | Type C, 54 FC, 2 fixture/1000 S.F. | 1.59 | 2.21 | 3.80 |
| 0440 | 2 watt/S.F., type E, 84 FC, 2 fixture/1000 S.F. | 3.28 | 4.02 | 7.30 |
| 0480 | Type G, 105 FC, 2 fixture/1000 S.F. | 3.28 | 4.02 | 7.30 |
| 0520 | Type C, 108 FC, 4 fixture/1000 S.F. | 3.17 | 4.42 | 7.59 |
| 0640 | 3 watt/S.F., type E, 126 FC, 3 fixture/1000 S.F. | 4.91 | 6 | 10.91 |
| 0680 | Type G, 157 FC, 3 fixture/1000 S.F. | 4.91 | 6 | 10.91 |
| 0720 | Type C, 162 FC, 6 fixture/1000 S.F. | 4.76 | 6.60 | 11.36 |
| 0840 | 4 watt/S.F., type E, 168 FC, 4 fixture/1000 S.F. | 6.55 | 8.05 | 14.60 |
| 0880 | Type G, 210 FC, 4 fixture/1000 S.F. | 6.55 | 8.05 | 14.60 |
| 0920 | Type C, 243 FC, 9 fixture/1000 S.F. | 6.85 | 9.25 | 16.10 |
| 1040 | 5 watt/S.F., type E, 210 FC, 5 fixture/1000 S.F. | 8.20 | 10 | 18.20 |
| 1080 | Type G, 262 FC, 5 fixture/1000 S.F. | 8.20 | 10 | 18.20 |
| 1120 | Type C, 297 FC, 11 fixture/1000 S.F. | 8.40 | 11.45 | 19.85 |

| D5020 234 | H.I.D. Fixture, High Bay, 30′ (by Wattage) | COST PER S.F. | | |
|---|---|---|---|---|
| | | MAT. | INST. | TOTAL |
| 0190 | High intensity discharge fixture, 30′ above work plane | | | |
| 0240 | 1 watt/S.F., type E, 37 FC, 1 fixture/1000 S.F. | 1.86 | 2.50 | 4.36 |
| 0280 | Type G, 45 FC., 1 fixture/1000 S.F. | 1.86 | 2.50 | 4.36 |
| 0320 | Type F, 50 FC, 1 fixture/1000 S.F. | 1.32 | 1.95 | 3.27 |
| 0440 | 2 watt/S.F., type E, 74 FC, 2 fixtures/1000 S.F. | 3.72 | 5 | 8.72 |
| 0480 | Type G, 92 FC, 2 fixtures/1000 S.F. | 3.72 | 5 | 8.72 |
| 0520 | Type F, 100 FC, 2 fixtures/1000 S.F. | 2.68 | 3.99 | 6.67 |
| 0640 | 3 watt/S.F., type E, 110 FC, 3 fixtures/1000 S.F. | 5.60 | 7.55 | 13.15 |
| 0680 | Type G, 138 FC, 3 fixtures/1000 S.F. | 5.60 | 7.55 | 13.15 |
| 0720 | Type F, 150 FC, 3 fixtures/1000 S.F. | 3.99 | 5.95 | 9.94 |
| 0840 | 4 watt/S.F., type E, 148 FC, 4 fixtures/1000 S.F. | 7.45 | 10.05 | 17.50 |
| 0880 | Type G, 185 FC, 4 fixtures/1000 S.F. | 7.45 | 10.05 | 17.50 |
| 0920 | Type F, 200 FC, 4 fixtures/1000 S.F. | 5.35 | 8 | 13.35 |
| 1040 | 5 watt/S.F., type E, 185 FC, 5 fixtures/1000 S.F. | 9.35 | 12.55 | 21.90 |
| 1080 | Type G, 230 FC, 5 fixtures/1000 S.F. | 9.35 | 12.55 | 21.90 |
| 1120 | Type F, 250 FC, 5 fixtures/1000 S.F. | 6.65 | 9.95 | 16.60 |

| D5020 238 | H.I.D. Fixture, Low Bay, 8′-10′ (by Wattage) | COST PER S.F. | | |
|---|---|---|---|---|
| | | MAT. | INST. | TOTAL |
| 0190 | High intensity discharge fixture, 8′-10′ above work plane | | | |
| 0240 | 1 watt/S.F., type J, 30 FC, 4 fixtures/1000 S.F. | 3.08 | 4.08 | 7.16 |
| 0280 | Type K, 29 FC, 5 fixtures/1000 S.F. | 3.07 | 3.66 | 6.73 |
| 0400 | 2 watt/S.F., type J, 52 FC, 7 fixtures/1000 S.F. | 5.55 | 7.50 | 13.05 |
| 0440 | Type K, 63 FC, 11 fixtures/1000 S.F. | 6.60 | 7.70 | 14.30 |
| 0560 | 3 watt/S.F., type J, 81 FC, 11 fixtures/1000 S.F. | 8.50 | 11.30 | 19.80 |

# D5020 Lighting and Branch Wiring

| D5020 238 | H.I.D. Fixture, Low Bay, 8′-10′ (by Wattage) | COST PER S.F. MAT. | INST. | TOTAL |
|---|---|---|---|---|
| 0600 | Type K, 92 FC, 16 fixtures/1000 S.F. | 9.70 | 11.35 | 21.05 |
| 0720 | 4 watt/S.F., type J, 103 FC, 14 fixtures/1000 S.F. | 11.05 | 14.85 | 25.90 |
| 0760 | Type K, 127 FC, 22 fixtures/1000 S.F. | 13.20 | 15.40 | 28.60 |
| 0880 | 5 watt/S.F., type J, 133 FC, 18 fixtures/1000 S.F. | 14.05 | 18.75 | 32.80 |
| 0920 | Type K, 155 FC, 27 fixtures/1000 S.F. | 16.30 | 19.05 | 35.35 |

| D5020 242 | H.I.D. Fixture, Low Bay, 16′ (by Wattage) | COST PER S.F. MAT. | INST. | TOTAL |
|---|---|---|---|---|
| 0190 | High intensity discharge fixture, mounted 16′ above work plane | | | |
| 0240 | 1 watt/S.F., type J, 28 FC, 4 fixt./1000 S.F. | 3.32 | 4.62 | 7.94 |
| 0280 | Type K, 27 FC, 5 fixt./1000 S.F. | 3.74 | 5.20 | 8.94 |
| 0400 | 2 watt/S.F., type J, 48 FC, 7 fixt/1000 S.F. | 6.20 | 8.95 | 15.15 |
| 0440 | Type K, 58 FC, 11 fixt/1000 S.F. | 7.85 | 10.60 | 18.45 |
| 0560 | 3 watt/S.F., type J, 75 FC, 11 fixt/1000 S.F. | 9.50 | 13.55 | 23.05 |
| 0600 | Type K, 85 FC, 16 fixt/1000 S.F. | 11.60 | 15.75 | 27.35 |
| 0720 | 4 watt/S.F., type J, 95 FC, 14 fixt/1000 S.F. | 12.40 | 17.90 | 30.30 |
| 0760 | Type K, 117 FC, 22 fixt/1000 S.F. | 15.75 | 21 | 36.75 |
| 0880 | 5 watt/S.F., type J, 122 FC, 18 fixt/1000 S.F. | 15.70 | 22.50 | 38.20 |
| 0920 | Type K, 143 FC, 27 fixt/1000 S.F. | 19.50 | 26.50 | 46 |

## D5030 Communications and Security

| D5030 910 | Communication & Alarm Systems | COST EACH | | |
|---|---|---|---|---|
| | | MAT. | INST. | TOTAL |
| 0200 | Communication & alarm systems, includes outlets, boxes, conduit & wire | | | |
| 0210 | Sound system, 6 outlets | 8,100 | 10,100 | 18,200 |
| 0220 | 12 outlets | 12,000 | 16,200 | 28,200 |
| 0240 | 30 outlets | 21,600 | 30,600 | 52,200 |
| 0280 | 100 outlets | 66,000 | 102,500 | 168,500 |
| 0320 | Fire detection systems, non-addressable, 12 detectors | 4,875 | 8,400 | 13,275 |
| 0360 | 25 detectors | 8,725 | 14,200 | 22,925 |
| 0400 | 50 detectors | 17,300 | 28,100 | 45,400 |
| 0440 | 100 detectors | 32,300 | 51,000 | 83,300 |
| 0450 | Addressable type, 12 detectors | 6,300 | 8,450 | 14,750 |
| 0452 | 25 detectors | 11,400 | 14,300 | 25,700 |
| 0454 | 50 detectors | 22,100 | 28,100 | 50,200 |
| 0456 | 100 detectors | 42,200 | 51,500 | 93,700 |
| 0458 | Fire alarm control panel, 8 zone, excluding wire and conduit | 725 | 1,600 | 2,325 |
| 0459 | 12 zone | 3,150 | 2,400 | 5,550 |
| 0460 | Fire alarm command center, addressable without voice, excl. wire & conduit | 2,425 | 1,400 | 3,825 |
| 0462 | Addressable with voice | 12,500 | 2,200 | 14,700 |
| 0480 | Intercom systems, 6 stations | 8,150 | 6,925 | 15,075 |
| 0560 | 25 stations | 25,700 | 26,500 | 52,200 |
| 0640 | 100 stations | 99,000 | 97,500 | 196,500 |
| 0680 | Master clock systems, 6 rooms | 6,250 | 11,300 | 17,550 |
| 0720 | 12 rooms | 10,400 | 19,200 | 29,600 |
| 0760 | 20 rooms | 14,700 | 27,200 | 41,900 |
| 0800 | 30 rooms | 25,600 | 50,000 | 75,600 |
| 0840 | 50 rooms | 42,500 | 84,500 | 127,000 |
| 0920 | Master TV antenna systems, 6 outlets | 3,250 | 7,150 | 10,400 |
| 0960 | 12 outlets | 6,175 | 13,300 | 19,475 |
| 1000 | 30 outlets | 19,400 | 30,800 | 50,200 |
| 1040 | 100 outlets | 69,500 | 100,500 | 170,000 |

## D5090 Other Electrical Systems

Generator System

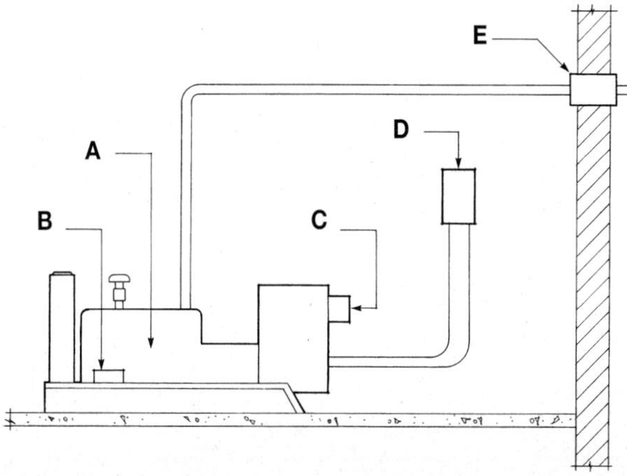


| D5090 210 | Generators (by kW) | COST PER kW | | |
|---|---|---|---|---|
| | | MAT. | INST. | TOTAL |
| 0190 | Generator sets, include battery, charger, muffler & transfer switch | | | |
| 0200 | Gas/gasoline operated, 3 phase, 4 wire, 277/480 volt, 7.5 kW | 1,200 | 355 | 1,555 |
| 0240 | 11.5 kW | 1,125 | 272 | 1,397 |
| 0280 | 20 kW | 650 | 176 | 826 |
| 0320 | 35 kW | 525 | 115 | 640 |
| 0360 | 80 kW | 365 | 148 | 513 |
| 0400 | 100 kW | 320 | 144 | 464 |
| 0440 | 125 kW | 279 | 136 | 415 |
| 0480 | 185 kW | 470 | 103 | 573 |
| 0560 | Diesel engine with fuel tank, 30 kW | 595 | 135 | 730 |
| 0600 | 50 kW | 410 | 106 | 516 |
| 0640 | 75 kW | 450 | 84.50 | 534.50 |
| 0680 | 100 kW | 395 | 71.50 | 466.50 |
| 0760 | 150 kW | 178 | 57 | 235 |
| 0840 | 200 kW | 390 | 46 | 436 |
| 0880 | 250 kW | 252 | 38.50 | 290.50 |
| 0960 | 350 kW | 249 | 31.50 | 280.50 |
| 1040 | 500 kW | 189 | 24.50 | 213.50 |

# E1010 Commercial Equipment

| E1010 110 | Security/Vault, EACH | COST EACH | | |
|---|---|---|---|---|
| | | MAT. | INST. | TOTAL |
| 0100 | Bank equipment, drive up window, drawer & mike, no glazing, economy | 4,725 | 1,600 | 6,325 |
| 0110 | Deluxe | 6,675 | 3,175 | 9,850 |
| 0120 | Night depository, economy | 1,050 | 1,600 | 2,650 |
| 0130 | Deluxe | 2,575 | 3,175 | 5,750 |
| 0140 | Pneumatic tube systems, 2 station, standard | 35,800 | 6,075 | 41,875 |
| 0150 | Teller, automated, 24 hour, single unit | 27,400 | 24,300 | 51,700 |
| 0160 | Teller window, bullet proof glazing, 44" x 60" | 5,050 | 1,100 | 6,150 |
| 0170 | Pass through, painted steel, 72" x 40" | 6,000 | 2,000 | 8,000 |
| 0300 | Safe, office type, 1 hr. rating, 34" x 20" x 20" | 1,900 | | 1,900 |
| 0310 | 4 hr. rating, 62" x 33" x 20" | 9,275 | | 9,275 |
| 0320 | Data storage, 4 hr. rating, 63" x 44" x 16" | 12,700 | | 12,700 |
| 0330 | Jewelers, 63" x 44" x 16" | 12,400 | | 12,400 |
| 0340 | Money, "B" label, 9" x 14" x 14" | 540 | | 540 |
| 0350 | Tool and torch resistive, 24" x 24" x 20" | 1,175 | 281 | 1,456 |
| 0500 | Security gates-scissors type, painted steel, single, 6' high, 5-1/2' wide | 282 | 400 | 682 |
| 0510 | Vault front, door and frame, clear opening, 32" door | 740 | 795 | 1,535 |
| 0514 | Vault front, door and frame, clear opening, 40" door | 7,100 | 1,175 | 8,275 |

| E1010 510 | Mercantile Equipment, EACH | COST EACH | | |
|---|---|---|---|---|
| | | MAT. | INST. | TOTAL |
| 0015 | Barber equipment, chair, hydraulic, economy | 850 | 29 | 879 |
| 0020 | Deluxe | 5,275 | 43.50 | 5,318.50 |
| 0100 | Checkout counter, single belt | 4,100 | 113 | 4,213 |
| 0110 | Double belt, power take-away | 5,650 | 125 | 5,775 |
| 0200 | Display cases, freestanding, glass and aluminum, 3'-6" x 3' x 1'-0" deep | 226 | 175 | 401 |
| 0220 | Wall mounted, glass and aluminum, 3' x 4' x 1'-4" deep | 2,250 | 279 | 2,529 |
| 0320 | Frozen food, chest type, 12 ft. long | 7,550 | 470 | 8,020 |

| E1010 610 | Laundry/Dry Cleaning, EACH | COST EACH | | |
|---|---|---|---|---|
| | | MAT. | INST. | TOTAL |
| 0100 | Laundry equipment, dryers, gas fired, residential, 16 lb. capacity | 1,450 | 287 | 1,737 |
| 0110 | Commercial, 30 lb. capacity, single | 1,925 | 287 | 2,212 |
| 0120 | Dry cleaners, electric, 20 lb. capacity | 44,500 | 8,300 | 52,800 |
| 0130 | 30 lb. capacity | 70,500 | 11,100 | 81,600 |
| 0140 | Ironers, commercial, 120" with canopy, 8 roll | 248,000 | 23,700 | 271,700 |
| 0150 | Institutional, 110", single roll | 44,300 | 4,000 | 48,300 |
| 0160 | Washers, residential, 4 cycle | 1,275 | 287 | 1,562 |
| 0170 | Commercial, coin operated, deluxe | 4,650 | 287 | 4,937 |

# E1020 Institutional Equipment

| E1020 110 | Ecclesiastical Equipment, EACH | COST EACH | | |
|---|---|---|---|---|
| | | MAT. | INST. | TOTAL |
| 0090 | Church equipment, altar, wood, custom, plain | 2,750 | 500 | 3,250 |
| 0100 | Granite, custom, deluxe | 34,700 | 6,850 | 41,550 |
| 0110 | Baptistry, fiberglass, economy | 4,000 | 1,825 | 5,825 |
| 0120 | Bells & carillons, keyboard operation | 18,300 | 11,200 | 29,500 |
| 0130 | Confessional, wood, single, economy | 3,175 | 1,175 | 4,350 |
| 0140 | Double, deluxe | 18,000 | 3,500 | 21,500 |
| 0150 | Steeples, translucent fiberglas, 30″ square, 15′ high | 2,000 | 2,975 | 4,975 |

| E1020 130 | Ecclesiastical Equipment, L.F. | COST PER L.F. | | |
|---|---|---|---|---|
| | | MAT. | INST. | TOTAL |
| 0100 | Arch. equip., church equip. pews, bench type, hardwood, economy | 199 | 35 | 234 |
| 0110 | Deluxe | 475 | 46.50 | 521.50 |

| E1020 210 | Library Equipment, EACH | COST EACH | | |
|---|---|---|---|---|
| | | MAT. | INST. | TOTAL |
| 0110 | Library equipment, carrels, metal, economy | 209 | 140 | 349 |
| 0120 | Hardwood, deluxe | 2,175 | 175 | 2,350 |

| E1020 230 | Library Equipment, L.F. | COST PER L.F. | | |
|---|---|---|---|---|
| | | MAT. | INST. | TOTAL |
| 0100 | Library equipment, book shelf, metal, single face, 90″ high x 10″ shelf | 133 | 58 | 191 |
| 0110 | Double face, 90″ high x 10″ shelf | 495 | 126 | 621 |
| 0120 | Charging desk, built-in, with counter, plastic laminate | 610 | 99.50 | 709.50 |

| E1020 310 | Theater and Stage Equipment, EACH | COST EACH | | |
|---|---|---|---|---|
| | | MAT. | INST. | TOTAL |
| 0200 | Movie equipment, changeover, economy | 630 | | 630 |
| 0210 | Film transport, incl. platters and autowind, economy | 7,825 | | 7,825 |
| 0220 | Lamphouses, incl. rectifiers, xenon, 1000W | 10,400 | 400 | 10,800 |
| 0230 | 4000W | 14,200 | 535 | 14,735 |
| 0240 | Projector mechanisms, 35 mm, economy | 15,500 | | 15,500 |
| 0250 | Deluxe | 21,400 | | 21,400 |
| 0260 | Sound systems, incl. amplifier, single, economy | 10,700 | 890 | 11,590 |
| 0270 | Dual, Dolby/super sound | 24,300 | 2,000 | 26,300 |
| 0280 | Projection screens, wall hung, manual operation, 50 S.F., economy | 460 | 140 | 600 |
| 0290 | Electric operation, 100 S.F., deluxe | 4,350 | 700 | 5,050 |

| E1020 320 | Theater and Stage Equipment, S.F. | COST PER S.F. | | |
|---|---|---|---|---|
| | | MAT. | INST. | TOTAL |
| 0090 | Movie equipment, projection screens, rigid in wall, acrylic, 1/4″ thick | 33.50 | 6.85 | 40.35 |
| 0100 | 1/2″ thick | 68 | 10.25 | 78.25 |
| 0110 | Stage equipment, curtains, velour, medium weight | 11.60 | 2.33 | 13.93 |
| 0120 | Silica based yarn, fireproof | 17.95 | 28 | 45.95 |
| 0130 | Stages, portable with steps, folding legs, 8″ high | 51 | | 51 |
| 0140 | Telescoping platforms, aluminum, deluxe | 59.50 | 36.50 | 96 |

| E1020 330 | Theater and Stage Equipment, L.F. | COST PER L.F. | | |
|---|---|---|---|---|
| | | MAT. | INST. | TOTAL |
| 0100 | Stage equipment, curtain track, heavy duty | 37.50 | 77.50 | 115 |
| 0110 | Lights, border, quartz, colored | 605 | 40 | 645 |

| E1020 610 | Detention Equipment, EACH | COST PER EACH | | |
|---|---|---|---|---|
| | | MAT. | INST. | TOTAL |
| 0110 | Detention equipment, cell front rolling door, 7/8″ bars, 5′ x 7′ high | 6,125 | 1,675 | 7,800 |
| 0120 | Cells, prefab., including front, 5′ x 7′ x 7′ deep | 10,400 | 2,225 | 12,625 |

## E1020 Institutional Equipment

| E1020 610 | Detention Equipment, EACH | COST PER EACH | | |
|---|---|---|---|---|
| | | MAT. | INST. | TOTAL |
| 0130 | Doors and frames, 3′ x 7′, single plate | 6,900 | 840 | 7,740 |
| 0140 | Double plate | 8,225 | 840 | 9,065 |
| 0150 | Toilet apparatus, incl wash basin | 2,725 | 1,225 | 3,950 |
| 0160 | Visitor cubicle, vision panel, no intercom | 4,650 | 1,675 | 6,325 |

| E1020 710 | Laboratory Equipment, EACH | COST PER EACH | | |
|---|---|---|---|---|
| | | MAT. | INST. | TOTAL |
| 0110 | Laboratory equipment, glassware washer, distilled water, economy | 9,150 | 920 | 10,070 |
| 0120 | Deluxe | 20,100 | 1,650 | 21,750 |
| 0140 | Radio isotope | 20,400 | | 20,400 |

| E1020 720 | Laboratory Equipment, S.F. | COST PER S.F. | | |
|---|---|---|---|---|
| | | MAT. | INST. | TOTAL |
| 0100 | Arch. equip., lab equip., counter tops, acid proof, economy | 131 | 17 | 148 |
| 0110 | Stainless steel | 78 | 17 | 95 |

| E1020 730 | Laboratory Equipment, L.F. | COST PER L.F. | | |
|---|---|---|---|---|
| | | MAT. | INST. | TOTAL |
| 0110 | Laboratory equipment, cabinets, wall, open | 214 | 70 | 284 |
| 0120 | Base, drawer units | 985 | 77.50 | 1,062.50 |
| 0130 | Fume hoods, not incl. HVAC, economy | 985 | 259 | 1,244 |
| 0140 | Deluxe incl. fixtures | 12,500 | 580 | 13,080 |

| E1020 810 | Medical Equipment, EACH | COST EACH | | |
|---|---|---|---|---|
| | | MAT. | INST. | TOTAL |
| 0100 | Dental equipment, central suction system, economy | 2,175 | 715 | 2,890 |
| 0110 | Compressor-air, deluxe | 11,200 | 1,475 | 12,675 |
| 0120 | Chair, hydraulic, economy | 4,600 | 1,475 | 6,075 |
| 0130 | Deluxe | 7,450 | 2,950 | 10,400 |
| 0140 | Drill console with accessories, economy | 5,350 | 460 | 5,810 |
| 0150 | Deluxe | 9,775 | 460 | 10,235 |
| 0160 | X-ray unit, portable | 5,025 | 184 | 5,209 |
| 0170 | Panoramic unit | 29,600 | 1,225 | 30,825 |
| 0300 | Medical equipment, autopsy table, standard | 9,400 | 860 | 10,260 |
| 0310 | Deluxe | 3,500 | 1,425 | 4,925 |
| 0320 | Incubators, economy | 2,950 | | 2,950 |
| 0330 | Deluxe | 2,425 | | 2,425 |
| 0700 | Station, scrub-surgical, single, economy | 1,775 | 287 | 2,062 |
| 0710 | Dietary, medium, with ice | 700 | | 700 |
| 0720 | Sterilizers, general purpose, single door, 20″ x 20″ x 28″ | 32,200 | | 32,200 |
| 0730 | Floor loading, double door, 28″ x 67″ x 52″ | 67,000 | | 67,000 |
| 0740 | Surgery tables, standard | 14,100 | 1,125 | 15,225 |
| 0750 | Deluxe | 22,000 | 1,600 | 23,600 |
| 0770 | Tables, standard, with base cabinets, economy | 1,375 | 465 | 1,840 |
| 0780 | Deluxe | 5,325 | 700 | 6,025 |
| 0790 | X-ray, mobile, economy | 16,200 | | 16,200 |
| 0800 | Stationary, deluxe | 264,500 | | 264,500 |

## E1030 Vehicular Equipment

| E1030 110 | Vehicular Service Equipment, EACH | COST EACH MAT. | INST. | TOTAL |
|---|---|---|---|---|
| 0110 | Automotive equipment, compressors, electric, 1-1/2 H.P., std. controls | 1,225 | 1,350 | 2,575 |
| 0120 | 5 H.P., dual controls | 1,775 | 2,025 | 3,800 |
| 0130 | Hoists, single post, 4 ton capacity, swivel arms | 7,325 | 5,050 | 12,375 |
| 0140 | Dual post, 12 ton capacity, adjustable frame | 50,500 | 1,050 | 51,550 |
| 0150 | Lube equipment, 3 reel type, with pumps | 12,900 | 4,025 | 16,925 |
| 0160 | Product dispenser, 6 nozzles, w/vapor recovery, not incl. piping, installed | 31,300 | | 31,300 |
| 0800 | Scales, dial type, built in floor, 5 ton capacity, 8′ x 6′ platform | 10,200 | 4,200 | 14,400 |
| 0810 | 10 ton capacity, 9′ x 7′ platform | 8,525 | 5,975 | 14,500 |
| 0820 | Truck (including weigh bridge), 20 ton capacity, 24′ x 10′ | 13,300 | 6,975 | 20,275 |

| E1030 210 | Parking Control Equipment, EACH | COST EACH MAT. | INST. | TOTAL |
|---|---|---|---|---|
| 0110 | Parking equipment, automatic gates, 8 ft. arm, one way | 2,575 | 1,450 | 4,025 |
| 0120 | Traffic detectors, single treadle | 325 | 665 | 990 |
| 0130 | Booth for attendant, economy | 13,800 | | 13,800 |
| 0140 | Deluxe | 37,300 | | 37,300 |
| 0150 | Ticket printer/dispenser, rate computing | 7,075 | 1,150 | 8,225 |
| 0160 | Key station on pedestal | 1,025 | 390 | 1,415 |

| E1030 310 | Loading Dock Equipment, EACH | COST EACH MAT. | INST. | TOTAL |
|---|---|---|---|---|
| 0110 | Dock bumpers, rubber blocks, 4-1/2″ thick, 10″ high, 14″ long | 63.50 | 27 | 90.50 |
| 0120 | 6″ thick, 20″ high, 11″ long | 130 | 53.50 | 183.50 |
| 0130 | Dock boards, H.D., 5′ x 5′, aluminum, 5000 lb. capacity | 1,525 | | 1,525 |
| 0140 | 16,000 lb. capacity | 2,125 | | 2,125 |
| 0150 | Dock levelers, hydraulic, 7′ x 8′, 10 ton capacity | 7,450 | 1,650 | 9,100 |
| 0160 | Dock lifters, platform, 6′ x 6′, portable, 3000 lb. capacity | 9,975 | | 9,975 |
| 0170 | Dock shelters, truck, scissor arms, economy | 3,000 | 700 | 3,700 |
| 0180 | Deluxe | 3,175 | 1,400 | 4,575 |

## E1090 Other Equipment

| E1090 210 | Solid Waste Handling Equipment, EACH | COST EACH MAT. | COST EACH INST. | COST EACH TOTAL |
|---|---|---|---|---|
| 0110 | Waste handling, compactors, single bag, 250 lbs./hr., hand fed | 17,600 | 840 | 18,440 |
| 0120 | Heavy duty industrial, 5 C.Y. capacity | 38,500 | 4,025 | 42,525 |
| 0130 | Incinerator, electric, 100 lbs./hr., economy | 68,000 | 3,850 | 71,850 |
| 0140 | Gas, 2000 lbs./hr., deluxe | 412,500 | 32,700 | 445,200 |
| 0150 | Shredder, no baling, 35 tons/hr. | 367,500 | | 367,500 |
| 0160 | Incl. baling, 50 tons/day | 734,500 | | 734,500 |

| E1090 350 | Food Service Equipment, EACH | COST EACH MAT. | COST EACH INST. | COST EACH TOTAL |
|---|---|---|---|---|
| 0110 | Kitchen equipment, bake oven, single deck | 4,850 | 193 | 5,043 |
| 0120 | Broiler, without oven | 4,225 | 193 | 4,418 |
| 0130 | Commercial dish washer, semiautomatic, 50 racks/hr. | 10,700 | 1,200 | 11,900 |
| 0140 | Automatic, 275 racks/hr. | 34,700 | 5,050 | 39,750 |
| 0150 | Cooler, beverage, reach-in, 6 ft. long | 4,275 | 258 | 4,533 |
| 0160 | Food warmer, counter, 1.65 kw | 720 | | 720 |
| 0170 | Fryers, with submerger, single | 1,650 | 221 | 1,871 |
| 0180 | Double | 5,250 | 310 | 5,560 |
| 0185 | Ice maker, 1000 lb. per day, with bin | 5,975 | 1,550 | 7,525 |
| 0190 | Kettles, steam jacketed, 20 gallons | 18,100 | 335 | 18,435 |
| 0200 | Range, restaurant type, burners, 2 ovens and 24" griddle | 6,825 | 258 | 7,083 |
| 0210 | Range hood, incl. carbon dioxide system, elect. stove | 2,200 | 515 | 2,715 |
| 0220 | Gas stove | 2,650 | 515 | 3,165 |

| E1090 360 | Food Service Equipment, S.F. | COST PER S.F. MAT. | COST PER S.F. INST. | COST PER S.F. TOTAL |
|---|---|---|---|---|
| 0110 | Refrigerators, prefab, walk-in, 7'-6" high, 6' x 6' | 115 | 25.50 | 140.50 |
| 0120 | 12' x 20' | 126 | 12.75 | 138.75 |

| E1090 410 | Residential Equipment, EACH | COST EACH MAT. | COST EACH INST. | COST EACH TOTAL |
|---|---|---|---|---|
| 0110 | Arch. equip., appliances, range, cook top, 4 burner, economy | 345 | 133 | 478 |
| 0120 | Built in, single oven 30" wide, economy | 1,425 | 133 | 1,558 |
| 0130 | Standing, single oven-21" wide, economy | 875 | 113 | 988 |
| 0135 | Free standing, 30" wide, 1 oven, average | 1,300 | 224 | 1,524 |
| 0140 | Double oven-30" wide, deluxe | 4,925 | 113 | 5,038 |
| 0150 | Compactor, residential, economy | 1,450 | 140 | 1,590 |
| 0160 | Deluxe | 1,650 | 233 | 1,883 |
| 0170 | Dish washer, built-in, 2 cycles, economy | 550 | 415 | 965 |
| 0180 | 4 or more cycles, deluxe | 870 | 830 | 1,700 |
| 0190 | Garbage disposer, sink type, economy | 136 | 166 | 302 |
| 0200 | Deluxe | 281 | 166 | 447 |
| 0210 | Refrigerator, no frost, 10 to 12 C.F., economy | 895 | 113 | 1,008 |
| 0220 | 21 to 29 C.F., deluxe | 2,450 | 375 | 2,825 |
| 0300 | Washing machine, automatic | 770 | 860 | 1,630 |

| E1090 610 | School Equipment, EACH | COST EACH MAT. | COST EACH INST. | COST EACH TOTAL |
|---|---|---|---|---|
| 0110 | School equipment, basketball backstops, wall mounted, wood, fixed | 2,300 | 1,250 | 3,550 |
| 0120 | Suspended type, electrically operated | 7,125 | 2,400 | 9,525 |
| 0130 | Bleachers-telescoping, manual operation, 15 tier, economy (per seat) | 118 | 43.50 | 161.50 |
| 0140 | Power operation, 30 tier, deluxe (per seat) | 2,400 | 77 | 2,477 |
| 0150 | Weight lifting gym, universal, economy | 370 | 1,125 | 1,495 |
| 0160 | Deluxe | 18,200 | 2,250 | 20,450 |
| 0170 | Scoreboards, basketball, 1 side, economy | 585 | 1,075 | 1,660 |
| 0180 | 4 sides, deluxe | 21,000 | 14,700 | 35,700 |

## E1090 Other Equipment

| E1090 610 | School Equipment, EACH | COST EACH MAT. | INST. | TOTAL |
|---|---|---|---|---|
| 0800 | Vocational shop equipment, benches, metal | 505 | 279 | 784 |
| 0810 | Wood | 720 | 279 | 999 |
| 0820 | Dust collector, not incl. ductwork, 6′ diam. | 10,800 | 770 | 11,570 |
| 0830 | Planer, 13″ x 6″ | 1,875 | 350 | 2,225 |

| E1090 620 | School Equipment, S.F. | COST PER S.F. MAT. | INST. | TOTAL |
|---|---|---|---|---|
| 0110 | School equipment, gym mats, naugahyde cover, 2″ thick | 7.75 | | 7.75 |
| 0120 | Wrestling, 1″ thick, heavy duty | 5.90 | | 5.90 |

| E1090 810 | Athletic, Recreational, and Therapeutic Equipment, EACH | COST EACH MAT. | INST. | TOTAL |
|---|---|---|---|---|
| 0050 | Bowling alley with gutters | 59,000 | 14,700 | 73,700 |
| 0060 | Combo. table and ball rack | 1,625 | | 1,625 |
| 0070 | Bowling alley automatic scorer | 12,000 | | 12,000 |
| 0110 | Sauna, prefabricated, incl. heater and controls, 7′ high, 6′ x 4′ | 6,425 | 1,075 | 7,500 |
| 0120 | 10′ x 12′ | 17,300 | 2,350 | 19,650 |
| 0130 | Heaters, wall mounted, to 200 C.F. | 1,250 | | 1,250 |
| 0140 | Floor standing, to 1000 C.F., 12500 W | 4,900 | 267 | 5,167 |
| 0610 | Shooting range incl. bullet traps, controls, separators, ceilings, economy | 9,550 | 9,025 | 18,575 |
| 0620 | Deluxe | 49,500 | 15,200 | 64,700 |
| 0650 | Sport court, squash, regulation, in existing building, economy | 50,500 | | 50,500 |
| 0660 | Deluxe | 56,000 | | 56,000 |
| 0670 | Racketball, regulation, in existing building, economy | 55,500 | 13,300 | 68,800 |
| 0680 | Deluxe | 59,000 | 26,600 | 85,600 |
| 0700 | Swimming pool equipment, diving stand, stainless steel, 1 meter | 18,700 | 515 | 19,215 |
| 0710 | 3 meter | 22,300 | 3,500 | 25,800 |
| 0720 | Diving boards, 16 ft. long, aluminum | 5,475 | 515 | 5,990 |
| 0730 | Fiberglass | 6,475 | 515 | 6,990 |
| 0740 | Filter system, sand, incl. pump, 6000 gal./hr. | 1,375 | 955 | 2,330 |
| 0750 | Lights, underwater, 12 volt with transformer, 300W | 320 | 800 | 1,120 |
| 0760 | Slides, fiberglass with aluminum handrails & ladder, 6′ high, straight | 4,875 | 875 | 5,750 |
| 0780 | 12′ high, straight with platform | 22,400 | 1,175 | 23,575 |

| E1090 820 | Athletic, Recreational, and Therapeutic Equipment, S.F. | COST PER S.F. MAT. | INST. | TOTAL |
|---|---|---|---|---|
| 0110 | Swimming pools, residential, vinyl liner, metal sides | 89 | 9.40 | 98.40 |
| 0120 | Concrete sides | 47.50 | 17.35 | 64.85 |
| 0130 | Gunite shell, plaster finish, 350 S.F. | 66.50 | 36 | 102.50 |
| 0140 | 800 S.F. | 53.50 | 21 | 74.50 |
| 0150 | Motel, gunite shell, plaster finish | 82 | 45 | 127 |
| 0160 | Municipal, gunite shell, tile finish, formed gutters | 315 | 78 | 393 |

## E2010 Fixed Furnishings

| E2010 310 | Window Treatment, EACH | COST EACH | | |
|---|---|---|---|---|
| | | MAT. | INST. | TOTAL |
| 0110 | Furnishings, blinds, exterior, aluminum, louvered, 1'-4" wide x 3'-0" long | 330 | 70 | 400 |
| 0120 | 1'-4" wide x 6'-8" long | 1,300 | 77.50 | 1,377.50 |
| 0130 | Hemlock, solid raised, 1-'4" wide x 3'-0" long | 127 | 70 | 197 |
| 0140 | 1'-4" wide x 6'-9" long | 223 | 77.50 | 300.50 |
| 0150 | Polystyrene, louvered, 1'-3" wide x 3'-3" long | 43.50 | 70 | 113.50 |
| 0160 | 1'-3" wide x 6'-8" long | 129 | 77.50 | 206.50 |
| 0200 | Interior, wood folding panels, louvered, 7" x 20" (per pair) | 107 | 41 | 148 |
| 0210 | 18" x 40" (per pair) | 202 | 41 | 243 |

| E2010 320 | Window Treatment, S.F. | COST PER S.F. | | |
|---|---|---|---|---|
| | | MAT. | INST. | TOTAL |
| 0110 | Furnishings, blinds-interior, venetian-aluminum, stock, 2" slats | 6.90 | 1.18 | 8.08 |
| 0120 | Custom, 1" slats, deluxe | 6 | 1.18 | 7.18 |
| 0130 | Vertical, PVC or cloth, T&B track, economy | 5.65 | 1.52 | 7.17 |
| 0140 | Deluxe | 6.20 | 1.75 | 7.95 |
| 0150 | Draperies, unlined, economy | 46.50 | | 46.50 |
| 0160 | Lightproof, deluxe | 6.15 | | 6.15 |
| 0510 | Shades, mylar, wood roller, single layer, non-reflective | 6.80 | 1.02 | 7.82 |
| 0520 | Metal roller, triple layer, heat reflective | 13.55 | 1.02 | 14.57 |
| 0530 | Vinyl, light weight, 4 ga. | 1.22 | 1.02 | 2.24 |
| 0540 | Heavyweight, 6 ga. | 3.80 | 1.02 | 4.82 |
| 0550 | Vinyl coated cotton, lightproof decorator shades | 9.05 | 1.02 | 10.07 |
| 0560 | Woven aluminum, 3/8" thick, light and fireproof | 11.20 | 1.99 | 13.19 |

| E2010 420 | Fixed Floor Grilles and Mats, S.F. | COST PER S.F. | | |
|---|---|---|---|---|
| | | MAT. | INST. | TOTAL |
| 0110 | Floor mats, recessed, inlaid black rubber, 3/8" thick, solid | 3.51 | 3.63 | 7.14 |
| 0120 | Colors, 1/2" thick, perforated | 6.60 | 3.63 | 10.23 |
| 0130 | Link-including nosings, steel-galvanized, 3/8" thick | 11 | 3.63 | 14.63 |
| 0140 | Vinyl, in colors | 34.50 | 3.63 | 38.13 |

| E2010 510 | Fixed Multiple Seating, EACH | COST EACH | | |
|---|---|---|---|---|
| | | MAT. | INST. | TOTAL |
| 0110 | Seating, painted steel, upholstered, economy | 415 | 40 | 455 |
| 0120 | Deluxe | 515 | 50 | 565 |
| 0400 | Seating, lecture hall, pedestal type, economy | 320 | 63.50 | 383.50 |
| 0410 | Deluxe | 680 | 96.50 | 776.50 |
| 0500 | Auditorium chair, veneer construction | 415 | 63.50 | 478.50 |
| 0510 | Fully upholstered, spring seat | 320 | 63.50 | 383.50 |

## E2020 Moveable Furnishings

| E2020 210 | Furnishings/EACH | COST EACH | | |
|---|---|---|---|---|
| | | MAT. | INST. | TOTAL |
| 0200 | Hospital furniture, beds, manual, economy | 620 | | 620 |
| 0210 | Deluxe | 3,450 | | 3,450 |
| 0220 | All electric, economy | 2,250 | | 2,250 |
| 0230 | Deluxe | 16,000 | | 16,000 |
| 0240 | Patient wall systems, no utilities, economy, per room | 1,525 | | 1,525 |
| 0250 | Deluxe, per room | 2,775 | | 2,775 |
| 0300 | Hotel furnishings, standard room set, economy, per room | 2,925 | | 2,925 |
| 0310 | Deluxe, per room | 9,300 | | 9,300 |
| 0500 | Office furniture, standard employee set, economy, per person | 990 | | 990 |
| 0510 | Deluxe, per person | 2,300 | | 2,300 |
| 0550 | Posts, portable, pedestrian traffic control, economy | 118 | | 118 |
| 0560 | Deluxe | 320 | | 320 |
| 0700 | Restaurant furniture, booth, molded plastic, stub wall and 2 seats, economy | 390 | 350 | 740 |
| 0710 | Deluxe | 1,950 | 465 | 2,415 |
| 0720 | Upholstered seats, foursome, single-economy | 1,025 | 140 | 1,165 |
| 0730 | Foursome, double-deluxe | 2,300 | 233 | 2,533 |

| E2020 220 | Furniture and Accessories, L.F. | COST PER L.F. | | |
|---|---|---|---|---|
| | | MAT. | INST. | TOTAL |
| 0210 | Dormitory furniture, desk top (built-in),laminated plastc, 24"deep, economy | 62 | 28 | 90 |
| 0220 | 30" deep, deluxe | 345 | 35 | 380 |
| 0230 | Dressing unit, built-in, economy | 241 | 116 | 357 |
| 0240 | Deluxe | 725 | 175 | 900 |
| 0310 | Furnishings, cabinets, hospital, base, laminated plastic | 435 | 140 | 575 |
| 0320 | Stainless steel | 800 | 140 | 940 |
| 0330 | Countertop, laminated plastic, no backsplash | 64.50 | 35 | 99.50 |
| 0340 | Stainless steel | 210 | 35 | 245 |
| 0350 | Nurses station, door type, laminated plastic | 505 | 140 | 645 |
| 0360 | Stainless steel | 960 | 140 | 1,100 |
| 0710 | Restaurant furniture, bars, built-in, back bar | 256 | 140 | 396 |
| 0720 | Front bar | 350 | 140 | 490 |
| 0910 | Wardrobes & coatracks, standing, steel, single pedestal, 30" x 18" x 63" | 310 | | 310 |
| 0920 | Double face rack, 39" x 26" x 70" | 234 | | 234 |
| 0930 | Wall mounted rack, steel frame & shelves, 12" x 15" x 26" | 22 | 10 | 32 |
| 0940 | 12" x 15" x 50" | 72.50 | 5.25 | 77.75 |

F Special Construction

## F1010 Special Structures

| F1010 120 | Air-Supported Structures, S.F. | COST PER S.F. | | |
|---|---|---|---|---|
| | | MAT. | INST. | TOTAL |
| 0110 | Air supported struc., polyester vinyl fabric, 24oz., warehouse, 5000 S.F. | 32.50 | .45 | 32.95 |
| 0120 | 50,000 S.F. | 14.50 | .36 | 14.86 |
| 0130 | Tennis, 7,200 S.F. | 28 | .38 | 28.38 |
| 0140 | 24,000 S.F. | 20.50 | .38 | 20.88 |
| 0150 | Woven polyethylene, 6 oz., shelter, 3,000 S.F. | 19.55 | .75 | 20.30 |
| 0160 | 24,000 S.F. | 14.65 | .38 | 15.03 |
| 0170 | Teflon coated fiberglass, stadium cover, economy | 71 | .19 | 71.19 |
| 0180 | Deluxe | 87.50 | .27 | 87.77 |
| 0190 | Air supported storage tank covers, reinf. vinyl fabric, 12 oz., 400 S.F. | 29 | .63 | 29.63 |
| 0200 | 18,000 S.F. | 10.75 | .57 | 11.32 |

| F1010 210 | Pre-Engineered Structures, EACH | COST EACH | | |
|---|---|---|---|---|
| | | MAT. | INST. | TOTAL |
| 0600 | Radio towers, guyed, 40 lb. section, 50′ high, 70 MPH basic wind speed | 4,525 | 1,600 | 6,125 |
| 0610 | 90 lb. section, 400′ high, wind load 70 MPH basic wind speed | 36,800 | 19,200 | 56,000 |
| 0620 | Self supporting, 60′ high, 70 MPH basic wind speed | 7,675 | 3,350 | 11,025 |
| 0630 | 190′ high, wind load 90 MPH basic wind speed | 42,100 | 13,400 | 55,500 |
| 0700 | Shelters, aluminum frame, acrylic glazing, 8′ high, 3′ x 9′ | 4,200 | 1,400 | 5,600 |
| 0710 | 9′ x 12′ | 8,275 | 2,175 | 10,450 |

| F1010 320 | Other Special Structures, S.F. | COST PER S.F. | | |
|---|---|---|---|---|
| | | MAT. | INST. | TOTAL |
| 0110 | Swimming pool enclosure, transluscent, freestanding, economy | 67.50 | 7 | 74.50 |
| 0120 | Deluxe | 184 | 19.95 | 203.95 |
| 0510 | Tension structures, steel frame, polyester vinyl fabric, 12,000 S.F. | 13.70 | 3.25 | 16.95 |
| 0520 | 20,800 S.F. | 23 | 2.94 | 25.94 |

| F1010 330 | Special Structures, EACH | COST EACH | | |
|---|---|---|---|---|
| | | MAT. | INST. | TOTAL |
| 0110 | Kiosks, round, 5′ diam., 7′ high, aluminum wall, illuminated | 25,600 | | 25,600 |
| 0120 | Rectangular, 5′ x 9′, 1″ insulated dbl. wall fiberglass, 7′-6″ high | 28,900 | | 28,900 |
| 0220 | Silos, steel prefab, 30,000 gal., painted, economy | 28,100 | 8,075 | 36,175 |
| 0230 | Epoxy-lined, deluxe | 58,500 | 16,200 | 74,700 |

| F1010 340 | Special Structures, S.F. | COST PER S.F. | | |
|---|---|---|---|---|
| | | MAT. | INST. | TOTAL |
| 0110 | Comfort stations, prefab, mobile on steel frame, economy | 221 | | 221 |
| 0120 | Permanent on concrete slab, deluxe | 243 | 54 | 297 |
| 0210 | Domes, bulk storage, wood framing, wood decking, 50′ diam. | 76.50 | 2.97 | 79.47 |
| 0220 | 116′ diam. | 37.50 | 3.44 | 40.94 |
| 0230 | Steel framing, metal decking, 150′ diam. | 38 | 15.35 | 53.35 |
| 0240 | 400′ diam. | 31 | 11.70 | 42.70 |
| 0250 | Geodesic, wood framing, wood panels, 30′ diam. | 54.50 | 2.50 | 57 |
| 0260 | 60′ diam. | 25.50 | 2.11 | 27.61 |
| 0270 | Aluminum framing, acrylic panels, 40′ diam. | 69.50 | | 69.50 |
| 0280 | Aluminum panels, 400′ diam. | 23.50 | | 23.50 |
| 0310 | Garden house, prefab, wood, shell only, 48 S.F. | 57.50 | 7 | 64.50 |
| 0320 | 200 S.F. | 68.50 | 29 | 97.50 |
| 0410 | Greenhouse, shell-stock, residential, lean-to, 8′-6″ long x 3′-10″ wide | 64.50 | 41 | 105.50 |
| 0420 | Freestanding, 8′-6″ long x 13′-6″ wide | 69.50 | 12.95 | 82.45 |
| 0430 | Commercial-truss frame, under 2000 S.F., deluxe | 26 | | 26 |
| 0440 | Over 5,000 S.F., economy | 31 | | 31 |
| 0450 | Institutional-rigid frame, under 500 S.F., deluxe | 41 | | 41 |
| 0460 | Over 2,000 S.F., economy | 21 | | 21 |
| 0510 | Hangar, prefab, galv. roof and walls, bottom rolling doors, economy | 15 | 6.05 | 21.05 |
| 0520 | Electric bifolding doors, deluxe | 14.05 | 7.95 | 22 |

## F1020 Integrated Construction

| F1020 110 | Integrated Construction, EACH | COST EACH | | |
|---|---|---|---|---|
| | | MAT. | INST. | TOTAL |
| 0110 | Integrated ceilings, radiant electric, 2' x 4' panel, manila finish | 325 | 32 | 357 |
| 0120 | ABS plastic finish | 131 | 61.50 | 192.50 |

| F1020 120 | Integrated Construction, S.F. | COST PER S.F. | | |
|---|---|---|---|---|
| | | MAT. | INST. | TOTAL |
| 0110 | Integrated ceilings, Luminaire, suspended, 5' x 5' modules, 50% lighted | 7.25 | 16.90 | 24.15 |
| 0120 | 100% lighted | 10.05 | 30.50 | 40.55 |
| 0130 | Dimensionaire, 2' x 4' module tile system, no air bar | 2.88 | 2.79 | 5.67 |
| 0140 | With air bar, deluxe | 4.23 | 2.79 | 7.02 |
| 0220 | Pedestal access floor pkg., inc. stl. pnls, peds. & stringers, w/vinyl cov. | 18.70 | 3.72 | 22.42 |
| 0230 | With high pressure laminate covering | 16.90 | 3.72 | 20.62 |
| 0240 | With carpet covering | 18.10 | 3.72 | 21.82 |
| 0250 | Aluminum panels, no stringers, no covering | 37.50 | 2.79 | 40.29 |

| F1020 250 | Special Purpose Room, EACH | COST EACH | | |
|---|---|---|---|---|
| | | MAT. | INST. | TOTAL |
| 0110 | Portable booth, acoustical, 27 db 1000 hz., 15 S.F. floor | 4,950 | | 4,950 |
| 0120 | 55 S.F. flr. | 10,200 | | 10,200 |

| F1020 260 | Special Purpose Room, S.F. | COST PER S.F. | | |
|---|---|---|---|---|
| | | MAT. | INST. | TOTAL |
| 0110 | Anechoic chambers, 7' high, 100 cps cutoff, 25 S.F. | 3,000 | | 3,000 |
| 0120 | 200 cps cutoff, 100 S.F. | 1,575 | | 1,575 |
| 0130 | Audiometric rooms, under 500 S.F. | 67 | 28.50 | 95.50 |
| 0140 | Over 500 S.F. | 63.50 | 23.50 | 87 |
| 0300 | Darkrooms, shell, not including door, 240 S.F., 8' high | 32.50 | 11.65 | 44.15 |
| 0310 | 64 S.F., 12' high | 84.50 | 22 | 106.50 |
| 0510 | Music practice room, modular, perforated steel, under 500 S.F. | 41.50 | 19.95 | 61.45 |
| 0520 | Over 500 S.F. | 35 | 17.45 | 52.45 |

| F1020 330 | Special Construction, L.F. | COST PER L.F. | | |
|---|---|---|---|---|
| | | MAT. | INST. | TOTAL |
| 0110 | Spec. const., air curtains, shipping & receiving, 8'high x 5'wide, economy | 1,000 | 169 | 1,169 |
| 0120 | 20' high x 8' wide, heated, deluxe | 4,525 | 425 | 4,950 |
| 0130 | Customer entrance, 10' high x 5' wide, economy | 1,375 | 169 | 1,544 |
| 0140 | 12' high x 4' wide, heated, deluxe | 3,075 | 211 | 3,286 |

# F1030 Special Construction Systems

| F1030 120 | Sound, Vibration, and Seismic Construction, S.F. | COST PER S.F. | | |
|---|---|---|---|---|
| | | MAT. | INST. | TOTAL |
| 0020 | Special construction, acoustical, enclosure, 4" thick, 8 psf panels | 56 | 29 | 85 |
| 0030 | Reverb chamber, 4" thick, parallel walls | 51.50 | 35 | 86.50 |
| 0110 | Sound absorbing panels, 2'-6" x 8', painted metal | 13.75 | 9.75 | 23.50 |
| 0120 | Vinyl faced | 10.75 | 8.75 | 19.50 |
| 0130 | Flexible transparent curtain, clear | 8.30 | 11.80 | 20.10 |
| 0140 | With absorbing foam, 75% coverage | 11.60 | 11.80 | 23.40 |
| 0150 | Strip entrance, 2/3 overlap | 9.95 | 18.80 | 28.75 |
| 0160 | Full overlap | 11.85 | 22 | 33.85 |
| 0200 | Audio masking system, plenum mounted, over 10,000 S.F. | .80 | .36 | 1.16 |
| 0210 | Ceiling mounted, under 5,000 S.F. | 1.33 | .67 | 2 |

| F1030 210 | Radiation Protection, EACH | COST EACH | | |
|---|---|---|---|---|
| | | MAT. | INST. | TOTAL |
| 0110 | Shielding, lead x-ray protection, radiography room, 1/16" lead, economy | 23,400 | 5,450 | 28,850 |
| 0120 | Deluxe | 28,100 | 9,100 | 37,200 |
| 0210 | Deep therapy x-ray, 1/4" lead, economy | 65,500 | 17,100 | 82,600 |
| 0220 | Deluxe | 80,500 | 22,700 | 103,200 |

| F1030 220 | Radiation Protection, S.F. | COST PER S.F. | | |
|---|---|---|---|---|
| | | MAT. | INST. | TOTAL |
| 0110 | Shielding, lead, gypsum board, 5/8" thick, 1/16" lead | 15.45 | 8.35 | 23.80 |
| 0120 | 1/8" lead | 30.50 | 9.50 | 40 |
| 0130 | Lath, 1/16" thick | 13.10 | 10.10 | 23.20 |
| 0140 | 1/8" thick | 29 | 11.35 | 40.35 |
| 0150 | Radio frequency, galvanized steel, prefab type, economy | 8.25 | 3.72 | 11.97 |
| 0160 | Radio frequency, door, copper/wood laminate, 4" x 7' | 13.95 | 9.95 | 23.90 |

| F1030 910 | Other Special Construction Systems, EACH | COST EACH | | |
|---|---|---|---|---|
| | | MAT. | INST. | TOTAL |
| 0110 | Disappearing stairways, folding, pine, 8'-6" ceiling | 106 | 175 | 281 |
| 0220 | Automatic electric, wood, 8' to 9' ceiling | 4,750 | 1,400 | 6,150 |
| 0300 | Fireplace prefabricated, freestanding or wall hung, painted | 5,000 | 535 | 5,535 |
| 0310 | Stainless steel | 2,800 | 775 | 3,575 |
| 0320 | Woodburning stoves, cast iron, economy, less than 1500 S.F. htg. area | 1,775 | 1,075 | 2,850 |
| 0330 | Greater than 2000 S.F. htg. area | 3,900 | 1,750 | 5,650 |

## F1040 Special Facilities

| F1040 210 | Ice Rinks, EACH | COAT EACH | | |
|---|---|---|---|---|
| | | MAT. | INST. | TOTAL |
| 0100 | Ice skating rink, 85′ x 200′, 55° system, 5 mos., 100 ton | 662,500 | | 662,500 |
| 0110 | 90° system, 12 mos., 135 ton | 753,500 | | 753,500 |
| 0120 | Dash boards, acrylic screens, polyethylene coated plywood | 152,000 | 46,900 | 198,900 |
| 0130 | Fiberglass and aluminum construction | 169,500 | 46,900 | 216,400 |

| F1040 510 | Liquid & Gas Storage Tanks, EACH | COST EACH | | |
|---|---|---|---|---|
| | | MAT. | INST. | TOTAL |
| 0100 | Tanks, steel, ground level, 100,000 gal. | 357,000 | | 357,000 |
| 0110 | 10,000,000 gal. | 8,287,000 | | 8,287,000 |
| 0120 | Elevated water, 50,000 gal. | 184,500 | 341,500 | 526,000 |
| 0130 | 1,000,000 gal. | 770,000 | 1,594,500 | 2,364,500 |
| 0150 | Cypress wood, ground level, 3,000 gal. | 8,050 | 14,000 | 22,050 |
| 0160 | Redwood, ground level, 45,000 gal. | 60,500 | 38,000 | 98,500 |

## F1040 Special Facilities

| F1040 910 | Special Construction, EACH | COST EACH | | |
|---|---|---|---|---|
| | | MAT. | INST. | TOTAL |
| 0110 | Special construction, bowling alley incl. pinsetter, scorer etc., economy | 47,900 | 14,000 | 61,900 |
| 0120 | Deluxe | 67,500 | 15,500 | 83,000 |
| 0130 | For automatic scorer, economy, add | 7,125 | | 7,125 |
| 0140 | Deluxe, add | 12,000 | | 12,000 |
| 0300 | Control tower, modular, 12' x 10', incl. instrumentation, economy | 931,500 | | 931,500 |
| 0310 | Deluxe | 1,433,000 | | 1,433,000 |
| 0400 | Garage costs, residential, prefab, wood, single car economy | 7,200 | 1,400 | 8,600 |
| 0410 | Two car deluxe | 23,400 | 2,800 | 26,200 |
| 0500 | Hangars, prefab, galv. steel, bottom rolling doors, economy (per plane) | 21,800 | 6,750 | 28,550 |
| 0510 | Electrical bi-folding doors, deluxe (per plane) | 15,000 | 9,250 | 24,250 |

## G1030 Site Earthwork

| G1030 805 | Trenching Common Earth | COST PER L.F. | | |
|---|---|---|---|---|
| | | MAT. | INST. | TOTAL |
| 1310 | Trenching, common earth, no slope, 2' wide, 2' deep, 3/8 C.Y. bucket | | 3.14 | 3.14 |
| 1330 | 4' deep, 3/8 C.Y. bucket | | 6.20 | 6.20 |
| 1360 | 10' deep, 1 C.Y. bucket | | 15.05 | 15.05 |
| 1400 | 4' wide, 2' deep, 3/8 C.Y. bucket | | 6.40 | 6.40 |
| 1420 | 4' deep, 1/2 C.Y. bucket | | 11.05 | 11.05 |
| 1450 | 10' deep, 1 C.Y. bucket | | 30.50 | 30.50 |
| 1480 | 18' deep, 2-1/2 C.Y. bucket | | 48 | 48 |
| 1520 | 6' wide, 6' deep, 5/8 C.Y. bucket w/trench box | | 30 | 30 |
| 1540 | 10' deep, 1 C.Y. bucket | | 39.50 | 39.50 |
| 1570 | 20' deep, 3-1/2 C.Y. bucket | | 64.50 | 64.50 |
| 1640 | 8' wide, 12' deep, 1-1/2 C.Y. bucket w/trench box | | 55 | 55 |
| 1680 | 24' deep, 3-1/2 C.Y. bucket | | 101 | 101 |
| 1730 | 10' wide, 20' deep, 3-1/2 C.Y. bucket w/trench box | | 91.50 | 91.50 |
| 1740 | 24' deep, 3-1/2 C.Y. bucket | | 118 | 118 |
| 3500 | 1 to 1 slope, 2' wide, 2' deep, 3/8 C.Y. bucket | | 6.20 | 6.20 |
| 3540 | 4' deep, 3/8 C.Y. bucket | | 18.50 | 18.50 |
| 3600 | 10' deep, 1 C.Y. bucket | | 90.50 | 90.50 |
| 3800 | 4' wide, 2' deep, 3/8 C.Y. bucket | | 9.45 | 9.45 |
| 3840 | 4' deep, 1/2 C.Y. bucket | | 22 | 22 |
| 3900 | 10' deep, 1 C.Y. bucket | | 109 | 109 |
| 4030 | 6' wide, 6' deep, 5/8 C.Y. bucket w/trench box | | 60 | 60 |
| 4050 | 10' deep, 1 C.Y. bucket | | 94 | 94 |
| 4080 | 20' deep, 3-1/2 C.Y. bucket | | 275 | 275 |
| 4500 | 8' wide, 12' deep, 1-1/2 C.Y. bucket w/trench box | | 140 | 140 |
| 4650 | 24' deep, 3-1/2 C.Y. bucket | | 415 | 415 |
| 4800 | 10' wide, 20' deep, 3-1/2 C.Y. bucket w/trench box | | 283 | 283 |
| 4850 | 24' deep, 3-1/2 C.Y. bucket | | 440 | 440 |

| G1030 806 | Trenching Loam & Sandy Clay | COST PER L.F. | | |
|---|---|---|---|---|
| | | MAT. | INST. | TOTAL |
| 1310 | Trenching, loam & sandy clay, no slope, 2' wide, 2' deep, 3/8 C.Y. bucket | | 3.08 | 3.08 |

| G1030 807 | Trenching Sand & Gravel | COST PER L.F. | | |
|---|---|---|---|---|
| | | MAT. | INST. | TOTAL |
| 1310 | Trenching, sand & gravel, no slope, 2' wide, 2' deep, 3/8 C.Y. bucket | | 2.90 | 2.90 |
| 1320 | 3' deep, 3/8 C.Y. bucket | | 4.77 | 4.77 |
| 1330 | 4' deep, 3/8 C.Y. bucket | | 5.75 | 5.75 |
| 1340 | 6' deep, 3/8 C.Y. bucket | | 7.90 | 7.90 |
| 1350 | 8' deep, 1/2 C.Y. bucket | | 10.50 | 10.50 |
| 1360 | 10' deep, 1 C.Y. bucket | | 11.05 | 11.05 |
| 1400 | 4' wide, 2' deep, 3/8 C.Y. bucket | | 5.90 | 5.90 |
| 1410 | 3' deep, 3/8 C.Y. bucket | | 8.75 | 8.75 |
| 1420 | 4' deep, 1/2 C.Y. bucket | | 10.30 | 10.30 |
| 1430 | 6' deep, 1/2 C.Y. bucket | | 16.20 | 16.20 |
| 1440 | 8' deep, 1/2 C.Y. bucket | | 23.50 | 23.50 |
| 1450 | 10' deep, 1 C.Y. bucket | | 22.50 | 22.50 |
| 1460 | 12' deep, 1 C.Y. bucket | | 28.50 | 28.50 |
| 1470 | 15' deep, 1-1/2 C.Y. bucket | | 33 | 33 |
| 1480 | 18' deep, 2-1/2 C.Y. bucket | | 36.50 | 36.50 |
| 1520 | 6' wide, 6' deep, 5/8 C.Y. bucket w/trench box | | 28 | 28 |
| 1530 | 8' deep, 3/4 C.Y. bucket | | 37 | 37 |
| 1540 | 10' deep, 1 C.Y. bucket | | 35 | 35 |
| 1550 | 12' deep, 1-1/2 C.Y. bucket | | 39.50 | 39.50 |
| 1560 | 16' deep, 2 C.Y. bucket | | 50.50 | 50.50 |
| 1570 | 20' deep, 3-1/2 C.Y. bucket | | 59 | 59 |
| 1580 | 24' deep, 3-1/2 C.Y. bucket | | 72.50 | 72.50 |

## G1030 Site Earthwork

| G1030 807 | Trenching Sand & Gravel | COST PER L.F. MAT. | INST. | TOTAL |
|---|---|---|---|---|
| 1640 | 8' wide, 12' deep, 1-1/2 C.Y. bucket w/trench box | | 51.50 | 51.50 |
| 1650 | 15' deep, 1-1/2 C.Y. bucket | | 64.50 | 64.50 |
| 1660 | 18' deep, 2-1/2 C.Y. bucket | | 73 | 73 |
| 1680 | 24' deep, 3-1/2 C.Y. bucket | | 95 | 95 |
| 1730 | 10' wide, 20' deep, 3-1/2 C.Y. bucket w/trench box | | 95.50 | 95.50 |
| 1740 | 24' deep, 3-1/2 C.Y. bucket | | 118 | 118 |
| 1780 | 12' wide, 20' deep, 3-1/2 C.Y. bucket w/trench box | | 114 | 114 |
| 1790 | 25' deep, 3-1/2 C.Y. bucket | | 147 | 147 |
| 1800 | 1/2:1 slope, 2' wide, 2' deep, 3/8 C.Y. bucket | | 4.33 | 4.33 |
| 1810 | 3' deep, 3/8 C.Y. bucket | | 7.55 | 7.55 |
| 1820 | 4' deep, 3/8 C.Y. bucket | | 11.45 | 11.45 |
| 1840 | 6' deep, 3/8 C.Y. bucket | | 19.65 | 19.65 |
| 1860 | 8' deep, 1/2 C.Y. bucket | | 31.50 | 31.50 |
| 1880 | 10' deep, 1 C.Y. bucket | | 39 | 39 |
| 2300 | 4' wide, 2' deep, 3/8 C.Y. bucket | | 7.30 | 7.30 |
| 2310 | 3' deep, 3/8 C.Y. bucket | | 11.95 | 11.95 |
| 2320 | 4' deep, 1/2 C.Y. bucket | | 15.35 | 15.35 |
| 2340 | 6' deep, 1/2 C.Y. bucket | | 28.50 | 28.50 |
| 2360 | 8' deep, 1/2 C.Y. bucket | | 46.50 | 46.50 |
| 2380 | 10' deep, 1 C.Y. bucket | | 51.50 | 51.50 |
| 2400 | 12' deep, 1 C.Y. bucket | | 86 | 86 |
| 2430 | 15' deep, 1-1/2 C.Y. bucket | | 96 | 96 |
| 2460 | 18' deep, 2-1/2 C.Y. bucket | | 148 | 148 |
| 2840 | 6' wide, 6' deep, 5/8 C.Y. bucket w/trench box | | 41.50 | 41.50 |
| 2860 | 8' deep, 3/4 C.Y. bucket | | 61.50 | 61.50 |
| 2880 | 10' deep, 1 C.Y. bucket | | 65.50 | 65.50 |
| 2900 | 12' deep, 1-1/2 C.Y. bucket | | 79.50 | 79.50 |
| 2940 | 16' deep, 2 C.Y. bucket | | 118 | 118 |
| 2980 | 20' deep, 3-1/2 C.Y. bucket | | 159 | 159 |
| 3020 | 24' deep, 3-1/2 C.Y. bucket | | 220 | 220 |
| 3100 | 8' wide, 12' deep, 1-1/4 C.Y. bucket w/trench box | | 91.50 | 91.50 |
| 3120 | 15' deep, 1-1/2 C.Y. bucket | | 127 | 127 |
| 3140 | 18' deep, 2-1/2 C.Y. bucket | | 159 | 159 |
| 3180 | 24' deep, 3-1/2 C.Y. bucket | | 243 | 243 |
| 3270 | 10' wide, 20' deep, 3-1/2 C.Y. bucket w/trench box | | 195 | 195 |
| 3280 | 24' deep, 3-1/2 C.Y. bucket | | 266 | 266 |
| 3370 | 12' wide, 20' deep, 3-1/2 C.Y. bucket w/trench box | | 218 | 218 |
| 3380 | 25' deep, 3-1/2 C.Y. bucket | | 310 | 310 |
| 3500 | 1:1 slope, 2' wide, 2' deep, 3/8 C.Y. bucket | | 7.80 | 7.80 |
| 3520 | 3' deep, 3/8 C.Y. bucket | | 10.75 | 10.75 |
| 3540 | 4' deep, 3/8 C.Y. bucket | | 17.20 | 17.20 |
| 3560 | 6' deep, 3/8 C.Y. bucket | | 19.65 | 19.65 |
| 3580 | 8' deep, 1/2 C.Y. bucket | | 52.50 | 52.50 |
| 3600 | 10' deep, 1 C.Y. bucket | | 66.50 | 66.50 |
| 3800 | 4' wide, 2' deep, 3/8 C.Y. bucket | | 8.75 | 8.75 |
| 3820 | 3' deep, 3/8 C.Y. bucket | | 15.15 | 15.15 |
| 3840 | 4' deep, 1/2 C.Y. bucket | | 20.50 | 20.50 |
| 3860 | 6' deep, 1/2 C.Y. bucket | | 40.50 | 40.50 |
| 3880 | 8' deep, 1/2 C.Y. bucket | | 69.50 | 69.50 |
| 3900 | 10' deep, 1 C.Y. bucket | | 80.50 | 80.50 |
| 3920 | 12' deep, 1 C.Y. bucket | | 115 | 115 |
| 3940 | 15' deep, 1-1/2 C.Y. bucket | | 159 | 159 |
| 3960 | 18' deep, 2-1/2 C.Y. bucket | | 203 | 203 |
| 4030 | 6' wide, 6' deep, 5/8 C.Y. bucket w/trench box | | 55.50 | 55.50 |
| 4040 | 8' deep, 3/4 C.Y. bucket | | 86 | 86 |
| 4050 | 10' deep, 1 C.Y. bucket | | 95.50 | 95.50 |
| 4060 | 12' deep, 1-1/2 C.Y. bucket | | 119 | 119 |
| 4070 | 16' deep, 2 C.Y. bucket | | 186 | 186 |

| G1030 807 | Trenching Sand & Gravel | COST PER L.F. MAT. | INST. | TOTAL |
|---|---|---|---|---|
| 4080 | 20′ deep, 3-1/2 C.Y. bucket | | 259 | 259 |
| 4090 | 24′ deep, 3-1/2 C.Y. bucket | | 370 | 370 |
| 4500 | 8′ wide, 12′ deep, 1-1/2 C.Y. bucket w/trench box | | 132 | 132 |
| 4550 | 15′ deep, 1-1/2 C.Y. bucket | | 190 | 190 |
| 4600 | 18′ deep, 2-1/2 C.Y. bucket | | 245 | 245 |
| 4650 | 24′ deep, 3-1/2 C.Y. bucket | | 390 | 390 |
| 4800 | 10′ wide, 20′ deep, 3-1/2 C.Y. bucket w/trench box | | 295 | 295 |
| 4850 | 24′ deep, 3-1/2 C.Y. bucket | | 415 | 415 |
| 4950 | 12′ wide, 20′ deep, 3-1/2 C.Y. bucket w/trench box | | 315 | 315 |
| 4980 | 25′ deep, 3-1/2 C.Y. bucket | | 470 | 470 |

| G1030 815 | Pipe Bedding | COST PER L.F. MAT. | INST. | TOTAL |
|---|---|---|---|---|
| 1440 | Pipe bedding, side slope 0 to 1, 1′ wide, pipe size 6″ diameter | 1.30 | 1.11 | 2.41 |
| 1460 | 2′ wide, pipe size 8″ diameter | 2.81 | 2.40 | 5.21 |
| 1500 | Pipe size 12″ diameter | 2.93 | 2.51 | 5.44 |
| 1600 | 4′ wide, pipe size 20″ diameter | 7 | 6 | 13 |
| 1660 | Pipe size 30″ diameter | 7.35 | 6.30 | 13.65 |
| 1680 | 6′ wide, pipe size 32″ diameter | 12.60 | 10.75 | 23.35 |
| 1740 | 8′ wide, pipe size 60″ diameter | 25 | 21.50 | 46.50 |
| 1780 | 12′ wide, pipe size 84″ diameter | 46 | 39 | 85 |

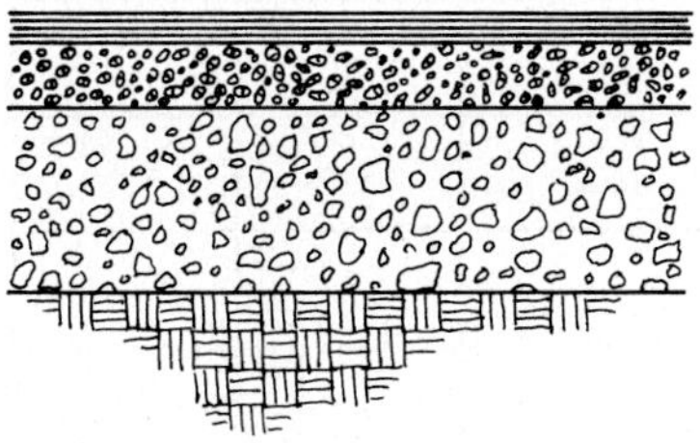

The Bituminous Roadway Systems are listed for pavement thicknesses between 3-1/2″ and 7″ and crushed stone bases from 3″ to 22″ in depth. Systems costs are expressed per linear foot for varying widths of two and multi-lane roads. Earth moving is not included. Granite curbs and line painting are added as required system components.

| G2010 232 | Bituminous Roadways Crushed Stone | COST PER L.F. | | |
|---|---|---|---|---|
| | | MAT. | INST. | TOTAL |
| 1050 | Bitum. roadway, two lanes, 3-1/2″ th. pvmt., 3″ th. crushed stone,24′ wide | 87.50 | 67 | 154.50 |
| 1100 | 28′ wide | 96 | 68 | 164 |
| 1150 | 32′ wide | 104 | 78 | 182 |
| 1200 | 4″ thick crushed stone, 24′ wide | 91 | 64 | 155 |
| 1210 | 28′ wide | 100 | 69 | 169 |
| 1220 | 32′ wide | 109 | 73.50 | 182.50 |
| 1222 | 36′ wide | 118 | 78.50 | 196.50 |
| 1224 | 40′ wide | 127 | 83 | 210 |
| 1230 | 6″ thick crushed stone, 24′ wide | 98.50 | 66 | 164.50 |
| 1240 | 28′ wide | 109 | 71.50 | 180.50 |
| 1250 | 32′ wide | 119 | 76.50 | 195.50 |
| 1252 | 36′ wide | 129 | 81.50 | 210.50 |
| 1254 | 40′ wide | 140 | 86.50 | 226.50 |
| 1256 | 8″ thick crushed stone, 24′ wide | 106 | 68 | 174 |
| 1258 | 28′ wide | 117 | 73.50 | 190.50 |
| 1260 | 32′ wide | 129 | 79 | 208 |
| 1262 | 36′ wide | 140 | 84.50 | 224.50 |
| 1264 | 40′ wide | 152 | 90 | 242 |
| 1300 | 9″ thick crushed stone, 24′ wide | 110 | 69.50 | 179.50 |
| 1350 | 28′ wide | 122 | 75.50 | 197.50 |
| 1400 | 32′ wide | 135 | 81 | 216 |
| 1410 | 10″ thick crushed stone, 24′ wide | 113 | 70 | 183 |
| 1412 | 28′ wide | 126 | 76 | 202 |
| 1414 | 32′ wide | 139 | 82 | 221 |
| 1416 | 36′ wide | 152 | 87.50 | 239.50 |
| 1418 | 40′ wide | 164 | 93.50 | 257.50 |
| 1420 | 12″ thick crushed stone, 24′ wide | 121 | 72 | 193 |
| 1422 | 28′ wide | 135 | 78.50 | 213.50 |
| 1424 | 32′ wide | 149 | 84.50 | 233.50 |
| 1426 | 36′ wide | 163 | 90.50 | 253.50 |
| 1428 | 40′ wide | 177 | 96.50 | 273.50 |
| 1430 | 15″ thick crushed stone, 24′ wide | 132 | 75.50 | 207.50 |
| 1432 | 28′ wide | 148 | 82 | 230 |
| 1434 | 32′ wide | 164 | 88.50 | 252.50 |
| 1436 | 36′ wide | 180 | 95 | 275 |
| 1438 | 40′ wide | 195 | 102 | 297 |
| 1440 | 18″ thick crushed stone, 24′ wide | 143 | 78.50 | 221.50 |
| 1442 | 28′ wide | 161 | 85.50 | 246.50 |
| 1444 | 32′ wide | 178 | 92.50 | 270.50 |
| 1446 | 36′ wide | 196 | 99.50 | 295.50 |
| 1448 | 40′ wide | 214 | 107 | 321 |
| 1550 | 4″ thick pavement., 4″ thick crushed stone, 24′ wide | 96.50 | 65 | 161.50 |

## G2010 Roadways

| G2010 232 | Bituminous Roadways Crushed Stone | COST PER L.F. MAT. | INST. | TOTAL |
|---|---|---|---|---|
| 1600 | 28′ wide | 107 | 70 | 177 |
| 1650 | 32′ wide | 117 | 75 | 192 |
| 1652 | 36′ wide | 127 | 79.50 | 206.50 |
| 1654 | 40′ wide | 137 | 84.50 | 221.50 |
| 1700 | 6″ thick crushed stone , 24′ wide | 104 | 67 | 171 |
| 1710 | 28′ wide | 115 | 72 | 187 |
| 1720 | 32′ wide | 127 | 77.50 | 204.50 |
| 1722 | 36′ wide | 138 | 82.50 | 220.50 |
| 1724 | 40′ wide | 149 | 88 | 237 |
| 1726 | 8″ thick crushed stone , 24′ wide | 111 | 69 | 180 |
| 1728 | 28′ wide | 124 | 74.50 | 198.50 |
| 1730 | 32′ wide | 136 | 80 | 216 |
| 1732 | 36′ wide | 149 | 85.50 | 234.50 |
| 1734 | 40′ wide | 161 | 91 | 252 |
| 1800 | 10″ thick crushed stone, 24′ wide | 119 | 71 | 190 |
| 1850 | 28′ wide | 133 | 75.50 | 208.50 |
| 1900 | 32′ wide | 147 | 83 | 230 |
| 1902 | 36′ wide | 160 | 88.50 | 248.50 |
| 1904 | 40′ wide | 164 | 92.50 | 256.50 |

## G2020 Parking Lots

| G2020 210 | Parking Lots Gravel Base | COST PER CAR | | |
|---|---|---|---|---|
| | | MAT. | INST. | TOTAL |
| 1500 | Parking lot, 90° angle parking, 3″ bituminous paving, 6″ gravel base | 1,050 | 550 | 1,600 |
| 1540 | 10″ gravel base | 1,275 | 640 | 1,915 |
| 1560 | 4″ bituminous paving, 6″ gravel base | 1,275 | 580 | 1,855 |
| 1600 | 10″ gravel base | 1,500 | 670 | 2,170 |
| 1620 | 6″ bituminous paving, 6″ gravel base | 1,650 | 620 | 2,270 |
| 1660 | 10″ gravel base | 1,875 | 710 | 2,585 |
| 1800 | 60° angle parking, 3″ bituminous paving, 6″ gravel base | 1,050 | 550 | 1,600 |
| 1840 | 10″ gravel base | 1,275 | 640 | 1,915 |
| 1860 | 4″ bituminous paving, 6″ gravel base | 1,275 | 580 | 1,855 |
| 1900 | 10″ gravel base | 1,500 | 670 | 2,170 |
| 1920 | 6″ bituminous paving, 6″ gravel base | 1,650 | 620 | 2,270 |
| 1960 | 10″ gravel base | 1,875 | 710 | 2,585 |
| 2200 | 45° angle parking, 3″ bituminous paving, 6″ gravel base | 1,075 | 565 | 1,640 |
| 2240 | 10″ gravel base | 1,325 | 660 | 1,985 |
| 2260 | 4″ bituminous paving, 6″ gravel base | 1,300 | 595 | 1,895 |
| 2300 | 10″ gravel base | 1,550 | 690 | 2,240 |
| 2320 | 6″ bituminous paving, 6″ gravel base | 1,675 | 635 | 2,310 |
| 2360 | 10″ gravel base | 1,925 | 730 | 2,655 |

## G2040 Site Development

| G2040 810 | Flagpoles | COST EACH MAT. | COST EACH INST. | COST EACH TOTAL |
|---|---|---|---|---|
| 0110 | Flagpoles, on grade, aluminum, tapered, 20' high | 1,175 | 880 | 2,055 |
| 0120 | 70' high | 12,100 | 2,225 | 14,325 |
| 0130 | Fiberglass, tapered, 23' high | 2,150 | 880 | 3,030 |
| 0140 | 59' high | 10,300 | 1,950 | 12,250 |
| 0150 | Concrete, internal halyard, 20' high | 279 | 700 | 979 |
| 0160 | 100' high | 31,800 | 1,750 | 33,550 |

| G2040 950 | Other Site Development, EACH | COST EACH MAT. | COST EACH INST. | COST EACH TOTAL |
|---|---|---|---|---|
| 0110 | Grandstands, permanent, closed deck, alum, economy (per seat) | 144 | | 144 |
| 0120 | Deluxe (per seat) | 31 | | 31 |
| 0130 | Composite design, economy (per seat) | 39.50 | | 39.50 |
| 0140 | Deluxe (per seat) | 93.50 | | 93.50 |

## G2040 Site Development

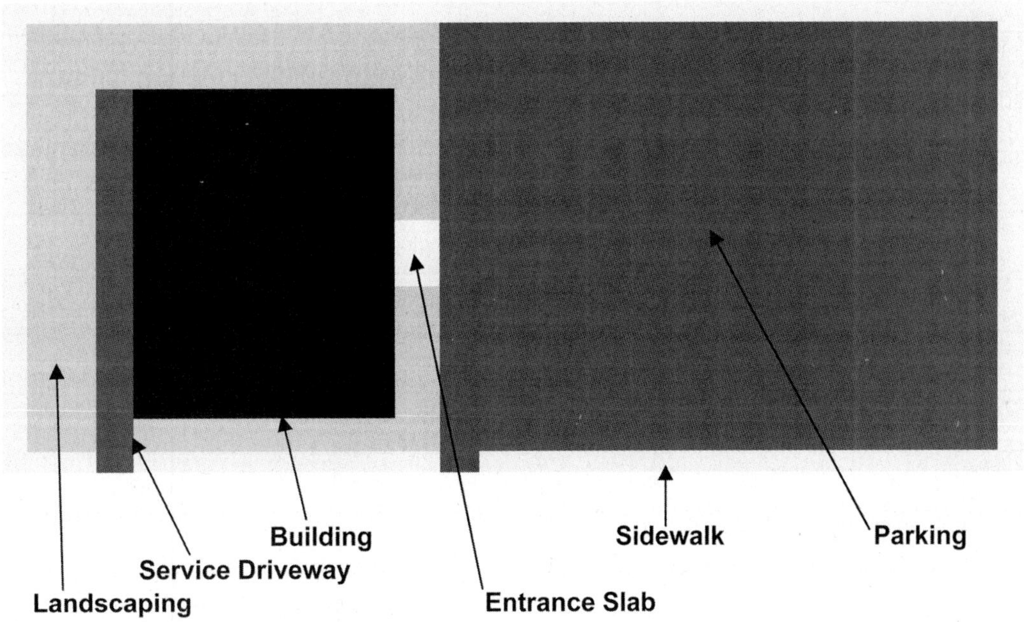


| G2040 990 | Site Development Components for Buildings | COST EACH | | |
|---|---|---|---|---|
| | | MAT. | INST. | TOTAL |
| 0970 | Assume minimal and balanced cut & fill, no rock, no demolition, no haz mat. | | | |
| 0975 | Lines can be adjusted linearly +/- 20% within same use & number of floors. | | | |
| 0980 | 60,000 S.F. 2-Story Office Bldg on 3.3 Acres w/20% Green Space | | | |
| 1000 | Site Preparation | 560 | 60,000 | 60,560 |
| 1002 | Utilities | 231,500 | 124,000 | 355,500 |
| 1004 | Pavement | 374,500 | 245,500 | 620,000 |
| 1006 | Stormwater Management | 348,500 | 73,500 | 422,000 |
| 1008 | Sidewalks | 25,900 | 23,000 | 48,900 |
| 1010 | Exterior lighting | 56,000 | 47,600 | 103,600 |
| 1014 | Landscaping | 91,000 | 63,500 | 154,500 |
| 1028 | 80,000 S.F. 4-Story Office Bldg on 3.5 Acres w/20% Green Space | | | |
| 1030 | Site preparation | 575 | 64,500 | 65,075 |
| 1032 | Utilities | 212,000 | 112,500 | 324,500 |
| 1034 | Pavement | 447,000 | 294,000 | 741,000 |
| 1036 | Stormwater Managmement | 367,000 | 77,500 | 444,500 |
| 1038 | Sidewalks | 21,100 | 18,800 | 39,900 |
| 1040 | Lighting | 55,000 | 50,500 | 105,500 |
| 1042 | Landscaping | 93,500 | 66,000 | 159,500 |
| 1058 | 16,000 S.F. 1-Story Medical Office Bldg on 1.7 Acres w/25% Green Space | | | |
| 1060 | Site preparation | 405 | 45,900 | 46,305 |
| 1062 | Utilities | 162,500 | 91,000 | 253,500 |
| 1064 | Pavement | 175,500 | 115,500 | 291,000 |
| 1066 | Stormwater Management | 170,000 | 35,800 | 205,800 |
| 1068 | Sidewalks | 18,900 | 16,800 | 35,700 |
| 1070 | Lighting | 35,100 | 27,600 | 62,700 |
| 1072 | Landscaping | 61,500 | 39,100 | 100,600 |
| 1098 | 36,000 S.F. 3-Story Apartment Bldg on 1.6 Acres w/25% Green Space | | | |
| 1100 | Site preparation | 390 | 45,300 | 45,690 |

## G2040 Site Development

| G2040 990 | Site Development Components for Buildings | COST EACH MAT. | COST EACH INST. | COST EACH TOTAL |
|---|---|---|---|---|
| 1102 | Utilities | 148,500 | 82,500 | 231,000 |
| 1104 | Pavement | 177,000 | 116,000 | 293,000 |
| 1106 | Stormwater Management | 158,500 | 33,300 | 191,800 |
| 1108 | Sidewalks | 16,400 | 14,500 | 30,900 |
| 1110 | Lighting | 32,500 | 26,200 | 58,700 |
| 1112 | Landscaping | 59,000 | 37,200 | 96,200 |
| 1128 | 130,000 S.F. 3-Story Hospital Bldg on 5.9 Acres w/17% Green Space | | | |
| 1130 | Site preparation | 755 | 84,500 | 85,255 |
| 1132 | Utilities | 314,500 | 162,500 | 477,000 |
| 1134 | Pavement | 759,500 | 499,500 | 1,259,000 |
| 1136 | Stormwater Management | 652,500 | 137,500 | 790,000 |
| 1138 | Sidewalks | 31,100 | 27,600 | 58,700 |
| 1140 | Lighting | 90,000 | 84,500 | 174,500 |
| 1142 | Landscaping | 130,500 | 100,500 | 231,000 |
| 1158 | 60,000 S.F. 1-Story Light Manufacturing Bldg on 3.9 Acres w/18% Green Space | | | |
| 1160 | Site preparation | 615 | 63,500 | 64,115 |
| 1162 | Utilities | 284,500 | 154,500 | 439,000 |
| 1164 | Pavement | 377,500 | 212,500 | 590,000 |
| 1166 | Stormwater Management | 429,500 | 90,500 | 520,000 |
| 1168 | Sidewalks | 36,600 | 32,500 | 69,100 |
| 1170 | Lighting | 69,000 | 54,500 | 123,500 |
| 1172 | Landscaping | 98,500 | 71,000 | 169,500 |
| 1198 | 8,000 S.F. 1-Story Restaurant Bldg on 1.4 Acres w/26% Green Space | | | |
| 1200 | Site preparation | 370 | 44,300 | 44,670 |
| 1202 | Utilities | 130,000 | 72,000 | 202,000 |
| 1204 | Pavement | 167,000 | 111,500 | 278,500 |
| 1206 | Stormwater Management | 139,500 | 29,400 | 168,900 |
| 1208 | Sidewalks | 13,400 | 11,900 | 25,300 |
| 1210 | Lighting | 28,800 | 24,200 | 53,000 |
| 1212 | Landscaping | 55,000 | 34,200 | 89,200 |
| 1228 | 20,000 S.F. 1-Story Retail Store Bldg on 2.1 Acres w/23% Green Space | | | |
| 1230 | Site preparation | 450 | 53,500 | 53,950 |
| 1232 | Utilities | 182,500 | 101,000 | 283,500 |
| 1234 | Pavement | 227,500 | 149,500 | 377,000 |
| 1236 | Stormwater Management | 217,500 | 45,800 | 263,300 |
| 1238 | Sidewalks | 21,100 | 18,800 | 39,900 |
| 1240 | Lighting | 40,000 | 32,000 | 72,000 |
| 1242 | Landscaping | 70,000 | 46,100 | 116,100 |
| 1258 | 60,000 S.F. 1-Story Warehouse on 3.1 Acres w/19% Green Space | | | |
| 1260 | Site preparation | 545 | 59,000 | 59,545 |
| 1262 | Utilities | 259,500 | 144,500 | 404,000 |
| 1264 | Pavement | 239,500 | 119,500 | 359,000 |
| 1266 | Stormwater Management | 334,500 | 70,500 | 405,000 |
| 1268 | Sidewalks | 36,600 | 32,500 | 69,100 |
| 1270 | Lighting | 59,000 | 42,300 | 101,300 |
| 1272 | Landscaping | 84,500 | 59,000 | 143,500 |

## G3030 Storm Sewer

| G3030 210 | Manholes & Catch Basins | COST PER EACH | | |
|---|---|---|---|---|
| | | MAT. | INST. | TOTAL |
| 1920 | Manhole/catch basin, brick, 4′ I.D. riser, 4′ deep | 3,300 | 2,175 | 5,475 |
| 1980 | 10′ deep | 6,750 | 5,150 | 11,900 |
| 3200 | Block, 4′ I.D. riser, 4′ deep | 2,200 | 1,750 | 3,950 |
| 3260 | 10′ deep | 3,825 | 4,250 | 8,075 |
| 4620 | Concrete, cast-in-place, 4′ I.D. riser, 4′ deep | 2,525 | 3,000 | 5,525 |
| 4680 | 10′ deep | 5,050 | 7,175 | 12,225 |
| 5820 | Concrete, precast, 4′ I.D. riser, 4′ deep | 3,000 | 1,600 | 4,600 |
| 5880 | 10′ deep | 5,250 | 3,775 | 9,025 |
| 6200 | 6′ I.D. riser, 4′ deep | 6,500 | 2,300 | 8,800 |
| 6260 | 10′ deep | 9,950 | 5,425 | 15,375 |

## G4020 Site Lighting

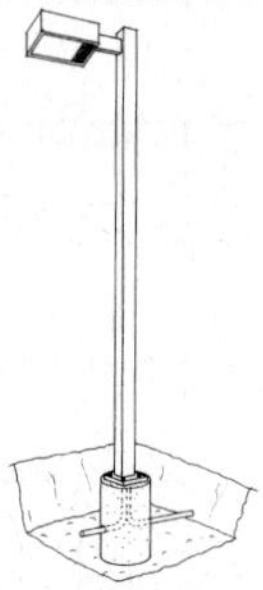

Light Pole

| G4020 210 | Light Pole (Installed) | COST EACH | | |
|---|---|---|---|---|
| | | MAT. | INST. | TOTAL |
| 0200 | Light pole, aluminum, 20' high, 1 arm bracket | 1,600 | 1,475 | 3,075 |
| 0240 | 2 arm brackets | 2,225 | 1,475 | 3,700 |
| 0280 | 3 arm brackets | 1,450 | 1,525 | 2,975 |
| 0320 | 4 arm brackets | 1,600 | 1,525 | 3,125 |
| 0360 | 30' high, 1 arm bracket | 2,625 | 1,850 | 4,475 |
| 0400 | 2 arm brackets | 3,275 | 1,850 | 5,125 |
| 0440 | 3 arm brackets | 2,500 | 1,900 | 4,400 |
| 0480 | 4 arm brackets | 2,650 | 1,925 | 4,575 |
| 0680 | 40' high, 1 arm bracket | 3,800 | 2,475 | 6,275 |
| 0720 | 2 arm brackets | 4,425 | 2,475 | 6,900 |
| 0760 | 3 arm brackets | 3,650 | 2,525 | 6,175 |
| 0800 | 4 arm brackets | 3,800 | 2,525 | 6,325 |
| 0840 | Steel, 20' high, 1 arm bracket | 2,075 | 1,550 | 3,625 |
| 0880 | 2 arm brackets | 2,475 | 1,550 | 4,025 |
| 0920 | 3 arm brackets | 2,575 | 1,600 | 4,175 |
| 0960 | 4 arm brackets | 2,800 | 1,600 | 4,400 |
| 1000 | 30' high, 1 arm bracket | 2,600 | 1,975 | 4,575 |
| 1040 | 2 arm brackets | 3,000 | 1,975 | 4,975 |
| 1080 | 3 arm brackets | 3,125 | 2,025 | 5,150 |
| 1120 | 4 arm brackets | 3,350 | 2,025 | 5,375 |
| 1320 | 40' high, 1 arm bracket | 3,400 | 2,650 | 6,050 |
| 1360 | 2 arm brackets | 3,825 | 2,650 | 6,475 |
| 1400 | 3 arm brackets | 3,925 | 2,700 | 6,625 |
| 1440 | 4 arm brackets | 4,150 | 2,700 | 6,850 |

# Reference Section

All the reference information is in one section making it easy to find what you need to know . . . and easy to use the data set on a daily basis. This section is visually identified by a vertical black bar on the edge of pages.

In this Reference Section, we've included General Conditions; Location Factors for adjusting costs to the region you are in; Historical Cost Indexes for cost comparisons over time; a Glossary; an explanation of all Abbreviations used in the data set; and sample Estimating Forms.

## Table of Contents

## General Conditions, Overhead & Profit

The total building costs in the Commercial/Industrial/Institutional section include a 10% allowance for general conditions and a 15% allowance for the general contractor's overhead and profit and contingencies.

General contractor overhead includes indirect costs such as permits, Workers' Compensation, insurances, supervision and bonding fees. Overhead will vary with the size of project, the contractor's operating procedures and location. Profits will vary with economic activity and local conditions.

Contingencies provide for unforeseen construction difficulties which include material shortages and weather. In all situations, the appraiser should give consideration to possible adjustment of the 25% factor used in developing the Commercial/Industrial/Institutional models.

## Architectural Fees

Tabulated below are typical percentage fees by project size, for good professional architectural service. Fees may vary from those listed depending upon degree of design difficulty and economic conditions in any particular area.

Rates can be interpolated horizontally and vertically. Various portions of the same project requiring different rates should be adjusted proportionately. For alterations, add 50% to the fee for the first $500,000 of project cost and add 25% to the fee for project cost over $500,000.

Architectural fees tabulated below include Engineering fees.

## Insurance Exclusions

Many insurance companies exclude from coverage such items as architect's fees, excavation, foundations below grade, underground piping and site preparation. Since exclusions vary among insurance companies, it is recommended that for greatest accuracy each exclusion be priced separately using the unit-in-place section.

As a rule of thumb, exclusions can be calculated at 9% of total building cost plus the appropriate allowance for architect's fees.

| | Total Project Size in Thousands of Dollars | | | | | | |
|---|---|---|---|---|---|---|---|
| Building Types | 100 | 250 | 500 | 1,000 | 5,000 | 10,000 | 50,000 |
| Factories, garages, warehouses, repetitive housing | 9.0% | 8.0% | 7.0% | 6.2% | 5.3% | 4.9% | 4.5% |
| Apartments, banks, schools, libraries, offices, municipal buildings | 12.2 | 12.3 | 9.2 | 8.0 | 7.0 | 6.6 | 6.2 |
| Churches, hospitals, homes, laboratories, museums, research | 15.0 | 13.6 | 12.7 | 11.9 | 9.5 | 8.8 | 8.0 |
| Memorials, monumental work, decorative furnishings | – | 16.0 | 14.5 | 13.1 | 10.0 | 9.0 | 8.3 |

# Location Factors - Residential/Commercial

Costs shown in *Square Foot Costs with RSMeans data* are based on national averages for materials and installation. To adjust these costs to a specific location, simply multiply the base cost by the factor for that city. The data is arranged alphabetically by state and postal zip code numbers. For a city not listed, use the factor for a nearby city with similar economic characteristics.

| STATE/ZIP | CITY | Residential | Commercial |
|---|---|---|---|
| **ALABAMA** | | | |
| 350-352 | Birmingham | .86 | .90 |
| 354 | Tuscaloosa | .85 | .88 |
| 355 | Jasper | .83 | .88 |
| 356 | Decatur | .83 | .87 |
| 357-358 | Huntsville | .86 | .89 |
| 359 | Gadsden | .81 | .89 |
| 360-361 | Montgomery | .85 | .89 |
| 362 | Anniston | .80 | .86 |
| 363 | Dothan | .85 | .88 |
| 364 | Evergreen | .78 | .85 |
| 365-366 | Mobile | .83 | .88 |
| 367 | Selma | .80 | .87 |
| 368 | Phenix City | .82 | .87 |
| 369 | Butler | .79 | .86 |
| **ALASKA** | | | |
| 995-996 | Anchorage | 1.16 | 1.14 |
| 997 | Fairbanks | 1.20 | 1.14 |
| 998 | Juneau | 1.16 | 1.14 |
| 999 | Ketchikan | 1.20 | 1.19 |
| **ARIZONA** | | | |
| 850,853 | Phoenix | .90 | .91 |
| 851,852 | Mesa/Tempe | .87 | .88 |
| 855 | Globe | .85 | .87 |
| 856-857 | Tucson | .88 | .87 |
| 859 | Show Low | .88 | .87 |
| 860 | Flagstaff | .92 | .90 |
| 863 | Prescott | .90 | .88 |
| 864 | Kingman | .86 | .87 |
| 865 | Chambers | .89 | .87 |
| **ARKANSAS** | | | |
| 716 | Pine Bluff | .76 | .85 |
| 717 | Camden | .77 | .83 |
| 718 | Texarkana | .79 | .84 |
| 719 | Hot Springs | .75 | .82 |
| 720-722 | Little Rock | .83 | .85 |
| 723 | West Memphis | .81 | .83 |
| 724 | Jonesboro | .79 | .84 |
| 725 | Batesville | .76 | .81 |
| 726 | Harrison | .78 | .81 |
| 727 | Fayetteville | .75 | .81 |
| 728 | Russellville | .77 | .81 |
| 729 | Fort Smith | .83 | .83 |
| **CALIFORNIA** | | | |
| 900-902 | Los Angeles | 1.15 | 1.13 |
| 903-905 | Inglewood | 1.14 | 1.07 |
| 906-908 | Long Beach | 1.12 | 1.08 |
| 910-912 | Pasadena | 1.11 | 1.08 |
| 913-916 | Van Nuys | 1.15 | 1.10 |
| 917-918 | Alhambra | 1.15 | 1.11 |
| 919-921 | San Diego | 1.14 | 1.11 |
| 922 | Palm Springs | 1.11 | 1.08 |
| 923-924 | San Bernardino | 1.13 | 1.06 |
| 925 | Riverside | 1.13 | 1.09 |
| 926-927 | Santa Ana | 1.14 | 1.07 |
| 928 | Anaheim | 1.13 | 1.09 |
| 930 | Oxnard | 1.15 | 1.10 |
| 931 | Santa Barbara | 1.14 | 1.09 |
| 932-933 | Bakersfield | 1.13 | 1.10 |
| 934 | San Luis Obispo | 1.17 | 1.09 |
| 935 | Mojave | 1.15 | 1.07 |
| 936-938 | Fresno | 1.19 | 1.11 |
| 939 | Salinas | 1.23 | 1.15 |
| 940-941 | San Francisco | 1.32 | 1.26 |
| 942,956-958 | Sacramento | 1.20 | 1.10 |
| 943 | Palo Alto | 1.28 | 1.17 |
| 944 | San Mateo | 1.32 | 1.18 |
| 945 | Vallejo | 1.25 | 1.14 |
| 946 | Oakland | 1.30 | 1.19 |
| 947 | Berkeley | 1.34 | 1.19 |
| 948 | Richmond | 1.34 | 1.16 |
| 949 | San Rafael | 1.32 | 1.18 |
| 950 | Santa Cruz | 1.24 | 1.17 |
| 951 | San Jose | 1.28 | 1.21 |
| 952 | Stockton | 1.19 | 1.12 |
| 953 | Modesto | 1.18 | 1.12 |

| STATE/ZIP | CITY | Residential | Commercial |
|---|---|---|---|
| **CALIFORNIA (CONT'D)** | | | |
| 954 | Santa Rosa | 1.24 | 1.17 |
| 955 | Eureka | 1.24 | 1.14 |
| 959 | Marysville | 1.19 | 1.12 |
| 960 | Redding | 1.18 | 1.14 |
| 961 | Susanville | 1.19 | 1.13 |
| **COLORADO** | | | |
| 800-802 | Denver | .92 | .92 |
| 803 | Boulder | .92 | .88 |
| 804 | Golden | .87 | .87 |
| 805 | Fort Collins | .90 | .89 |
| 806 | Greeley | .88 | .88 |
| 807 | Fort Morgan | .91 | .87 |
| 808-809 | Colorado Springs | .86 | .88 |
| 810 | Pueblo | .89 | .89 |
| 811 | Alamosa | .88 | .88 |
| 812 | Salida | .89 | .88 |
| 813 | Durango | .92 | .87 |
| 814 | Montrose | .85 | .87 |
| 815 | Grand Junction | .94 | .91 |
| 816 | Glenwood Springs | .87 | .87 |
| **CONNECTICUT** | | | |
| 060 | New Britain | 1.10 | 1.04 |
| 061 | Hartford | 1.09 | 1.06 |
| 062 | Willimantic | 1.10 | 1.04 |
| 063 | New London | 1.09 | 1.01 |
| 064 | Meriden | 1.09 | 1.03 |
| 065 | New Haven | 1.10 | 1.05 |
| 066 | Bridgeport | 1.10 | 1.05 |
| 067 | Waterbury | 1.10 | 1.05 |
| 068 | Norwalk | 1.09 | 1.04 |
| 069 | Stamford | 1.09 | 1.05 |
| **D.C.** | | | |
| 200-205 | Washington | .94 | .97 |
| **DELAWARE** | | | |
| 197 | Newark | 1.02 | 1.03 |
| 198 | Wilmington | 1.04 | 1.04 |
| 199 | Dover | 1.04 | 1.04 |
| **FLORIDA** | | | |
| 320,322 | Jacksonville | .84 | .87 |
| 321 | Daytona Beach | .84 | .88 |
| 323 | Tallahassee | .86 | .88 |
| 324 | Panama City | .85 | .88 |
| 325 | Pensacola | .87 | .89 |
| 326,344 | Gainesville | .83 | .87 |
| 327-328,347 | Orlando | .87 | .89 |
| 329 | Melbourne | .84 | .91 |
| 330-332,340 | Miami | .85 | .89 |
| 333 | Fort Lauderdale | .82 | .87 |
| 334,349 | West Palm Beach | .82 | .84 |
| 335-336,346 | Tampa | .84 | .88 |
| 337 | St. Petersburg | .82 | .89 |
| 338 | Lakeland | .80 | .87 |
| 339,341 | Fort Myers | .80 | .87 |
| 342 | Sarasota | .84 | .87 |
| **GEORGIA** | | | |
| 300-303,399 | Atlanta | .92 | .91 |
| 304 | Statesboro | .81 | .87 |
| 305 | Gainesville | .81 | .83 |
| 306 | Athens | .79 | .82 |
| 307 | Dalton | .81 | .85 |
| 308-309 | Augusta | .88 | .87 |
| 310-312 | Macon | .85 | .88 |
| 313-314 | Savannah | .88 | .89 |
| 315 | Waycross | .81 | .86 |
| 316 | Valdosta | .82 | .88 |
| 317,398 | Albany | .86 | .88 |
| 318-319 | Columbus | .86 | .89 |
| **HAWAII** | | | |
| 967 | Hilo | 1.13 | 1.12 |
| 968 | Honolulu | 1.16 | 1.16 |

# Location Factors - Residential/Commercial

| STATE/ZIP | CITY | Residential | Commercial |
|---|---|---|---|
| **STATES & POSS.** | | | |
| 969 | Guam | .98 | 1.08 |
| **IDAHO** | | | |
| 832 | Pocatello | .90 | .93 |
| 833 | Twin Falls | .90 | .92 |
| 834 | Idaho Falls | .87 | .92 |
| 835 | Lewiston | .98 | .97 |
| 836-837 | Boise | .91 | .93 |
| 838 | Coeur d'Alene | .98 | .97 |
| **ILLINOIS** | | | |
| 600-603 | North Suburban | 1.18 | 1.13 |
| 604 | Joliet | 1.18 | 1.13 |
| 605 | South Suburban | 1.18 | 1.13 |
| 606-608 | Chicago | 1.20 | 1.16 |
| 609 | Kankakee | 1.10 | 1.07 |
| 610-611 | Rockford | 1.10 | 1.08 |
| 612 | Rock Island | .95 | .96 |
| 613 | La Salle | 1.10 | 1.06 |
| 614 | Galesburg | .99 | .99 |
| 615-616 | Peoria | 1.03 | 1.01 |
| 617 | Bloomington | .98 | .99 |
| 618-619 | Champaign | 1.04 | 1.03 |
| 620-622 | East St. Louis | 1.01 | 1.01 |
| 623 | Quincy | 1.03 | 1.00 |
| 624 | Effingham | 1.02 | .99 |
| 625 | Decatur | 1.03 | 1.01 |
| 626-627 | Springfield | 1.04 | 1.02 |
| 628 | Centralia | 1.01 | .97 |
| 629 | Carbondale | 1.00 | .98 |
| **INDIANA** | | | |
| 460 | Anderson | .86 | .89 |
| 461-462 | Indianapolis | .90 | .94 |
| 463-464 | Gary | .96 | .98 |
| 465-466 | South Bend | .88 | .92 |
| 467-468 | Fort Wayne | .87 | .89 |
| 469 | Kokomo | .87 | .86 |
| 470 | Lawrenceburg | .84 | .85 |
| 471 | New Albany | .85 | .85 |
| 472 | Columbus | .89 | .88 |
| 473 | Muncie | .88 | .88 |
| 474 | Bloomington | .92 | .90 |
| 475 | Washington | .89 | .88 |
| 476-477 | Evansville | .89 | .90 |
| 478 | Terre Haute | .87 | .89 |
| 479 | Lafayette | .89 | .87 |
| **IOWA** | | | |
| 500-503,509 | Des Moines | .95 | .96 |
| 504 | Mason City | .83 | .85 |
| 505 | Fort Dodge | .83 | .85 |
| 506-507 | Waterloo | .88 | .90 |
| 508 | Creston | .86 | .89 |
| 510-511 | Sioux City | .90 | .90 |
| 512 | Sibley | .75 | .82 |
| 513 | Spencer | .76 | .82 |
| 514 | Carroll | .85 | .88 |
| 515 | Council Bluffs | .85 | .91 |
| 516 | Shenandoah | .84 | .88 |
| 520 | Dubuque | .86 | .90 |
| 521 | Decorah | .84 | .85 |
| 522-524 | Cedar Rapids | .94 | .92 |
| 525 | Ottumwa | .87 | .87 |
| 526 | Burlington | .90 | .88 |
| 527-528 | Davenport | .97 | .95 |
| **KANSAS** | | | |
| 660-662 | Kansas City | .98 | .98 |
| 664-666 | Topeka | .86 | .90 |
| 667 | Fort Scott | .88 | .86 |
| 668 | Emporia | .81 | .86 |
| 669 | Belleville | .80 | .85 |
| 670-672 | Wichita | .83 | .88 |
| 673 | Independence | .88 | .87 |
| 674 | Salina | .80 | .87 |
| 675 | Hutchinson | .77 | .83 |
| 676 | Hays | .81 | .85 |
| 677 | Colby | .83 | .86 |
| 678 | Dodge City | .81 | .88 |
| 679 | Liberal | .79 | .85 |
| **KENTUCKY** | | | |
| 400-402 | Louisville | .89 | .91 |
| 403-405 | Lexington | .87 | .89 |

| STATE/ZIP | CITY | Residential | Commercial |
|---|---|---|---|
| **KENTUCKY (CONT'D)** | | | |
| 406 | Frankfort | .89 | .90 |
| 407-409 | Corbin | .80 | .85 |
| 410 | Covington | .81 | .85 |
| 411-412 | Ashland | .83 | .88 |
| 413-414 | Campton | .82 | .85 |
| 415-416 | Pikeville | .85 | .88 |
| 417-418 | Hazard | .81 | .85 |
| 420 | Paducah | .83 | .85 |
| 421-422 | Bowling Green | .84 | .87 |
| 423 | Owensboro | .85 | .88 |
| 424 | Henderson | .84 | .85 |
| 425-426 | Somerset | .80 | .84 |
| 427 | Elizabethtown | .79 | .83 |
| **LOUISIANA** | | | |
| 700-701 | New Orleans | .86 | .88 |
| 703 | Thibodaux | .80 | .82 |
| 704 | Hammond | .76 | .81 |
| 705 | Lafayette | .84 | .83 |
| 706 | Lake Charles | .85 | .84 |
| 707-708 | Baton Rouge | .84 | .86 |
| 710-711 | Shreveport | .84 | .86 |
| 712 | Monroe | .78 | .84 |
| 713-714 | Alexandria | .79 | .84 |
| **MAINE** | | | |
| 039 | Kittery | .89 | .88 |
| 040-041 | Portland | .96 | .95 |
| 042 | Lewiston | .94 | .92 |
| 043 | Augusta | .92 | .94 |
| 044 | Bangor | .92 | .91 |
| 045 | Bath | .88 | .89 |
| 046 | Machias | .90 | .89 |
| 047 | Houlton | .91 | .89 |
| 048 | Rockland | .91 | .88 |
| 049 | Waterville | .88 | .89 |
| **MARYLAND** | | | |
| 206 | Waldorf | .89 | .91 |
| 207-208 | College Park | .85 | .91 |
| 209 | Silver Spring | .87 | .90 |
| 210-212 | Baltimore | .93 | .95 |
| 214 | Annapolis | .91 | .93 |
| 215 | Cumberland | .88 | .89 |
| 216 | Easton | .84 | .86 |
| 217 | Hagerstown | .90 | .92 |
| 218 | Salisbury | .86 | .84 |
| 219 | Elkton | .90 | .89 |
| **MASSACHUSETTS** | | | |
| 010-011 | Springfield | 1.05 | 1.00 |
| 012 | Pittsfield | 1.01 | .98 |
| 013 | Greenfield | 1.01 | .98 |
| 014 | Fitchburg | 1.03 | .98 |
| 015-016 | Worcester | 1.08 | 1.03 |
| 017 | Framingham | 1.08 | 1.01 |
| 018 | Lowell | 1.09 | 1.05 |
| 019 | Lawrence | 1.09 | 1.05 |
| 020-022, 024 | Boston | 1.18 | 1.13 |
| 023 | Brockton | 1.07 | 1.03 |
| 025 | Buzzards Bay | 1.04 | .97 |
| 026 | Hyannis | 1.03 | 1.00 |
| 027 | New Bedford | 1.06 | 1.02 |
| **MICHIGAN** | | | |
| 480,483 | Royal Oak | .94 | .93 |
| 481 | Ann Arbor | .97 | .96 |
| 482 | Detroit | 1.00 | 1.00 |
| 484-485 | Flint | .93 | .93 |
| 486 | Saginaw | .89 | .92 |
| 487 | Bay City | .89 | .91 |
| 488-489 | Lansing | .91 | .94 |
| 490 | Battle Creek | .88 | .89 |
| 491 | Kalamazoo | .89 | .90 |
| 492 | Jackson | .87 | .90 |
| 493,495 | Grand Rapids | .89 | .91 |
| 494 | Muskegon | .87 | .89 |
| 496 | Traverse City | .82 | .85 |
| 497 | Gaylord | .84 | .87 |
| 498-499 | Iron Mountain | .85 | .88 |
| **MINNESOTA** | | | |
| 550-551 | Saint Paul | 1.07 | 1.08 |
| 553-555 | Minneapolis | 1.08 | 1.07 |
| 556-558 | Duluth | 1.03 | 1.04 |

# Location Factors - Residential/Commercial

| STATE/ZIP | CITY | Residential | Commercial |
|---|---|---|---|
| **MINNESOTA (CONT'd)** | | | |
| 559 | Rochester | 1.02 | 1.02 |
| 560 | Mankato | .98 | .97 |
| 561 | Windom | .87 | .92 |
| 562 | Willmar | .94 | .97 |
| 563 | St. Cloud | 1.00 | 1.02 |
| 564 | Brainerd | .93 | .97 |
| 565 | Detroit Lakes | .88 | .94 |
| 566 | Bemidji | .91 | .95 |
| 567 | Thief River Falls | .91 | .94 |
| **MISSISSIPPI** | | | |
| 386 | Clarksdale | .73 | .80 |
| 387 | Greenville | .79 | .86 |
| 388 | Tupelo | .74 | .81 |
| 389 | Greenwood | .78 | .80 |
| 390-392 | Jackson | .87 | .87 |
| 393 | Meridian | .80 | .84 |
| 394 | Laurel | .77 | .80 |
| 395 | Biloxi | .85 | .85 |
| 396 | McComb | .74 | .78 |
| 397 | Columbus | .75 | .80 |
| **MISSOURI** | | | |
| 630-631 | St. Louis | 1.00 | 1.00 |
| 633 | Bowling Green | .92 | .91 |
| 634 | Hannibal | .89 | .89 |
| 635 | Kirksville | .84 | .89 |
| 636 | Flat River | .92 | .90 |
| 637 | Cape Girardeau | .87 | .91 |
| 638 | Sikeston | .83 | .88 |
| 639 | Poplar Bluff | .83 | .87 |
| 640-641 | Kansas City | .99 | 1.00 |
| 644-645 | St. Joseph | .95 | .93 |
| 646 | Chillicothe | .90 | .89 |
| 647 | Harrisonville | .91 | .91 |
| 648 | Joplin | .88 | .88 |
| 650-651 | Jefferson City | .92 | .95 |
| 652 | Columbia | .88 | .94 |
| 653 | Sedalia | .85 | .91 |
| 654-655 | Rolla | .92 | .93 |
| 656-658 | Springfield | .88 | .92 |
| **MONTANA** | | | |
| 590-591 | Billings | .92 | .93 |
| 592 | Wolf Point | .87 | .90 |
| 593 | Miles City | .89 | .89 |
| 594 | Great Falls | .92 | .93 |
| 595 | Havre | .82 | .88 |
| 596 | Helena | .90 | .91 |
| 597 | Butte | .85 | .90 |
| 598 | Missoula | .86 | .89 |
| 599 | Kalispell | .86 | .88 |
| **NEBRASKA** | | | |
| 680-681 | Omaha | .90 | .92 |
| 683-685 | Lincoln | .88 | .91 |
| 686 | Columbus | .86 | .87 |
| 687 | Norfolk | .85 | .86 |
| 688 | Grand Island | .88 | .89 |
| 689 | Hastings | .85 | .86 |
| 690 | McCook | .80 | .84 |
| 691 | North Platte | .85 | .87 |
| 692 | Valentine | .79 | .85 |
| 693 | Alliance | .80 | .86 |
| **NEVADA** | | | |
| 889-891 | Las Vegas | 1.04 | 1.05 |
| 893 | Ely | .99 | .95 |
| 894-895 | Reno | .91 | .94 |
| 897 | Carson City | .93 | .94 |
| 898 | Elko | .99 | .92 |
| **NEW HAMPSHIRE** | | | |
| 030 | Nashua | 1.00 | .96 |
| 031 | Manchester | 1.00 | .97 |
| 032-033 | Concord | 1.00 | .97 |
| 034 | Keene | .92 | .90 |
| 035 | Littleton | .95 | .87 |
| 036 | Charleston | .90 | .89 |
| 037 | Claremont | .91 | .89 |
| 038 | Portsmouth | .94 | .93 |

| STATE/ZIP | CITY | Residential | Commercial |
|---|---|---|---|
| **NEW JERSEY** | | | |
| 070-071 | Newark | 1.16 | 1.13 |
| 072 | Elizabeth | 1.18 | 1.10 |
| 073 | Jersey City | 1.13 | 1.10 |
| 074-075 | Paterson | 1.14 | 1.11 |
| 076 | Hackensack | 1.13 | 1.09 |
| 077 | Long Branch | 1.13 | 1.08 |
| 078 | Dover | 1.13 | 1.09 |
| 079 | Summit | 1.14 | 1.09 |
| 080,083 | Vineland | 1.15 | 1.09 |
| 081 | Camden | 1.17 | 1.11 |
| 082,084 | Atlantic City | 1.21 | 1.09 |
| 085-086 | Trenton | 1.17 | 1.11 |
| 087 | Point Pleasant | 1.12 | 1.07 |
| 088-089 | New Brunswick | 1.20 | 1.11 |
| **NEW MEXICO** | | | |
| 870-872 | Albuquerque | .87 | .89 |
| 873 | Gallup | .87 | .88 |
| 874 | Farmington | .87 | .89 |
| 875 | Santa Fe | .87 | .90 |
| 877 | Las Vegas | .87 | .87 |
| 878 | Socorro | .87 | .87 |
| 879 | Truth/Consequences | .86 | .86 |
| 880 | Las Cruces | .85 | .86 |
| 881 | Clovis | .86 | .88 |
| 882 | Roswell | .86 | .89 |
| 883 | Carrizozo | .86 | .89 |
| 884 | Tucumcari | .87 | .88 |
| **NEW YORK** | | | |
| 100-102 | New York | 1.31 | 1.25 |
| 103 | Staten Island | 1.25 | 1.20 |
| 104 | Bronx | 1.28 | 1.19 |
| 105 | Mount Vernon | 1.11 | 1.09 |
| 106 | White Plains | 1.17 | 1.11 |
| 107 | Yonkers | 1.19 | 1.14 |
| 108 | New Rochelle | 1.15 | 1.07 |
| 109 | Suffern | 1.09 | 1.01 |
| 110 | Queens | 1.27 | 1.25 |
| 111 | Long Island City | 1.32 | 1.26 |
| 112 | Brooklyn | 1.33 | 1.26 |
| 113 | Flushing | 1.30 | 1.25 |
| 114 | Jamaica | 1.30 | 1.25 |
| 115,117,118 | Hicksville | 1.17 | 1.16 |
| 116 | Far Rockaway | 1.29 | 1.25 |
| 119 | Riverhead | 1.20 | 1.18 |
| 120-122 | Albany | 1.04 | 1.02 |
| 123 | Schenectady | 1.05 | 1.01 |
| 124 | Kingston | 1.08 | 1.07 |
| 125-126 | Poughkeepsie | 1.15 | 1.09 |
| 127 | Monticello | 1.10 | 1.07 |
| 128 | Glens Falls | .95 | .95 |
| 129 | Plattsburgh | .97 | .93 |
| 130-132 | Syracuse | 1.00 | .98 |
| 133-135 | Utica | .99 | .98 |
| 136 | Watertown | .93 | .97 |
| 137-139 | Binghamton | 1.00 | .98 |
| 140-142 | Buffalo | 1.07 | 1.04 |
| 143 | Niagara Falls | .97 | .97 |
| 144-146 | Rochester | 1.00 | 1.00 |
| 147 | Jamestown | .90 | .93 |
| 148-149 | Elmira | .94 | .97 |
| **NORTH CAROLINA** | | | |
| 270,272-274 | Greensboro | .98 | .87 |
| 271 | Winston-Salem | .98 | .87 |
| 275-276 | Raleigh | .96 | .87 |
| 277 | Durham | .98 | .89 |
| 278 | Rocky Mount | .93 | .85 |
| 279 | Elizabeth City | .91 | .85 |
| 280 | Gastonia | 1.00 | .88 |
| 281-282 | Charlotte | .99 | .89 |
| 283 | Fayetteville | .95 | .88 |
| 284 | Wilmington | .95 | .85 |
| 285 | Kinston | .92 | .83 |
| 286 | Hickory | .94 | .86 |
| 287-288 | Asheville | .95 | .85 |
| 289 | Murphy | .96 | .83 |
| **NORTH DAKOTA** | | | |
| 580-581 | Fargo | .87 | .91 |
| 582 | Grand Forks | .89 | .91 |
| 583 | Devils Lake | .90 | .90 |
| 584 | Jamestown | .87 | .89 |
| 585 | Bismarck | .93 | .95 |

# Location Factors - Residential/Commercial

| STATE/ZIP | CITY | Residential | Commercial |
|---|---|---|---|
| **NORTH DAKOTA (CONT'D)** | | | |
| 586 | Dickinson | .86 | .89 |
| 587 | Minot | .85 | .90 |
| 588 | Williston | .89 | .90 |
| **OHIO** | | | |
| 430-432 | Columbus | .91 | .93 |
| 433 | Marion | .86 | .87 |
| 434-436 | Toledo | .93 | .93 |
| 437-438 | Zanesville | .84 | .87 |
| 439 | Steubenville | .86 | .89 |
| 440 | Lorain | .92 | .91 |
| 441 | Cleveland | .96 | .96 |
| 442-443 | Akron | .94 | .92 |
| 444-445 | Youngstown | .91 | .91 |
| 446-447 | Canton | .91 | .90 |
| 448-449 | Mansfield | .86 | .88 |
| 450 | Hamilton | .86 | .87 |
| 451-452 | Cincinnati | .87 | .90 |
| 453-454 | Dayton | .88 | .89 |
| 455 | Springfield | .88 | .89 |
| 456 | Chillicothe | .87 | .88 |
| 457 | Athens | .87 | .91 |
| 458 | Lima | .83 | .88 |
| **OKLAHOMA** | | | |
| 730-731 | Oklahoma City | .84 | .87 |
| 734 | Ardmore | .79 | .83 |
| 735 | Lawton | .82 | .86 |
| 736 | Clinton | .79 | .84 |
| 737 | Enid | .81 | .85 |
| 738 | Woodward | .80 | .84 |
| 739 | Guymon | .79 | .82 |
| 740-741 | Tulsa | .83 | .84 |
| 743 | Miami | .79 | .81 |
| 744 | Muskogee | .82 | .84 |
| 745 | McAlester | .77 | .81 |
| 746 | Ponca City | .78 | .80 |
| 747 | Durant | .76 | .80 |
| 748 | Shawnee | .76 | .82 |
| 749 | Poteau | .77 | .80 |
| **OREGON** | | | |
| 970-972 | Portland | 1.03 | 1.04 |
| 973 | Salem | 1.01 | 1.04 |
| 974 | Eugene | 1.02 | 1.02 |
| 975 | Medford | 1.00 | 1.02 |
| 976 | Klamath Falls | 1.00 | 1.01 |
| 977 | Bend | 1.04 | 1.01 |
| 978 | Pendleton | 1.00 | 1.00 |
| 979 | Vale | 1.00 | .94 |
| **PENNSYLVANIA** | | | |
| 150-152 | Pittsburgh | 1.01 | 1.01 |
| 153 | Washington | .93 | .96 |
| 154 | Uniontown | .89 | .95 |
| 155 | Bedford | .86 | .92 |
| 156 | Greensburg | .90 | .94 |
| 157 | Indiana | .91 | .95 |
| 158 | Dubois | .87 | .94 |
| 159 | Johnstown | .89 | .95 |
| 160 | Butler | .90 | .92 |
| 161 | New Castle | .91 | .92 |
| 162 | Kittanning | .89 | .93 |
| 163 | Oil City | .88 | .90 |
| 164-165 | Erie | .96 | .94 |
| 166 | Altoona | .89 | .93 |
| 167 | Bradford | .91 | .93 |
| 168 | State College | .93 | .94 |
| 169 | Wellsboro | .88 | .91 |
| 170-171 | Harrisburg | .98 | .99 |
| 172 | Chambersburg | .86 | .89 |
| 173-174 | York | .91 | .94 |
| 175-176 | Lancaster | .94 | .94 |
| 177 | Williamsport | .89 | .91 |
| 178 | Sunbury | .88 | .90 |
| 179 | Pottsville | .87 | .91 |
| 180 | Lehigh Valley | .97 | .97 |
| 181 | Allentown | 1.03 | 1.00 |
| 182 | Hazleton | .88 | .91 |
| 183 | Stroudsburg | .90 | .94 |
| 184-185 | Scranton | .97 | .97 |
| 186-187 | Wilkes-Barre | .92 | .93 |
| 188 | Montrose | .88 | .91 |
| 189 | Doylestown | 1.00 | 1.01 |

| STATE/ZIP | CITY | Residential | Commercial |
|---|---|---|---|
| **PENNSYLVANIA (CONT'D)** | | | |
| 190-191 | Philadelphia | 1.18 | 1.14 |
| 193 | Westchester | 1.04 | 1.04 |
| 194 | Norristown | 1.03 | 1.04 |
| 195-196 | Reading | .99 | .98 |
| **PUERTO RICO** | | | |
| 009 | San Juan | .81 | .87 |
| **RHODE ISLAND** | | | |
| 028 | Newport | 1.06 | 1.01 |
| 029 | Providence | 1.06 | 1.04 |
| **SOUTH CAROLINA** | | | |
| 290-292 | Columbia | .96 | .87 |
| 293 | Spartanburg | .96 | .87 |
| 294 | Charleston | .98 | .88 |
| 295 | Florence | .90 | .85 |
| 296 | Greenville | .94 | .87 |
| 297 | Rock Hill | .93 | .85 |
| 298 | Aiken | .94 | .84 |
| 299 | Beaufort | .95 | .85 |
| **SOUTH DAKOTA** | | | |
| 570-571 | Sioux Falls | .91 | .92 |
| 572 | Watertown | .83 | .86 |
| 573 | Mitchell | .81 | .83 |
| 574 | Aberdeen | .88 | .90 |
| 575 | Pierre | .93 | .91 |
| 576 | Mobridge | .78 | .83 |
| 577 | Rapid City | .86 | .87 |
| **TENNESSEE** | | | |
| 370-372 | Nashville | .87 | .90 |
| 373-374 | Chattanooga | .84 | .87 |
| 375,380-381 | Memphis | .85 | .89 |
| 376 | Johnson City | .75 | .83 |
| 377-379 | Knoxville | .81 | .85 |
| 382 | McKenzie | .72 | .80 |
| 383 | Jackson | .82 | .87 |
| 384 | Columbia | .76 | .82 |
| 385 | Cookeville | .69 | .80 |
| **TEXAS** | | | |
| 750 | McKinney | .78 | .83 |
| 751 | Waxahachie | .82 | .86 |
| 752-753 | Dallas | .85 | .87 |
| 754 | Greenville | .78 | .83 |
| 755 | Texarkana | .82 | .83 |
| 756 | Longview | .77 | .82 |
| 757 | Tyler | .80 | .83 |
| 758 | Palestine | .75 | .80 |
| 759 | Lufkin | .77 | .81 |
| 760-761 | Fort Worth | .83 | .85 |
| 762 | Denton | .84 | .82 |
| 763 | Wichita Falls | .84 | .83 |
| 764 | Eastland | .81 | .80 |
| 765 | Temple | .79 | .78 |
| 766-767 | Waco | .84 | .83 |
| 768 | Brownwood | .79 | .81 |
| 769 | San Angelo | .79 | .82 |
| 770-772 | Houston | .83 | .86 |
| 773 | Huntsville | .76 | .81 |
| 774 | Wharton | .75 | .82 |
| 775 | Galveston | .78 | .82 |
| 776-777 | Beaumont | .84 | .84 |
| 778 | Bryan | .74 | .80 |
| 779 | Victoria | .77 | .81 |
| 780 | Laredo | .80 | .83 |
| 781-782 | San Antonio | .82 | .85 |
| 783-784 | Corpus Christi | .84 | .85 |
| 785 | McAllen | .83 | .81 |
| 786-787 | Austin | .81 | .84 |
| 788 | Del Rio | .79 | .81 |
| 789 | Giddings | .78 | .80 |
| 790-791 | Amarillo | .82 | .85 |
| 792 | Childress | .81 | .82 |
| 793-794 | Lubbock | .82 | .86 |
| 795-796 | Abilene | .83 | .85 |
| 797 | Midland | .86 | .87 |
| 798-799,885 | El Paso | .83 | .86 |
| **UTAH** | | | |
| 840-841 | Salt Lake City | .87 | .91 |
| 842,844 | Ogden | .85 | .88 |
| 843 | Logan | .85 | .89 |

# Location Factors - Residential/Commercial

| STATE/ZIP | CITY | Residential | Commercial |
|---|---|---|---|
| **UTAH (CONT'd)** | | | |
| 845 | Price | .84 | .87 |
| 846-847 | Provo | .86 | .89 |
| **VERMONT** | | | |
| 050 | White River Jct. | .93 | .88 |
| 051 | Bellows Falls | .97 | .90 |
| 052 | Bennington | .96 | .90 |
| 053 | Brattleboro | .97 | .91 |
| 054 | Burlington | .96 | .93 |
| 056 | Montpelier | .98 | .92 |
| 057 | Rutland | .94 | .91 |
| 058 | St. Johnsbury | .94 | .88 |
| 059 | Guildhall | .94 | .87 |
| **VIRGINIA** | | | |
| 220-221 | Fairfax | .99 | .92 |
| 222 | Arlington | 1.01 | .93 |
| 223 | Alexandria | 1.05 | .93 |
| 224-225 | Fredericksburg | .98 | .90 |
| 226 | Winchester | .96 | .88 |
| 227 | Culpeper | .99 | .91 |
| 228 | Harrisonburg | .95 | .88 |
| 229 | Charlottesville | .93 | .87 |
| 230-232 | Richmond | .98 | .88 |
| 233-235 | Norfolk | .98 | .88 |
| 236 | Newport News | .98 | .87 |
| 237 | Portsmouth | .92 | .86 |
| 238 | Petersburg | .95 | .87 |
| 239 | Farmville | .96 | .84 |
| 240-241 | Roanoke | .98 | .88 |
| 242 | Bristol | .90 | .82 |
| 243 | Pulaski | .92 | .86 |
| 244 | Staunton | .92 | .86 |
| 245 | Lynchburg | .94 | .86 |
| 246 | Grundy | .91 | .84 |
| **WASHINGTON** | | | |
| 980-981,987 | Seattle | 1.10 | 1.07 |
| 982 | Everett | 1.12 | 1.04 |
| 983-984 | Tacoma | 1.07 | 1.04 |
| 985 | Olympia | 1.04 | 1.04 |
| 986 | Vancouver | 1.04 | 1.04 |
| 988 | Wenatchee | .99 | .96 |
| 989 | Yakima | 1.01 | 1.01 |
| 990-992 | Spokane | .95 | .93 |
| 993 | Richland | .93 | .95 |
| 994 | Clarkston | .87 | .88 |
| **WEST VIRGINIA** | | | |
| 247-248 | Bluefield | .89 | .91 |
| 249 | Lewisburg | .88 | .92 |
| 250-253 | Charleston | .95 | .95 |
| 254 | Martinsburg | .87 | .89 |
| 255-257 | Huntington | .95 | .95 |
| 258-259 | Beckley | .89 | .91 |
| 260 | Wheeling | .91 | .95 |
| 261 | Parkersburg | .91 | .94 |
| 262 | Buckhannon | .90 | .94 |
| 263-264 | Clarksburg | .89 | .94 |
| 265 | Morgantown | .90 | .94 |
| 266 | Gassaway | .89 | .92 |
| 267 | Romney | .89 | .92 |
| 268 | Petersburg | .90 | .92 |
| **WISCONSIN** | | | |
| 530,532 | Milwaukee | 1.04 | 1.02 |
| 531 | Kenosha | 1.04 | .99 |
| 534 | Racine | 1.00 | .99 |
| 535 | Beloit | .94 | .95 |
| 537 | Madison | 1.00 | .99 |
| 538 | Lancaster | .93 | .91 |
| 539 | Portage | .90 | .92 |
| 540 | New Richmond | .92 | .92 |
| 541-543 | Green Bay | 1.06 | .99 |
| 544 | Wausau | .93 | .92 |
| 545 | Rhinelander | .92 | .93 |
| 546 | La Crosse | .93 | .96 |
| 547 | Eau Claire | .97 | .97 |
| 548 | Superior | .91 | .93 |
| 549 | Oshkosh | .93 | .92 |
| **WYOMING** | | | |
| 820 | Cheyenne | .89 | .90 |
| 821 | Yellowstone Nat. Pk. | .85 | .87 |
| 822 | Wheatland | .84 | .87 |

| STATE/ZIP | CITY | Residential | Commercial |
|---|---|---|---|
| **WYOMING (CONT'd)** | | | |
| 823 | Rawlins | .86 | .88 |
| 824 | Worland | .85 | .87 |
| 825 | Riverton | .84 | .88 |
| 826 | Casper | .87 | .90 |
| 827 | Newcastle | .85 | .87 |
| 828 | Sheridan | .89 | .89 |
| 829-831 | Rock Springs | .91 | .90 |
| **CANADIAN FACTORS (reflect Canadian currency)** | | | |
| **ALBERTA** | | | |
| | Calgary | 1.05 | 1.19 |
| | Edmonton | 1.10 | 1.19 |
| | Fort McMurray | 1.07 | 1.14 |
| | Lethbridge | 1.05 | 1.10 |
| | Lloydminster | 1.00 | 1.05 |
| | Medicine Hat | 1.01 | 1.05 |
| | Red Deer | 1.01 | 1.05 |
| **BRITISH COLUMBIA** | | | |
| | Kamloops | .96 | 1.06 |
| | Prince George | .96 | 1.07 |
| | Vancouver | 1.05 | 1.15 |
| | Victoria | 1.01 | 1.10 |
| **MANITOBA** | | | |
| | Brandon | 1.03 | 1.07 |
| | Portage la Prairie | .96 | 1.00 |
| | Winnipeg | .97 | 1.09 |
| **NEW BRUNSWICK** | | | |
| | Bathurst | .88 | .96 |
| | Dalhousie | .90 | .98 |
| | Fredericton | .94 | 1.07 |
| | Moncton | .92 | 1.01 |
| | Newcastle | .88 | .96 |
| | St. John | 1.00 | 1.03 |
| **NEWFOUNDLAND** | | | |
| | Corner Brook | 1.01 | 1.09 |
| | St. Johns | 1.03 | 1.13 |
| **NORTHWEST TERRITORIES** | | | |
| | Yellowknife | 1.08 | 1.19 |
| **NOVA SCOTIA** | | | |
| | Bridgewater | .90 | 1.00 |
| | Dartmouth | .96 | 1.07 |
| | Halifax | 1.02 | 1.09 |
| | New Glasgow | .96 | 1.06 |
| | Sydney | .95 | 1.05 |
| | Truro | .90 | 1.00 |
| | Yarmouth | .96 | 1.06 |
| **ONTARIO** | | | |
| | Barrie | 1.10 | 1.07 |
| | Brantford | 1.06 | 1.09 |
| | Cornwall | 1.06 | 1.07 |
| | Hamilton | 1.06 | 1.17 |
| | Kingston | 1.06 | 1.08 |
| | Kitchener | 1.01 | 1.09 |
| | London | 1.05 | 1.16 |
| | North Bay | 1.10 | 1.13 |
| | Oshawa | 1.05 | 1.11 |
| | Ottawa | 1.03 | 1.16 |
| | Owen Sound | 1.09 | 1.06 |
| | Peterborough | 1.04 | 1.07 |
| | Sarnia | 1.07 | 1.09 |
| | Sault Ste. Marie | 1.01 | 1.05 |
| | St. Catharines | 1.01 | 1.08 |
| | Sudbury | .99 | 1.07 |
| | Thunder Bay | 1.04 | 1.08 |
| | Timmins | 1.04 | 1.07 |
| | Toronto | 1.07 | 1.18 |
| | Windsor | 1.03 | 1.08 |
| **PRINCE EDWARD ISLAND** | | | |
| | Charlottetown | .95 | 1.04 |
| | Summerside | .91 | 1.03 |
| **QUEBEC** | | | |
| | Cap-de-la-Madeleine | 1.06 | 1.03 |
| | Charlesbourg | 1.06 | 1.03 |
| | Chicoutimi | 1.10 | 1.05 |
| | Gatineau | 1.05 | 1.03 |

| STATE/ZIP | CITY | Residential | Commercial |
|---|---|---|---|
| **QUEBEC (CONT'D)** | | | |
| | Granby | 1.05 | |
| | Hull | 1.05 | 1.03 |
| | Joliette | 1.06 | 1.03 |
| | Laval | 1.05 | 1.03 |
| | Montreal | 1.02 | 1.14 |
| | Quebec City | 1.02 | 1.14 |
| | Rimouski | 1.10 | 1.06 |
| | Rouyn-Noranda | 1.05 | 1.03 |
| | Saint-Hyacinthe | 1.06 | 1.02 |
| | Sherbrooke | 1.05 | 1.03 |
| | Sorel | 1.06 | 1.03 |
| | Saint-Jerome | 1.05 | 1.03 |
| | Trois-Rivieres | 1.13 | 1.09 |
| **SASKATCHEWAN** | | | |
| | Moose Jaw | .88 | .96 |
| | Prince Albert | .87 | .95 |
| | Regina | 1.08 | 1.18 |
| | Saskatoon | 1.00 | 1.05 |
| **YUKON** | | | |
| | Whitehorse | 1.02 | 1.16 |

# Historical Cost Indexes

The following tables are the estimated Historical Cost Indexes based on a 30-city national average with a base of 100 on January 1, 1993.

The indexes may be used to:

1. Estimate and compare construction costs for different years in the same city.
2. Estimate and compare construction costs in different cities for the same year.
3. Estimate and compare construction costs in different cities for different years.
4. Compare construction trends in any city with the national average.

## EXAMPLES

1. Estimate and compare construction costs for different years in the same city.

A. To estimate the construction cost of a building in Lexington, KY in 1970, knowing that it cost $915,000 in 2023.

Index Lexington, KY in 1970 = 26.9
Index Lexington, KY in 2023 = 257.4

$$\frac{\text{Index 1970}}{\text{Index 2023}} \times \text{Cost 2023} = \text{Cost 1970}$$

$$\frac{26.9}{257.4} \times \$915{,}000 = \$95{,}624$$

Construction Cost in Lexington, KY in 1970 = $95,624

B. To estimate the current construction cost of a building in Boston, MA that was built in 1980 for $900,000.

Index Boston, MA in 1980 = 64.0
Index Boston, MA in 2023 = 337.1

$$\frac{\text{Index 2023}}{\text{Index 1980}} \times \text{Cost 1980} = \text{Cost 2023}$$

$$\frac{337.1}{64.0} \times \$900{,}000 = \$4{,}740{,}469$$

Construction Cost in Boston in 2023 = $4,740,469

2. Estimate and compare construction costs in different cities for the same year.

To compare the construction cost of a building in Topeka, KS in 2023 with the known cost of $800,000 in Baltimore, MD in 2023

Index Topeka, KS in 2023 = 264.6
Index Baltimore, MD in 2023 = 280.5

$$\frac{\text{Index Topeka}}{\text{Index Baltimore}} \times \text{Cost Baltimore} = \text{Cost Topeka}$$

$$\frac{264.6}{280.5} \times \$800{,}000 = \$754{,}652$$

Construction Cost in Topeka in 2023 = $754,652

3. Estimate and compare construction costs in different cities for different years.

To compare the construction cost of a building in Detroit, MI in 2023 with the known construction cost of $5,000,000 for the same building in San Francisco, CA in 1980.

Index Detroit, MI in 2023 = 298.0
Index San Francisco, CA in 1980 = 75.2

$$\frac{\text{Index Detroit 2023}}{\text{Index San Francisco 1980}} \times \text{Cost San Francisco 1980} = \text{Cost Detroit 2023}$$

$$\frac{298.0}{75.2} \times \$5{,}000{,}000 = \$19{,}813{,}830$$

Construction Cost in Detroit in 2023 = $19,813,830

4. Compare construction trends in any city with the national average.

To compare the construction cost in Las Vegas, NV from 1975 to 2023 with the increase in the National Average during the same time period.

Index Las Vegas, NV for 1975 = 42.8 For 2023 = 310.8
Index 30 City Average for 1975 = 43.7 For 2023 = 318.8

A. National Average escalation From 1975 to 2023 $= \frac{\text{Index — 30 City 2023}}{\text{Index — 30 City 1975}} = \frac{318.8}{43.7}$

National Average escalation From 1975 to 2023 = 7.30 or increased by 730%

B. Escalation for Las Vegas, NV From 1975 to 2023 $= \frac{\text{Index Las Vegas, NV 2023}}{\text{Index Las Vegas, NV 1975}} = \frac{310.8}{42.8}$

Las Vegas escalation From 1975 to 2023 = 7.26 or increased by 726%

Conclusion: Construction costs in Las Vegas are higher than National Average costs and increased at a greater rate from 1975 to 2023 than the National Average.

| | National | Alabama | | | | | Alaska | Arizona | | Arkansas | | California | | | | |
|---|---|---|---|---|---|---|---|---|---|---|---|---|---|---|---|---|
| Year | 30 City Average | Birming-ham | Hunts-ville | Mobile | Mont-gomery | Tusca-loosa | Anchor-age | Phoenix | Tuscon | Fort Smith | Little Rock | Anaheim | Bakers-field | Fresno | Los Angeles | Oxnard |
| Jan 2023 | 318.8E | 263.2E | 261.3E | 257.3E | 261E | 259.9E | 339.5E | 268.6E | 257.6E | 242.8E | 245.4E | 327.6E | 328.1E | 332.3E | 338.9E | 326.7E |
| 2022 | 276.9 | 245.3 | 243.5 | 239.8 | 243.3 | 242.2 | 316.4 | 250.3 | 240.1 | 226.3 | 228.7 | 305.3 | 305.8 | 309.7 | 315.9 | 304.5 |
| 2021 | 238.3 | 204.8 | 202.8 | 202 | 205.5 | 202.6 | 272.2 | 208.2 | 203.9 | 191.8 | 193.6 | 263 | 261 | 265.9 | 267.3 | 261.1 |
| 2020 | 234.3 | 201.7 | 201.1 | 200.1 | 202.5 | 200.2 | 272.3 | 205.3 | 200.3 | 187.6 | 191.5 | 260.3 | 256.9 | 263.1 | 262.9 | 258.6 |
| 2019 | 227.3 | 190.0 | 189.2 | 186.5 | 188.7 | 189.8 | 258.5 | 196.1 | 191.3 | 180.4 | 183.6 | 247.3 | 244.6 | 248.1 | 252.3 | 244.9 |
| 2018 | 217.7 | 186.4 | 185.6 | 183.0 | 185.1 | 186.2 | 253.6 | 192.4 | 187.7 | 177.0 | 180.1 | 242.6 | 240.0 | 243.4 | 247.5 | 240.3 |
| 2017 | 209.4 | 178.6 | 178.3 | 177.9 | 178.5 | 179.6 | 246.2 | 183.8 | 181.3 | 170.6 | 172.8 | 233.6 | 229.2 | 232.0 | 237.8 | 231.9 |
| 2016 | 207.7 | 185.6 | 184.2 | 184.1 | 183.5 | 186.3 | 246.3 | 181.7 | 178.1 | 169.8 | 174.6 | 223.6 | 221.3 | 224.3 | 226.2 | 222.5 |
| 2015 | 204.0 | 184.8 | 182.1 | 185.4 | 182.7 | 184.5 | 244.7 | 181.0 | 177.9 | 167.6 | 171.1 | 217.3 | 214.6 | 218.8 | 218.5 | 215.7 |
| 2014 | 203.0 | 180.3 | 175.8 | 170.6 | 163.1 | 165.9 | 241.0 | 180.0 | 177.0 | 165.1 | 168.4 | 214.2 | 215.2 | 217.0 | 217.3 | 214.8 |
| 2013 | 196.9 | 173.3 | 168.7 | 165.7 | 158.7 | 161.6 | 235.3 | 174.1 | 169.2 | 161.2 | 163.2 | 207.0 | 205.6 | 210.3 | 210.7 | 207.8 |
| 2012 | 194.0 | 169.1 | 162.7 | 163.2 | 153.8 | 154.6 | 232.5 | 172.2 | 166.4 | 158.7 | 161.0 | 204.1 | 202.9 | 207.3 | 207.2 | 204.7 |
| 2011 | 185.7 | 163.0 | 156.3 | 156.9 | 147.6 | 148.3 | 225.1 | 163.8 | 159.5 | 152.0 | 154.1 | 196.1 | 194.6 | 199.8 | 199.2 | 197.0 |
| 2010 | 181.6 | 159.6 | 152.9 | 153.1 | 144.4 | 144.9 | 218.3 | 160.7 | 157.3 | 150.3 | 152.5 | 192.8 | 190.8 | 195.0 | 194.9 | 192.8 |
| 2009 | 182.5 | 162.7 | 157.2 | 155.6 | 148.8 | 149.4 | 222.9 | 161.3 | 156.8 | 149.2 | 156.3 | 194.5 | 192.3 | 195.0 | 196.6 | 194.5 |
| 2008 | 171.0 | 150.3 | 146.9 | 143.7 | 138.4 | 138.8 | 210.8 | 152.2 | 148.4 | 138.6 | 145.4 | 182.7 | 179.8 | 183.2 | 184.7 | 182.6 |
| 2007 | 165.0 | 146.9 | 143.3 | 140.3 | 134.8 | 135.4 | 206.8 | 147.7 | 143.1 | 134.8 | 141.7 | 175.1 | 173.7 | 176.7 | 177.5 | 176.2 |
| 2006 | 156.2 | 135.7 | 133.6 | 126.7 | 124.0 | 122.2 | 196.4 | 137.9 | 134.8 | 123.2 | 127.2 | 166.8 | 164.9 | 169.8 | 167.3 | 167.4 |
| 2005 | 146.7 | 127.9 | 125.4 | 119.3 | 116.6 | 114.6 | 185.6 | 128.5 | 124.1 | 115.4 | 119.4 | 156.5 | 153.0 | 157.9 | 157.1 | 156.4 |
| 2004 | 132.8 | 115.9 | 112.9 | 107.0 | 104.9 | 102.9 | 167.0 | 116.5 | 113.6 | 103.8 | 108.6 | 142.1 | 139.5 | 143.8 | 142.0 | 140.9 |
| 2003 | 129.7 | 113.1 | 110.7 | 104.8 | 102.6 | 100.8 | 163.5 | 113.9 | 110.6 | 101.8 | 105.8 | 139.4 | 137.2 | 142.1 | 139.6 | 138.7 |
| 2002 | 126.7 | 110.0 | 103.4 | 103.6 | 101.7 | 99.7 | 159.5 | 113.3 | 110.2 | 100.4 | 102.1 | 136.5 | 133.4 | 136.0 | 136.4 | 136.3 |
| 2001 | 122.2 | 106.0 | 100.5 | 100.6 | 98.3 | 95.9 | 152.6 | 109.0 | 106.4 | 97.3 | 98.7 | 132.5 | 129.3 | 132.8 | 132.4 | 132.4 |
| 2000 | 118.9 | 104.1 | 98.9 | 99.1 | 94.2 | 94.6 | 148.3 | 106.9 | 104.9 | 94.4 | 95.7 | 129.4 | 125.2 | 129.4 | 129.9 | 129.7 |
| 1990 | 93.2 | 79.4 | 77.6 | 82.7 | 78.4 | 75.2 | 125.8 | 86.4 | 87.0 | 77.1 | 77.9 | 107.7 | 102.7 | 103.3 | 107.5 | 107.4 |
| 1985 | 81.8 | 71.1 | 70.5 | 72.7 | 70.9 | 67.9 | 116.0 | 78.1 | 77.7 | 69.6 | 71.0 | 95.4 | 92.2 | 92.6 | 94.6 | 96.6 |
| 1980 | 60.7 | 55.2 | 54.1 | 56.8 | 56.8 | 54.0 | 91.4 | 63.7 | 62.4 | 53.1 | 55.8 | 68.7 | 69.4 | 68.7 | 67.4 | 69.9 |
| 1975 | 43.7 | 40.0 | 40.9 | 41.8 | 40.1 | 37.8 | 57.3 | 44.5 | 45.2 | 39.0 | 38.7 | 47.6 | 46.6 | 47.7 | 48.3 | 47.0 |
| 1970 | 27.8 | 24.1 | 25.1 | 25.8 | 25.4 | 24.2 | 43.0 | 27.2 | 28.5 | 24.3 | 22.3 | 31.0 | 30.8 | 31.1 | 29.0 | 31.0 |
| 1965 | 21.5 | 19.6 | 19.3 | 19.6 | 19.5 | 18.7 | 34.9 | 21.8 | 22.0 | 18.7 | 18.5 | 23.9 | 23.7 | 24.0 | 22.7 | 23.9 |
| 1960 | 19.5 | 17.9 | 17.5 | 17.8 | 17.7 | 16.9 | 31.7 | 19.9 | 20.0 | 17.0 | 16.8 | 21.7 | 21.5 | 21.8 | 20.6 | 21.7 |
| 1955 | 16.3 | 14.8 | 14.7 | 14.9 | 14.9 | 14.2 | 26.6 | 16.7 | 16.7 | 14.3 | 14.5 | 18.2 | 18.1 | 18.3 | 17.3 | 18.2 |
| ▼ 1950 | 13.5 | 12.2 | 12.1 | 12.3 | 12.3 | 11.7 | 21.9 | 13.8 | 13.8 | 11.8 | 11.6 | 15.1 | 15.0 | 15.1 | 14.3 | 15.1 |

| | National | California | | | | | | | Colorado | | | Connecticut | | | | |
|---|---|---|---|---|---|---|---|---|---|---|---|---|---|---|---|---|
| Year | 30 City Average | River-side | Sacra-mento | San Diego | San Francisco | Santa Barbara | Stockton | Vallejo | Colorado Springs | Denver | Pueblo | Bridge-Port | Bristol | Hartford | New Britain | New Haven |
| Jan 2023 | 318.8E | 326.8E | 331.8E | 329.8E | 379.7E | 324.9E | 336.9E | 343.2E | 261E | 273.5E | 262.6E | 311.7E | 311.3E | 314.6E | 309.9E | 312.3E |
| 2022 | 276.9 | 304.6 | 309.2 | 307.4 | 353.9 | 302.8 | 314 | 319.9 | 243.3 | 254.9 | 244.7 | 290.5 | 290.1 | 293.2 | 288.8 | 291.1 |
| 2021 | 238.3 | 262.9 | 272.7 | 261.9 | 311.7 | 259.3 | 271.6 | 282.5 | 210.4 | 218.2 | 208.1 | 253.7 | 252.8 | 256.6 | 252.2 | 254.8 |
| 2020 | 234.3 | 260.2 | 269.5 | 256.9 | 305.7 | 257.6 | 267.8 | 276 | 208 | 213.5 | 206.3 | 249.9 | 248 | 250.9 | 247.4 | 250.2 |
| 2019 | 227.3 | 246.7 | 253.7 | 245.8 | 286.7 | 243.9 | 252.0 | 259.7 | 197.1 | 201.4 | 196.7 | 237.0 | 236.5 | 237.4 | 236.0 | 238.3 |
| 2018 | 217.7 | 242.1 | 248.9 | 241.2 | 281.3 | 239.3 | 247.3 | 254.8 | 193.4 | 197.6 | 193.0 | 232.5 | 232.0 | 232.9 | 231.6 | 233.8 |
| 2017 | 209.4 | 233.2 | 237.9 | 229.3 | 270.8 | 231.1 | 236.2 | 246.8 | 187.3 | 187.8 | 183.1 | 224.4 | 222.9 | 223.9 | 222.5 | 225.0 |
| 2016 | 207.7 | 223.3 | 227.3 | 218.3 | 256.6 | 221.9 | 227.9 | 236.0 | 189.4 | 191.0 | 186.2 | 226.4 | 225.6 | 226.1 | 225.0 | 226.9 |
| 2015 | 204.0 | 217.1 | 221.0 | 213.1 | 250.2 | 215.7 | 222.8 | 230.2 | 185.1 | 186.6 | 183.5 | 224.1 | 223.3 | 224.2 | 222.8 | 225.0 |
| 2014 | 203.0 | 214.1 | 221.5 | 211.4 | 248.0 | 214.7 | 218.4 | 227.9 | 187.8 | 189.1 | 184.7 | 223.8 | 222.8 | 223.9 | 222.4 | 224.1 |
| 2013 | 196.9 | 207.0 | 215.0 | 203.2 | 241.0 | 207.9 | 211.8 | 222.2 | 180.7 | 183.4 | 180.0 | 217.8 | 217.2 | 218.4 | 216.8 | 218.5 |
| 2012 | 194.0 | 204.1 | 211.9 | 198.9 | 237.6 | 204.8 | 208.8 | 218.9 | 179.4 | 182.2 | 177.9 | 213.9 | 213.3 | 214.4 | 212.9 | 214.7 |
| 2011 | 185.7 | 195.8 | 203.1 | 192.3 | 227.9 | 196.2 | 201.3 | 210.3 | 171.7 | 174.1 | 170.7 | 205.2 | 204.2 | 205.1 | 203.9 | 205.8 |
| 2010 | 181.6 | 192.7 | 196.7 | 188.2 | 223.0 | 192.9 | 195.9 | 204.6 | 170.5 | 172.6 | 168.1 | 198.8 | 199.1 | 199.8 | 198.8 | 200.7 |
| 2009 | 182.5 | 193.1 | 198.1 | 191.6 | 224.9 | 193.6 | 194.5 | 202.7 | 168.4 | 172.0 | 166.7 | 199.0 | 197.7 | 198.7 | 197.4 | 199.3 |
| 2008 | 171.0 | 181.3 | 186.0 | 179.9 | 210.6 | 181.5 | 183.2 | 191.6 | 158.8 | 161.9 | 157.9 | 185.8 | 184.8 | 185.7 | 184.5 | 186.1 |
| 2007 | 165.0 | 174.7 | 179.1 | 173.6 | 201.1 | 175.2 | 178.2 | 185.9 | 152.6 | 155.9 | 152.3 | 179.6 | 178.3 | 179.6 | 178.0 | 179.5 |
| 2006 | 156.2 | 166.0 | 172.2 | 164.0 | 191.2 | 166.4 | 171.0 | 177.9 | 146.1 | 149.2 | 145.0 | 169.5 | 168.0 | 169.5 | 167.7 | 169.8 |
| 2005 | 146.7 | 155.4 | 161.1 | 153.8 | 179.7 | 155.7 | 160.0 | 167.2 | 138.3 | 141.1 | 136.4 | 160.8 | 159.4 | 159.6 | 159.1 | 160.8 |
| 2004 | 132.8 | 141.0 | 147.2 | 139.0 | 163.6 | 141.4 | 144.2 | 148.6 | 125.6 | 127.2 | 123.5 | 143.6 | 142.9 | 142.4 | 142.7 | 144.3 |
| 2003 | 129.7 | 138.7 | 144.9 | 136.6 | 162.1 | 139.2 | 141.8 | 146.4 | 123.1 | 123.7 | 120.7 | 141.3 | 140.2 | 140.3 | 140.0 | 141.6 |
| 2002 | 126.7 | 135.3 | 138.4 | 134.2 | 157.9 | 135.9 | 136.9 | 143.8 | 118.7 | 121.3 | 116.7 | 133.8 | 133.6 | 133.1 | 133.3 | 134.8 |
| 2001 | 122.2 | 131.4 | 135.5 | 129.7 | 151.8 | 131.5 | 134.1 | 140.2 | 113.3 | 117.2 | 113.1 | 128.6 | 128.5 | 128.5 | 128.3 | 128.6 |
| 2000 | 118.9 | 128.0 | 131.5 | 127.1 | 146.9 | 128.7 | 130.7 | 137.1 | 109.8 | 111.8 | 108.8 | 122.7 | 122.6 | 122.9 | 122.4 | 122.7 |
| 1990 | 93.2 | 107.0 | 104.9 | 105.6 | 121.8 | 106.4 | 105.4 | 111.4 | 86.9 | 88.8 | 88.8 | 96.3 | 95.9 | 96.6 | 95.9 | 96.5 |
| 1985 | 81.8 | 94.8 | 92.2 | 94.2 | 106.2 | 93.2 | 93.7 | 97.0 | 79.6 | 81.0 | 80.4 | 86.1 | 86.2 | 87.2 | 86.1 | 86.3 |
| 1980 | 60.7 | 68.7 | 71.3 | 68.1 | 75.2 | 71.1 | 71.2 | 71.9 | 60.7 | 60.9 | 59.5 | 61.5 | 60.7 | 61.9 | 60.7 | 61.4 |
| 1975 | 43.7 | 47.3 | 49.1 | 47.7 | 49.8 | 46.1 | 47.6 | 46.5 | 43.1 | 42.7 | 42.5 | 45.2 | 45.5 | 46.0 | 45.2 | 46.0 |
| 1970 | 27.8 | 31.0 | 32.1 | 30.7 | 31.6 | 31.3 | 31.8 | 31.8 | 27.6 | 26.1 | 27.3 | 29.2 | 28.2 | 29.6 | 28.2 | 29.3 |
| 1965 | 21.5 | 23.9 | 24.8 | 24.0 | 23.7 | 24.1 | 24.5 | 24.5 | 21.3 | 20.9 | 21.0 | 22.4 | 21.7 | 22.6 | 21.7 | 23.2 |
| 1960 | 19.5 | 21.7 | 22.5 | 21.7 | 21.5 | 21.9 | 22.3 | 22.2 | 19.3 | 19.0 | 19.1 | 20.0 | 19.8 | 20.0 | 19.8 | 20.0 |
| 1955 | 16.3 | 18.2 | 18.9 | 18.2 | 18.0 | 18.4 | 18.7 | 18.6 | 16.2 | 15.9 | 16.0 | 16.8 | 16.6 | 16.8 | 16.6 | 16.8 |
| ▼ 1950 | 13.5 | 15.0 | 15.6 | 15.0 | 14.9 | 15.2 | 15.4 | 15.4 | 13.4 | 13.2 | 13.2 | 13.9 | 13.7 | 13.8 | 13.7 | 13.9 |

| Year | National | Connecticut | | | Delaware | D.C. | Florida | | | | | | Georgia | | | |
|---|---|---|---|---|---|---|---|---|---|---|---|---|---|---|---|---|
| | 30 City Average | Norwalk | Stamford | Waterbury | Wilmington | Washington | Fort Lauderdale | Jacksonville | Miami | Orlando | Tallahassee | Tampa | Albany | Atlanta | Columbus | Macon |
| Jan 2023 | 318.8E | 311.2E | 311.8E | 311.4E | 307.6E | 288.1E | 256E | 253.8E | 261.2E | 259.3E | 257.9E | 260.8E | 259E | 267.4E | 260.7E | 257.6E |
| 2022 | 276.9 | 290.0 | 290.6 | 290.2 | 286.7 | 268.5 | 238.6 | 236.5 | 243.4 | 241.7 | 240.4 | 243.1 | 241.4 | 249.2 | 243.0 | 240.1 |
| 2021 | 238.3 | 253.1 | 260.5 | 253.6 | 245.4 | 227.7 | 202.9 | 199.0 | 200.6 | 198.9 | 200.2 | 200.0 | 203.1 | 211.6 | 204.2 | 203.6 |
| 2020 | 234.3 | 249.4 | 255.9 | 249.1 | 239.4 | 223.8 | 195.3 | 197.6 | 199.2 | 197 | 197.6 | 199.2 | 200.5 | 205.6 | 201.8 | 200.1 |
| 2019 | 227.3 | 236.7 | 243.3 | 237.1 | 229.9 | 211.2 | 182.8 | 182.6 | 183.6 | 186.0 | 184.5 | 186.2 | 190.2 | 196.0 | 190.5 | 190.3 |
| 2018 | 217.7 | 232.2 | 238.7 | 232.6 | 225.6 | 207.2 | 179.4 | 179.2 | 180.1 | 182.5 | 181.0 | 182.7 | 186.6 | 192.3 | 186.9 | 186.7 |
| 2017 | 209.4 | 224.2 | 230.8 | 224.2 | 217.7 | 199.1 | 173.7 | 172.7 | 173.4 | 176.5 | 174.1 | 177.0 | 179.4 | 185.1 | 180.1 | 179.4 |
| 2016 | 207.7 | 232.7 | 233.3 | 225.7 | 215.7 | 201.3 | 177.7 | 176.3 | 179.1 | 180.4 | 173.4 | 180.6 | 176.3 | 185.0 | 173.6 | 172.4 |
| 2015 | 204.0 | 230.2 | 230.3 | 223.8 | 211.7 | 197.3 | 176.1 | 174.2 | 178.1 | 178.3 | 172.5 | 178.9 | 168.6 | 178.3 | 171.3 | 170.0 |
| 2014 | 203.0 | 230.3 | 230.5 | 223.2 | 210.2 | 197.0 | 176.5 | 171.0 | 178.4 | 176.5 | 164.4 | 183.2 | 166.6 | 177.5 | 170.2 | 168.2 |
| 2013 | 196.9 | 223.1 | 224.2 | 217.3 | 203.6 | 191.7 | 173.2 | 168.4 | 175.8 | 174.8 | 160.8 | 180.2 | 163.2 | 173.3 | 166.7 | 164.9 |
| 2018 | 194.0 | 219.8 | 220.0 | 213.4 | 201.0 | 189.6 | 170.9 | 165.8 | 173.7 | 172.8 | 158.5 | 177.8 | 158.3 | 170.7 | 160.6 | 159.3 |
| 2011 | 185.7 | 211.0 | 211.2 | 204.6 | 193.3 | 182.3 | 164.4 | 159.4 | 167.0 | 166.1 | 151.7 | 171.4 | 151.8 | 164.0 | 154.3 | 152.7 |
| 2010 | 181.6 | 198.3 | 203.8 | 199.4 | 187.7 | 179.0 | 160.3 | 155.4 | 163.3 | 162.5 | 148.1 | 167.5 | 148.3 | 160.1 | 150.9 | 149.4 |
| 2009 | 182.5 | 198.8 | 204.3 | 198.4 | 188.9 | 181.4 | 160.7 | 152.0 | 165.2 | 163.9 | 145.1 | 165.1 | 152.0 | 164.5 | 155.6 | 153.5 |
| 2008 | 171.0 | 185.2 | 189.2 | 185.3 | 177.5 | 170.4 | 149.6 | 142.5 | 152.9 | 153.0 | 135.3 | 155.6 | 140.4 | 153.2 | 143.9 | 142.5 |
| 2007 | 165.0 | 178.6 | 183.3 | 179.1 | 173.4 | 163.1 | 145.6 | 139.0 | 148.9 | 148.1 | 131.7 | 152.0 | 135.8 | 148.0 | 140.1 | 138.1 |
| 2006 | 156.2 | 169.7 | 173.7 | 169.1 | 158.3 | 153.0 | 136.0 | 126.5 | 136.7 | 134.3 | 118.4 | 136.6 | 123.6 | 139.9 | 126.3 | 124.3 |
| 2005 | 146.7 | 160.9 | 164.1 | 160.5 | 149.6 | 142.7 | 126.0 | 119.2 | 127.1 | 126.0 | 110.7 | 127.7 | 115.7 | 131.7 | 118.9 | 116.1 |
| 2004 | 132.8 | 143.6 | 146.5 | 143.2 | 136.1 | 126.8 | 114.8 | 107.8 | 115.6 | 113.2 | 100.6 | 116.6 | 102.8 | 119.6 | 102.0 | 105.0 |
| 2003 | 129.7 | 140.6 | 145.1 | 140.8 | 133.0 | 124.6 | 109.0 | 105.6 | 110.5 | 107.8 | 98.0 | 103.5 | 100.5 | 115.8 | 99.1 | 102.7 |
| 2002 | 126.7 | 133.5 | 136.2 | 133.9 | 129.4 | 120.3 | 107.1 | 104.6 | 107.4 | 106.7 | 97.3 | 102.8 | 99.7 | 113.0 | 98.3 | 101.9 |
| 2001 | 122.2 | 128.2 | 131.5 | 128.8 | 124.8 | 115.9 | 104.3 | 100.8 | 104.6 | 103.8 | 94.8 | 100.3 | 96.4 | 109.1 | 95.5 | 99.0 |
| 2000 | 118.9 | 121.5 | 126.4 | 123.2 | 117.4 | 113.8 | 102.4 | 99.0 | 101.8 | 101.2 | 93.6 | 98.9 | 94.9 | 106.1 | 94.1 | 97.0 |
| 1990 | 93.2 | 96.3 | 98.9 | 95.1 | 92.5 | 90.4 | 83.9 | 81.1 | 84.0 | 82.9 | 78.4 | 85.0 | 75.0 | 80.4 | 74.0 | 76.9 |
| 1985 | 81.8 | 85.3 | 86.8 | 85.6 | 81.1 | 78.8 | 76.7 | 73.4 | 78.3 | 73.9 | 70.6 | 77.3 | 66.9 | 70.3 | 66.1 | 68.1 |
| 1980 | 60.7 | 60.7 | 60.9 | 62.3 | 58.5 | 59.6 | 55.3 | 55.8 | 56.5 | 56.7 | 53.5 | 57.2 | 51.7 | 54.0 | 51.1 | 51.3 |
| 1975 | 43.7 | 44.7 | 45.0 | 46.3 | 42.9 | 43.7 | 42.1 | 40.3 | 43.2 | 41.5 | 38.1 | 41.3 | 37.5 | 38.4 | 36.2 | 36.5 |
| 1970 | 27.8 | 28.1 | 28.2 | 28.9 | 27.0 | 26.3 | 25.7 | 22.8 | 27.0 | 26.2 | 24.5 | 24.2 | 23.8 | 25.2 | 22.8 | 23.4 |
| 1965 | 21.5 | 21.6 | 21.7 | 22.2 | 20.9 | 21.8 | 19.8 | 17.4 | 19.3 | 20.2 | 18.9 | 18.6 | 18.3 | 19.8 | 17.6 | 18.0 |
| 1960 | 19.5 | 19.7 | 19.7 | 20.2 | 18.9 | 19.4 | 18.0 | 15.8 | 17.6 | 18.3 | 17.2 | 16.9 | 16.7 | 17.1 | 16.0 | 16.4 |
| 1955 | 16.3 | 16.5 | 16.5 | 17.0 | 15.9 | 16.3 | 15.1 | 13.2 | 14.7 | 15.4 | 14.4 | 14.1 | 14.0 | 14.4 | 13.4 | 13.7 |
| ▼ 1950 | 13.5 | 13.6 | 13.7 | 14.0 | 13.1 | 13.4 | 12.5 | 11.0 | 12.2 | 12.7 | 11.9 | 11.7 | 11.5 | 11.9 | 11.0 | 11.3 |

| Year | National | Georgia | Hawaii | Idaho | | Illinois | | | | | | Indiana | | | | |
|---|---|---|---|---|---|---|---|---|---|---|---|---|---|---|---|---|
| | 30 City Average | Savannah | Honolulu | Boise | Pocatello | Chicago | Decatur | Joliet | Peoria | Rockford | Springfield | Anderson | Evansville | Fort Wayne | Gary | Indianapolis |
| Jan 2023 | 318.8E | 262.7E | 348.6E | 273E | 274.2E | 348E | 302.4E | 341.4E | 301.8E | 323.1E | 305.7E | 262.3E | 267.9E | 263.7E | 292.2E | 275E |
| 2022 | 276.9 | 244.8 | 324.9 | 254.4 | 255.6 | 324.3 | 281.8 | 318.2 | 281.3 | 301.1 | 284.9 | 244.5 | 249.7 | 245.8 | 272.3 | 256.3 |
| 2021 | 238.3 | 205.1 | 280.4 | 216.8 | 216.2 | 286.4 | 241.6 | 282.3 | 245.2 | 264.5 | 243.7 | 211.7 | 213.4 | 208.0 | 239.5 | 220.3 |
| 2020 | 234.3 | 203.2 | 278.4 | 215.4 | 214.5 | 282.7 | 238.5 | 269.1 | 237.9 | 253 | 242.2 | 208.9 | 210.6 | 206.3 | 238.6 | 217.7 |
| 2019 | 227.3 | 191.7 | 266.9 | 203.9 | 204.5 | 266.1 | 226.3 | 262.3 | 232.2 | 247.7 | 227.9 | 199.8 | 202.4 | 196.8 | 227.3 | 203.6 |
| 2018 | 217.7 | 188.1 | 261.9 | 200.1 | 200.6 | 261.1 | 222.0 | 257.4 | 227.8 | 243.0 | 223.6 | 196.0 | 198.6 | 193.1 | 223.0 | 199.8 |
| 2017 | 209.4 | 180.5 | 249.7 | 192.5 | 193.4 | 251.7 | 215.3 | 247.9 | 220.4 | 233.1 | 216.0 | 189.8 | 192.3 | 185.2 | 216.8 | 191.8 |
| 2016 | 207.7 | 175.1 | 251.7 | 191.1 | 190.2 | 244.9 | 212.9 | 244.3 | 217.5 | 229.6 | 215.1 | 190.5 | 192.3 | 184.4 | 216.8 | 192.5 |
| 2015 | 204.0 | 170.5 | 250.5 | 185.4 | 185.3 | 238.9 | 209.0 | 238.7 | 213.7 | 225.3 | 210.5 | 186.4 | 190.1 | 183.0 | 212.4 | 189.6 |
| 2014 | 203.0 | 167.2 | 239.7 | 184.1 | 184.4 | 238.1 | 206.0 | 236.8 | 212.5 | 224.4 | 208.2 | 184.5 | 188.1 | 180.8 | 210.1 | 188.4 |
| 2013 | 196.9 | 163.5 | 231.5 | 179.6 | 179.9 | 231.1 | 200.8 | 228.7 | 207.2 | 217.2 | 203.2 | 177.8 | 182.5 | 175.9 | 203.6 | 182.7 |
| 2012 | 194.0 | 158.9 | 227.9 | 170.4 | 171.5 | 226.2 | 195.7 | 222.7 | 199.7 | 211.8 | 197.2 | 175.2 | 177.8 | 171.8 | 197.9 | 180.6 |
| 2011 | 185.7 | 151.7 | 219.0 | 162.8 | 163.6 | 217.6 | 187.9 | 216.8 | 193.4 | 205.8 | 189.4 | 168.4 | 169.7 | 165.0 | 191.0 | 173.0 |
| 2010 | 181.6 | 147.9 | 214.6 | 161.7 | 162.4 | 210.6 | 181.2 | 208.3 | 186.2 | 197.6 | 182.2 | 162.8 | 165.9 | 160.0 | 183.7 | 168.1 |
| 2009 | 182.5 | 152.8 | 218.6 | 162.6 | 163.4 | 209.0 | 182.2 | 205.9 | 186.2 | 196.5 | 184.0 | 164.9 | 166.9 | 163.0 | 185.2 | 170.3 |
| 2008 | 171.0 | 141.1 | 205.5 | 153.2 | 152.8 | 195.7 | 168.7 | 185.5 | 172.2 | 180.2 | 168.5 | 152.4 | 155.8 | 151.0 | 169.0 | 159.2 |
| 2007 | 165.0 | 136.9 | 200.4 | 148.0 | 148.1 | 186.5 | 160.5 | 177.7 | 166.0 | 175.0 | 159.2 | 149.0 | 152.6 | 147.7 | 165.4 | 154.1 |
| 2006 | 156.2 | 124.0 | 191.9 | 141.6 | 141.2 | 177.8 | 153.8 | 168.7 | 155.2 | 163.3 | 152.8 | 139.8 | 144.4 | 139.1 | 154.5 | 144.6 |
| 2005 | 146.7 | 116.9 | 181.2 | 133.8 | 132.5 | 164.4 | 145.0 | 158.3 | 146.5 | 151.2 | 145.4 | 131.4 | 136.2 | 131.0 | 146.4 | 137.4 |
| 2004 | 132.8 | 105.6 | 161.2 | 122.0 | 120.5 | 149.3 | 129.3 | 145.1 | 133.9 | 138.1 | 130.3 | 120.9 | 123.5 | 120.1 | 132.2 | 125.0 |
| 2003 | 129.7 | 103.0 | 159.4 | 120.2 | 118.7 | 146.2 | 127.4 | 143.5 | 132.4 | 137.3 | 128.4 | 119.7 | 121.4 | 118.2 | 131.4 | 122.5 |
| 2002 | 126.7 | 102.0 | 157.2 | 118.3 | 117.1 | 141.2 | 123.8 | 138.5 | 129.6 | 132.9 | 125.3 | 117.5 | 119.0 | 116.4 | 129.1 | 120.5 |
| 2001 | 122.2 | 99.0 | 150.0 | 114.3 | 113.4 | 135.8 | 120.1 | 133.7 | 124.3 | 127.8 | 119.8 | 113.4 | 115.6 | 112.1 | 123.4 | 116.4 |
| 2000 | 118.9 | 97.5 | 144.8 | 112.9 | 112.1 | 131.2 | 115.1 | 124.6 | 119.0 | 122.2 | 116.2 | 109.8 | 111.5 | 108.4 | 117.8 | 113.2 |
| 1990 | 93.2 | 77.9 | 104.7 | 88.2 | 88.1 | 98.4 | 90.9 | 98.4 | 93.7 | 94.0 | 90.1 | 84.6 | 89.3 | 83.4 | 88.4 | 87.1 |
| 1985 | 81.8 | 68.9 | 94.7 | 78.0 | 78.0 | 82.4 | 81.9 | 83.4 | 83.7 | 83.0 | 81.5 | 75.2 | 79.8 | 75.0 | 77.8 | 77.1 |
| 1980 | 60.7 | 52.2 | 68.9 | 60.3 | 59.5 | 62.8 | 62.3 | 63.4 | 64.5 | 61.6 | 61.1 | 56.5 | 59.0 | 56.7 | 59.8 | 57.9 |
| 1975 | 43.7 | 36.9 | 44.6 | 40.8 | 40.5 | 45.7 | 43.1 | 44.5 | 44.7 | 42.7 | 42.4 | 39.5 | 41.7 | 39.9 | 41.9 | 40.6 |
| 1970 | 27.8 | 21.0 | 30.4 | 26.7 | 26.6 | 29.1 | 28.0 | 28.6 | 29.0 | 27.5 | 27.6 | 25.4 | 26.4 | 25.5 | 27.1 | 26.2 |
| 1965 | 21.5 | 16.4 | 21.8 | 20.6 | 20.5 | 22.7 | 21.5 | 22.1 | 22.4 | 21.2 | 21.3 | 19.5 | 20.4 | 19.7 | 20.8 | 20.7 |
| 1960 | 19.5 | 14.9 | 19.8 | 18.7 | 18.6 | 20.2 | 19.6 | 20.0 | 20.3 | 19.2 | 19.3 | 17.7 | 18.7 | 17.9 | 18.9 | 18.4 |
| 1955 | 16.3 | 12.5 | 16.6 | 15.7 | 15.6 | 16.9 | 16.4 | 16.8 | 17.0 | 16.1 | 16.2 | 14.9 | 15.7 | 15.0 | 15.9 | 15.5 |
| ▼ 1950 | 13.5 | 10.3 | 13.7 | 13.0 | 12.9 | 14.0 | 13.6 | 13.9 | 14.0 | 13.3 | 13.4 | 12.3 | 12.9 | 12.4 | 13.1 | 12.8 |

| Year | National | Indiana | | | Iowa | | | | | Kansas | | Kentucky | | Louisiana | | |
|---|---|---|---|---|---|---|---|---|---|---|---|---|---|---|---|---|
| | 30 City Average | Muncie | South Bend | Terre Haute | Cedar Rapids | Davenport | Des Moines | Sioux City | Waterloo | Topeka | Wichita | Lexington | Louisville | Baton Rouge | Lake Charles | New Orleans |
| Jan 2023 | 318.8E | 260.7E | 272.7E | 264.1E | 272.9E | 281.9E | 277.7E | 265.2E | 259.8E | 264.6E | 255.5E | 257.4E | 263.9E | 250.7E | 246.3E | 258.7E |
| 2022 | 276.9 | 243 | 254.2 | 246.1 | 254.3 | 262.7 | 258.8 | 247.2 | 242.1 | 246.6 | 238.1 | 239.9 | 246 | 233.7 | 229.6 | 241.1 |
| 2021 | 238.3 | 209.9 | 218.4 | 214.2 | 219.6 | 228.4 | 221.9 | 212.8 | 209.1 | 210.8 | 202.9 | 206.5 | 208.3 | 199.1 | 197 | 202.4 |
| 2020 | 234.3 | 207.2 | 214.5 | 210.7 | 217.6 | 227.3 | 218.8 | 211.5 | 205.2 | 207.2 | 202.8 | 203.1 | 206 | 197.9 | 196 | 200.9 |
| 2019 | 227.3 | 198.9 | 203.6 | 202.4 | 206.9 | 216.6 | 205.7 | 199.6 | 198.8 | 198.7 | 192.6 | 195.3 | 194.4 | 188.2 | 187.5 | 189.8 |
| 2018 | 217.7 | 195.2 | 199.8 | 198.6 | 203.0 | 212.5 | 201.8 | 195.8 | 195.1 | 195.0 | 189.0 | 191.6 | 190.7 | 184.7 | 184.0 | 186.2 |
| 2017 | 209.4 | 189.5 | 192.4 | 193.1 | 194.8 | 205.7 | 195.0 | 188.2 | 188.5 | 188.1 | 183.0 | 186.2 | 185.0 | 179.2 | 178.2 | 179.3 |
| 2016 | 207.7 | 191.0 | 190.7 | 192.8 | 191.4 | 199.9 | 190.0 | 184.0 | 181.0 | 181.0 | 191.0 | 186.0 | 188.1 | 180.1 | 176.7 | 180.0 |
| 2015 | 204.0 | 186.0 | 188.6 | 190.6 | 188.8 | 196.9 | 189.0 | 179.1 | 177.8 | 175.7 | 175.1 | 184.4 | 185.9 | 176.6 | 175.4 | 177.6 |
| 2014 | 203.0 | 185.0 | 185.5 | 189.2 | 188.3 | 195.9 | 188.5 | 178.9 | 177.4 | 173.6 | 173.7 | 183.7 | 186.1 | 171.3 | 170.9 | 177.5 |
| 2013 | 196.9 | 179.3 | 179.3 | 182.6 | 183.4 | 190.8 | 181.8 | 173.2 | 171.3 | 168.8 | 167.3 | 179.1 | 182.4 | 166.3 | 166.2 | 173.1 |
| 2012 | 194.0 | 175.8 | 174.3 | 178.9 | 180.3 | 184.6 | 179.2 | 168.8 | 169.2 | 162.3 | 161.4 | 174.8 | 177.5 | 164.4 | 163.8 | 171.7 |
| 2011 | 185.7 | 169.2 | 168.1 | 171.3 | 173.8 | 178.1 | 172.7 | 162.3 | 162.8 | 156.3 | 155.3 | 167.8 | 170.8 | 156.9 | 156.5 | 162.1 |
| 2010 | 181.6 | 163.1 | 163.5 | 167.8 | 170.4 | 175.6 | 170.2 | 159.0 | 160.2 | 152.8 | 151.3 | 158.7 | 166.9 | 153.7 | 153.4 | 160.3 |
| 2009 | 182.5 | 164.5 | 167.1 | 168.0 | 165.9 | 172.0 | 162.1 | 156.3 | 147.6 | 154.5 | 152.4 | 160.7 | 167.5 | 156.9 | 154.4 | 161.9 |
| 2008 | 171.0 | 153.0 | 153.1 | 155.9 | 157.3 | 163.4 | 152.4 | 147.8 | 139.2 | 144.9 | 143.1 | 152.0 | 156.8 | 144.0 | 141.5 | 149.3 |
| 2007 | 165.0 | 149.7 | 149.5 | 152.7 | 152.4 | 157.6 | 148.9 | 144.0 | 135.0 | 141.0 | 138.7 | 147.6 | 150.9 | 139.4 | 138.0 | 145.2 |
| 2006 | 156.2 | 141.2 | 141.3 | 144.0 | 145.8 | 151.1 | 142.9 | 137.3 | 128.4 | 134.7 | 132.9 | 129.0 | 143.0 | 129.4 | 129.8 | 135.8 |
| 2005 | 146.7 | 131.0 | 133.8 | 135.2 | 135.7 | 142.1 | 133.5 | 129.4 | 120.0 | 125.9 | 125.6 | 121.5 | 135.1 | 120.8 | 117.7 | 126.2 |
| 2004 | 132.8 | 120.0 | 120.6 | 123.0 | 122.7 | 128.6 | 121.6 | 116.2 | 108.3 | 112.6 | 113.4 | 110.1 | 120.3 | 105.6 | 109.0 | 115.3 |
| 2003 | 129.7 | 118.7 | 119.2 | 121.7 | 120.9 | 126.4 | 120.2 | 114.6 | 105.9 | 109.4 | 111.3 | 107.8 | 118.7 | 103.3 | 106.1 | 112.4 |
| 2002 | 126.7 | 116.7 | 117.1 | 119.9 | 116.0 | 122.1 | 116.7 | 111.4 | 103.7 | 107.8 | 109.6 | 106.2 | 116.4 | 102.5 | 105.0 | 110.6 |
| 2001 | 122.2 | 112.8 | 111.6 | 115.5 | 112.5 | 117.5 | 113.2 | 107.7 | 100.6 | 104.3 | 105.2 | 103.3 | 112.7 | 99.4 | 101.3 | 104.6 |
| 2000 | 118.9 | 109.1 | 106.9 | 110.8 | 108.8 | 112.6 | 108.9 | 99.0 | 98.1 | 101.0 | 101.1 | 101.4 | 109.3 | 97.8 | 99.7 | 102.1 |
| 1990 | 93.2 | 83.9 | 85.1 | 89.1 | 87.1 | 86.5 | 86.9 | 80.4 | 80.3 | 83.2 | 82.6 | 82.8 | 82.6 | 82.0 | 84.1 | 84.5 |
| 1985 | 81.8 | 75.2 | 76.0 | 79.2 | 75.9 | 77.6 | 77.1 | 72.1 | 72.3 | 75.0 | 74.7 | 75.5 | 74.5 | 74.9 | 78.5 | 78.2 |
| 1980 | 60.7 | 56.1 | 58.3 | 59.7 | 62.7 | 59.6 | 61.8 | 59.3 | 57.7 | 58.9 | 58.0 | 59.3 | 59.8 | 59.1 | 60.0 | 57.2 |
| 1975 | 43.7 | 39.2 | 40.3 | 41.9 | 43.1 | 41.0 | 43.1 | 41.0 | 40.0 | 42.0 | 43.1 | 42.7 | 42.5 | 40.4 | 40.6 | 41.5 |
| 1970 | 27.8 | 25.3 | 26.2 | 27.0 | 28.2 | 26.9 | 27.6 | 26.6 | 25.9 | 27.0 | 25.5 | 26.9 | 25.9 | 25.0 | 26.7 | 27.2 |
| 1965 | 21.5 | 19.5 | 20.2 | 20.9 | 21.7 | 20.8 | 21.7 | 20.5 | 20.0 | 20.8 | 19.6 | 20.7 | 20.3 | 19.4 | 20.6 | 20.4 |
| 1960 | 19.5 | 17.8 | 18.3 | 18.9 | 19.7 | 18.8 | 19.5 | 18.6 | 18.2 | 18.9 | 17.8 | 18.8 | 18.4 | 17.6 | 18.7 | 18.5 |
| 1955 | 16.3 | 14.9 | 15.4 | 15.9 | 16.6 | 15.8 | 16.3 | 15.6 | 15.2 | 15.8 | 15.0 | 15.8 | 15.4 | 14.8 | 15.7 | 15.6 |
| ▼ 1950 | 13.5 | 12.3 | 12.7 | 13.1 | 13.7 | 13.1 | 13.5 | 12.9 | 12.6 | 13.1 | 12.4 | 13.0 | 12.8 | 12.2 | 13.0 | 12.8 |

| Year | National | Louisiana | Maine | | Maryland | Massachusetts | | | | | | | | | Michigan | |
|---|---|---|---|---|---|---|---|---|---|---|---|---|---|---|---|---|
| | 30 City Average | Shreveport | Lewiston | Portland | Baltimore | Boston | Brockton | Fall River | Lawrence | Lowell | New Bedford | Pittsfield | Springfield | Worcester | Ann Arbor | Dearborn |
| Jan 2023 | 318.8E | 249.8E | 274.9E | 281.3E | 280.5E | 337.1E | 306.9E | 304.3E | 315.7E | 316E | 304.2E | 292.1E | 300.3E | 309E | 287.2E | 291.3E |
| 2022 | 276.9 | 232.8 | 256.2 | 262.2 | 261.4 | 314.2 | 286.0 | 283.6 | 294.2 | 294.5 | 283.5 | 272.2 | 279.9 | 288.0 | 267.7 | 271.5 |
| 2021 | 238.3 | 198.8 | 220.0 | 225.8 | 223.8 | 271.9 | 252.3 | 250.0 | 260.0 | 260.3 | 249.8 | 238.8 | 245.3 | 253.2 | 232.8 | 236.7 |
| 2020 | 234.3 | 196 | 217.8 | 221.4 | 220.8 | 266 | 248.6 | 247.2 | 256.6 | 254.8 | 246 | 232.7 | 239.3 | 248 | 228.1 | 228.9 |
| 2019 | 227.3 | 186.5 | 201.1 | 203.7 | 208.7 | 253.2 | 237.2 | 235.0 | 243.7 | 242.3 | 234.5 | 222.9 | 225.6 | 237.0 | 219.7 | 220.7 |
| 2018 | 217.7 | 183.0 | 197.3 | 199.9 | 204.8 | 248.4 | 232.7 | 230.6 | 239.1 | 237.7 | 230.1 | 218.7 | 221.4 | 232.5 | 215.6 | 216.5 |
| 2017 | 209.4 | 177.9 | 192.0 | 194.7 | 197.7 | 240.0 | 226.4 | 225.0 | 233.9 | 231.3 | 224.4 | 211.7 | 213.5 | 226.1 | 208.7 | 211.1 |
| 2016 | 207.7 | 173.2 | 197.2 | 200.0 | 193.8 | 245.0 | 230.5 | 229.0 | 236.9 | 235.5 | 228.2 | 216.1 | 218.3 | 230.1 | 211.3 | 212.5 |
| 2015 | 204.0 | 170.9 | 193.7 | 196.9 | 189.2 | 240.7 | 228.3 | 228.2 | 234.5 | 233.2 | 227.4 | 212.8 | 214.6 | 226.8 | 209.8 | 211.5 |
| 2014 | 203.0 | 167.7 | 192.4 | 195.4 | 187.6 | 239.1 | 229.1 | 229.3 | 234.8 | 233.9 | 228.5 | 213.3 | 214.8 | 227.3 | 206.1 | 208.4 |
| 2013 | 196.9 | 159.0 | 187.9 | 189.5 | 183.2 | 232.9 | 221.6 | 221.8 | 225.3 | 223.4 | 221.1 | 205.9 | 206.5 | 219.3 | 201.2 | 202.4 |
| 2012 | 194.0 | 153.2 | 180.7 | 182.4 | 180.8 | 229.3 | 217.2 | 217.8 | 221.6 | 219.3 | 217.0 | 200.2 | 201.9 | 215.2 | 196.1 | 199.2 |
| 2011 | 185.7 | 146.7 | 167.4 | 169.1 | 173.6 | 219.3 | 208.2 | 206.0 | 211.6 | 210.1 | 205.2 | 191.2 | 194.5 | 206.6 | 186.7 | 189.4 |
| 2010 | 181.6 | 145.1 | 162.1 | 163.7 | 168.3 | 214.3 | 202.7 | 200.7 | 204.9 | 204.7 | 200.0 | 185.9 | 189.4 | 201.1 | 183.3 | 186.8 |
| 2009 | 182.5 | 147.6 | 159.4 | 161.8 | 169.1 | 211.8 | 199.2 | 197.6 | 201.9 | 201.9 | 196.9 | 185.1 | 187.1 | 198.2 | 179.2 | 186.9 |
| 2008 | 171.0 | 135.9 | 149.1 | 150.9 | 157.7 | 198.6 | 186.4 | 185.1 | 188.7 | 189.1 | 184.5 | 171.3 | 173.7 | 184.5 | 169.6 | 176.4 |
| 2007 | 165.0 | 132.4 | 146.4 | 148.2 | 152.5 | 191.8 | 180.4 | 179.7 | 182.0 | 181.7 | 179.1 | 166.8 | 169.1 | 180.4 | 166.8 | 172.5 |
| 2006 | 156.2 | 125.2 | 140.2 | 139.8 | 144.9 | 180.4 | 171.6 | 170.4 | 172.3 | 173.5 | 170.4 | 157.3 | 159.7 | 171.6 | 161.1 | 165.5 |
| 2005 | 146.7 | 117.4 | 131.7 | 131.4 | 135.8 | 169.6 | 161.3 | 159.6 | 162.2 | 162.3 | 159.6 | 147.6 | 150.7 | 158.8 | 147.5 | 155.8 |
| 2004 | 132.8 | 105.7 | 119.8 | 119.4 | 121.4 | 154.1 | 144.4 | 143.6 | 146.4 | 146.7 | 143.6 | 131.9 | 136.5 | 143.2 | 135.9 | 142.1 |
| 2003 | 129.7 | 103.9 | 117.7 | 117.3 | 118.1 | 150.2 | 139.6 | 140.6 | 143.3 | 143.6 | 140.5 | 128.9 | 133.8 | 139.0 | 134.1 | 139.0 |
| 2002 | 126.7 | 102.1 | 117.5 | 117.1 | 115.6 | 145.6 | 136.0 | 135.0 | 136.9 | 137.3 | 134.9 | 124.7 | 128.3 | 134.9 | 131.4 | 134.3 |
| 2001 | 122.2 | 98.3 | 114.6 | 114.3 | 111.7 | 140.9 | 132.1 | 131.4 | 133.1 | 132.9 | 131.3 | 120.3 | 124.5 | 130.1 | 126.8 | 129.8 |
| 2000 | 118.9 | 96.2 | 105.7 | 105.4 | 107.7 | 138.9 | 129.4 | 128.4 | 129.7 | 130.3 | 128.3 | 116.7 | 121.0 | 127.3 | 124.3 | 125.8 |
| 1990 | 93.2 | 80.3 | 88.5 | 88.6 | 85.6 | 110.9 | 103.7 | 102.9 | 105.2 | 102.8 | 102.6 | 98.7 | 101.4 | 103.2 | 93.2 | 96.5 |
| 1985 | 81.8 | 73.6 | 76.7 | 77.0 | 72.7 | 92.8 | 88.8 | 88.7 | 89.4 | 88.2 | 88.6 | 85.0 | 85.6 | 86.7 | 80.1 | 82.7 |
| 1980 | 60.7 | 58.7 | 57.3 | 58.5 | 53.6 | 64.0 | 63.7 | 64.1 | 63.4 | 62.7 | 63.1 | 61.8 | 62.0 | 62.3 | 62.9 | 64.0 |
| 1975 | 43.7 | 40.5 | 41.9 | 42.1 | 39.8 | 46.6 | 45.8 | 45.7 | 46.2 | 45.7 | 46.1 | 45.5 | 45.8 | 46.0 | 44.1 | 44.9 |
| 1970 | 27.8 | 26.4 | 26.5 | 25.8 | 25.1 | 29.2 | 29.1 | 29.2 | 29.1 | 28.9 | 29.0 | 28.6 | 28.5 | 28.7 | 28.5 | 28.9 |
| 1965 | 21.5 | 20.3 | 20.4 | 19.4 | 20.2 | 23.0 | 22.5 | 22.5 | 22.5 | 22.2 | 22.4 | 22.0 | 22.4 | 22.1 | 22.0 | 22.3 |
| 1960 | 19.5 | 18.5 | 18.6 | 17.6 | 17.5 | 20.5 | 20.4 | 20.4 | 20.4 | 20.2 | 20.3 | 20.0 | 20.1 | 20.1 | 20.0 | 20.2 |
| 1955 | 16.3 | 15.5 | 15.6 | 14.7 | 14.7 | 17.2 | 17.1 | 17.1 | 17.1 | 16.9 | 17.1 | 16.8 | 16.9 | 16.8 | 16.7 | 16.9 |
| ▼ 1950 | 13.5 | 12.8 | 12.9 | 12.2 | 12.1 | 14.2 | 14.1 | 14.1 | 14.1 | 14.0 | 14.1 | 13.8 | 14.0 | 13.9 | 13.8 | 14.0 |

| Year | National | Michigan | | | | | | | Minnesota | | | Mississippi | | Missouri | | |
|---|---|---|---|---|---|---|---|---|---|---|---|---|---|---|---|---|
| Year | 30 City Average | Detroit | Flint | Grand Rapids | Kalamazoo | Lansing | Saginaw | Duluth | Minneapolis | Rochester | Biloxi | Jackson | Kansas City | St. Joseph | St. Louis | Springfield |
| Jan 2023 | 318.8E | 298E | 277.5E | 269.5E | 265.8E | 279.5E | 271.9E | 307.7E | 319.3E | 302.5E | 249.8E | 254.2E | 295.4E | 276.5E | 296.1E | 269.5E |
| 2022 | 276.9 | 277.7 | 258.6 | 251.2 | 247.7 | 260.5 | 253.4 | 286.8 | 297.6 | 281.9 | 232.8 | 236.9 | 275.3 | 257.7 | 276 | 251.2 |
| 2021 | 238.3 | 239 | 222.4 | 216.3 | 212.4 | 224.6 | 218 | 242.5 | 256.8 | 240.5 | 197.7 | 200.9 | 236.9 | 223.7 | 241 | 212.4 |
| 2020 | 234.3 | 234.7 | 216.6 | 211.7 | 207.1 | 217.1 | 212.8 | 238.5 | 252.1 | 234.8 | 193.9 | 197.1 | 233.7 | 218.8 | 234.4 | 208.3 |
| 2019 | 227.3 | 223.8 | 208.7 | 201.3 | 198.5 | 208.3 | 204.9 | 223.8 | 237.1 | 220.2 | 183.6 | 184.4 | 224.8 | 212.8 | 227.1 | 203 |
| 2018 | 217.7 | 219.6 | 204.8 | 197.5 | 194.8 | 204.4 | 201 | 219.6 | 232.6 | 216.1 | 180.1 | 180.9 | 220.6 | 208.8 | 222.8 | 199.2 |
| 2017 | 209.4 | 212.1 | 199.2 | 190.9 | 189.6 | 198.1 | 195.3 | 212.1 | 221.2 | 207.6 | 175.3 | 175.6 | 212.9 | 202.8 | 213.1 | 192.9 |
| 2016 | 207.7 | 212.8 | 200.2 | 191.0 | 189.7 | 200.9 | 195.9 | 217.6 | 227.2 | 212.4 | 173.3 | 177.7 | 213.2 | 205.5 | 212.1 | 194.6 |
| 2015 | 204.0 | 211.8 | 198.9 | 191.2 | 190.4 | 199.6 | 194.1 | 212.9 | 222.0 | 209.1 | 167.3 | 174.2 | 210.0 | 202.3 | 210.1 | 191.8 |
| 2014 | 203.0 | 208.7 | 196.0 | 187.9 | 188.4 | 195.7 | 191.7 | 211.1 | 220.7 | 207.5 | 164.6 | 169.8 | 210.8 | 199.3 | 208.6 | 189.5 |
| 2013 | 196.9 | 203.1 | 190.6 | 182.4 | 182.4 | 190.2 | 186.5 | 205.1 | 216.3 | 201.4 | 160.9 | 164.3 | 204.7 | 193.1 | 202.4 | 181.6 |
| 2012 | 194.0 | 200.2 | 186.3 | 176.4 | 178.9 | 185.9 | 182.8 | 203.1 | 214.7 | 199.7 | 157.6 | 160.5 | 200.8 | 189.0 | 198.0 | 177.7 |
| 2011 | 185.7 | 190.3 | 178.5 | 169.9 | 171.9 | 178.0 | 174.6 | 195.7 | 208.1 | 193.8 | 151.4 | 154.3 | 191.1 | 178.8 | 190.6 | 168.3 |
| 2010 | 181.6 | 187.5 | 176.2 | 160.6 | 167.3 | 175.8 | 171.9 | 193.1 | 203.8 | 188.9 | 148.0 | 151.0 | 186.1 | 174.2 | 185.9 | 164.3 |
| 2009 | 182.5 | 187.8 | 176.0 | 156.7 | 166.3 | 173.7 | 168.6 | 191.8 | 203.1 | 188.0 | 152.8 | 156.6 | 185.6 | 172.3 | 187.2 | 163.7 |
| 2008 | 171.0 | 177.0 | 164.4 | 140.2 | 155.7 | 161.6 | 158.7 | 177.4 | 190.6 | 175.0 | 141.8 | 147.1 | 175.5 | 164.2 | 176.2 | 152.9 |
| 2007 | 165.0 | 172.9 | 161.7 | 137.2 | 152.6 | 158.7 | 156.1 | 174.2 | 184.5 | 171.4 | 137.7 | 131.2 | 169.0 | 157.8 | 170.6 | 145.3 |
| 2006 | 156.2 | 165.8 | 153.8 | 131.1 | 146.0 | 152.5 | 150.6 | 166.2 | 173.9 | 161.9 | 123.3 | 117.1 | 162.0 | 152.4 | 159.3 | 139.4 |
| 2005 | 146.7 | 156.2 | 145.1 | 123.1 | 134.9 | 142.0 | 140.6 | 157.3 | 164.6 | 152.8 | 116.0 | 109.9 | 151.3 | 143.1 | 149.4 | 131.7 |
| 2004 | 132.8 | 141.9 | 129.6 | 112.8 | 122.5 | 129.7 | 127.6 | 139.1 | 150.1 | 137.0 | 105.3 | 99.3 | 135.1 | 126.9 | 135.5 | 116.3 |
| 2003 | 129.7 | 138.7 | 127.9 | 110.9 | 120.8 | 127.7 | 126.0 | 136.7 | 146.5 | 134.5 | 101.4 | 96.7 | 131.9 | 124.8 | 133.3 | 113.9 |
| 2002 | 126.7 | 134.2 | 126.9 | 107.4 | 119.9 | 125.3 | 124.4 | 131.9 | 139.5 | 130.0 | 101.0 | 96.3 | 128.4 | 122.7 | 129.6 | 112.5 |
| 2001 | 122.2 | 129.4 | 122.4 | 104.3 | 115.2 | 120.1 | 119.7 | 131.4 | 136.1 | 124.9 | 98.7 | 93.9 | 121.8 | 114.7 | 125.5 | 106.7 |
| 2000 | 118.9 | 125.3 | 119.8 | 102.7 | 111.6 | 117.6 | 115.9 | 124.1 | 131.1 | 120.1 | 97.2 | 92.9 | 118.2 | 111.9 | 122.4 | 104.3 |
| 1990 | 93.2 | 96.0 | 91.7 | 84.0 | 87.4 | 90.2 | 88.9 | 94.3 | 100.5 | 95.6 | 76.4 | 75.6 | 89.5 | 86.8 | 94.0 | 82.6 |
| 1985 | 81.8 | 81.6 | 80.7 | 75.8 | 79.4 | 80.0 | 80.5 | 85.2 | 87.9 | 86.5 | 69.4 | 68.5 | 78.2 | 77.3 | 80.8 | 73.2 |
| 1980 | 60.7 | 62.5 | 63.1 | 59.8 | 61.7 | 60.3 | 63.3 | 63.4 | 64.1 | 64.8 | 54.3 | 54.3 | 59.1 | 60.4 | 59.7 | 56.7 |
| 1975 | 43.7 | 45.8 | 44.9 | 41.8 | 43.7 | 44.1 | 44.8 | 45.2 | 46.0 | 45.3 | 37.9 | 37.7 | 42.7 | 45.4 | 44.8 | 41.1 |
| 1970 | 27.8 | 29.7 | 28.5 | 26.7 | 28.1 | 27.8 | 28.7 | 28.9 | 29.5 | 28.9 | 24.4 | 21.3 | 25.3 | 28.3 | 28.4 | 26.0 |
| 1965 | 21.5 | 22.1 | 21.9 | 20.6 | 21.7 | 21.5 | 22.2 | 22.3 | 23.4 | 22.3 | 18.8 | 16.4 | 20.6 | 21.8 | 21.8 | 20.0 |
| 1960 | 19.5 | 20.1 | 20.0 | 18.7 | 19.7 | 19.5 | 20.1 | 20.3 | 20.5 | 20.2 | 17.1 | 14.9 | 19.0 | 19.8 | 19.5 | 18.2 |
| 1955 | 16.3 | 16.8 | 16.7 | 15.7 | 16.5 | 16.3 | 16.9 | 17.0 | 17.2 | 17.0 | 14.3 | 12.5 | 16.0 | 16.6 | 16.3 | 15.2 |
| ▼ 1950 | 13.5 | 13.9 | 13.8 | 13.0 | 13.6 | 13.5 | 13.9 | 14.0 | 14.2 | 14.0 | 11.8 | 10.3 | 13.2 | 13.7 | 13.5 | 12.6 |

| Year | National | Montana | | Nebraska | | Nevada | | New Hampshire | | New Jersey | | | | | NM | NY |
|---|---|---|---|---|---|---|---|---|---|---|---|---|---|---|---|---|
| Year | 30 City Average | Billings | Great Falls | Lincoln | Omaha | Las Vegas | Reno | Manchester | Nashua | Camden | Jersey City | Newark | Paterson | Trenton | Albuquerque | Albany |
| Jan 2023 | 318.8E | 274.9E | 274.2E | 265.7E | 268.5E | 310.8E | 280.9E | 286.4E | 284E | 331.9E | 330.9E | 339.1E | 332.9E | 334.5E | 259E | 303.8E |
| 2022 | 276.9 | 256.2 | 255.6 | 247.6 | 250.2 | 289.7 | 261.8 | 266.9 | 264.7 | 309.3 | 308.4 | 316.0 | 310.3 | 311.8 | 241.4 | 283.1 |
| 2021 | 238.3 | 214.4 | 216.3 | 214.8 | 216.7 | 248.6 | 224.9 | 229.1 | 226.7 | 271.7 | 272.0 | 278.4 | 274.7 | 273.1 | 205.0 | 245.0 |
| 2020 | 234.3 | 214.4 | 213.5 | 213.2 | 213.8 | 245.4 | 225.5 | 226.8 | 224.8 | 268.3 | 265.9 | 273 | 269.1 | 262.2 | 204.9 | 239.9 |
| 2019 | 227.3 | 199.8 | 200.3 | 199.5 | 200.1 | 232.4 | 211.0 | 211.0 | 210.2 | 248.0 | 251.7 | 256.3 | 254.7 | 250.5 | 195.8 | 226.3 |
| 2018 | 217.7 | 196.0 | 196.5 | 195.7 | 196.3 | 228.0 | 207.0 | 207.0 | 206.2 | 243.3 | 247.0 | 251.5 | 249.9 | 245.8 | 192.1 | 222.0 |
| 2017 | 209.4 | 190.4 | 191.0 | 189.6 | 190.1 | 220.1 | 199.8 | 200.7 | 200.0 | 236.3 | 238.7 | 242.7 | 240.8 | 239.2 | 185.9 | 213.5 |
| 2016 | 207.7 | 191.8 | 191.1 | 186.8 | 187.6 | 221.1 | 198.8 | 200.9 | 200.5 | 228.8 | 229.6 | 232.9 | 231.3 | 229.3 | 181.6 | 209.6 |
| 2015 | 204.0 | 188.1 | 188.4 | 183.7 | 184.7 | 215.5 | 194.9 | 198.7 | 197.8 | 224.5 | 226.1 | 230.1 | 228.5 | 227.6 | 178.3 | 208.1 |
| 2014 | 203.0 | 185.4 | 186.3 | 181.1 | 183.7 | 210.9 | 195.7 | 198.8 | 197.3 | 224.6 | 226.6 | 230.6 | 227.8 | 226.6 | 178.0 | 205.1 |
| 2013 | 196.9 | 180.5 | 181.1 | 175.5 | 180.6 | 206.8 | 190.4 | 193.8 | 192.5 | 217.7 | 219.3 | 223.6 | 221.2 | 218.7 | 173.6 | 195.3 |
| 2012 | 194.0 | 178.6 | 179.5 | 169.3 | 177.1 | 202.6 | 186.8 | 189.2 | 188.3 | 213.6 | 215.2 | 219.2 | 217.5 | 213.7 | 171.0 | 191.2 |
| 2011 | 185.7 | 168.8 | 170.8 | 162.8 | 169.6 | 195.7 | 179.8 | 176.8 | 176.1 | 205.5 | 207.0 | 210.3 | 209.2 | 206.4 | 163.3 | 180.9 |
| 2010 | 181.6 | 166.5 | 168.6 | 159.3 | 165.8 | 193.7 | 175.6 | 172.5 | 172.0 | 201.2 | 203.3 | 206.3 | 205.3 | 200.8 | 162.5 | 177.8 |
| 2009 | 182.5 | 165.3 | 166.0 | 161.7 | 165.0 | 191.5 | 176.5 | 174.0 | 173.5 | 196.8 | 200.5 | 203.6 | 202.0 | 198.6 | 163.0 | 178.1 |
| 2008 | 171.0 | 153.1 | 154.6 | 152.0 | 154.8 | 176.2 | 167.0 | 162.5 | 161.9 | 184.0 | 187.3 | 189.6 | 188.7 | 185.6 | 152.6 | 166.0 |
| 2007 | 165.0 | 147.7 | 147.8 | 147.7 | 150.3 | 166.7 | 161.4 | 159.3 | 158.7 | 179.3 | 183.3 | 185.2 | 184.6 | 181.7 | 146.7 | 159.4 |
| 2006 | 156.2 | 140.5 | 140.8 | 132.4 | 140.7 | 160.0 | 154.5 | 146.7 | 146.4 | 167.7 | 171.0 | 173.6 | 172.2 | 169.9 | 140.1 | 151.6 |
| 2005 | 146.7 | 131.9 | 132.4 | 124.1 | 132.8 | 149.5 | 145.4 | 136.8 | 136.5 | 159.0 | 162.4 | 163.9 | 163.0 | 161.5 | 130.4 | 142.2 |
| 2004 | 132.8 | 118.2 | 117.9 | 112.1 | 119.4 | 137.1 | 130.5 | 124.2 | 123.9 | 143.4 | 145.4 | 147.2 | 146.6 | 146.0 | 118.3 | 128.6 |
| 2003 | 129.7 | 115.8 | 115.8 | 110.2 | 117.3 | 133.8 | 128.3 | 122.4 | 122.2 | 142.0 | 144.3 | 145.7 | 145.0 | 143.0 | 116.4 | 126.8 |
| 2002 | 126.7 | 114.6 | 114.5 | 108.2 | 115.0 | 131.9 | 126.4 | 119.9 | 119.6 | 135.9 | 138.5 | 140.2 | 140.1 | 137.6 | 114.6 | 122.6 |
| 2001 | 122.2 | 117.5 | 117.7 | 101.3 | 111.6 | 127.8 | 122.5 | 116.2 | 116.2 | 133.4 | 136.7 | 136.9 | 136.8 | 136.0 | 111.4 | 119.2 |
| 2000 | 118.9 | 113.7 | 113.9 | 98.8 | 107.0 | 125.8 | 118.2 | 111.9 | 111.9 | 128.4 | 130.5 | 132.6 | 132.4 | 130.6 | 109.0 | 116.5 |
| 1990 | 93.2 | 92.9 | 93.8 | 78.8 | 85.0 | 96.3 | 94.5 | 86.3 | 86.3 | 93.0 | 93.5 | 93.8 | 97.2 | 94.5 | 84.9 | 93.2 |
| 1985 | 81.8 | 83.9 | 84.3 | 71.5 | 77.5 | 87.6 | 85.0 | 78.1 | 78.1 | 81.3 | 83.3 | 83.5 | 84.5 | 82.8 | 76.7 | 79.5 |
| 1980 | 60.7 | 63.9 | 64.6 | 58.5 | 63.5 | 64.6 | 63.0 | 56.6 | 56.0 | 58.6 | 60.6 | 60.1 | 60.0 | 58.9 | 59.0 | 59.5 |
| 1975 | 43.7 | 43.1 | 43.8 | 40.9 | 43.2 | 42.8 | 41.9 | 41.3 | 40.8 | 42.3 | 43.4 | 44.2 | 43.9 | 43.8 | 40.3 | 43.9 |
| 1970 | 27.8 | 28.5 | 28.9 | 26.4 | 26.8 | 29.4 | 28.0 | 26.2 | 25.6 | 27.2 | 27.8 | 29.0 | 27.8 | 27.4 | 26.4 | 28.3 |
| 1965 | 21.5 | 22.0 | 22.3 | 20.3 | 20.6 | 22.4 | 21.6 | 20.6 | 19.7 | 20.9 | 21.4 | 23.8 | 21.4 | 21.3 | 20.6 | 22.3 |
| 1960 | 19.5 | 20.0 | 20.3 | 18.5 | 18.7 | 20.2 | 19.6 | 18.0 | 17.9 | 19.0 | 19.4 | 19.4 | 19.4 | 19.2 | 18.5 | 19.3 |
| 1955 | 16.3 | 16.7 | 17.0 | 15.5 | 15.7 | 16.9 | 16.4 | 15.1 | 15.0 | 16.0 | 16.3 | 16.3 | 16.3 | 16.1 | 15.6 | 16.2 |
| ▼ 1950 | 13.5 | 13.9 | 14.0 | 12.8 | 13.0 | 14.0 | 13.6 | 12.5 | 12.4 | 13.2 | 13.5 | 13.5 | 13.5 | 13.3 | 12.9 | 13.4 |

# Historical Cost Indexes

| Year | National | New York | | | | | | | | North Carolina | | | | | N. Dakota | Ohio |
|---|---|---|---|---|---|---|---|---|---|---|---|---|---|---|---|---|
| Year | 30 City Average | Binghamton | Buffalo | New York | Rochester | Schenectady | Syracuse | Utica | Yonkers | Charlotte | Durham | Greensboro | Raleigh | Winston-Salem | Fargo | Akron |
| Jan 2023 | 318.8E | 290.9E | 310.1E | 376.8E | 299.5E | 302.6E | 293.2E | 290.9E | 343.9E | 259.8E | 259.3E | 255.5E | 254.1E | 254.8E | 267.9E | 275.4E |
| 2022 | 276.9 | 271.1 | 289.0 | 351.2 | 279.1 | 282.0 | 273.3 | 271.1 | 320.5 | 242.1 | 241.7 | 238.1 | 236.8 | 237.5 | 249.7 | 256.7 |
| 2021 | 238.3 | 235.0 | 248.1 | 313.0 | 238.9 | 243.7 | 236.2 | 234.4 | 286.2 | 204.8 | 203.9 | 201.9 | 200.9 | 201.6 | 213.4 | 223.2 |
| 2020 | 234.3 | 232 | 245.1 | 306 | 237.4 | 239.6 | 233.3 | 231.7 | 281.2 | 203.6 | 201.3 | 199.3 | 198 | 199 | 213.1 | 218.7 |
| 2019 | 227.3 | 219.5 | 234.0 | 296.1 | 223.6 | 226.3 | 219.6 | 215.8 | 268.4 | 187.3 | 191.1 | 189.1 | 186.8 | 188.6 | 203.4 | 210.3 |
| 2018 | 217.7 | 215.4 | 229.6 | 290.5 | 219.4 | 222.0 | 215.5 | 211.7 | 263.3 | 183.8 | 187.5 | 185.5 | 183.3 | 185.0 | 199.6 | 206.3 |
| 2017 | 209.4 | 208.4 | 220.8 | 282.9 | 213.0 | 213.8 | 208.9 | 205.9 | 256.8 | 177.0 | 180.3 | 178.2 | 175.8 | 178.0 | 192.8 | 199.4 |
| 2016 | 207.7 | 202.6 | 213.7 | 270.5 | 208.4 | 209.8 | 203.6 | 200.8 | 247.9 | 180.6 | 182.0 | 179.8 | 174.6 | 179.6 | 185.5 | 202.4 |
| 2015 | 204.0 | 202.4 | 209.6 | 268.0 | 203.5 | 207.4 | 200.9 | 198.1 | 243.4 | 173.1 | 172.3 | 170.5 | 167.6 | 170.6 | 181.0 | 199.1 |
| 2014 | 203.0 | 202.4 | 207.8 | 267.7 | 202.2 | 204.2 | 198.8 | 196.4 | 245.6 | 165.5 | 165.2 | 163.9 | 161.6 | 164.3 | 177.1 | 199.2 |
| 2013 | 196.9 | 195.5 | 200.7 | 259.4 | 194.3 | 195.5 | 193.6 | 188.5 | 230.0 | 159.6 | 158.4 | 158.7 | 157.5 | 159.1 | 169.6 | 191.8 |
| 2012 | 194.0 | 192.9 | 198.1 | 256.3 | 191.2 | 191.4 | 189.6 | 185.2 | 227.1 | 156.4 | 155.6 | 156.3 | 155.4 | 157.2 | 167.3 | 187.7 |
| 2011 | 185.7 | 176.1 | 188.1 | 245.6 | 181.9 | 181.5 | 180.8 | 173.5 | 218.9 | 142.6 | 143.8 | 142.2 | 142.8 | 140.9 | 160.3 | 180.8 |
| 2010 | 181.6 | 173.8 | 184.0 | 241.4 | 179.6 | 179.0 | 176.7 | 170.5 | 217.1 | 140.5 | 141.6 | 140.0 | 140.6 | 138.8 | 156.2 | 174.5 |
| 2009 | 182.5 | 172.9 | 184.4 | 239.9 | 179.6 | 178.8 | 176.9 | 171.3 | 217.5 | 145.1 | 145.8 | 144.0 | 145.1 | 142.7 | 154.3 | 175.7 |
| 2008 | 171.0 | 160.7 | 173.9 | 226.8 | 168.0 | 167.2 | 165.9 | 161.6 | 202.1 | 135.8 | 136.6 | 134.6 | 135.3 | 133.8 | 145.0 | 165.4 |
| 2007 | 165.0 | 155.7 | 168.6 | 215.2 | 163.5 | 159.8 | 159.8 | 155.0 | 196.5 | 132.8 | 133.7 | 131.7 | 132.1 | 131.0 | 139.8 | 159.0 |
| 2006 | 156.2 | 147.5 | 159.2 | 204.5 | 155.2 | 151.1 | 150.9 | 146.4 | 186.0 | 125.1 | 124.6 | 123.8 | 124.2 | 123.0 | 133.2 | 152.8 |
| 2005 | 146.7 | 137.5 | 149.4 | 194.0 | 147.3 | 142.2 | 141.9 | 136.9 | 176.1 | 110.5 | 112.1 | 112.1 | 112.1 | 111.1 | 125.3 | 144.4 |
| 2004 | 132.8 | 123.5 | 136.1 | 177.7 | 132.0 | 128.4 | 127.3 | 124.4 | 161.8 | 98.9 | 100.0 | 100.1 | 100.3 | 99.4 | 113.0 | 131.9 |
| 2003 | 129.7 | 121.8 | 132.8 | 173.4 | 130.3 | 126.7 | 124.7 | 121.7 | 160.0 | 96.2 | 97.5 | 97.5 | 97.8 | 96.8 | 110.6 | 129.6 |
| 2002 | 126.7 | 119.0 | 128.5 | 170.1 | 127.1 | 123.0 | 121.8 | 118.4 | 154.8 | 94.8 | 96.1 | 96.1 | 96.3 | 95.5 | 106.3 | 127.2 |
| 2001 | 122.2 | 116.0 | 125.2 | 164.4 | 123.1 | 120.1 | 118.6 | 115.3 | 151.4 | 91.5 | 92.9 | 92.9 | 93.3 | 92.3 | 103.1 | 123.5 |
| 2000 | 118.9 | 112.4 | 122.3 | 159.2 | 120.0 | 117.5 | 115.1 | 112.4 | 144.8 | 90.3 | 91.6 | 91.6 | 91.9 | 91.0 | 97.9 | 117.8 |
| 1990 | 93.2 | 87.0 | 94.1 | 118.1 | 94.6 | 93.9 | 91.0 | 85.6 | 111.4 | 74.8 | 75.4 | 75.5 | 75.5 | 75.3 | 81.3 | 94.6 |
| 1985 | 81.8 | 77.5 | 83.2 | 94.9 | 81.6 | 80.1 | 81.0 | 77.0 | 92.8 | 66.9 | 67.6 | 67.7 | 67.6 | 67.5 | 73.4 | 86.8 |
| 1980 | 60.7 | 58.0 | 60.6 | 66.0 | 60.5 | 60.3 | 61.6 | 58.5 | 65.9 | 51.1 | 52.2 | 52.5 | 51.7 | 50.8 | 57.4 | 62.3 |
| 1975 | 43.7 | 42.5 | 45.1 | 49.5 | 44.8 | 43.7 | 44.8 | 42.7 | 47.1 | 36.1 | 37.0 | 37.0 | 37.3 | 36.1 | 39.3 | 44.7 |
| 1970 | 27.8 | 27.0 | 28.9 | 32.8 | 29.2 | 27.8 | 28.5 | 26.9 | 30.0 | 20.9 | 23.7 | 23.6 | 23.4 | 23.0 | 25.8 | 28.3 |
| 1965 | 21.5 | 20.8 | 22.2 | 25.5 | 22.8 | 21.4 | 21.9 | 20.7 | 23.1 | 16.0 | 18.2 | 18.2 | 18.0 | 17.7 | 19.9 | 21.8 |
| 1960 | 19.5 | 18.9 | 19.9 | 21.5 | 19.7 | 19.5 | 19.9 | 18.8 | 21.0 | 14.4 | 16.6 | 16.6 | 16.4 | 16.1 | 18.1 | 19.9 |
| 1955 | 16.3 | 15.8 | 16.7 | 18.1 | 16.5 | 16.3 | 16.7 | 15.8 | 17.6 | 12.1 | 13.9 | 13.9 | 13.7 | 13.5 | 15.2 | 16.6 |
| ▼ 1950 | 13.5 | 13.1 | 13.8 | 14.9 | 13.6 | 13.5 | 13.8 | 13.0 | 14.5 | 10.0 | 11.5 | 11.5 | 11.4 | 11.2 | 12.5 | 13.7 |

| Year | National | Ohio | | | | | | | | | Oklahoma | | | Oregon | | PA |
|---|---|---|---|---|---|---|---|---|---|---|---|---|---|---|---|---|
| Year | 30 City Average | Canton | Cincinnati | Cleveland | Columbus | Dayton | Lorain | Springfield | Toledo | Youngstown | Lawton | Oklahoma City | Tulsa | Eugene | Portland | Allentown |
| Jan 2023 | 318.8E | 267.1E | 267.3E | 283E | 273.2E | 260E | 269.2E | 261.5E | 278.2E | 269.6E | 253.6E | 254.7E | 247.6E | 305.3E | 309.5E | 296.8E |
| 2022 | 276.9 | 248.9 | 249.1 | 263.8 | 254.6 | 242.3 | 250.9 | 243.7 | 259.3 | 251.3 | 236.4 | 237.4 | 230.8 | 284.5 | 288.5 | 276.6 |
| 2021 | 238.3 | 216.6 | 214.4 | 227.9 | 221.3 | 211.2 | 218.5 | 212.5 | 226.6 | 219.3 | 200.4 | 201.4 | 197.4 | 241.5 | 243.1 | 242.9 |
| 2020 | 234.3 | 212 | 211.6 | 225.6 | 218.4 | 208.3 | 216 | 208.7 | 222.7 | 214.2 | 195.3 | 197.2 | 193.6 | 235.2 | 240.1 | 240.1 |
| 2019 | 227.3 | 203.3 | 199.4 | 213.8 | 203.2 | 194.7 | 207.1 | 196.8 | 212.5 | 204.6 | 187.4 | 186.2 | 184.8 | 219.1 | 221.7 | 226.1 |
| 2018 | 217.7 | 199.5 | 195.6 | 209.8 | 199.4 | 191.0 | 203.2 | 193.1 | 208.5 | 200.7 | 183.9 | 182.7 | 181.3 | 215.0 | 217.5 | 221.8 |
| 2017 | 209.4 | 192.2 | 186.1 | 202.6 | 191.6 | 186.1 | 196.9 | 187.8 | 201.4 | 194.2 | 178.0 | 177.0 | 174.8 | 207.3 | 209.5 | 213.7 |
| 2016 | 207.7 | 195.0 | 190.1 | 205.9 | 195.2 | 189.3 | 199.9 | 190.6 | 206.1 | 197.9 | 177.7 | 180.1 | 172.0 | 209.1 | 209.2 | 214.8 |
| 2015 | 204.0 | 191.1 | 188.1 | 203.4 | 192.4 | 187.9 | 196.7 | 188.1 | 201.0 | 193.3 | 175.1 | 177.1 | 170.0 | 203.1 | 204.3 | 209.8 |
| 2014 | 203.0 | 190.8 | 188.1 | 203.1 | 192.4 | 185.8 | 196.7 | 187.2 | 199.7 | 193.8 | 169.3 | 170.9 | 166.7 | 200.4 | 201.4 | 209.0 |
| 2013 | 196.9 | 183.9 | 181.9 | 195.5 | 187.1 | 180.7 | 187.6 | 181.5 | 193.5 | 186.5 | 162.7 | 165.5 | 161.7 | 194.7 | 195.6 | 203.2 |
| 2012 | 194.0 | 180.2 | 178.6 | 191.4 | 183.5 | 177.6 | 184.1 | 178.0 | 190.4 | 183.3 | 158.1 | 158.0 | 151.3 | 190.1 | 191.8 | 199.3 |
| 2011 | 185.7 | 172.1 | 171.3 | 184.0 | 175.7 | 168.4 | 176.8 | 168.4 | 183.1 | 176.5 | 151.7 | 151.6 | 144.8 | 184.9 | 186.6 | 192.2 |
| 2010 | 181.6 | 167.5 | 166.5 | 180.2 | 170.3 | 163.4 | 173.0 | 164.6 | 176.5 | 171.7 | 149.5 | 149.4 | 143.1 | 181.5 | 182.9 | 187.9 |
| 2009 | 182.5 | 168.4 | 168.1 | 181.6 | 171.2 | 165.3 | 174.0 | 166.0 | 178.5 | 172.8 | 152.5 | 153.3 | 146.8 | 181.3 | 183.6 | 188.3 |
| 2008 | 171.0 | 158.4 | 159.0 | 170.6 | 160.2 | 157.5 | 163.9 | 157.5 | 168.2 | 161.5 | 141.3 | 140.6 | 136.2 | 172.3 | 174.7 | 175.7 |
| 2007 | 165.0 | 153.2 | 152.4 | 164.9 | 155.1 | 149.4 | 158.1 | 150.3 | 161.6 | 156.7 | 136.2 | 135.6 | 132.5 | 168.5 | 169.5 | 169.4 |
| 2006 | 156.2 | 147.0 | 144.9 | 156.9 | 146.9 | 142.9 | 151.8 | 143.4 | 154.5 | 150.3 | 129.5 | 129.5 | 125.7 | 160.5 | 161.7 | 160.1 |
| 2005 | 146.7 | 137.7 | 136.8 | 147.9 | 138.0 | 134.5 | 143.3 | 134.8 | 145.5 | 141.1 | 121.6 | 121.6 | 117.8 | 150.9 | 152.2 | 150.2 |
| 2004 | 132.8 | 125.6 | 124.3 | 135.6 | 126.2 | 121.1 | 131.5 | 122.0 | 132.8 | 129.3 | 109.3 | 109.4 | 107.3 | 136.8 | 137.8 | 133.9 |
| 2003 | 129.7 | 123.7 | 121.3 | 132.7 | 123.7 | 119.4 | 126.1 | 120.0 | 130.4 | 126.2 | 107.5 | 107.8 | 105.0 | 134.2 | 135.9 | 130.3 |
| 2002 | 126.7 | 120.9 | 119.2 | 130.0 | 120.9 | 117.5 | 124.3 | 118.0 | 128.4 | 123.6 | 106.3 | 106.0 | 104.1 | 132.2 | 133.9 | 128.1 |
| 2001 | 122.2 | 117.7 | 115.9 | 125.9 | 117.1 | 114.0 | 120.4 | 114.7 | 123.8 | 119.9 | 102.0 | 102.1 | 99.7 | 129.8 | 131.2 | 123.5 |
| 2000 | 118.9 | 112.7 | 110.1 | 121.3 | 112.5 | 109.0 | 115.0 | 109.2 | 115.7 | 114.1 | 98.7 | 98.9 | 97.5 | 126.3 | 127.4 | 119.9 |
| 1990 | 93.2 | 92.1 | 86.7 | 95.1 | 88.1 | 85.9 | 89.4 | 83.4 | 92.9 | 91.8 | 77.1 | 79.9 | 80.0 | 98.0 | 99.4 | 95.0 |
| 1985 | 81.8 | 83.7 | 78.2 | 86.2 | 77.7 | 76.3 | 80.7 | 74.3 | 84.7 | 82.7 | 71.2 | 73.9 | 73.8 | 88.7 | 90.1 | 81.9 |
| 1980 | 60.7 | 60.6 | 59.8 | 61.0 | 58.6 | 56.6 | 60.8 | 56.2 | 64.0 | 61.5 | 52.2 | 55.5 | 57.2 | 68.9 | 68.4 | 58.7 |
| 1975 | 43.7 | 44.0 | 43.7 | 44.6 | 42.2 | 40.5 | 42.7 | 40.0 | 44.9 | 44.5 | 38.6 | 38.6 | 39.2 | 44.6 | 44.9 | 42.3 |
| 1970 | 27.8 | 27.8 | 28.2 | 29.6 | 26.7 | 27.0 | 27.5 | 25.4 | 29.1 | 29.6 | 24.1 | 23.4 | 24.1 | 30.4 | 30.0 | 27.3 |
| 1965 | 21.5 | 21.5 | 20.7 | 21.1 | 20.2 | 20.0 | 21.1 | 19.6 | 21.3 | 21.0 | 18.5 | 17.8 | 20.6 | 23.4 | 22.6 | 21.0 |
| 1960 | 19.5 | 19.5 | 19.3 | 19.6 | 18.7 | 18.1 | 19.2 | 17.8 | 19.4 | 19.1 | 16.9 | 16.1 | 18.1 | 21.2 | 21.1 | 19.1 |
| 1955 | 16.3 | 16.3 | 16.2 | 16.5 | 15.7 | 15.2 | 16.1 | 14.9 | 16.2 | 16.0 | 14.1 | 13.5 | 15.1 | 17.8 | 17.7 | 16.0 |
| ▼ 1950 | 13.5 | 13.5 | 13.3 | 13.6 | 13.0 | 12.5 | 13.3 | 12.3 | 13.4 | 13.2 | 11.7 | 11.2 | 12.5 | 14.7 | 14.6 | 13.2 |

| Year | National | Pennsylvania | | | | | | RI | South Carolina | | South Dakota | | Tennessee | | | |
|---|---|---|---|---|---|---|---|---|---|---|---|---|---|---|---|---|
| | 30 City Average | Erie | Harris-burg | Phila-delphia | Pitts burgh | Reading | Scranton | Provi-dence | Charles-ton | Colum-bia | Rapid City | Sioux Falls | Chatta-nooga | Knox-ville | Memphis | Nash-ville |
| Jan 2023 | 318.8E | 278E | 291E | 339.1E | 299.8E | 291.6E | 286.9E | 311.5E | 259.4E | 256.1E | 256.5E | 271.7E | 255.3E | 250.2E | 261.9E | 265.9E |
| 2022 | 276.9 | 259.1 | 271.2 | 316.0 | 279.4 | 271.8 | 267.4 | 290.3 | 241.8 | 238.7 | 239.1 | 253.2 | 237.9 | 233.2 | 244.1 | 247.8 |
| 2021 | 238.3 | 225.1 | 230.6 | 275.3 | 239.3 | 236.7 | 232.6 | 250.7 | 201.3 | 200.4 | 204.0 | 215.9 | 202.8 | 195.5 | 205.2 | 210.8 |
| 2020 | 234.3 | 221.9 | 229.6 | 268.8 | 234.6 | 236.2 | 229.7 | 248.8 | 200.6 | 199.9 | 204 | 210.3 | 200.4 | 191.3 | 203.3 | 209.2 |
| 2019 | 227.3 | 209.9 | 213.7 | 253.5 | 224.9 | 221.0 | 217.7 | 232.7 | 189.1 | 187.4 | 196.5 | 200.8 | 191.3 | 182.8 | 191.3 | 190.9 |
| 2018 | 217.7 | 205.9 | 209.7 | 248.7 | 220.7 | 216.8 | 213.6 | 228.3 | 185.5 | 183.9 | 192.8 | 197.0 | 187.7 | 179.4 | 187.7 | 187.3 |
| 2017 | 209.4 | 199.5 | 202.4 | 239.8 | 213.6 | 210.7 | 207.4 | 218.6 | 178.4 | 176.5 | 185.3 | 184.8 | 181.9 | 173.3 | 180.9 | 180.5 |
| 2016 | 207.7 | 199.7 | 202.4 | 238.2 | 212.2 | 207.6 | 207.0 | 221.6 | 176.8 | 176.6 | 174.7 | 175.2 | 177.4 | 173.9 | 181.9 | 181.8 |
| 2015 | 204.0 | 194.5 | 200.3 | 234.7 | 209.5 | 204.2 | 201.7 | 219.9 | 171.3 | 171.9 | 167.7 | 168.0 | 174.3 | 171.0 | 177.5 | 179.9 |
| 2014 | 203.0 | 191.4 | 200.3 | 232.1 | 207.1 | 201.4 | 201.4 | 220.3 | 171.0 | 162.5 | 168.6 | 166.8 | 174.1 | 170.9 | 176.5 | 178.2 |
| 2013 | 196.9 | 187.2 | 192.5 | 223.6 | 201.4 | 196.1 | 196.0 | 213.4 | 166.3 | 157.9 | 159.6 | 161.2 | 167.4 | 159.3 | 169.3 | 172.8 |
| 2012 | 194.0 | 182.0 | 187.9 | 221.8 | 196.8 | 190.8 | 191.5 | 209.3 | 155.3 | 148.1 | 156.7 | 158.8 | 163.8 | 155.8 | 166.3 | 167.5 |
| 2011 | 185.7 | 176.0 | 180.9 | 212.8 | 187.7 | 184.3 | 185.3 | 196.8 | 149.4 | 142.3 | 149.5 | 151.3 | 157.3 | 149.3 | 158.4 | 160.7 |
| 2010 | 181.6 | 171.0 | 175.2 | 209.3 | 182.3 | 179.8 | 180.8 | 192.8 | 147.4 | 140.2 | 147.3 | 149.0 | 152.4 | 144.7 | 154.2 | 156.7 |
| 2009 | 182.5 | 171.9 | 176.5 | 209.5 | 181.7 | 180.7 | 181.3 | 192.9 | 150.8 | 144.3 | 148.2 | 151.1 | 155.7 | 148.0 | 157.2 | 159.8 |
| 2008 | 171.0 | 161.0 | 165.7 | 196.2 | 169.2 | 169.3 | 167.9 | 178.2 | 142.1 | 134.8 | 138.4 | 141.3 | 136.7 | 133.4 | 146.0 | 147.5 |
| 2007 | 165.0 | 156.0 | 159.4 | 188.4 | 163.2 | 164.9 | 163.1 | 174.4 | 139.3 | 131.7 | 129.5 | 133.0 | 133.7 | 130.6 | 143.1 | 144.4 |
| 2006 | 156.2 | 148.7 | 150.7 | 177.8 | 155.5 | 155.0 | 153.9 | 163.6 | 122.4 | 118.7 | 122.8 | 126.6 | 127.0 | 123.9 | 136.5 | 135.5 |
| 2005 | 146.7 | 140.6 | 141.5 | 166.4 | 146.6 | 145.5 | 142.9 | 155.6 | 110.2 | 109.6 | 115.2 | 118.5 | 116.0 | 115.1 | 128.6 | 127.9 |
| 2004 | 132.8 | 127.0 | 126.2 | 148.4 | 133.1 | 128.7 | 129.0 | 138.8 | 98.9 | 98.4 | 103.9 | 107.3 | 105.0 | 104.5 | 115.6 | 115.8 |
| 2003 | 129.7 | 124.5 | 123.8 | 145.5 | 130.5 | 126.3 | 126.0 | 135.9 | 96.1 | 95.7 | 101.3 | 104.0 | 102.8 | 102.3 | 111.1 | 110.9 |
| 2002 | 126.7 | 122.1 | 121.1 | 142.0 | 127.8 | 123.4 | 124.2 | 131.1 | 94.8 | 93.9 | 100.2 | 103.2 | 102.2 | 101.2 | 107.6 | 109.2 |
| 2001 | 122.2 | 118.9 | 118.4 | 136.9 | 124.1 | 120.4 | 121.1 | 127.8 | 92.1 | 91.3 | 96.8 | 99.7 | 98.2 | 96.5 | 102.6 | 104.3 |
| 2000 | 118.9 | 114.6 | 114.0 | 132.1 | 120.9 | 115.9 | 117.7 | 122.8 | 89.9 | 89.1 | 94.2 | 98.0 | 96.9 | 95.0 | 100.8 | 100.8 |
| 1990 | 93.2 | 88.5 | 89.5 | 98.5 | 91.2 | 90.8 | 91.3 | 94.1 | 73.7 | 74.5 | 77.2 | 78.4 | 79.9 | 75.1 | 81.3 | 77.1 |
| 1985 | 81.8 | 79.6 | 77.2 | 82.2 | 81.5 | 77.7 | 80.0 | 83.0 | 65.9 | 66.9 | 69.7 | 71.2 | 72.5 | 67.7 | 74.3 | 66.7 |
| 1980 | 60.7 | 59.4 | 56.9 | 58.7 | 61.3 | 57.7 | 58.4 | 59.2 | 50.6 | 51.1 | 54.8 | 57.1 | 55.0 | 51.6 | 55.9 | 53.1 |
| 1975 | 43.7 | 43.4 | 42.2 | 44.5 | 44.5 | 43.6 | 41.9 | 42.7 | 35.0 | 36.4 | 37.7 | 39.6 | 39.1 | 37.3 | 40.7 | 37.0 |
| 1970 | 27.8 | 27.5 | 25.8 | 27.5 | 28.7 | 27.1 | 27.0 | 27.3 | 22.8 | 22.9 | 24.8 | 25.8 | 24.9 | 22.0 | 23.0 | 22.8 |
| 1965 | 21.5 | 21.1 | 20.1 | 21.7 | 22.4 | 20.9 | 20.8 | 21.9 | 17.6 | 17.6 | 19.1 | 19.9 | 19.2 | 17.1 | 18.3 | 17.4 |
| 1960 | 19.5 | 19.1 | 18.6 | 19.4 | 19.7 | 19.0 | 18.9 | 19.1 | 16.0 | 16.0 | 17.3 | 18.1 | 17.4 | 15.5 | 16.6 | 15.8 |
| 1955 | 16.3 | 16.1 | 15.6 | 16.3 | 16.5 | 15.9 | 15.9 | 16.0 | 13.4 | 13.4 | 14.5 | 15.1 | 14.6 | 13.0 | 13.9 | 13.3 |
| ▼ 1950 | 13.5 | 13.3 | 12.9 | 13.5 | 13.6 | 13.2 | 13.1 | 13.2 | 11.1 | 11.1 | 12.0 | 12.5 | 12.1 | 10.7 | 11.5 | 10.9 |

| Year | National | Texas | | | | | | | | | | | | | | Utah |
|---|---|---|---|---|---|---|---|---|---|---|---|---|---|---|---|---|
| | 30 City Average | Abi-lene | Ama-rillo | Austin | Beau-mont | Corpus Christi | Dallas | El Paso | Fort Worth | Houston | Lubbock | Odessa | San Antonio | Waco | Wichita Falls | Ogden |
| Jan 2023 | 318.8E | 247.3E | 249.5E | 248.1E | 247.7E | 249.2E | 260E | 251.6E | 251.5E | 256.1E | 251.5E | 248.5E | 250.4E | 245.5E | 244.3E | 261.6E |
| 2022 | 276.9 | 230.5 | 232.5 | 231.2 | 230.9 | 232.3 | 242.3 | 234.5 | 234.4 | 238.7 | 234.4 | 231.6 | 233.4 | 228.8 | 227.7 | 243.8 |
| 2021 | 238.3 | 195.4 | 196.7 | 195.7 | 198.7 | 200.1 | 203.2 | 196.2 | 197.6 | 204.8 | 196.3 | 194.4 | 199.5 | 192.6 | 192.8 | 207.3 |
| 2020 | 234.3 | 192.6 | 193.7 | 191.3 | 195.8 | 193.7 | 199.5 | 194.1 | 194.4 | 202.2 | 195.5 | 193.4 | 195.5 | 189.3 | 190.6 | 205.6 |
| 2019 | 227.3 | 182.1 | 181.4 | 182.3 | 186.2 | 184.5 | 188.6 | 181.9 | 183.9 | 188.7 | 184.7 | 183.6 | 184.5 | 180.1 | 179.7 | 194.3 |
| 2018 | 217.7 | 178.7 | 178.0 | 178.9 | 182.7 | 181.0 | 185.0 | 178.5 | 180.4 | 185.1 | 181.2 | 180.1 | 181.0 | 176.7 | 176.3 | 190.6 |
| 2017 | 209.4 | 174.0 | 172.8 | 172.6 | 178.0 | 178.9 | 180.0 | 173.5 | 174.9 | 179.2 | 176.6 | 175.6 | 175.5 | 170.7 | 170.4 | 183.3 |
| 2016 | 207.7 | 173.7 | 171.0 | 173.3 | 178.3 | 175.5 | 177.9 | 172.8 | 174.1 | 180.5 | 175.2 | 172.6 | 173.1 | 170.3 | 170.1 | 179.4 |
| 2015 | 204.0 | 170.8 | 170.7 | 172.3 | 174.0 | 172.8 | 174.4 | 168.8 | 172.5 | 176.4 | 173.3 | 171.5 | 171.8 | 167.3 | 169.0 | 177.1 |
| 2014 | 203.0 | 160.9 | 167.2 | 167.5 | 165.2 | 167.3 | 172.4 | 156.2 | 169.5 | 176.0 | 166.9 | 159.2 | 169.5 | 161.7 | 160.6 | 174.2 |
| 2013 | 196.9 | 155.2 | 161.7 | 158.7 | 160.2 | 157.7 | 167.4 | 151.2 | 161.7 | 169.4 | 159.3 | 151.5 | 164.3 | 156.1 | 155.9 | 167.7 |
| 2012 | 194.0 | 152.5 | 158.6 | 154.3 | 158.2 | 151.8 | 165.2 | 149.1 | 159.4 | 167.8 | 156.6 | 149.1 | 160.7 | 153.8 | 152.9 | 165.6 |
| 2011 | 185.7 | 145.9 | 151.9 | 147.6 | 152.4 | 145.0 | 157.9 | 142.5 | 152.8 | 160.8 | 150.0 | 142.5 | 152.6 | 147.3 | 146.6 | 158.7 |
| 2010 | 181.6 | 144.2 | 150.1 | 144.7 | 150.5 | 142.1 | 155.1 | 140.8 | 149.6 | 157.3 | 148.1 | 140.7 | 147.9 | 145.8 | 145.0 | 157.5 |
| 2009 | 182.5 | 143.5 | 147.3 | 146.4 | 149.8 | 141.7 | 155.5 | 141.1 | 150.1 | 160.9 | 144.6 | 139.1 | 150.8 | 146.7 | 146.1 | 155.1 |
| 2008 | 171.0 | 132.4 | 137.0 | 137.5 | 140.3 | 133.2 | 144.1 | 130.7 | 138.3 | 149.1 | 134.7 | 128.9 | 141.0 | 136.1 | 136.1 | 144.8 |
| 2007 | 165.0 | 128.5 | 132.2 | 131.6 | 137.1 | 128.8 | 138.6 | 126.2 | 134.8 | 146.0 | 130.2 | 125.0 | 136.4 | 132.1 | 132.1 | 140.0 |
| 2006 | 156.2 | 121.6 | 125.7 | 125.5 | 130.1 | 122.0 | 131.1 | 120.3 | 127.6 | 138.2 | 123.2 | 118.3 | 129.8 | 125.2 | 125.3 | 133.4 |
| 2005 | 146.7 | 113.8 | 117.3 | 117.9 | 121.3 | 114.4 | 123.7 | 112.5 | 119.4 | 129.0 | 115.5 | 110.5 | 121.3 | 116.1 | 117.3 | 126.0 |
| 2004 | 132.8 | 102.9 | 106.3 | 105.7 | 108.5 | 102.9 | 112.0 | 101.5 | 108.4 | 115.9 | 104.7 | 99.9 | 108.4 | 104.8 | 105.1 | 115.2 |
| 2003 | 129.7 | 100.5 | 104.4 | 103.9 | 106.1 | 100.4 | 109.3 | 99.5 | 105.5 | 113.4 | 102.3 | 97.6 | 104.8 | 102.7 | 103.0 | 112.7 |
| 2002 | 126.7 | 99.9 | 101.9 | 102.4 | 104.5 | 98.9 | 107.9 | 98.7 | 104.6 | 111.5 | 100.5 | 95.9 | 103.7 | 100.5 | 101.4 | 110.8 |
| 2001 | 122.2 | 93.4 | 98.4 | 99.8 | 102.3 | 96.6 | 103.8 | 95.5 | 100.9 | 107.8 | 97.6 | 93.4 | 100.5 | 97.8 | 97.3 | 107.7 |
| 2000 | 118.9 | 93.4 | 98.1 | 99.1 | 101.6 | 96.9 | 102.7 | 92.4 | 99.9 | 106.0 | 97.6 | 93.4 | 99.4 | 97.3 | 96.9 | 104.6 |
| 1990 | 93.2 | 78.0 | 80.1 | 81.3 | 86.5 | 79.3 | 84.5 | 76.7 | 82.1 | 85.4 | 81.5 | 78.6 | 80.7 | 79.6 | 80.3 | 83.4 |
| 1985 | 81.8 | 71.1 | 72.5 | 74.5 | 79.3 | 72.3 | 77.6 | 69.4 | 75.1 | 79.6 | 74.0 | 71.2 | 73.9 | 71.7 | 73.3 | 75.2 |
| 1980 | 60.7 | 53.4 | 55.2 | 54.5 | 57.6 | 54.5 | 57.9 | 53.1 | 57.0 | 59.4 | 55.6 | 57.2 | 55.0 | 54.9 | 55.4 | 62.2 |
| 1975 | 43.7 | 37.6 | 39.0 | 39.0 | 39.6 | 38.1 | 40.7 | 38.0 | 40.4 | 41.2 | 38.9 | 37.9 | 39.0 | 38.6 | 38.0 | 40.0 |
| 1970 | 27.8 | 24.5 | 24.9 | 24.9 | 25.7 | 24.5 | 25.5 | 23.7 | 25.9 | 25.4 | 25.1 | 24.6 | 23.3 | 24.8 | 24.5 | 26.8 |
| 1965 | 21.5 | 18.9 | 19.2 | 19.2 | 19.9 | 18.9 | 19.9 | 19.0 | 19.9 | 20.0 | 19.4 | 19.0 | 18.5 | 19.2 | 18.9 | 20.6 |
| 1960 | 19.5 | 17.1 | 17.4 | 17.4 | 18.1 | 17.1 | 18.2 | 17.0 | 18.1 | 18.2 | 17.6 | 17.3 | 16.8 | 17.4 | 17.2 | 18.8 |
| 1955 | 16.3 | 14.4 | 14.6 | 14.6 | 15.1 | 14.4 | 15.3 | 14.3 | 15.2 | 15.2 | 14.8 | 14.5 | 14.1 | 14.6 | 14.4 | 15.7 |
| ▼ 1950 | 13.5 | 11.9 | 12.1 | 12.1 | 12.5 | 11.9 | 12.6 | 11.8 | 12.5 | 12.6 | 12.2 | 12.0 | 11.6 | 12.1 | 11.9 | 13.0 |

| Year | National | Utah | Vermont | | Virginia | | | | | Washington | | | West Virginia | | Wisconsin | |
|---|---|---|---|---|---|---|---|---|---|---|---|---|---|---|---|---|
| | 30 City Average | Salt Lake City | Burlington | Rutland | Alexandria | Newport News | Norfolk | Richmond | Roanoke | Seattle | Spokane | Tacoma | Charleston | Huntington | Green Bay | Kenosha |
| Jan 2023 | 318.8E | 269.5E | 276E | 269.7E | 274.9E | 256.8E | 260.3E | 259.3E | 258.9E | 316.6E | 278.9E | 309.2E | 278.4E | 279.2E | 294.7E | 296.5E |
| 2022 | 276.9 | 251.2 | 257.2 | 251.4 | 256.2 | 239.3 | 242.6 | 241.7 | 241.3 | 295.1 | 259.9 | 288.2 | 259.5 | 260.2 | 274.7 | 276.3 |
| 2021 | 238.3 | 213.2 | 221.3 | 215.8 | 220.5 | 203.7 | 204.5 | 209.2 | 205.0 | 256.4 | 225.0 | 249.6 | 222.7 | 224.6 | 237.9 | 241.1 |
| 2020 | 234.3 | 211.8 | 220.1 | 215.3 | 217.6 | 202.3 | 204.3 | 208.2 | 202.9 | 252.3 | 216.5 | 240.4 | 221.9 | 222 | 232.2 | 237.7 |
| 2019 | 227.3 | 199.5 | 203.9 | 200.4 | 206.2 | 189.6 | 190.3 | 197.5 | 194.5 | 235.3 | 209.2 | 228.6 | 211.8 | 215.7 | 218.3 | 226.2 |
| 2018 | 217.7 | 195.7 | 200.1 | 196.6 | 202.3 | 186.0 | 186.7 | 193.8 | 190.8 | 230.9 | 205.3 | 224.3 | 207.8 | 211.6 | 214.2 | 221.9 |
| 2017 | 209.4 | 188.8 | 192.8 | 189.5 | 195.6 | 180.7 | 180.5 | 182.8 | 185.1 | 219.3 | 198.8 | 215.8 | 201.5 | 204.5 | 206.9 | 213.6 |
| 2016 | 207.7 | 184.7 | 193.6 | 190.2 | 195.6 | 178.3 | 178.2 | 178.9 | 178.0 | 213.4 | 195.1 | 209.7 | 204.2 | 206.5 | 207.4 | 212.8 |
| 2015 | 204.0 | 182.1 | 191.6 | 188.5 | 192.5 | 175.8 | 177.4 | 177.2 | 175.3 | 209.9 | 193.1 | 207.2 | 199.9 | 201.3 | 200.8 | 205.4 |
| 2014 | 203.0 | 177.1 | 191.3 | 188.6 | 190.5 | 174.4 | 175.7 | 176.4 | 173.5 | 209.8 | 190.8 | 205.2 | 197.0 | 199.5 | 198.9 | 205.2 |
| 2013 | 196.9 | 171.1 | 178.7 | 176.6 | 185.0 | 170.0 | 171.5 | 170.7 | 168.3 | 203.4 | 184.3 | 199.1 | 187.2 | 193.2 | 193.9 | 201.2 |
| 2012 | 194.0 | 168.8 | 172.4 | 170.5 | 182.4 | 168.3 | 169.7 | 169.4 | 166.4 | 201.9 | 181.6 | 194.3 | 183.4 | 186.4 | 190.0 | 195.5 |
| 2011 | 185.7 | 161.8 | 158.8 | 157.1 | 174.5 | 159.8 | 161.1 | 159.0 | 154.2 | 194.1 | 175.5 | 187.6 | 177.5 | 180.3 | 181.4 | 187.6 |
| 2010 | 181.6 | 160.9 | 156.3 | 154.6 | 170.9 | 156.7 | 158.0 | 156.6 | 151.8 | 191.8 | 171.5 | 186.0 | 171.6 | 176.1 | 179.0 | 185.1 |
| 2009 | 182.5 | 160.4 | 158.3 | 156.7 | 172.5 | 160.0 | 161.9 | 160.7 | 155.6 | 188.5 | 173.0 | 186.3 | 174.6 | 177.4 | 175.5 | 182.5 |
| 2008 | 171.0 | 149.7 | 147.2 | 145.8 | 161.8 | 150.8 | 150.8 | 150.9 | 145.9 | 176.9 | 162.4 | 174.9 | 162.8 | 165.7 | 165.6 | 172.2 |
| 2007 | 165.0 | 144.6 | 144.4 | 143.2 | 155.0 | 146.2 | 146.1 | 147.3 | 142.9 | 171.4 | 156.7 | 168.7 | 158.7 | 160.1 | 159.4 | 164.8 |
| 2006 | 156.2 | 137.7 | 131.7 | 130.7 | 146.2 | 133.7 | 134.6 | 134.8 | 129.7 | 162.9 | 150.1 | 160.7 | 149.4 | 151.4 | 152.7 | 157.1 |
| 2005 | 146.7 | 129.4 | 124.6 | 123.8 | 136.5 | 123.5 | 124.4 | 125.4 | 112.2 | 153.9 | 141.9 | 151.5 | 140.8 | 141.0 | 144.4 | 148.3 |
| 2004 | 132.8 | 117.8 | 113.0 | 112.3 | 121.5 | 108.9 | 110.2 | 110.9 | 99.7 | 138.0 | 127.6 | 134.5 | 124.8 | 125.6 | 128.9 | 132.4 |
| 2003 | 129.7 | 116.0 | 110.7 | 110.1 | 119.5 | 104.8 | 106.2 | 108.6 | 97.0 | 134.9 | 125.9 | 133.0 | 123.3 | 123.6 | 127.4 | 130.9 |
| 2002 | 126.7 | 113.7 | 109.0 | 108.4 | 115.1 | 102.9 | 104.1 | 106.6 | 95.2 | 132.7 | 123.9 | 131.4 | 121.2 | 120.9 | 123.0 | 127.3 |
| 2001 | 122.2 | 109.1 | 105.7 | 105.2 | 110.8 | 99.8 | 100.3 | 102.9 | 92.1 | 127.9 | 120.3 | 125.7 | 114.6 | 117.5 | 119.1 | 123.6 |
| 2000 | 118.9 | 106.5 | 98.9 | 98.3 | 108.1 | 96.5 | 97.6 | 100.2 | 90.7 | 124.6 | 118.3 | 122.9 | 111.5 | 114.4 | 114.6 | 119.1 |
| 1990 | 93.2 | 84.3 | 83.0 | 82.9 | 86.1 | 76.3 | 76.7 | 77.6 | 76.1 | 100.1 | 98.5 | 100.5 | 86.1 | 86.8 | 86.7 | 87.8 |
| 1985 | 81.8 | 75.9 | 74.8 | 74.9 | 75.1 | 68.7 | 68.8 | 69.5 | 67.2 | 88.3 | 89.0 | 91.2 | 77.7 | 77.7 | 76.7 | 77.4 |
| 1980 | 60.7 | 57.0 | 55.3 | 58.3 | 57.3 | 52.5 | 52.4 | 54.3 | 51.3 | 67.9 | 66.3 | 66.7 | 57.7 | 58.3 | 58.6 | 58.3 |
| 1975 | 43.7 | 40.1 | 41.8 | 43.9 | 41.7 | 37.2 | 36.9 | 37.1 | 37.1 | 44.9 | 44.4 | 44.5 | 41.0 | 40.0 | 40.9 | 40.5 |
| 1970 | 27.8 | 26.1 | 25.4 | 26.8 | 26.2 | 23.9 | 21.5 | 22.0 | 23.7 | 28.8 | 29.3 | 29.6 | 26.1 | 25.8 | 26.4 | 26.5 |
| 1965 | 21.5 | 20.0 | 19.8 | 20.6 | 20.2 | 18.4 | 17.1 | 17.2 | 18.3 | 22.4 | 22.5 | 22.8 | 20.1 | 19.9 | 20.3 | 20.4 |
| 1960 | 19.5 | 18.4 | 18.0 | 18.8 | 18.4 | 16.7 | 15.4 | 15.6 | 16.6 | 20.4 | 20.8 | 20.8 | 18.3 | 18.1 | 18.4 | 18.6 |
| 1955 | 16.3 | 15.4 | 15.1 | 15.7 | 15.4 | 14.0 | 12.9 | 13.1 | 13.9 | 17.1 | 17.4 | 17.4 | 15.4 | 15.2 | 15.5 | 15.6 |
| ▼ 1950 | 13.5 | 12.7 | 12.4 | 13.0 | 12.7 | 11.6 | 10.7 | 10.8 | 11.5 | 14.1 | 14.4 | 14.4 | 12.7 | 12.5 | 12.8 | 12.9 |

| Year | National | Wisconsin | | | Wyoming | Canada | | | | | | | | | |
|---|---|---|---|---|---|---|---|---|---|---|---|---|---|---|---|
| | 30 City Average | Madison | Milwaukee | Racine | Cheyenne | Calgary | Edmonton | Hamilton | London | Montreal | Ottawa | Quebec | Toronto | Vancouver | Winnipeg |
| Jan 2023 | 318.8E | 296.9E | 300.1E | 295E | 263.2E | 342.8E | 345.1E | 328.1E | 326.6E | 321.2E | 314.6E | 321.6E | 337.6E | 328.3E | 308.5E |
| 2022 | 276.9 | 276.7 | 279.7 | 274.9 | 245.3 | 319.5 | 321.6 | 305.8 | 304.4 | 299.4 | 293.2 | 299.7 | 314.6 | 306.0 | 287.5 |
| 2021 | 238.3 | 240.3 | 244.5 | 240.1 | 209.4 | 257.9 | 260.8 | 255.1 | 253.8 | 254.8 | 255.6 | 255.4 | 260.9 | 256.6 | 237.7 |
| 2020 | 234.3 | 233.8 | 240.5 | 238.5 | 207 | 256 | 259.4 | 254.4 | 252.2 | 249.7 | 254.1 | 249.8 | 259.5 | 250.9 | 235.6 |
| 2019 | 227.3 | 221.1 | 228.3 | 226.0 | 197.8 | 244.2 | 245.2 | 230.9 | 239.0 | 237.4 | 241.2 | 236.1 | 246.1 | 234.0 | 221.8 |
| 2018 | 217.7 | 216.9 | 224.0 | 221.7 | 194.1 | 239.6 | 240.6 | 226.6 | 234.5 | 232.9 | 236.7 | 231.7 | 241.5 | 229.6 | 217.6 |
| 2017 | 209.4 | 207.4 | 215.2 | 213.8 | 185.0 | 231.4 | 232.3 | 227.8 | 225.0 | 221.8 | 227.7 | 222.9 | 231.4 | 221.5 | 207.7 |
| 2016 | 207.7 | 207.4 | 214.4 | 212.4 | 178.6 | 229.1 | 229.4 | 221.7 | 221.3 | 218.5 | 223.4 | 218.9 | 228.6 | 219.3 | 205.3 |
| 2015 | 204.0 | 202.0 | 209.4 | 205.1 | 175.4 | 226.6 | 226.3 | 221.2 | 217.0 | 220.4 | 220.4 | 220.4 | 225.9 | 217.1 | 204.1 |
| 2014 | 203.0 | 202.4 | 210.2 | 205.3 | 173.6 | 228.2 | 229.1 | 222.1 | 218.9 | 219.8 | 214.8 | 218.3 | 227.4 | 218.8 | 202.9 |
| 2013 | 196.9 | 197.8 | 204.6 | 200.5 | 167.6 | 222.7 | 223.3 | 216.0 | 213.7 | 214.5 | 214.1 | 212.6 | 220.9 | 216.2 | 200.2 |
| 2012 | 194.0 | 191.2 | 202.2 | 194.9 | 165.0 | 219.1 | 219.6 | 211.1 | 208.2 | 209.6 | 209.7 | 207.5 | 216.6 | 214.0 | 200.7 |
| 2011 | 185.7 | 183.4 | 191.9 | 187.0 | 155.3 | 212.6 | 212.4 | 204.2 | 200.1 | 202.1 | 202.0 | 200.6 | 209.6 | 207.1 | 192.6 |
| 2010 | 181.6 | 181.3 | 187.1 | 184.4 | 154.4 | 200.6 | 200.7 | 197.7 | 193.7 | 193.9 | 195.6 | 192.7 | 200.7 | 192.7 | 182.9 |
| 2009 | 182.5 | 180.0 | 187.3 | 182.8 | 155.2 | 205.4 | 206.6 | 203.0 | 198.9 | 198.8 | 200.1 | 197.4 | 205.6 | 199.6 | 188.5 |
| 2008 | 171.0 | 168.4 | 176.3 | 173.0 | 146.5 | 190.2 | 191.0 | 194.3 | 188.6 | 186.7 | 188.0 | 186.8 | 194.6 | 184.9 | 174.4 |
| 2007 | 165.0 | 160.7 | 168.9 | 164.7 | 141.3 | 183.1 | 184.4 | 186.8 | 182.4 | 181.7 | 182.4 | 182.0 | 187.7 | 180.6 | 170.1 |
| 2006 | 156.2 | 152.8 | 158.8 | 157.2 | 128.0 | 163.6 | 164.8 | 169.0 | 164.9 | 158.6 | 163.7 | 159.0 | 170.6 | 169.3 | 155.9 |
| 2005 | 146.7 | 145.2 | 148.4 | 147.9 | 118.9 | 154.4 | 155.7 | 160.0 | 156.2 | 149.2 | 155.1 | 150.1 | 162.6 | 159.4 | 146.9 |
| 2004 | 132.8 | 129.7 | 134.2 | 132.7 | 104.7 | 138.8 | 139.4 | 142.6 | 140.4 | 134.5 | 141.0 | 135.7 | 146.0 | 141.7 | 129.7 |
| 2003 | 129.7 | 128.4 | 131.1 | 131.5 | 102.6 | 133.6 | 134.2 | 139.1 | 137.0 | 130.2 | 137.4 | 131.4 | 142.3 | 137.0 | 124.4 |
| 2002 | 126.7 | 124.5 | 128.2 | 126.5 | 101.7 | 122.5 | 122.2 | 136.3 | 134.1 | 127.2 | 134.9 | 128.4 | 139.8 | 134.6 | 121.4 |
| 2001 | 122.2 | 120.6 | 123.9 | 123.3 | 99.0 | 117.5 | 117.4 | 131.5 | 129.1 | 124.4 | 130.2 | 125.5 | 134.7 | 130.2 | 117.2 |
| 2000 | 118.9 | 116.6 | 120.5 | 118.7 | 98.1 | 115.9 | 115.8 | 130.0 | 127.5 | 122.8 | 128.8 | 124.1 | 133.1 | 128.4 | 115.6 |
| 1990 | 93.2 | 84.3 | 88.9 | 87.3 | 79.1 | 98.0 | 97.1 | 103.8 | 101.4 | 99.0 | 102.7 | 96.8 | 104.6 | 103.2 | 95.1 |
| 1985 | 81.8 | 74.3 | 77.4 | 77.0 | 72.3 | 90.2 | 89.1 | 85.8 | 84.9 | 82.4 | 83.9 | 79.9 | 86.5 | 89.8 | 83.4 |
| 1980 | 60.7 | 56.8 | 58.8 | 58.1 | 56.9 | 64.9 | 63.3 | 63.7 | 61.9 | 59.2 | 60.9 | 59.3 | 60.9 | 65.0 | 61.7 |
| 1975 | 43.7 | 40.7 | 43.3 | 40.7 | 40.6 | 42.2 | 41.6 | 42.9 | 41.6 | 39.7 | 41.5 | 39.0 | 42.2 | 42.4 | 39.2 |
| 1970 | 27.8 | 26.5 | 29.4 | 26.5 | 26.0 | 28.9 | 28.6 | 28.5 | 27.8 | 25.6 | 27.6 | 26.0 | 25.6 | 26.0 | 23.1 |
| 1965 | 21.5 | 20.6 | 21.8 | 20.4 | 20.0 | 22.3 | 22.0 | 22.0 | 21.4 | 18.7 | 21.2 | 20.1 | 19.4 | 20.5 | 17.5 |
| 1960 | 19.5 | 18.1 | 19.0 | 18.6 | 18.2 | 20.2 | 20.0 | 20.0 | 19.5 | 17.0 | 19.3 | 18.2 | 17.6 | 18.6 | 15.8 |
| 1955 | 16.3 | 15.2 | 15.9 | 15.6 | 15.2 | 17.0 | 16.8 | 16.7 | 16.3 | 14.3 | 16.2 | 15.3 | 14.8 | 15.5 | 13.3 |
| ▼ 1950 | 13.5 | 12.5 | 13.2 | 12.9 | 12.6 | 14.0 | 13.9 | 13.8 | 13.5 | 11.8 | 13.4 | 12.6 | 12.2 | 12.8 | 10.9 |

## Back by customer demand!

You asked and we listened. For customer convenience and estimating ease, we have made the 2023 Project Costs available for download at **RSMeans.com/2023books**. You will also find sample estimates, an RSMeans data overview video, and a book registration form to receive quarterly data updates throughout 2023.

## Estimating Tips

- The cost figures available in the download were derived from hundreds of projects contained in the RSMeans database of completed construction projects. They include the contractor's overhead and profit. The figures have been adjusted to January of the current year.
- These projects were located throughout the U.S. and reflect a tremendous variation in square foot (S.F.) costs. This is due to differences, not only in labor and material costs, but also in individual owners' requirements. For instance, a bank in a large city would have different features than one in a rural area. This is true of all the different types of buildings analyzed. Therefore, caution should be exercised when using these Project Costs. For example, for courthouses, costs in the database are local courthouse costs and will not apply to the larger, more elaborate federal courthouses.
- None of the figures "go with" any others. All individual cost items were computed and tabulated separately. Thus, the sum of the median figures for plumbing, HVAC, and electrical will not normally total up to the total mechanical and electrical costs arrived at by separate analysis and tabulation of the projects.
- Each building was analyzed as to total and component costs and percentages. The figures were arranged in ascending order with the results tabulated as shown. The 1/4 column shows that 25% of the projects had lower costs and 75% had higher. The 3/4 column shows that 75% of the projects had lower costs and 25% had higher. The median column shows that 50% of the projects had lower costs and 50% had higher.
- Project Costs are useful in the conceptual stage when no details are available. As soon as details become available in the project design, the square foot approach should be discontinued and the project should be priced as to its particular components. When more precision is required, or for estimating the replacement cost of specific buildings, the current edition of *Square Foot Costs with RSMeans data* should be used.
- In using the figures in this section, it is recommended that the median column be used for preliminary figures if no additional information is available. The median figures, when multiplied by the total city construction cost index figures (see City Cost Indexes) and then multiplied by the project size modifier at the end of this section, should present a fairly accurate base figure, which would then have to be adjusted in view of the estimator's experience, local economic conditions, code requirements, and the owner's particular requirements. There is no need to factor in the percentage figures, as these should remain constant from city to city.
- The editors of this data would greatly appreciate receiving cost figures on one or more of your recent projects, which would then be included in the averages for next year. All cost figures received will be kept confidential, except that they will be averaged with other similar projects to arrive at square foot cost figures for next year.

*See the website above for details and the discount available for submitting one or more of your projects.*

| | 50 17 00 \| Project Costs | | UNIT | UNIT COSTS 1/4 | UNIT COSTS MEDIAN | UNIT COSTS 3/4 | % OF TOTAL 1/4 | % OF TOTAL MEDIAN | % OF TOTAL 3/4 | |
|---|---|---|---|---|---|---|---|---|---|---|
| 01 | 0000 | **Auto Sales with Repair** | S.F. | | | | | | | 01 |
| | 0100 | Architectural | | 146 | 163 | 176 | 58% | 64% | 67% | |
| | 0200 | Plumbing | | 12.20 | 12.75 | 17.05 | 4.84% | 5.20% | 6.80% | |
| | 0300 | Mechanical | | 16.30 | 22 | 24 | 6.40% | 8.70% | 10.15% | |
| | 0400 | Electrical | | 25 | 31 | 39 | 9.05% | 11.70% | 15.90% | |
| | 0500 | Total Project Costs | ↓ | 244 | 255 | 262 | | | | |
| 02 | 0000 | **Banking Institutions** | S.F. | | | | | | | 02 |
| | 0100 | Architectural | | 220 | 270 | 330 | 59% | 65% | 69% | |
| | 0200 | Plumbing | | 8.85 | 12.35 | 17.15 | 2.12% | 3.39% | 4.19% | |
| | 0300 | Mechanical | | 17.60 | 24.50 | 28.50 | 4.41% | 5.10% | 10.75% | |
| | 0400 | Electrical | | 43 | 52 | 80 | 10.45% | 13.05% | 15.90% | |
| | 0500 | Total Project Costs | ↓ | 365 | 410 | 505 | | | | |
| 03 | 0000 | **Courthouse** | S.F. | | | | | | | 03 |
| | 0100 | Architectural | | 116 | 228 | 320 | 54.50% | 58.50% | 61% | |
| | 0200 | Plumbing | | 4.38 | 16.30 | 16.30 | 2.07% | 3.13% | 3.13% | |
| | 0300 | Mechanical | | 27.50 | 32.50 | 32.50 | 6.25% | 12.95% | 12.95% | |
| | 0400 | Electrical | | 35 | 40 | 40 | 7.65% | 16.60% | 16.60% | |
| | 0500 | Total Project Costs | ↓ | 211 | 390 | 520 | | | | |
| 04 | 0000 | **Data Centers** | S.F. | | | | | | | 04 |
| | 0100 | Architectural | | 262 | 262 | 262 | 68% | 68% | 68% | |
| | 0200 | Plumbing | | 14.35 | 14.35 | 14.35 | 3.71% | 3.71% | 3.71% | |
| | 0300 | Mechanical | | 36.50 | 36.50 | 36.50 | 9.45% | 9.45% | 9.45% | |
| | 0400 | Electrical | | 34.50 | 34.50 | 34.50 | 9% | 9% | 9% | |
| | 0500 | Total Project Costs | ↓ | 385 | 385 | 385 | | | | |
| 05 | 0000 | **Detention Centers** | S.F. | | | | | | | 05 |
| | 0100 | Architectural | | 243 | 256 | 272 | 52% | 53% | 60.50% | |
| | 0200 | Plumbing | | 25.50 | 31 | 37.50 | 5.15% | 7.10% | 7.25% | |
| | 0300 | Mechanical | | 32.50 | 46.50 | 55.50 | 7.55% | 9.50% | 13.80% | |
| | 0400 | Electrical | | 53.50 | 63 | 82 | 10.90% | 14.85% | 17.95% | |
| | 0500 | Total Project Costs | ↓ | 410 | 435 | 510 | | | | |
| 06 | 0000 | **Fire Stations** | S.F. | | | | | | | 06 |
| | 0100 | Architectural | | 141 | 180 | 284 | 46% | 54.50% | 61.50% | |
| | 0200 | Plumbing | | 14.75 | 19.70 | 25.50 | 4.67% | 5.60% | 6.35% | |
| | 0300 | Mechanical | | 22 | 31 | 42 | 6.10% | 8.25% | 10.20% | |
| | 0400 | Electrical | | 33.50 | 41 | 57.50 | 10.75% | 12.55% | 14.95% | |
| | 0500 | Total Project Costs | ↓ | 292 | 350 | 465 | | | | |
| 07 | 0000 | **Gymnasium** | S.F. | | | | | | | 07 |
| | 0100 | Architectural | | 121 | 160 | 160 | 57% | 64.50% | 64.50% | |
| | 0200 | Plumbing | | 2.97 | 9.75 | 9.75 | 1.58% | 3.48% | 3.48% | |
| | 0300 | Mechanical | | 4.56 | 41 | 41 | 2.42% | 14.65% | 14.65% | |
| | 0400 | Electrical | | 14.95 | 29 | 29 | 7.95% | 10.35% | 10.35% | |
| | 0500 | Total Project Costs | ↓ | 189 | 280 | 280 | | | | |
| 08 | 0000 | **Hospitals** | S.F. | | | | | | | 08 |
| | 0100 | Architectural | | 147 | 242 | 263 | 41.50% | 47.50% | 48% | |
| | 0200 | Plumbing | | 10.80 | 44.50 | 53 | 6% | 7.65% | 10.35% | |
| | 0300 | Mechanical | | 65 | 80.50 | 105 | 12.55% | 17.95% | 23.50% | |
| | 0400 | Electrical | | 32.50 | 73.50 | 84.50 | 10.95% | 14.10% | 16.85% | |
| | 0500 | Total Project Costs | ↓ | 345 | 520 | 555 | | | | |
| 09 | 0000 | **Industrial Buildings** | S.F. | | | | | | | 09 |
| | 0100 | Architectural | | 80.50 | 158 | 320 | 52% | 56% | 82% | |
| | 0200 | Plumbing | | 2.32 | 6.30 | 18.20 | 1.57% | 2.11% | 6.30% | |
| | 0300 | Mechanical | | 6.60 | 12.55 | 60 | 4.77% | 5.55% | 14.80% | |
| | 0400 | Electrical | | 10.10 | 11.50 | 96 | 7.85% | 13.55% | 16.20% | |
| | 0500 | Total Project Costs | ↓ | 119 | 181 | 595 | | | | |
| 10 | 0000 | **Medical Clinics & Offices** | S.F. | | | | | | | 10 |
| | 0100 | Architectural | | 134 | 166 | 218 | 48.50% | 54% | 62% | |
| | 0200 | Plumbing | | 12.30 | 18.55 | 30.50 | 4.50% | 6.65% | 8.75% | |
| | 0300 | Mechanical | | 19.90 | 30.50 | 54.50 | 7.80% | 10.85% | 15.75% | |
| | 0400 | Electrical | | 27 | 33.50 | 51 | 8.90% | 11.20% | 13.85% | |
| | 0500 | Total Project Costs | ↓ | 231 | 305 | 400 | | | | |

| | | 50 17 00 \| Project Costs | UNIT | UNIT COSTS 1/4 | UNIT COSTS MEDIAN | UNIT COSTS 3/4 | % OF TOTAL 1/4 | % OF TOTAL MEDIAN | % OF TOTAL 3/4 | |
|---|---|---|---|---|---|---|---|---|---|---|
| 11 | 0000 | **Mixed Use** | S.F. | | | | | | | 11 |
| | 0100 | Architectural | | 151 | 209 | 285 | 45.50% | 52.50% | 61.50% | |
| | 0200 | Plumbing | | 8.55 | 15.55 | 16.55 | 3.31% | 3.47% | 4.18% | |
| | 0300 | Mechanical | | 22.50 | 49 | 65 | 6.10% | 13.60% | 17.05% | |
| | 0400 | Electrical | | 30 | 50.50 | 72.50 | 8.60% | 11.65% | 15.65% | |
| | 0500 | Total Project Costs | ↓ | 264 | 460 | 470 | | | | |
| 12 | 0000 | **Multi-Family Housing** | S.F. | | | | | | | 12 |
| | 0100 | Architectural | | 105 | 143 | 233 | 54.50% | 62% | 69% | |
| | 0200 | Plumbing | | 9.40 | 15.15 | 20.50 | 5.25% | 6.65% | 8% | |
| | 0300 | Mechanical | | 9.65 | 13 | 37 | 4.41% | 6.05% | 10.25% | |
| | 0400 | Electrical | | 12.70 | 21.50 | 31 | 5.65% | 7.90% | 10.25% | |
| | 0500 | Total Project Costs | ↓ | 174 | 286 | 370 | | | | |
| 13 | 0000 | **Nursing Home & Assisted Living** | S.F. | | | | | | | 13 |
| | 0100 | Architectural | | 99 | 143 | 162 | 51.50% | 55.50% | 63.50% | |
| | 0200 | Plumbing | | 10.60 | 15.95 | 19 | 6.25% | 7.40% | 9.20% | |
| | 0300 | Mechanical | | 8.70 | 12.85 | 25 | 4.04% | 6.70% | 9.55% | |
| | 0400 | Electrical | | 14.60 | 25.50 | 33.50 | 7.25% | 11% | 13.10% | |
| | 0500 | Total Project Costs | ↓ | 174 | 224 | 296 | | | | |
| 14 | 0000 | **Office Buildings** | S.F. | | | | | | | 14 |
| | 0100 | Architectural | | 130 | 177 | 244 | 54.50% | 61% | 69% | |
| | 0200 | Plumbing | | 7 | 11 | 20.50 | 2.70% | 3.78% | 5.20% | |
| | 0300 | Mechanical | | 13.70 | 23.50 | 36 | 5.55% | 8.15% | 11.10% | |
| | 0400 | Electrical | | 18.35 | 30 | 48 | 7.80% | 10.10% | 12.90% | |
| | 0500 | Total Project Costs | ↓ | 221 | 292 | 400 | | | | |
| 15 | 0000 | **Parking Garage** | S.F. | | | | | | | 15 |
| | 0100 | Architectural | | 43.50 | 53 | 55.50 | 70% | 79% | 88% | |
| | 0200 | Plumbing | | 1.43 | 1.50 | 2.80 | 2.05% | 2.70% | 2.83% | |
| | 0300 | Mechanical | | 1.11 | 1.71 | 6.50 | 2.11% | 3.62% | 3.81% | |
| | 0400 | Electrical | | 3.81 | 4.19 | 8.75 | 5.30% | 6.35% | 7.95% | |
| | 0500 | Total Project Costs | ↓ | 53 | 64.50 | 70 | | | | |
| 16 | 0000 | **Parking Garage/Mixed Use** | S.F. | | | | | | | 16 |
| | 0100 | Architectural | | 141 | 154 | 157 | 61% | 62% | 65.50% | |
| | 0200 | Plumbing | | 4.52 | 5.95 | 9.10 | 2.47% | 2.72% | 3.66% | |
| | 0300 | Mechanical | | 19.35 | 22 | 31.50 | 7.80% | 13.10% | 13.60% | |
| | 0400 | Electrical | | 20.50 | 29 | 30 | 8.20% | 12.65% | 18.15% | |
| | 0500 | Total Project Costs | ↓ | 230 | 240 | 248 | | | | |
| 17 | 0000 | **Police Stations** | S.F. | | | | | | | 17 |
| | 0100 | Architectural | | 159 | 225 | 277 | 49% | 61% | 61.50% | |
| | 0200 | Plumbing | | 21 | 25.50 | 25.50 | 5.05% | 5.55% | 7.70% | |
| | 0300 | Mechanical | | 47.50 | 66.50 | 69 | 12.35% | 14.55% | 16.55% | |
| | 0400 | Electrical | | 36 | 41.50 | 61.50 | 9.15% | 12.10% | 14% | |
| | 0500 | Total Project Costs | ↓ | 298 | 415 | 455 | | | | |
| 18 | 0000 | **Police/Fire** | S.F. | | | | | | | 18 |
| | 0100 | Architectural | | 155 | 155 | 475 | 55.50% | 66% | 68% | |
| | 0200 | Plumbing | | 12.40 | 12.85 | 47.50 | 5.45% | 5.50% | 5.55% | |
| | 0300 | Mechanical | | 19 | 30 | 109 | 8.35% | 12.70% | 12.80% | |
| | 0400 | Electrical | | 21.50 | 27.50 | 124 | 9.50% | 11.75% | 14.55% | |
| | 0500 | Total Project Costs | ↓ | 228 | 235 | 855 | | | | |
| 19 | 0000 | **Public Assembly Buildings** | S.F. | | | | | | | 19 |
| | 0100 | Architectural | | 158 | 206 | 320 | 56.50% | 61% | 64% | |
| | 0200 | Plumbing | | 8.35 | 12.25 | 18.10 | 2.63% | 3.36% | 4.39% | |
| | 0300 | Mechanical | | 17.60 | 30.50 | 48.50 | 6.45% | 8.75% | 12.45% | |
| | 0400 | Electrical | | 26 | 35 | 56 | 8.60% | 10.70% | 12.80% | |
| | 0500 | Total Project Costs | ↓ | 254 | 340 | 505 | | | | |
| 20 | 0000 | **Recreational** | S.F. | | | | | | | 20 |
| | 0100 | Architectural | | 152 | 230 | 325 | 49.50% | 59% | 64.50% | |
| | 0200 | Plumbing | | 11.35 | 18.30 | 30 | 3.08% | 4.67% | 7.40% | |
| | 0300 | Mechanical | | 18.10 | 27.50 | 41 | 5.15% | 6.65% | 11.35% | |
| | 0400 | Electrical | | 22 | 37.50 | 54.50 | 7.10% | 8.95% | 10.80% | |
| | 0500 | Total Project Costs | ↓ | 270 | 390 | 610 | | | | |

## 50 17 00 | Project Costs

| | | 50 17 00 \| Project Costs | UNIT | UNIT COSTS 1/4 | UNIT COSTS MEDIAN | UNIT COSTS 3/4 | % OF TOTAL 1/4 | % OF TOTAL MEDIAN | % OF TOTAL 3/4 | |
|---|---|---|---|---|---|---|---|---|---|---|
| 21 | 0000 | **Restaurants** | S.F. | | | | | | | 21 |
| | 0100 | Architectural | | 172 | 270 | 340 | 57.50% | 60% | 63.50% | |
| | 0200 | Plumbing | | 18.95 | 38 | 50 | 7.35% | 7.70% | 8.75% | |
| | 0300 | Mechanical | | 20.50 | 27 | 51 | 6.50% | 8.15% | 11.15% | |
| | 0400 | Electrical | | 20.50 | 33 | 66 | 6.75% | 10.30% | 11.60% | |
| | 0500 | Total Project Costs | ↓ | 285 | 470 | 570 | | | | |
| 22 | 0000 | **Retail** | S.F. | | | | | | | 22 |
| | 0100 | Architectural | | 77 | 120 | 248 | 54.50% | 60% | 64.50% | |
| | 0200 | Plumbing | | 9.60 | 13.40 | 16.65 | 4.18% | 5.45% | 8.45% | |
| | 0300 | Mechanical | | 9 | 12.75 | 23.50 | 4.98% | 6.15% | 7.05% | |
| | 0400 | Electrical | | 14.30 | 29 | 43 | 7.90% | 11.25% | 12.45% | |
| | 0500 | Total Project Costs | ↓ | 117 | 208 | 400 | | | | |
| 23 | 0000 | **Schools** | S.F. | | | | | | | 23 |
| | 0100 | Architectural | | 133 | 169 | 226 | 50.50% | 55.50% | 60.50% | |
| | 0200 | Plumbing | | 10.60 | 14.55 | 21 | 3.66% | 4.57% | 6.95% | |
| | 0300 | Mechanical | | 25 | 36 | 52.50 | 8.90% | 11.95% | 14.55% | |
| | 0400 | Electrical | | 25 | 34.50 | 44.50 | 9.45% | 11.25% | 13.30% | |
| | 0500 | Total Project Costs | ↓ | 242 | 310 | 415 | | | | |
| 24 | 0000 | **University, College & Private School Classroom & Admin Buildings** | S.F. | | | | | | | 24 |
| | 0100 | Architectural | | 172 | 224 | 272 | 50% | 53.50% | 58.50% | |
| | 0200 | Plumbing | | 11.75 | 16.10 | 29.50 | 3.04% | 4.30% | 6.35% | |
| | 0300 | Mechanical | | 34 | 51.50 | 66 | 9.20% | 11.40% | 14.40% | |
| | 0400 | Electrical | | 28.50 | 41 | 53.50 | 7.70% | 9.95% | 12.55% | |
| | 0500 | Total Project Costs | ↓ | 297 | 415 | 540 | | | | |
| 25 | 0000 | **University, College & Private School Dormitories** | S.F. | | | | | | | 25 |
| | 0100 | Architectural | | 111 | 195 | 207 | 53% | 61.50% | 68% | |
| | 0200 | Plumbing | | 14.65 | 21 | 24 | 6.35% | 6.65% | 8.95% | |
| | 0300 | Mechanical | | 6.60 | 28 | 44.50 | 4.13% | 9% | 11.80% | |
| | 0400 | Electrical | | 7.80 | 27 | 41.50 | 4.75% | 7.35% | 10.60% | |
| | 0500 | Total Project Costs | ↓ | 164 | 310 | 370 | | | | |
| 26 | 0000 | **University, College & Private School Science, Eng. & Lab Buildings** | S.F. | | | | | | | 26 |
| | 0100 | Architectural | | 191 | 226 | 335 | 48% | 54.50% | 58% | |
| | 0200 | Plumbing | | 13.15 | 19.90 | 33.50 | 3.29% | 3.77% | 5% | |
| | 0300 | Mechanical | | 50.50 | 94 | 96.50 | 11.70% | 19.40% | 23.50% | |
| | 0400 | Electrical | | 39.50 | 51.50 | 53 | 9% | 12.05% | 13.15% | |
| | 0500 | Total Project Costs | ↓ | 400 | 430 | 585 | | | | |
| 27 | 0000 | **University, College & Private School Student Union Buildings** | S.F. | | | | | | | 27 |
| | 0100 | Architectural | | 151 | 395 | 395 | 54.50% | 54.50% | 59.50% | |
| | 0200 | Plumbing | | 23 | 23 | 34 | 3.13% | 4.27% | 11.45% | |
| | 0300 | Mechanical | | 43.50 | 70 | 70 | 9.60% | 9.60% | 14.55% | |
| | 0400 | Electrical | | 38 | 66 | 66 | 9.05% | 12.80% | 13.15% | |
| | 0500 | Total Project Costs | ↓ | 297 | 730 | 730 | | | | |
| 28 | 0000 | **Warehouses** | S.F. | | | | | | | 28 |
| | 0100 | Architectural | | 65 | 98.50 | 180 | 60.50% | 67% | 71.50% | |
| | 0200 | Plumbing | | 3.37 | 7.20 | 13.90 | 2.82% | 3.72% | 5% | |
| | 0300 | Mechanical | | 3.99 | 22.50 | 35.50 | 4.56% | 8.15% | 10.70% | |
| | 0400 | Electrical | | 8.40 | 27 | 45.50 | 7.75% | 10.10% | 18.30% | |
| | 0500 | Total Project Costs | ↓ | 96.50 | 154 | 310 | | | | |

# Square Foot Project Size Modifier

One factor that affects the S.F. cost of a particular building is the size. In general, for buildings built to the same specifications in the same locality, the larger building will have the lower S.F. cost. This is due mainly to the decreasing contribution of the exterior walls plus the economy of scale usually achievable in larger buildings. The Area Conversion Scale shown below will give a factor to convert costs for the typical size building to an adjusted cost for the particular project.

The Square Foot Base Size lists the median costs, most typical project size in our accumulated data, and the range in size of the projects.

The Size Factor for your project is determined by dividing your project area in S.F. by the typical project size for the particular Building Type. With this factor, enter the Area Conversion Scale at the appropriate Size Factor and determine the appropriate Cost Multiplier for your building size.

**Example:** Determine the cost per S.F. for a 107,200 S.F. Multi-family housing.

$$\frac{\text{Proposed building area} = 107{,}200 \text{ S.F.}}{\text{Typical size from below} = 53{,}600 \text{ S.F.}} = 2.00$$

Enter Area Conversion Scale at 2.0, intersect curve, read horizontally the appropriate cost multiplier of .94. Size adjusted cost becomes .94 x \$286.00 = \$268.84 based on national average costs.

Note: For Size Factors less than .50, the Cost Multiplier is 1.1
For Size Factors greater than 3.5, the Cost Multiplier is .90

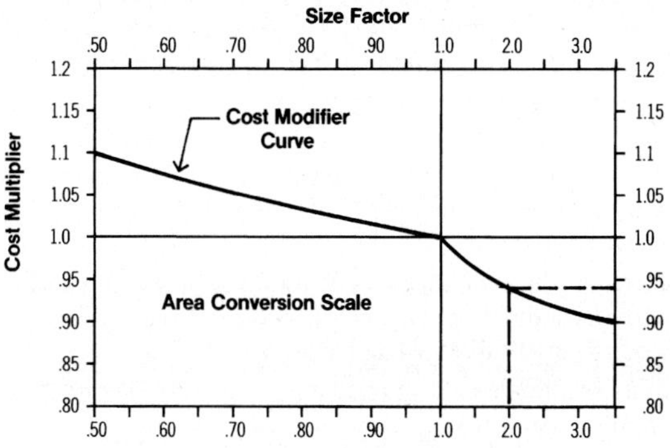


| System | Median Cost (Total Project Costs) | Typical Size Gross S.F. (Median of Projects) | Typical Range (Low – High) (Projects) |
|---|---|---|---|
| Auto Sales with Repair | \$255.00 | 24,900 | 4,700 – 29,300 |
| Banking Institutions | 410.00 | 9,300 | 3,300 – 38,100 |
| Courthouse | 390.00 | 56,000 | 24,700 – 70,500 |
| Data Centers | 385.00 | 14,400 | 14,400 – 14,400 |
| Detention Centers | 435.00 | 37,800 | 12,300 – 183,330 |
| Fire Stations | 350.00 | 12,400 | 6,300 – 49,600 |
| Gymnasium | 280.00 | 52,400 | 22,800 – 82,000 |
| Hospitals | 520.00 | 73,300 | 12,700 – 410,300 |
| Industrial Buildings | 181.00 | 21,100 | 5,100 – 200,600 |
| Medical Clinics & Offices | 305.00 | 24,200 | 2,300 – 327,000 |
| Mixed Use | 460.00 | 31,800 | 7,200 – 188,900 |
| Multi-Family Housing | 286.00 | 53,600 | 2,500 – 1,161,500 |
| Nursing Home & Assisted Living | 224.00 | 38,700 | 1,500 – 242,600 |
| Office Buildings | 292.00 | 21,000 | 1,100 – 930,000 |
| Parking Garage | 64.50 | 151,800 | 99,900 – 287,000 |
| Parking Garage/Mixed Use | 240.00 | 254,200 | 5,300 – 318,000 |
| Police Stations | 415.00 | 25,200 | 12,700 – 88,600 |
| Police/Fire | 235.00 | 44,300 | 8,600 – 50,300 |
| Public Assembly Buildings | 340.00 | 20,800 | 2,200 – 235,300 |
| Recreational | 390.00 | 27,700 | 1,000 – 223,800 |
| Restaurants | 470.00 | 5,900 | 2,100 – 42,000 |
| Retail | 208.00 | 26,000 | 4,000 – 84,300 |
| Schools | 310.00 | 69,400 | 1,300 – 410,800 |
| University, College & Private School Classroom & Admin Buildings | 415.00 | 48,300 | 2,400 – 196,200 |
| University, College & Private School Dormitories | 310.00 | 39,200 | 1,500 – 126,900 |
| University, College & Private School Science, Eng. & Lab Buildings | 430.00 | 60,000 | 5,300 – 117,600 |
| University, College & Private School Student Union Buildings | 730.00 | 48,700 | 42,100 – 50,000 |
| Warehouses | 154.00 | 10,900 | 600 – 303,800 |

**Accent lighting**–Fixtures or directional beams of light arranged to bring attention to an object or area.

**Acoustical material**–A material fabricated for the sole purpose of absorbing sound.

**Addition**–An expansion to an existing structure generally in the form of a room, floor(s) or wing(s). An increase in the floor area or volume of a structure.

**Aggregate**–Materials such as sand, gravel, stone, vermiculite, perlite and fly ash (slag) which are essential components in the production of concrete, mortar or plaster.

**Air conditioning system**–An air treatment to control the temperature, humidity and cleanliness of air and to provide for its distribution throughout the structure.

**Air curtain**–A stream of air directed downward to prevent the loss of hot or cool air from the structure and inhibit the entrance of dust and insects. Generally installed at loading platforms.

**Anodized aluminum**–Aluminum treated by an electrolytic process to produce an oxide film that is corrosion resistant.

**Arcade**–A covered passageway between buildings often with shops and offices on one or both sides.

**Ashlar**–A square-cut building stone or a wall constructed of cut stone.

**Asphalt paper**–A sheet paper material either coated or saturated with asphalt to increase its strength and resistance to water.

**Asphalt shingles**–Shingles manufactured from saturated roofing felts, coated with asphalt and topped with mineral granules to prevent weathering.

**Assessment ratio**–The ratio between the market value and assessed valuation of a property.

**Back-up**–That portion of a masonry wall behind the exterior facing-usually load bearing.

**Balcony**–A platform projecting from a building either supported from below or cantilevered. Usually protected by railing.

**Bay**–Structural component consisting of beams and columns occurring consistently throughout the structure.

**Beam**–A horizontal structural framing member that transfers loads to vertical members (columns) or bearing walls.

**Bid**–An offer to perform work described in a contract at a specified price.

**Board foot**–A unit or measure equal in volume to a board one foot long, one foot wide and one inch thick.

**Booster pump**–A supplemental pump installed to increase or maintain adequate pressure in the system.

**Bowstring roof**–A roof supported by trusses fabricated in the shape of a bow and tied together by a straight member.

**Brick veneer**–A facing of brick laid against, but not bonded to, a wall.

**Bridging**–A method of bracing joists for stiffness, stability and load distribution.

**Broom finish**–A method of finishing concrete by lightly dragging a broom over freshly placed concrete.

**Built-up roofing**–Installed on flat or extremely low-pitched roofs, a roof covering composed of plies or laminations of saturated roofing felts alternated with layers of coal tar pitch or asphalt and surfaced with a layer of gravel or slag in a thick coat of asphalt and finished with a capping sheet.

**Caisson**–A watertight chamber to expedite work on foundations or structure below water level.

**Cantilever**–A structural member supported only at one end.

**Carport**–An automobile shelter having one or more sides open to the weather.

**Casement window**–A vertical opening window having one side fixed.

**Caulking**–A resilient compound generally having a silicone or rubber base used to prevent infiltration of water or outside air.

**Cavity wall**–An exterior wall usually of masonry having an inner and outer wall separated by a continuous air space for thermal insulation.

**Cellular concrete**–A lightweight concrete consisting of cement mixed with gas-producing materials which, in turn, forms bubbles resulting in good insulating qualities.

**Chattel mortgage**–A secured interest in a property as collateral for payment of a note.

**Clapboard**–A wood siding used as exterior covering in frame construction. It is applied horizontally with grain running lengthwise. The thickest section of the board is on the bottom.

**Clean room**–An environmentally controlled room usually found in medical facilities or precision manufacturing spaces where it is essential to eliminate dust, lint or pathogens.

**Close studding**–A method of construction whereby studs are spaced close together and the intervening spaces are plastered.

**Cluster housing**–A closely grouped series of houses resulting in a high density land use.

**Cofferdam**–A watertight enclosure used for foundation construction in waterfront areas. Water is pumped out of the cofferdam allowing free access to the work area.

**Collar joint**–Joint between the collar beam and roof rafters.

**Column**–A vertical structural member supporting horizontal members (beams) along the direction of its longitudinal axis.

**Combination door (windows)**–Door (windows) having interchangeable screens and glass for seasonal use.

**Common area**–Spaces either inside or outside the building designated for use by the occupant of the building but not the general public.

**Common wall**–A wall used jointly by two dwelling units.

**Compound wall**–A wall constructed of more than one material.

**Concrete**–A composite material consisting of sand, coarse aggregate (gravel, stone or slag), cement and water that when mixed and allowed to harden forms a hard stone-like material.

**Concrete floor hardener**–A mixture of chemicals applied to the surface of concrete to produce a dense, wear-resistant bearing surface.

**Conduit**–A tube or pipe used to protect electric wiring.

**Coping**–The top cover or capping on a wall.

**Craneway**–Steel or concrete column and beam supports and rails on which a crane travels.

**Curtain wall**–A non-bearing exterior wall not supported by beams or girders of the steel frame.

**Dampproofing**–Coating of a surface to prevent the passage of water or moisture.

**Dead load**–Total weight of all structural components plus permanently attached fixtures and equipment.

**Decibel**–Unit of acoustical measurement.

**Decorative block**–A concrete masonry unit having a special treatment on its face.

**Deed restriction**–A restriction on the use of a property as set forth in the deed.

**Depreciation**–A loss in property value caused by physical aging, functional or economic obsolescence.

**Direct heating**–Heating of spaces by means of exposed heated surfaces (stove, fire, radiators, etc.).

**Distributed load**–A load that acts evenly over a structural member.

**Dock bumper**–A resilient material attached to a loading dock to absorb the impact of trucks backing in.

**Dome**–A curved roof shape spanning an area.

**Dormer**–A structure projecting from a sloping roof.

**Double-hung window**–A window having two vertical sliding sashes-one covering the upper section and one covering the lower.

**Downspout**–A vertical pipe for carrying rain water from the roof to the ground.

**Drain tile**–A hollow tile used to drain water-soaked soil.

**Dressed size**–In lumber about 3/8″ - 1/2″ less than nominal size after planing and sawing.

**Drop panel**–The depressed surface on the bottom side of a flat concrete slab which surrounds a column.

**Dry pipe sprinkler system**–A sprinkler system that is activated with water only in case of fire. Used in areas susceptible to freezing or to avoid the hazards of leaking pipes.

**Drywall**–An interior wall constructed of gypsum board, plywood or wood paneling. No water is required for application.

**Duct**–Pipe for transmitting warm or cold air. A pipe containing electrical cable or wires.

**Dwelling**–A structure designed as living quarters for one or more families.

**Easement**–A right of way or free access over land owned by another.

**Eave**–The lower edge of a sloping roof that overhangs the side wall of the structure.

**Economic rent**–That rent on a property sufficient to pay all operating costs exclusive of services and utilities.

**Economic life**–The term during which a structure is expected to be profitable. Generally shorter than the physical life of the structure.

**Economic obsolescence**–Loss in value due to unfavorable economic influences occurring from outside the structure itself.

**Effective age**–The age a structure appears to be based on observed physical condition determined by degree of maintenance and repair.

**Elevator**–A mechanism for vertical transport of personnel or freight equipped with car or platform.

**Ell**–A secondary wing or addition to a structure at right angles to the main structure.

**Eminent domain**–The right of the state to take private property for public use.

**Envelope**–The shape of a building indicating volume.

**Equity**–Value of an owner's interest calculated by subtracting outstanding mortgages and expenses from the value of the property.

**Escheat**–The assumption of ownership by the state, of property whose owner cannot be determined.

**Facade**–The exterior face of a building sometimes decorated with elaborate detail.

**Face brick**–Brick manufactured to present an attractive appearance.

**Facing block**–A concrete masonry unit having a decorative exterior finish.

**Feasibility study**–A detailed evaluation of a proposed project to determine its financial potential.

**Felt paper**–Paper sheathing used on walls as an insulator and to prevent infiltration of moisture.

**Fenestration**–Pertaining to the density and arrangement of windows in a structure.

**Fiberboard**–A building material composed of wood fiber compressed with a binding agent, produced in sheet form.

**Fiberglass**–Fine spun filaments of glass processed into various densities to produce thermal and acoustical insulation.

**Field house**–A long structure used for indoor athletic events.

**Finish floor**–The top or wearing surface of the floor system.

**Fireproofing**–The use of fire-resistant materials for the protection of structural members to ensure structural integrity in the event of fire.

**Fire stop**–A material or member used to seal an opening to prevent the spread of fire.

**Flashing**–A thin, impervious material such as copper or sheet metal used to prevent air or water penetration.

**Float finish**–A concrete finish accomplished by using a flat tool with a handle on the back.

**Floor drain**–An opening installed in a floor for removing excess water into a plumbing system.

**Floor load**–The live load the floor system has been designed for and which may be applied safely.

**Flue**–A heat-resistant enclosed passage in a chimney to remove gaseous products of combustion from a fireplace or boiler.

**Footing**–The lowest portion of the foundation wall that transmits the load directly to the soil.

**Foundation**–Below grade wall system that supports the structure.

**Foyer**–A portion of the structure that serves as a transitional space between the interior and exterior.

**Frontage**–That portion of a lot that is placed facing a street, public way or body of water.

**Frost action**–The effects of freezing and thawing on materials and the resultant structural damage.

**Functional obsolescence**–An inadequacy caused by outmoded design, dated construction materials or over or undersized areas, all of which cause excessive operating costs.

**Furring strips**–Wood or metal channels used for attaching gypsum or metal lath to masonry walls as a finish or for leveling purposes.

**Gambrel roof (mansard)**–A roof system having two pitches on each side.

**Garden apartment**–Two or three story apartment building with common outside areas.

**General contractor**–The prime contractor responsible for work on the construction site.

**Girder**–A principal horizontal supporting member.

**Girt**–A horizontal framing member for adding rigid support to columns which also acts as a support for sheathing or siding.

**Grade beam**–That portion of the foundation system that directly supports the exterior walls of the building.

**Gross area**–The total enclosed floor area of a building.

**Ground area**–The area computed by the exterior dimensions of the structure.

**Ground floor**–The floor of a building in closest proximity to the ground.

**Grout**–A mortar containing a high water content used to fill joints and cavities in masonry work.

**Gutter**–A wood or sheet metal conduit set along the building eaves used to channel rainwater to leaders or downspouts.

**Gunite**–A concrete mix placed pneumatically.

**Gypsum**–Hydrated calcium sulphate used as both a retarder in Portland cement and as a major ingredient in plaster of Paris. Used in sheets as a substitute for plaster.

**Hall**–A passageway providing access to various parts of a building-a large room for entertainment or assembly.

**Hangar**–A structure for the storage or repair of aircraft.

**Head room**–The distance between the top of the finished floor to the bottom of the finished ceiling.

**Hearth**–The floor of a fireplace and the adjacent area of fireproof material.

**Heat pump**–A mechanical device for providing either heating or air conditioning.

**Hip roof**–A roof whose four sides meet at a common point with no gabled ends.

**I-beam**–A structural member having a cross-section resembling the letter "I".

**Insulation**–Material used to reduce the effects of heat, cold or sound.

**Jack rafter**–An unusually short rafter generally found in hip roofs.

**Jalousie**–Adjustable glass louvers which pivot simultaneously in a common frame.

**Jamb**–The vertical member on either side of a door frame or window frame.

**Joist**–Parallel beams of timber, concrete or steel used to support floor and ceiling.

**Junction box**–A box that protects splices or joints in electrical wiring.

**Kalamein door**–Solid core wood doors clad with galvanized sheet metal.

**Kip**–A unit of weight equal to 1,000 pounds.

**Lally column**–A concrete-filled steel pipe used as a vertical support.

**Laminated beam**–A beam built up by gluing together several pieces of timber.

**Landing**–A platform between flights of stairs.

**Lath**–Strips of wood or metal used as a base for plaster.

**Lead-lined door, sheetrock**–Doors or sheetrock internally lined with sheet lead to provide protection from X-ray radiation.

**Lean-to**–A small shed or building addition with a single pitched roof attached to the exterior wall of the main building.

**Lintel**–A horizontal framing member used to carry a load over a wall opening.

**Live load**–The moving or movable load on a structure composed of furnishings, equipment or personnel weight.

**Load bearing partition**–A partition that supports a load in addition to its own weight.

**Loading dock leveler**–An adjustable platform for handling off-on loading of trucks.

**Loft building**–A commercial/industrial type building containing large, open unpartitioned floor areas.

**Louver window**–A window composed of a series of sloping, overlapping blades or slats that may be adjusted to admit varying degrees of air or light.

**Main beam**–The principal load bearing beam used to transmit loads directly to columns.

**Mansard roof**–A roof having a double pitch on all four sides, the lower level having the steeper pitch.

**Mansion**–An extremely large and imposing residence.

**Masonry**–The utilization of brick, stone, concrete or block for walls and other building components.

**Mastic**–A sealant or adhesive compound generally used as either a binding agent or floor finish.

**Membrane fireproofing**–A coating of metal lath and plaster to provide resistance to fire and heat.

**Mesh reinforcement**–An arrangement of wire tied or welded at their intersection to provide strength and resistance to cracking.

**Metal lath**–A diamond-shaped metallic base for plaster.

**Mezzanine**–A low story situated between two main floors.

**Mill construction**–A heavy timber construction that achieves fire resistance by using large wood structural members, noncombustible bearing and non-bearing walls and omitting concealed spaces under floors and roof.

**Mixed occupancy**–Two or more classes of occupancy in a single structure.

**Molded brick**–A specially shaped brick used for decorative purposes.

**Monolithic concrete**–Concrete poured in a continuous process so there are no joints.

**Movable partition**–A non-load bearing demountable partition that can be relocated and can be either ceiling height or partial height.

**Moving walk**–A continually moving horizontal passenger carrying device.

**Multi-zone system**–An air conditioning system that is capable of handling several individual zones simultaneously.

**Net floor area**–The usable, occupied area of a structure excluding stairwells, elevator shafts and wall thicknesses.

**Non-combustible construction**–Construction in which the walls, partitions and the structural members are of non-combustible materials.

**Nurses call system**–An electrically operated system for use by patients or personnel for summoning a nurse.

**Occupancy rate**–The number of persons per room, per dwelling unit, etc.

**One-way joist connection**–A framing system for floors and roofs in a concrete building consisting of a series of parallel joists supported by girders between columns.

**Open web joist**–A lightweight prefabricated metal chord truss.

**Parapet**–A low guarding wall at the point of a drop. That portion of the exterior wall that extends above the roof line.

**Parging**–A thin coat of mortar applied to a masonry wall used primarily for waterproofing purposes.

**Parquet**–Inlaid wood flooring set in a simple design.

**Peaked roof**–A roof of two or more slopes that rises to a peak.

**Penthouse**–A structure occupying usually half the roof area and used to house elevator, HVAC equipment, or other mechanical or electrical systems.

**Pier**–A column designed to support a concentrated load.

**Pilaster**–A column usually formed of the same material and integral with, but projecting from, a wall.

**Pile**–A concrete, wood or steel column usually less than 2′ in diameter which is driven or otherwise introduced into the soil to carry a vertical load or provide vertical support.

**Pitched roof**–A roof having one or more surfaces with a pitch greater than 10°.

**Plenum**–The space between the suspended ceiling and the floor above.

**Plywood**–Structural wood made of three or more layers of veneer and bonded together with glue.

**Porch**–A structure attached to a building to provide shelter for an entranceway or to serve as a semi-enclosed space.

**Post and beam framing**–A structural framing system where beams rest on posts rather than bearing walls.

**Post-tensioned concrete**–Concrete that has the reinforcing tendons tensioned after the concrete has set.

**Pre-cast concrete**–Concrete structural components fabricated at a location other than in-place.

**Pre-stressed concrete**–Concrete that has the reinforcing tendons tensioned prior to the concrete setting.

**Purlins**–A horizontal structural member supporting the roof deck and resting on the trusses, girders, beams or rafters.

**Rafters**–Structural members supporting the roof deck and covering.

**Resilient flooring**–A manufactured interior floor covering material in either sheet or tile form, that is resilient.

**Ridge**–The horizontal line at the junction of two sloping roof edges.

**Rigid frame**–A structural framing system in which all columns and beams are rigidly connected; there are no hinged joints.

**Roof drain**–A drain designed to accept rainwater and discharge it into a leader or downspout.

**Rough floor**–A layer of boards or plywood nailed to the floor joists that serves as a base for the finished floor.

**Sanitary sewer**–A sewer line designed to carry only liquid or waterborne waste from the structure to a central treatment plant.

**Sawtooth roof**–Roof shape found primarily in industrial roofs that creates the appearance of the teeth of a saw.

**Semi-rigid frame**–A structural system wherein the columns and beams are so attached that there is some flexibility at the joints.

**Septic tank**–A covered tank in which waste matter is decomposed by natural bacterial action.

**Service elevator**–A combination passenger and freight elevator.

**Sheathing**–The first covering of exterior studs by boards, plywood or particle board.

**Shoring**–Temporary bracing for structural components during construction.

**Span**–The horizontal distance between supports.

**Specification**–A detailed list of materials and requirements for construction of a building.

**Storm sewer**–A system of pipes used to carry rainwater or surface waters.

**Stucco**–A cement plaster used to cover exterior wall surfaces usually applied over a wood or metal lath base.

**Stud**–A vertical wooden structural component.

**Subfloor**–A system of boards, plywood or particle board laid over the floor joists to form a base.

**Superstructure**–That portion of the structure above the foundation or ground level.

**Terrazzo**–A durable floor finish made of small chips of colored stone or marble, embedded in concrete, then polished to a high sheen.

**Tile**–A thin piece of fired clay, stone or concrete used for floor, roof or wall finishes.

**Unit cost**–The cost per unit of measurement.

**Vault**–A room especially designed for storage.

**Veneer**–A thin surface layer covering a base of common material.

**Vent**–An opening serving as an outlet for air.

**Wainscot**–The lower portion of an interior wall whose surface differs from that of the upper wall.

**Wall bearing construction**–A structural system where the weight of the floors and roof are carried directly by the masonry walls rather than the structural framing system.

**Waterproofing**–Any of a number of materials applied to various surfaces to prevent the infiltration of water.

**Weatherstrip**–A thin strip of metal, wood or felt used to cover the joint between the door or window sash and the jamb, casing or sill to keep out air, dust, rain, etc.

**Wing**–A building section or addition projecting from the main structure.

**X-ray protection**–Lead encased in sheetrock or plaster to prevent the escape of radiation.

# Abbreviations

| | |
|---|---|
| A | Area Square Feet; Ampere |
| AAFES | Army and Air Force Exchange Service |
| ABS | Acrylonitrile Butadiene Stryrene; Asbestos Bonded Steel |
| A.C., AC | Alternating Current; Air-Conditioning; Asbestos Cement; Plywood Grade A & C |
| ACI | American Concrete Institute |
| ACR | Air Conditioning Refrigeration |
| ADA | Americans with Disabilities Act |
| AD | Plywood, Grade A & D |
| Addit. | Additional |
| Adh. | Adhesive |
| Adj. | Adjustable |
| af | Audio-frequency |
| AFFF | Aqueous Film Forming Foam |
| AFUE | Annual Fuel Utilization Efficiency |
| AGA | American Gas Association |
| Agg. | Aggregate |
| A.H., Ah | Ampere Hours |
| A hr. | Ampere-hour |
| A.H.U., AHU | Air Handling Unit |
| A.I.A. | American Institute of Architects |
| AIC | Ampere Interrupting Capacity |
| Allow. | Allowance |
| alt., alt | Alternate |
| Alum. | Aluminum |
| a.m. | Ante Meridiem |
| Amp. | Ampere |
| Anod. | Anodized |
| ANSI | American National Standards Institute |
| APA | American Plywood Association |
| Approx. | Approximate |
| Apt. | Apartment |
| Asb. | Asbestos |
| A.S.B.C. | American Standard Building Code |
| Asbe. | Asbestos Worker |
| ASCE | American Society of Civil Engineers |
| A.S.H.R.A.E. | American Society of Heating, Refrig. & AC Engineers |
| ASME | American Society of Mechanical Engineers |
| ASTM | American Society for Testing and Materials |
| Attchmt. | Attachment |
| Avg., Ave. | Average |
| AWG | American Wire Gauge |
| AWWA | American Water Works Assoc. |
| Bbl. | Barrel |
| B&B, BB | Grade B and Better; Balled & Burlapped |
| B&S | Bell and Spigot |
| B.&W. | Black and White |
| b.c.c. | Body-centered Cubic |
| B.C.Y. | Bank Cubic Yards |
| BE | Bevel End |
| B.F. | Board Feet |
| Bg. cem. | Bag of Cement |
| BHP | Boiler Horsepower; Brake Horsepower |
| B.I. | Black Iron |
| bidir. | bidirectional |
| Bit., Bitum. | Bituminous |
| Bit., Conc. | Bituminous Concrete |
| Bk. | Backed |
| Bkrs. | Breakers |
| Bldg., bldg | Building |
| Blk. | Block |
| Bm. | Beam |
| Boil. | Boilermaker |
| bpm | Blows per Minute |
| BR | Bedroom |
| Brg., brng. | Bearing |
| Brhe. | Bricklayer Helper |
| Bric. | Bricklayer |
| Brk., brk | Brick |
| brkt | Bracket |
| Brs. | Brass |
| Brz. | Bronze |
| Bsn. | Basin |
| Btr. | Better |
| BTU | British Thermal Unit |
| BTUH | BTU per Hour |
| Bu. | Bushels |
| BUR | Built-up Roofing |
| BX | Interlocked Armored Cable |
| °C | Degree Centigrade |
| c | Conductivity, Copper Sweat |
| C | Hundred; Centigrade |
| C/C | Center to Center, Cedar on Cedar |
| C-C | Center to Center |
| Cab | Cabinet |
| Cair. | Air Tool Laborer |
| Cal. | Caliper |
| Calc | Calculated |
| Cap. | Capacity |
| Carp. | Carpenter |
| C.B. | Circuit Breaker |
| C.C.A. | Chromate Copper Arsenate |
| C.C.F. | Hundred Cubic Feet |
| cd | Candela |
| cd/sf | Candela per Square Foot |
| CD | Grade of Plywood Face & Back |
| CDX | Plywood, Grade C & D, exterior glue |
| Cefi. | Cement Finisher |
| Cem. | Cement |
| CF | Hundred Feet |
| C.F. | Cubic Feet |
| CFM | Cubic Feet per Minute |
| CFRP | Carbon Fiber Reinforced Plastic |
| c.g. | Center of Gravity |
| CHW | Chilled Water; Commercial Hot Water |
| C.I., CI | Cast Iron |
| C.I.P., CIP | Cast in Place |
| Circ. | Circuit |
| C.L. | Carload Lot |
| CL | Chain Link |
| Clab. | Common Laborer |
| Clam | Common Maintenance Laborer |
| C.L.F. | Hundred Linear Feet |
| CLF | Current Limiting Fuse |
| CLP | Cross Linked Polyethylene |
| cm | Centimeter |
| CMP | Corr. Metal Pipe |
| CMU | Concrete Masonry Unit |
| CN | Change Notice |
| Col. | Column |
| $CO_2$ | Carbon Dioxide |
| Comb. | Combination |
| comm. | Commercial, Communication |
| Compr. | Compressor |
| Conc. | Concrete |
| Cont., cont | Continuous; Continued, Container |
| Corkbd. | Cork Board |
| Corr. | Corrugated |
| Cos | Cosine |
| Cot | Cotangent |
| Cov. | Cover |
| C/P | Cedar on Paneling |
| CPA | Control Point Adjustment |
| Cplg. | Coupling |
| CPM | Critical Path Method |
| CPVC | Chlorinated Polyvinyl Chloride |
| C.Pr. | Hundred Pair |
| CRC | Cold Rolled Channel |
| Creos. | Creosote |
| Crpt. | Carpet & Linoleum Layer |
| CRT | Cathode-ray Tube |
| CS | Carbon Steel, Constant Shear Bar Joist |
| Csc | Cosecant |
| C.S.F. | Hundred Square Feet |
| CSI | Construction Specifications Institute |
| CT | Current Transformer |
| CTS | Copper Tube Size |
| Cu | Copper, Cubic |
| Cu. Ft. | Cubic Foot |
| cw | Continuous Wave |
| C.W. | Cool White; Cold Water |
| Cwt. | 100 Pounds |
| C.W.X. | Cool White Deluxe |
| C.Y. | Cubic Yard (27 cubic feet) |
| C.Y./Hr. | Cubic Yard per Hour |
| Cyl. | Cylinder |
| d | Penny (nail size) |
| D | Deep; Depth; Discharge |
| Dis., Disch. | Discharge |
| Db | Decibel |
| Dbl. | Double |
| DC | Direct Current |
| DDC | Direct Digital Control |
| Demob. | Demobilization |
| d.f.t. | Dry Film Thickness |
| d.f.u. | Drainage Fixture Units |
| D.H. | Double Hung |
| DHW | Domestic Hot Water |
| DI | Ductile Iron |
| Diag. | Diagonal |
| Diam., Dia | Diameter |
| Distrib. | Distribution |
| Div. | Division |
| Dk. | Deck |
| D.L. | Dead Load; Diesel |
| DLH | Deep Long Span Bar Joist |
| dlx | Deluxe |
| Do. | Ditto |
| DOP | Dioctyl Phthalate Penetration Test (Air Filters) |
| Dp., dp | Depth |
| D.P.S.T. | Double Pole, Single Throw |
| Dr. | Drive |
| DR | Dimension Ratio |
| Drink. | Drinking |
| D.S. | Double Strength |
| D.S.A. | Double Strength A Grade |
| D.S.B. | Double Strength B Grade |
| Dty. | Duty |
| DWV | Drain Waste Vent |
| DX | Deluxe White, Direct Expansion |
| dyn | Dyne |
| e | Eccentricity |
| E | Equipment Only; East; Emissivity |
| Ea. | Each |
| EB | Encased Burial |
| Econ. | Economy |
| E.C.Y | Embankment Cubic Yards |
| EDP | Electronic Data Processing |
| EIFS | Exterior Insulation Finish System |
| E.D.R. | Equiv. Direct Radiation |
| Eq. | Equation |
| EL | Elevation |
| Elec. | Electrician; Electrical |
| Elev. | Elevator; Elevating |
| EMT | Electrical Metallic Conduit; Thin Wall Conduit |
| Eng. | Engine, Engineered |
| EPDM | Ethylene Propylene Diene Monomer |
| EPS | Expanded Polystyrene |
| Eqhv. | Equip. Oper., Heavy |
| Eqlt. | Equip. Oper., Light |
| Eqmd. | Equip. Oper., Medium |
| Eqmm. | Equip. Oper., Master Mechanic |
| Eqol. | Equip. Oper., Oilers |
| Equip. | Equipment |
| ERW | Electric Resistance Welded |

# Abbreviations

| | |
|---|---|
| E.S. | Energy Saver |
| Est. | Estimated |
| esu | Electrostatic Units |
| E.W. | Each Way |
| EWT | Entering Water Temperature |
| Excav. | Excavation |
| excl | Excluding |
| Exp., exp | Expansion, Exposure |
| Ext., ext | Exterior; Extension |
| Extru. | Extrusion |
| f. | Fiber Stress |
| F | Fahrenheit; Female; Fill |
| Fab., fab | Fabricated; Fabric |
| FBGS | Fiberglass |
| F.C. | Footcandles |
| f.c.c. | Face-centered Cubic |
| f'c. | Compressive Stress in Concrete; Extreme Compressive Stress |
| F.E. | Front End |
| FEP | Fluorinated Ethylene Propylene (Teflon) |
| F.G. | Flat Grain |
| F.H.A. | Federal Housing Administration |
| Fig. | Figure |
| Fin. | Finished |
| FIPS | Female Iron Pipe Size |
| Fixt. | Fixture |
| FJP | Finger jointed and primed |
| Fl. Oz. | Fluid Ounces |
| Flr. | Floor |
| Flrs. | Floors |
| FM | Frequency Modulation; Factory Mutual |
| Fmg. | Framing |
| FM/UL | Factory Mutual/Underwriters Labs |
| Fdn. | Foundation |
| FNPT | Female National Pipe Thread |
| Fori. | Foreman, Inside |
| Foro. | Foreman, Outside |
| Fount. | Fountain |
| fpm | Feet per Minute |
| FPT | Female Pipe Thread |
| Fr | Frame |
| F.R. | Fire Rating |
| FRK | Foil Reinforced Kraft |
| FSK | Foil/Scrim/Kraft |
| FRP | Fiberglass Reinforced Plastic |
| FS | Forged Steel |
| FSC | Cast Body; Cast Switch Box |
| Ft., ft | Foot; Feet |
| Ftng. | Fitting |
| Ftg. | Footing |
| Ft lb. | Foot Pound |
| Furn. | Furniture |
| FVNR | Full Voltage Non-Reversing |
| FVR | Full Voltage Reversing |
| FXM | Female by Male |
| Fy. | Minimum Yield Stress of Steel |
| g | Gram |
| G | Gauss |
| Ga. | Gauge |
| Gal., gal. | Gallon |
| Galv., galv | Galvanized |
| GC/MS | Gas Chromatograph/Mass Spectrometer |
| Gen. | General |
| GFI | Ground Fault Interrupter |
| GFRC | Glass Fiber Reinforced Concrete |
| Glaz. | Glazier |
| GPD | Gallons per Day |
| gpf | Gallon per Flush |
| GPH | Gallons per Hour |
| gpm, GPM | Gallons per Minute |
| GR | Grade |
| Gran. | Granular |
| Grnd. | Ground |
| GVW | Gross Vehicle Weight |
| GWB | Gypsum Wall Board |
| H | High Henry |
| HC | High Capacity |
| H.D., HD | Heavy Duty; High Density |
| H.D.O. | High Density Overlaid |
| HDPE | High Density Polyethylene Plastic |
| Hdr. | Header |
| Hdwe. | Hardware |
| H.I.D., HID | High Intensity Discharge |
| Help. | Helper Average |
| HEPA | High Efficiency Particulate Air Filter |
| Hg | Mercury |
| HIC | High Interrupting Capacity |
| HM | Hollow Metal |
| HMWPE | High Molecular Weight Polyethylene |
| HO | High Output |
| Horiz. | Horizontal |
| H.P., HP | Horsepower; High Pressure |
| H.P.F. | High Power Factor |
| Hr. | Hour |
| Hrs./Day | Hours per Day |
| HSC | High Short Circuit |
| Ht. | Height |
| Htg. | Heating |
| Htrs. | Heaters |
| HVAC | Heating, Ventilation & Air-Conditioning |
| Hvy. | Heavy |
| HW | Hot Water |
| Hyd.; Hydr. | Hydraulic |
| Hz | Hertz (cycles) |
| I. | Moment of Inertia |
| IBC | International Building Code |
| I.C. | Interrupting Capacity |
| ID | Inside Diameter |
| I.D. | Inside Dimension; Identification |
| I.F. | Inside Frosted |
| I.M.C. | Intermediate Metal Conduit |
| In. | Inch |
| Incan. | Incandescent |
| Incl. | Included; Including |
| Int. | Interior |
| Inst. | Installation |
| Insul., insul | Insulation/Insulated |
| I.P. | Iron Pipe |
| I.P.S., IPS | Iron Pipe Size |
| IPT | Iron Pipe Threaded |
| I.W. | Indirect Waste |
| J | Joule |
| J.I.C. | Joint Industrial Council |
| K | Thousand; Thousand Pounds; Heavy Wall Copper Tubing, Kelvin |
| K.A.H. | Thousand Amp. Hours |
| kcmil | Thousand Circular Mils |
| KD | Knock Down |
| K.D.A.T. | Kiln Dried After Treatment |
| kg | Kilogram |
| kG | Kilogauss |
| kgf | Kilogram Force |
| kHz | Kilohertz |
| Kip | 1000 Pounds |
| KJ | Kilojoule |
| K.L. | Effective Length Factor |
| K.L.F. | Kips per Linear Foot |
| Km | Kilometer |
| KO | Knock Out |
| K.S.F. | Kips per Square Foot |
| K.S.I. | Kips per Square Inch |
| kV | Kilovolt |
| kVA | Kilovolt Ampere |
| kVAR | Kilovar (Reactance) |
| KW | Kilowatt |
| KWh | Kilowatt-hour |
| L | Labor Only; Length; Long; Medium Wall Copper Tubing |
| Lab. | Labor |
| lat | Latitude |
| Lath. | Lather |
| Lav. | Lavatory |
| lb.; # | Pound |
| L.B., LB | Load Bearing; L Conduit Body |
| L. & E. | Labor & Equipment |
| lb./hr. | Pounds per Hour |
| lb./L.F. | Pounds per Linear Foot |
| lbf/sq.in. | Pound-force per Square Inch |
| L.C.L. | Less than Carload Lot |
| L.C.Y. | Loose Cubic Yard |
| Ld. | Load |
| LE | Lead Equivalent |
| LED | Light Emitting Diode |
| L.F. | Linear Foot |
| L.F. Hdr | Linear Feet of Header |
| L.F. Nose | Linear Foot of Stair Nosing |
| L.F. Rsr | Linear Foot of Stair Riser |
| Lg. | Long; Length; Large |
| L & H | Light and Heat |
| LH | Long Span Bar Joist |
| L.H. | Labor Hours |
| L.L., LL | Live Load |
| L.L.D. | Lamp Lumen Depreciation |
| lm | Lumen |
| lm/sf | Lumen per Square Foot |
| lm/W | Lumen per Watt |
| LOA | Length Over All |
| log | Logarithm |
| L-O-L | Lateralolet |
| long. | Longitude |
| L.P., LP | Liquefied Petroleum; Low Pressure |
| L.P.F. | Low Power Factor |
| LR | Long Radius |
| L.S. | Lump Sum |
| Lt. | Light |
| Lt. Ga. | Light Gauge |
| L.T.L. | Less than Truckload Lot |
| Lt. Wt. | Lightweight |
| L.V. | Low Voltage |
| M | Thousand; Material; Male; Light Wall Copper Tubing |
| $M^2CA$ | Meters Squared Contact Area |
| m/hr.; M.H. | Man-hour |
| mA | Milliampere |
| Mach. | Machine |
| Mag. Str. | Magnetic Starter |
| Maint. | Maintenance |
| Marb. | Marble Setter |
| Mat; Mat'l. | Material |
| Max. | Maximum |
| MBF | Thousand Board Feet |
| MBH | Thousand BTU's per hr. |
| MC | Metal Clad Cable |
| MCC | Motor Control Center |
| M.C.F. | Thousand Cubic Feet |
| MCFM | Thousand Cubic Feet per Minute |
| M.C.M. | Thousand Circular Mils |
| MCP | Motor Circuit Protector |
| MD | Medium Duty |
| MDF | Medium-density fibreboard |
| M.D.O. | Medium Density Overlaid |
| Med. | Medium |
| MF | Thousand Feet |
| M.F.B.M. | Thousand Feet Board Measure |
| Mfg. | Manufacturing |
| Mfrs. | Manufacturers |
| mg | Milligram |
| MGD | Million Gallons per Day |
| MGPH | Million Gallons per Hour |
| MH, M.H. | Manhole; Metal Halide; Man-Hour |
| MHz | Megahertz |
| Mi. | Mile |
| MI | Malleable Iron; Mineral Insulated |
| MIPS | Male Iron Pipe Size |
| mj | Mechanical Joint |
| m | Meter |
| mm | Millimeter |
| Mill. | Millwright |
| Min., min. | Minimum, Minute |

# Abbreviations

| | |
|---|---|
| Misc. | Miscellaneous |
| ml | Milliliter, Mainline |
| M.L.F. | Thousand Linear Feet |
| Mo. | Month |
| Mobil. | Mobilization |
| Mog. | Mogul Base |
| MPH | Miles per Hour |
| MPT | Male Pipe Thread |
| MRGWB | Moisture Resistant Gypsum Wallboard |
| MRT | Mile Round Trip |
| ms | Millisecond |
| M.S.F. | Thousand Square Feet |
| Mstz. | Mosaic & Terrazzo Worker |
| M.S.Y. | Thousand Square Yards |
| Mtd., mtd., mtd | Mounted |
| Mthe. | Mosaic & Terrazzo Helper |
| Mtng. | Mounting |
| Mult. | Multi; Multiply |
| MUTCD | Manual on Uniform Traffic Control Devices |
| M.V.A. | Million Volt Amperes |
| M.V.A.R. | Million Volt Amperes Reactance |
| MV | Megavolt |
| MW | Megawatt |
| MXM | Male by Male |
| MYD | Thousand Yards |
| N | Natural; North |
| nA | Nanoampere |
| NA | Not Available; Not Applicable |
| N.B.C. | National Building Code |
| NC | Normally Closed |
| NEMA | National Electrical Manufacturers Assoc. |
| NEHB | Bolted Circuit Breaker to 600V. |
| NFPA | National Fire Protection Association |
| NLB | Non-Load-Bearing |
| NM | Non-Metallic Cable |
| nm | Nanometer |
| No. | Number |
| NO | Normally Open |
| N.O.C. | Not Otherwise Classified |
| Nose. | Nosing |
| NPT | National Pipe Thread |
| NQOD | Combination Plug-on/Bolt on Circuit Breaker to 240V. |
| N.R.C., NRC | Noise Reduction Coefficient/ Nuclear Regulator Commission |
| N.R.S. | Non Rising Stem |
| ns | Nanosecond |
| NTP | Notice to Proceed |
| nW | Nanowatt |
| OB | Opposing Blade |
| OC | On Center |
| OD | Outside Diameter |
| O.D. | Outside Dimension |
| ODS | Overhead Distribution System |
| O.G. | Ogee |
| O.H. | Overhead |
| O&P | Overhead and Profit |
| Oper. | Operator |
| Opng. | Opening |
| Orna. | Ornamental |
| OSB | Oriented Strand Board |
| OS&Y | Outside Screw and Yoke |
| OSHA | Occupational Safety and Health Act |
| Ovhd. | Overhead |
| OWG | Oil, Water or Gas |
| Oz. | Ounce |
| P. | Pole; Applied Load; Projection |
| p. | Page |
| Pape. | Paperhanger |
| P.A.P.R. | Powered Air Purifying Respirator |
| PAR | Parabolic Reflector |
| P.B., PB | Push Button |
| Pc., Pcs. | Piece, Pieces |
| P.C. | Portland Cement; Power Connector |
| P.C.F. | Pounds per Cubic Foot |
| PCM | Phase Contrast Microscopy |
| PDCA | Painting and Decorating Contractors of America |
| P.E., PE | Professional Engineer; Porcelain Enamel; Polyethylene; Plain End |
| P.E.C.I. | Porcelain Enamel on Cast Iron |
| Perf. | Perforated |
| PEX | Cross Linked Polyethylene |
| Ph. | Phase |
| P.I. | Pressure Injected |
| Pile. | Pile Driver |
| Pkg. | Package |
| Pl. | Plate |
| Plah. | Plasterer Helper |
| Plas. | Plasterer |
| plf | Pounds Per Linear Foot |
| Pluh. | Plumber Helper |
| Plum. | Plumber |
| Ply. | Plywood |
| p.m. | Post Meridiem |
| Pntd. | Painted |
| Pord. | Painter, Ordinary |
| pp | Pages |
| PP, PPL | Polypropylene |
| P.P.M. | Parts per Million |
| Pr. | Pair |
| P.E.S.B. | Pre-engineered Steel Building |
| Prefab. | Prefabricated |
| Prefin. | Prefinished |
| Prop. | Propelled |
| PSF, psf | Pounds per Square Foot |
| PSI, psi | Pounds per Square Inch |
| PSIG | Pounds per Square Inch Gauge |
| PSP | Plastic Sewer Pipe |
| Pspr. | Painter, Spray |
| Psst. | Painter, Structural Steel |
| P.T. | Potential Transformer |
| P. & T. | Pressure & Temperature |
| Ptd. | Painted |
| Ptns. | Partitions |
| Pu | Ultimate Load |
| PVC | Polyvinyl Chloride |
| Pvmt. | Pavement |
| PRV | Pressure Relief Valve |
| Pwr. | Power |
| Q | Quantity Heat Flow |
| Qt. | Quart |
| Quan., Qty. | Quantity |
| Q.C. | Quick Coupling |
| r | Radius of Gyration |
| R | Resistance |
| R.C.P. | Reinforced Concrete Pipe |
| Rect. | Rectangle |
| recpt. | Receptacle |
| Reg. | Regular |
| Reinf. | Reinforced |
| Req'd. | Required |
| Res. | Resistant |
| Resi. | Residential |
| RF | Radio Frequency |
| RFID | Radio-frequency Identification |
| Rgh. | Rough |
| RGS | Rigid Galvanized Steel |
| RHW | Rubber, Heat & Water Resistant; Residential Hot Water |
| rms | Root Mean Square |
| Rnd. | Round |
| Rodm. | Rodman |
| Rofc. | Roofer, Composition |
| Rofp. | Roofer, Precast |
| Rohe. | Roofer Helpers (Composition) |
| Rots. | Roofer, Tile & Slate |
| R.O.W. | Right of Way |
| RPM | Revolutions per Minute |
| R.S. | Rapid Start |
| Rsr | Riser |
| RT | Round Trip |
| S. | Suction; Single Entrance; South |
| SBS | Styrene Butadiere Styrene |
| SC | Screw Cover |
| SCFM | Standard Cubic Feet per Minute |
| Scaf. | Scaffold |
| Sch., Sched. | Schedule |
| S.C.R. | Modular Brick |
| S.D. | Sound Deadening |
| SDR | Standard Dimension Ratio |
| S.E. | Surfaced Edge |
| Sel. | Select |
| SER, SEU | Service Entrance Cable |
| S.F. | Square Foot |
| S.F.C.A. | Square Foot Contact Area |
| S.F. Flr. | Square Foot of Floor |
| S.F.G. | Square Foot of Ground |
| S.F. Hor. | Square Foot Horizontal |
| SFR | Square Feet of Radiation |
| S.F. Shlf. | Square Foot of Shelf |
| S4S | Surface 4 Sides |
| Shee. | Sheet Metal Worker |
| Sin. | Sine |
| Skwk. | Skilled Worker |
| SL | Saran Lined |
| S.L. | Slimline |
| Sldr. | Solder |
| SLH | Super Long Span Bar Joist |
| S.N. | Solid Neutral |
| SO | Stranded with oil resistant inside insulation |
| S-O-L | Socketolet |
| sp | Standpipe |
| S.P. | Static Pressure; Single Pole; Self-Propelled |
| Spri. | Sprinkler Installer |
| spwg | Static Pressure Water Gauge |
| S.P.D.T. | Single Pole, Double Throw |
| SPF | Spruce Pine Fir; Sprayed Polyurethane Foam |
| S.P.S.T. | Single Pole, Single Throw |
| SPT | Standard Pipe Thread |
| Sq. | Square; 100 Square Feet |
| Sq. Hd. | Square Head |
| Sq. In. | Square Inch |
| S.S. | Single Strength; Stainless Steel |
| S.S.B. | Single Strength B Grade |
| sst, ss | Stainless Steel |
| Sswk. | Structural Steel Worker |
| Sswl. | Structural Steel Welder |
| St.; Stl. | Steel |
| STC | Sound Transmission Coefficient |
| Std. | Standard |
| Stg. | Staging |
| STK | Select Tight Knot |
| STP | Standard Temperature & Pressure |
| Stpi. | Steamfitter, Pipefitter |
| Str. | Strength; Starter; Straight |
| Strd. | Stranded |
| Struct. | Structural |
| Sty. | Story |
| Subj. | Subject |
| Subs. | Subcontractors |
| Surf. | Surface |
| Sw. | Switch |
| Swbd. | Switchboard |
| S.Y. | Square Yard |
| Syn. | Synthetic |
| S.Y.P. | Southern Yellow Pine |
| Sys. | System |
| t. | Thickness |
| T | Temperature; Ton |
| Tan | Tangent |
| T.C. | Terra Cotta |
| T & C | Threaded and Coupled |
| T.D. | Temperature Difference |
| TDD | Telecommunications Device for the Deaf |
| T.E.M. | Transmission Electron Microscopy |
| temp | Temperature, Tempered, Temporary |
| TFFN | Nylon Jacketed Wire |

# Abbreviations

| | |
|---|---|
| TFE | Tetrafluoroethylene (Teflon) |
| T. & G. | Tongue & Groove; Tar & Gravel |
| Th., Thk. | Thick |
| Thn. | Thin |
| Thrded | Threaded |
| Tilf. | Tile Layer, Floor |
| Tilh. | Tile Layer, Helper |
| THHN | Nylon Jacketed Wire |
| THW. | Insulated Strand Wire |
| THWN | Nylon Jacketed Wire |
| T.L., TL | Truckload |
| T.M. | Track Mounted |
| Tot. | Total |
| T-O-L | Threadolet |
| tmpd | Tempered |
| TPO | Thermoplastic Polyolefin |
| T.S. | Trigger Start |
| Tr. | Trade |
| Transf. | Transformer |
| Trhv. | Truck Driver, Heavy |
| Trlr | Trailer |
| Trlt. | Truck Driver, Light |
| TTY | Teletypewriter |
| TV | Television |
| T.W. | Thermoplastic Water Resistant Wire |
| UCI | Uniform Construction Index |
| UF | Underground Feeder |
| UGND | Underground Feeder |
| UHF | Ultra High Frequency |
| U.I. | United Inch |
| U.L., UL | Underwriters Laboratory |
| Uld. | Unloading |
| Unfin. | Unfinished |
| UPS | Uninterruptible Power Supply |
| URD | Underground Residential Distribution |
| US | United States |
| USGBC | U.S. Green Building Council |
| USP | United States Primed |
| UTMCD | Uniform Traffic Manual For Control Devices |
| UTP | Unshielded Twisted Pair |
| V | Volt |
| VA | Volt Amperes |
| VAT | Vinyl Asbestos Tile |
| V.C.T. | Vinyl Composition Tile |
| VAV | Variable Air Volume |
| VC | Veneer Core |
| VDC | Volts Direct Current |
| Vent. | Ventilation |
| Vert. | Vertical |
| V.F. | Vinyl Faced |
| V.G. | Vertical Grain |
| VHF | Very High Frequency |
| VHO | Very High Output |
| Vib. | Vibrating |
| VLF | Vertical Linear Foot |
| VOC | Volatile Organic Compound |
| Vol. | Volume |
| VRP | Vinyl Reinforced Polyester |
| W | Wire; Watt; Wide; West |
| w/ | With |
| W.C., WC | Water Column; Water Closet |
| W.F. | Wide Flange |
| W.G. | Water Gauge |
| Wldg. | Welding |
| W. Mile | Wire Mile |
| W-O-L | Weldolet |
| W.R. | Water Resistant |
| Wrck. | Wrecker |
| WSFU | Water Supply Fixture Unit |
| W.S.P. | Water, Steam, Petroleum |
| WT., Wt. | Weight |
| WWF | Welded Wire Fabric |
| XFER | Transfer |
| XFMR | Transformer |
| XHD | Extra Heavy Duty |
| XHHW | Cross-Linked Polyethylene Wire |
| XLPE | Insulation |
| XLP | Cross-linked Polyethylene |
| Xport | Transport |
| Y | Wye |
| yd | Yard |
| yr | Year |
| Δ | Delta |
| % | Percent |
| ~ | Approximately |
| Ø | Phase; diameter |
| @ | At |
| # | Pound; Number |
| < | Less Than |
| > | Greater Than |
| Z | Zone |

## RESIDENTIAL COST ESTIMATE

OWNER'S NAME: ______ APPRAISER: ______

RESIDENCE ADDRESS: ______ PROJECT: ______

CITY, STATE, ZIP CODE: ______ DATE: ______

CLASS OF CONSTRUCTION
- ☐ ECONOMY
- ☐ AVERAGE
- ☐ CUSTOM
- ☐ LUXURY

RESIDENCE TYPE
- ☐ 1 STORY
- ☐ 1-1/2 STORY
- ☐ 2 STORY
- ☐ 2-1/2 STORY
- ☐ 3 STORY
- ☐ BI-LEVEL
- ☐ TRI-LEVEL

CONFIGURATION
- ☐ DETACHED
- ☐ TOWN/ROW HOUSE
- ☐ SEMI-DETACHED

OCCUPANCY
- ☐ ONE STORY
- ☐ TWO FAMILY
- ☐ THREE FAMILY
- ☐ OTHER ______

EXTERIOR WALL SYSTEM
- ☐ WOOD SIDING—WOOD FRAME
- ☐ BRICK VENEER—WOOD FRAME
- ☐ STUCCO ON WOOD FRAME
- ☐ PAINTED CONCRETE BLOCK
- ☐ SOLID MASONRY (AVERAGE & CUSTOM)
- ☐ STONE VENEER—WOOD FRAME
- ☐ SOLID BRICK (LUXURY)
- ☐ SOLID STONE (LUXURY)

| *LIVING AREA (Main Building) | | *LIVING AREA (Wing or Ell) ( ) | | *LIVING AREA (Wing or Ell) ( ) | |
|---|---|---|---|---|---|
| First Level | ______ S.F. | First Level | ______ S.F. | First Level | ______ S.F. |
| Second Level | ______ S.F. | Second Level | ______ S.F. | Second Level | ______ S.F. |
| Third Level | ______ S.F. | Third Level | ______ S.F. | Third Level | ______ S.F. |
| Total | ______ S.F. | Total | ______ S.F. | Total | ______ S.F. |

*Basement Area is not part of living area.

| MAIN BUILDING | COSTS PER S.F. LIVING AREA |
|---|---|
| Cost per Square Foot of Living Area, from Page ______ | $ |
| Basement Addition: ______ % Finished, ______ % Unfinished | + |
| Roof Cover Adjustment: ______ Type, Page ______ (Add or Deduct) | ( ) |
| Central Air Conditioning: ☐ Separate Ducts ☐ Heating Ducts, Page ______ | + |
| Heating System Adjustment: ______ Type, Page ______ (Add or Deduct) | ( ) |
| Main Building: Adjusted Cost per S.F. of Living Area | $ |

MAIN BUILDING TOTAL COST: $ ______ /S.F. (Cost per S.F. Living Area) x ______ S.F. (Living Area) x ______ (Town/Row House Multiplier (Use 1 for Detached)) = $ ______ (TOTAL COST)

| WING OR ELL ( ) ______ STORY | COSTS PER S.F. LIVING AREA |
|---|---|
| Cost per Square Foot of Living Area, from Page ______ | $ |
| Basement Addition: ______ % Finished, ______ % Unfinished | + |
| Roof Cover Adjustment: ______ Type, Page ______ (Add or Deduct) | ( ) |
| Central Air Conditioning: ☐ Separate Ducts ☐ Heating Ducts, Page ______ | + |
| Heating System Adjustment: ______ Type, Page ______ (Add or Deduct) | ( ) |
| Wing or Ell ( ): Adjusted Cost per S.F. of Living Area | $ |

WING OR ELL ( ) TOTAL COST: $ ______ /S.F. (Cost per S.F. Living Area) x ______ S.F. (Living Area) = $ ______ (TOTAL COST)

| WING OR ELL ( ) ______ STORY | COSTS PER S.F. LIVING AREA |
|---|---|
| Cost per Square Foot of Living Area, from Page ______ | $ |
| Basement Addition: ______ % Finished, ______ % Unfinished | + |
| Roof Cover Adjustment: ______ Type, Page ______ (Add or Deduct) | ( ) |
| Central Air Conditioning: ☐ Separate Ducts ☐ Heating Ducts, Page ______ | + |
| Heating System Adjustment: ______ Type, Page ______ (Add or Deduct) | ( ) |
| Wing or Ell ( ): Adjusted Cost per S.F. of Living Area | $ |

WING OR ELL ( ) TOTAL COST: $ ______ /S.F. (Cost per S.F. Living Area) x ______ S.F. (Living Area) = $ ______ (TOTAL COST)

TOTAL THIS PAGE ______

Page 1 of 2

## RESIDENTIAL COST ESTIMATE

| | | | |
|---|---|---|---|
| Total Page 1 | | | $ |
| | QUANTITY | UNIT COST | |
| Additional Bathrooms: ________ Full, ________ Half | | | |
| Finished Attic: ________ Ft. x ________ Ft. | S.F. | | + |
| Breezeway: ☐ Open ☐ Enclosed ________ Ft. x ________ Ft. | S.F. | | + |
| Covered Porch: ☐ Open ☐ Enclosed ________ Ft. x ________ Ft. | S.F. | | + |
| Fireplace: ☐ Interior Chimney ☐ Exterior Chimney<br>☐ No. of Flues ☐ Additional Fireplaces | | | + |
| Appliances: | | | + |
| Kitchen Cabinets Adjustment: (+/–) | | | |
| ☐ Garage ☐ Carport: ________ Car(s) Description ________________ (+/–) | | | |
| Miscellaneous: | | | + |

ADJUSTED TOTAL BUILDING COST $

| REPLACEMENT COST | |
|---|---|
| ADJUSTED TOTAL BUILDING COST | $ ________ |
| Site Improvements | |
| (A) Paving & Sidewalks | $ ________ |
| (B) Landscaping | $ ________ |
| (C) Fences | $ ________ |
| (D) Swimming Pool | $ ________ |
| (E) Miscellaneous | $ ________ |
| TOTAL | $ ________ |
| Location Factor | x ________ |
| Location Replacement Cost | $ ________ |
| Depreciation | –$ ________ |
| LOCAL DEPRECIATED COST | $ ________ |

| INSURANCE COST | |
|---|---|
| ADJUSTED TOTAL BUILDING COST | $ ________ |
| Insurance Exclusions | |
| (A) Footings, Site Work, Underground Piping | –$ ________ |
| (B) Architects' Fees | –$ ________ |
| Total Building Cost Less Exclusion | $ ________ |
| Location Factor | x ________ |
| LOCAL INSURABLE REPLACEMENT COST | $ ________ |

**SKETCH AND ADDITIONAL CALCULATIONS**

Page 2 of 2

**CII APPRAISAL**

5. DATE: ____________________

1. SUBJECT PROPERTY: ____________________

6. APPRAISER: ____________________

2. BUILDING: ____________________

3. ADDRESS: ____________________

4. BUILDING USE: ____________________

7. YEAR BUILT: ____________________

8. EXTERIOR WALL CONSTRUCTION: ____________________

9. FRAME: ____________________

10. GROUND FLOOR AREA: ____________________ S.F.

11. GROSS FLOOR AREA (EXCL. BASEMENT): ____________________ S.F.

12. NUMBER OF STORIES: ____________________

13. STORY HEIGHT: ____________________

14. PERIMETER: ____________________ L.F.

15. BASEMENT AREA: ____________________ S.F.

16. GENERAL COMMENTS: ____________________

| | NO. | DESCRIPTION | UNIT | UNIT COST | NEW SF COST | MODEL SF COST | +/- CHANGE |
|---|---|---|---|---|---|---|---|
| A | SUBSTRUCTURE | | | | | | |
| A | 1010 | Standard Foundations Bay size: | S.F. Gnd. | | | | |
| A | 1030 | Slab on Grade Material: Thickness: | S.F. Slab | | | | |
| A | 2010 | Basement Excavation Depth: Area: | S.F. Gnd. | | | | |
| A | 2020 | Basement Walls | L.F. Walls | | | | |
| B | SHELL | | | | | | |
| | B10 Superstructure | | | | | | |
| B | 1010 | Floor Construction Elevated floors: | S.F. Floor | | | | |
| | | | S.F. Floor | | | | |
| B | 1020 | Roof Construction | S.F. Roof | | | | |
| | B20 Exterior Enclosure | | | | | | |
| B | 2010 | Exterior walls Material: Thickness: *% of wall* | S.F. Walls | | | | |
| | | Material: Thickness: *% of wall* | S.F. Walls | | | | |
| B | 2020 | Exterior Windows Type: *% of wall* | S.F. Wind. | | | | |
| | | Type: *% of wall* Each | S.F. Wind. | | | | |
| B | 2030 | Exterior Doors Type: Number: | Each | | | | |
| | | Type: Number: | Each | | | | |
| | B30 Roofing | | | | | | |
| B | 3010 | Roof Coverings Material: | S.F. Roof | | | | |
| | | Material: | S.F. Roof | | | | |
| B | 3020 | Roof Openings | S.F. Opng. | | | | |
| C | INTERIORS | | | | | | |
| C | 1010 | Partitions: Material: Density: | S.F. Part. | | | | |
| | | Material: Density: | | | | | |
| C | 1020 | Interior Doors Type: Number: | Each | | | | |
| C | 1030 | Fittings | Each | | | | |
| C | 2010 | Stair Construction | Flight | | | | |
| C | 3010 | Wall Finishes Material: % of Wall | S.F. Walls | | | | |
| | | Material: | S.F. Walls | | | | |
| C | 3020 | Floor Finishes Material: | S.F. Floor | | | | |
| | | Material: | S.F. Floor | | | | |
| | | Material: | S.F. Floor | | | | |
| C | 3030 | Ceiling Finishes Material: | S.F. Ceil. | | | | |

| | NO. | SYSTEM/COMPONENT | DESCRIPTION | UNIT | UNIT COST | NEW S.F. COST | MODEL S.F. COST | +/- CHANGE |
|---|---|---|---|---|---|---|---|---|
| **D SERVICES** | | | | | | | | |
| | **D10 Conveying** | | | | | | | |
| D | 1010 | Elevators & Lifts | Type: Capacity: Stops: | Each | | | | |
| D | 1020 | Escalators & Moving Walks | Type: | Each | | | | |
| | **D20 Plumbing** | | | | | | | |
| D | 2010 | Plumbing | | Each | | | | |
| D | 2020 | Domestic Water Distribution | | S.F. Floor | | | | |
| D | 2040 | Rain Water Drainage | | S.F. Roof | | | | |
| | **D30 HVAC** | | | | | | | |
| D | 3010 | Energy Supply | | Each | | | | |
| D | 3020 | Heat Generating Systems | Type: | S.F. Floor | | | | |
| D | 3030 | Cooling Generating Systems | Type: | S.F. Floor | | | | |
| D | 3090 | Other HVAC Sys. & Equipment | | Each | | | | |
| | **D40 Fire Protection** | | | | | | | |
| D | 4010 | Sprinklers | | S.F. Floor | | | | |
| D | 4020 | Standpipes | | S.F. Floor | | | | |
| | **D50 Electrical** | | | | | | | |
| D | 5010 | Electrical Service/Distribution | | S.F. Floor | | | | |
| D | 5020 | Lighting & Branch Wiring | | S.F. Floor | | | | |
| D | 5030 | Communications & Security | | S.F. Floor | | | | |
| D | 5090 | Other Electrical Systems | | S.F. Floor | | | | |
| **E EQUIPMENT & FURNISHINGS** | | | | | | | | |
| E | 1010 | Commercial Equipment | | Each | | | | |
| E | 1020 | Institutional Equipment | | Each | | | | |
| E | 1030 | Vehicular Equipment | | Each | | | | |
| E | 1090 | Other Equipment | | Each | | | | |
| **F SPECIAL CONSTRUCTION** | | | | | | | | |
| F | 1020 | Integrated Construction | | S.F. | | | | |
| F | 1040 | Special Facilities | | S.F. | | | | |
| **G BUILDING SITEWORK** | | | | | | | | |

| ITEM | | Total Change |
|---|---|---|
| 17 | Model 020 total ___ $ ______ | |
| 18 | Adjusted S.F. cost ___ $ ______ item 17 +/- changes | |
| 19 | Building area - from item 11 ______ S.F. x adjusted S.F. cost | $ |
| 20 | Basement area - from item 15 ______ S.F. x S.F. cost $ | $ |
| 21 | Base building sub-total - item 20 + item 19 | $ |
| 22 | Miscellaneous addition (quality, etc.) | $ |
| 23 | Sub-total - item 22 + 21 | $ |
| 24 | General conditions -25 % of item 23 | $ |
| 25 | Sub-total - item 24 + item 23 | $ |
| 26 | Architects fees ______ % of item 25 | $ |
| 27 | Sub-total - item 26 + item 27 | $ |
| 28 | Location modifier | x |
| 29 | Local replacement cost - item 28 x item 27 | $ |
| 30 | Depreciation ______ % of item 29 | $ |
| 31 | Depreciated local replacement cost - item 29 less item 30 | $ |
| 32 | Exclusions | $ |
| 33 | Net depreciated replacement cost - item 31 less item 32 | $ |

Base Cost per square foot floor area: *(from square foot table)*

Specify source: Page: ________, Model # __________, Area __________ S.F., Exterior wall ____________, Frame ______________

Adjustments for exterior wall variation:

Size Adjustment:
*(Interpolate)*

Height Adjustment: __________ + __________ = __________

Adjusted Base Cost per square foot:

Building Cost $ ______________ x ______________ = ______________
*Adjusted Base Cost per square foot* *Floor Area*

Basement Cost $ ______________ x ______________ = ______________
*Basement Cost* *Basement Area*

Lump Sum Additions

TOTAL BUILDING COST *(Sum of above costs)* ______________

Modifications: *(complexity, workmanship, size)* +/- ______________ % ______________

Location Modifier: City ______________________ Date ______________ x ______________

Local cost of replacement ______________

Less depreciation: ______________________________ - ______________

Local cost of replacement less depreciation $ ______________

# Notes

# Notes

# Notes

# Notes

# Notes

# Notes

# Notes

# Notes

# Notes

# Notes

**Virtual classes offered monthly. Call for the schedule.** 877.620.6245

Gordian offers training classes in a variety of formats—eLearning training modules, instructor-led classes, on-site training, and virtual training classes, as well as custom solutions. Please visit our website at rsmeans.com/products/training/seminars for our current schedule of class offerings.

Training classes that are offered in one or more of our formats are: Building Systems and the Construction Process; Construction Cost Estimating: Concepts & Practice; Introduction to Estimating; Scope of Work for Facilities Estimating; Facilities Construction Estimating; Fundamentals to Construction Cost Estimating; Maintenance & Repair Estimating for Facilities; Mechanical & Electrical Estimating; RSMeans CostWorks CD; and RSMeans Data Online Training.

# Registration Information

**How to register**

*By Phone*

Register by phone at 877.620.6245

*Online*

Register online at rsmeans.com/products/services/training

*Note: Purchase orders or credits cards are required to register.*

**Instructor-led Government Pricing**

All federal government employees save off the regular seminar price. Other promotional discounts cannot be combined with the government discount. Call 781.422.5115 for government pricing.

**If you have any questions or you would like to register for any class or purchase a training module, call us at 877.620.6245.**

## Construction Cost Estimating: Concepts and Practice

This one- or two-day introductory course to improve estimating skills and effectiveness starts with the details of interpreting bid documents and ends with the summary of the estimate and bid submission.

Topics include:

- Using plans and specifications to create estimates
- The takeoff process – deriving all tasks with correct quantities
- Summarizing the estimate to arrive at the final number
- Formulas for area and cubic measure, adding waste and adjusting productivity to specific projects
- Evaluating subcontractors' proposals and prices
- Adding insurance and bonds
- Understanding how labor costs are calculated
- Submitting bids and proposals

Who should attend: project managers, architects, engineers, owners' representatives, contractors, and anyone responsible for budgeting or estimating construction projects.

## Fundamentals to Construction Cost Estimating

This self-paced course focuses on unit price estimating for facilities renovation, repair, and remodeling. Combining hands-on skill building with a discussion of best estimating practices and real-life problems this informative online course will boost your estimating skills, bring you up to date with key concepts, and provide tips and guidelines that can save you time and help you avoid costly estimating oversights and errors.

Topics include:

- The three phases of estimating
- Bid document review
- How to perform quantity takeoffs
- How to price the work

Who should attend: facilities professionals and anyone involved in facilities planning, design, and construction.

For novice estimators, this course can serve as a primer to Facilities Construction Estimating Self-Paced Training or the following live training courses: Facilities Construction Estimating, Mechanical & Electrical Estimating, Assessing Scope of Work for Facilities Estimating, or Maintenance & Repair Estimating.

## Mechanical & Electrical Estimating

This two-day course teaches attendees how to prepare more accurate and complete mechanical/electrical estimates, avoid the pitfalls of omission and double-counting, and understand the composition and rationale within the RSMeans data mechanical/electrical database.

Topics include:
- The unique way mechanical and electrical systems are interrelated
- M&E estimates – conceptual, planning, budgeting, and bidding stages
- Order of magnitude, square foot, assemblies and unit price estimating
- Comparative cost analysis of equipment and design alternatives

Who should attend: architects, engineers, facilities managers, mechanical and electrical contractors, and others who need a highly reliable method for developing, understanding, and evaluating mechanical and electrical contracts.

## Facilities Construction Estimating

In this two-day course, professionals working in facilities management can get help with their daily challenges to establish budgets for all phases of a project.

Topics include:
- Determining the full scope of a project
- Understanding of RSMeans data and what is included in prices
- Identifying appropriate factors to be included in your estimate
- Creative solutions to estimating issues
- Organizing estimates for presentation and discussion
- Special estimating techniques for repair/remodel and maintenance projects
- Appropriate use of contingency, city cost indexes and reference notes
- Techniques to get to the correct estimate quickly

Who should attend: facility managers, engineers, contractors, facility tradespeople, planners and project managers.

## Assessing Scope of Work for Facilities Construction Estimating

This two-day practical training program addresses the vital importance of understanding the scope of projects in order to produce accurate cost estimates for facilities repair and remodeling.

Topics include:
- Discussions of site visits, plans/specs, record drawings of facilities and site-specific lists
- Review of CSI divisions, including means, methods, materials and the challenges of scoping each topic
- Exercises in scope identification and scope writing for accurate estimating of projects
- Hands-on exercises that require scope, takeoff and pricing

Who should attend: corporate and government estimators, planners, facility managers and others who need to produce accurate project estimates.

## CostWorks CD Self-Paced Training Course

This self-paced course helps users become more familiar with the functionality of the CD. Each menu, icon, screen, and function found in the program is explained in depth. Time is devoted to hands-on estimating exercises.

Topics include:
- Searching the database using all navigation methods
- Exporting RSMeans data to your preferred spreadsheet format
- Viewing crews, assembly components and much more
- Automatically regionalizing the database

This training session requires users to bring a laptop computer to class and to follow along using a purchased copy of RSMeans data CostWorks CD.

When you register for this course you will receive an outline for your laptop requirements.

## Maintenance & Repair Estimating for Facilities

This two-day course teaches attendees how to plan, budget and estimate the cost of ongoing and preventive maintenance and repair for existing buildings and grounds.

Topics include:
- The most financially favorable maintenance, repair, and replacement scheduling and estimating
- Preventive planning and facilities upgrading
- Determining both in-house and contract-out service costs
- Annual asset-protecting M&R plan

Who should attend: facility managers, maintenance supervisors, buildings and grounds superintendents, plant managers, planners, estimators, and others involved in facilities planning and budgeting.

## RSMeans Data Online Training

Construction estimating is vital to the decision-making process at each state of every project. Our online solution works the way you do. It's systematic, flexible and intuitive. In this self-paced course you will see how you can estimate any phase of any project faster and better.

Topics include:
- Customizing our online estimating solution
- Making the most of RSMeans data "Circle Reference" numbers
- How to integrate your cost data
- Generating reports, exporting estimates to MS Excel, sharing, collaborating and more

Also offered as a self-paced or on-site training program!

# RSMeans data Training Cancellation Policy

## Virtual Training (Individual)

If you are unable to attend a training class, a colleague may substitute at any time before the session starts by notifying the training registrar at 781.422.5115 or your sales representative. Gordian is not responsible for sending duplicate materials to the substitute colleague.

If you are unable to find a substitute and cancel fewer than ten (10) business days prior to the training class, you will either forfeit the registration fee or be allowed to apply your registration fee to the same class only once within the same calendar year. No-shows will forfeit their registration fees and no rescheduling is permitted. In the unfortunate circumstance that Gordian must cancel your event, Gordian will work with you to reschedule your attendance in the same training class at a later date or will fully refund your registration fee.

Any on-demand (self-paced) training modules are not eligible for cancellation, substitution, transfer, return or refund.

## Virtual Training (Private Group)

If you provide notice more than ten (10) business days prior to the training class, Gordian will work to reschedule your event. If you cancel your event fewer than ten (10) business days prior to the training class, you are responsible for paying for the trainer's time for the cancelled training, as well as the full cost of materials and shipping. In the unfortunate circumstance that Gordian must cancel your event, Gordian will work with you to reschedule your attendance in the same training class at a later date or will fully refund your registration fee.

## Public Training Events (Individual)

If you are unable to attend a training conference, a colleague may substitute no fewer than ten (10) business days before the session starts by notifying the training registrar at 781.422.5115 or your sales representative. Gordian is not responsible for sending duplicate materials to the substitute colleague.

If you are unable to find a substitute and cancel fewer than ten (10) business days prior to the conference, you will forfeit the registration fee. No-shows will forfeit their registration fees and no rescheduling is permitted. In the unfortunate circumstance that Gordian must cancel your event, Gordian will fully refund your registration fee.

## On-Site Training (Private Group)

If you provide notice more than ten (10) business days prior to the training class, Gordian will work with you to reschedule your event, but you are responsible for rescheduling fees associated with the trainer's time, airfare and lodging. If you cancel fewer than ten (10) business days before your event, you are responsible for the full cost of the event. In the unfortunate event that Gordian must cancel your event, Gordian will work with you to reschedule your attendance at a later date or will fully refund your registration fee.

## AACE Approved Courses

The AACE recognizes .1 CEUs per hour of training attended for all of Gordian's virtual training courses.

## AIA Continuing Education

We are registered with the AIA Continuing Education System (AIA/CES) and are committed to developing quality learning activities in accordance with the CES criteria. Many seminars meet the AIA/CES criteria for Quality Level 2. AIA members may receive 14 learning units (LUs) for each two-day course.

## Daily Course Schedule

The first day of each seminar session begins at 8:30 a.m. and ends at 4:30 p.m. The second day begins at 8:00 a.m. and ends at 4:00 p.m. Participants are urged to bring a hand-held calculator since many actual problems will be worked out in each session.

## Continental Breakfast

Your registration includes the cost of a continental breakfast and a morning and afternoon refreshment break. These informal segments allow you to discuss topics of mutual interest with other seminar attendees. You are free to make your own lunch and dinner arrangements.

## Hotel/Transportation Arrangements

We arrange to hold a block of rooms at most host hotels. To take advantage of special group rates when making your reservation, be sure to mention that you are attending the Gordian RSMeans data seminar. You are, of course, free to stay at the lodging place of your choice. Hotel reservations and transportation arrangements should be made directly by seminar attendees.

## Important

Class sizes are limited, so please register as soon as possible.